Contents

3   Introduction to Graphing   147

Systems of Equations in Two Variables   227

5   Polynomials   285

6   Polynomials and Factoring   361

7   Rational Expressions and Equations   433

8   Functions and Graphs   501

12

Exponents and Radical Functions   717

13

Quadratic Functions and Equations   797

14

Exponential Functions and Logarithmic Functions   875

Preface

The Bittinger Graphs and Models series helps students "see the math" and learn algebra by making connections between mathematical concepts and their real-world applications. The authors use a variety of tools and techniques—including side-by-side algebraic and graphical solutions and graphing calculators, when appropriate—to engage and motivate all types of learners. The authors have included an abundance of applications, many of which use real data, giving students a lens through which to learn the math.

Appropriate for two consecutive courses or a course combining the study of elementary and intermediate algebra, *Elementary and Intermediate Algebra: Graphs and Models,* Fourth Edition, covers both elementary and intermediate topics without the repetition necessary in two separate texts. This text is more interactive than most other elementary and intermediate texts. Our goal is to enhance the learning process by encouraging students to visualize the mathematics and by providing as much support as possible to help students in their study of algebra. *Intermediate Algebra: Graphs and Models,* Fourth Edition, is also part of this series.

New and Updated Features in This Edition

Responding to both user and reviewer feedback, we have refined the pedagogy, content, design, and art and have expanded the supplements package for this edition. The following is a list of major changes:

New! • **Chapter openers** pose real-world questions that relate to the chapter contents. Real-data graphs help students consider the answers to the questions. (See p. 671.)

New! • **"Try" exercises** conclude nearly every example by pointing students to one or more parallel exercises in the corresponding exercise set so they can immediately reinforce the skills and concepts presented in the examples. Answers to these exercises appear at the end of each exercise set, as well as in the answer section.

New! • **Your Turn** exercises encourage immediate practice of graphing calculator features discussed in the text. Many of these exercises include keystrokes, and answers are included where appropriate. (See p. 725.)

New! • A **Mid-Chapter Review** gives students the opportunity to reinforce their understanding of the mathematical skills and concepts before moving on to new material. Section and objective references are included for convenient studying. (See p. 835.)

  • **Guided Solutions** are worked-out problems with blanks for students to fill in the correct expression to complete the solution. (See p. 836.)

  • **Mixed Review** provides free-response exercises, similar to those in the preceding sections in the chapter, reinforcing mastery of skills and concepts. (See p. 836.)

New! • **Skill Review** exercises in the section exercise sets offer just-in-time review of previously presented skills that students will need to learn before moving on to the next section. (See p. 253.)

- In total, **27% of the exercises are new or updated.** All exercises have been carefully reviewed and revised to improve their grading and to update applications.
- The **Study Summary** at the end of each chapter is expanded to provide more comprehensive in-text practice and review. Important Concepts are paired with a worked-out example for reference and review and a similar practice exercise for students to solve. (See p. 280.)
- **New design!** While incorporating a new layout, a fresh palette of colors, and new features, we have increased the page dimension for an open look and a typeface that is easy to read. As always, it is our goal to make the text look mature without being intimidating. In addition, we continue to pay close attention to the pedagogical use of color to make sure that it is used to present concepts in the clearest possible manner.

Content Changes

- Section 12.7 now contains the distance formula and the midpoint formula.
- Sections 13.3 and 13.4 from the previous edition have switched order.
- The appendixes have been removed.

New and Updated Student and Instructor Resources

- The *Instructor's Resource Manual* includes new **Mini-Lectures** for every section of the text.
- **Enhancements to the Bittinger MyMathLab course** include the following:
  - **Increased exercise coverage** provides more practice options for students.
  - **New math games** help students practice math skills in a fun, interactive environment.
  - **Premade homework assignments** are available for each section of the text. In addition to the section-level premade assignments, the Bittinger MyMathLab courses include premade **mid-chapter review assignments** for each chapter.
  - **Interactive Translating for Success** matching activities help students learn to associate word problems (through translation) with their appropriate mathematical equations. These activities are now assignable.
  - **Interactive Visualizing for Success** activities ask students to match equations and inequalities with their graphs, allowing them to recognize the important characteristics of the equation and visualize the corresponding attributes of its graph. These activities are now assignable.
  - **The English/Spanish Audio Glossary** allows students to see key mathematical terms and hear their definitions in either English or Spanish.

Hallmark Features

Problem Solving

One distinguishing feature of our approach is our treatment of and emphasis on problem solving. We use problem solving and applications to motivate the material wherever possible, and we include real-life applications and problem-solving techniques throughout the text. Problem solving not only encourages students to think about how mathematics can be used, it helps to prepare them for more advanced material in future courses.

We introduce the five-step process for solving problems: (1) *Familiarize*, (2) *Translate*, (3) *Carry out*, (4) *Check*, and (5) *State* the answer. These steps are then used consistently throughout the text whenever we encounter a problem-solving situation. Repeated use of this problem-solving strategy gives students a sense that they have a starting point for any type of problem they encounter, and frees them to focus on the mathematics necessary to successfully translate the problem situation. We often use estimation and carefully checked guesses to help with the *Familiarize* and *Check* steps.

Algebraic/Graphical Side-by-Sides

Algebraic/graphical side-by-sides give students a direct comparison between these two problem-solving approaches. They show the connection between algebraic and graphical or visual solutions and demonstrate that there is more than one way to obtain a result. This feature also illustrates the comparative efficiency and accuracy of the two methods. (See p. 635) Instructors using this text have found that it works superbly both in courses where the graphing calculator is required and in courses where it is optional.

Applications

Interesting applications of mathematics help motivate both students and instructors. Solving applied problems gives students the opportunity to see their conceptual understanding put to use in a real way. In the fourth edition of *Elementary and Intermediate Algebra: Graphs and Models*, the number of applications and source lines has been increased, and effort has been made to present the most current and relevant applications. As in the past, art is integrated into the applications and exercises to aid the student in visualizing the mathematics.

Interactive Discoveries

Interactive Discoveries invite students to develop analytical and reasoning skills while taking an active role in the learning process. These discoveries can be used as lecture launchers to introduce new topics at the beginning of a class and quickly guide students through a concept, or as out-of-class concept discoveries.

Pedagogical Features

Concept Reinforcement Exercises. This feature is designed to help students build their confidence and comprehension through true/false, matching, and fill-in-the-blank exercises at the beginning of most exercise sets. Whenever possible, special attention is devoted to increasing student understanding of the new vocabulary and notation developed in that section. (See p. 237)

Translating for Success. These problem sets give extra practice with the important *Translate* step of the process for solving word problems. After translating each of ten problems into its appropriate equation or inequality, students are asked to choose from fifteen possible translations, encouraging them to comprehend the problem before matching.

Visualizing for Success. These matching exercises provide students with an opportunity to match an equation with its graph by focusing on the characteristics of the equation and the corresponding attributes of the graph. This feature occurs once in each chapter at the end of a related section. (See p. 236)

Student Notes. These comments, strategically located in the margin within each section, are specific to the mathematics appearing on that page. Remarks are often more casual in format than the typical exposition and range from suggestions on how to avoid common mistakes to how to best read new mathematical notation. (See p. 232)

Connecting the Concepts. To help students understand the big picture, Connecting the Concepts subsections relate the concept at hand to previously learned and upcoming concepts. Because students occasionally lose sight of the forest because of the trees, this feature helps students keep their bearings as they encounter new material. (See p. 654)

Study Tips. These remarks, located in the margin near the beginning of each section, provide suggestions for successful study habits that can be applied to both this and other college courses. Ranging from ideas for better time management to suggestions for test preparation, these comments can be useful even to experienced college students.

Skill Review Exercises. Retention of skills is critical to a student's success in this and future courses. Thus, every exercise set includes Skill Review exercises that review skills and concepts from preceding sections of the text. Often, these exercises provide practice with specific skills needed for the next section of the text. (See p. 253)

Synthesis Exercises. Following the Skill Review section, every exercise set ends with a group of Synthesis exercises that offers opportunities for students to synthesize skills and concepts from earlier sections with the present material, and often provides students with deeper insights into the current topic. Synthesis exercises are generally more challenging than those in the main body of the exercise set and occasionally include Aha! exercises (exercises that can be solved more quickly by reasoning than by computation).

Thinking and Writing Exercises. Writing exercises have been found to aid in student comprehension, critical thinking, and conceptualization. Thus every set of exercises includes at least four Thinking and Writing exercises. Two of these appear just before the Skill Review exercises. The others are more challenging and appear as Synthesis exercises. All are marked with TW and require answers that are one or more complete sentences. Because some instructors may collect answers to writing exercises, and because more than one answer may be correct, answers to the Thinking and Writing exercises are listed at the back of the text only when they are within review exercises.

Collaborative Corners. Studies have shown that students who work together generally outperform those who do not. Throughout the text, we provide optional Collaborative Corner features that require students to work in groups to explore and solve problems. There is at least one Collaborative Corner per chapter, each one appearing after the appropriate exercise set. (See p. 270)

Study Summary. Each three-column study summary contains a list of key terms and concepts from the chapter, with definitions, as well as formulas from the chapter. Examples of important concepts are shown in the second column, with a practice exercise relating to that concept appearing in the third column. Section references are provided so students can reference the corresponding exposition in the chapter. The Summary provides a terrific point from which to begin reviewing for a chapter test. (See p. 280)

Ancillaries

The following ancillaries are available to help both instructors and students use this text more effectively.

STUDENT SUPPLEMENTS

Student's Solutions Manual
(ISBN 978-0-321-72660-5)

- By Math Made Visible
- Contains completely worked-out solutions for all the odd-numbered exercises in the text, with the exception of the Thinking and Writing exercises, as well as completely worked-out solutions to all the exercises in the Chapter Reviews, Chapter Tests, and Cumulative Reviews.

Worksheets for Classroom or Lab Practice
(ISBN 978-0-321-72666-7)

These classroom- and lab-friendly workbooks offer the following resources for every section of the text: a list of learning objectives, vocabulary practice problems, and extra practice exercises with ample workspace.

Graphing Calculator Manual
(ISBN 978-0-321-73726-7)

- By Math Made Visible
- Uses actual examples and exercises from the text to help teach students to use the graphing calculator.
- Order of topics mirrors the order of the text, providing a just-in-time mode of instruction.

Video Resources on DVD
(ISBN 978-0-321-72662-9)

- Complete set of digitized videos on DVDs for student use at home or on campus.
- Presents a series of lectures correlated directly to the content of each section of the text.
- Features an engaging team of instructors, including authors Barbara Johnson and David Ellenbogen, who present material in a format that stresses student interaction, often using examples and exercises from the text.
- Ideal for distance learning or supplemental instruction.
- Includes an expandable window that shows text captioning. Captions can be turned on or off.

INSTRUCTOR SUPPLEMENTS

Annotated Instructor's Edition
(ISBN 978-0-321-72663-6)

- Includes answers to all exercises printed in blue on the same page as those exercises.

Instructor's Solutions Manual
(ISBN 978-0-321-72664-3)

- By Math Made Visible
- Contains full, worked-out solutions to all the exercises in the exercise sets, including the Thinking and Writing exercises, and worked-out solutions to all the exercises in the Chapter Reviews, Chapter Tests, and Cumulative Reviews.

Instructor's Resource Manual with Printable Test Forms

- By Math Made Visible
- Download at www.pearsonhighered.com
- Features resources and teaching tips designed to help both new and adjunct faculty with course preparation and classroom management, including general/first-time advice, sample syllabi, and teaching tips arranged by textbook section.
- New! Includes mini-lectures, one for every section of the text, with objectives, key examples, and teaching tips.
- Provides 5 revised test forms for every chapter and revised test forms for the final exam.
- For the chapter tests, test forms are organized by topic order following the chapter tests in the text, and 2 test forms are multiple choice.
- Resources include extra practice sheets, conversion guide, video index, and transparency masters.
- Available electronically so course/adjunct coordinators can customize material specific to their schools.

TestGen® (www.pearsoned.com/testgen)
(ISBN 978-0-321-72661-2)

- Enables instructors to build, edit, print, and administer tests.
- Features a computerized bank of questions developed to cover all text objectives.
- Algorithmically based content allows instructors to create multiple but equivalent versions of the same question or test with a click of a button.
- Instructors can also modify test-bank questions or add new questions.
- The software and testbank are available for download from Pearson Education's online catalog.

MathXL® Online Course (access code required).   MathXL is a powerful online homework, tutorial, and assessment system that accompanies Pearson Education's textbooks in mathematics or statistics. With MathXL, instructors can create, edit, and assign online homework and tests using algorithmically generated exercises correlated at the objective level to the textbook. They can also create and assign their own online exercises and import TestGen tests for added flexibility. All student work is tracked and records maintained in MathXL's online gradebook. Students can take chapter tests in MathXL and receive personalized study plans and/or personalized homework assignments based on their test results. The study plan diagnoses weaknesses and links students directly to tutorial exercises for the objectives they need to study and retest. Students can also access supplemental animations and video clips directly from selected exercises. MathXL is available to qualified adopters. For more information, visit our Web site at www.mathxl.com or contact your Pearson representative.

MyMathLab® Online Course (access code required).   MyMathLab is a text-specific, easily customizable online course that integrates interactive multimedia instruction with textbook content. MyMathLab gives you the tools you need to deliver all or a portion of your course online, whether your students are in a lab setting or working from home.

* **Interactive homework exercises,** correlated to your textbook at the objective level, are algorithmically generated for unlimited practice and mastery. Most exercises are free-response and provide guided solutions, sample problems, and tutorial learning aids for extra help.

* **Personalized homework** assignments can be designed to meet the needs of your class. MyMathLab tailors the assignment for each student on the basis of their test or quiz scores. Each student receives a homework assignment that contains only the problems he or she still needs to master.

* **Personalized Study Plan,** generated when students complete a test or quiz or homework, indicates which topics have been mastered and links to tutorial exercises for topics students have not mastered. You can customize the Study Plan so that the topics available match your course content.

* **Multimedia learning aids,** such as video lectures and podcasts, animations, interpactive games, and a complete multimedia textbook, help students independently improve their understanding and performance. You can assign these multimedia learning aids as homework to help your students grasp the concepts.

* **Homework and Test Manager** lets you assign homework, quizzes, and tests that are automatically graded. Select just the right mix of questions from the MyMathLab exercise bank, instructor-created custom exercises, and/or TestGen® test items.

* **Gradebook,** designed specifically for mathematics and statistics, automatically tracks students' results, lets you stay on top of student performance, and gives you control over how to calculate final grades. You can also add offline (paper-and-pencil) grades to the gradebook.

* **MathXL Exercise Builder** allows you to create static and algorithmic exercises for your online assignments. You can use the library of sample exercises as an easy starting point, or you can edit any course-related exercise.

* **Pearson Tutor Center** (www.pearsontutorservices.com) access is automatically included with MyMathLab. The Tutor Center is staffed by qualified math instructors who provide textbook-specific tutoring for students via toll-free phone, fax, email, and interactive Web sessions.

Students do their assignments in the Flash®-based MathXL Player, which is compatible with almost any browser (Firefox®, Safari™, or Internet Explorer®) on almost any platform (Macintosh® or Windows®). MyMathLab is powered by CourseCompass™, Pearson Education's online teaching and learning environment, and by MathXL®, our online homework, tutorial, and assessment system. MyMathLab is available to qualified adopters. For more information, visit www.mymathlab.com or contact your Pearson representative.

InterAct Math Tutorial Web site, www.interactmath.com.   Get practice and tutorial help online! This interactive tutorial Web site provides algorithmically generated practice exercises that correlate directly to the exercises in the textbook. Students can retry an exercise as many times as they like with new values each time for unlimited practice and mastery. Every exercise is accompanied by an interactive guided solution that provides helpful feedback for incorrect answers, and students can also view a worked-out sample problem that steps them through an exercise similar to the one they're working on.

Pearson Math Adjunct Support Center.   The Pearson Math Adjunct Support Center (http://www.pearsontutorservices.com/math-adjunct.html) is staffed by qualified instructors with over 100 years of combined experience at both the community college and university levels. Assistance is provided for faculty in the following areas:

- Suggested syllabus consultation
- Tips on using materials packed with your book
- Book-specific content assistance
- Teaching suggestions including advice on classroom strategies

Acknowledgments

No book can be produced without a team of professionals who take pride in their work and are willing to put in long hours. Thanks to Math Made Visible for their work on the print (or printable) supplements. Holly Martinez, Mindy Pergl, Jeremy Pletcher, Art Bouvier, David Johnson, Beverly Fusfield, Christine Verity, Carrie Green, and Gary Williams provided enormous help, often in the face of great time pressure, as accuracy checkers. Michael Avidon, Ebony Harvey, and Robert Pierce from the Pearson Tutor Center also made valuable contributions. We are also indebted to Michelle Lanosga for her help with applications research.

Martha Morong, of Quadrata, Inc., provided editorial and production services of the highest quality imaginable—she is simply a joy to work with. Geri Davis, of the Davis Group, Inc., performed superb work as designer, art editor, and photo researcher, and always with a disposition that can brighten an otherwise gray day. Network Graphics generated the graphs, the charts, and many of the illustrations. Not only are the people at Network reliable, but they clearly take pride in their work. The many representational illustrations appear thanks to Bill Melvin, a gifted artist with true mathematical sensibilities.

Our team at Pearson deserves special thanks. Assistant Editor Jonathan Wooding managed many of the day-to-day details—always in a pleasant and reliable manner. Executive Content Editor Kari Heen expertly provided information and a steadying influence along with gentle prodding at just the right moments. Executive Editor Cathy Cantin provided many fine suggestions along with unflagging support. Production Manager Ron Hampton exhibited careful supervision and an eye for detail throughout production. Executive Marketing Manager Michelle Renda and Marketing Coordinator Alicia Frankel skillfully kept us in touch with the needs of faculty. Associate Media Producer Nathaniel Koven provided us with the technological guidance so necessary for our many supplements and our fine video series. To all of these people, we owe a real debt of gratitude.

Reviewers

Reviewers of *Elementary and Intermediate Algebra: Graphs and Models,* Fourth Edition

Susan Bradley, *Angelina College*
Ben Franklin, *Indiana University–Kokomo*
Julie Mays, *Angelina College*
Melissa Reid, *Rowan-Cabarrus Community College*
Pansy Waycaster, *Virginia Highlands Community College*
Kevin Yokoyama, *College of the Redwoods*

Reviewers of *Intermediate Algebra: Graphs and Models*, Fourth Edition

Clark Brown, *Mohave Community College–Kingman*
Steve Drucker, *Santa Rosa Junior College*
Diana Hunt, *Arapahoe Community Colleg*

M.L.B.
D.J.E.
B.L.J.

Introduction to Algebraic Expressions

BRIAN BUSBY
CHIEF METEOROLOGIST
Kansas City, Missouri

All weather measurements are a series of numbers and values. Temperature, relative humidity, wind speed and direction, precipitation amount, and air pressure are all expressed in various numbers and percentages. Because weather systems move north and south, east and west, up and down, *and* over time, high-level math like calculus is the only way to represent that movement. But before you study calculus, you must begin with algebra.

AN APPLICATION

On December 10, Jenna notes that the temperature is −3°F at 6:00 A.M. She predicts that the temperature will rise at a rate of 2° per hour for 3 hr, and then rise at a rate of 3° per hour for 6 hr. She also predicts that the temperature will then fall at a rate of 2° per hour for 3 hr, and then fall at a rate of 5° per hour for 2 hr. What is Jenna's temperature forecast for 8:00 P.M.?

This problem appears as Exercise 135 in Section 1.7.

Taken from *Elementary and Intermediate Algebra Concepts and Applications*, Fifth Edition by Marvin L. Bittinger, David J. Ellenbogen, and Barbara L. Johnson.

P roblem solving is the focus of this text. Chapter 1 presents important preliminaries that are needed for the problem-solving approach that is developed in Chapter 2 and used throughout the rest of the book. These preliminaries include a review of arithmetic, a discussion of real numbers and their properties, and an examination of how real numbers are added, subtracted, multiplied, divided, and raised to powers.

1.1   Introduction to Algebra

Algebraic Expressions   ▪   Translating to Algebraic Expressions   ▪   Translating to Equations

This section introduces some basic concepts and expressions used in algebra. Solving real-world problems is an important part of algebra, so we will focus on the wordings and mathematical expressions that often arise in applications.

Algebraic Expressions

Probably the greatest difference between arithmetic and algebra is the use of *variables* in algebra. When a letter can be any one of a set of numbers, that letter is a **variable**. For example, if n represents the number of tickets purchased for a Maroon 5 concert, then n will vary, depending on factors like price and day of the week. This makes n a variable. If each ticket costs \$40, then 3 tickets cost $40 \cdot 3$ dollars, 4 tickets cost $40 \cdot 4$ dollars, and n tickets cost $40 \cdot n$, or $40n$ dollars. Note that both $40 \cdot n$ and $40n$ mean 40 *times n*. The number 40 is an example of a **constant** because it does not change.

Price per Ticket (in dollars)	Number of Tickets Purchased	Total Paid (in dollars)
40	n	$40n$

The expression $40n$ is a **variable expression** because its value varies with the replacement for n. In this case, the total amount paid, $40n$, will change with the number of tickets purchased. In the following chart, we replace n with a variety of values and compute the total amount paid. In doing so, we are **evaluating the expression** $40n$.

Price per Ticket (in dollars), 40	Number of Tickets Purchased, n	Total Paid (in dollars), $40n$
40	400	$16,000
40	500	20,000
40	600	24,000

Variable expressions are examples of *algebraic expressions*. An **algebraic expression** consists of variables and/or numerals, often with operation signs and grouping symbols. Examples are

$$t + 97, \quad 5 \cdot x, \quad 3a - b, \quad 18 \div y, \quad \frac{9}{7}, \quad \text{and} \quad 4r(s + t).$$

Recall that a fraction bar is a division symbol: $\frac{9}{7}$, or 9/7, means $9 \div 7$. Similarly, multiplication can be written in several ways. For example, "5 times x" can be written as $5 \cdot x$, $5 \times x$, $5(x)$, or simply $5x$. On many calculators, this appears as $5 * x$.

To **evaluate** an algebraic expression, we substitute a number for each variable in the expression. We then calculate the result.

EXAMPLE 1

Evaluate each expression for the given values.

a) $x + y$ for $x = 37$ and $y = 28$

b) $5ab$ for $a = 2$ and $b = 3$

SOLUTION

a) We substitute 37 for x and 28 for y and carry out the addition:

$$x + y = 37 + 28 = 65.$$

The number 65 is called the **value** of the expression.

b) We substitute 2 for a and 3 for b and multiply:

$$5ab = 5 \cdot 2 \cdot 3 = 10 \cdot 3 = 30. \qquad \text{$5ab$ means 5 times a times b.}$$

TRY EXERCISE 17

STUDENT NOTES

As we will see later, it is sometimes necessary to use parentheses when substituting a number for a variable. You may wish to use parentheses whenever you substitute. In Example 1, we could write

$$x + y = (37) + (28) = 65$$

and

$$5ab = 5(2)(3) = 30.$$

EXAMPLE 2

The area A of a rectangle of length l and width w is given by the formula $A = lw$. Find the area when l is 17 in. and w is 10 in.

SOLUTION   We evaluate, using 17 in. for l and 10 in. for w, and carry out the multiplication:

$$A = lw$$
$$A = (17 \text{ in.})(10 \text{ in.})$$
$$A = (17)(10)(\text{in.})(\text{in.})$$
$$A = 170 \text{ in}^2, \text{ or } 170 \text{ square inches.}$$

Note that we always use square units for area and $(\text{in.})(\text{in.}) = \text{in}^2$. Exponents like the 2 within the expression in^2 are discussed further in Section 1.8.

TRY EXERCISE 25

EXAMPLE 3   The area of a triangle with a base of length b and a height of length h is given by the formula $A = \frac{1}{2}bh$. Find the area when b is 8 m (meters) and h is 6.4 m.

SOLUTION   We substitute 8 m for b and 6.4 m for h and then multiply:

$$A = \tfrac{1}{2}bh$$
$$A = \tfrac{1}{2}(8\,\text{m})(6.4\,\text{m})$$
$$A = \tfrac{1}{2}(8)(6.4)(\text{m})(\text{m})$$
$$A = 4(6.4)\,\text{m}^2$$
$$A = 25.6\,\text{m}^2,\text{ or } 25.6 \text{ square meters.}$$

TRY EXERCISE   27

Translating to Algebraic Expressions

Before attempting to translate problems to equations, we need to be able to translate certain phrases to algebraic expressions.

Important Words	Sample Phrase or Sentence	Translation
Addition (+)		
added to	700 pounds was added to the car's weight.	$w + 700$
sum of	The sum of a number and 12	$n + 12$
plus	53 plus some number	$53 + x$
more than	800 more than Biloxi's population	$p + 800$
increased by	Ty's original estimate, increased by 4	$n + 4$
Subtraction (−)		
subtracted from	2 ounces was subtracted from the bag's weight.	$w - 2$
difference of	The difference of two scores	$m - n$
minus	A team of size s, minus 2 injured players	$s - 2$
less than	9 less than the number of volunteers last month	$v - 9$
decreased by	The car's speed, decreased by 8 mph	$s - 8$
Multiplication (·)		
multiplied by	The number of reservations, multiplied by 3	$r \cdot 3$
product of	The product of two numbers	$m \cdot n$
times	5 times the dog's weight	$5w$
twice	Twice the wholesale cost	$2c$
of	$\frac{1}{2}$ of Amelia's salary	$\frac{1}{2}s$
Division (÷)		
divided by	A 2-pound coffee cake, divided by 3	$2 \div 3$
quotient of	The quotient of 14 and 7	$14 \div 7$
divided into	4 divided into the delivery fee	$f \div 4$
ratio of	The ratio of \$500 to the price of a new car	$500/p$
per	There were 18 computers per class of size s.	$18/s$

     Any variable can be used to represent an unknown quantity; however, it is helpful to choose a descriptive letter. For example, w suggests weight and p suggests population or price. It is important to write down what the chosen variable represents.

EXAMPLE 4

Translate each phrase to an algebraic expression.

a) Four less than Ava's height, in inches
b) Eighteen more than a number
c) A day's pay, in dollars, divided by eight

SOLUTION   To help think through a translation, we sometimes begin with a specific number in place of a variable.

a) If the height were 60, then 4 less than 60 would mean $60 - 4$. If the height were 65, the translation would be $65 - 4$. If we use h to represent "Ava's height, in inches," the translation of "Four less than Ava's height, in inches" is $h - 4$.

b) If we knew the number to be 10, the translation would be $10 + 18$, or $18 + 10$. If we use t to represent "a number," the translation of "Eighteen more than a number" is

$$t + 18, \quad \text{or} \quad 18 + t.$$

c) We let d represent "a day's pay, in dollars." If the pay were \$78, the translation would be $78 \div 8$, or $\frac{78}{8}$. Thus our translation of "A day's pay, in dollars, divided by eight" is

$$d \div 8, \quad \text{or} \quad \frac{d}{8}.$$

TRY EXERCISE 31

CAUTION!   The order in which we subtract and divide affects the answer! Answering $4 - h$ or $8 \div d$ in Examples 4(a) and 4(c) is incorrect.

EXAMPLE 5

Translate each phrase to an algebraic expression.

a) Half of some number
b) Seven more than twice the weight
c) Six less than the product of two numbers
d) Nine times the difference of a number and 10
e) Eighty-two percent of last year's enrollment

SOLUTION

	Phrase	*Variable(s)*	*Algebraic Expression*
a)	Half of some number	Let n represent the number.	$\frac{1}{2}n$, or $\frac{n}{2}$, or $n \div 2$
b)	Seven more than twice the weight	Let w represent the weight.	$2w + 7$, or $7 + 2w$
c)	Six less than the product of two numbers	Let m and n represent the numbers.	$mn - 6$
d)	Nine times the difference of a number and 10	Let a represent the number.	$9(a - 10)$
e)	Eighty-two percent of last year's enrollment	Let r represent last year's enrollment.	82% of r, or $0.82r$

TRY EXERCISE 45

Translating to Equations

The symbol = ("equals") indicates that the expressions on either side of the equals sign represent the same number. An **equation** is a number sentence with the verb =. Equations may be true, false, or neither true nor false.

EXAMPLE **6** Determine whether each equation is true, false, or neither.

a) $8 \cdot 4 = 32$ **b)** $7 - 2 = 4$ **c)** $x + 6 = 13$

SOLUTION

a) $8 \cdot 4 = 32$ The equation is *true*.

b) $7 - 2 = 4$ The equation is *false*.

c) $x + 6 = 13$ The equation is *neither* true nor false, because we do not know what number x represents.

Solution

A replacement or substitution that makes an equation true is called a *solution*. Some equations have more than one solution, and some have no solution. When all solutions have been found, we have *solved* the equation.

To see if a number is a solution, we evaluate all expressions in the equation. If the values on both sides of the equation are the same, the number is a solution.

EXAMPLE **7** Determine whether 7 is a solution of $x + 6 = 13$.

SOLUTION   We evaluate $x + 6$ and compare both sides of the equation.

$$x + 6 = 13 \quad \text{Writing the equation}$$
$$7 + 6 \;\Big|\; 13 \quad \text{Substituting 7 for } x$$
$$13 \overset{?}{=} 13 \quad 13 = 13 \text{ is TRUE.}$$

Since the left-hand side and the right-hand side are the same, 7 is a solution.

TRY EXERCISE   57

Although we do not study solving equations until Chapter 2, we can translate certain problem situations to equations now. The words "is the same as," "equal," "is," and "are" often translate to "=."

Words indicating equality, = : "is the same as," "equal," "is," "are"

When translating a problem to an equation, we translate phrases to algebraic expressions, and the entire statement to an equation containing those expressions.

EXAMPLE **8**   Translate the following problem to an equation.

What number plus 478 is 1019?

SOLUTION   We let y represent the unknown number. The translation then comes almost directly from the English sentence.

What number   plus   478   is   1019?

$$y \qquad + \qquad 478 \quad = \quad 1019$$

Note that "what number plus 478" translates to "$y + 478$" and "is" translates to "=."

TRY EXERCISE 63

Sometimes it helps to reword a problem before translating.

EXAMPLE **9**   Translate the following problem to an equation.

The Taipei Financial Center, or Taipei 101, in Taiwan is the world's tallest building. At 1666 ft, it is 183 ft taller than the Petronas Twin Towers in Kuala Lumpur. How tall are the Petronas Twin Towers?

Source: *Guinness World Records* 2007

SOLUTION   We let h represent the height, in feet, of the Petronas Towers. A rewording and translation follow:

Rewording: The height of   is   183 ft more than the height
Taipei 101   of the Petronas Towers

Translating: 1666   = $h + 183$

TRY EXERCISE 69

TECHNOLOGY CONNECTION

Technology Connections are activities that make use of features that are common to most graphing calculators. In some cases, students may find the user's manual for their particular calculator helpful for exact keystrokes.

Although all graphing calculators are not the same, most share the following characteristics.

Screen.   The large screen can show graphs and tables as well as the expressions entered. The screen has a different layout for different functions. Computations are performed in the **home screen**. On many calculators, the home screen is accessed by pressing **2ND** (QUIT). The **cursor** shows location on the screen, and the **contrast** (set by **2ND** ⌃ or **2ND** ⌄) determines how dark the characters appear.

Keypad.   There are options written above the keys as well as on them. To access those above the keys, we press **2ND** or **ALPHA** and then the key. Expressions are usually entered as they would appear in print. For example, to evaluate $3xy + x$ for $x = 65$ and $y = 92$, we press 3 (×) 65 (×) 92 (+) 65 and then **ENTER**. The value of the expression, 18005, will appear at the right of the screen.

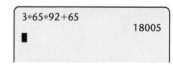

Evaluate each of the following.

1. $27a - 18b$, for $a = 136$ and $b = 13$
2. $19xy - 9x + 13y$, for $x = 87$ and $y = 29$

STUDY SKILLS

Get the Facts

Throughout this textbook, you will find a feature called Study Skills. These tips are intended to help improve your math study skills. On the first day of class, you should complete this chart.

Instructor: Name _____

Office hours and location _____

Phone number _____

Fax number _____

E-mail address _____

Find the names of two students whom you could contact for information or study questions:

1. Name _____

   Phone number _____

   E-mail address _____

2. Name _____

   Phone number _____

   E-mail address _____

Math lab on campus:

Location _____

Hours _____

Phone _____

Tutoring:

Campus location _____

Hours _____

Important supplements:

(See the preface for a complete list of available supplements.)

Supplements recommended by the instructor.

_____

_____

Translating for Success

1. Twice the difference of a number and 11

2. The product of a number and 11 is 2.

3. Twice the difference of two numbers is 11.

4. The quotient of twice a number and 11

5. The quotient of 11 and the product of two numbers

6. Eleven times the sum of a number and twice the number

7. Twice the sum of two numbers is 11.

8. Two more than twice a number is 11.

9. Twice the sum of 11 times a number and 2

10. Twenty percent of some number is 11.

Translate to an expression or an equation and match that translation with one of the choices A–O below. Do not solve.

A. $x = 0.2(11)$

B. $\dfrac{2x}{11}$

C. $2x + 2 = 11$

D. $2(11x + 2)$

E. $11x = 2$

F. $0.2x = 11$

G. $11(2x - y)$

H. $2(x - 11)$

I. $11 + 2x = 2$

J. $2x + y = 11$

K. $2(x - y) = 11$

L. $11(x + 2x)$

M. $2(x + y) = 11$

N. $2 + \dfrac{x}{11}$

O. $\dfrac{11}{xy}$

Answers on page A-1

An additional, animated version of this activity appears in MyMathLab. To use MyMathLab, you need a course ID and a student access code. Contact your instructor for more information.

1.1   EXERCISE SET

↪ *Concept Reinforcement*   *Classify each of the following as either an expression or an equation.*

1. $10n - 1$

2. $3x = 21$

3. $2x - 5 = 9$

4. $5(x + 2)$

5. $38 = 2t$

6. $45 = a - 1$

7. $4a - 5b$

8. $3s + 4t = 19$

9. $2x - 3y = 8$

10. $12 - 4xy$

11. $r(t + 7) + 5$

12. $9a + b$

To the student and the instructor: *The* ▸ TRY EXERCISES *for examples are indicated by a shaded block* ▮ *on the exercise number. Complete step-by-step solutions for these exercises appear online at www.pearsonhighered.com/ bittingerellenbogen.*

Evaluate.

13. $5a$, for $a = 9$

14. $11y$, for $y = 7$

15. $12 - r$, for $r = 4$

16. $t + 8$, for $t = 2$

17. $\dfrac{a}{b}$, for $a = 45$ and $b = 9$

18. $\dfrac{c + d}{3}$, for $c = 14$ and $d = 13$

19. $\dfrac{x + y}{4}$, for $x = 2$ and $y = 14$

20. $\dfrac{m}{n}$, for $m = 54$ and $n = 9$

21. $\dfrac{p - q}{7}$, for $p = 55$ and $q = 20$

22. $\dfrac{9m}{q}$, for $m = 6$ and $q = 18$

23. $\dfrac{5z}{y}$, for $z = 9$ and $y = 15$

24. $\dfrac{m - n}{2}$, for $m = 20$ and $n = 8$

Substitute to find the value of each expression.

25. *Hockey.*   The area of a rectangle with base b and height h is bh. A regulation hockey goal is 6 ft wide and 4 ft high. Find the area of the opening.

6 ft

4 ft

26. *Orbit time.*   A communications satellite orbiting 300 mi above the earth travels about 27,000 mi in one orbit. The time, in hours, for an orbit is

$$\frac{27{,}000}{v},$$

where v is the velocity, in miles per hour. How long will an orbit take at a velocity of 1125 mph?

27. *Zoology.*   A great white shark has triangular teeth. Each tooth measures about 5 cm across the base and has a height of 6 cm. Find the surface area of the front side of one such tooth. (See Example 3.)

6 cm

5 cm

28. *Work time.*   Javier takes three times as long to do a job as Luis does. Suppose t represents the time it takes Luis to do the job. Then $3t$ represents the time it takes Javier. How long does it take Javier if Luis takes **(a)** 30 sec? **(b)** 90 sec? **(c)** 2 min?

29. *Women's softball.*   A softball player's batting average is h/a, where h is the number of hits and a is the number of "at bats." In the 2007 Women's College World Series, Caitlin Lowe of the Arizona Wildcats had 10 hits in 29 at bats. What was her batting average? Round to the nearest thousandth.

30. *Area of a parallelogram.* The area of a parallelogram with base b and height h is bh. Find the area of the parallelogram when the height is 6 cm (centimeters) and the base is 7.5 cm.

Translate to an algebraic expression.

31. 5 more than Ron's age

32. The product of 4 and a

33. 6 times b

34. 7 more than Lori's weight

35. 9 less than c

36. 4 less than d

37. 6 increased by q

38. 11 increased by z

39. 8 times Mai's speed

40. m subtracted from n

41. x less than y

42. 2 less than Than's age

43. x divided by w

44. The quotient of two numbers

45. The sum of the box's length and height

46. The sum of d and f

47. The product of 9 and twice m

48. Pemba's speed minus twice the wind speed

49. Thirteen less than one quarter of some number

50. Four less than ten times a number

51. Five times the difference of two numbers

52. One third of the sum of two numbers

53. 64% of the women attending

54. 38% of a number

Determine whether the given number is a solution of the given equation.

55. 25; $x + 17 = 42$

56. 75; $93 - y = 28$

57. 93; $a - 28 = 75$

58. 12; $8t = 96$

59. 63; $\dfrac{t}{7} = 9$

60. 52; $\dfrac{x}{8} = 6$

61. 3; $\dfrac{108}{x} = 36$

62. 7; $\dfrac{94}{y} = 12$

Translate each problem to an equation. Do not solve.

63. What number added to 73 is 201?

64. Seven times what number is 1596?

65. When 42 is multiplied by a number, the result is 2352. Find the number.

66. When 345 is added to a number, the result is 987. Find the number.

67. *Chess.* A chess board has 64 squares. If pieces occupy 19 squares, how many squares are unoccupied?

68. *Hours worked.* A carpenter charges \$35 an hour. How many hours did she work if she billed a total of \$3640?

69. *Recycling.* Currently, Americans recycle or compost 32% of all municipal solid waste. This is the same as recycling or composting 79 million tons. What is the total amount of waste generated?
Source: U.S. EPA, Municipal Solid Waste Department

70. *Travel to work.* In 2005, the average commuting time to work in New York was 31.2 min. The average commuting time in North Dakota was 14.9 min shorter. How long was the average commute in North Dakota?
Source: American Community Survey

In each of Exercises 71–78, match the phrase or sentence with the appropriate expression or equation from the column on the right.

71. ____ Twice the sum of two numbers

a) $\dfrac{x}{y} + 6$

72. ____ Five less than a number is twelve.

b) $2(x + y) = 48$

73. ____ Twelve more than a number is five.

c) $\dfrac{1}{2} \cdot a \cdot b$

74. ____ Half of the product of two numbers

d) $t + 12 = 5$

75. ____ Three times the sum of a number and five

e) $ab - 1 = 48$

76. ____ Twice the sum of two numbers is 48.

f) $2(m + n)$

77. ____ One less than the product of two numbers is 48.

g) $3(t + 5)$

78. ____ Six more than the quotient of two numbers

h) $x - 5 = 12$

To the student and the instructor: Writing exercises, denoted by ✍️, *should be answered using one or more English sentences. Because answers to many writing exercises will vary, solutions are not listed in the answers at the back of the book.*

✍️ **79.** What is the difference between a variable, a variable expression, and an equation?

✍️ **80.** What does it mean to evaluate an algebraic expression?

Synthesis

To the student and the instructor: Synthesis exercises *are designed to challenge students to extend the concepts or skills studied in each section. Many synthesis exercises will require the assimilation of skills and concepts from several sections.*

✍️ **81.** If the lengths of the sides of a square are doubled, is the area doubled? Why or why not?

✍️ **82.** Write a problem that translates to $1998 + t = 2006$.

83. Signs of Distinction charges $120 per square foot for handpainted signs. The town of Belmar commissioned a triangular sign with a base of 3 ft and a height of 2.5 ft. How much will the sign cost?

84. Find the area that is shaded.

85. Evaluate $\dfrac{x - y}{3}$ when x is twice y and $x = 12$.

86. Evaluate $\dfrac{x + y}{2}$ when y is twice x and $x = 6$.

87. Evaluate $\dfrac{a + b}{4}$ when a is twice b and $a = 16$.

88. Evaluate $\dfrac{a - b}{3}$ when a is three times b and $a = 18$.

Answer each question with an algebraic expression.

89. If $w + 3$ is a whole number, what is the next whole number after it?

90. If $d + 2$ is an odd number, what is the preceding odd number?

Translate to an algebraic expression.

91. The perimeter of a rectangle with length l and width w (perimeter means distance around)

92. The perimeter of a square with side s (perimeter means distance around)

93. Ellie's race time, assuming she took 5 sec longer than Joe and Joe took 3 sec longer than Molly. Assume that Molly's time was t seconds.

94. Ray's age 7 yr from now if he is 2 yr older than Monique and Monique is a years old

✍️ **95.** If the length of the height of a triangle is doubled, is its area also doubled? Why or why not?

COLLABORATIVE CORNER

Teamwork

Focus: Group problem solving; working collaboratively

Time: 15 minutes

Group size: 2

Working and studying as a team often enables students to solve problems that are difficult to solve alone.

ACTIVITY

1. The left-hand column below contains the names of 12 colleges. A scrambled list of the names of their sports teams is on the right. As a group, match the names of the colleges to the teams.

   1. University of Texas
   2. Western State College of Colorado
   3. University of North Carolina
   4. University of Massachusetts
   5. Hawaii Pacific University
   6. University of Nebraska
   7. University of California, Santa Cruz
   8. University of Louisiana at Lafayette
   9. Grand Canyon University
   10. Palm Beach Atlantic University
   11. University of Alaska, Anchorage
   12. University of Florida

   a) Antelopes
   b) Banana Slugs
   c) Sea Warriors
   d) Gators
   e) Mountaineers
   f) Sailfish
   g) Longhorns
   h) Tar Heels
   i) Seawolves
   j) Ragin' Cajuns
   k) Cornhuskers
   l) Minutemen

2. After working for 5 min, confer with another group and reach mutual agreement.

3. Does the class agree on all 12 pairs?

4. Do you agree that group collaboration enhances our ability to solve problems?

1.2 The Commutative, Associative, and Distributive Laws

Equivalent Expressions ▪ The Commutative Laws ▪ The Associative Laws ▪ The Distributive Law ▪ The Distributive Law and Factoring

In order to solve equations, we must be able to manipulate algebraic expressions. The commutative, associative, and distributive laws discussed in this section enable us to write *equivalent expressions* that will simplify our work. Indeed, much of this text is devoted to finding equivalent expressions.

Equivalent Expressions

The expressions $4 + 4 + 4, 3 \cdot 4$, and $4 \cdot 3$ all represent the same number, 12. Expressions that represent the same number are said to be **equivalent**. The equivalent expressions $t + 18$ and $18 + t$ were used on p. 5 when we translated "eighteen more than a number." These expressions are equivalent because they represent the same number for any value of *t*. We can illustrate this by making some choices for *t*.

$$\text{When } t = 3, \quad t + 18 = 3 + 18 = 21$$
$$\text{and} \quad 18 + t = 18 + 3 = 21.$$
$$\text{When } t = 40, \quad t + 18 = 40 + 18 = 58$$
$$\text{and} \quad 18 + t = 18 + 40 = 58.$$

The Commutative Laws

Recall that changing the order in addition or multiplication does not change the result. Equations like $3 + 78 = 78 + 3$ and $5 \cdot 14 = 14 \cdot 5$ illustrate this idea and show that addition and multiplication are **commutative**.

The Commutative Laws

For Addition.   For any numbers *a* and *b*,

$$a + b = b + a.$$

(Changing the order of addition does not affect the answer.)

For Multiplication.   For any numbers *a* and *b*,

$$ab = ba.$$

(Changing the order of multiplication does not affect the answer.)

EXAMPLE **1**   Use the commutative laws to write an expression equivalent to each of the following: **(a)** $y + 5$; **(b)** $9x$; **(c)** $7 + ab$.

SOLUTION

a) $y + 5$ is equivalent to $5 + y$ by the commutative law of addition.

b) $9x$ is equivalent to $x \cdot 9$ by the commutative law of multiplication.

c) $7 + ab$ is equivalent to $ab + 7$ by the commutative law of *addition*.

   $7 + ab$ is also equivalent to $7 + ba$ by the commutative law of *multiplication*.

   $7 + ab$ is also equivalent to $ba + 7$ by the two commutative laws, used together.

> TRY EXERCISE   11

The Associative Laws

Parentheses are used to indicate groupings. We generally simplify within the parentheses first. For example,

$$3 + (8 + 4) = 3 + 12 = 15$$

and

$$(3 + 8) + 4 = 11 + 4 = 15.$$

Similarly,

$$4 \cdot (2 \cdot 3) = 4 \cdot 6 = 24$$

and

$$(4 \cdot 2) \cdot 3 = 8 \cdot 3 = 24.$$

Note that, so long as only addition or only multiplication appears in an expression, changing the grouping does not change the result. Equations such as $3 + (7 + 5) = (3 + 7) + 5$ and $4(5 \cdot 3) = (4 \cdot 5)3$ illustrate that addition and multiplication are **associative**.

The Associative Laws

For Addition.   For any numbers a, b, and c,

$$a + (b + c) = (a + b) + c.$$

(Numbers can be grouped in any manner for addition.)

For Multiplication.   For any numbers a, b, and c,

$$a \cdot (b \cdot c) = (a \cdot b) \cdot c.$$

(Numbers can be grouped in any manner for multiplication.)

EXAMPLE   2   Use an associative law to write an expression equivalent to each of the following:
(a) $y + (z + 3)$; **(b)** $(8x)y$.

SOLUTION

a) $y + (z + 3)$ is equivalent to $(y + z) + 3$ by the associative law of addition.

b) $(8x)y$ is equivalent to $8(xy)$ by the associative law of multiplication.

> TRY EXERCISE 27

When only addition or only multiplication is involved, parentheses do not change the result. For that reason, we sometimes omit them altogether. Thus,

$$x + (y + 7) = x + y + 7 \quad \text{and} \quad l(wh) = lwh.$$

A sum such as $(5 + 1) + (3 + 5) + 9$ can be simplified by pairing numbers that add to 10. The associative and commutative laws allow us to do this:

$$(5 + 1) + (3 + 5) + 9 = 5 + 5 + 9 + 1 + 3$$
$$= 10 + 10 + 3 = 23.$$

EXAMPLE   3   Use the commutative and/or associative laws of addition to write two expressions equivalent to $(7 + x) + 3$. Then simplify.

SOLUTION

$$(7 + x) + 3 = (x + 7) + 3 \qquad \text{Using the commutative law;}$$
$$(x + 7) + 3 \text{ is one equivalent expression.}$$

$$= x + (7 + 3) \qquad \text{Using the associative law; } x + (7 + 3)$$
$$\text{is another equivalent expression.}$$

$$= x + 10 \qquad \text{Simplifying} \qquad \text{> TRY EXERCISE 39}$$

EXAMPLE 4   Use the commutative and/or associative laws of multiplication to write two expressions equivalent to $2(x \cdot 3)$.

SOLUTION

$$2(x \cdot 3) = 2(3x) \qquad \text{Using the commutative law; } 2(3x) \text{ is one equivalent expression.}$$
$$= (2 \cdot 3)x \qquad \text{Using the associative law; } (2 \cdot 3)x \text{ is another equivalent expression.}$$
$$= 6x \qquad \text{Simplifying} \qquad \boxed{\text{TRY EXERCISE } 41}$$

The Distributive Law

The *distributive law* is probably the single most important law for manipulating algebraic expressions. Unlike the commutative and associative laws, the distributive law uses multiplication together with addition.

You have already used the distributive law although you may not have realized it at the time. To illustrate, try to multiply $3 \cdot 21$ mentally. Many people find the product, 63, by thinking of 21 as $20 + 1$ and then multiplying 20 by 3 and 1 by 3. The sum of the two products, $60 + 3$, is 63. Note that if the 3 does not multiply *both* 20 and 1, the result will not be correct.

EXAMPLE 5   Compute in two ways: $4(7 + 2)$.

SOLUTION

a) As in the discussion of $3(20 + 1)$ above, to compute $4(7 + 2)$, we can multiply both 7 and 2 by 4 and add the results:

$$4(7 + 2) = 4 \cdot 7 + 4 \cdot 2 \qquad \text{Multiplying both 7 and 2 by 4}$$
$$= 28 + 8 = 36. \qquad \text{Adding}$$

b) By first adding inside the parentheses, we get the same result in a different way:

$$4(7 + 2) = 4(9) \qquad \text{Adding; } 7 + 2 = 9$$
$$= 36. \qquad \text{Multiplying}$$

> ### The Distributive Law
> For any numbers a, b, and c,
> $$a(b + c) = ab + ac.$$
> (The product of a number and a sum can be written as the sum of two products.)

EXAMPLE 6   Multiply: $3(x + 2)$.

SOLUTION   Since $x + 2$ cannot be simplified unless a value for x is given, we use the distributive law:

$$3(x + 2) = 3 \cdot x + 3 \cdot 2 \qquad \text{Using the distributive law}$$
$$= 3x + 6. \qquad \text{Note that } 3 \cdot x \text{ is the same as } 3x.$$

$$\boxed{\text{TRY EXERCISE } 47}$$

The expression $3x + 6$ has two *terms*, $3x$ and 6. In general, a **term** is a number, a variable, or a product or a quotient of numbers and/or variables. Thus, $t, 29, 5ab$, and $2x/y$ are terms in $t + 29 + 5ab + 2x/y$. Note that terms are separated by plus signs.

EXAMPLE 7

List the terms in the expression $7s + st + \dfrac{3}{t}$.

SOLUTION   Terms are separated by plus signs, so the terms in $7s + st + \dfrac{3}{t}$ are

$7s, st$, and $\dfrac{3}{t}$.

TRY EXERCISE 61

The distributive law can also be used when more than two terms are inside the parentheses.

EXAMPLE 8

Multiply: $6(s + 2 + 5w)$.

SOLUTION

$$6(s + 2 + 5w) = 6 \cdot s + 6 \cdot 2 + 6 \cdot 5w \quad \text{Using the distributive law}$$
$$= 6s + 12 + (6 \cdot 5)w \quad \text{Using the associative law for multiplication}$$
$$= 6s + 12 + 30w$$

TRY EXERCISE 55

Because of the commutative law of multiplication, the distributive law can be used on the "right": $(b + c)a = ba + ca$.

EXAMPLE 9

Multiply: $(c + 4)5$.

SOLUTION

$$(c + 4)5 = c \cdot 5 + 4 \cdot 5 \quad \text{Using the distributive law on the right}$$
$$= 5c + 20 \quad \text{Using the commutative law; } c \cdot 5 = 5c$$

TRY EXERCISE 57

CAUTION!   To use the distributive law for removing parentheses, be sure to multiply *each* term inside the parentheses by the multiplier outside. Thus,

$\cancel{a(b + c) = ab + c}$ but $a(b + c) = ab + ac$.

The Distributive Law and Factoring

If we use the distributive law in reverse, we have the basis of a process called **factoring**: $ab + ac = a(b + c)$. To **factor** an expression means to write an equivalent expression that is a product. The parts of the product are called **factors**. Note that "factor" can be used as either a verb or a noun. Thus in the expression $5t$, the factors are 5 and t. In the expression $4(m + n)$, the factors are 4 and $(m + n)$. A **common factor** is a factor that appears in every term in an expression.

EXAMPLE 10 Use the distributive law to factor each of the following.

a) $3x + 3y$ **b)** $7x + 21y + 7$

SOLUTION

a) By the distributive law,

$$3x + 3y = 3(x + y).$$ The common factor for $3x$ and $3y$ is 3.

b) $7x + 21y + 7 = 7 \cdot x + 7 \cdot 3y + 7 \cdot 1$ The common factor is 7.

$$= 7(x + 3y + 1)$$ Using the distributive law.
Be sure to include both the 1 and the common factor, 7.

TRY EXERCISE 69

To check our factoring, we multiply to see if the original expression is obtained. For example, to check the **factorization** in Example 10(b), note that

$$7(x + 3y + 1) = 7 \cdot x + 7 \cdot 3y + 7 \cdot 1$$
$$= 7x + 21y + 7.$$

Since $7x + 21y + 7$ is what we started with in Example 10(b), we have a check.

CAUTION! Do not confuse **terms** with **factors**. Terms are separated by plus signs, and factors are parts of products. The distributive law is used when there are two or more terms inside parentheses. For example, in the expression $a(b \cdot c)$, b and c are factors, not terms. We can use the commutative and associative laws to reorder and regroup the factors, but the distributive law does not apply here. Thus,

$$\cancel{a(b \cdot c) = a \cdot b \cdot a \cdot c} \quad \text{but} \quad a(b \cdot c) = (a \cdot b) \cdot c.$$

1.2   EXERCISE SET

For Extra Help

🔄 *Concept Reinforcement* *Complete each sentence using one of these terms:* commutative, associative, *or* distributive.

1. $8 + t$ is equivalent to $t + 8$ by the _____ law for addition.

2. $3(xy)$ is equivalent to $(3x)y$ by the _____ law for multiplication.

3. $(5b)c$ is equivalent to $5(bc)$ by the _____ law for multiplication.

4. mn is equivalent to nm by the _____ law for multiplication.

5. $x(y + z)$ is equivalent to $xy + xz$ by the _____ law.

6. $(9 + a) + b$ is equivalent to $9 + (a + b)$ by the _____ law for addition.

7. $a + (6 + d)$ is equivalent to $(a + 6) + d$ by the _____ law for addition.

8. $3(t + 4)$ is equivalent to $3(4 + t)$ by the _____ law for addition.

9. $5(x + 2)$ is equivalent to $(x + 2)5$ by the _____ law for multiplication.

10. $2(a + b)$ is equivalent to $2 \cdot a + 2 \cdot b$ by the _____ law.

Use the commutative law of addition to write an equivalent expression.

11. $11 + t$

12. $a + 2$

13. $4 + 8x$

14. $ab + c$

15. $9x + 3y$

16. $3a + 7b$

17. $5(a + 1)$

18. $9(x + 5)$

Use the commutative law of multiplication to write an equivalent expression.

19. $7x$

20. xy

21. st

22. $13m$

23. $5 + ab$

24. $x + 3y$

25. $5(a + 1)$

26. $9(x + 5)$

Use the associative law of addition to write an equivalent expression.

27. $(x + 8) + y$

28. $(5 + m) + r$

29. $u + (v + 7)$

30. $x + (2 + y)$

31. $(ab + c) + d$

32. $(m + np) + r$

Use the associative law of multiplication to write an equivalent expression.

33. $(8x)y$

34. $(4u)v$

35. $2(ab)$

36. $9(7r)$

37. $3[2(a + b)]$

38. $5[x(2 + y)]$

Use the commutative and/or associative laws to write two equivalent expressions. Answers may vary.

39. $s + (t + 6)$

40. $7 + (v + w)$

41. $(17a)b$

42. $x(3y)$

Use the commutative and/or associative laws to show why the expression on the left is equivalent to the expression on the right. Write a series of steps with labels, as in Example 4.

43. $(1 + x) + 2$ is equivalent to $x + 3$

44. $(2a)4$ is equivalent to $8a$

45. $(m \cdot 3)7$ is equivalent to $21m$

46. $4 + (9 + x)$ is equivalent to $x + 13$

Multiply.

47. $2(x + 15)$

48. $3(x + 5)$

49. $4(1 + a)$

50. $6(v + 4)$

51. $8(3 + y)$

52. $7(s + 1)$

53. $10(9x + 6)$

54. $9(6m + 7)$

55. $5(r + 2 + 3t)$

56. $4(5x + 8 + 3p)$

57. $(a + b)2$

58. $(x + 2)7$

59. $(x + y + 2)5$

60. $(2 + a + b)6$

List the terms in each expression.

61. $x + xyz + 1$

62. $9 + 17a + abc$

63. $2a + \dfrac{a}{3b} + 5b$

64. $3xy + 20 + \dfrac{4a}{b}$

65. $4(x + y)$

66. $(7 + y)2$

67. $4x + 4y$

68. $14 + 2y$

Use the distributive law to factor each of the following. Check by multiplying.

69. $2a + 2b$

70. $5y + 5z$

71. $7 + 7y$

72. $13 + 13x$

73. $32x + 4$

74. $20a + 5$

75. $5x + 10 + 15y$

76. $3 + 27b + 6c$

77. $7a + 35b$

78. $8x + 24y$

79. $44x + 11y + 22z$

80. $14a + 56b + 7$

List the factors in each expression.

81. $5n$

82. uv

83. $3(x + y)$

84. $(a + b)12$

85. $7 \cdot a \cdot b$

86. $m \cdot n \cdot 2$

87. $(a - b)(x - y)$

88. $(3 - a)(b + c)$

89. Is subtraction commutative? Why or why not?

90. Is division associative? Why or why not?

Skill Review

To the student and the instructor: **Exercises included for Skill Review include skills previously studied in the text. Often these exercises provide preparation for the next section of the text. The numbers in brackets immediately following the directions or exercise indicate the section in which the skill was introduced. The answers to all Skill Review exercises appear at the back of the book. If a Skill Review exercise gives you difficulty, review the material in the indicated section of the text.**

Translate to an algebraic expression. [1.1]

91. Half of Kara's salary

92. Twice the sum of m and 3

Synthesis

 93. Give an example illustrating the distributive law, and identify the terms and the factors in your example. Explain how you can determine terms and factors in an expression.

94. Explain how the distributive, commutative, and associative laws can be used to show that $2(3x + 4y)$ is equivalent to $6x + 8y$.

Tell whether the expressions in each pairing are equivalent. Then explain why or why not.

95. $8 + 4(a + b)$ and $4(2 + a + b)$

96. $5(a \cdot b)$ and $5 \cdot a \cdot 5 \cdot b$

97. $7 \div 3m$ and $m \cdot 3 \div 7$

98. $(rt + st)5$ and $5t(r + s)$

99. $30y + x \cdot 15$ and $5[2(x + 3y)]$

100. $[c(2 + 3b)]5$ and $10c + 15bc$

101. Evaluate the expressions $3(2 + x)$ and $6 + x$ for $x = 0$. Do your results indicate that $3(2 + x)$ and $6 + x$ are equivalent? Why or why not?

102. Factor $15x + 40$. Then evaluate both $15x + 40$ and the factorization for $x = 4$. Do your results *guarantee* that the factorization is correct? Why or why not? (*Hint:* See Exercise 101.)

COLLABORATIVE CORNER

Mental Addition

Focus: Application of commutative and associative laws

Time: 10 minutes

Group size: 2–3

Legend has it that while still in grade school, the mathematician Carl Friedrich Gauss (1777–1855) was able to add the numbers from 1 to 100 mentally. Gauss did not add them sequentially, but rather paired 1 with 99, 2 with 98, and so on.

ACTIVITY

1. Use a method similar to Gauss's to simplify the following:

$$1 + 2 + 3 + 4 + 5 + 6 + 7 + 8 + 9 + 10.$$

One group member should add from left to right as a check.

2. Use Gauss's method to find the sum of the first 25 counting numbers:

$$1 + 2 + 3 + \cdots + 23 + 24 + 25.$$

Again, one student should add from left to right as a check.

3. How were the associative and commutative laws applied in parts (1) and (2) above?

4. Now use a similar approach involving both addition and division to find the sum of the first 10 counting numbers:

$$\begin{array}{r} 1 + 2 + 3 + \cdots + 10 \\ + 10 + 9 + 8 + \cdots + 1 \\ \hline \end{array}$$

5. Use the approach in step (4) to find the sum of the first 100 counting numbers. Are the associative and commutative laws applied in this method, too? How is the distributive law used in this approach?

1.3   Fraction Notation

Factors and Prime Factorizations ■ Fraction Notation ■ Multiplication, Division, and Simplification ■
More Simplifying ■ Addition and Subtraction

This section covers multiplication, addition, subtraction, and division with fractions. Although much of this may be review, note that fraction expressions that contain variables are also included.

Factors and Prime Factorizations

In preparation for work with fraction notation, we first review how *natural numbers* are factored. **Natural numbers** can be thought of as the counting numbers:

$$1, 2, 3, 4, 5, \ldots .*$$

(The dots indicate that the established pattern continues without ending.)

Since factors are parts of products, to factor a number, we express it as a product of two or more numbers.

Several factorizations of 12 are

$$1 \cdot 12, \quad 2 \cdot 6, \quad 3 \cdot 4, \quad 2 \cdot 2 \cdot 3.$$

It is easy to miss a factor of a number if the factorizations are not written methodically.

EXAMPLE **1**   List all factors of 18.

SOLUTION   Beginning at 1, we check all natural numbers to see if they are factors of 18. If they are, we write the factorization. We stop when we have already included the next natural number in a factorization.

1 is a factor of every number.	$1 \cdot 18$
2 is a factor of 18.	$2 \cdot 9$
3 is a factor of 18.	$3 \cdot 6$
4 is *not* a factor of 18.	
5 is *not* a factor of 18.	

6 is the next natural number, but we have already listed 6 as a factor in the product $3 \cdot 6$.

We need check no additional numbers, because any natural number greater than 6 must be paired with a factor less than 6.

We now write the factors of 18 beginning with 1, going down the list of factorizations writing the first factor, then up the list of factorizations writing the second factor:

$$1, \quad 2, \quad 3, \quad 6, \quad 9, \quad 18.$$

> TRY EXERCISE   15

Some numbers have only two different factors, the number itself and 1. Such numbers are called **prime**.

---

*A similar collection of numbers, the **whole numbers,** includes 0: 0, 1, 2, 3, ...

> ### Prime Number
>
> A *prime number* is a natural number that has exactly two different factors: the number itself and 1. The first several primes are 2, 3, 5, 7, 11, 13, 17, 19, and 23.

If a natural number other than 1 is not prime, we call it **composite**.

EXAMPLE **2** Label each number as prime, composite, or neither: 29, 4, 1.

SOLUTION

29 is prime. It has exactly two different factors, 29 and 1.

4 is not prime. It has three different factors, 1, 2, and 4. It is composite.

1 is not prime. It does not have two *different* factors. The number 1 is not considered composite. It is neither prime nor composite.

> TRY EXERCISE 5

Every composite number can be factored into a product of prime numbers. Such a factorization is called the **prime factorization** of that composite number.

EXAMPLE **3** Find the prime factorization of 36.

SOLUTION   We first factor 36 in any way that we can. One way is like this:

$$36 = 4 \cdot 9.$$

The factors 4 and 9 are not prime, so we factor them:

$$36 = 4 \cdot 9$$
$$= 2 \cdot 2 \cdot 3 \cdot 3. \quad \text{2 and 3 are both prime.}$$

The prime factorization of 36 is $2 \cdot 2 \cdot 3 \cdot 3$.

> TRY EXERCISE 25

STUDENT NOTES

When writing a factorization, you are writing an equivalent expression for the original number. Some students do this with a tree diagram:

$$36$$
$$36 = 4 \quad \cdot \quad 9$$
$$36 = 2 \cdot 2 \cdot 3 \cdot 3$$

All prime

Fraction Notation

An example of **fraction notation** for a number is

$$\frac{2}{3}. \quad \begin{array}{l} \leftarrow \text{Numerator} \\ \leftarrow \text{Denominator} \end{array}$$

The top number is called the **numerator**, and the bottom number is called the **denominator**. When the numerator and the denominator are the same nonzero number, we have fraction notation for the number 1.

> ### Fraction Notation for 1
>
> For any number a, except 0,
>
> $$\frac{a}{a} = 1.$$
>
> (Any nonzero number divided by itself is 1.)

Note that in the definition for fraction notation for the number 1, we have excluded 0. In fact, 0 cannot be the denominator of *any* fraction. In this section, we limit our discussion to natural numbers, so this situation does not arise. Later in this chapter, we will discuss why denominators cannot be 0.

Multiplication, Division, and Simplification

Recall from arithmetic that fractions are multiplied as follows.

Multiplication of Fractions

For any two fractions a/b and c/d,

$$\frac{a}{b} \cdot \frac{c}{d} = \frac{ac}{bd}.$$

(The numerator of the product is the product of the two numerators. The denominator of the product is the product of the two denominators.)

EXAMPLE   4   Multiply: **(a)** $\dfrac{2}{3} \cdot \dfrac{5}{7}$;   **(b)** $\dfrac{4}{x} \cdot \dfrac{8}{y}$.

SOLUTION   We multiply numerators as well as denominators.

a) $\dfrac{2}{3} \cdot \dfrac{5}{7} = \dfrac{2 \cdot 5}{3 \cdot 7} = \dfrac{10}{21}$

b) $\dfrac{4}{x} \cdot \dfrac{8}{y} = \dfrac{4 \cdot 8}{x \cdot y} = \dfrac{32}{xy}$

> TRY EXERCISE   53

Two numbers whose product is 1 are **reciprocals**, or **multiplicative inverses**, of each other. All numbers, except zero, have reciprocals. For example,

the reciprocal of $\dfrac{2}{3}$ is $\dfrac{3}{2}$ because $\dfrac{2}{3} \cdot \dfrac{3}{2} = \dfrac{6}{6} = 1$;

the reciprocal of 9 is $\dfrac{1}{9}$ because $9 \cdot \dfrac{1}{9} = \dfrac{9}{9} = 1$; and

the reciprocal of $\dfrac{1}{4}$ is 4 because $\dfrac{1}{4} \cdot 4 = 1$.

Reciprocals are used to rewrite division in an equivalent form that uses multiplication.

Division of Fractions

To divide two fractions, multiply by the reciprocal of the divisor:

$$\frac{a}{b} \div \frac{c}{d} = \frac{a}{b} \cdot \frac{d}{c}.$$

EXAMPLE 5   Divide: $\dfrac{1}{2} \div \dfrac{3}{5}$.

SOLUTION

$$\frac{1}{2} \div \frac{3}{5} = \frac{1}{2} \cdot \frac{5}{3} \qquad \frac{5}{3} \text{ is the reciprocal of } \frac{3}{5}.$$

$$= \frac{5}{6}$$

TRY EXERCISE 73

When one of the fractions being multiplied is 1, multiplying yields an equivalent expression because of the *identity property of* 1. A similar property could be stated for division, but there is no need to do so here.

The Identity Property of 1

For any number a,

$$a \cdot 1 = 1 \cdot a = a.$$

(Multiplying a number by 1 gives that same number.) The number 1 is called the *multiplicative identity*.

EXAMPLE 6   Multiply $\dfrac{4}{5} \cdot \dfrac{6}{6}$ to find an expression equivalent to $\dfrac{4}{5}$.

SOLUTION   Since $\frac{6}{6} = 1$, the expression $\frac{4}{5} \cdot \frac{6}{6}$ is equivalent to $\frac{4}{5} \cdot 1$, or simply $\frac{4}{5}$. We have

$$\frac{4}{5} \cdot \frac{6}{6} = \frac{4 \cdot 6}{5 \cdot 6} = \frac{24}{30}.$$

Thus, $\frac{24}{30}$ is equivalent to $\frac{4}{5}$.

The steps of Example 6 are reversed by "removing a factor equal to 1"—in this case, $\frac{6}{6}$. By removing a factor that equals 1, we can *simplify* an expression like $\frac{24}{30}$ to an equivalent expression like $\frac{4}{5}$.

To simplify, we factor the numerator and the denominator, looking for the largest factor common to both. This is sometimes made easier by writing prime factorizations. After identifying common factors, we can express the fraction as a product of two fractions, one of which is in the form a/a.

EXAMPLE 7   Simplify: **(a)** $\dfrac{15}{40}$; **(b)** $\dfrac{36}{24}$.

SOLUTION

a) Note that 5 is a factor of both 15 and 40:

$$\frac{15}{40} = \frac{3 \cdot 5}{8 \cdot 5} \qquad \text{Factoring the numerator and the denominator, using the common factor, 5}$$

$$= \frac{3}{8} \cdot \frac{5}{5} \qquad \text{Rewriting as a product of two fractions; } \frac{5}{5} = 1$$

$$= \frac{3}{8} \cdot 1 = \frac{3}{8}. \qquad \text{Using the identity property of 1 (removing a factor equal to 1)}$$

The following rules can help you quickly determine whether 2, 3, or 5 is a factor of a number.

2 is a factor of a number if the number is even (the ones digit is 0, 2, 4, 6, or 8).

3 is a factor of a number if the sum of its digits is divisible by 3.

5 is a factor of a number if its ones digit is 0 or 5.

b) $\dfrac{36}{24} = \dfrac{2 \cdot 2 \cdot 3 \cdot 3}{2 \cdot 2 \cdot 2 \cdot 3}$ Writing the prime factorizations and identifying common factors; 12/12 could also be used.

$\qquad = \dfrac{3}{2} \cdot \dfrac{2 \cdot 2 \cdot 3}{2 \cdot 2 \cdot 3}$ Rewriting as a product of two fractions; $\dfrac{2 \cdot 2 \cdot 3}{2 \cdot 2 \cdot 3} = 1$

$\qquad = \dfrac{3}{2} \cdot 1 = \dfrac{3}{2}$ Using the identity property of 1   `TRY EXERCISE` 35

It is always wise to check your result to see if any common factors of the numerator and the denominator remain. (This will never happen if prime factorizations are used correctly.) If common factors remain, repeat the process by removing another factor equal to 1 to simplify your result.

More Simplifying

"Canceling" is a shortcut that you may have used for removing a factor equal to 1 when working with fraction notation. With *great* concern, we mention it as a possible way to speed up your work. Canceling can be used only when removing common factors in numerators and denominators. Canceling *cannot* be used in sums or differences. Our concern is that "canceling" be used with understanding. Example 7(b) might have been done faster as follows:

$$\frac{36}{24} = \frac{\cancel{2} \cdot \cancel{2} \cdot 3 \cdot \cancel{3}}{\cancel{2} \cdot \cancel{2} \cdot 2 \cdot \cancel{3}} = \frac{3}{2}, \quad \text{or} \quad \frac{36}{24} = \frac{3 \cdot \cancel{12}}{2 \cdot \cancel{12}} = \frac{3}{2}, \quad \text{or} \quad \frac{\cancel{\cancel{36}}^{\,\,3}}{\cancel{\cancel{24}}_{\,\,2}} = \frac{3}{2}.$$

CAUTION!   Unfortunately, canceling is often performed incorrectly:

$$\frac{\cancel{2} + 3}{\cancel{2}} = 3, \qquad \frac{\cancel{4} - 1}{\cancel{4} - 2} = \frac{1}{2}, \qquad \frac{1\cancel{5}}{\cancel{5}4} = \frac{1}{4}.$$

The above cancellations are incorrect because the expressions canceled are *not* factors. For example, in 2 + 3, the 2 and the 3 are not factors. Correct simplifications are as follows:

$$\frac{2 + 3}{2} = \frac{5}{2}, \qquad \frac{4 - 1}{4 - 2} = \frac{3}{2}, \qquad \frac{15}{54} = \frac{5 \cdot \cancel{3}}{18 \cdot \cancel{3}} = \frac{5}{18}.$$

***Remember*: If you can't factor, you can't cancel! If in doubt, don't cancel!**

Sometimes it is helpful to use 1 as a factor in the numerator or the denominator when simplifying.

EXAMPLE **8**   Simplify: $\dfrac{9}{72}$.

SOLUTION

$$\frac{9}{72} = \frac{1 \cdot 9}{8 \cdot 9}$$ Factoring and using the identity property of 1 to write 9 as $1 \cdot 9$

$$\qquad = \frac{1 \cdot \cancel{9}}{8 \cdot \cancel{9}} = \frac{1}{8}$$ Simplifying by removing a factor equal to 1: $\dfrac{9}{9} = 1$ `TRY EXERCISE` 39

Addition and Subtraction

When denominators are the same, fractions are added or subtracted by adding or subtracting numerators and keeping the same denominator.

Addition and Subtraction of Fractions

For any two fractions a/d and b/d,

$$\frac{a}{d} + \frac{b}{d} = \frac{a+b}{d} \quad \text{and} \quad \frac{a}{d} - \frac{b}{d} = \frac{a-b}{d}.$$

EXAMPLE 9   Add and simplify: $\dfrac{4}{8} + \dfrac{5}{8}$.

SOLUTION   The common denominator is 8. We add the numerators and keep the common denominator:

$$\frac{4}{8} + \frac{5}{8} = \frac{4+5}{8} = \frac{9}{8}.$$

You can think of this as
$$4 \cdot \frac{1}{8} + 5 \cdot \frac{1}{8} = 9 \cdot \frac{1}{8}, \text{ or } \frac{9}{8}.$$

TRY EXERCISE 63

In arithmetic, we often write $1\frac{1}{8}$ rather than the "improper" fraction $\frac{9}{8}$. In algebra, $\frac{9}{8}$ is generally more useful and is quite "proper" for our purposes.

When denominators are different, we use the identity property of 1 and multiply to find a common denominator. Then we add, as in Example 9.

EXAMPLE 10   Add or subtract as indicated: **(a)** $\dfrac{7}{8} + \dfrac{5}{12}$; **(b)** $\dfrac{9}{8} - \dfrac{4}{5}$.

SOLUTION

a) The number 24 is divisible by both 8 and 12. We multiply both $\frac{7}{8}$ and $\frac{5}{12}$ by suitable forms of 1 to obtain two fractions with denominators of 24:

$$\frac{7}{8} + \frac{5}{12} = \frac{7}{8} \cdot \frac{3}{3} + \frac{5}{12} \cdot \frac{2}{2}$$

Multiplying by 1. Since $8 \cdot 3 = 24$, we multiply $\frac{7}{8}$ by $\frac{3}{3}$. Since $12 \cdot 2 = 24$, we multiply $\frac{5}{12}$ by $\frac{2}{2}$.

$$= \frac{21}{24} + \frac{10}{24}$$

Performing the multiplication

$$= \frac{31}{24}.$$

Adding fractions

b) $\dfrac{9}{8} - \dfrac{4}{5} = \dfrac{9}{8} \cdot \dfrac{5}{5} - \dfrac{4}{5} \cdot \dfrac{8}{8}$

Using 40 as a common denominator

$$= \frac{45}{40} - \frac{32}{40} = \frac{13}{40}$$

Subtracting fractions

TRY EXERCISE 69

After adding, subtracting, multiplying, or dividing, we may still need to simplify the answer.

STUDY SKILLS

Do the Exercises

- When you complete an odd-numbered exercise, you can check your answers at the back of the book. If you miss any, closely examine your work, and if necessary, consult the *Student's Solutions Manual* or your instructor for guidance.

- Do some even-numbered exercises, even if none are assigned. Because there are no answers given for them, you will gain practice doing exercises in a context similar to taking a quiz or a test. Check your answers later with a friend or your instructor.

EXAMPLE 11   Perform the indicated operation and, if possible, simplify.

a) $\dfrac{7}{10} - \dfrac{1}{5}$ b) $8 \cdot \dfrac{5}{12}$ c) $\dfrac{\frac{5}{6}}{\frac{25}{9}}$

SOLUTION

a) $\dfrac{7}{10} - \dfrac{1}{5} = \dfrac{7}{10} - \dfrac{1}{5} \cdot \dfrac{2}{2}$ Using 10 as the common denominator

$\qquad = \dfrac{7}{10} - \dfrac{2}{10}$

$\qquad = \dfrac{5}{10} = \dfrac{1 \cdot 5}{2 \cdot 5} = \dfrac{1}{2}$ Removing a factor equal to 1: $\dfrac{5}{5} = 1$

b) $8 \cdot \dfrac{5}{12} = \dfrac{8 \cdot 5}{12}$ Multiplying numerators and denominators. Think of 8 as $\frac{8}{1}$.

$\qquad = \dfrac{2 \cdot 2 \cdot 2 \cdot 5}{2 \cdot 2 \cdot 3}$ Factoring; $\dfrac{4 \cdot 2 \cdot 5}{4 \cdot 3}$ can also be used.

$\qquad = \dfrac{2 \cdot 2 \cdot 2 \cdot 5}{2 \cdot 2 \cdot 3}$ Removing a factor equal to 1: $\dfrac{2 \cdot 2}{2 \cdot 2} = 1$

$\qquad = \dfrac{10}{3}$ Simplifying

c) $\dfrac{\frac{5}{6}}{\frac{25}{9}} = \dfrac{5}{6} \div \dfrac{25}{9}$ Rewriting horizontally. Remember that a fraction bar indicates division.

$\qquad = \dfrac{5}{6} \cdot \dfrac{9}{25}$ Multiplying by the reciprocal of $\frac{25}{9}$

$\qquad = \dfrac{5 \cdot 3 \cdot 3}{2 \cdot 3 \cdot 5 \cdot 5}$ Writing as one fraction and factoring

$\qquad = \dfrac{5 \cdot 3 \cdot 3}{2 \cdot 3 \cdot 5 \cdot 5}$ Removing a factor equal to 1: $\dfrac{5 \cdot 3}{3 \cdot 5} = 1$

$\qquad = \dfrac{3}{10}$ Simplifying   TRY EXERCISE ▶ 65

TECHNOLOGY CONNECTION

Some graphing calculators can perform operations using fraction notation. Others can convert answers given in decimal notation to fraction notation. Often this conversion is done using a command found in a **menu** of options that appears when a key is pressed. To select an item from a menu, we highlight its number and press **ENTER** or simply press the number of the item.

For example, to find fraction notation for $\frac{2}{15} + \frac{7}{12}$, we enter the expression as 2/15 + 7/12. The answer is given in decimal notation. To convert this to fraction notation, we press **MATH** and select the Frac option. In this case, the notation Ans ▶ Frac shows that the graphing calculator will convert .7166666667 to fraction notation.

```
2/15+7/12
              .7166666667
Ans▶Frac
                    43/60
```

We see that $\frac{2}{15} + \frac{7}{12} = \frac{43}{60}$.

1.3   **EXERCISE SET**

For Extra Help   MyMathLab   Math XL   WATCH   DOWNLOAD

To the student and the instructor: *Beginning in this section, selected exercises are marked with the symbol* Aha!. *Students who pause to inspect an Aha! exercise should find the answer more readily than those who proceed mechanically. This is done to discourage rote memorization. Some later "Aha!" exercises in this exercise set are unmarked, to encourage students to always pause before working a problem.*

👈 *Concept Reinforcement*   *In each of Exercises 1–4, match the description with a number from the list on the right.*

1. ____ A factor of 35   a) 2

2. ____ A number that has 3 as a factor   b) 7

3. ____ An odd composite number   c) 60

4. ____ The only even prime number   d) 65

Label each of the following numbers as prime, composite, or neither.

5. 9   **6.** 15   **7.** 41   **8.** 49

9. 77   **10.** 37   **11.** 2   **12.** 1

13. 0   **14.** 16

Write all two-factor factorizations of each number. Then list all the factors of the number.

15. 50   **16.** 70   **17.** 42   **18.** 60

Find the prime factorization of each number. If the number is prime, state this.

19. 39   **20.** 34   **21.** 30

22. 55   **23.** 27   **24.** 98

25. 150   **26.** 54   **27.** 40

28. 56   **29.** 31   **30.** 180

31. 210   **32.** 79   **33.** 115

34. 143

Simplify.

35. $\dfrac{21}{35}$ **36.** $\dfrac{20}{26}$ **37.** $\dfrac{16}{56}$

38. $\dfrac{72}{27}$ **39.** $\dfrac{12}{48}$ **40.** $\dfrac{18}{84}$

41. $\dfrac{52}{13}$ **42.** $\dfrac{132}{11}$ **43.** $\dfrac{19}{76}$

44. $\dfrac{17}{51}$ **45.** $\dfrac{150}{25}$ **46.** $\dfrac{180}{36}$

47. $\dfrac{42}{50}$ **48.** $\dfrac{75}{80}$ **49.** $\dfrac{120}{82}$

50. $\dfrac{75}{45}$ **51.** $\dfrac{210}{98}$ **52.** $\dfrac{140}{350}$

Perform the indicated operation and, if possible, simplify.

53. $\dfrac{1}{2} \cdot \dfrac{3}{5}$ **54.** $\dfrac{11}{10} \cdot \dfrac{8}{5}$ **55.** $\dfrac{9}{2} \cdot \dfrac{4}{3}$

Aha! **56.** $\dfrac{11}{12} \cdot \dfrac{12}{11}$ **57.** $\dfrac{1}{8} + \dfrac{3}{8}$ **58.** $\dfrac{1}{2} + \dfrac{1}{8}$

59. $\dfrac{4}{9} + \dfrac{13}{18}$ **60.** $\dfrac{4}{5} + \dfrac{8}{15}$ **61.** $\dfrac{3}{a} \cdot \dfrac{b}{7}$

62. $\dfrac{x}{5} \cdot \dfrac{y}{z}$ **63.** $\dfrac{4}{n} + \dfrac{6}{n}$ **64.** $\dfrac{9}{x} - \dfrac{5}{x}$

65. $\dfrac{3}{10} + \dfrac{8}{15}$ **66.** $\dfrac{7}{8} + \dfrac{5}{12}$ **67.** $\dfrac{11}{7} - \dfrac{4}{7}$

68. $\dfrac{12}{5} - \dfrac{2}{5}$ **69.** $\dfrac{13}{18} - \dfrac{4}{9}$ **70.** $\dfrac{13}{15} - \dfrac{11}{45}$

Aha! **71.** $\dfrac{20}{30} - \dfrac{2}{3}$ **72.** $\dfrac{5}{7} - \dfrac{5}{21}$ **73.** $\dfrac{7}{6} \div \dfrac{3}{5}$

74. $\dfrac{7}{5} \div \dfrac{10}{3}$ **75.** $\dfrac{8}{9} \div \dfrac{4}{15}$ **76.** $\dfrac{9}{4} \div 9$

77. $12 \div \dfrac{4}{9}$ **78.** $\dfrac{1}{10} \div \dfrac{1}{5}$ Aha! **79.** $\dfrac{7}{13} \div \dfrac{7}{13}$

80. $\dfrac{17}{8} \div \dfrac{5}{6}$ **81.** $\dfrac{\frac{2}{7}}{\frac{5}{3}}$ **82.** $\dfrac{\frac{3}{8}}{\frac{1}{5}}$

83. $\dfrac{9}{\frac{1}{2}}$ **84.** $\dfrac{\frac{3}{7}}{6}$

85. Under what circumstances would the sum of two fractions be easier to compute than the product of the same two fractions?

86. Under what circumstances would the product of two fractions be easier to compute than the sum of the same two fractions?

Skill Review

Use a commutative law to write an equivalent expression. There can be more than one correct answer. [1.2]

87. $5(x + 3)$ **88.** $7 + (a + b)$

Synthesis

89. Bryce insists that $(2 + x)/8$ is equivalent to $(1 + x)/4$. What mistake do you think is being made and how could you demonstrate to Bryce that the two expressions are not equivalent?

90. Why are 0 and 1 considered neither prime nor composite?

91. In the following table, the top number can be factored in such a way that the sum of the factors is the bottom number. For example, in the first column, 56 is factored as $7 \cdot 8$, since $7 + 8 = 15$, the bottom number. Find the missing numbers in each column.

Product	56	63	36	72	140	96	168
Factor	7						
Factor	8						
Sum	15	16	20	38	24	20	29

92. *Packaging.* Tritan Candies uses two sizes of boxes, 6 in. long and 8 in. long. These are packed end to end in bigger cartons to be shipped. What is the shortest-length carton that will accommodate boxes of either size without any room left over? (Each carton must contain boxes of only one size; no mixing is allowed.)

Simplify.

93. $\dfrac{16 \cdot 9 \cdot 4}{15 \cdot 8 \cdot 12}$

94. $\dfrac{9 \cdot 8xy}{2xy \cdot 36}$

95. $\dfrac{45pqrs}{9prst}$

96. $\dfrac{247}{323}$

97. $\dfrac{15 \cdot 4xy \cdot 9}{6 \cdot 25x \cdot 15y}$

98. $\dfrac{10x \cdot 12 \cdot 25y}{2z \cdot 30x \cdot 20y}$

99. $\dfrac{\frac{27ab}{15mn}}{\frac{18bc}{25np}}$

100. $\dfrac{\frac{45xyz}{24ab}}{\frac{30xz}{32ac}}$

101. $\dfrac{5\frac{3}{4}rs}{4\frac{1}{2}st}$

102. $\dfrac{3\frac{5}{7}mn}{2\frac{4}{5}np}$

Find the area of each figure.

103.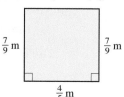

$\frac{7}{9}$ m, $\frac{7}{9}$ m, $\frac{4}{5}$ m

104.

$\frac{5}{4}$ m, $\frac{10}{7}$ m

105. Find the perimeter of a square with sides of length $3\frac{5}{9}$ m.

$3\frac{5}{9}$ m

106. Find the perimeter of the rectangle in Exercise 103.

107. Find the total length of the edges of a cube with sides of length $2\frac{3}{10}$ cm.

$2\frac{3}{10}$ cm

1.4   Positive and Negative Real Numbers

The Integers ▪ The Rational Numbers ▪ Real Numbers and Order ▪ Absolute Value

A **set** is a collection of objects. The set containing 1, 3, and 7 is usually written $\{1, 3, 7\}$. In this section, we examine some important sets of numbers. More on sets can be found in Appendix B.

The Integers

Natural numbers = $\{1, 2, 3, \dots\}$

0 1 2 3 4 5 6 7

Whole numbers = $\{0, 1, 2, 3, \dots\}$

Two sets of numbers were mentioned in Section 1.3. We represent these sets using dots on a number line, as shown at left.

To create the set of *integers,* we include all whole numbers, along with their *opposites.* To find the opposite of a number, we locate the number that is the same distance from 0 but on the other side of the number line. For example,

the opposite of 1 is negative 1, written −1;

and

the opposite of 3 is negative 3, written −3.

The **integers** consist of all whole numbers and their opposites.

STUDENT NOTES

It is not uncommon in mathematics for a symbol to have more than one meaning in different contexts. The symbol "−" in 5 − 3 indicates subtraction. The same symbol in −10 indicates the opposite of 10, or negative 10.

Opposites are discussed in more detail in Section 1.6. Note that, except for 0, opposites occur in pairs. Thus, 5 is the opposite of −5, just as −5 is the opposite of 5. Note that 0 acts as its own opposite.

Set of Integers

The set of integers = $\{\ldots, -4, -3, -2, -1, 0, 1, 2, 3, 4, \ldots\}$.

Integers are associated with many real-world problems and situations.

EXAMPLE **1**   State which integer(s) corresponds to each situation.

a) In 2006, there was $13 trillion in outstanding mortgage debt in the United States.
Source: Board of Governors of the Federal Reserve System

b) Part of Death Valley is 200 ft below sea level.

c) To lose one pound of fat, it is necessary for most people to create a 3500-calorie deficit.
Source: World Health Organization

SOLUTION

a) The integer −13,000,000,000,000 corresponds to a debt of $13 trillion.

b) The integer −200 corresponds to 200 ft below sea level.

c) The integer −3500 corresponds to a deficit of 3500 calories.

TRY EXERCISE 9

Try to Get Ahead

Try to keep one section ahead of your instructor. If you study ahead of your lectures, you can concentrate on what is being explained in class, rather than trying to write everything down. You can then write notes on only special points or questions related to what is happening in class.

The Rational Numbers

A number like $\frac{5}{9}$, although built out of integers, is not itself an integer. Another set of numbers, the **rational numbers**, contains integers, fractions, and decimals. Some examples of rational numbers are

$$\frac{5}{9}, \quad -\frac{4}{7}, \quad 95, \quad -16, \quad 0, \quad \frac{-35}{8}, \quad 2.4, \quad -0.31.$$

In Section 1.7, we show that $-\frac{4}{7}$ can be written as $\frac{-4}{7}$ or $\frac{4}{-7}$. Indeed, every number listed above can be written as an integer over an integer. For example, 95 can be written as $\frac{95}{1}$ and 2.4 can be written as $\frac{24}{10}$. In this manner, any *ratio*nal number can be expressed as the *ratio* of two integers. Rather than attempt to list all rational numbers, we use this idea of ratio to describe the set as follows.

> ### Set of Rational Numbers
>
> The set of rational numbers $= \left\{ \dfrac{a}{b} \,\middle|\, a \text{ and } b \text{ are integers and } b \neq 0 \right\}$.
>
> This is read "the set of all numbers a over b, where a and b are integers and b does not equal zero."

In Section 1.7, we explain why b cannot equal 0.

To *graph* a number is to mark its location on a number line.

EXAMPLE 2 Graph each of the following rational numbers: **(a)** $\frac{5}{2}$; **(b)** -3.2; **(c)** $\frac{11}{8}$.

SOLUTION

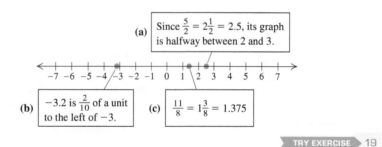

(a) Since $\frac{5}{2} = 2\frac{1}{2} = 2.5$, its graph is halfway between 2 and 3.

(b) -3.2 is $\frac{2}{10}$ of a unit to the left of -3.

(c) $\frac{11}{8} = 1\frac{3}{8} = 1.375$

TRY EXERCISE 19

It is important to remember that every rational number can be written using fraction notation or decimal notation.

EXAMPLE 3 Convert to decimal notation: $-\frac{5}{8}$.

SOLUTION   We first find decimal notation for $\frac{5}{8}$. Since $\frac{5}{8}$ means $5 \div 8$, we divide.

$$
\begin{array}{r}
0.6\,2\,5 \\
8\overline{)5.0\,0\,0} \\
\underline{4\,8\,0\,0} \\
2\,0\,0 \\
\underline{1\,6\,0} \\
4\,0 \\
\underline{4\,0} \\
0 \quad \leftarrow \text{ The remainder is 0.}
\end{array}
$$

Thus, $\frac{5}{8} = 0.625$, so $-\frac{5}{8} = -0.625$.

TRY EXERCISE 25

Because the division in Example 3 ends with the remainder 0, we consider −0.625 a **terminating decimal**. If we are "bringing down" zeros and a remainder reappears, we have a **repeating decimal**, as shown in the next example.

EXAMPLE 4

Convert to decimal notation: $\frac{7}{11}$.

SOLUTION   We divide:

$$
\begin{array}{r}
0.6\,3\,6\,3\ldots \\
11\overline{)7.0\,0\,0\,0} \\
6\,6 \\
\overline{4\,0} \\
3\,3 \\
\overline{7\,0} \\
6\,6 \\
\overline{4\,0}
\end{array}
$$

4 reappears as a remainder, so the pattern of 6's and 3's in the quotient will continue.

We abbreviate repeating decimals by writing a bar over the repeating part—in this case, $0.\overline{63}$. Thus, $\frac{7}{11} = 0.\overline{63}$.

TRY EXERCISE 29

Although we do not prove it here, every rational number can be expressed as either a terminating or repeating decimal, and every terminating or repeating decimal can be expressed as a ratio of two integers.

Real Numbers and Order

Some numbers, when written in decimal form, neither terminate nor repeat. Such numbers are called **irrational numbers**.

What sort of numbers are irrational? One example is π (the Greek letter *pi*, read "pie"), which is used to find the area and the circumference of a circle: $A = \pi r^2$ and $C = 2\pi r$.

Another irrational number, $\sqrt{2}$ (read "the square root of 2"), is the length of the diagonal of a square with sides of length 1. It is also the number that, when multiplied by itself, gives 2. No rational number can be multiplied by itself to get 2, although some approximations come close:

1.4 is an *approximation* of $\sqrt{2}$ because $(1.4)(1.4) = 1.96$;

1.41 is a better approximation because $(1.41)(1.41) = 1.9881$;

1.4142 is an even better approximation because $(1.4142)(1.4142) = 1.99996164$.

To approximate $\sqrt{2}$ on some calculators, we simply press ② and then ⱱ. With other calculators, we press ⱱ, ②, and **ENTER**, or consult a manual.

EXAMPLE 5

Graph the real number $\sqrt{3}$ on the number line.

SOLUTION   We use a calculator and approximate: $\sqrt{3} \approx 1.732$ ("$\approx$" means "approximately equals"). Then we locate this number on the number line.

TRY EXERCISE 37

TECHNOLOGY CONNECTION

To approximate $\sqrt{3}$ on most graphing calculators, we press ⟨√⟩ and then enter 3 enclosed by parentheses. Some graphing calculators will supply the left parenthesis automatically when ⟨√⟩ is pressed.

Approximate each of the following to nine decimal places.

1. $\sqrt{5}$ 2. $\sqrt{7}$

3. $\sqrt{13}$ 4. $\sqrt{27}$

5. $\sqrt{38}$ 6. $\sqrt{50}$

The rational numbers and the irrational numbers together correspond to all the points on the number line and make up what is called the **real-number system**.

> ### Set of Real Numbers
>
> The set of real numbers = The set of all numbers corresponding to points on the number line.

The following figure shows the relationships among various kinds of numbers.

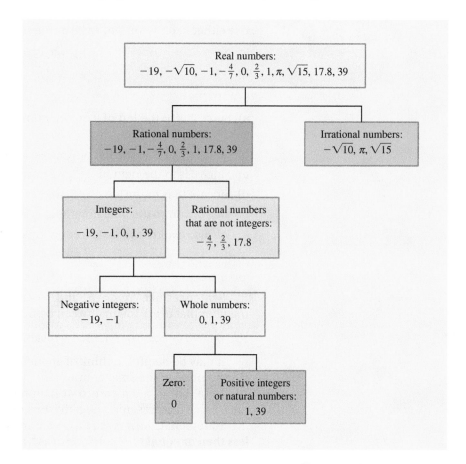

EXAMPLE   6   Which numbers in the following list are **(a)** whole numbers? **(b)** integers? **(c)** rational numbers? **(d)** irrational numbers? **(e)** real numbers?

$$-38, \quad -\frac{8}{5}, \quad 0, \quad 0.\overline{3}, \quad 4.5, \quad \sqrt{30}, \quad 52$$

SOLUTION

a) 0 and 52 are whole numbers.

b) -38, 0, and 52 are integers.

c) -38, $-\frac{8}{5}$, 0, $0.\overline{3}$, 4.5, and 52 are rational numbers.

d) $\sqrt{30}$ is an irrational number.

e) -38, $-\frac{8}{5}$, 0, $0.\overline{3}$, 4.5, $\sqrt{30}$, and 52 are real numbers.

▶ TRY EXERCISE ▶ 75

Real numbers are named in order on the number line, with larger numbers further to the right. For any two numbers, the one to the left is less than the one to the right. We use the symbol **<** to mean "**is less than.**" The sentence $-8 < 6$ means "-8 is less than 6." The symbol **>** means "**is greater than.**" The sentence $-3 > -7$ means "-3 is greater than -7."

EXAMPLE 7 Use either $<$ or $>$ for ▨ to write a true sentence.

a) 2 ▨ 9   **b)** -3.45 ▨ 1.32   **c)** 6 ▨ -12

d) -18 ▨ -5 **e)** $\frac{7}{11}$ ▨ $\frac{5}{8}$

SOLUTION

a) Since 2 is to the left of 9 on the number line, we know that 2 is less than 9, so $2 < 9$.

b) Since -3.45 is to the left of 1.32, we have $-3.45 < 1.32$.

c) Since 6 is to the right of -12, we have $6 > -12$.

d) Since -18 is to the left of -5, we have $-18 < -5$.

e) We convert to decimal notation: $\frac{7}{11} = 0.\overline{63}$ and $\frac{5}{8} = 0.625$. Thus, $\frac{7}{11} > \frac{5}{8}$.

　　We also could have used a common denominator: $\frac{7}{11} = \frac{56}{88} > \frac{55}{88} = \frac{5}{8}$.

TRY EXERCISES 41 and 45

Sentences like "$a < -5$" and "$-3 > -8$" are **inequalities**. It is useful to remember that every inequality can be written in two ways. For example,

$$-3 > -8 \quad \text{has the same meaning as} \quad -8 < -3.$$

It may be helpful to think of an inequality sign as an "arrow" with the smaller side pointing to the smaller number.

Note that $a > 0$ means that a represents a positive real number and $a < 0$ means that a represents a negative real number.

Statements like $a \leq b$ and $b \geq a$ are also inequalities. We read $a \leq b$ as "**a is less than or equal to** b" and $a \geq b$ as "**a is greater than or equal to** b."

EXAMPLE 8 Classify each inequality as true or false.

a) $-3 \leq 5$ **b)** $-3 \leq -3$ **c)** $-5 \geq 4$

SOLUTION

a) $-3 \leq 5$ is *true* because $-3 < 5$ is true.

b) $-3 \leq -3$ is *true* because $-3 = -3$ is true.

c) $-5 \geq 4$ is *false* since neither $-5 > 4$ nor $-5 = 4$ is true.

TRY EXERCISE 57

STUDENT NOTES ──────

It is important to remember that just because an equation or inequality is written or printed, it is not necessarily *true*. For instance, $6 = 7$ is an equation and $2 > 5$ is an inequality. Of course, both statements are *false*.

Absolute Value

There is a convenient terminology and notation for the distance a number is from 0 on the number line. It is called the **absolute value** of the number.

> ### Absolute Value
> We write $|a|$, read "the absolute value of a," to represent the number of units that a is from zero.

EXAMPLE 9   Find each absolute value: **(a)** $|-3|$; **(b)** $|7.2|$; **(c)** $|0|$.

SOLUTION

a) $|-3| = 3$ since -3 is 3 units from 0.

b) $|7.2| = 7.2$ since 7.2 is 7.2 units from 0.

c) $|0| = 0$ since 0 is 0 units from itself.

TRY EXERCISE 63

Distance is never negative, so numbers that are opposites have the same absolute value. If a number is nonnegative, its absolute value is the number itself. If a number is negative, its absolute value is its opposite.

TECHNOLOGY CONNECTION

Most graphing calculators use the notation abs (2) to indicate the absolute value of 2. This is often accessed using the NUM option of the MATH key. When using a graphing calculator for this, be sure to distinguish between the ⊖ and ⊙ keys (see p. 46 in Section 1.6).

1.4   EXERCISE SET

Concept Reinforcement *In each of Exercises 1–8, fill in the blank using one of the following words:* natural number, whole number, integer, rational number, terminating, repeating, irrational number, absolute value.

1. Division can be used to show that $\frac{4}{7}$ can be written as a(n) _____ decimal.

2. Division can be used to show that $\frac{3}{20}$ can be written as a(n) _____ decimal.

3. If a number is a(n) _____, it is either a whole number or the opposite of a whole number.

4. 0 is the only _____ that is not a natural number.

5. Any number of the form a/b, where a and b are integers, with $b \neq 0$, is an example of a(n) _____.

6. A number like $\sqrt{5}$, which cannot be written precisely in fraction notation or decimal notation, is an example of a(n) _____.

7. If a number is a(n) _____, then it can be thought of as a counting number.

8. When two numbers are opposites, they have the same _____.

State which real number(s) correspond to each situation.

9. *Student loans and grants.* The maximum amount that a student may borrow each year with a Stafford Loan is $10,500. The maximum annual award for the Nurse Educator Scholarship Program is $27,482.
   Sources: www.studentaid.ed.gov and www.collegezone.com

10. Using a NordicTrack exercise machine, LaToya burned 150 calories. She then drank an isotonic drink containing 65 calories.

11. The highest temperature ever recorded in a desert was 136 degrees Fahrenheit (°F) at Al-Aziziyah in the Sahara, Libya. The coldest temperature recorded in a desert was 4°F below zero in the McMurdo Dry Valleys, Antarctica.
Source: *Guinness World Records* 2007

12. The Dead Sea is 1312 ft below sea level, whereas Mt. Everest is 29,035 ft above sea level.
Source: *Guinness World Records* 2007

13. *Stock market.* The Dow Jones Industrial Average is an indicator of the stock market. On October 12, 1997, the Dow Jones fell a record 554 points. On March 16, 2002, the Dow Jones gained a record 499.19 points.
Source: www.finfacts.ie

14. Ignition occurs 10 sec before liftoff. A spent fuel tank is detached 235 sec after liftoff.

15. Kim deposited $650 in a savings account. Two weeks later, she withdrew $180.

16. *Birth and death rates.* Recently, the world birth rate was 20.09 per thousand. The death rate was 8.37 per thousand.
Source: Central Intelligence Agency, 2007

17. The halfback gained 8 yd on the first play. The quarterback was tackled for a 5-yd loss on the second play.

18. In the 2007 Masters Tournament, golfer Tiger Woods finished 3 over par. In the World Golf Championship, he finished 10 under par.
Source: PGA Tour Inc.

Graph each rational number on a number line.

19. $\frac{10}{3}$

20. $-\frac{17}{5}$

21. -4.3

22. 3.87

23. -2

24. 5

Write decimal notation for each number.

25. $\frac{7}{8}$

26. $-\frac{1}{8}$

27. $-\frac{3}{4}$

28. $\frac{11}{6}$

29. $-\frac{7}{6}$

30. $-\frac{5}{12}$

31. $\frac{2}{3}$

32. $\frac{1}{4}$

33. $-\frac{1}{2}$

34. $-\frac{1}{9}$

Aha! 35. $\frac{13}{100}$

36. $-\frac{9}{20}$

Graph each irrational number on a number line.

37. $\sqrt{5}$

38. $\sqrt{92}$

39. $-\sqrt{22}$

40. $-\sqrt{54}$

Write a true sentence using either < or >.

41. $5 \ \square \ 0$

42. $8 \ \square \ -8$

43. $-9 \ \square \ 9$

44. $0 \ \square \ -7$

45. $-8 \ \square \ -5$

46. $-4 \ \square \ -3$

47. $-5 \ \square \ -11$

48. $-3 \ \square \ -4$

49. $-12.5 \ \square \ -10.2$

50. $-10.3 \ \square \ -14.5$

51. $\frac{5}{12} \ \square \ \frac{11}{25}$

52. $-\frac{14}{17} \ \square \ -\frac{27}{35}$

For each of the following, write a second inequality with the same meaning.

53. $-2 > x$

54. $a > 9$

55. $10 \le y$

56. $-12 \ge t$

Classify each inequality as either true or false.

57. $-3 \ge -11$

58. $5 \le -5$

59. $0 \ge 8$

60. $-5 \le 7$

61. $-8 \le -8$

62. $10 \ge 10$

Find each absolute value.

63. $|-58|$

64. $|-47|$

65. $|-12.2|$

66. $|4.3|$

67. $|\sqrt{2}|$

68. $|-456|$

69. $|-\frac{9}{7}|$

70. $|-\sqrt{3}|$

71. $|0|$

72. $|-\frac{3}{4}|$

73. $|x|$, for $x = -8$

74. $|a|$, for $a = -5$

For Exercises 75–80, consider the following list:
$$-83, \quad -4.7, \quad 0, \quad \frac{5}{9}, \quad 2.\overline{16}, \quad \pi, \quad \sqrt{17}, \quad 62.$$

75. List all rational numbers.

76. List all natural numbers.

77. List all integers.

78. List all irrational numbers.

79. List all real numbers.

80. List all nonnegative integers.

81. Is every integer a rational number? Why or why not?

82. Is every integer a natural number? Why or why not?

Skill Review

83. Evaluate $3xy$ for $x = 2$ and $y = 7$. [1.1]

84. Use a commutative law to write an expression equivalent to $ab + 5$. [1.2]

Synthesis

85. Is the absolute value of a number always positive? Why or why not?

86. How many rational numbers are there between 0 and 1? Justify your answer.

87. Does "nonnegative" mean the same thing as "positive"? Why or why not?

List in order from least to greatest.

88. $13, -12, 5, -17$

89. $-23, 4, 0, -17$

90. $-\frac{2}{3}, \frac{1}{2}, -\frac{3}{4}, -\frac{5}{6}, \frac{3}{8}, \frac{1}{6}$

91. $\frac{4}{5}, \frac{4}{3}, \frac{4}{8}, \frac{4}{6}, \frac{4}{9}, \frac{4}{2}, -\frac{4}{3}$

Write a true sentence using either $<$, $>$, or $=$.

92. $|-5| \quad |-2|$

93. $|4| \quad |-7|$

94. $|-8| \quad |8|$

95. $|23| \quad |-23|$

96. $|-11| \quad |5|$

Solve. Consider only integer replacements.

Aha! **97.** $|x| = 19$

98. $|x| < 3$

99. $2 < |x| < 5$

Given that $0.3\overline{3} = \frac{1}{3}$ and $0.6\overline{6} = \frac{2}{3}$, express each of the following as a ratio of two integers.

100. $0.1\overline{1}$

101. $0.9\overline{9}$

102. $5.5\overline{5}$

103. $7.7\overline{7}$

Translate to an inequality.

104. A number a is negative.

105. A number x is nonpositive.

106. The distance from x to 0 is no more than 10.

107. The distance from t to 0 is at least 20.

To the student and the instructor: *The calculator icon, ▦, is used to indicate those exercises designed to be solved with a calculator.*

108. When Helga's calculator gives a decimal value for $\sqrt{2}$ and that value is promptly squared, the result is 2. Yet when that same decimal approximation is entered by hand and then squared, the result is not exactly 2. Why do you suppose this is?

109. Is the following statement true? Why or why not?
$$\sqrt{a^2} = |a| \quad \text{for any real number } a.$$

1.5   Addition of Real Numbers

Adding with the Number Line ▪ Adding Without the Number Line ▪ Problem Solving ▪ Combining Like Terms

We now consider addition of real numbers. To gain understanding, we will use the number line first. After observing the principles involved, we will develop rules that allow us to work more quickly without the number line.

Adding with the Number Line

To add $a + b$ on the number line, we start at a and move according to b.

a) If b is positive, we move to the right (the positive direction).

b) If b is negative, we move to the left (the negative direction).

c) If b is 0, we stay at a.

EXAMPLE   **1**   Add: $-4 + 9$.

SOLUTION   To add on the number line, we locate the first number, -4, and then move 9 units to the right. Note that it requires 4 units to reach 0. The difference between 9 and 4 is where we finish.

$$-4 + 9 = 5$$

> TRY EXERCISE   9

EXAMPLE   **2**   Add: $3 + (-5)$.

STUDENT NOTES

Parentheses are essential when a negative sign follows an operation. Just as we would never write $8 \div \times 2$, it is improper to write $3 + -5$.

SOLUTION   We locate the first number, 3, and then move 5 units to the left. Note that it requires 3 units to reach 0. The difference between 5 and 3 is 2, so we finish 2 units to the left of 0.

$$3 + (-5) = -2$$

> TRY EXERCISE   7

EXAMPLE   **3**   Add: $-4 + (-3)$.

SOLUTION   After locating -4, we move 3 units to the left. We finish a total of 7 units to the left of 0.

$$-4 + (-3) = -7$$

> TRY EXERCISE   13

EXAMPLE   **4**   Add: $-5.2 + 0$.

SOLUTION   We locate -5.2 and move 0 units. Thus we finish where we started, at -5.2.

$$-5.2 + 0 = -5.2$$

> TRY EXERCISE   11

From Examples 1–4, the following rules emerge.

Rules for Addition of Real Numbers

1. *Positive numbers*: Add as usual. The answer is positive.
2. *Negative numbers*: Add absolute values and make the answer negative (see Example 3).
3. *A positive number and a negative number*: Subtract the smaller absolute value from the greater absolute value. Then:

   a) If the positive number has the greater absolute value, the answer is positive (see Example 1).
   b) If the negative number has the greater absolute value, the answer is negative (see Example 2).
   c) If the numbers have the same absolute value, the answer is 0.

4. *One number is zero*: The sum is the other number (see Example 4).

Rule 4 is known as the **identity property of 0**.

Identity Property of 0

For any real number a,

$$a + 0 = 0 + a = a.$$

(Adding 0 to a number gives that same number.) The number 0 is called the *additive identity*.

Adding Without the Number Line

The rules listed above can be used without drawing the number line.

EXAMPLE 5   Add without using the number line.

a) $-12 + (-7)$ b) $-1.4 + 8.5$
c) $-36 + 21$ d) $1.5 + (-1.5)$
e) $-\frac{7}{8} + 0$ f) $\frac{2}{3} + \left(-\frac{5}{8}\right)$

SOLUTION

a) $-12 + (-7) = -19$ Two negatives. *Think:* Add the absolute values, 12 and 7, to get 19. Make the answer *negative*, -19.

b) $-1.4 + 8.5 = 7.1$ A negative and a positive. *Think:* The difference of absolute values is $8.5 - 1.4$, or 7.1. The positive number has the greater absolute value, so the answer is *positive*, 7.1.

c) $-36 + 21 = -15$ A negative and a positive. *Think:* The difference of absolute values is $36 - 21$, or 15. The negative number has the greater absolute value, so the answer is *negative*, -15.

d) $1.5 + (-1.5) = 0$ A negative and a positive. *Think:* Since the numbers are opposites, they have the same absolute value and the answer is 0.

e) $-\dfrac{7}{8} + 0 = -\dfrac{7}{8}$ **One number is zero.** The sum is the other number, $-\frac{7}{8}$.

f) $\dfrac{2}{3} + \left(-\dfrac{5}{8}\right) = \dfrac{16}{24} + \left(-\dfrac{15}{24}\right)$ This is similar to part (b) above. We find a common denominator and then add.

$\qquad\qquad = \dfrac{1}{24}$ **TRY EXERCISES** ▸ 15 and 21

If we are adding several numbers, some positive and some negative, the commutative and associative laws allow us to add all the positives, then add all the negatives, and then add the results. Of course, we can also add from left to right, if we prefer.

EXAMPLE 6   Add: $15 + (-2) + 7 + 14 + (-5) + (-12)$.

SOLUTION

$15 + (-2) + 7 + 14 + (-5) + (-12)$

$= 15 + 7 + 14 + (-2) + (-5) + (-12)$ Using the commutative law of addition

$= (15 + 7 + 14) + [(-2) + (-5) + (-12)]$ Using the associative law of addition

$= 36 + (-19)$ Adding the positives; adding the negatives

$= 17$ Adding a positive and a negative

TRY EXERCISE ▸ 55

Problem Solving

EXAMPLE 7   *Interest rates.*   Between 1994 and 2007, the average interest rate for a 30-yr fixed-rate mortgage dropped 2.5 percent, rose 1.75 percent, dropped 3.25 percent, and rose 1 percent. By how much did the average interest rate change?

Source: Mortgage-X.com

SOLUTION   The problem translates to a sum:

Rewording:	The 1st change	plus	the 2nd change	plus	the 3rd change	plus	the 4th change	is	the total change.
	↓	↓	↓	↓	↓	↓	↓	↓	↓
Translating:	-2.5	$+$	1.75	$+$	(-3.25)	$+$	1	$=$	Total change

Adding from left to right, we have

$$-2.5 + 1.75 + (-3.25) + 1 = -0.75 + (-3.25) + 1 = -4 + 1 = -3.$$

The average interest rate dropped 3 percent between 1994 and 2007.

TRY EXERCISE ▸ 59

Combining Like Terms

When two terms have variable factors that are exactly the same, like $5a$ and $-7a$, the terms are called **like**, or **similar**, **terms**.* The distributive law enables us to **combine**, or **collect**, **like terms**. The above rules for addition will again apply.

EXAMPLE 8   Combine like terms.

a) $-7x + 9x$

b) $2a + (-3b) + (-5a) + 9b$

c) $6 + y + (-3.5y) + 2$

SOLUTION

a)
$$-7x + 9x = (-7 + 9)x \qquad \text{Using the distributive law}$$
$$= 2x \qquad \text{Adding } -7 \text{ and } 9$$

b) $2a + (-3b) + (-5a) + 9b$
$$= 2a + (-5a) + (-3b) + 9b \qquad \text{Using the commutative law of addition}$$
$$= (2 + (-5))a + (-3 + 9)b \qquad \text{Using the distributive law}$$
$$= -3a + 6b \qquad \text{Adding}$$

c) $6 + y + (-3.5y) + 2 = y + (-3.5y) + 6 + 2 \qquad$ Using the commutative law of addition
$$= (1 + (-3.5))y + 6 + 2 \qquad \text{Using the distributive law}$$
$$= -2.5y + 8 \qquad \text{Adding}$$

> **TRY EXERCISE** 69

With practice we can omit some steps, combining like terms mentally. Note that numbers like 6 and 2 in the expression $6 + y + (-3.5y) + 2$ are constants and are also considered to be like terms.

1.5   EXERCISE SET

For Extra Help   MyMathLab   Math XL PRACTICE WATCH   DOWNLOAD

↪ *Concept Reinforcement   In each of Exercises 1–6, match the term with a like term from the column on the right.*

1. ____ $8n$

2. ____ $7m$

3. ____ 43

4. ____ $28z$

5. ____ $-2x$

6. ____ $-9t$

a) $-3z$

b) $5x$

c) $2t$

d) $-4m$

e) 9

f) $-3n$

Add using the number line.

7. $5 + (-8)$

8. $2 + (-5)$

9. $-6 + 10$

10. $-3 + 8$

11. $-7 + 0$

12. $-6 + 0$

13. $-3 + (-5)$

14. $-4 + (-6)$

Add. Do not use a number line except as a check.

15. $-35 + 0$

16. $-68 + 0$

17. $0 + (-8)$

18. $0 + (-2)$

19. $12 + (-12)$

20. $17 + (-17)$

---

*Like terms are discussed in greater detail in Section 1.8.

21. $-24 + (-17)$

22. $-17 + (-25)$

23. $-13 + 13$

24. $-31 + 31$

25. $20 + (-11)$

26. $8 + (-5)$

27. $10 + (-12)$

28. $9 + (-13)$

29. $-3 + 14$

30. $25 + (-6)$

31. $-24 + (-19)$

32. $11 + (-9)$

33. $19 + (-19)$

34. $-20 + (-6)$

35. $23 + (-5)$

36. $-15 + (-7)$

37. $-31 + (-14)$

38. $40 + (-8)$

39. $40 + (-40)$

40. $-25 + 25$

41. $85 + (-69)$

42. $63 + (-13)$

43. $-3.6 + 2.8$

44. $-6.5 + 4.7$

45. $-5.4 + (-3.7)$

46. $-3.8 + (-9.4)$

47. $\frac{4}{5} + \left(\frac{-1}{5}\right)$

48. $\frac{-2}{7} + \frac{3}{7}$

49. $\frac{-4}{7} + \frac{-2}{7}$

50. $\frac{-5}{9} + \frac{-2}{9}$

51. $-\frac{2}{5} + \frac{1}{3}$

52. $-\frac{4}{13} + \frac{1}{2}$

53. $\frac{-4}{9} + \frac{2}{3}$

54. $\frac{1}{9} + \left(\frac{-1}{3}\right)$

55. $35 + (-14) + (-19) + (-5)$

56. $-28 + (-44) + 17 + 31 + (-94)$

Aha! **57.** $-4.9 + 8.5 + 4.9 + (-8.5)$

58. $24 + 3.1 + (-44) + (-8.2) + 63$

Solve. Write your answer as a complete sentence.

59. *Gasoline prices.* In a recent year, the price of a gallon of 87-octane gasoline was $2.89. The price rose 15¢, then dropped 3¢, and then rose 17¢. By how much did the price change during that period?

60. *Natural gas prices.* In a recent year, the price of a gallon of natural gas was $1.88. The price dropped 2¢, then rose 25¢, and then dropped 43¢. By how much did the price change during that period?

61. *Telephone bills.* Chloe's cell-phone bill for July was $82. She sent a check for $50 and then ran up $63 in charges for August. What was her new balance?

62. *Profits and losses.* The following table lists the profits and losses of Premium Sales over a 3-yr period. Find the profit or loss after this period of time.

Year	Profit or loss
2006	−$26,500
2007	−$10,200
2008	+$32,400

63. *Yardage gained.* In an intramural football game, the quarterback attempted passes with the following results.

First try	13-yd loss
Second try	12-yd gain
Third try	21-yd gain

Find the total gain (or loss).

64. *Account balance.* Aiden has $450 in a checking account. He writes a check for $530, makes a deposit of $75, and then writes a check for $90. What is the balance in the account?

65. *Lake level.* Between October 2003 and February 2005, the south end of the Great Salt Lake dropped $\frac{2}{5}$ ft, rose $1\frac{1}{5}$ ft, and dropped $\frac{1}{2}$ ft. By how much did the level change?
Source: U.S. Geological Survey

66. *Peak elevation.* The tallest mountain in the world, as measured from base to peak, is Mauna Kea in Hawaii. From a base 19,684 ft below sea level, it rises 33,480 ft. What is the elevation of its peak?
Source: *Guinness World Records* 2007

67. *Credit-card bills.* Logan's credit-card bill indicates that he owes $470. He sends a check to the credit-card company for $45, charges another $160 in merchandise, and then pays off another $500 of his bill. What is Logan's new balance?

68. *Class size.* During the first two weeks of the semester, 5 students withdrew from Hailey's algebra class, 8 students were added to the class, and 4 students were dropped as "no-shows." By how many students did the original class size change?

Combine like terms.

69. $7a + 10a$

70. $3x + 8x$

71. $-3x + 12x$

72. $-2m + (-7m)$

73. $4t + 21t$

74. $5a + 8a$

75. $7m + (-9m)$

76. $-4x + 4x$

77. $-8y + (-2y)$

78. $10n + (-17n)$

79. $-3 + 8x + 4 + (-10x)$

80. $8a + 5 + (-a) + (-3)$

Find the perimeter of each figure.

81.

82.

83.

84.

85.

86.

87. Explain in your own words why the sum of two negative numbers is negative.

88. Without performing the actual addition, explain why the sum of all integers from −10 to 10 is 0.

Skill Review

89. Multiply: $7(3z + 2y + 1)$. [1.2]

90. Divide and simplify: $\frac{7}{2} \div \frac{3}{8}$. [1.3]

Synthesis

91. Under what circumstances will the sum of one positive number and several negative numbers be positive?

92. Is it possible to add real numbers without knowing how to calculate $a - b$ with a and b both nonnegative and $a \geq b$? Why or why not?

93. *Banking.* Travis had $257.33 in his checking account. After depositing $152 in the account and writing a check, his account was overdrawn by $42.37. What was the amount of the check?

94. *Sports-card values.* The value of a sports card dropped $12 and then rose $17.50 before settling at $61. What was the original value of the card?

Find the missing term or terms.

95. $4x + \underline{\quad} + (-9x) + (-2y) = -5x - 7y$

96. $-3a + 9b + \underline{\quad} + 5a = 2a - 6b$

97. $3m + 2n + \underline{\quad} + (-2m) = 2n + (-6m)$

98. $\underline{\quad} + 9x + (-4y) + x = 10x - 7y$

Aha! **99.** $7t + 23 + \underline{\quad} + \underline{\quad} = 0$

100. *Geometry.* The perimeter of a rectangle is $7x + 10$. If the length of the rectangle is 5, express the width in terms of x.

101. *Golfing.* After five rounds of golf, a golf pro was 3 under par twice, 2 over par once, 2 under par once, and 1 over par once. On average, how far above or below par was the golfer?

1.6   Subtraction of Real Numbers

Opposites and Additive Inverses ▪ Subtraction ▪ Problem Solving

In arithmetic, when a number b is subtracted from another number a, the difference, $a - b$, is the number that when added to b gives a. For example, $45 - 17 = 28$ because $28 + 17 = 45$. We will use this approach to develop an efficient way of finding the value of $a - b$ for any real numbers a and b. Before doing so, however, we must develop some terminology.

Opposites and Additive Inverses

Numbers such as 6 and −6 are *opposites*, or *additive inverses*, of each other. Whenever opposites are added, the result is 0; and whenever two numbers add to 0, those numbers are opposites.

EXAMPLE   **1**   Find the opposite of each number: **(a)** 34; **(b)** −8.3; **(c)** 0.

SOLUTION

a) The opposite of 34 is −34: $34 + (-34) = 0.$
b) The opposite of −8.3 is 8.3: $-8.3 + 8.3 = 0.$
c) The opposite of 0 is 0: $0 + 0 = 0.$

▶ **TRY EXERCISE** ▶ 19

To write the opposite, we use the symbol −, as follows.

> ## Opposite
>
> The *opposite*, or *additive inverse*, of a number a is written $-a$ (read "the opposite of a" or "the additive inverse of a").

Note that if we take a number, say 8, and find its opposite, −8, and then find the opposite of the result, we will have the original number, 8, again.

EXAMPLE   **2**   Find $-x$ and $-(-x)$ when $x = 16$.

SOLUTION

If $x = 16$, then $-x = -16$.   The opposite of 16 is −16.
If $x = 16$, then $-(-x) = -(-16) = 16$.   The opposite of the opposite of 16 is 16.

▶ **TRY EXERCISE** ▶ 25

> ## The Opposite of an Opposite
>
> For any real number a,
>
> $$-(-a) = a.$$
>
> (The opposite of the opposite of a is a.)

EXAMPLE   **3**   Find $-x$ and $-(-x)$ when $x = -3$.

SOLUTION

If $x = -3$, then $-x = -(-3) = 3$.   The opposite of −3 is 3.
Since $-(-x) = x$, it follows that $-(-(-3)) = -3$.   Finding the opposite of an opposite

▶ **TRY EXERCISE** ▶ 31

Note in Example 3 that an extra set of parentheses is used to show that we are substituting the negative number −3 for x. The notation $- -x$ is not used.

A symbol such as −8 is usually read "negative 8." It could be read "the additive inverse of 8," because the additive inverse of 8 is negative 8. It could also be read "the opposite of 8," because the opposite of 8 is −8.

A symbol like $-x$, which has a variable, should be read "the opposite of x" or "the additive inverse of x" and *not* "negative x," since to do so suggests that $-x$ represents a negative number.

The symbol "$-$" is read differently depending on where it appears. For example, $-5 - (-x)$ should be read "negative five minus the opposite of x."

EXAMPLE 4   Write each of the following in words.

a) $2 - 8$ **b)** $5 - (-4)$ **c)** $-6 - (-x)$

SOLUTION

a) $2 - 8$ is read "two minus eight."

b) $5 - (-4)$ is read "five minus negative four."

c) $-6 - (-x)$ is read "negative six minus the opposite of x."

> TRY EXERCISE 11

STUDENT NOTES

As you read mathematics, it is important to verbalize correctly the words and symbols to yourself. Consistently reading the expression $-x$ as "the opposite of x" is a good step in this direction.

As we saw in Example 3, $-x$ can represent a positive number. This notation can be used to restate a result from Section 1.5 as *the law of opposites*.

The Law of Opposites

For any two numbers a and $-a$,

$$a + (-a) = 0.$$

(When opposites are added, their sum is 0.)

A negative number is said to have a "negative *sign*." A positive number is said to have a "positive *sign*." If we change a number to its opposite, or additive inverse, we say that we have "changed or reversed its sign."

EXAMPLE 5   Change the sign (find the opposite) of each number: **(a)** -3; **(b)** -10; **(c)** 14.

SOLUTION

a) When we change the sign of -3, we obtain 3.

b) When we change the sign of -10, we obtain 10.

c) When we change the sign of 14, we obtain -14.

> TRY EXERCISE 35

Subtraction

Opposites are helpful when subtraction involves negative numbers. To see why, look for a pattern in the following:

Subtracting		*Adding the Opposite*
$9 - 5 = 4$	since $4 + 5 = 9$	$9 + (-5) = 4$
$5 - 8 = -3$	since $-3 + 8 = 5$	$5 + (-8) = -3$
$-6 - 4 = -10$	since $-10 + 4 = -6$	$-6 + (-4) = -10$
$-7 - (-10) = 3$	since $3 + (-10) = -7$	$-7 + 10 = 3$
$-7 - (-2) = -5$	since $-5 + (-2) = -7$	$-7 + 2 = -5$

The matching results suggest that we can subtract by adding the opposite of the number being subtracted. This can always be done and often provides the easiest way to subtract real numbers.

Subtraction of Real Numbers

For any real numbers a and b,

$$a - b = a + (-b).$$

(To subtract, add the opposite, or additive inverse, of the number being subtracted.)

EXAMPLE **6**   Subtract each of the following and then check with addition.

a) $2 - 6$ **b)** $4 - (-9)$ **c)** $-4.2 - (-3.6)$

d) $-1.8 - (-7.5)$ **e)** $\frac{1}{5} - \left(-\frac{3}{5}\right)$

SOLUTION

a) $2 - 6 = 2 + (-6) = -4$ The opposite of 6 is -6. We change the subtraction to addition and add the opposite.
Check: $-4 + 6 = 2$.

b) $4 - (-9) = 4 + 9 = 13$ The opposite of -9 is 9. We change the subtraction to addition and add the opposite.
Check: $13 + (-9) = 4$.

c) $-4.2 - (-3.6) = -4.2 + 3.6$ Adding the opposite of -3.6
$\quad\quad\quad\quad\quad\quad = -0.6$ *Check:* $-0.6 + (-3.6) = -4.2$.

d) $-1.8 - (-7.5) = -1.8 + 7.5$ Adding the opposite
$\quad\quad\quad\quad\quad\quad = 5.7$ *Check:* $5.7 + (-7.5) = -1.8$.

e) $\dfrac{1}{5} - \left(-\dfrac{3}{5}\right) = \dfrac{1}{5} + \dfrac{3}{5}$ Adding the opposite

$\quad\quad\quad\quad\quad = \dfrac{1+3}{5}$ A common denominator exists so we add in the numerator.

$\quad\quad\quad\quad\quad = \dfrac{4}{5}$

Check: $\dfrac{4}{5} + \left(-\dfrac{3}{5}\right) = \dfrac{4}{5} + \dfrac{-3}{5} = \dfrac{4 + (-3)}{5} = \dfrac{1}{5}$.

TRY EXERCISES 39 and 47

EXAMPLE **7**   Simplify: $8 - (-4) - 2 - (-5) + 3$.

SOLUTION

$8 - (-4) - 2 - (-5) + 3 = 8 + 4 + (-2) + 5 + 3$ To subtract, we add the opposite.
$\quad\quad\quad\quad\quad\quad\quad\quad\quad = 18$

TRY EXERCISE 109

TECHNOLOGY CONNECTION

On nearly all graphing calculators, it is essential to distinguish between the key for negation and the key for subtraction. To enter a negative number, we use ⊙ and to subtract, we use ⊖. This said, be careful not to rely on a calculator for computations that you will be expected to do by hand.

Recall from Section 1.2 that the terms of an algebraic expression are separated by plus signs. This means that the terms of $5x - 7y - 9$ are $5x$, $-7y$, and -9, since $5x - 7y - 9 = 5x + (-7y) + (-9)$.

EXAMPLE 8   Identify the terms of $4 - 2ab + 7a - 9$.

SOLUTION   We have

$$4 - 2ab + 7a - 9 = 4 + (-2ab) + 7a + (-9),$$ Rewriting as addition

so the terms are 4, $-2ab$, $7a$, and -9.

> **TRY EXERCISE** 117

EXAMPLE 9   Combine like terms.

a) $1 + 3x - 7x$

b) $-5a - 7b - 4a + 10b$

c) $4 - 3m - 9 + 2m$

SOLUTION

a)
$$
\begin{aligned}
1 + 3x - 7x &= 1 + 3x + (-7x) && \text{Adding the opposite} \\
&= 1 + (3 + (-7))x && \text{Using the distributive law.} \\
&= 1 + (-4)x && \text{Try to do this mentally.} \\
&= 1 - 4x && \text{Rewriting as subtraction to be more concise}
\end{aligned}
$$

b)
$$
\begin{aligned}
-5a - 7b - 4a + 10b &= -5a + (-7b) + (-4a) + 10b && \text{Adding the opposite} \\
&= -5a + (-4a) + (-7b) + 10b && \text{Using the commutative law of addition} \\
&= -9a + 3b && \text{Combining like terms mentally}
\end{aligned}
$$

c)
$$
\begin{aligned}
4 - 3m - 9 + 2m &= 4 + (-3m) + (-9) + 2m && \text{Rewriting as addition} \\
&= 4 + (-9) + (-3m) + 2m && \text{Using the commutative law of addition} \\
&= -5 + (-1m) && \text{We can write } -1m \text{ as } -m. \\
&= -5 - m
\end{aligned}
$$

> **TRY EXERCISE** 121

Problem Solving

We use subtraction to solve problems involving differences. These include problems that ask "How much more?" or "How much higher?"

EXAMPLE 10   *Record elevations.*   The current world records for the highest parachute jump and the lowest manned vessel ocean dive were both set in 1960. On August 16 of that year, Captain Joseph Kittinger jumped from a height of 102,800 ft above sea level. Earlier, on January 23, Jacques Piccard and Navy Lieutenant Donald Walsh descended in a bathyscaphe 35,797 ft below sea level. What was the difference in elevation between the highest parachute jump and the lowest ocean dive?

Sources: www.firstflight.org and www.seasky.org

102,800 ft   35,797 ft

SOLUTION   To find the difference between two elevations, we always subtract the lower elevation from the higher elevation:

$$\underbrace{\text{Higher elevation}} \quad - \quad \underbrace{\text{Lower elevation}}$$

$$102{,}800 \quad - \quad (-35{,}797)$$
$$= 102{,}800 + 35{,}797$$
$$= 138{,}597.$$

The parachute jump began 138,597 ft higher than the ocean dive ended.

TRY EXERCISE ▶ 135

1.6   EXERCISE SET

Concept Reinforcement   *In each of Exercises 1–8, match the expression with the appropriate wording from the column on the right.*

1. _____ $-x$

2. _____ $12 - x$

3. _____ $12 - (-x)$

4. _____ $x - 12$

5. _____ $x - (-12)$

6. _____ $-x - 12$

7. _____ $-x - x$

8. _____ $-x - (-12)$

a) x minus negative twelve

b) The opposite of x minus x

c) The opposite of x minus twelve

d) The opposite of x

e) The opposite of x minus negative twelve

f) Twelve minus the opposite of x

g) Twelve minus x

h) x minus twelve

Write each of the following in words.

9. $6 - 10$

10. $5 - 13$

11. $2 - (-12)$

12. $4 - (-1)$

13. $9 - (-t)$

14. $8 - (-m)$

15. $-x - y$

16. $-a - b$

17. $-3 - (-n)$

18. $-7 - (-m)$

Find the opposite, or additive inverse.

19. 51

20. -17

21. $-\frac{11}{3}$

22. $\frac{7}{2}$

23. -3.14

24. 48.2

Find $-x$ when x is each of the following.

25. -45

26. 26

27. $-\frac{14}{3}$

28. $\frac{1}{328}$

29. 0.101

30. 0

Find −(−x) when x is each of the following.

31. 37   **32.** 29

33. $-\frac{2}{5}$ **34.** −9.1

Change the sign. (Find the opposite.)

35. −1   **36.** −7

37. 15   **38.** 10

Subtract.

39. 7 − 10   **40.** 4 − 13

41. 0 − 6   **42.** 0 − 8

43. 2 − 5   **44.** 3 − 13

45. −4 − 3   **46.** −5 − 6

47. −9 − (−3)   **48.** −9 − (−5)

Aha! **49.** −8 − (−8)   **50.** −10 − (−10)

51. 14 − 19   **52.** 12 − 16

53. 30 − 40   **54.** 20 − 27

55. 0 − 11   **56.** 0 − 31

57. −9 − (−9)   **58.** −40 − (−40)

59. 5 − 5   **60.** 7 − 7

61. 4 − (−4)   **62.** 6 − (−6)

63. −7 − 4   **64.** −6 − 8

65. 6 − (−10)   **66.** 3 − (−12)

67. −4 − 15   **68.** −14 − 2

69. −6 − (−7)   **70.** −4 − (−7)

71. 5 − (−12)   **72.** 5 − (−6)

73. 0 − (−3)   **74.** 0 − (−5)

75. −5 − (−2)   **76.** −3 − (−1)

77. −7 − 14   **78.** −9 − 16

79. 0 − (−10)   **80.** 0 − (−1)

81. −8 − 0   **82.** −9 − 0

83. −52 − 8   **84.** −63 − 11

85. 2 − 25   **86.** 18 − 63

87. −4.2 − 3.1   **88.** −10.1 − 2.6

89. −1.3 − (−2.4)   **90.** −5.8 − (−7.3)

91. 3.2 − 8.7   **92.** 1.5 − 9.4

93. 0.072 − 1   **94.** 0.825 − 1

95. $\frac{2}{11} - \frac{9}{11}$ **96.** $\frac{3}{7} - \frac{5}{7}$

97. $\frac{-1}{5} - \frac{3}{5}$ **98.** $\frac{-2}{9} - \frac{5}{9}$

99. $-\frac{4}{17} - \left(-\frac{9}{17}\right)$ **100.** $-\frac{2}{13} - \left(-\frac{5}{13}\right)$

In each of Exercises 101–104, translate the phrase to mathematical language and simplify. See the solution to Example 10.

101. The difference between 3.8 and −5.2

102. The difference between −2.1 and −5.9

103. The difference between 114 and −79

104. The difference between 23 and −17

105. Subtract 32 from −8.

106. Subtract 19 from −7.

107. Subtract −25 from 18.

108. Subtract −31 from −5.

Simplify.

109. 16 − (−12) − 1 − (−2) + 3

110. 22 − (−18) + 7 + (−42) − 27

111. −31 + (−28) − (−14) − 17

112. −43 − (−19) − (−21) + 25

113. −34 − 28 + (−33) − 44

114. 39 + (−88) − 29 − (−83)

Aha! **115.** −93 + (−84) − (−93) − (−84)

116. 84 + (−99) + 44 − (−18) − 43

Identify the terms in each expression.

117. −3y − 8x

118. 7a − 9b

119. 9 − 5t − 3st

120. −4 − 3x + 2xy

Combine like terms.

121. 10x − 13x

122. 3a − 14a

123. 7a − 12a + 4

124. −9x − 13x + 7

125. −8n − 9 + 7n

126. −7 + 9n − 8n

127. 5 − 3x − 11

128. $2 + 3a - 7$

129. $2 - 6t - 9 - 2t$

130. $-5 + 4b - 7 - 5b$

131. $5y + (-3x) - 9x + 1 - 2y + 8$

132. $14 - (-5x) + 2z - (-32) + 4z - 2x$

133. $13x - (-2x) + 45 - (-21) - 7x$

134. $8t - (-2t) - 14 - (-5t) + 53 - 9t$

Solve.

135. *Temperature extremes.*   The highest temperature ever recorded in the United States is 134°F in Greenland Ranch, California, on July 10, 1913. The lowest temperature ever recorded is −80°F in Prospect Creek, Alaska, on January 23, 1971. How much higher was the temperature in Greenland Ranch than that in Prospect Creek?
Source: Information Please Database 2007, Pearson Education, Inc.

136. *Temperature change.*   In just 12 hr on February 21, 1918, the temperature in Granville, North Dakota, rose from −33°F to 50°F. By how much did the temperature change?
Source: Information Please Database 2007, Pearson Education, Inc.

137. *Elevation extremes.*   The lowest elevation in Asia, the Dead Sea, is 1312 ft below sea level. The highest elevation in Asia, Mount Everest, is 29,035 ft. Find the difference in elevation.
Source: Guinness World Records 2007

138. *Elevation extremes.*   The elevation of Mount Whitney, the highest peak in California, is 14,776 ft more than the elevation of Death Valley, California.

If Death Valley is 282 ft below sea level, find the elevation of Mount Whitney.
Source: *The Columbia Electronic Encyclopedia*, 6th ed., 2007 (New York: Columbia University Press)

139. *Changes in elevation.*   The lowest point in Africa is Lake Assal, which is 156 m below sea level. The lowest point in South America is the Valdes Peninsula, which is 40 m below sea level. How much lower is Lake Assal than the Valdes Peninsula?
Source: Information Please Database 2007, Pearson Education, Inc.

140. *Underwater elevation.*   The deepest point in the Pacific Ocean is the Marianas Trench, with a depth of 10,911 m. The deepest point in the Atlantic Ocean is the Puerto Rico Trench, with a depth of 8648 m. What is the difference in elevation of the two trenches?
Source: *Guinness World Records* 2007

141. Jeremy insists that if you can *add* real numbers, then you can also *subtract* real numbers. Do you agree? Why or why not?

142. Are the expressions $-a + b$ and $a + (-b)$ opposites of each other? Why or why not?

Skill Review

143. Find the area of a rectangle when the length is 36 ft and the width is 12 ft. [1.1]

144. Find the prime factorization of 864. [1.3]

Synthesis

145. Explain the different uses of the symbol "−". Give examples of each and how they should be read.

146. If a and b are both negative, under what circumstances will $a - b$ be negative?

147. *Power outages.*   During the Northeast's electrical blackout of August 14, 2003, residents of Bloomfield, New Jersey, lost power at 4:00 P.M. One resident returned from vacation at 3:00 P.M. the following day to find the clocks in her apartment reading 8:00 A.M. At what time, and on what day, was power restored?

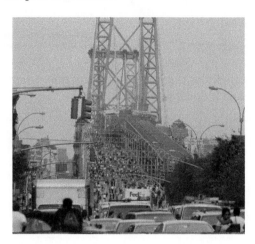

Tell whether each statement is true or false for all real numbers m and n. Use various replacements for m and n to support your answer.

148. If $m > n$, then $m - n > 0$.

149. If $m > n$, then $m + n > 0$.

150. If m and n are opposites, then $m - n = 0$.

151. If $m = -n$, then $m + n = 0$.

152. A gambler loses a wager and then loses "double or nothing" (meaning the gambler owes twice as much) twice more. After the three losses, the gambler's assets are $-\$20$. Explain how much the gambler originally bet and how the \$20 debt occurred.

153. List the keystrokes needed to compute $-9 - (-7)$.

154. If n is positive and m is negative, what is the sign of $n + (-m)$? Why?

1.7   Multiplication and Division of Real Numbers

Multiplication ■ Division

We now develop rules for multiplication and division of real numbers. Because multiplication and division are closely related, the rules are quite similar.

Multiplication

We already know how to multiply two nonnegative numbers. To see how to multiply a positive number and a negative number, consider the following pattern in which multiplication is regarded as repeated addition:

This number → $4(-5) = (-5) + (-5) + (-5) + (-5) = -20$ ← This number
decreases by $3(-5) = \qquad\quad (-5) + (-5) + (-5) = -15$ increases by
1 each time. $2(-5) = \qquad\qquad\qquad (-5) + (-5) = -10$ 5 each time.
                 $1(-5) = \qquad\qquad\qquad\qquad\quad (-5) = \;\; -5$
                 $0(-5) = \qquad\qquad\qquad\qquad\qquad\;\; 0 = \quad 0$

This pattern illustrates that the product of a negative number and a positive number is negative.

> ### The Product of a Negative Number and a Positive Number
>
> To multiply a positive number and a negative number, multiply their absolute values. The answer is negative.

EXAMPLE   **1**   Multiply: **(a)** $8(-5)$; **(b)** $-\frac{1}{3} \cdot \frac{5}{7}$.

SOLUTION

a) $8(-5) = -40$ *Think:* $8 \cdot 5 = 40$; make the answer negative.

b) $-\frac{1}{3} \cdot \frac{5}{7} = -\frac{5}{21}$ *Think:* $\frac{1}{3} \cdot \frac{5}{7} = \frac{5}{21}$; make the answer negative.

     TRY EXERCISE 11

The pattern developed above includes not just products of positive numbers and negative numbers, but a product involving zero as well.

The Multiplicative Property of Zero

For any real number a,

$$0 \cdot a = a \cdot 0 = 0.$$

(The product of 0 and any real number is 0.)

EXAMPLE   **2**   Multiply: $173(-452)0$.

SOLUTION   We have

$$173(-452)0 = 173[(-452)0]$$ Because of the associative law of multiplication, we can multiply the last two factors first.

$$= 173[0]$$ Using the multiplicative property of zero

$$= 0.$$ Using the multiplicative property of zero again

Note that whenever 0 appears as a factor, the product is 0.

     TRY EXERCISE 33

We can extend the above pattern still further to examine the product of two negative numbers.

This number → $2(-5) = \quad (-5) + (-5) = -10$ ← This number increases
decreases by $1(-5) = \qquad\qquad (-5) = \;-5$ by 5 each time.
1 each time. $0(-5) = \qquad\qquad\quad 0 = \quad 0$
         $-1(-5) = \qquad\quad -(-5) = \quad 5$
         $-2(-5) = -(-5) - (-5) = \quad 10$

According to the pattern, the product of two negative numbers is positive.

The Product of Two Negative Numbers

To multiply two negative numbers, multiply their absolute values. The answer is positive.

EXAMPLE 3

Multiply: **(a)** $(-6)(-8)$; **(b)** $(-1.2)(-3)$.

SOLUTION

a) The absolute value of -6 is 6 and the absolute value of -8 is 8. Thus,

$$(-6)(-8) = 6 \cdot 8 \qquad \text{Multiplying absolute values. The answer is positive.}$$
$$= 48.$$

b) $(-1.2)(-3) = (1.2)(3) \qquad \text{Multiplying absolute values. The answer is positive.}$
$$= 3.6 \qquad\qquad \text{Try to go directly to this step.}$$

> TRY EXERCISE 17

When three or more numbers are multiplied, we can order and group the numbers as we please, because of the commutative and associative laws.

EXAMPLE 4

Multiply: **(a)** $-3(-2)(-5)$; **(b)** $-4(-6)(-1)(-2)$.

SOLUTION

a) $-3(-2)(-5) = 6(-5) \qquad \text{Multiplying the first two numbers. The product of two negatives is positive.}$

$$= -30 \qquad\qquad \text{The product of a positive and a negative is negative.}$$

b) $-4(-6)(-1)(-2) = 24 \cdot 2 \qquad \text{Multiplying the first two numbers and the last two numbers}$

$$= 48$$

> TRY EXERCISE 43

We can see the following pattern in the results of Example 4.

The product of an even number of negative numbers is positive.

The product of an odd number of negative numbers is negative.

Division

Recall that $a \div b$, or $\dfrac{a}{b}$, is the number, if one exists, that when multiplied by b gives a. For example, to show that $10 \div 2$ is 5, we need only note that $5 \cdot 2 = 10$. Thus division can always be checked with multiplication.

EXAMPLE 5

Divide, if possible, and check your answer.

a) $14 \div (-7)$

b) $\dfrac{-32}{-4}$

c) $\dfrac{-10}{9}$

d) $\dfrac{-17}{0}$

SOLUTION

a) $14 \div (-7) = -2 \qquad \text{We look for a number that when multiplied by } -7 \text{ gives } 14. \text{ That number is } -2. \textit{ Check: } (-2)(-7) = 14.$

b) $\dfrac{-32}{-4} = 8 \qquad \text{We look for a number that when multiplied by } -4 \text{ gives } -32. \text{ That number is } 8. \textit{ Check: } 8(-4) = -32.$

STUDENT NOTES

Try to regard "undefined" as a mathematical way of saying "we do not give any meaning to this expression."

c) $\dfrac{-10}{9} = -\dfrac{10}{9} \qquad \text{We look for a number that when multiplied by 9 gives } -10. \text{ That number is } -\tfrac{10}{9}. \textit{ Check: } -\tfrac{10}{9} \cdot 9 = -10.$

d) $\dfrac{-17}{0}$ is **undefined**. $\qquad \text{We look for a number that when multiplied by 0 gives } -17. \text{ There is no such number because if 0 is a factor, the product is 0, not } -17.$

> TRY EXERCISE 57

The rules for signs for division are the same as those for multiplication: The quotient of a positive number and a negative number is negative; the quotient of two negative numbers is positive.

> ## Rules for Multiplication and Division
>
> To multiply or divide two nonzero real numbers:
>
> 1. Using the absolute values, multiply or divide, as indicated.
> 2. If the signs are the same, the answer is positive.
> 3. If the signs are different, the answer is negative.

Had Example 5(a) been written as $-14 \div 7$ or $-\frac{14}{7}$, rather than $14 \div (-7)$, the result would still have been -2. Thus from Examples 5(a)–5(c), we have the following:

$$\frac{-a}{b} = \frac{a}{-b} = -\frac{a}{b} \quad \text{and} \quad \frac{-a}{-b} = \frac{a}{b}.$$

EXAMPLE 6 Rewrite each of the following in two equivalent forms: **(a)** $\frac{5}{-2}$; **(b)** $-\frac{3}{10}$.

SOLUTION   We use one of the properties just listed.

a) $\dfrac{5}{-2} = \dfrac{-5}{2}$ and $\dfrac{5}{-2} = -\dfrac{5}{2}$

b) $-\dfrac{3}{10} = \dfrac{-3}{10}$ and $-\dfrac{3}{10} = \dfrac{3}{-10}$

Since $\dfrac{-a}{b} = \dfrac{a}{-b} = -\dfrac{a}{b}$

TRY EXERCISE 81

When a fraction contains a negative sign, it can be helpful to rewrite (or simply visualize) the fraction in an equivalent form.

EXAMPLE 7 Perform the indicated operation: **(a)** $\left(-\frac{4}{5}\right)\left(\frac{-7}{3}\right)$; **(b)** $-\frac{2}{7} + \frac{9}{-7}$.

SOLUTION

a) $\left(-\dfrac{4}{5}\right)\left(\dfrac{-7}{3}\right) = \left(-\dfrac{4}{5}\right)\left(-\dfrac{7}{3}\right)$ Rewriting $\dfrac{-7}{3}$ as $-\dfrac{7}{3}$

$= \dfrac{28}{15}$ Try to go directly to this step.

b) Given a choice, we generally choose a positive denominator:

$-\dfrac{2}{7} + \dfrac{9}{-7} = \dfrac{-2}{7} + \dfrac{-9}{7}$ Rewriting both fractions with a common denominator of 7

$= \dfrac{-11}{7}, \text{ or } -\dfrac{11}{7}.$

TRY EXERCISE 101

To divide with fraction notation, it is usually easiest to find a reciprocal and then multiply.

EXAMPLE 8   Find the reciprocal of each number, if it exists.

a) -27 **b)** $\frac{-3}{4}$

c) $-\frac{1}{5}$ **d)** 0

SOLUTION   Recall from Section 1.3 that we can check that two numbers are reciprocals of each other by confirming that their product is 1.

a) The reciprocal of -27 is $\frac{1}{-27}$. More often, this number is written as $-\frac{1}{27}$.
   Check: $(-27)\left(-\frac{1}{27}\right) = \frac{27}{27} = 1$.

b) The reciprocal of $\frac{-3}{4}$ is $\frac{4}{-3}$, or, equivalently, $-\frac{4}{3}$.   *Check:* $\frac{-3}{4} \cdot \frac{4}{-3} = \frac{-12}{-12} = 1$.

c) The reciprocal of $-\frac{1}{5}$ is -5.   *Check:* $-\frac{1}{5}(-5) = \frac{5}{5} = 1$.

d) The reciprocal of 0 does not exist. To see this, recall that there is no number r for which $0 \cdot r = 1$.   **TRY EXERCISE** ▶ 89

EXAMPLE 9   Divide: **(a)** $-\frac{2}{3} \div \left(-\frac{5}{4}\right)$; **(b)** $-\frac{3}{4} \div \frac{3}{10}$.

SOLUTION   We divide by multiplying by the reciprocal of the divisor.

a) $-\dfrac{2}{3} \div \left(-\dfrac{5}{4}\right) = -\dfrac{2}{3} \cdot \left(-\dfrac{4}{5}\right) = \dfrac{8}{15}$ Multiplying by the reciprocal

> Be careful not to change the sign when taking a reciprocal!

b) $-\dfrac{3}{4} \div \dfrac{3}{10} = -\dfrac{3}{4} \cdot \left(\dfrac{10}{3}\right) = -\dfrac{30}{12} = -\dfrac{5}{2} \cdot \dfrac{6}{6} = -\dfrac{5}{2}$ Removing a factor equal to 1: $\frac{6}{6} = 1$

TRY EXERCISE ▶ 109

To divide with decimal notation, it is usually easiest to carry out the division.

EXAMPLE 10   Divide: $27.9 \div (-3)$.

SOLUTION

$$27.9 \div (-3) = \frac{27.9}{-3} = -9.3$$ Dividing: $3\overline{)27.9}$ with quotient 9.3.
The answer is negative.

TRY EXERCISE ▶ 67

In Example 5(d), we explained why we cannot divide -17 by 0. To see why *no* nonzero number b can be divided by 0, remember that $b \div 0$ would have to be the number that when multiplied by 0 gives b. But since the product of 0 and any number is 0, not b, we say that $b \div 0$ is **undefined** for $b \neq 0$. In the special case of $0 \div 0$, we look for a number r such that $0 \div 0 = r$ and $r \cdot 0 = 0$. But, $r \cdot 0 = 0$ for *any* number r. For this reason, we say that $b \div 0$ is undefined for any choice of b.*

Finally, note that $0 \div 7 = 0$ since $0 \cdot 7 = 0$. This can be written $0/7 = 0$. It is important not to confuse division *by* 0 with division *into* 0.

---

*Sometimes $0 \div 0$ is said to be *indeterminate*.

EXAMPLE **11**   Divide, if possible: **(a)** $\frac{0}{-2}$; **(b)** $\frac{5}{0}$.

SOLUTION

a) $\dfrac{0}{-2} = 0$ We can divide 0 by a nonzero number.
   Check: $0(-2) = 0$.

b) $\dfrac{5}{0}$ is undefined.   We cannot divide by 0.

> TRY EXERCISE 73

Division Involving Zero

For any real number a,

$$\frac{a}{0} \text{ is undefined,}$$

and for $a \neq 0$,

$$\frac{0}{a} = 0.$$

It is important *not* to confuse *opposite* with *reciprocal*. Keep in mind that the opposite, or additive inverse, of a number is what we add to the number to get 0. The reciprocal, or multiplicative inverse, is what we multiply the number by to get 1.

Compare the following.

Number	Opposite (Change the sign.)	Reciprocal (Invert but do not change the sign.)	
$-\dfrac{3}{8}$	$\dfrac{3}{8}$	$-\dfrac{8}{3}$	$\left(-\dfrac{3}{8}\right)\left(-\dfrac{8}{3}\right) = 1$
19	-19	$\dfrac{1}{19}$	$-\dfrac{3}{8} + \dfrac{3}{8} = 0$
$\dfrac{18}{7}$	$-\dfrac{18}{7}$	$\dfrac{7}{18}$	
-7.9	7.9	$-\dfrac{1}{7.9}$, or $-\dfrac{10}{79}$	
0	0	Undefined	

1.7   EXERCISE SET

Concept Reinforcement   *In each of Exercises 1–10, replace the blank with either 0 or 1 to match the description given.*

1. The product of two reciprocals ____

2. The sum of a pair of opposites ____

3. The sum of a pair of additive inverses ____

4. The product of two multiplicative inverses ____

5. This number has no reciprocal. ____

6. This number is its own reciprocal. ____

7. This number is the multiplicative identity. ____

8. This number is the additive identity. ____

9. A nonzero number divided by itself ____

10. Division by this number is undefined. ____

Multiply.

11. $-4 \cdot 10$

12. $-5 \cdot 6$

13. $-8 \cdot 7$

14. $-9 \cdot 2$

15. $4 \cdot (-10)$

16. $9 \cdot (-5)$

17. $-9 \cdot (-8)$

18. $-10 \cdot (-11)$

19. $-6 \cdot 7$

20. $-2 \cdot 5$

21. $-5 \cdot (-9)$

22. $-9 \cdot (-2)$

23. $-19 \cdot (-10)$

24. $-12 \cdot (-10)$

25. $11 \cdot (-12)$

26. $-13 \cdot (-15)$

27. $-25 \cdot (-48)$

28. $15 \cdot (-43)$

29. $4.5 \cdot (-28)$

30. $-49 \cdot (-2.1)$

31. $-5 \cdot (-2.3)$

32. $-6 \cdot 4.8$

33. $(-25) \cdot 0$

34. $0 \cdot (-4.7)$

35. $\frac{2}{5} \cdot \left(-\frac{5}{7}\right)$

36. $\frac{5}{7} \cdot \left(-\frac{2}{3}\right)$

37. $-\frac{3}{8} \cdot \left(-\frac{2}{9}\right)$

38. $-\frac{5}{8} \cdot \left(-\frac{2}{5}\right)$

39. $(-5.3)(2.1)$

40. $(9.5)(-3.7)$

41. $-\frac{5}{9} \cdot \frac{3}{4}$

42. $-\frac{8}{3} \cdot \frac{9}{4}$

43. $3 \cdot (-7) \cdot (-2) \cdot 6$

44. $9 \cdot (-2) \cdot (-6) \cdot 7$

Aha! 45. $27 \cdot (-34) \cdot 0$

46. $-43 \cdot (-74) \cdot 0$

47. $-\frac{1}{3} \cdot \frac{1}{4} \cdot \left(-\frac{3}{7}\right)$

48. $-\frac{1}{2} \cdot \frac{3}{5} \cdot \left(-\frac{2}{7}\right)$

49. $-2 \cdot (-5) \cdot (-3) \cdot (-5)$

50. $-3 \cdot (-5) \cdot (-2) \cdot (-1)$

51. $(-31) \cdot (-27) \cdot 0 \cdot (-13)$

52. $7 \cdot (-6) \cdot 5 \cdot (-4) \cdot 3 \cdot (-2) \cdot 1 \cdot 0$

53. $(-8)(-9)(-10)$

54. $(-7)(-8)(-9)(-10)$

55. $(-6)(-7)(-8)(-9)(-10)$

56. $(-5)(-6)(-7)(-8)(-9)(-10)$

Divide, if possible, and check. If a quotient is undefined, state this.

57. $18 \div (-2)$

58. $\frac{24}{-3}$

59. $\frac{36}{-9}$

60. $26 \div (-13)$

61. $\frac{-56}{8}$

62. $\frac{-35}{-7}$

63. $\frac{-48}{-12}$

64. $-63 \div (-9)$

65. $-72 \div 8$

66. $\frac{-50}{25}$

67. $-10.2 \div (-2)$

68. $-2 \div 0.8$

69. $-100 \div (-11)$

70. $\frac{-64}{-7}$

71. $\frac{400}{-50}$

72. $-300 \div (-13)$

73. $\frac{48}{0}$

74. $\frac{0}{-5}$

75. $-4.8 \div 1.2$

76. $-3.9 \div 1.3$

77. $\frac{0}{-9}$

78. $0 \div 18$

Aha! 79. $\frac{9.7(-2.8)0}{4.3}$

80. $\frac{(-4.9)(7.2)}{0}$

Write each expression in two equivalent forms, as in Example 6.

81. $\frac{-8}{3}$

82. $\frac{18}{-7}$

83. $\frac{29}{-35}$

84. $\frac{-10}{3}$

85. $-\frac{7}{3}$

86. $-\frac{4}{15}$

87. $\frac{-x}{2}$

88. $\frac{9}{-a}$

Find the reciprocal of each number, if it exists.

89. $-\frac{4}{5}$

90. $-\frac{13}{11}$

91. $\frac{51}{-10}$

92. $\frac{43}{-24}$

93. -10

94. 34

95. 4.3

96. -1.7

97. $\frac{-9}{4}$

98. $\frac{-6}{11}$

99. 0

100. -1

Perform the indicated operation and, if possible, simplify. If a quotient is undefined, state this.

101. $\left(\frac{-7}{4}\right)\left(-\frac{3}{5}\right)$

102. $\left(-\frac{5}{6}\right)\left(\frac{-1}{3}\right)$

103. $\frac{-3}{8} + \frac{-5}{8}$

104. $\frac{-4}{5} + \frac{7}{5}$

Aha! **105.** $\left(\frac{-9}{5}\right)\left(\frac{5}{-9}\right)$ **106.** $\left(-\frac{2}{7}\right)\left(\frac{5}{-8}\right)$

107. $\left(-\frac{3}{11}\right) - \left(-\frac{6}{11}\right)$ **108.** $\left(-\frac{4}{7}\right) - \left(-\frac{2}{7}\right)$

109. $\frac{7}{8} \div \left(-\frac{1}{2}\right)$ **110.** $\frac{3}{4} \div \left(-\frac{2}{3}\right)$

Aha! **111.** $-\frac{5}{9} \div \left(-\frac{5}{9}\right)$ **112.** $\frac{-5}{12} \div \frac{15}{7}$

113. $\frac{-3}{10} + \frac{2}{5}$ **114.** $\frac{-5}{9} + \frac{2}{3}$

115. $\frac{7}{10} \div \left(\frac{-3}{5}\right)$ **116.** $\left(\frac{-3}{5}\right) \div \frac{6}{15}$

117. $\frac{14}{-9} \div \frac{0}{3}$ **118.** $\frac{0}{-10} \div \frac{-3}{8}$

119. $\frac{-4}{15} + \frac{2}{-3}$ **120.** $\frac{3}{-10} + \frac{-1}{5}$

121. Most calculators have a key, often appearing as **1/x**, for finding reciprocals. To use this key, we enter a number and then press **1/x** to find its reciprocal. What should happen if we enter a number and then press the reciprocal key twice? Why?

122. Multiplication can be regarded as repeated addition. Using this idea and a number line, explain why $3 \cdot (-5) = -15$.

Skill Review

123. Simplify: $\frac{264}{468}$. [1.3]

124. Combine like terms: $x + 12y + 11x - 13y - 9$. [1.5]

Synthesis

125. If two nonzero numbers are opposites of each other, are their reciprocals opposites of each other? Why or why not?

126. If two numbers are reciprocals of each other, are their opposites reciprocals of each other? Why or why not?

Translate to an algebraic expression or equation.

127. The reciprocal of a sum

128. The sum of two reciprocals

129. The opposite of a sum

130. The sum of two opposites

131. A real number is its own opposite.

132. A real number is its own reciprocal.

133. Show that the reciprocal of a sum is *not* the sum of the two reciprocals.

134. Which real numbers are their own reciprocals?

135. Jenna is a meteorologist. On December 10, she notes that the temperature is $-3°F$ at 6:00 A.M. She predicts that the temperature will rise at a rate of 2° per hour for 3 hr, and then rise at a rate of 3° per hour for 6 hr. She also predicts that the temperature will then fall at a rate of 2° per hour for 3 hr, and then fall at a rate of 5° per hour for 2 hr. What is Jenna's temperature forecast for 8:00 P.M?

Tell whether each expression represents a positive number or a negative number when m and n are negative.

136. $\frac{m}{-n}$

137. $\frac{-n}{-m}$

138. $-m \cdot \left(\frac{-n}{m}\right)$

139. $-\left(\frac{n}{-m}\right)$

140. $(m + n) \cdot \frac{m}{n}$

141. $(-n - m)\frac{n}{m}$

142. What must be true of m and n if $-mn$ is to be **(a)** positive? **(b)** zero? **(c)** negative?

143. The following is a proof that a positive number times a negative number is negative. Provide a reason for each step. Assume that $a > 0$ and $b > 0$.

$$a(-b) + ab = a[-b + b]$$
$$= a(0)$$
$$= 0$$

Therefore, $a(-b)$ is the opposite of ab.

144. Is it true that for any numbers a and b, if a is larger than b, then the reciprocal of a is smaller than the reciprocal of b? Why or why not?

CONNECTING the CONCEPTS

The rules for multiplication and division of real numbers differ significantly from the rules for addition and subtraction. When simplifying an expression, look at the operation first to determine which set of rules to follow.

Addition

If the signs are the same, add absolute values.

- *Both numbers are positive:* Add as usual. The answer is positive.
- *Both numbers are negative:* Add absolute values and make the answer negative.

If the signs are different, subtract absolute values.

- *The positive number has the greater absolute value:* The answer is positive.
- *The negative number has the greater absolute value:* The answer is negative.
- *The numbers have the same absolute value:* The answer is 0.

If one number is zero, the sum is the other number.

Subtraction

Add the opposite of the number being subtracted.

Multiplication

If the signs are the same, multiply absolute values. The answer is positive.

If the signs are different, multiply absolute values. The answer is negative.

If one number is zero, the product is 0.

Division

Multiply by the reciprocal of the divisor.

MIXED REVIEW

Perform the indicated operation and, if possible, simplify.

1. $-8 + (-2)$
2. $-8 \cdot (-2)$
3. $-8 \div (-2)$
4. $-8 - (-2)$
5. $12 \cdot (-10)$
6. $13 - 20$
7. $-5 - 18$
8. $-12 \div 4$
9. $\dfrac{3}{5} - \dfrac{8}{5}$
10. $\dfrac{-12}{5} + \left(\dfrac{-3}{5}\right)$
11. $-5.6 + 4.8$
12. $1.3 \cdot (-2.9)$
13. $-44.1 \div 6.3$
14. $6.6 + (-10.7)$
15. $\dfrac{9}{5} \cdot \left(-\dfrac{20}{3}\right)$
16. $-\dfrac{5}{4} \div \left(-\dfrac{3}{4}\right)$
17. $38 - (-62)$
18. $-17 + 94$
19. $(-15) \cdot (-12)$
20. $-26 - 26$

1.8   Exponential Notation and Order of Operations

Exponential Notation   ▪   Order of Operations   ▪   Simplifying and the Distributive Law   ▪
The Opposite of a Sum

Algebraic expressions often contain *exponential notation*. In this section, we learn how to use exponential notation as well as rules for the *order of operations* in performing certain algebraic manipulations.

Exponential Notation

A product like $3 \cdot 3 \cdot 3 \cdot 3$, in which the factors are the same, is called a **power**. Powers occur often enough that a simpler notation called **exponential notation** is used. For

$$\underbrace{3 \cdot 3 \cdot 3 \cdot 3}_{4 \text{ factors}}, \quad \text{we write} \quad 3^4.$$

Because $3^4 = 81$, we can say that 81 "is a power of 3."

This is read "three to the fourth power," or simply, "three to the fourth." The number 4 is called an **exponent** and the number 3 a **base**.

Expressions like s^2 and s^3 are usually read "s squared" and "s cubed," respectively. This comes from the fact that a square with sides of length s has an area A given by $A = s^2$ and a cube with sides of length s has a volume V given by $V = s^3$.

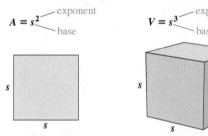

$A = s^2$ — exponent — base
$V = s^3$ — exponent — base

EXAMPLE 1   Write exponential notation for $10 \cdot 10 \cdot 10 \cdot 10 \cdot 10$.

SOLUTION

Exponential notation is 10^5.   5 is the exponent.
10 is the base.   **TRY EXERCISE** 3

EXAMPLE 2   Simplify: **(a)** 5^2;   **(b)** $(-5)^3$;   **(c)** $(2n)^3$.

SOLUTION

a) $5^2 = 5 \cdot 5 = 25$ The exponent 2 indicates two factors of 5.

b) $(-5)^3 = (-5)(-5)(-5)$ The exponent 3 indicates three factors of -5.
$ = 25(-5)$ Using the associative law of multiplication
$ = -125$

c) $(2n)^3 = (2n)(2n)(2n)$ The exponent 3 indicates three factors of $2n$.
$ = 2 \cdot 2 \cdot 2 \cdot n \cdot n \cdot n$ Using the associative and commutative laws of multiplication
$ = 8n^3$ **TRY EXERCISE** 13

STUDENT NOTES

Although most scientific and graphing calculators follow the rules for order of operations when evaluating expressions, some calculators do not. Try calculating $4 + 2 \times 5$ on your calculator. If the result shown is 30, your calculator does not follow the rules for order of operations. In this case, you will have to multiply 2×5 first and then add 4.

To determine what the exponent 1 will mean, look for a pattern in the following:

$$
\begin{aligned}
7 \cdot 7 \cdot 7 \cdot 7 &= 7^4 \\
7 \cdot 7 \cdot 7 &= 7^3 \\
7 \cdot 7 &= 7^2 \\
? &= 7^1
\end{aligned}
$$

The exponent decreases by 1 each time.

The number of factors decreases by 1 each time. To extend the pattern, we say that

$$7 = 7^1.$$

Exponential Notation

For any natural number n,

$$b^n \text{ means } \overbrace{b \cdot b \cdot b \cdot b \cdots b}^{n \text{ factors}}.$$

Order of Operations

How should $4 + 2 \times 5$ be computed? If we multiply 2 by 5 and then add 4, the result is 14. If we add 2 and 4 first and then multiply by 5, the result is 30. Since these results differ, the order in which we perform operations matters. If grouping symbols such as parentheses ( ), brackets [ ], braces { }, absolute-value symbols | |, or fraction bars appear, they tell us what to do first. For example,

$$(4 + 2) \times 5 \quad \text{indicates} \quad 6 \times 5, \quad \text{resulting in 30,}$$

and

$$4 + (2 \times 5) \quad \text{indicates} \quad 4 + 10, \quad \text{resulting in 14.}$$

Besides grouping symbols, the following conventions exist for determining the order in which operations should be performed.

Rules for Order of Operations

1. Calculate within the innermost grouping symbols, ( ), [ ], { }, | |, and above or below fraction bars.
2. Simplify all exponential expressions.
3. Perform all multiplications and divisions, working from left to right.
4. Perform all additions and subtractions, working from left to right.

Thus the correct way to compute $4 + 2 \times 5$ is to first multiply 2 by 5 and then add 4. The result is 14.

EXAMPLE 3

Simplify: $15 - 2 \cdot 5 + 3$.

SOLUTION   When no groupings or exponents appear, we *always* multiply or divide before adding or subtracting:

$$
\begin{aligned}
15 - 2 \cdot 5 + 3 &= 15 - 10 + 3 &&\text{Multiplying} \\
&= 5 + 3 \\
&= 8.
\end{aligned}
\left. \vphantom{\begin{aligned}a\\b\end{aligned}} \right\} \text{Subtracting and adding from left to right}
$$

TRY EXERCISE 31

Always calculate within parentheses first. When there are exponents and no parentheses, we simplify powers before multiplying or dividing.

EXAMPLE 4

Simplify: **(a)** $(3 \cdot 4)^2$; **(b)** $3 \cdot 4^2$.

SOLUTION

a) $(3 \cdot 4)^2 = (12)^2$ Working within parentheses first

$= 144$

b) $3 \cdot 4^2 = 3 \cdot 16$ Simplifying the power

$= 48$ Multiplying

Note that $(3 \cdot 4)^2 \neq 3 \cdot 4^2$.   ▶ TRY EXERCISE 37

CAUTION! Example 4 illustrates that, in general, $(ab)^2 \neq ab^2$.

EXAMPLE 5

Evaluate when $x = 5$: **(a)** $(-x)^2$; **(b)** $-x^2$.

SOLUTION

a) $(-x)^2 = (-5)^2 = (-5)(-5) = 25$ We square the opposite of 5.

b) $-x^2 = -5^2 = -25$ We square 5 and then find the opposite.

▶ TRY EXERCISE 15

CAUTION! Example 5 illustrates that, in general, $(-x)^2 \neq -x^2$.

To simplify $-x^2$, it may help to write

$$-x^2 = (-1)x^2.$$

EXAMPLE 6

Evaluate $-15 \div 3(6 - a)^3$ when $a = 4$.

SOLUTION

$$-15 \div 3(6 - a)^3 = -15 \div 3(6 - 4)^3 \quad \text{Substituting 4 for } a$$
$$= -15 \div 3(2)^3 \quad \text{Working within parentheses first}$$
$$= -15 \div 3 \cdot 8 \quad \text{Simplifying the exponential expression}$$
$$= -5 \cdot 8 \Big\} \quad \text{Dividing and multiplying from}$$
$$= -40 \quad \text{left to right}$$

▶ TRY EXERCISE 67

STUDENT NOTES ────────

When simplifying an expression, it is important to copy the entire expression on each line, not just the parts that have been simplified in a given step. As shown in Examples 6 and 7, each line should be equivalent to the line above it.

────────

The symbols ( ), [ ], and { } are all used in the same way. Used inside or next to each other, they make it easier to locate the left and right sides of a grouping. When combinations of grouping symbols are used, we begin with the innermost grouping symbols and work to the outside.

EXAMPLE 7   Simplify: $8 \div 4 + 3[9 + 2(3 - 5)^3]$.

SOLUTION

$8 \div 4 + 3[9 + 2(3 - 5)^3] = 8 \div 4 + 3[9 + 2(-2)^3]$ Doing the calculations in the innermost grouping symbols first

$= 8 \div 4 + 3[9 + 2(-8)]$ $(-2)^3 = (-2)(-2)(-2)$
$= -8$

$= 8 \div 4 + 3[9 + (-16)]$

$= 8 \div 4 + 3[-7]$ Completing the calculations within the brackets

$= 2 + (-21)$ Multiplying and dividing from left to right

$= -19$ TRY EXERCISE 47

EXAMPLE 8   Calculate: $\dfrac{12(9 - 7) + 4 \cdot 5}{3^4 + 2^3}$.

SOLUTION   An equivalent expression with brackets is

$[12(9 - 7) + 4 \cdot 5] \div [3^4 + 2^3]$.   Here the grouping symbols are necessary.

In effect, we need to simplify the numerator, simplify the denominator, and then divide the results:

$\dfrac{12(9 - 7) + 4 \cdot 5}{3^4 + 2^3} = \dfrac{12(2) + 4 \cdot 5}{81 + 8}$

$= \dfrac{24 + 20}{89} = \dfrac{44}{89}$.   TRY EXERCISE 55

Simplifying and the Distributive Law

Sometimes we cannot simplify within grouping symbols. When a sum or a difference is being grouped, the distributive law provides a method for removing the grouping symbols.

EXAMPLE 9   Simplify: $5x - 9 + 2(4x + 5)$.

SOLUTION

$5x - 9 + 2(4x + 5) = 5x - 9 + 8x + 10$ Using the distributive law

$= 13x + 1$ Combining like terms

TRY EXERCISE 85

Now that exponents have been introduced, we can make our definition of *like* or *similar terms* more precise. **Like**, or **similar**, **terms** are either constant terms or terms containing the same variable(s) raised to the same power(s). Thus, 5 and -7, $19xy$ and $2yx$, and $4a^3b$ and a^3b are all pairs of like terms.

EXAMPLE **10**   Simplify: $7x^2 + 3[x^2 + 2x] - 5x$.

SOLUTION

$$7x^2 + 3[x^2 + 2x] - 5x = 7x^2 + 3x^2 + 6x - 5x \qquad \text{Using the distributive law}$$

$$= 10x^2 + x \qquad \text{Combining like terms}$$

TRY EXERCISE 91

The Opposite of a Sum

When a number is multiplied by -1, the result is the opposite of that number. For example, $-1(7) = -7$ and $-1(-5) = 5$.

> ### The Property of -1
> For any real number a,
> $$-1 \cdot a = -a.$$
> (Negative one times a is the opposite of a.)

An expression such as $-(x + y)$ indicates the *opposite*, or *additive inverse*, of the sum of x and y. When a sum within grouping symbols is preceded by a "$-$" symbol, we can multiply the sum by -1 and use the distributive law. In this manner, we can find an equivalent expression for the opposite of a sum.

EXAMPLE **11**   Write an expression equivalent to $-(3x + 2y + 4)$ without using parentheses.

SOLUTION

$$-(3x + 2y + 4) = -1(3x + 2y + 4) \qquad \text{Using the property of } -1$$

$$= -1(3x) + (-1)(2y) + (-1)4 \qquad \text{Using the distributive law}$$

$$= -3x - 2y - 4 \qquad \text{Using the associative law and the property of } -1$$

TRY EXERCISE 73

Example 11 illustrates an important property of real numbers.

> ### The Opposite of a Sum
> For any real numbers a and b,
> $$-(a + b) = -a + (-b) = -a - b.$$
> (The opposite of a sum is the sum of the opposites.)

To remove parentheses from an expression like $-(x - 7y + 5)$, we can first rewrite the subtraction as addition:

$$-(x - 7y + 5) = -(x + (-7y) + 5) \qquad \text{Rewriting as addition}$$

$$= -x + 7y - 5. \qquad \text{Taking the opposite of a sum}$$

This procedure is normally streamlined to one step in which we find the opposite by "removing parentheses and changing the sign of every term":

$$-(x - 7y + 5) = -x + 7y - 5.$$

EXAMPLE 12   Simplify: $3x - (4x + 2)$.

SOLUTION

$$
\begin{aligned}
3x - (4x + 2) &= 3x + [-(4x + 2)] && \text{Adding the opposite of } 4x + 2 \\
&= 3x + [-4x - 2] && \text{Taking the opposite of } 4x + 2 \\
&= 3x + (-4x) + (-2) && \\
&= 3x - 4x - 2 && \text{Try to go directly to this step.} \\
&= -x - 2 && \text{Combining like terms}
\end{aligned}
$$

> **TRY EXERCISE** 81

In practice, the first three steps of Example 12 are generally skipped.

EXAMPLE 13   Simplify: $5t^2 - 2t - (-4t^2 + 9t)$.

SOLUTION

$$
\begin{aligned}
5t^2 - 2t - (-4t^2 + 9t) &= 5t^2 - 2t + 4t^2 - 9t && \text{Removing parentheses and changing the sign of each term inside} \\
&= 9t^2 - 11t && \text{Combining like terms}
\end{aligned}
$$

> **TRY EXERCISE** 89

Expressions such as $7 - 3(x + 2)$ can be simplified as follows:

$$
\begin{aligned}
7 - 3(x + 2) &= 7 + [-3(x + 2)] && \text{Adding the opposite of } 3(x + 2) \\
&= 7 + [-3x - 6] && \text{Multiplying } x + 2 \text{ by } -3 \\
&= 7 - 3x - 6 && \text{Try to go directly to this step.} \\
&= 1 - 3x. && \text{Combining like terms}
\end{aligned}
$$

EXAMPLE 14   Simplify: **(a)** $3n - 2(4n - 5)$; **(b)** $7x^3 + 2 - [5(x^3 - 1) + 8]$.

SOLUTION

a)
$$
\begin{aligned}
3n - 2(4n - 5) &= 3n - 8n + 10 && \text{Multiplying each term inside the parentheses by } -2 \\
&= -5n + 10 && \text{Combining like terms}
\end{aligned}
$$

b)
$$
\begin{aligned}
7x^3 + 2 - [5(x^3 - 1) + 8] &= 7x^3 + 2 - [5x^3 - 5 + 8] && \text{Removing parentheses} \\
&= 7x^3 + 2 - [5x^3 + 3] && \\
&= 7x^3 + 2 - 5x^3 - 3 && \text{Removing brackets} \\
&= 2x^3 - 1 && \text{Combining like terms}
\end{aligned}
$$

> **TRY EXERCISE** 93

As we progress through our study of algebra, it is important that we be able to distinguish between the two tasks of **simplifying an expression** and **solving an equation**. In Chapter 1, we have not solved equations, but we have simplified expressions. This enabled us to write *equivalent expressions* that were simpler than the given expression. In Chapter 2, we will continue to simplify expressions, but we will also begin to solve equations.

1.8 EXERCISE SET

 Concept Reinforcement   In each part of Exercises 1 and 2, name the operation that should be performed first. Do not perform the calculations.

1. a) $4 + 8 \div 2 \cdot 2$

   b) $7 - 9 + 15$

   c) $5 - 2(3 + 4)$

   d) $6 + 7 \cdot 3$

   e) $18 - 2[4 + (3 - 2)]$

   f) $\dfrac{5 - 6 \cdot 7}{2}$

2. a) $9 - 3 \cdot 4 \div 2$

   b) $8 + 7(6 - 5)$

   c) $5 \cdot [2 - 3(4 + 1)]$

   d) $8 - 7 + 2$

   e) $4 + 6 \div 2 \cdot 3$

   f) $\dfrac{37}{8 - 2 \cdot 2}$

Write exponential notation.

3. $x \cdot x \cdot x \cdot x \cdot x \cdot x$

4. $y \cdot y \cdot y \cdot y \cdot y \cdot y$

5. $(-5)(-5)(-5)$

6. $(-7)(-7)(-7)(-7)$

7. $3t \cdot 3t \cdot 3t \cdot 3t \cdot 3t$

8. $5m \cdot 5m \cdot 5m \cdot 5m \cdot 5m$

9. $2 \cdot n \cdot n \cdot n \cdot n$

10. $8 \cdot a \cdot a \cdot a$

Simplify.

11. 4^2

12. 5^3

13. $(-3)^2$

14. $(-7)^2$

15. -3^2

16. -7^2

17. 4^3

18. 9^1

19. $(-5)^4$

20. 5^4

21. 7^1

22. $(-1)^7$

23. $(-2)^5$

24. -2^5

25. $(3t)^4$

26. $(5t)^2$

27. $(-7x)^3$

28. $(-5x)^4$

29. $5 + 3 \cdot 7$

30. $3 - 4 \cdot 2$

31. $10 \cdot 5 + 1 \cdot 1$

32. $19 - 5 \cdot 4 + 3$

33. $6 - 70 \div 7 - 2$

34. $12 \div 3 + 18 \div 2$

Aha! 35. $14 \cdot 19 \div (19 \cdot 14)$

36. $18 - 6 \div 3 \cdot 2 + 7$

37. $3(-10)^2 - 8 \div 2^2$

38. $9 - 3^2 \div 9(-1)$

39. $8 - (2 \cdot 3 - 9)$

40. $(8 - 2 \cdot 3) - 9$

41. $(8 - 2)(3 - 9)$

42. $32 \div (-2)^2 \cdot 4$

43. $13(-10)^2 + 45 \div (-5)$

44. $2^4 + 2^3 - 10 \div (-1)^4$

45. $5 + 3(2 - 9)^2$

46. $9 - (3 - 5)^3 - 4$

47. $[2 \cdot (5 - 8)]^2$

48. $3(5 - 7)^3 \div 4$

49. $\dfrac{7 + 2}{5^2 - 4^2}$

50. $\dfrac{(5^2 - 3^2)^2}{2 \cdot 6 - 4}$

51. $8(-7) + |3(-4)|$

52. $|10(-5)| + 1(-1)$

53. $36 \div (-2)^2 + 4[5 - 3(8 - 9)^5]$

54. $-48 \div (7 - 9)^3 - 2[1 - 5(2 - 6) + 3^2]$

55. $\dfrac{7^2 - (-1)^7}{5 \cdot 7 - 4 \cdot 3^2 - 2^2}$

56. $\dfrac{(-2)^3 + 4^2}{2 \cdot 3 - 5^2 + 3 \cdot 7}$

57. $\dfrac{-3^3 - 2 \cdot 3^2}{8 \div 2^2 - (6 - |2 - 15|)}$

58. $\dfrac{(-5)^2 - 3 \cdot 5}{3^2 + 4 \cdot |6 - 7| \cdot (-1)^5}$

Evaluate.

59. $9 - 4x$, for $x = 7$

60. $1 + x^3$, for $x = -2$

61. $24 \div t^3$, for $t = -2$

62. $-100 \div a^2$, for $a = -5$

63. $45 \div a \cdot 5$, for $a = -3$

64. $50 \div 2 \cdot t$, for $t = 5$

65. $5x \div 15x^2$, for $x = 3$

66. $6a \div 12a^3$, for $a = 2$

67. $45 \div 3^2 x(x - 1)$, for $x = 3$

68. $-30 \div t(t + 4)^2$, for $t = -6$

69. $-x^2 - 5x$, for $x = -3$

70. $(-x)^2 - 5x$, for $x = -3$

71. $\dfrac{3a - 4a^2}{a^2 - 20}$, for $a = 5$

72. $\dfrac{a^3 - 4a}{a(a - 3)}$, for $a = -2$

Write an equivalent expression without using grouping symbols.

73. $-(9x + 1)$ **74.** $-(3x + 5)$

75. $-[-7n + 8]$ **76.** $-(6x - 7)$

77. $-(4a - 3b + 7c)$ **78.** $-[5n - m - 2p]$

79. $-(3x^2 + 5x - 1)$ **80.** $-(-9x^3 + 8x + 10)$

Simplify.

81. $8x - (6x + 7)$

82. $2a - (5a - 9)$

83. $2x - 7x - (4x - 6)$

84. $2a + 5a - (6a + 8)$

85. $9t - 7r + 2(3r + 6t)$

86. $4m - 9n + 3(2m - n)$

87. $15x - y - 5(3x - 2y + 5z)$

88. $4a - b - 4(5a - 7b + 8c)$

89. $3x^2 + 11 - (2x^2 + 5)$

90. $5x^4 + 3x - (5x^4 + 3x)$

91. $5t^3 + t + 3(t - 2t^3)$

92. $8n^2 - 3n + 2(n - 4n^2)$

93. $12a^2 - 3ab + 5b^2 - 5(-5a^2 + 4ab - 6b^2)$

94. $-8a^2 + 5ab - 12b^2 - 6(2a^2 - 4ab - 10b^2)$

95. $-7t^3 - t^2 - 3(5t^3 - 3t)$

96. $9t^4 + 7t - 5(9t^3 - 2t)$

97. $5(2x - 7) - [4(2x - 3) + 2]$

98. $3(6x - 5) - [3(1 - 8x) + 5]$

99. Some students use the mnemonic device PEMDAS to help remember the rules for the order of operations. Explain how this can be done and how the order of the letters in PEMDAS could lead a student to a wrong conclusion about the order of some operations.

100. Jake keys 18/2 · 3 into his calculator and expects the result to be 3. What mistake is he probably making?

Skill Review

Translate to an algebraic expression. [1.1]

101. Nine less than twice a number

102. Half of the sum of two numbers

Synthesis

103. Write the sentence $(-x)^2 \neq -x^2$ in words. Explain why $(-x)^2$ and $-x^2$ are not equivalent.

104. Write the sentence $-|x| \neq -x$ in words. Explain why $-|x|$ and $-x$ are not equivalent.

Simplify.

105. $5t - \{7t - [4r - 3(t - 7)] + 6r\} - 4r$

106. $z - \{2z - [3z - (4z - 5z) - 6z] - 7z\} - 8z$

107. $\{x - [f - (f - x)] + [x - f]\} - 3x$

108. Is it true that for all real numbers a and b,
$$ab = (-a)(-b)?$$
Why or why not?

109. Is it true that for all real numbers a, b, and c,
$$a|b - c| = ab - ac?$$
Why or why not?

If $n > 0$, $m > 0$, and $n \neq m$, classify each of the following as either true or false.

110. $-n + m = -(n + m)$

111. $m - n = -(n - m)$

112. $n(-n - m) = -n^2 + nm$

113. $-m(n - m) = -(mn + m^2)$

114. $-n(-n - m) = n(n + m)$

Evaluate.

Aha! **115.** $[x + 3(2 - 5x) \div 7 + x](x - 3)$, for $x = 3$

Aha! **116.** $[x + 2 \div 3x] \div [x + 2 \div 3x]$, for $x = -7$

117. $\dfrac{x^2 + 2^x}{x^2 - 2^x}$, for $x = 3$

118. $\dfrac{x^2 + 2^x}{x^2 - 2^x}$, for $x = 2$

119. In Mexico, between 500 B.C. and 600 A.D., the Mayans represented numbers using powers of 20 and certain symbols. For example, the symbols

represent $4 \cdot 20^3 + 17 \cdot 20^2 + 10 \cdot 20^1 + 0 \cdot 20^0$. Evaluate this number.

Source: National Council of Teachers of Mathematics, 1906 Association Drive, Reston, VA 22091

120. Examine the Mayan symbols and the numbers in Exercise 119. What numbers do

       and

each represent?

121. Calculate the volume of the tower shown below.

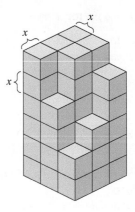

COLLABORATIVE

CORNER

Select the Symbols

Focus: Order of operations

Time: 15 minutes

Group size: 2

One way to master the rules for the order of operations is to insert symbols within a display of numbers in order to obtain a predetermined result. For example, the display

1   2   3   4   5

can be used to obtain the result 21 as follows:

$$(1 + 2) \div 3 + 4 \cdot 5.$$

Note that without an understanding of the rules for the order of operations, solving a problem of this sort is impossible.

ACTIVITY

1. Each group should prepare an exercise similar to the example shown above. (Exponents are not allowed.) To do so, first select five single-digit numbers for display. Then insert operations and grouping symbols and calculate the result.

2. Pair with another group. Each group should give the other its result along with its five-number display, and challenge the other group to insert symbols that will make the display equal the result given.

3. Share with the entire class the various mathematical statements developed by each group.

Study Summary

KEY TERMS AND CONCEPTS	EXAMPLES

SECTION 1.1: INTRODUCTION TO ALGEBRA

An **algebraic expression** is a collection of **variables** and **constants** on which operations are performed.

$5ab^3$ is an algebraic expression; 5 is a constant; and a and b are variables.

To **evaluate** an algebraic expression, substitute a number for each variable and carry out the operations. The result is a **value** of that expression.

Evaluate $\dfrac{x + y}{8}$ *for* $x = 15$ *and* $y = 9$.

$$\frac{x + y}{8} = \frac{15 + 9}{8} = \frac{24}{8} = 3$$

To find the area of a rectangle, a triangle, or a parallelogram, evaluate the appropriate formula for the given values.

Find the area of a triangle with base 3.1 m *and height* 6 m.

$$A = \tfrac{1}{2}bh = \tfrac{1}{2}(3.1 \text{ m})(6 \text{ m}) = \tfrac{1}{2}(3.1)(6)(\text{m} \cdot \text{m}) = 9.3 \text{ m}^2$$

Many problems can be solved by **translating** phrases to algebraic expressions and then forming an equation. The table on p. 4 shows translations of many words that occur in problems.

Translate to an equation. Do not solve.

When 34 is subtracted from a number, the result is 13. What is the number?

Let n represent the number.

Rewording:	34 subtracted from a number	is	13
Translating:	$n - 34$	$=$	13

An **equation** is a number sentence with the verb $=$. A substitution for the variable in an equation that makes the equation true is a **solution** of the equation.

Determine whether 9 *is a solution of* $47 - n = 38$.

$$47 - n = 38$$

$$\frac{47 - 9 \ \big| \ 38}{ 38 \overset{?}{=} 38 \quad \text{TRUE}}$$

Since $38 = 38$ is true, 9 is a solution.

SECTION 1.2: THE COMMUTATIVE, ASSOCIATIVE, AND DISTRIBUTIVE LAWS

Equivalent expressions represent the same value for any replacement of the variable.

$x + 10$ and $3 + 7 + x$ are equivalent expressions.

The Commutative Laws

$$a + b = b + a;$$
$$ab = ba$$

$3 + (-5) = -5 + 3;$

$8(10) = 10(8)$

The Associative Laws

$$a + (b + c) = (a + b) + c;$$
$$a \cdot (b \cdot c) = (a \cdot b) \cdot c$$

$-5 + (5 + 6) = (-5 + 5) + 6;$

$2 \cdot (5 \cdot 9) = (2 \cdot 5) \cdot 9$

The Distributive Law

$$a(b + c) = ab + ac$$

$$4(x + 2) = 4 \cdot x + 4 \cdot 2 = 4x + 8$$

The distributive law is used to multiply and to **factor** expressions.

Multiply: $3(2x + 5y)$.

$$3(2x + 5y) = 3 \cdot 2x + 3 \cdot 5y = 6x + 15y$$

Factor: $16x + 24y + 8$.

$$16x + 24y + 8 = 8(2x + 3y + 1)$$

SECTION 1.3: FRACTION NOTATION

Natural numbers: $\{1, 2, 3, \ldots\}$
Whole numbers: $\{0, 1, 2, 3, \ldots\}$

15, 39, and 1567 are some natural numbers.
0, 5, 16, and 2890 are some whole numbers.

A **prime** number has only two different factors, the number itself and 1. Natural numbers that have factors other than 1 and the number itself are **composite** numbers.

2, 3, 5, 7, 11, and 13 are the first six prime numbers.
4, 6, 8, 24, and 100 are examples of composite numbers.

The **prime factorization** of a composite number expresses that number as a product of prime numbers.

The prime factorization of 136 is $2 \cdot 2 \cdot 2 \cdot 17$.

For any nonzero number a,

$$\frac{a}{a} = 1.$$

$$\frac{15}{15} = 1 \quad \text{and} \quad \frac{2x}{2x} = 1$$

The Identity Property of 1

$$a \cdot 1 = 1 \cdot a = a$$

The number 1 is called the **multiplicative identity**.

$$\frac{2}{3} = \frac{2}{3} \cdot \frac{5}{5} \quad \text{since} \quad \frac{5}{5} = 1.$$

$$\frac{a}{d} + \frac{b}{d} = \frac{a + b}{d}$$

$$\frac{a}{d} - \frac{b}{d} = \frac{a - b}{d}$$

$$\frac{a}{b} \cdot \frac{c}{d} = \frac{a \cdot c}{b \cdot d}$$

$$\frac{a}{b} \div \frac{c}{d} = \frac{a}{b} \cdot \frac{d}{c}$$

$$\frac{1}{6} + \frac{3}{8} = \frac{4}{24} + \frac{9}{24} = \frac{13}{24}$$

$$\frac{5}{12} - \frac{1}{6} = \frac{5}{12} - \frac{2}{12} = \frac{3}{12} = \frac{1 \cdot 3}{4 \cdot 3} = \frac{1}{4} \cdot \frac{3}{3} = \frac{1}{4} \cdot 1 = \frac{1}{4}$$

$$\frac{2}{5} \cdot \frac{7}{8} = \frac{2 \cdot 7}{5 \cdot 2 \cdot 4} = \frac{7}{20} \qquad \text{Removing a factor equal to 1: } \frac{2}{2} = 1$$

$$\frac{10}{9} \div \frac{4}{15} = \frac{10}{9} \cdot \frac{15}{4} = \frac{2 \cdot 5 \cdot 3 \cdot 5}{3 \cdot 3 \cdot 2 \cdot 2} = \frac{25}{6} \qquad \text{Removing a factor equal to 1: } \frac{2 \cdot 3}{2 \cdot 3} = 1$$

SECTION 1.4: POSITIVE AND NEGATIVE REAL NUMBERS

Integers:
$\{\ldots, -3, -2, -1, 0, 1, 2, 3, \ldots\}$

Rational numbers:

$\left\{\dfrac{a}{b} \;\middle|\; a \text{ and } b \text{ are integers and } b \neq 0\right\}$

The rational numbers and the **irrational numbers** make up the set of **real numbers**.

$-25, -2, 0, 1,$ and 2000 are some integers.

$\dfrac{1}{6}, \dfrac{-3}{7}, 0, 17, 0.758,$ and $9.\overline{608}$ are some rational numbers.

$\sqrt{7}$ and π are some irrational numbers.

Every rational number can be written using fraction notation or decimal notation. When written in decimal notation, a rational number either **repeats** or **terminates**.

$-\dfrac{1}{16} = -0.0625$ This is a terminating decimal.

$\dfrac{5}{6} = 0.8333\ldots = 0.8\overline{3}$ This is a repeating decimal.

Every real number corresponds to a point on the number line. For any two numbers, the one to the left is less than the one to the right. The symbol $<$ means "**is less than**" and the symbol $>$ means "**is greater than.**"

$4 > -3.1 \qquad -\dfrac{1}{2} < \sqrt{2}$

The **absolute value** of a number is the number of units that number is from zero on the number line.

$|3| = 3$ since 3 is 3 units from $0.$
$|-3| = 3$ since -3 is 3 units from $0.$

SECTION 1.5: ADDITION OF REAL NUMBERS

To **add** two real numbers, use the rules on p. 39.

$-8 + (-3) = -11;$
$-8 + 3 = -5;$
$8 + (-3) = 5;$
$-8 + 8 = 0$

The Identity Property of 0

$$a + 0 = 0 + a = a$$

The number 0 is called the **additive identity**.

$-35 + 0 = -35;$

$0 + \dfrac{2}{9} = \dfrac{2}{9}$

SECTION 1.6: SUBTRACTION OF REAL NUMBERS

The **opposite**, or **additive inverse**, of a number a is written $-a.$ The opposite of the opposite of a is $a.$

$$-(-a) = a$$

Find $-x$ *and* $-(-x)$ *when* $x = -11.$

$\qquad -x = -(-11) = 11;$
$\qquad -(-x) = -(-(-11)) = -11 \qquad {\scriptstyle -(-x) = x}$

To **subtract** two real numbers, add the opposite of the number being subtracted.	$-10 - 12 = -10 + (-12) = -22;$ $-10 - (-12) = -10 + 12 = 2$
The **terms** of an expression are separated by plus signs. **Like terms** either are constants or have the same variable factors raised to the same power. Like terms can be **combined** using the distributive law.	In the expression $-2x + 3y + 5x - 7y$: The terms are $-2x, 3y, 5x,$ and $-7y$. The like terms are $-2x$ and $5x$, and $3y$ and $-7y$. Combining like terms gives $$-2x + 3y + 5x - 7y = -2x + 5x + 3y - 7y$$ $$= (-2 + 5)x + (3 - 7)y = 3x - 4y.$$

SECTION 1.7: MULTIPLICATION AND DIVISION OF REAL NUMBERS

To **multiply** or **divide** two real numbers, use the rules on p. 54. Division by 0 is undefined.	$(-5)(-2) = 10;$ $30 \div (-6) = -5;$ $0 \div (-3) = 0;$ $-3 \div 0$ is undefined.

SECTION 1.8: EXPONENTIAL NOTATION AND ORDER OF OPERATIONS

Exponential notation: Exponent $\overbrace{b^n = b \cdot b \cdot b \cdots b}^{n \text{ factors}}$ Base	$6^2 = 6 \cdot 6 = 36;$ $(-6)^2 = (-6) \cdot (-6) = 36;$ $-6^2 = -6 \cdot 6 = -36;$ $(6x)^2 = (6x) \cdot (6x) = 36x^2$
To perform multiple operations, use the rules for **order of operations** on p. 61.	$-3 + (3 - 5)^3 \div 4(-1) = -3 + (-2)^3 \div 4(-1)$ $= -3 + (-8) \div 4(-1)$ $= -3 + (-2)(-1)$ $= -3 + 2$ $= -1$
The Property of -1 For any real number a, $-1 \cdot a = -a.$	$-1 \cdot 5x = -5x$ and $-5x = -1(5x)$
The Opposite of a Sum For any real numbers a and b, $-(a + b) = -a - b.$	$-(2x - 3y) = -(2x) - (-3y) = -2x + 3y$
Expressions containing parentheses can be simplified by removing parentheses using the distributive law.	*Simplify:* $3x^2 - 5(x^2 - 4xy + 2y^2) - 7y^2.$ $3x^2 - 5(x^2 - 4xy + 2y^2) - 7y^2 = 3x^2 - 5x^2 + 20xy - 10y^2 - 7y^2$ $= -2x^2 + 20xy - 17y^2$

Review Exercises: Chapter 1

In each of Exercises 1–10, classify the statement as either true or false.

1. $4x - 5y$ and $12 - 7a$ are both algebraic expressions containing two terms. [1.2]

2. $3t + 1 = 7$ and $8 - 2 = 9$ are both equations. [1.1]

3. The fact that $2 + x$ is equivalent to $x + 2$ is an illustration of the associative law for addition. [1.2]

4. The statement $4(a + 3) = 4 \cdot a + 4 \cdot 3$ illustrates the distributive law. [1.2]

5. The number 2 is neither prime nor composite. [1.3]

6. Every irrational number can be written as a repeating decimal or a terminating decimal. [1.4]

7. Every natural number is a whole number and every whole number is an integer. [1.4]

8. The expressions $9r^2s$ and $5rs^2$ are like terms. [1.8]

9. The opposite of x, written $-x$, never represents a positive number. [1.6]

10. The number 0 has no reciprocal. [1.7]

Evaluate.

11. $8t$, for $t = 3$ [1.1]

12. $\dfrac{x - y}{3}$, for $x = 17$ and $y = 5$ [1.1]

13. $9 - y^2$, for $y = -5$ [1.8]

14. $-10 + a^2 \div (b + 1)$, for $a = 5$ and $b = -6$ [1.8]

Translate to an algebraic expression. [1.1]

15. 7 less than y

16. 10 more than the product of x and z

17. 15 times the difference of Brandt's speed and the wind speed

18. Determine whether 35 is a solution of $x/5 = 8$. [1.1]

19. Translate to an equation. Do not solve. [1.1]

   According to Photo Marketing Association International, in 2006, 14.1 billion prints were made from film. This number is 3.2 billion more than the number of digital prints made. How many digital prints were made in 2006?

20. Use the commutative law of multiplication to write an expression equivalent to $3t + 5$. [1.2]

21. Use the associative law of addition to write an expression equivalent to $(2x + y) + z$. [1.2]

22. Use the commutative and associative laws to write three expressions equivalent to $4(xy)$. [1.2]

Multiply. [1.2]

23. $6(3x + 5y)$

24. $8(5x + 3y + 2)$

Factor. [1.2]

25. $21x + 15y$

26. $22a + 99b + 11$

27. Find the prime factorization of 56. [1.3]

Simplify. [1.3]

28. $\dfrac{20}{48}$

29. $\dfrac{18}{8}$

Perform the indicated operation and, if possible, simplify. [1.3]

30. $\dfrac{5}{12} + \dfrac{3}{8}$

31. $\dfrac{9}{16} \div 3$

32. $\dfrac{2}{3} - \dfrac{1}{15}$

33. $\dfrac{9}{10} \cdot \dfrac{6}{5}$

34. Tell which integers correspond to this situation. [1.4]

   Natalie borrowed \$3600 for an entertainment center. Sean has \$1350 in his savings account.

35. Graph on a number line: $\frac{-1}{3}$. [1.4]

36. Write an inequality with the same meaning as $-3 < x$. [1.4]

37. Classify as true or false: $2 \geq -8$. [1.4]

38. Classify as true or false: $0 \leq -1$. [1.4]

39. Find decimal notation: $-\dfrac{4}{9}$. [1.4]

40. Find the absolute value: $|-1|$. [1.4]

41. Find $-(-x)$ when x is -12. [1.6]

Simplify.

42. $-3 + (-7)$ [1.5]

43. $-\frac{2}{3} + \frac{1}{12}$ [1.5]

44. $10 + (-9) + (-8) + 7$ [1.5]

45. $-3.8 + 5.1 + (-12) + (-4.3) + 10$ [1.5]

46. $-2 - (-10)$ [1.6]

47. $-\frac{9}{10} - \frac{1}{2}$ [1.6]

48. $-3.8 - 4.1$ [1.6]

49. $-9 \cdot (-7)$ [1.7]

50. $-2.7(3.4)$ [1.7]

51. $\frac{2}{3} \cdot \left(-\frac{3}{7}\right)$ [1.7]

52. $2 \cdot (-7) \cdot (-2) \cdot (-5)$ [1.7]

53. $35 \div (-5)$ [1.7]

54. $-5.1 \div 1.7$ [1.7]

55. $-\frac{3}{5} \div \left(-\frac{4}{15}\right)$ [1.7]

56. $120 - 6^2 \div 4 \cdot 8$ [1.8]

57. $(120 - 6^2) \div 4 \cdot 8$ [1.8]

58. $(120 - 6^2) \div (4 \cdot 8)$ [1.8]

59. $16 \div (-2)^3 - 5[3 - 1 + 2(4 - 7)]$ [1.8]

60. $|-3 \cdot 5 - 4 \cdot 8| - 3(-2)$ [1.8]

61. $\dfrac{4(18 - 8) + 7 \cdot 9}{9^2 - 8^2}$ [1.8]

Combine like terms.

62. $11a + 2b + (-4a) + (-3b)$ [1.5]

63. $7x - 3y - 11x + 8y$ [1.6]

64. Find the opposite of -7. [1.6]

65. Find the reciprocal of -7. [1.7]

66. Write exponential notation for $2x \cdot 2x \cdot 2x \cdot 2x$. [1.8]

67. Simplify: $(-5x)^3$. [1.8]

Remove parentheses and simplify. [1.8]

68. $2a - (5a - 9)$

69. $5b + 3(2b - 9)$

70. $11x^4 + 2x + 8(x - x^4)$

71. $2n^2 - 5(-3n^2 + m^2 - 4mn) + 6m^2$

72. $8(x + 4) - 6 - [3(x - 2) + 4]$

Synthesis

73. Explain the difference between a constant and a variable. [1.1]

74. Explain the difference between a term and a factor. [1.2]

75. Describe at least three ways in which the distributive law was used in this chapter. [1.2]

76. Devise a rule for determining the sign of a negative number raised to a power. [1.8]

77. Evaluate $a^{50} - 20a^{25}b^4 + 100b^8$ for $a = 1$ and $b = 2$. [1.8]

78. If $0.090909\ldots = \frac{1}{11}$ and $0.181818\ldots = \frac{2}{11}$, what rational number is named by each of the following?

    a) $0.272727\ldots$ [1.4]   **b)** $0.909090\ldots$ [1.4]

Simplify. [1.8]

79. $-\left|\frac{7}{8} - \left(-\frac{1}{2}\right) - \frac{3}{4}\right|$

80. $(|2.7 - 3| + 3^2 - |-3|) \div (-3)$

Match each phrase in the left column with the most appropriate choice from the right column.

81. ____ A number is nonnegative. [1.4]

82. ____ The product of a number and its reciprocal is 1. [1.7]

83. ____ A number squared [1.8]

84. ____ A sum of squares [1.8]

85. ____ The opposite of an opposite is the original number. [1.6]

86. ____ The order in which numbers are added does not change the result. [1.2]

87. ____ A number is positive. [1.4]

88. ____ The absolute value of a product [1.4]

89. ____ A sum of a number and its reciprocal [1.7]

90. ____ The square of a sum [1.8]

91. ____ The absolute value of one number is less than the absolute value of another number. [1.4]

a) a^2

b) $a + b = b + a$

c) $a > 0$

d) $a + \dfrac{1}{a}$

e) $|ab|$

f) $(a + b)^2$

g) $|a| < |b|$

h) $a^2 + b^2$

i) $a \geq 0$

j) $a \cdot \dfrac{1}{a} = 1$

k) $-(-a) = a$

Test: Chapter 1

CHAPTER Test Prep VIDEO CD *Step-by-step test solutions are found on the video CD in the front of this book.*

1. Evaluate $\dfrac{2x}{y}$ for $x = 10$ and $y = 5$.

2. Write an algebraic expression: Nine less than the product of two numbers.

3. Find the area of a triangle when the height h is 30 ft and the base b is 16 ft.

4. Use the commutative law of addition to write an expression equivalent to $3p + q$.

5. Use the associative law of multiplication to write an expression equivalent to $x \cdot (4 \cdot y)$.

6. Determine whether 7 is a solution of $65 - x = 69$.

7. Translate to an equation. Do not solve.

   In the summer of 2005, member utilities of the Florida Reliability Coordinating Council had a demand of 45,950 megawatts. This is only 4250 megawatts less than its maximum production capability. What is the maximum capability of production?
   Source: Energy Information Administration

Multiply.

8. $7(5 + x)$

9. $-5(y - 2)$

Factor.

10. $11 + 44x$

11. $7x + 7 + 49y$

12. Find the prime factorization of 300.

13. Simplify: $\dfrac{24}{56}$.

Write a true sentence using either $<$ or $>$.

14. $-4 \quad 0$ 15. $-3 \quad -8$

Find the absolute value.

16. $\left|\dfrac{9}{4}\right|$ 17. $|-3.8|$

18. Find the opposite of $-\dfrac{2}{3}$.

19. Find the reciprocal of $-\dfrac{4}{7}$.

20. Find $-x$ when x is -10.

21. Write an inequality with the same meaning as $x \le -5$.

Perform the indicated operations and, if possible, simplify.

22. $3.1 - (-4.7)$ 23. $-8 + 4 + (-7) + 3$

24. $3.2 - 5.7$ 25. $-\dfrac{1}{8} - \dfrac{3}{4}$

26. $4 \cdot (-12)$

27. $-\dfrac{1}{2} \cdot \left(-\dfrac{4}{9}\right)$

28. $-66 \div 11$

29. $-\dfrac{3}{5} \div \left(-\dfrac{4}{5}\right)$

30. $4.864 \div (-0.5)$

31. $-2(16) - |2(-8) - 5^3|$

32. $9 + 7 - 4 - (-3)$

33. $256 \div (-16) \cdot 4$

34. $2^3 - 10[4 - (-2 + 18)3]$

35. Combine like terms: $18y + 30a - 9a + 4y$.

36. Simplify: $(-2x)^4$.

Remove parentheses and simplify.

37. $4x - (3x - 7)$

38. $4(2a - 3b) + a - 7$

39. $3[5(y - 3) + 9] - 2(8y - 1)$

Synthesis

40. Evaluate $\dfrac{5y - x}{2}$ when $x = 20$ and y is 4 less than half of x.

41. Insert one pair of parentheses to make the following a true statement:
$$9 - 3 - 4 + 5 = 15.$$

Simplify.

42. $|-27 - 3(4)| - |-36| + |-12|$

43. $a - \{3a - [4a - (2a - 4a)]\}$

44. Classify the following as either true or false:
$$a|b - c| = |ab| - |ac|.$$

Equations, Inequalities, and Problem Solving

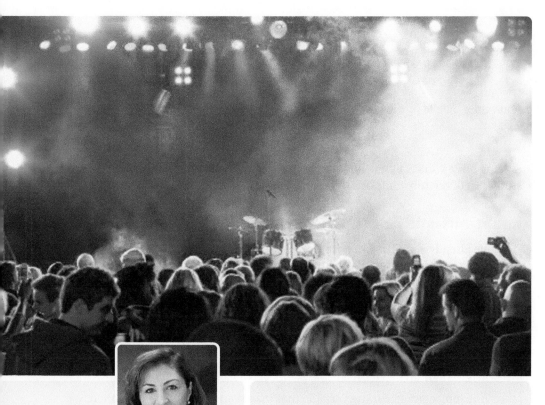

DEBORAH ELIAS
EVENT COORDINATOR
Houston, Texas

As an event planner, I am constantly using math. Calculations range from figuring the tax and gratuity percentage to add to the final bill to finding dimensions of linens to fit a table properly. For every client, I also determine a budget with income and expenses.

AN APPLICATION

Event promoters use the formula

$$p = \frac{1.2x}{s}$$

to determine a ticket price p for an event with x dollars of expenses and s anticipated ticket sales. Grand Events expects expenses for an upcoming concert to be $80,000 and anticipates selling 4000 tickets. What should the ticket price be?

Source: *The Indianapolis Star, 2/27/03*

This problem appears as Example 1 in Section 2.3.

77

S olving equations and inequalities is a recurring theme in much of mathematics. In this chapter, we will study some of the principles used to solve equations and inequalities. We will then use equations and inequalities to solve applied problems.

2.1 Solving Equations

Equations and Solutions ▪ The Addition Principle ▪ The Multiplication Principle ▪
Selecting the Correct Approach

Solving equations is essential for problem solving in algebra. In this section, we study two of the most important principles used for this task.

Equations and Solutions

We have already seen that an equation is a number sentence stating that the expressions on either side of the equals sign represent the same number. Some equations, like $3 + 2 = 5$ or $2x + 6 = 2(x + 3)$, are *always* true and some, like $3 + 2 = 6$ or $x + 2 = x + 3$, are *never* true. In this text, we will concentrate on equations like $x + 6 = 13$ or $7x = 141$ that are *sometimes* true, depending on the replacement value for the variable.

> #### Solution of an Equation
> Any replacement for the variable that makes an equation true is called a *solution* of the equation. To *solve* an equation means to find all of its solutions.

To determine whether a number is a solution, we substitute that number for the variable throughout the equation. If the values on both sides of the equals sign are the same, then the number that was substituted is a solution.

EXAMPLE **1** Determine whether 7 is a solution of $x + 6 = 13$.

SOLUTION   We have

$$
\begin{array}{ll}
x + 6 = 13 & \text{Writing the equation} \\
\overline{7 + 6 \mid 13} & \text{Substituting 7 for } x \\
13 \stackrel{?}{=} 13 \quad \text{TRUE} & 13 = 13 \text{ is a true statement.}
\end{array}
$$

Since the left-hand side and the right-hand side are the same, 7 is a solution.

> *CAUTION!* Note that in Example 1, the solution is 7, not 13.

EXAMPLE   2   Determine whether $\frac{2}{3}$ is a solution of $156x = 117$.

SOLUTION   We have

$$156x = 117 \qquad \text{Writing the equation}$$

$$156\left(\frac{2}{3}\right) \mid 117 \qquad \text{Substituting } \frac{2}{3} \text{ for } x$$

$$104 \overset{?}{=} 117 \quad \text{FALSE} \qquad \text{The statement } 104 = 117 \text{ is false.}$$

Since the left-hand side and the right-hand side differ, $\frac{2}{3}$ is not a solution.

The Addition Principle

Consider the equation

$$x = 7.$$

We can easily see that the solution of this equation is 7. Replacing x with 7, we get

$$7 = 7, \quad \text{which is true.}$$

Now consider the equation

$$x + 6 = 13.$$

In Example 1, we found that the solution of $x + 6 = 13$ is also 7. Although the solution of $x = 7$ may seem more obvious, because $x + 6 = 13$ and $x = 7$ have identical solutions, the equations are said to be **equivalent**.

STUDENT NOTES

Be sure to remember the difference between an expression and an equation. For example, $5a - 10$ and $5(a - 2)$ are *equivalent expressions* because they represent the same value for all replacements for a. The *equations* $5a = 10$ and $a = 2$ are *equivalent* because they have the same solution, 2.

> ### Equivalent Equations
>
> Equations with the same solutions are called *equivalent equations*.

There are principles that enable us to begin with one equation and end up with an equivalent equation, like $x = 7$, for which the solution is obvious. One such principle concerns addition. The equation $a = b$ says that a and b stand for the same number. Suppose this is true, and some number c is added to a. We get the same result if we add c to b, because a and b are the same number.

> ### The Addition Principle
>
> For any real numbers a, b, and c,
>
> $$a = b \quad \text{is equivalent to} \quad a + c = b + c.$$

To visualize the addition principle, consider a balance similar to one a jeweler might use. When the two sides of a balance hold equal weight, the balance is level. If weight is then added or removed, equally, on both sides, the balance will remain level.

$a = b$ $a + c = b + c$

When using the addition principle, we often say that we "add the same number to both sides of an equation." We can also "subtract the same number from both sides," since subtraction can be regarded as the addition of an opposite.

EXAMPLE 3

Solve: $x + 5 = -7$.

SOLUTION   We can add any number we like to both sides. Since -5 is the opposite, or additive inverse, of 5, we add -5 to each side:

$$x + 5 = -7$$
$$x + 5 - 5 = -7 - 5 \qquad \text{Using the addition principle: adding } -5 \text{ to both sides or subtracting 5 from both sides}$$
$$x + 0 = -12 \qquad \text{Simplifying; } x + 5 - 5 = x + 5 + (-5) = x + 0$$
$$x = -12. \qquad \text{Using the identity property of 0}$$

The equation $x = -12$ is equivalent to the equation $x + 5 = -7$ by the addition principle, so the solution of $x = -12$ is the solution of $x + 5 = -7$.

It is obvious that the solution of $x = -12$ is the number -12. To check the answer in the original equation, we substitute.

Check:
$$\begin{array}{c|c} x + 5 = -7 \\ \hline -12 + 5 & -7 \\ -7 \stackrel{?}{=} -7 & \text{TRUE} \qquad -7 = -7 \text{ is true.} \end{array}$$

The solution of the original equation is -12.

> TRY EXERCISE 11

In Example 3, note that because we added the *opposite*, or *additive inverse*, of 5, the left side of the equation simplified to x plus the *additive identity*, 0, or simply x. These steps effectively replaced the 5 on the left with a 0. To solve $x + a = b$ for x, we add $-a$ to (or subtract a from) both sides.

EXAMPLE 4

Solve: $-6.5 = y - 8.4$.

SOLUTION   The variable is on the right side this time. We can isolate y by adding 8.4 to each side:

$$-6.5 = y - 8.4 \qquad y - 8.4 \text{ can be regarded as } y + (-8.4).$$
$$-6.5 + 8.4 = y - 8.4 + 8.4 \qquad \text{Using the addition principle: Adding 8.4 to both sides "eliminates" } -8.4 \text{ on the right side.}$$
$$1.9 = y. \qquad y - 8.4 + 8.4 = y + (-8.4) + 8.4 = y + 0 = y$$

STUDENT NOTES

We can also think of "undoing" operations in order to isolate a variable. In Example 4, we began with $y - 8.4$ on the right side. To undo the subtraction, we *add* 8.4.

Check:
$$\begin{array}{c|c} -6.5 = y - 8.4 \\ \hline -6.5 & 1.9 - 8.4 \\ -6.5 \stackrel{?}{=} -6.5 & \text{TRUE} \qquad -6.5 = -6.5 \text{ is true.} \end{array}$$

The solution is 1.9.

> TRY EXERCISE 15

Note that the equations $a = b$ and $b = a$ have the same meaning. Thus, $-6.5 = y - 8.4$ could have been rewritten as $y - 8.4 = -6.5$.

The Multiplication Principle

A second principle for solving equations concerns multiplying. Suppose a and b are equal. If a and b are multiplied by some number c, then ac and bc will also be equal.

The Multiplication Principle

For any real numbers a, b, and c, with $c \neq 0$,

$$a = b \quad \text{is equivalent to} \quad a \cdot c = b \cdot c.$$

EXAMPLE 5

Solve: $\frac{5}{4}x = 10$.

SOLUTION   We can multiply both sides by any nonzero number we like. Since $\frac{4}{5}$ is the reciprocal of $\frac{5}{4}$, we decide to multiply both sides by $\frac{4}{5}$:

$$\frac{5}{4}x = 10$$

$$\frac{4}{5} \cdot \frac{5}{4}x = \frac{4}{5} \cdot 10 \qquad \text{Using the multiplication principle: Multiplying both sides by } \frac{4}{5} \text{ "eliminates" the } \frac{5}{4} \text{ on the left.}$$

$$1 \cdot x = 8 \qquad \text{Simplifying}$$

$$x = 8. \qquad \text{Using the identity property of 1}$$

Check:

$$\begin{array}{c|c} \frac{5}{4}x = 10 \\ \hline \frac{5}{4} \cdot 8 & 10 \\ \frac{40}{4} & \\ 10 \stackrel{?}{=} 10 & \text{TRUE} \end{array}$$

Think of 8 as $\frac{8}{1}$.

$10 = 10$ is true.

The solution is 8.

> **TRY EXERCISE** 49

In Example 5, to get x alone, we multiplied by the *reciprocal*, or *multiplicative inverse* of $\frac{5}{4}$. We then simplified the left-hand side to x times the *multiplicative identity*, 1, or simply x. These steps effectively replaced the $\frac{5}{4}$ on the left with 1.

Because division is the same as multiplying by a reciprocal, the multiplication principle also tells us that we can "divide both sides by the same nonzero number." That is,

$$\text{if } a = b, \text{ then } \quad \frac{1}{c} \cdot a = \frac{1}{c} \cdot b \quad \text{and} \quad \frac{a}{c} = \frac{b}{c} \qquad (\text{provided } c \neq 0).$$

In a product like $3x$, the multiplier 3 is called the **coefficient**. *When the coefficient of the variable is an integer or a decimal, it is usually easiest to solve an equation by dividing on both sides. When the coefficient is in fraction notation, it is usually easiest to multiply by the reciprocal.*

EXAMPLE 6

Solve: **(a)** $-4x = 9$; **(b)** $-x = 5$; **(c)** $\dfrac{2y}{9} = \dfrac{8}{3}$.

SOLUTION

a) In $-4x = 9$, the coefficient of x is an integer, so we *divide* on both sides:

$$\frac{-4x}{-4} = \frac{9}{-4} \qquad \text{Using the multiplication principle: Dividing both sides by } -4 \text{ is the same as multiplying by } -\frac{1}{4}.$$

$$1 \cdot x = -\frac{9}{4} \qquad \text{Simplifying}$$

$$x = -\frac{9}{4}. \qquad \text{Using the identity property of 1}$$

STUDENT NOTES

In Example 6(a), we can think of undoing the multiplication $-4 \cdot x$ by *dividing* by -4.

Check:
$$\begin{array}{c|c} \multicolumn{2}{c}{-4x = 9} \\ \hline -4\left(-\frac{9}{4}\right) & 9 \\ 9 \overset{?}{=} 9 & \text{TRUE} \qquad 9 = 9 \text{ is true.} \end{array}$$

The solution is $-\frac{9}{4}$.

b) To solve an equation like $-x = 5$, remember that when an expression is multiplied or divided by -1, its sign is changed. Here we divide both sides by -1 to change the sign of $-x$:

$$-x = 5 \qquad \text{Note that } -x = -1 \cdot x.$$

$$\frac{-x}{-1} = \frac{5}{-1} \qquad \begin{array}{l}\text{Dividing both sides by } -1. \text{ (Multiplying by } -1 \text{ would also} \\ \text{work. Note that the reciprocal of } -1 \text{ is } -1.)\end{array}$$

$$x = -5. \qquad \text{Note that } \frac{-x}{-1} \text{ is the same as } \frac{x}{1}.$$

Check:
$$\begin{array}{c|c} \multicolumn{2}{c}{-x = 5} \\ \hline -(-5) & 5 \\ 5 \overset{?}{=} 5 & \text{TRUE} \qquad 5 = 5 \text{ is true.} \end{array}$$

The solution is -5.

c) To solve an equation like $\dfrac{2y}{9} = \dfrac{8}{3}$, we rewrite the left-hand side as $\dfrac{2}{9} \cdot y$ and then use the multiplication principle, multiplying by the reciprocal of $\dfrac{2}{9}$:

$$\frac{2y}{9} = \frac{8}{3}$$

$$\frac{2}{9} \cdot y = \frac{8}{3} \qquad \text{Rewriting } \frac{2y}{9} \text{ as } \frac{2}{9} \cdot y$$

$$\frac{9}{2} \cdot \frac{2}{9} \cdot y = \frac{9}{2} \cdot \frac{8}{3} \qquad \text{Multiplying both sides by } \frac{9}{2}$$

$$1y = \frac{3 \cdot \cancel{3} \cdot \cancel{2} \cdot 4}{\cancel{2} \cdot \cancel{3}} \qquad \text{Removing a factor equal to 1: } \frac{3 \cdot 2}{2 \cdot 3} = 1$$

$$y = 12.$$

Check:
$$\begin{array}{c|c} \multicolumn{2}{c}{\dfrac{2y}{9} = \dfrac{8}{3}} \\ \hline \dfrac{2 \cdot 12}{9} & \dfrac{8}{3} \\[2mm] \dfrac{24}{9} & \\[2mm] \dfrac{8}{3} \overset{?}{=} \dfrac{8}{3} & \text{TRUE} \qquad \dfrac{8}{3} = \dfrac{8}{3} \text{ is true.} \end{array}$$

The solution is 12.

TRY EXERCISE ▶ 35

Selecting the Correct Approach

It is important that you be able to determine which principle should be used to solve a particular equation.

EXAMPLE 7   Solve: **(a)** $-\frac{2}{3} + x = \frac{5}{2}$; **(b)** $12.6 = 3t$.

SOLUTION

a) To undo addition of $-\frac{2}{3}$, we subtract $-\frac{2}{3}$ from both sides. Subtracting $-\frac{2}{3}$ is the same as adding $\frac{2}{3}$.

$$-\frac{2}{3} + x = \frac{5}{2}$$
$$-\frac{2}{3} + x + \frac{2}{3} = \frac{5}{2} + \frac{2}{3} \quad\quad \text{Using the addition principle}$$
$$x = \frac{5}{2} + \frac{2}{3}$$
$$x = \frac{5}{2} \cdot \frac{3}{3} + \frac{2}{3} \cdot \frac{2}{2} \quad\quad \text{Finding a common denominator}$$
$$x = \frac{15}{6} + \frac{4}{6}$$
$$x = \frac{19}{6}$$

Check:
$$-\frac{2}{3} + x = \frac{5}{2}$$

$$\begin{array}{c|c} -\frac{2}{3} + \frac{19}{6} & \frac{5}{2} \\ -\frac{4}{6} + \frac{19}{6} & \\ \frac{15}{6} & \\ \frac{5 \cdot 3}{2 \cdot 3} & \\ \frac{5}{2} \overset{?}{=} \frac{5}{2} & \text{TRUE} \end{array}$$

$-\frac{2}{3} \cdot \frac{2}{2} = -\frac{4}{6}$

Removing a factor equal to 1: $\frac{3}{3} = 1$

$\frac{5}{2} = \frac{5}{2}$ is true.

The solution is $\frac{19}{6}$.

b) To undo multiplication by 3, we either divide both sides by 3 or multiply both sides by $\frac{1}{3}$:

$$12.6 = 3t$$
$$\frac{12.6}{3} = \frac{3t}{3} \quad\quad \text{Using the multiplication principle}$$
$$4.2 = t. \quad\quad \text{Simplifying}$$

Check:
$$12.6 = 3t$$
$$\begin{array}{c|c} 12.6 & 3(4.2) \\ 12.6 \overset{?}{=} 12.6 & \text{TRUE} \end{array}$$

$12.6 = 12.6$ is true.

The solution is 4.2.

▶ **TRY EXERCISES** 59 and 67

2.1 **EXERCISE SET**

↪ *Concept Reinforcement*   *For each of Exercises 1–6, match the statement with the most appropriate choice from the column on the right.*

1. ____ The equations $x + 3 = 7$ and $6x = 24$ a) Coefficient

2. ____ The expressions $3(x - 2)$ and $3x - 6$ b) Equivalent expressions

3. ____ A replacement that makes an equation true   c) Equivalent equations

4. ____ The role of 9 in $9ab$ d) The multiplication principle

5. ____ The principle used to solve $\frac{2}{3} \cdot x = -4$ e) The addition principle

6. ____ The principle used to solve $\frac{2}{3} + x = -4$ f) Solution

For each of Exercises 7–10, match the equation with the step, from the column on the right, that would be used to solve the equation.

7. $6x = 30$ **a)** Add 6 to both sides.

8. $x + 6 = 30$ **b)** Subtract 6 from both sides.

9. $\frac{1}{6}x = 30$ **c)** Multiply both sides by 6.

10. $x - 6 = 30$ **d)** Divide both sides by 6.

To the student and the instructor: The ▶TRY EXERCISES▶ *for examples are indicated by a shaded block ▬▬ on the exercise number. Complete step-by-step solutions for these exercises appear online at www.pearsonhighered.com/ bittingerellenbogen.*

Solve using the addition principle. Don't forget to check!

11. $x + 10 = 21$ **12.** $t + 9 = 47$

13. $y + 7 = -18$ **14.** $x + 12 = -7$

15. $-6 = y + 25$ **16.** $-5 = x + 8$

17. $x - 18 = 23$ **18.** $x - 19 = 16$

19. $12 = -7 + y$ **20.** $15 = -8 + z$

21. $-5 + t = -11$ **22.** $-6 + y = -21$

23. $r + \frac{1}{3} = \frac{8}{3}$ **24.** $t + \frac{3}{8} = \frac{5}{8}$

25. $x - \frac{3}{5} = -\frac{7}{10}$ **26.** $x - \frac{2}{3} = -\frac{5}{6}$

27. $x - \frac{5}{6} = \frac{7}{8}$ **28.** $y - \frac{3}{4} = \frac{5}{6}$

29. $-\frac{1}{5} + z = -\frac{1}{4}$ **30.** $-\frac{2}{3} + y = -\frac{3}{4}$

31. $m - 2.8 = 6.3$ **32.** $y - 5.3 = 8.7$

33. $-9.7 = -4.7 + y$ **34.** $-7.8 = 2.8 + x$

Solve using the multiplication principle. Don't forget to check!

35. $8a = 56$ **36.** $6x = 72$

37. $84 = 7x$ **38.** $45 = 9t$

39. $-x = 38$ **40.** $100 = -x$

Aha! **41.** $-t = -8$ **42.** $-68 = -r$

43. $-7x = 49$ **44.** $-4x = 36$

45. $-1.3a = -10.4$ **46.** $-3.4t = -20.4$

47. $\frac{y}{8} = 11$ **48.** $\frac{a}{4} = 13$

49. $\frac{4}{5}x = 16$ **50.** $\frac{3}{4}x = 27$

51. $\frac{-x}{6} = 9$ **52.** $\frac{-t}{4} = 8$

53. $\frac{1}{9} = \frac{z}{-5}$ **54.** $\frac{2}{7} = \frac{x}{-3}$

Aha! **55.** $-\frac{3}{5}r = -\frac{3}{5}$ **56.** $-\frac{2}{5}y = -\frac{4}{15}$

57. $\frac{-3r}{2} = -\frac{27}{4}$ **58.** $\frac{5x}{7} = -\frac{10}{14}$

Solve. The icon ▤ indicates an exercise designed to give practice using a calculator.

59. $4.5 + t = -3.1$ **60.** $\frac{3}{4}x = 18$

61. $-8.2x = 20.5$ **62.** $t - 7.4 = -12.9$

63. $x - 4 = -19$ **64.** $y - 6 = -14$

65. $t - 3 = -8$ **66.** $t - 9 = -8$

67. $-12x = 14$ **68.** $-15x = 20$

69. $48 = -\frac{3}{8}y$ **70.** $14 = t + 27$

71. $a - \frac{1}{6} = -\frac{2}{3}$ **72.** $-\frac{x}{6} = \frac{2}{9}$

73. $-24 = \frac{8x}{5}$ **74.** $\frac{1}{5} + y = -\frac{3}{10}$

75. $-\frac{4}{3}t = -12$ **76.** $\frac{17}{35} = -x$

▤ **77.** $-483.297 = -794.053 + t$

▤ **78.** $-0.2344x = 2028.732$

📝 **79.** When solving an equation, how do you determine what number to add, subtract, multiply, or divide by on both sides of that equation?

📝 **80.** What is the difference between equivalent expressions and equivalent equations?

Skill Review

To prepare for Section 2.2, review the rules for order of operations (Section 1.8).

Simplify. [1.8]

81. $3 \cdot 4 - 18$

82. $14 - 2(7 - 1)$

83. $16 \div (2 - 3 \cdot 2) + 5$

84. $12 - 5 \cdot 2^3 + 4 \cdot 3$

Synthesis

📝 **85.** To solve $-3.5 = 14t$, Anita adds 3.5 to both sides. Will this form an equivalent equation? Will it help solve the equation? Explain.

📝 **86.** Explain why it is not necessary to state a subtraction principle: For any real numbers a, b, and c, $a = b$ is equivalent to $a - c = b - c$.

Solve for x. Assume a, c, m ≠ 0.

87. $mx = 11.6m$

88. $x - 4 + a = a$

89. $cx + 5c = 7c$

90. $c \cdot \dfrac{21}{a} = \dfrac{7cx}{2a}$

91. $7 + |x| = 30$

92. $ax - 3a = 5a$

93. If $t - 3590 = 1820$, find $t + 3590$.

94. If $n + 268 = 124$, find $n - 268$.

95. Lydia makes a calculation and gets an answer of 22.5. On the last step, she multiplies by 0.3 when she should have divided by 0.3. What should the correct answer be?

96. Are the equations $x = 5$ and $x^2 = 25$ equivalent? Why or why not?

2.2 Using the Principles Together

Applying Both Principles   ▪   Combining Like Terms   ▪   Clearing Fractions and Decimals   ▪
Contradictions and Identities

An important strategy for solving new problems is to find a way to make a new problem look like a problem that we already know how to solve. This is precisely the approach taken in this section. You will find that the last steps of the examples in this section are nearly identical to the steps used for solving the equations of Section 2.1. What is new in this section appears in the early steps of each example.

Applying Both Principles

The addition and multiplication principles, along with the laws discussed in Chapter 1, are our tools for solving equations. In this section, we will find that the sequence and manner in which these tools are used is especially important.

EXAMPLE 1   Solve: $5 + 3x = 17$.

SOLUTION   Were we to evaluate $5 + 3x$, the rules for the order of operations direct us to *first* multiply by 3 and *then* add 5. Because of this, we can isolate $3x$ and then x by reversing these operations: We first subtract 5 from both sides and then divide both sides by 3. Our goal is an equivalent equation of the form $x = a$.

$$5 + 3x = 17$$

$$5 + 3x - 5 = 17 - 5 \qquad \text{Using the addition principle: subtracting 5 from both sides (adding } -5)$$

$$5 + (-5) + 3x = 12 \qquad \text{Using a commutative law. Try to perform this step mentally.}$$

Isolate the x-term. $\quad 3x = 12 \qquad \text{Simplifying}$

$$\dfrac{3x}{3} = \dfrac{12}{3} \qquad \text{Using the multiplication principle: dividing both sides by 3 (multiplying by } \tfrac{1}{3})$$

Isolate x. $\quad x = 4 \qquad \text{Simplifying}$

Check:

$$\begin{array}{c|c} 5 + 3x = 17 & \\ \hline 5 + 3 \cdot 4 & 17 \\ 5 + 12 & \\ 17 \overset{?}{=} 17 & \text{TRUE} \end{array}$$

We use the rules for order of operations: Find the product, $3 \cdot 4$, and then add.

The solution is 4.

TRY EXERCISE 7

EXAMPLE   2   Solve: $\frac{4}{3}x - 7 = 1$.

SOLUTION   In $\frac{4}{3}x - 7$, we multiply first and then subtract. To reverse these steps, we first add 7 and then either divide by $\frac{4}{3}$ or multiply by $\frac{3}{4}$.

$$\frac{4}{3}x - 7 = 1$$

$$\frac{4}{3}x - 7 + 7 = 1 + 7 \qquad \text{Adding 7 to both sides}$$

$$\frac{4}{3}x = 8$$

$$\frac{3}{4} \cdot \frac{4}{3}x = \frac{3}{4} \cdot 8 \qquad \text{Multiplying both sides by } \frac{3}{4}$$

$$\left.\begin{array}{c} 1 \cdot x = \dfrac{3 \cdot 4 \cdot 2}{4} \\[2mm] x = 6 \end{array}\right\} \quad \text{Simplifying}$$

Check:

$$\begin{array}{c|c} \frac{4}{3}x - 7 = 1 \\ \hline \frac{4}{3} \cdot 6 - 7 & 1 \\ 8 - 7 & \\ 1 \overset{?}{=} 1 & \text{TRUE} \end{array}$$

The solution is 6.   ▸ **TRY EXERCISE** ▸ 27

STUDY SKILLS ─────────

Use the Answer Section Carefully

When using the answers listed at the back of this book, try not to "work backward" from the answer. If you frequently require two or more attempts to answer an exercise correctly, you probably need to work more carefully and/or reread the section preceding the exercise set. Remember that on quizzes and tests you have only one attempt per problem and no answer section to consult.

EXAMPLE   3   Solve: $45 - t = 13$.

SOLUTION   We have

$$45 - t = 13$$

$$45 - t - 45 = 13 - 45 \qquad \text{Subtracting 45 from both sides}$$

$$\left.\begin{array}{l} 45 + (-t) + (-45) = 13 - 45 \\ 45 + (-45) + (-t) = 13 - 45 \end{array}\right\} \quad \text{Try to do these steps mentally.}$$

$$-t = -32 \qquad \text{Try to go directly to this step.}$$

$$(-1)(-t) = (-1)(-32) \qquad \begin{array}{l}\text{Multiplying both sides by } -1 \\ \text{(Dividing by } -1 \text{ would also} \\ \text{work.)}\end{array}$$

$$t = 32.$$

Check:

$$\begin{array}{c|c} 45 - t = 13 \\ \hline 45 - 32 & 13 \\ 13 \overset{?}{=} 13 & \text{TRUE} \end{array}$$

The solution is 32.   ▸ **TRY EXERCISE** ▸ 19

As our skills improve, certain steps can be streamlined.

EXAMPLE 4   Solve: $16.3 - 7.2y = -8.18$.

SOLUTION   We have

$$16.3 - 7.2y = -8.18$$
$$16.3 - 7.2y - 16.3 = -8.18 - 16.3 \qquad \text{Subtracting 16.3 from both sides}$$
$$-7.2y = -24.48 \qquad \text{Simplifying}$$
$$\frac{-7.2y}{-7.2} = \frac{-24.48}{-7.2} \qquad \text{Dividing both sides by } -7.2$$
$$y = 3.4. \qquad \text{Simplifying}$$

Check:

$$\begin{array}{c|c} 16.3 - 7.2y = -8.18 \\ \hline 16.3 - 7.2(3.4) & -8.18 \\ 16.3 - 24.48 & \\ -8.18 \overset{?}{=} -8.18 & \text{TRUE} \end{array}$$

The solution is 3.4.

TRY EXERCISE 23

Combining Like Terms

If like terms appear on the same side of an equation, we combine them and then solve. Should like terms appear on both sides of an equation, we can use the addition principle to rewrite all like terms on one side.

EXAMPLE 5   Solve.

a) $3x + 4x = -14$ **b)** $-x + 5 = -8x + 6$

c) $6x + 5 - 7x = 10 - 4x + 7$ **d)** $2 - 5(x + 5) = 3(x - 2) - 1$

SOLUTION

a) $3x + 4x = -14$

$$7x = -14 \qquad \text{Combining like terms}$$
$$\frac{7x}{7} = \frac{-14}{7} \qquad \text{Dividing both sides by 7}$$
$$x = -2 \qquad \text{Simplifying}$$

The check is left to the student. The solution is -2.

b) To solve $-x + 5 = -8x + 6$, we must first write only variable terms on one side and only constant terms on the other. This can be done by subtracting 5 from both sides, to get all constant terms on the right, and adding $8x$ to both sides, to get all variable terms on the left.

$$-x + 5 = -8x + 6$$

> Isolate variable terms on one side and constant terms on the other side.

$$-x + 8x + 5 = -8x + 8x + 6 \qquad \text{Adding } 8x \text{ to both sides}$$
$$7x + 5 = 6 \qquad \text{Simplifying}$$
$$7x + 5 - 5 = 6 - 5 \qquad \text{Subtracting 5 from both sides}$$
$$7x = 1 \qquad \text{Combining like terms}$$
$$\frac{7x}{7} = \frac{1}{7} \qquad \text{Dividing both sides by 7}$$
$$x = \frac{1}{7}$$

The check is left to the student. The solution is $\frac{1}{7}$.

Most graphing calculators have a TABLE feature that lists the value of a variable expression for different choices of x. For example, to evaluate $6x + 5 - 7x$ for $x = 0, 1, 2, \ldots,$ we first use ⟨ Y= ⟩ to enter $6x + 5 - 7x$ as y_1. We then use 2ND (TBLSET) to specify TblStart $= 0$, ΔTbl $= 1$, and select AUTO twice. By pressing 2ND (TABLE), we can generate a table in which the value of $6x + 5 - 7x$ is listed for values of x starting at 0 and increasing by ones.

X	Y1	
0	5	
1	4	
2	3	
3	2	
4	1	
5	0	
6	−1	

X = 0

1. Create the above table on your graphing calculator. Scroll up and down to extend the table.
2. Enter $10 - 4x + 7$ as y_2. Your table should now have three columns.
3. For what x-value is y_1 the same as y_2? Compare this with the solution of Example 5(c). Is this a reliable way to solve equations? Why or why not?

c)
$$6x + 5 - 7x = 10 - 4x + 7$$
$$-x + 5 = 17 - 4x \qquad \text{Combining like terms within each side}$$
$$-x + 5 + 4x = 17 - 4x + 4x \qquad \text{Adding } 4x \text{ to both sides}$$
$$5 + 3x = 17 \qquad \text{Simplifying. This is identical to Example 1.}$$
$$3x = 12 \qquad \text{Subtracting 5 from both sides}$$
$$\frac{3x}{3} = \frac{12}{3} \qquad \text{Dividing both sides by 3}$$
$$x = 4$$

Check:
$$
\begin{array}{c|c}
6x + 5 - 7x = 10 - 4x + 7 \\
\hline
6 \cdot 4 + 5 - 7 \cdot 4 & 10 - 4 \cdot 4 + 7 \\
24 + 5 - 28 & 10 - 16 + 7 \\
1 \stackrel{?}{=} 1 & \text{TRUE}
\end{array}
$$

The student can confirm that 4 checks and is the solution.

d)
$$2 - 5(x + 5) = 3(x - 2) - 1$$
$$2 - 5x - 25 = 3x - 6 - 1 \qquad \text{Using the distributive law. This is now similar to part (c) above.}$$
$$-5x - 23 = 3x - 7 \qquad \text{Combining like terms on each side}$$
$$\left.\begin{array}{l} -5x - 23 + 7 = 3x \\ -23 + 7 = 3x + 5x \end{array}\right\} \qquad \text{Adding 7 and } 5x \text{ to both sides. This isolates the } x\text{-terms on one side and the constant terms on the other.}$$
$$-16 = 8x \qquad \text{Simplifying}$$
$$\frac{-16}{8} = \frac{8x}{8} \qquad \text{Dividing both sides by 8}$$
$$-2 = x \qquad \text{This is equivalent to } x = -2.$$

The student can confirm that -2 checks and is the solution.

TRY EXERCISE ▶ 39

Clearing Fractions and Decimals

Equations are generally easier to solve when they do not contain fractions or decimals. The multiplication principle can be used to "clear" fractions or decimals, as shown here.

Clearing Fractions	Clearing Decimals
$\frac{1}{2}x + 5 = \frac{3}{4}$	$2.3x + 7 = 5.4$
$4\left(\frac{1}{2}x + 5\right) = 4 \cdot \frac{3}{4}$	$10(2.3x + 7) = 10 \cdot 5.4$
$2x + 20 = 3$	$23x + 70 = 54$

In each case, the resulting equation is equivalent to the original equation, but easier to solve.

The easiest way to clear an equation of fractions is to multiply *both sides* of the equation by the smallest, or *least*, common denominator of the fractions in the equation.

EXAMPLE 6 Solve: **(a)** $\frac{2}{3}x - \frac{1}{6} = 2x$; **(b)** $\frac{2}{5}(3x + 2) = 8$.

SOLUTION

a) We multiply both sides by 6, the least common denominator of $\frac{2}{3}$ and $\frac{1}{6}$.

$$6\left(\frac{2}{3}x - \frac{1}{6}\right) = 6 \cdot 2x \qquad \text{Multiplying both sides by 6}$$

$$6 \cdot \frac{2}{3}x - 6 \cdot \frac{1}{6} = 6 \cdot 2x \leftarrow \boxed{\begin{array}{l} \textit{CAUTION!} \quad \text{Be sure the distributive law} \\ \text{is used to multiply } \textit{all} \text{ the terms by 6.} \end{array}}$$

$$4x - 1 = 12x \qquad \begin{array}{l}\text{Simplifying. Note that the fractions are} \\ \text{cleared: } 6 \cdot \frac{2}{3} = 4, 6 \cdot \frac{1}{6} = 1, \text{ and } 6 \cdot 2 = 12.\end{array}$$

$$-1 = 8x \qquad \text{Subtracting } 4x \text{ from both sides}$$

$$\frac{-1}{8} = \frac{8x}{8} \qquad \text{Dividing both sides by 8}$$

$$-\frac{1}{8} = x$$

The student can confirm that $-\frac{1}{8}$ checks and is the solution.

b) To solve $\frac{2}{5}(3x + 2) = 8$, we can multiply both sides by $\frac{5}{2}$ (or divide by $\frac{2}{5}$) to "undo" the multiplication by $\frac{2}{5}$ on the left side.

$$\frac{5}{2} \cdot \frac{2}{5}(3x + 2) = \frac{5}{2} \cdot 8 \qquad \text{Multiplying both sides by } \frac{5}{2}$$

$$3x + 2 = 20 \qquad \text{Simplifying; } \frac{5}{2} \cdot \frac{2}{5} = 1 \text{ and } \frac{5}{2} \cdot \frac{8}{1} = 20$$

$$3x = 18 \qquad \text{Subtracting 2 from both sides}$$

$$x = 6 \qquad \text{Dividing both sides by 3}$$

The student can confirm that 6 checks and is the solution.

TRY EXERCISE 69

To clear an equation of decimals, we count the greatest number of decimal places in any one number. If the greatest number of decimal places is 1, we multiply both sides by 10; if it is 2, we multiply by 100; and so on. This procedure is the same as multiplying by the least common denominator after converting the decimals to fractions.

EXAMPLE 7 Solve: $16.3 - 7.2y = -8.18$.

SOLUTION The greatest number of decimal places in any one number is *two*. Multiplying by 100 will clear all decimals.

$$100(16.3 - 7.2y) = 100(-8.18) \qquad \text{Multiplying both sides by 100}$$

$$100(16.3) - 100(7.2y) = 100(-8.18) \qquad \text{Using the distributive law}$$

$$1630 - 720y = -818 \qquad \text{Simplifying}$$

$$-720y = -818 - 1630 \qquad \begin{array}{l}\text{Subtracting 1630 from both} \\ \text{sides}\end{array}$$

$$-720y = -2448 \qquad \text{Combining like terms}$$

$$y = \frac{-2448}{-720} \qquad \text{Dividing both sides by } -720$$

$$y = 3.4$$

In Example 4, the same solution was found without clearing decimals. Finding the same answer in two ways is a good check. The solution is 3.4.

TRY EXERCISE 75

STUDENT NOTES ————

Compare the steps of Examples 4 and 7. Note that although the two approaches differ, they yield the same solution. Whenever you can use two approaches to solve a problem, try to do so, both as a check and as a valuable learning experience.

An Equation-Solving Procedure

1. Use the multiplication principle to clear any fractions or decimals. (This is optional, but can ease computations. See Examples 6 and 7.)
2. If necessary, use the distributive law to remove parentheses. Then combine like terms on each side. (See Example 5.)
3. Use the addition principle, as needed, to isolate all variable terms on one side. Then combine like terms. (See Examples 1–7.)
4. Multiply or divide to solve for the variable, using the multiplication principle. (See Examples 1–7.)
5. Check all possible solutions in the original equation. (See Examples 1–4.)

Contradictions and Identities

All of the equations we have examined so far had a solution. Equations that are true for some values (solutions), but not for others, are called **conditional equations**. Equations that have no solution, such as $x + 1 = x + 2$, are called **contradictions**. If, when solving an equation, we obtain an equation that is false for any value of x, the equation has no solution.

EXAMPLE 8   Solve: $3x - 5 = 3(x - 2) + 4$.

SOLUTION

$$3x - 5 = 3(x - 2) + 4$$
$$3x - 5 = 3x - 6 + 4 \qquad \text{Using the distributive law}$$
$$3x - 5 = 3x - 2 \qquad \text{Combining like terms}$$
$$-3x + 3x - 5 = -3x + 3x - 2 \qquad \text{Using the addition principle}$$
$$-5 = -2$$

Since the original equation is equivalent to $-5 = -2$, which is false regardless of the choice of x, the original equation has no solution. There is no solution of $3x - 5 = 3(x - 2) + 4$. The equation is a contradiction. It is *never* true.

> **TRY EXERCISE** 45

Some equations, like $x + 1 = x + 1$, are true for all replacements. Such an equation is called an **identity**.

EXAMPLE 9   Solve: $2x + 7 = 7(x + 1) - 5x$.

SOLUTION

$$2x + 7 = 7(x + 1) - 5x$$
$$2x + 7 = 7x + 7 - 5x \qquad \text{Using the distributive law}$$
$$2x + 7 = 2x + 7 \qquad \text{Combining like terms}$$

The equation $2x + 7 = 2x + 7$ is true regardless of the replacement for x, so all real numbers are solutions. Note that $2x + 7 = 2x + 7$ is equivalent to $2x = 2x$, $7 = 7$, or $0 = 0$. All real numbers are solutions and the equation is an identity.

> **TRY EXERCISE** 33

For Extra Help
MyMathLab | Math XL PRACTICE | WATCH | DOWNLOAD

Concept Reinforcement *In each of Exercises 1–6, match the equation with an equivalent equation from the column on the right that could be the next step in finding a solution.*

1. _____ $3x - 1 = 7$
2. _____ $4x + 5x = 12$
3. _____ $6(x - 1) = 2$
4. _____ $7x = 9$
5. _____ $4x = 3 - 2x$
6. _____ $8x - 5 = 6 - 2x$

a) $6x - 6 = 2$
b) $4x + 2x = 3$
c) $3x = 7 + 1$
d) $8x + 2x = 6 + 5$
e) $9x = 12$
f) $x = \frac{9}{7}$

Solve and check. Label any contradictions or identities.

7. $2x + 9 = 25$
8. $3x - 11 = 13$
9. $6z + 5 = 47$
10. $5z + 2 = 57$
11. $7t - 8 = 27$
12. $6x - 5 = 2$
13. $3x - 9 = 1$
14. $5x - 9 = 41$
15. $8z + 2 = -54$
16. $4x + 3 = -21$
17. $-37 = 9t + 8$
18. $-39 = 1 + 5t$
19. $12 - t = 16$
20. $9 - t = 21$
21. $-6z - 18 = -132$
22. $-7x - 24 = -129$
23. $5.3 + 1.2n = 1.94$
24. $6.4 - 2.5n = 2.2$
25. $32 - 7x = 11$
26. $27 - 6x = 99$
27. $\frac{3}{5}t - 1 = 8$
28. $\frac{2}{3}t - 1 = 5$

29. $6 + \frac{7}{2}x = -15$
30. $6 + \frac{5}{4}x = -4$
31. $-\frac{4a}{5} - 8 = 2$
32. $-\frac{8a}{7} - 2 = 4$
33. $4x = x + 3x$
34. $-3z + 8z = 45$
35. $4x - 6 = 6x$
36. $5x - x = x + 3x$
37. $2 - 5y = 26 - y$
38. $6x - 5 = 7 + 2x$
39. $7(2a - 1) = 21$
40. $5(3 - 3t) = 30$

Aha! 41. $11 = 11(x + 1)$
42. $9 = 3(5x - 2)$
43. $2(3 + 4m) - 6 = 48$
44. $3(5 + 3m) - 8 = 7$
45. $3(x + 4) = 3(x - 1)$
46. $5(x - 7) = 3(x - 2) + 2x$
47. $2r + 8 = 6r + 10$
48. $3b - 2 = 7b + 4$
49. $6x + 3 = 2x + 3$
50. $5y + 3 = 2y + 15$
51. $5 - 2x = 3x - 7x + 25$
52. $10 - 3x = x - 2x + 40$
53. $7 + 3x - 6 = 3x + 5 - x$
54. $5 + 4x - 7 = 4x - 2 - x$
55. $4y - 4 + y + 24 = 6y + 20 - 4y$
56. $5y - 10 + y = 7y + 18 - 5y$
57. $4 + 7x = 7(x + 1)$
58. $3(t + 2) + t = 2(3 + 2t)$
59. $19 - 3(2x - 1) = 7$

60. $5(d + 4) = 7(d - 2)$

61. $7(5x - 2) = 6(6x - 1)$

62. $5(t + 1) + 8 = 3(t - 2) + 6$

63. $2(3t + 1) - 5 = t - (t + 2)$

64. $4x - (x + 6) = 5(3x - 1) + 8$

65. $2(7 - x) - 20 = 7x - 3(2 + 3x)$

66. $5(x - 7) = 3(x - 2) + 2x$

67. $19 - (2x + 3) = 2(x + 3) + x$

68. $13 - (2c + 2) = 2(c + 2) + 3c$

Clear fractions or decimals, solve, and check.

69. $\frac{2}{3} + \frac{1}{4}t = 2$

70. $-\frac{5}{6} + x = -\frac{1}{2} - \frac{2}{3}$

71. $\frac{2}{3} + 4t = 6t - \frac{2}{15}$

72. $\frac{1}{2} + 4m = 3m - \frac{5}{2}$

73. $\frac{1}{3}x + \frac{2}{5} = \frac{4}{5} + \frac{3}{5}x - \frac{2}{3}$

74. $1 - \frac{2}{3}y = \frac{9}{5} - \frac{1}{5}y + \frac{3}{5}$

75. $2.1x + 45.2 = 3.2 - 8.4x$

76. $0.91 - 0.2z = 1.23 - 0.6z$

77. $0.76 + 0.21t = 0.96t - 0.49$

78. $1.7t + 8 - 1.62t = 0.4t - 0.32 + 8$

79. $\frac{2}{5}x - \frac{3}{2}x = \frac{3}{4}x + 3$

80. $\frac{5}{16}y + \frac{3}{8}y = 2 + \frac{1}{4}y$

81. $\frac{1}{3}(2x - 1) = 7$

82. $\frac{1}{5}(4x - 1) = 7$

83. $\frac{3}{4}(3t - 4) = 15$

84. $\frac{3}{2}(2x + 5) = -\frac{15}{2}$

85. $\frac{1}{6}\left(\frac{3}{4}x - 2\right) = -\frac{1}{5}$

86. $\frac{2}{3}\left(\frac{7}{8} - 4x\right) - \frac{5}{8} = \frac{3}{8}$

87. $0.7(3x + 6) = 1.1 - (x - 3)$

88. $0.9(2x - 8) = 4 - (x + 5)$

89. $a + (a - 3) = (a + 2) - (a + 1)$

90. $0.8 - 4(b - 1) = 0.2 + 3(4 - b)$

✍ 91. Tyla solves $45 - t = 13$ (Example 3) by adding $t - 13$ to both sides. Is this approach preferable to the one used in Example 3? Why or why not?

✍ 92. Why must the rules for the order of operations be understood before solving the equations in this section?

Skill Review

To prepare for Section 2.3, review evaluating algebraic expressions (Section 1.8).

Evaluate. [1.8]

93. $3 - 5a$, for $a = 2$

94. $12 \div 4 \cdot t$, for $t = 5$

95. $7x - 2x$, for $x = -3$

96. $t(8 - 3t)$, for $t = -2$

Synthesis

✍ 97. What procedure would you use to solve an equation like $0.23x + \frac{17}{3} = -0.8 + \frac{3}{4}x$? Could your procedure be streamlined? If so, how?

✍ 98. Dave is determined to solve $3x + 4 = -11$ by first using the multiplication principle to "eliminate" the 3. How should he proceed and why?

Solve. Label any contradictions or identities.

▦ 99. $8.43x - 2.5(3.2 - 0.7x) = -3.455x + 9.04$

▦ 100. $0.008 + 9.62x - 42.8 = 0.944x + 0.0083 - x$

101. $-2[3(x - 2) + 4] = 4(5 - x) - 2x$

102. $0 = t - (-6) - (-7t)$

103. $2x(x + 5) - 3(x^2 + 2x - 1) = 9 - 5x - x^2$

104. $x(x - 4) = 3x(x + 1) - 2(x^2 + x - 5)$

105. $9 - 3x = 2(5 - 2x) - (1 - 5x)$

Aha! **106.** $[7 - 2(8 \div (-2))]x = 0$

107. $\dfrac{x}{14} - \dfrac{5x + 2}{49} = \dfrac{3x - 4}{7}$

108. $\dfrac{5x + 3}{4} + \dfrac{25}{12} = \dfrac{5 + 2x}{3}$

109. $2\{9 - 3[-2x - 4]\} = 12x + 42$

110. $-9t + 2 = 2 - 9t - 5(8 \div 4(1 + 3^4))$

CORNER

Step-by-Step Solutions

Focus: Solving linear equations

Time: 20 minutes

Group size: 3

In general, there is more than one correct sequence of steps for solving an equation. This makes it important that you write your steps clearly and logically so that others can follow your approach.

ACTIVITY

1. Each group member should select a different one of the following equations and, on a fresh sheet of paper, perform the first step of the solution.

$$4 - 3(x - 3) = 7x + 6(2 - x)$$
$$5 - 7[x - 2(x - 6)] = 3x + 4(2x - 7) + 9$$
$$4x - 7[2 + 3(x - 5) + x] = 4 - 9(-3x - 19)$$

2. Pass the papers around so that the second and third steps of each solution are performed by the other two group members. Before writing, make sure that the previous step is correct. If a mistake is discovered, return the problem to the person who made the mistake for repairs. Continue passing the problems around until all equations have been solved.

3. Each group should reach a consensus on what the three solutions are and then compare their answers to those of other groups.

2.3   Formulas

Evaluating Formulas ▪ Solving for a Variable

Many applications of mathematics involve relationships among two or more quantities. An equation that represents such a relationship will use two or more letters and is known as a **formula**. Most of the letters in this book are variables, but some are constants. For example, c in $E = mc^2$ represents the speed of light.

Evaluating Formulas

EXAMPLE 1   *Event promotion.*   Event promoters use the formula

$$p = \frac{1.2x}{s}$$

to determine a ticket price p for an event with x dollars of expenses and s anticipated ticket sales. Grand Events expects expenses for an upcoming concert to be $80,000 and anticipates selling 4000 tickets. What should the ticket price be?

Source: *The Indianapolis Star,* 2/27/03

SOLUTION   We substitute 80,000 for x and 4000 for s in the formula and calculate p:

$$p = \frac{1.2x}{s} = \frac{1.2(80{,}000)}{4000} = 24.$$

The ticket price should be $24.   **TRY EXERCISE** ▶ 1

Solving for a Variable

In the Northeast, the formula $B = 30a$ is used to determine the minimum furnace output B, in British thermal units (Btu's), for a well-insulated home with a square feet of flooring. Suppose that a contractor has an extra furnace and wants to determine the size of the largest (well-insulated) house in which it can be used. The contractor can substitute the amount of the furnace's output in Btu's—say, 63,000—for B, and then solve for a:

$$63{,}000 = 30a \qquad \text{Replacing } B \text{ with } 63{,}000$$
$$2100 = a. \qquad \text{Dividing both sides by 30}$$

The home should have no more than 2100 ft^2 of flooring.

Were these calculations to be performed for a variety of furnaces, the contractor would find it easier to first solve $B = 30a$ for a, and *then* substitute values for B. Solving for a variable can be done in much the same way that we solved equations in Sections 2.1 and 2.2.

EXAMPLE   2

Solve for a: $B = 30a$.

SOLUTION   We have

$$B = 30a \qquad \text{We want this letter alone.}$$
$$\frac{B}{30} = a. \qquad \text{Dividing both sides by 30}$$

The equation $a = B/30$ gives a quick, easy way to determine the floor area of the largest (well-insulated) house that a furnace supplying B Btu's could heat.

                                                                    TRY EXERCISE ▶ 9

To see how solving a formula is just like solving an equation, compare the following. In (A), we solve as usual; in (B), we show steps but do not simplify; and in (C), we *cannot* simplify because a, b, and c are unknown.

A. $5x + 2 = 12$ **B.** $5x + 2 = 12$ **C.** $ax + b = c$

$5x = 12 - 2$ $5x = 12 - 2$ $ax = c - b$

$5x = 10$ $x = \dfrac{12 - 2}{5}$ $x = \dfrac{c - b}{a}$

$x = \dfrac{10}{5} = 2$

TECHNOLOGY CONNECTION

Suppose that after calculating $63{,}000 \div 30$, we wish to find $72{,}000 \div 30$. Pressing **2ND** **ENTRY** gives the following.

```
63000/30
                2100
63000/30■
```

Moving the cursor left, we can change 63,000 to 72,000 and press **ENTER**.

```
63000/30
                2100
72000/30
                2400
```

1. Verify the work above and then use **2ND** **ENTRY** to find $72{,}000 \div 90$.

EXAMPLE 3

Circumference of a circle. The formula $C = 2\pi r$ gives the *circumference C* of a circle with radius r. Solve for r.

SOLUTION   The **circumference** is the distance around a circle.

Given a radius r, we can use this equation to find a circle's circumference C.

Given a circle's circumference C, we can use this equation to find the radius r.

$C = 2\pi r$ We want this variable alone.

$\dfrac{C}{2\pi} = \dfrac{2\pi r}{2\pi}$ Dividing both sides by 2π

$\dfrac{C}{2\pi} = r$

TRY EXERCISE 13

EXAMPLE 4

Solve for y: $3x - 4y = 10$.

SOLUTION   There is one term that contains y, so we begin by isolating that term on one side of the equation.

$3x - 4y = 10$ We want this variable alone.

$-4y = 10 - 3x$ Subtracting $3x$ from both sides

$-\frac{1}{4}(-4y) = -\frac{1}{4}(10 - 3x)$ Multiplying both sides by $-\frac{1}{4}$

$y = -\frac{10}{4} + \frac{3}{4}x$ Multiplying using the distributive law

$y = -\frac{5}{2} + \frac{3}{4}x$ Simplifying the fraction

TRY EXERCISE 33

EXAMPLE 5

Nutrition.   The number of calories K needed each day by a moderately active woman who weighs w pounds, is h inches tall, and is a years old, can be estimated using the formula

$$K = 917 + 6(w + h - a).*$$

Solve for w.

SOLUTION   We reverse the order in which the operations occur on the right side:

We want w alone.

$K = 917 + 6(w + h - a)$

$K - 917 = 6(w + h - a)$ Subtracting 917 from both sides

$\dfrac{K - 917}{6} = w + h - a$ Dividing both sides by 6

$\dfrac{K - 917}{6} + a - h = w.$ Adding a and subtracting h on both sides

This formula can be used to estimate a woman's weight, if we know her age, height, and caloric needs.

TRY EXERCISE 43

————————

*Based on information from M. Parker (ed.), *She Does Math!* (Washington, D.C.: Mathematical Association of America, 1995), p. 96.

The above steps are similar to those used in Section 2.2 to solve equations. We use the addition and multiplication principles just as before. An important difference that we will see in the next example is that we will sometimes need to factor.

> **To Solve a Formula for a Given Variable**
> 1. If the variable for which you are solving appears in a fraction, use the multiplication principle to clear fractions.
> 2. Isolate the term(s), with the variable for which you are solving on one side of the equation.
> 3. If two or more terms contain the variable for which you are solving, factor the variable out.
> 4. Multiply or divide to solve for the variable in question.

We can also solve for a letter that represents a constant.

EXAMPLE **6**

Surface area of a right circular cylinder. The formula $A = 2\pi rh + 2\pi r^2$ gives the surface area A of a right circular cylinder of height h and radius r. Solve for π.

SOLUTION We have

$$A = 2\pi rh + 2\pi r^2 \qquad \text{We want this letter alone.}$$
$$A = \pi(2rh + 2r^2) \qquad \text{Factoring}$$
$$\frac{A}{2rh + 2r^2} = \pi. \qquad \begin{array}{l}\text{Dividing both sides by } 2rh + 2r^2,\\ \text{or multiplying both sides by}\\ 1/(2rh + 2r^2)\end{array}$$

We can also write this as

$$\pi = \frac{A}{2rh + 2r^2}.$$

> TRY EXERCISE 47

> *CAUTION!* Had we performed the following steps in Example 6, we would *not* have solved for π:
>
> $$A = 2\pi rh + 2\pi r^2 \qquad \text{We want } \pi \text{ alone.}$$
> $$A - 2\pi r^2 = 2\pi rh \qquad \text{Subtracting } 2\pi r^2 \text{ from both sides}$$
> $$\qquad\qquad\qquad\qquad\quad \text{Two occurrences of } \pi$$
> $$\frac{A - 2\pi r^2}{2rh} = \pi. \qquad \text{Dividing both sides by } 2rh$$
>
> The mathematics of each step is correct, but because π occurs on both sides of the formula, *we have not solved the formula for π*. Remember that the letter being solved for should be alone on one side of the equation, with no occurrence of that letter on the other side!

1. *Outdoor concerts.*   The formula $d = 344t$ can be used to determine how far d, in meters, sound travels through room-temperature air in t seconds. At a large concert, fans near the back of the crowd experienced a 0.9-sec time lag between the time each word was pronounced on stage (as shown on large video monitors) and the time the sound reached their ears. How far were these fans from the stage?

2. *Furnace output.*   Contractors in the Northeast use the formula $B = 30a$ to determine the minimum furnace output B, in British thermal units (Btu's), for a well-insulated house with a square feet of flooring. Determine the minimum furnace output for an 1800-ft^2 house that is well insulated.
   Source: U.S. Department of Energy

3. *College enrollment.*   At many colleges, the number of "full-time-equivalent" students f is given by

   $$f = \frac{n}{15},$$

   where n is the total number of credits for which students have enrolled in a given semester. Determine the number of full-time-equivalent students on a campus in which students registered for a total of 21,345 credits.

4. *Distance from a storm.*   The formula $M = \frac{1}{5}t$ can be used to determine how far M, in miles, you are from lightning when its thunder takes t seconds to reach your ears. If it takes 10 sec for the sound of thunder to reach you after you have seen the lightning, how far away is the storm?

5. *Federal funds rate.*   The Federal Reserve Board sets a target f for the federal funds rate, that is, the interest rate that banks charge each other for overnight borrowing of Federal funds. This target rate can be estimated by

   $$f = 8.5 + 1.4(I - U),$$

   where I is the core inflation rate over the previous 12 months and U is the seasonally adjusted unemployment rate. If core inflation is 0.025 and unemployment is 0.044, what should the federal funds rate be?
   Source: Greg Mankiw, Harvard University, www.gregmankiw.blogspot.com/2006/06/what-would-alan-do.html

6. *Calorie density.*   The calorie density D, in calories per ounce, of a food that contains c calories and weighs w ounces is given by

   $$D = \frac{c}{w}.^*$$

   Eight ounces of fat-free milk contains 84 calories. Find the calorie density of fat-free milk.

7. *Absorption of ibuprofen.*   When 400 mg of the painkiller ibuprofen is swallowed, the number of milligrams n in the bloodstream t hours later (for $0 \le t \le 6$) is estimated by

   $$n = 0.5t^4 + 3.45t^3 - 96.65t^2 + 347.7t.$$

   How many milligrams of ibuprofen remain in the blood 1 hr after 400 mg has been swallowed?

8. *Size of a league schedule.*   When all n teams in a league play every other team twice, a total of N games are played, where

   $$N = n^2 - n.$$

   If a soccer league has 7 teams and all teams play each other twice, how many games are played?

In Exercises 9–48, solve each formula for the indicated letter.

9. $A = bh$, for b
   (Area of parallelogram with base b and height h)

10. $A = bh$, for h

11. $d = rt$, for r
    (A distance formula, where d is distance, r is speed, and t is time)

Source: Nutrition Action Healthletter, March 2000, p. 9. Center for Science in the Public Interest, Suite 300; 1875 Connecticut Ave NW, Washington, D.C. 20008.

12. $d = rt$, for t

13. $I = Prt$, for P
(Simple-interest formula, where I is interest, P is principal, r is interest rate, and t is time)

14. $I = Prt$, for t

15. $H = 65 - m$, for m
(To determine the number of heating degree days H for a day with m degrees Fahrenheit as the average temperature)

16. $d = h - 64$, for h
(To determine how many inches d above average an h-inch-tall woman is)

17. $P = 2l + 2w$, for l
(Perimeter of a rectangle of length l and width w)

18. $P = 2l + 2w$, for w

19. $A = \pi r^2$, for π
(Area of a circle with radius r)

20. $A = \pi r^2$, for r^2

21. $A = \frac{1}{2}bh$, for h
(Area of a triangle with base b and height h)

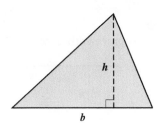

22. $A = \frac{1}{2}bh$, for b

23. $E = mc^2$, for c^2
(A relativity formula from physics)

24. $E = mc^2$, for m

25. $Q = \dfrac{c + d}{2}$, for d **26.** $Q = \dfrac{p - q}{2}$, for p

27. $A = \dfrac{a + b + c}{3}$, for b **28.** $A = \dfrac{a + b + c}{3}$, for c

29. $w = \dfrac{r}{f}$, for r
(To compute the wavelength w of a musical note with frequency f and speed of sound r)

30. $M = \dfrac{A}{s}$, for A
(To compute the Mach number M for speed A and speed of sound s)

31. $F = \dfrac{9}{5}C + 32$, for C
(To convert the Celsius temperature C to the Fahrenheit temperature F)

32. $M = \dfrac{5}{9}n + 18$, for n

33. $2x - y = 1$, for y

34. $3x - y = 7$, for y

35. $2x + 5y = 10$, for y

36. $3x + 2y = 12$, for y

37. $4x - 3y = 6$, for y

38. $5x - 4y = 8$, for y

39. $9x + 8y = 4$, for y

40. $x + 10y = 2$, for y

41. $3x - 5y = 8$, for y

42. $7x - 6y = 7$, for y

43. $z = 13 + 2(x + y)$, for x

44. $A = 115 + \dfrac{1}{2}(p + s)$, for s

45. $t = 27 - \dfrac{1}{4}(w - l)$, for l

46. $m = 19 - 5(x - n)$, for n

47. $A = at + bt$, for t

48. $S = rx + sx$, for x

49. *Area of a trapezoid.* The formula
$$A = \tfrac{1}{2}ah + \tfrac{1}{2}bh$$
can be used to find the area A of a trapezoid with bases a and b and height h. Solve for h. (*Hint*: First clear fractions.)

50. *Compounding interest.*   The formula

$$A = P + Prt$$

is used to find the amount A in an account when simple interest is added to an investment of P dollars (see Exercise 13). Solve for P.

51. *Chess rating.*   The formula

$$R = r + \frac{400(W - L)}{N}$$

is used to establish a chess player's rating R after that player has played N games, won W of them, and lost L of them. Here r is the average rating of the opponents. Solve for L.
Source: The U.S. Chess Federation

52. *Angle measure.*   The angle measure S of a sector of a circle is given by

$$S = \frac{360A}{\pi r^2},$$

where r is the radius, A is the area of the sector, and S is in degrees. Solve for r^2.

53. Naomi has a formula that allows her to convert Celsius temperatures to Fahrenheit temperatures. She needs a formula for converting Fahrenheit temperatures to Celsius temperatures. What advice can you give her?

54. Under what circumstances would it be useful to solve $d = rt$ for r? (See Exercise 11.)

Skill Review

Review simplifying expressions (Sections 1.6, 1.7, and 1.8).

Perform the indicated operations.

55. $-2 + 5 - (-4) - 17$ [1.6]

56. $-98 \div \frac{1}{2}$ [1.7]

Aha! **57.** $4.2(-11.75)(0)$ [1.7]

58. $(-2)^5$ [1.8]

Simplify. [1.8]

59. $20 \div (-4) \cdot 2 - 3$

60. $5|8 - (2 - 7)|$

Synthesis

61. The equations

$$P = 2l + 2w \quad \text{and} \quad w = \frac{P}{2} - l$$

are equivalent formulas involving the perimeter P, length l, and width w of a rectangle. Devise a problem for which the second of the two formulas would be more useful.

62. While solving $2A = ah + bh$ for h, Lea writes $\frac{2A - ah}{b} = h$. What is her mistake?

63. The Harris–Benedict formula gives the number of calories K needed each day by a moderately active man who weighs w kilograms, is h centimeters tall, and is a years old as

$$K = 21.235w + 7.75h - 10.54a + 102.3.$$

If Janos is moderately active, weighs 80 kg, is 190 cm tall, and needs to consume 2852 calories a day, how old is he?

64. *Altitude and temperature.*   Air temperature drops about 1° Celsius (C) for each 100-m rise above ground level, up to 12 km. If the ground level temperature is t°C, find a formula for the temperature T at an elevation of h meters.
Source: *A Sourcebook of School Mathematics*, Mathematical Association of America, 1980

65. *Surface area of a cube.*   The surface area A of a cube with side s is given by

$$A = 6s^2.$$

If a cube's surface area is 54 in^2, find the volume of the cube.

66. *Weight of a fish.*   An ancient fisherman's formula for estimating the weight of a fish is

$$w = \frac{lg^2}{800},$$

where w is the weight, in pounds, l is the length, in inches, and g is the girth (distance around the midsection), in inches. Estimate the girth of a 700-lb yellow tuna that is 8 ft long.

67. *Dosage size.*   Clark's rule for determining the size of a particular child's medicine dosage c is

$$c = \frac{w}{a} \cdot d,$$

where w is the child's weight, in pounds, and d is the usual adult dosage for an adult weighing a pounds. Solve for a.

Source: Olsen, June Looby, et al., *Medical Dosage Calculations.* Redwood City, CA: Addison-Wesley, 1995

Solve each formula for the given letter.

68. $\frac{y}{z} \div \frac{z}{t} = 1$, for y

69. $ac = bc + d$, for c

70. $qt = r(s + t)$, for t

71. $3a = c - a(b + d)$, for a

72. *Furnace output.*   The formula

$$B = 50a$$

is used in New England to estimate the minimum furnace output B, in Btu's, for an old, poorly insulated house with a square feet of flooring. Find an equation for determining the number of Btu's saved by insulating an old house. (*Hint*: See Exercise 2.)

73. Revise the formula in Exercise 63 so that a man's weight in pounds (2.2046 lb $= 1$ kg) and his height in inches (0.3937 in. $= 1$ cm) are used.

74. Revise the formula in Example 5 so that a woman's weight in kilograms (2.2046 lb $= 1$ kg) and her height in centimeters (0.3937 in. $= 1$ cm) are used.

2.4   Applications with Percent

Converting Between Percent Notation and Decimal Notation   ■   Solving Percent Problems

Percent problems arise so frequently in everyday life that most often we are not even aware of them. In this section, we will solve some real-world percent problems. Before doing so, however, we need to review a few basics.

Converting Between Percent Notation and Decimal Notation

Nutritionists recommend that no more than 30% of the calories in a person's diet come from fat. This means that of every 100 calories consumed, no more than 30 should come from fat. Thus, 30% is a ratio of 30 to 100.

Calories consumed

Calories from fat
30%

The percent symbol % means "per hundred." We can regard the percent symbol as part of a name for a number. For example,

$$30\% \quad \text{is defined to mean} \quad \frac{30}{100}, \quad \text{or} \quad 30 \times \frac{1}{100}, \quad \text{or} \quad 30 \times 0.01.$$

Percent Notation

$n\%$ means $\dfrac{n}{100}$,   or $n \times \dfrac{1}{100}$,   or $n \times 0.01$.

EXAMPLE 1   Convert to decimal notation: **(a)** 78%; **(b)** 1.3%.

SOLUTION

a) 78% = 78 × 0.01   Replacing % with × 0.01

       = 0.78

b) 1.3% = 1.3 × 0.01   Replacing % with × 0.01

        = 0.013

TRY EXERCISE 19

As shown above, multiplication by 0.01 simply moves the decimal point two places to the left.

To convert from percent notation to decimal notation, move the decimal point two places to the left and drop the percent symbol.

EXAMPLE 2   Convert the percent notation in the following sentence to decimal notation: Only 20% of teenagers get 8 hr of sleep a night.

Source: National Sleep Foundation

SOLUTION

20% = 20.0%   0.20.0   20% = 0.20, or simply 0.2

Move the decimal point two places to the left.

TRY EXERCISE 11

The procedure used in Examples 1 and 2 can be reversed:

0.38 = 38 × 0.01

     = 38%.   Replacing × 0.01 with %

To convert from decimal notation to percent notation, move the decimal point two places to the right and write a percent symbol.

EXAMPLE 3   Convert to percent notation: **(a)** 1.27; **(b)** $\frac{1}{4}$; **(c)** 0.3.

SOLUTION

a) We first move the decimal point two places to the right: 1.27.

and then write a % symbol: 127%   This is the same as multiplying 1.27 by 100 and writing %.

b) Note that $\frac{1}{4}$ = 0.25. We move the decimal point two places to the right: 0.25.

and then write a % symbol: 25%   Multiplying by 100 and writing %

c) We first move the decimal point two places to the right (recall that 0.3 = 0.30):   0.30.

and then write a % symbol: 30%   Multiplying by 100 and writing %

TRY EXERCISE 33

Solving Percent Problems

In solving percent problems, we first *translate* the problem to an equation. Then we *solve* the equation using the techniques discussed in Sections 2.1–2.3. The key words in the translation are as follows.

> ### Key Words in Percent Translations
>
> "**Of**" translates to "$\cdot$" or "$\times$".   "**Is**" or "**Was**" translates to "$=$".
> "**What**" translates to a variable.   "**%**" translates to "$\times \frac{1}{100}$" or "$\times 0.01$".

EXAMPLE 4

STUDENT NOTES

A way of checking answers is by estimating as follows:

$$11\% \times 49 \approx 10\% \times 50$$
$$= 0.10 \times 50 = 5.$$

Since 5 is close to 5.39, our answer is reasonable.

What is 11% of 49?

SOLUTION

Translate: What is 11% of 49?
                 ↓   ↓   ↓   ↓   ↓
                 a $=$ 0.11 $\cdot$ 49   "of" means multiply;
                                                        11% = 0.11
                          $a = 5.39$

Thus, 5.39 is 11% of 49. The answer is 5.39.   **TRY EXERCISE** 51

EXAMPLE 5

3 is 16 percent of what?

SOLUTION

Translate: 3   is   16 percent   of   what?
                ↓   ↓   ↓   ↓   ↓
                3   $=$ 0.16 $\cdot$ y

                $\dfrac{3}{0.16} = y$ Dividing both sides by 0.16

                $18.75 = y$

Thus, 3 is 16 percent of 18.75. The answer is 18.75.   **TRY EXERCISE** 47

EXAMPLE 6

What percent of $50 is $34?

SOLUTION

Translate: What percent   of $50   is $34?
                    ↓   ↓   ↓   ↓   ↓
                    n $\cdot$ 50 $=$ 34

                $n = \dfrac{34}{50}$ Dividing both sides by 50

                $n = 0.68 = 68\%$ Converting to
                                           percent notation

Thus, $34 is 68% of $50. The answer is 68%.   **TRY EXERCISE** 43

Examples 4–6 represent the three basic types of percent problems. Note that in all the problems, the following quantities are present:

- a percent, expressed in decimal notation in the translation,
- a base amount, indicated by "of" in the problem, and
- a percentage of the base, found by multiplying the base times the percent.

EXAMPLE 7

STUDENT NOTES

Always look for connections between examples. Here you should look for similarities between Examples 4 and 7 as well as between Examples 5 and 8 and between Examples 6 and 9.

Discount stores.   In 2006, there were 300 million people in the United States, and 62.2% of them lived within 5 mi of a Wal-Mart store. How many lived within 5 mi of a Wal-Mart store?

Source: *The Wall Street Journal,* 9/25/06

SOLUTION   We first reword and then translate. We let a = the number of people in the United States, in millions, who live within 5 mi of a Wal-Mart store.

Rewording: What   is   62.2%   of   300?

Translating: a =   0.622   ×   300

The letter is by itself. To solve the equation, we need only multiply:

$$a = 0.622 \times 300 = 186.6.$$

Since 186.6 million is 62.2% of 300 million, we have found that in 2006 about 186.6 million people in the United States lived within 5 mi of a Wal-Mart store.

TRY EXERCISE 65

EXAMPLE 8

College enrollment.   About 1.6 million students who graduated from high school in 2006 were attending college in the fall of 2006. This was 66% of all 2006 high school graduates. How many students graduated from high school in 2006?

Source: U.S. Bureau of Labor Statistics

SOLUTION   Before translating the problem to mathematics, we reword and let S represent the total number of students, in millions, who graduated from high school in 2006.

Rewording: 1.6   is   66%   of S.

Translating: 1.6   =   0.66   · S

$$\frac{1.6}{0.66} = S \qquad \text{Dividing both sides by 0.66}$$

$$2.4 \approx S \qquad \text{The symbol} \approx \text{means } \textit{is approximately equal to.}$$

About 2.4 million students graduated from high school in 2006.

TRY EXERCISE 67

EXAMPLE 9

Automobile prices.   Recently, Harken Motors reduced the price of a Flex Fuel 2007 Chevy Impala from the manufacturer's suggested retail price (MSRP) of $20,830 to $18,955.

a) What percent of the MSRP does the sale price represent?
b) What is the percent of discount?

SOLUTION

a) We reword and translate, using n for the unknown percent.

Rewording: What percent   of   20,830   is   18,955?

Translating: n ·   20,830   =   18,955

$$n = \frac{18,955}{20,830} \qquad \text{Dividing both sides by 20,830}$$

$$n \approx 0.91 = 91\% \qquad \text{Converting to percent notation}$$

The sale price is about 91% of the MSRP.

b) Since the original price of $20,830 represents 100% of the MSRP, the sale price represents a discount of $(100 - 91)$%, or 9%.

Alternatively, we could find the amount of discount and then calculate the percent of discount:

Amount of discount: $20,830 - \$18,955 = \$1875$.

Rewording: <u>What percent</u> of 20,830 is 1875?

Translating: n $\cdot$ 20,830   =   1875

$$n = \frac{1875}{20,830}$$ Dividing both sides by 20,830

$$n \approx 0.09 = 9\%$$ Converting to percent notation

Again we find that the percent of discount is 9%.   TRY EXERCISE ▸ 69

2.4   EXERCISE SET

For Extra Help   MyMathLab   Math XL PRACTICE   WATCH   DOWNLOAD

🖙 *Concept Reinforcement*   *In each of Exercises 1–10, match the question with the most appropriate translation from the column on the right. Some choices are used more than once.*

1. ___ What percent of 57 is 23?

2. ___ What percent of 23 is 57?

3. ___ 23 is 57% of what number?

4. ___ 57 is 23% of what number?

5. ___ 57 is what percent of 23?

6. ___ 23 is what percent of 57?

7. ___ What is 23% of 57?

8. ___ What is 57% of 23?

9. ___ 23% of what number is 57?

10. ___ 57% of what number is 23?

a) $a = (0.57)23$

b) $57 = 0.23y$

c) $n \cdot 23 = 57$

d) $n \cdot 57 = 23$

e) $23 = 0.57y$

f) $a = (0.23)57$

Convert the percent notation in each sentence to decimal notation.

11. *Energy use.*   Heating accounts for 49% of all household energy use.
Source: Chevron

12. *Energy use.*   Water heating accounts for 15% of all household energy use.
Source: Chevron

13. *Drinking water.*   Only 1% of the water on earth is suitable for drinking.
Source: www.drinktap.org

Drinking water, 1%

14. *Dehydration.*   A 2% drop in water content of the body can affect one's ability to study mathematics.
Source: High Performance Nutrition

15. *College tuition.*   Tuition and fees at two-year public colleges increased 4.1 percent in 2006.
Source: College Board 2006 tuition survey

16. *Plant species.*   Trees make up about 3.5% of all plant species found in the United States.
Source: South Dakota Project Learning Tree

17. *Women in the workforce.*   Women comprise 20% of all database administrators.
Source: U.S. Census Bureau

18. *Women in the workforce.*   Women comprise 60% of all accountants and auditors.
Source: U.S. Census Bureau

Convert to decimal notation.

19. 6.25%
20. 8.375%
21. 0.2%
22. 0.8%
23. 175%
24. 250%

Convert the decimal notation in each sentence to percent notation.

25. *NASCAR fans.*   Auto racing is the seventh most popular sport in the United States, with 0.38 of the adult population saying they are NASCAR fans.
Source: ESPN Sports poll

26. *Baseball fans.*   Baseball is the second most popular sport in the United States, with 0.61 of the adult population saying they are baseball fans.
Source: ESPN Sports poll

27. *Food security.*   The USDA defines food security as access to enough nutritious food for a healthy life. In 2005, 0.039 of U.S. households had very low food security.
Source: USDA

28. *Poverty rate.*   In 2005, 0.199 of Americans age 65 and older were under the poverty level.
Source: www.census.gov

29. *Music downloads.*   In 2006, 0.45 of Americans downloaded music.
Source: Solutions Research Group

30. *Music downloads.*   In 2006, 0.23 of Americans paid to download a song.
Source: Solutions Research Group

31. *Composition of the sun.*   The sun is 0.7 hydrogen.

32. *Jupiter's atmosphere.*   The atmosphere of Jupiter is 0.1 helium.

Convert to percent notation.

33. 0.0009
34. 0.0056
35. 1.06
36. 1.08
37. 1.8
38. 2.4
39. $\dfrac{3}{5}$
40. $\dfrac{3}{4}$
41. $\dfrac{8}{25}$
42. $\dfrac{5}{8}$

Solve.

43. What percent of 76 is 19?

44. What percent of 125 is 30?

45. What percent of 150 is 39?

46. What percent of 360 is 270?

47. 14 is 30% of what number?

48. 54 is 24% of what number?

49. 0.3 is 12% of what number?

50. 7 is 175% of what number?

51. What number is 1% of one million?

52. What number is 35% of 240?

53. What percent of 60 is 75?

Aha! **54.** What percent of 70 is 70?

55. What is 2% of 40?

56. What is 40% of 2?

Aha! **57.** 25 is what percent of 50?

58. 0.8 is 2% of what number?

59. What percent of 69 is 23?

60. What percent of 40 is 9?

Riding bicycles.   There are 57 million Americans who ride a bicycle at least occasionally. The following circle graph shows the reasons people ride. In each of Exercises 61–64, determine the number of Americans who ride a bicycle for the given reason.

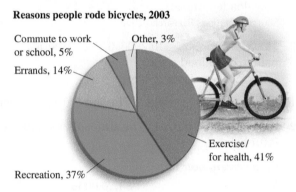

Reasons people rode bicycles, 2003

Commute to work or school, 5%
Other, 3%
Errands, 14%
Exercise/ for health, 41%
Recreation, 37%

Sources: U.S. Census Bureau; Bureau of Transportation Statistics

61. Commute to school or work

62. Run errands

63. Exercise for health

64. Recreation

65. *College graduation.*   To obtain his bachelor's degree in nursing, Cody must complete 125 credit hours of instruction. If he has completed 60% of his requirement, how many credits did Cody complete?

66. *College graduation.*   To obtain her bachelor's degree in journalism, Addy must complete 125 credit hours of instruction. If 20% of Addy's credit hours remain to be completed, how many credits does she still need to take?

67. *Batting average.*   In the 2007 season, Magglio Ordonez of the Detroit Tigers had 216 hits. His batting average was 0.363, the highest in major league baseball for that season. This means that of the total number of at bats, 36.3% were hits. How many at bats did he have?
Source: ESPN

68. *Pass completions.*   At one point in a recent season, Peyton Manning of the Indianapolis Colts had completed 357 passes. This was 62.5% of his attempts. How many attempts did he make?
Source: National Football League

69. *Tipping.*   Trent left a $4 tip for a meal that cost $25.
   a) What percent of the cost of the meal was the tip?
   b) What was the total cost of the meal including the tip?

70. *Tipping.*   Selena left a $12.76 tip for a meal that cost $58.
   a) What percent of the cost of the meal was the tip?
   b) What was the total cost of the meal including the tip?

71. *Crude oil imports.*   In April 2007, crude oil imports to the United States averaged 10.2 million barrels per day. Of this total, 3.4 million came from Canada and Mexico. What percent of crude oil imports came from Canada and Mexico? What percent came from the rest of the world?
Source: Energy Information Administration

72. *Alternative-fuel vehicles.*   Of the 550,000 alternative-fuel vehicles produced in the United States in 2004, 150,000 were E85 flexible-fuel vehicles. What percent of alternative-fuel vehicles used E85? What percent used other alternative fuels?
Source: Energy Information Administration

73. *Student loans.*   Glenn takes out a subsidized federal Stafford loan for $2400. After a year, Glenn decides to pay off the interest, which is 7% of $2400. How much will he pay?

74. *Student loans.*   To finance her community college education, LaTonya takes out a Stafford loan for $3500. After a year, LaTonya decides to pay off the interest, which is 8% of $3500. How much will she pay?

75. *Infant health.*   In a study of 300 pregnant women with "good-to-excellent" diets, 95% had babies in good or excellent health. How many women in this group had babies in good or excellent health?

76. *Infant health.*   In a study of 300 pregnant women with "poor" diets, 8% had babies in good or excellent health. How many women in this group had babies in good or excellent health?

77. *Cost of self-employment.*   Because of additional taxes and fewer benefits, it has been estimated that a self-employed person must earn 20% more than a non–self-employed person performing the same task(s). If Tia earns $16 an hour working for Village

Copy, how much would she need to earn on her own for a comparable income?

78. Refer to Exercise 77. Rik earns $18 an hour working for Round Edge stairbuilders. How much would Rik need to earn on his own for a comparable income?

79. *Budget overruns.* The Indianapolis Central Library expansion, begun in 2002, was expected to cost $103 million. By 2006, library officials estimated the cost would be $45 million over budget. By what percent did the actual cost exceed the initial estimate?
Source: *The Indianapolis Star*, 5/23/06

80. *Fastest swimmer.* In 1990, Tom Jager of the United States set a world record by swimming 50 m at a rate of 2.29 m/s. Previously, the fastest swimming rate on record was 2.26 m/s, set in 1975 by David Holmes Edgar, also of the United States. Calculate the percentage by which the rate increased.
Source: *Guinness Book of World Records* 1975 and 1998

81. A bill at Officeland totaled $47.70. How much did the merchandise cost if the sales tax is 6%?

82. Marta's checkbook shows that she wrote a check for $987 for building materials. What was the price of the materials if the sales tax is 5%?

83. *Deducting sales tax.* A tax-exempt school group received a bill of $157.41 for educational software. The bill incorrectly included sales tax of 6%. How much should the school group pay?

84. *Deducting sales tax.* A tax-exempt charity received a bill of $145.90 for a sump pump. The bill incorrectly included sales tax of 5%. How much does the charity owe?

85. *Body fat.* One author of this text exercises regularly at a local YMCA that recently offered a body-fat percentage test to its members. The device used measures the passage of a very low voltage of electricity through the body. The author's body-fat percentage was found to be 16.5% and he weighs 191 lb. What part, in pounds, of his body weight is fat?

86. *Areas of Alaska and Arizona.* The area of Arizona is 19% of the area of Alaska. The area of Alaska is 586,400 mi². What is the area of Arizona?

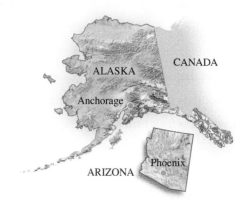

87. *Direct mail.* Only 2.15% of mailed ads lead to a sale or a response from customers. In 2006, businesses sent out 114 billion pieces of direct mail (catalogs, coupons, and so on). How many pieces of mail led to a response from customers?
Sources: Direct Marketing Association; U.S. Postal Service

88. *Kissing and colds.* In a medical study, it was determined that if 800 people kiss someone else who has a cold, only 56 will actually catch the cold. What percent is this?

89. *Calorie content.* Pepperidge Farm Light Style 7 Grain Bread® has 140 calories in a 3-slice serving. This is 15% less than the number of calories in a serving of regular bread. How many calories are in a serving of regular bread?

90. *Fat content.* Peek Freans Shortbread Reduced Fat Cookies® contain 35 calories of fat in each serving. This is 40% less than the fat content in the leading imported shortbread cookie. How many calories of fat are in a serving of the leading shortbread cookie?

91. Campus Bookbuyers pays $30 for a book and sells it for $60. Is this a 100% markup or a 50% markup? Explain.

92. If Julian leaves a $12 tip for a $90 dinner, is he being generous, stingy, or neither? Explain.

Skill Review

To prepare for Section 2.5, review translating to algebraic expressions and equations (Section 1.1).

Translate to an algebraic expression or equation. [1.1]

93. Twice the length plus twice the width

94. 5% of $180

95. 5 fewer than the number of points Tino scored

96. 15 plus the product of 1.5 and x

97. The product of 10 and half of a

98. 10 more than three times a number

99. The width is 2 in. less than the length.

100. A number is four times as large as a second number.

Synthesis

101. How is the use of statistics in the following misleading?

  a) A business explaining new restrictions on sick leave cited a recent survey indicating that 40% of all sick days were taken on Monday or Friday.

  b) An advertisement urging summer installation of a security system quoted FBI statistics stating that over 26% of home burglaries occur between Memorial Day and Labor Day.

102. Erin is returning a tent that she bought during a 25%-off storewide sale that has ended. She is offered store credit for 125% of what she paid (not to be used on sale items). Is this fair to Erin? Why or why not?

103. The community of Bardville has 1332 left-handed females. If 48% of the community is female and 15% of all females are left-handed, how many people are in the community?

104. It has been determined that at the age of 10, a girl has reached 84.4% of her final adult height. Dana is 4 ft 8 in. at the age of 10. What will her final adult height be?

105. It has been determined that at the age of 15, a boy has reached 96.1% of his final adult height. Jaraan is 6 ft 4 in. at the age of 15. What will his final adult height be?

106. *Dropout rate.*   Between 2002 and 2004, the high school dropout rate in the United States decreased from 105 to 103 per thousand. Calculate the percent by which the dropout rate decreased and use that percentage to estimate dropout rates for the United States in 2005 and in 2006.
Source: www.childrendsdatabank.org

107. *Photography.*   A 6-in. by 8-in. photo is framed using a mat meant for a 5-in. by 7-in. photo. What percentage of the photo will be hidden by the mat?

108. Would it be better to receive a 5% raise and then, a year later, an 8% raise or the other way around? Why?

Aha!

109. Jorge is in the 30% tax bracket. This means that 30¢ of each dollar earned goes to taxes. Which would cost him the least: contributing $50 that is tax-deductible or contributing $40 that is not tax-deductible? Explain.

CORNER

Sales and Discounts

Focus: Applications and models using percent

Time: 15 minutes

Group size: 3

Materials: Calculators are optional.

Often a store will reduce the price of an item by a fixed percentage. When the sale ends, the items are returned to their original prices. Suppose a department store reduces all sporting goods 20%, all clothing 25%, and all electronics 10%.

ACTIVITY

1. Each group member should select one of the following items: a $50 basketball, an $80 jacket, or a $200 MP3 player. Fill in the first three columns of the first three rows of the chart below.

2. Apply the appropriate discount and determine the sale price of your item. Fill in the fourth column of the chart.

3. Next, find a multiplier that can be used to convert the sale price back to the original price and fill in the remaining column of the chart. Does this multiplier depend on the price of the item?

4. Working as a group, compare the results of part (3) for all three items. Then develop a formula for a multiplier that will restore a sale price to its original price, p, after a discount r has been applied. Complete the fourth row of the table and check that your formula will duplicate the results of part (3).

5. Use the formula from part (4) to find the multiplier that a store would use to return an item to its original price after a "30% off" sale expires. Fill in the last line on the chart.

6. Inspect the last column of your chart. How can these multipliers be used to determine the percentage by which a sale price is increased when a sale ends?

Original Price, p	Discount, r	$1 - r$	Sale Price	Multiplier to convert back to p
p	r	$1 - r$		
	0.30			

2.5 Problem Solving

Five Steps for Problem Solving   ▪   Applying the Five Steps

Probably the most important use of algebra is as a tool for problem solving. In this section, we develop a problem-solving approach that is used throughout the remainder of the text.

Five Steps for Problem Solving

In Section 2.4, we solved several real-world problems. To solve them, we first *familiarized* ourselves with percent notation. We then *translated* each problem into an equation, *solved* the equation, *checked* the solution, and *stated* the answer.

Five Steps for Problem Solving in Algebra

1. *Familiarize* yourself with the problem.
2. *Translate* to mathematical language. (This often means writing an equation.)
3. *Carry out* some mathematical manipulation. (This often means *solving* an equation.)
4. *Check* your possible answer in the original problem.
5. *State* the answer clearly, using a complete English sentence.

Of the five steps, the most important is probably the first one: becoming familiar with the problem. Here are some hints for familiarization.

To Become Familiar with a Problem

1. Read the problem carefully. Try to visualize the problem.
2. Reread the problem, perhaps aloud. Make sure you understand all important words and any symbols or abbreviations.
3. List the information given and the question(s) to be answered. Choose a variable (or variables) to represent the unknown and specify exactly what the variable represents. For example, let L = length in centimeters, d = distance in miles, and so on.
4. Look for similarities between the problem and other problems you have already solved. Ask yourself what type of problem this is.
5. Find more information. Look up a formula in a book, at a library, or online. Consult a reference librarian or an expert in the field.
6. Make a table that uses all the information you have available. Look for patterns that may help in the translation.
7. Make a drawing and label it with known and unknown information, using specific units if given.
8. Think of a possible answer and check the guess. Note the manner in which the guess is checked.

Applying the Five Steps

EXAMPLE 1

Bicycling.   After finishing college, Nico spent a week touring Tuscany, Italy, by bicycle. He biked 260 km from Pisa through Siena to Florence. At Siena, he had biked three times as far from Pisa as he would then bike to Florence. How far had he biked, and how far did he have left to go?

SOLUTION

1. **Familiarize.** It is often helpful to make a drawing. In this case, we can use a map of Nico's trip.

   To gain familiarity, let's suppose that Nico has 50 km to go. Then he would have traveled three times 50 km, or 150 km, already. Since 50 km + 150 km = 200 km and 200 km < 260 km, we see that our guess is too small. Rather than guess again, we let

   d = the distance, in kilometers, from Siena to Florence

   and

   $3d$ = the distance, in kilometers, from Siena to Pisa.

   (We could also let x = the distance to Pisa; then the distance to Florence would be $\frac{1}{3}x$.)

2. **Translate.** The lengths of the two parts of the trip must add up to 260 km. This leads to our translation.

   Rewording: Distance to Florence plus distance to Pisa is 260 km

   Translating: d + $3d$ =   260

3. **Carry out.** We solve the equation:

   $$d + 3d = 260$$
   $$4d = 260 \qquad \text{Combining like terms}$$
   $$d = 65. \qquad \text{Dividing both sides by 4}$$

4. **Check.** As predicted in the *Familiarize* step, d is greater than 50 km. If d = 65 km, then $3d$ = 195 km. Since 65 km + 195 km = 260 km, we have a check.

5. **State.** At Siena, Nico had biked 195 km and had 65 km left to go to arrive in Florence.

   TRY EXERCISE 9

Before we solve the next problem, we need to learn some additional terminology regarding integers.

The following are examples of **consecutive integers:** 16, 17, 18, 19, 20; and −31, −30, −29, −28. Note that consecutive integers can be represented in the form $x, x + 1, x + 2$, and so on.

The following are examples of **consecutive even integers:** 16, 18, 20, 22, 24; and −52, −50, −48, −46. Note that consecutive even integers can be represented in the form $x, x + 2, x + 4$, and so on.

The following are examples of **consecutive odd integers:** 21, 23, 25, 27, 29; and −71, −69, −67, −65. Note that consecutive odd integers can be also represented in the form $x, x + 2, x + 4$, and so on.

EXAMPLE   2

Interstate mile markers.   U.S. interstate highways post numbered markers at every mile to indicate location in case of an emergency. The sum of two consecutive mile markers on I-70 in Kansas is 559. Find the numbers on the markers.

Source: Federal Highway Administration, Ed Rotalewski

x	$x + 1$	Sum of x and $x + 1$
114	115	229
252	253	505
302	303	605

SOLUTION

1. **Familiarize.** The numbers on the mile markers are consecutive positive integers. Thus if we let x = the smaller number, then $x + 1$ = the larger number.

   To become familiar with the problem, we can make a table, as shown at left. First, we guess a value for x; then we find $x + 1$. Finally, we add the two numbers and check the sum.

   From the table, we see that the first marker will be between 252 and 302. We could continue guessing and solve the problem this way, but let's work on developing our algebra skills.

2. **Translate.** We reword the problem and translate as follows.

   Rewording: First integer   plus   second integer   is   559.

   Translating: x $+$ $(x + 1)$ $=$ 559

3. **Carry out.** We solve the equation:

   $$x + (x + 1) = 559$$
   $$2x + 1 = 559 \quad \text{Using an associative law and combining like terms}$$
   $$2x = 558 \quad \text{Subtracting 1 from both sides}$$
   $$x = 279. \quad \text{Dividing both sides by 2}$$

   If x is 279, then $x + 1$ is 280.

4. **Check.** Our possible answers are 279 and 280. These are consecutive positive integers and $279 + 280 = 559$, so the answers check.

5. **State.** The mile markers are 279 and 280.

> TRY EXERCISE   13

EXAMPLE   3

Color printers.   Egads Computer Corporation rents a Xerox Phaser 8400 Color Laser Printer for $300 a month. A new art gallery is leasing a printer for a 2-month advertising campaign. The ink and paper for the brochures will cost an additional 21.5¢ per copy. If the gallery allots a budget of $3000, how many brochures can they print?

Source: egadscomputer.com

SOLUTION

1. **Familiarize.** Suppose that the art gallery prints 20,000 brochures. Then the cost is the monthly charges plus ink and paper cost, or

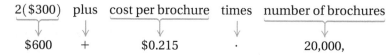

   2($300) plus cost per brochure times number of brochures

   $600   + $0.215   ·   20,000,

   which is $4900. Our guess of 20,000 is too large, but we have familiarized ourselves with the way in which a calculation is made. Note that we convert 21.5¢ to $0.215 so that all information is in the same unit, dollars. We let c = the number of brochures that can be printed for $3000.

2. **Translate.** We reword the problem and translate as follows.

   Rewording: Monthly cost   plus   ink and paper cost   is $3000.

   Translating: 2($300)   +   ($0.215)c = $3000

3. **Carry out.** We solve the equation:

$$2(300) + 0.215c = 3000$$
$$600 + 0.215c = 3000$$
$$0.215c = 2400 \qquad \text{Subtracting 600 from both sides}$$
$$c = \frac{2400}{0.215} \qquad \text{Dividing both sides by 0.215}$$
$$c \approx 11{,}162. \qquad \text{We round } down \text{ to avoid going over the budget.}$$

4. **Check.** We check in the original problem. The cost for 11,162 brochures is 11,162($0.215) = $2399.83. The rental for 2 months is 2($300) = $600. The total cost is then $2399.83 + $600 = $2999.83, which is just under the amount that was allotted. Our answer is less than 20,000, as we expected from the *Familiarize* step.

5. **State.** The art gallery can make 11,162 brochures with the rental allotment of $3000.

> TRY EXERCISE 37

STUDENT NOTES

For most students, the most challenging step is step (2), "Translate." The table on p. 4 (Section 1.1) can be helpful in this regard.

EXAMPLE   4

Perimeter of NBA court.   The perimeter of an NBA basketball court is 288 ft. The length is 44 ft longer than the width. Find the dimensions of the court.

Source: National Basketball Association

SOLUTION

1. **Familiarize.** Recall that the perimeter of a rectangle is twice the length plus twice the width. Suppose the court were 30 ft wide. The length would then be 30 + 44, or 74 ft, and the perimeter would be 2 · 30 ft + 2 · 74 ft, or 208 ft. This shows that in order for the perimeter to be 288 ft, the width must exceed 30 ft. Instead of guessing again, we let w = the width of the court, in feet.

Since the court is "44 ft longer than it is wide," we let $w + 44 =$ the length of the court, in feet.

$w + 44$

w

2. **Translate.** To translate, we use $w + 44$ as the length and 288 as the perimeter. To double the length, $w + 44$, parentheses are essential.

Rewording: Twice the   twice the
                length   plus   width   is   288 ft.

Translating: $2(w + 44)$ $+$ $2w$ $=$ 288

3. **Carry out.** We solve the equation:

$$2(w + 44) + 2w = 288$$
$$2w + 88 + 2w = 288 \quad \text{Using the distributive law}$$
$$4w + 88 = 288 \quad \text{Combining like terms}$$
$$4w = 200$$
$$w = 50.$$

The dimensions appear to be $w = 50\,\text{ft}$, and $l = w + 44 = 94\,\text{ft}$.

4. **Check.** If the width is 50 ft and the length is 94 ft, then the court is 44 ft longer than it is wide. The perimeter is $2(50\,\text{ft}) + 2(94\,\text{ft}) = 100\,\text{ft} + 188\,\text{ft}$, or 288 ft, as specified. We have a check.

5. **State.** An NBA court is 50 ft wide and 94 ft long.

TRY EXERCISE ▶ 25

CAUTION!   Always be sure to answer the original problem completely. For instance, in Example 1 we needed to find *two* numbers: the distances from *each* city to Siena. Similarly, in Example 4 we needed to find two dimensions, not just the width. Be sure to label each answer with the proper unit.

EXAMPLE   5

Selling at an auction.   Jared is selling his collection of Transformers at an auction. He wants to be left with $1150 after paying a seller's premium of 8% on the final bid (hammer price) for the collection. What must the hammer price be in order for him to clear $1150?

SOLUTION

1. **Familiarize.** Suppose the collection sells for $1200. The 8% seller's premium can be determined by finding 8% of $1200:

$$8\% \text{ of } \$1200 = 0.08(\$1200) = \$96.$$

Subtracting this premium from $1200 would leave Jared with

$$\$1200 - \$96 = \$1104.$$

This shows that in order for Jared to clear $1150, the collection must sell for more than $1200. We let $x =$ the hammer price, in dollars. Jared then must pay a seller's premium of $0.08x$.

2. **Translate.** We reword the problem and translate as follows.

Rewording: <u>Hammer price</u>   less   <u>seller's premium</u>   is   <u>amount remaining.</u>

Translating: x $-$ $0.08x$ $=$ $\$1150$

3. **Carry out.** We solve the equation:

$$x - 0.08x = 1150$$
$$1x - 0.08x = 1150$$
$$0.92x = 1150$$ Combining like terms. Had we noted that after the premium has been paid, 92% remains, we could have begun with this equation.

$$x = \frac{1150}{0.92}$$ Dividing both sides by 0.92

$$x = 1250.$$

4. **Check.** To check, we first find 8% of $1250:

   8% of $\$1250 = 0.08(\$1250) = \$100.$ This is the premium.

   Next, we subtract the premium to find the remaining amount:

   $\$1250 - \$100 = \$1150.$

   Since, after Jared pays the seller's premium, he is left with $1150, our answer checks. Note that the $1250 hammer price is greater than $1200, as predicted in the *Familiarize* step.

5. **State.** Jared's collection must sell for $1250 in order for him to be left with $1150.

   TRY EXERCISE 7

EXAMPLE 6

Cross section of a roof.   In a triangular gable end of a roof, the angle of the peak is twice as large as the angle on the back side of the house. The measure of the angle on the front side is 20° greater than the angle on the back side. How large are the angles?

SOLUTION

1. **Familiarize.** We make a drawing. In this case, the measure of the back angle is x, the measure of the front angle is $x + 20$, and the measure of the peak angle is $2x$.

2. **Translate.** To translate, we need to recall that the sum of the measures of the angles in a triangle is 180°.

Rewording: Measure of back angle + measure of front angle + measure of peak angle is 180°.

Translating: x + $(x + 20)$ + $2x$ = 180

3. **Carry out.** We solve:

$$x + (x + 20) + 2x = 180$$
$$4x + 20 = 180$$
$$4x = 160$$
$$x = 40.$$

The measures for the angles appear to be:

Back angle: $x = 40°$,

Front angle: $x + 20 = 40 + 20 = 60°$,

Peak angle: $2x = 2(40) = 80°$.

4. **Check.** Consider 40°, 60°, and 80°, as listed above. The measure of the front angle is 20° greater than the measure of the back angle, the measure of the peak angle is twice the measure of the back angle, and the sum is 180°. These numbers check.

5. **State.** The measures of the angles are 40°, 60°, and 80°.   **TRY EXERCISE** 31

We close this section with some tips to aid you in problem solving.

> **Problem-Solving Tips**
>
> 1. The more problems you solve, the more your skills will improve.
> 2. Look for patterns when solving problems. Each time you study an example or solve an exercise, you may observe a pattern for problems found later.
> 3. Clearly define variables before translating to an equation.
> 4. Consider the dimensions of the variables and constants in the equation. The variables that represent length should all be in the same unit, those that represent money should all be in dollars or all in cents, and so on.
> 5. Make sure that units appear in the answer whenever appropriate and that you completely answer the original problem.

2.5   EXERCISE SET

Solve. Even though you might find the answer quickly in some other way, practice using the five-step problem-solving process in order to build the skill of problem solving.

1. Three less than twice a number is 19. What is the number?

2. Two fewer than ten times a number is 78. What is the number?

3. Five times the sum of 3 and twice some number is 70. What is the number?

4. Twice the sum of 4 and three times some number is 34. What is the number?

5. *Price of an iPod.* Kyle paid $120 for an iPod nano during a 20%-off sale. What was the regular price?

6. *Price of sneakers.* Amy paid $102 for a pair of New Balance 1122 running shoes during a 15%-off sale. What was the regular price?

7. *Price of a calculator.* Kayla paid $137.80, including 6% tax, for her graphing calculator. How much did the calculator itself cost?

8. *Price of a printer.* Laura paid $219.45, including 5% tax, for an all-in-one color printer. How much did the printer itself cost?

9. *Unicycling.* In 2005, Ken Looi of New Zealand set a record by covering 235.3 mi in 24 hr on his unicycle. After 8 hr, he was approximately twice as far from the finish line as he was from the start. How far had he traveled?
Source: *Guinness World Records* 2007

10. *Sled-dog racing.* The Iditarod sled-dog race extends for 1049 mi from Anchorage to Nome. If a musher is twice as far from Anchorage as from Nome, how many miles has the musher traveled?

11. *Indy Car racing.* In April 2008, Danica Patrick won the Indy Japan 300 with a time of 01:51:02.6739 for the 300-mi race. At one point, Patrick was 20 mi closer to the finish than to the start. How far had Patrick traveled at that point?

12. *NASCAR racing.* In June 2007, Carl Edwards won the Michigan 400 with a time of 2:42:5 for the 400-mi race. At one point, Edwards was 80 mi closer to the finish than to the start. How far had Edwards traveled at that point?

13. *Apartment numbers.* The apartments in Erica's apartment house are consecutively numbered on each floor. The sum of her number and her next-door neighbor's number is 2409. What are the two numbers?

14. *Apartment numbers.* The apartments in Brian's apartment house are numbered consecutively on each floor. The sum of his number and his next-door neighbor's number is 1419. What are the two numbers?

15. *Street addresses.* The houses on the west side of Lincoln Avenue are consecutive odd numbers. Sam and Colleen are next-door neighbors and the sum of their house numbers is 572. Find their house numbers.

16. *Street addresses.* The houses on the south side of Elm Street are consecutive even numbers. Wanda and Larry are next-door neighbors and the sum of their house numbers is 794. Find their house numbers.

17. The sum of three consecutive page numbers is 99. Find the numbers.

18. The sum of three consecutive page numbers is 60. Find the numbers.

19. *Longest marriage.* As half of the world's longest-married couple, the woman was 2 yr younger than her husband. Together, their ages totaled 204 yr. How old were the man and the woman?
Source: *Guinness World Records* 2007

20. *Oldest bride.* The world's oldest bride was 19 yr older than her groom. Together, their ages totaled 185 yr. How old were the bride and the groom?
Source: *Guinness World Records* 2007

21. *e-mail.* In 2006, approximately 125 billion e-mail messages were sent each day. The number of spam messages was about four times the number of non-spam messages. How many of each type of message were sent each day in 2006?
Source: Ferris Research

22. *Home remodeling.* In 2005, Americans spent a total of $26 billion to remodel bathrooms and kitchens. They spent $5 billion more on kitchens than on bathrooms. How much was spent on each?
Source: Joint Center for Housing Studies, Harvard University

23. *Page numbers.* The sum of the page numbers on the facing pages of a book is 281. What are the page numbers?

24. *Perimeter of a triangle.* The perimeter of a triangle is 195 mm. If the lengths of the sides are consecutive odd integers, find the length of each side.

25. *Hancock Building dimensions.* The top of the John Hancock Building in Chicago is a rectangle whose length is 60 ft more than the width. The perimeter is 520 ft. Find the width and the length of the rectangle. Find the area of the rectangle.

26. *Dimensions of a state.* The perimeter of the state of Wyoming is 1280 mi. The width is 90 mi less than the length. Find the width and the length.

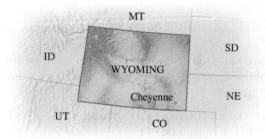

27. A rectangular community garden is to be enclosed with 92 m of fencing. In order to allow for compost storage, the garden must be 4 m longer than it is wide. Determine the dimensions of the garden.

28. *Perimeter of a high school basketball court.* The perimeter of a standard high school basketball court is 268 ft. The length is 34 ft longer than the width. Find the dimensions of the court.
Source: Indiana High School Athletic Association

29. *Two-by-four.* The perimeter of a cross section of a "two-by-four" piece of lumber is $10\frac{1}{2}$ in. The length is twice the width. Find the actual dimensions of the cross section of a two-by-four.

$P = 10\frac{1}{2}$ in.

30. *Standard billboard sign.* A standard rectangular highway billboard sign has a perimeter of 124 ft. The length is 6 ft more than three times the width. Find the dimensions of the sign.

$3w + 6$

w

31. *Angles of a triangle.* The second angle of an architect's triangle is three times as large as the first. The third angle is 30° more than the first. Find the measure of each angle.

32. *Angles of a triangle.* The second angle of a triangular garden is four times as large as the first. The third angle is 45° less than the sum of the other two angles. Find the measure of each angle.

33. *Angles of a triangle.* The second angle of a triangular kite is four times as large as the first. The third angle is 5° more than the sum of the other two angles. Find the measure of the second angle.

34. *Angles of a triangle.* The second angle of a triangular building lot is three times as large as the first. The third angle is 10° more than the sum of the other two angles. Find the measure of the third angle.

35. *Rocket sections.* A rocket is divided into three sections: the payload and navigation section in the top, the fuel section in the middle, and the rocket engine section in the bottom. The top section is one-sixth the length of the bottom section. The middle section is one-half the length of the bottom section. The total length is 240 ft. Find the length of each section.

240 ft

36. *Gourmet sandwiches.*   Jenny, Demi, and Drew buy an 18-in. long gourmet sandwich and take it back to their apartment. Since they have different appetites, Jenny cuts the sandwich so that Demi gets half of what Jenny gets and Drew gets three-fourths of what Jenny gets. Find the length of each person's sandwich.

37. *Taxi rates.*   In Chicago, a taxi ride costs $2.25 plus $1.80 for each mile traveled. Debbie has budgeted $18 for a taxi ride (excluding tip). How far can she travel on her $18 budget?
Source: City of Chicago

38. *Taxi fares.*   In New York City, taxis charge $2.50 plus $2.00 per mile for off-peak fares. How far can Ralph travel for $17.50 (assuming an off-peak fare)?
Source: New York City Taxi and Limousine Commission

39. *Truck rentals.*   Truck-Rite Rentals rents trucks at a daily rate of $49.95 plus 39¢ per mile. Concert Productions has budgeted $100 for renting a truck to haul equipment to an upcoming concert. How far can they travel in one day and stay within their budget?

40. *Truck rentals.*   Fine Line Trucks rents an 18-ft truck for $42 plus 35¢ per mile. Judy needs a truck for one day to deliver a shipment of plants. How far can she drive and stay within a budget of $70?

41. *Complementary angles.*   The sum of the measures of two *complementary* angles is 90°. If one angle measures 15° more than twice the measure of its complement, find the measure of each angle.

Complementary
angles

42. *Complementary angles.*   Two angles are complementary. (See Exercise 41.) The measure of one angle is $1\frac{1}{2}$ times the measure of the other. Find the measure of each angle.

43. *Supplementary angles.*   The sum of the measures of two *supplementary* angles is 180°. If the measure of one angle is $3\frac{1}{2}$ times the measure of the other, find the measure of each angle.

Supplementary
angles

44. *Supplementary angles.*   Two angles are supplementary. (See Exercise 43.) If one angle measures 45° less than twice the measure of its supplement, find the measure of each angle.

45. *Copier paper.*   The perimeter of standard-size copier paper is 99 cm. The width is 6.3 cm less than the length. Find the length and the width.

46. *Stock prices.*   Sarah's investment in Jet Blue stock grew 28% to $448. How much did she originally invest?

47. *Savings interest.*   Janeka invested money in a savings account at a rate of 6% simple interest. After 1 yr, she has $6996 in the account. How much did Janeka originally invest?

48. *Credit cards.*   The balance in Will's Mastercard® account grew 2%, to $870, in one month. What was his balance at the beginning of the month?

49. *Scrabble®.*   In a single game on October 12, 2006, Michael Cresta and Wayne Yorra set three North American Scrabble records: the most points in one game by one player, the most total points in the game, and the most points on a single turn. Cresta scored 340 points more than Yorra, and together they scored 1320 points. What was the winning score?
Source: www.slate.com

50. *Color printers.* The art gallery in Example 3 decides to raise its budget to $5000 for the 2-month period. How many brochures can they print for $5000?

51. *Selling a home.* The Brannons are planning to sell their home. If they want to be left with $117,500 after paying 6% of the selling price to a realtor as a commission, for how much must they sell the house?

52. *Budget overruns.* The massive roadworks project in Boston known as The Big Dig cost approximately $14.6 billion. This cost was 484% more than the original estimate. What was the original estimate of the cost of The Big Dig?
Sources: Taxpayers for Common Sense; www.msnbc.cmsn.com

53. *Cricket chirps and temperature.* The equation $T = \frac{1}{4}N + 40$ can be used to determine the temperature T, in degrees Fahrenheit, given the number of times N a cricket chirps per minute. Determine the number of chirps per minute for a temperature of 80°F.

54. *Race time.* The equation $R = -0.028t + 20.8$ can be used to predict the world record in the 200-m dash, where R is the record in seconds and t is the number of years since 1920. In what year will the record be 18.0 sec?

55. Sean claims he can solve most of the problems in this section by guessing. Is there anything wrong with this approach? Why or why not?

56. When solving Exercise 20, Beth used a to represent the bride's age and Ben used a to represent the groom's age. Is one of these approaches preferable to the other? Why or why not?

Skill Review

To prepare for Section 2.6, review inequalities (Section 1.4).

Write a true sentence using either $<$ *or* $>$. [1.4]

57. -8 ▮ 1

58. -2 ▮ -5

59. $\frac{1}{2}$ ▮ 0

60. -3 ▮ -1

Write a second inequality with the same meaning. [1.4]

61. $x \geq -4$

62. $x < 5$

63. $5 > y$

64. $-10 \leq t$

Synthesis

65. Write a problem for a classmate to solve. Devise it so that the problem can be translated to the equation $x + (x + 2) + (x + 4) = 375$.

66. Write a problem for a classmate to solve. Devise it so that the solution is "Audrey can drive the rental truck for 50 mi without exceeding her budget."

67. *Discounted dinners.* Kate's "Dining Card" entitles her to $10 off the price of a meal after a 15% tip has been added to the cost of the meal. If, after the discount, the bill is $32.55, how much did the meal originally cost?

68. *Test scores.* Pam scored 78 on a test that had 4 fill-in questions worth 7 points each and 24 multiple-choice questions worth 3 points each. She had one fill-in question wrong. How many multiple-choice questions did Pam get right?

69. *Gettysburg Address.* Abraham Lincoln's 1863 Gettysburg Address refers to the year 1776 as "four *score* and seven years ago." Determine what a score is.

70. One number is 25% of another. The larger number is 12 more than the smaller. What are the numbers?

71. A storekeeper goes to the bank to get $10 worth of change. She requests twice as many quarters as half dollars, twice as many dimes as quarters, three times as many nickels as dimes, and no pennies or dollars. How many of each coin did the storekeeper get?

72. *Perimeter of a rectangle.* The width of a rectangle is three fourths of the length. The perimeter of the rectangle becomes 50 cm when the length and the width are each increased by 2 cm. Find the length and the width.

73. *Discounts.* In exchange for opening a new credit account, Macy's Department Stores® subtracts 10% from all purchases made the day the account is established. Julio is opening an account and has a coupon for which he receives 10% off the first day's reduced price of a camera. If Julio's final price is $77.75, what was the price of the camera before the two discounts?

74. *Sharing fruit.* Apples are collected in a basket for six people. One third, one fourth, one eighth, and one fifth of the apples are given to four people, respectively. The fifth person gets ten apples, and one apple remains for the sixth person. Find the original number of apples in the basket.

75. *eBay purchases.* An eBay seller charges $9.99 for the first DVD purchased and $6.99 for all others. For shipping and handling, he charges the full shipping fee of $3 for the first DVD, one half of the shipping charge for the second item, and one third of the shipping charge per item for all remaining items. The total cost of a shipment (excluding tax) was $45.45. How many DVDs were in the shipment?

76. *Winning percentage.* In a basketball league, the Falcons won 15 of their first 20 games. In order to win 60% of the total number of games, how many more games will they have to play, assuming they win only half of the remaining games?

77. *Taxi fares.* In New York City, a taxi ride costs $2.50 plus 40¢ per $\frac{1}{5}$ mile and 40¢ per minute stopped in traffic. Due to traffic, Glenda's taxi took 20 min to complete what is usually a 10-min drive. If she is charged $18.50 for the ride, how far did Glenda travel?
Source: New York City Taxi and Limousine Commission

78. *Test scores.* Ella has an average score of 82 on three tests. Her average score on the first two tests is 85. What was the score on the third test?

79. A school purchases a piano and must choose between paying $2000 at the time of purchase or $2150 at the end of one year. Which option should the school select and why?

80. Annette claims the following problem has no solution: "The sum of the page numbers on facing pages is 191. Find the page numbers." Is she correct? Why or why not?

81. The perimeter of a rectangle is 101.74 cm. If the length is 4.25 cm longer than the width, find the dimensions of the rectangle.

82. The second side of a triangle is 3.25 cm longer than the first side. The third side is 4.35 cm longer than the second side. If the perimeter of the triangle is 26.87 cm, find the length of each side.

2.6 Solving Inequalities

Solutions of Inequalities ■ Graphs of Inequalities ■ Set-Builder and Interval Notation ■
Solving Inequalities Using the Addition Principle ■ Solving Inequalities Using the Multiplication Principle ■
Using the Principles Together

Many real-world situations translate to *inequalities*. For example, a student might need to register for *at least* 12 credits; an elevator might be designed to hold *at most* 2000 pounds; a tax credit might be allowable for families with incomes of *less than* $25,000; and so on. Before solving applications of this type, we must adapt our equation-solving principles to the solving of inequalities.

Solutions of Inequalities

Recall from Section 1.4 that an inequality is a number sentence containing > (is greater than), < (is less than), ≥ (is greater than or equal to), or ≤ (is less than or equal to). Inequalities like

$$-7 > x, \quad t < 5, \quad 5x - 2 \geq 9, \quad \text{and} \quad -3y + 8 \leq -7$$

are true for some replacements of the variable and false for others.

Any value for the variable that makes an inequality true is called a **solution**. The set of all solutions is called the **solution set**. When all solutions of an inequality are found, we say that we have **solved** the inequality.

EXAMPLE   1

Determine whether the given number is a solution of $x < 2$: **(a)** -3; **(b)** 2.

SOLUTION

a) Since $-3 < 2$ is true, -3 is a solution.

b) Since $2 < 2$ is false, 2 is not a solution.

TRY EXERCISE   9

EXAMPLE   2

Determine whether the given number is a solution of $y \geq 6$: **(a)** 6; **(b)** -4.

SOLUTION

a) Since $6 \geq 6$ is true, 6 is a solution.

b) Since $-4 \geq 6$ is false, -4 is not a solution.

TRY EXERCISE   11

Graphs of Inequalities

Because the solutions of inequalities like $x < 2$ are too numerous to list, it is help-ful to make a drawing that represents all the solutions. The **graph** of an inequality is such a drawing. Graphs of inequalities in one variable can be drawn on the number line by shading all points that are solutions. Parentheses are used to indi-cate endpoints that are *not* solutions and brackets to indicate endpoints that *are* solutions.*

EXAMPLE   3

Graph each inequality: **(a)** $x < 2$; **(b)** $y \geq -3$; **(c)** $-2 < x \leq 3$.

SOLUTION

a) The solutions of $x < 2$ are those numbers less than 2. They are shown on the graph by shading all points to the left of 2. The parenthesis at 2 and the shad-ing to its left indicate that 2 is *not* part of the graph, but numbers like 1.2 and 1.99 are.

b) The solutions of $y \geq -3$ are shown on the number line by shading the point for -3 and all points to the right of -3. The bracket at -3 indicates that -3 *is* part of the graph.

STUDENT NOTES

Note that $-2 < x < 3$ means $-2 < x$ *and* $x < 3$. Because of this, statements like $2 < x < 1$ make no sense—no number is both greater than 2 and less than 1.

c) The inequality $-2 < x \leq 3$ is read "-2 is less than x *and* x is less than or equal to 3," or "x is greater than -2 *and* less than or equal to 3." To be a solution of $-2 < x \leq 3$, a number must be a solution of both $-2 < x$ *and* $x \leq 3$. The number 1 is a solution, as are -0.5, 1.9, and 3. The parenthesis indicates that -2 is *not* a solution, whereas the bracket indicates that 3 *is* a solution. The other solutions are shaded.

TRY EXERCISE   17

*An alternative notation uses open dots to indicate endpoints that are not solutions and closed dots to indicate endpoints that are solutions. Using this notation, the solutions of $x < 2$ are graphed as ←++++++◦++→ and the solutions of $y \geq -3$ are graphed as ←+●++++++→.

Set–Builder and Interval Notation

To write the solution set of $x < 3$, we can use **set-builder notation:**

$$\{x\,|\,x < 3\}.$$

This is read "The set of all x such that x is less than 3."

Another way to write solutions of an inequality in one variable is to use **interval notation**. Interval notation uses parentheses, ( ), and brackets, [ ].

If a and b are real numbers with $a < b$, we define the **open interval (a, b)** as the set of all numbers x for which $a < x < b$. Using set-builder notation, we write

$$(a, b) = \{x\,|\,a < x < b\}. \qquad \text{Parentheses are used to exclude endpoints.}$$

Its graph excludes the endpoints:

(a, b) $\{x\,|\,a < x < b\}$

The **closed interval $[a, b]$** is defined as the set of all numbers x for which $a \le x \le b$. Thus,

$$[a, b] = \{x\,|\,a \le x \le b\}. \qquad \text{Brackets are used to include endpoints.}$$

Its graph includes the endpoints:

$[a, b]$ $\{x\,|\,a \le x \le b\}$

There are two kinds of **half-open intervals**, defined as follows:

1. $(a, b] = \{x\,|\,a < x \le b\}$. This is open on the left. Its graph is as follows:

$(a, b]$ $\{x\,|\,a < x \le b\}$

2. $[a, b) = \{x\,|\,a \le x < b\}$. This is open on the right. Its graph is as follows:

$[a, b)$ $\{x\,|\,a \le x < b\}$

We use the symbols ∞ and $-\infty$ to represent positive infinity and negative infinity, respectively. Thus the notation (a, ∞) represents the set of all real numbers greater than a, and $(-\infty, a)$ represents the set of all real numbers less than a.

(a, ∞) $\{x\,|\,x > a\}$

$(-\infty, a)$ $\{x\,|\,x < a\}$

The notation $[a, \infty)$ or $(-\infty, a]$ is used when we want to include the endpoint a.

CAUTION! Do not confuse the *interval* (a, b) with the *ordered pair* (a, b). The context in which the notation appears should make the meaning clear.

STUDENT NOTES

You may have noticed which inequality signs in set-builder notation correspond to brackets and which correspond to parentheses. The relationship could be written informally as

$$\le \quad \ge \qquad [\;]$$
$$< \quad > \qquad (\;).$$

EXAMPLE 4   Graph $y \ge -2$ on a number line and write the solution set using both set-builder and interval notations.

SOLUTION   Using set-builder notation, we write the solution set as $\{y\,|\,y \ge -2\}$.

Using interval notation, we write $[-2, \infty)$.

To graph the solution, we shade all numbers to the right of -2 and use a bracket to indicate that -2 is also a solution.

TRY EXERCISE 27

Solving Inequalities Using the Addition Principle

Consider a balance similar to one that appears in Section 2.1. When one side of
the balance holds more weight than the other, the balance tips in that direction. If
equal amounts of weight are then added to or subtracted from both sides of the
balance, the balance remains tipped in the same direction.

The balance illustrates the idea that when a number, such as 2, is added to (or
subtracted from) both sides of a true inequality, such as $3 < 7$, we get another
true inequality:

$$3 + 2 < 7 + 2, \quad \text{or} \quad 5 < 9.$$

Similarly, if we add -4 to both sides of $x + 4 < 10$, we get an *equivalent*
inequality:

$$x + 4 + (-4) < 10 + (-4), \quad \text{or} \quad x < 6.$$

We say that $x + 4 < 10$ and $x < 6$ are **equivalent**, which means that both inequalities have the same solution set.

The Addition Principle for Inequalities

For any real numbers a, b, and c:

$a < b$ is equivalent to $a + c < b + c$;

$a \leq b$ is equivalent to $a + c \leq b + c$;

$a > b$ is equivalent to $a + c > b + c$;

$a \geq b$ is equivalent to $a + c \geq b + c$.

As with equations, our goal is to isolate the variable on one side.

EXAMPLE 5   Solve $x + 2 > 8$ and then graph the solution.

SOLUTION   We use the addition principle, subtracting 2 from both sides:

$$x + 2 - 2 > 8 - 2 \qquad \text{Subtracting 2 from, or adding } -2 \text{ to, both sides}$$
$$x > 6.$$

From the inequality $x > 6$, we can determine the solutions easily. Any number
greater than 6 makes $x > 6$ true and is a solution of that inequality as well as the
inequality $x + 2 > 8$. Using set-builder notation, the solution set is $\{x \mid x > 6\}$.
Using interval notation, the solution set is $(6, \infty)$. The graph is as follows:

Because most inequalities have an infinite number of solutions, we cannot possibly check them all. A partial check can be made using one of the possible solutions. For this example, we can substitute any number greater than 6—say, 6.1—into the original inequality:

$$\frac{x + 2 > 8}{6.1 + 2 \mid 8}$$
$$8.1 \overset{?}{>} 8 \quad \text{TRUE} \qquad 8.1 > 8 \text{ is a true statement.}$$

Since $8.1 > 8$ is true, 6.1 is a solution. Any number greater than 6 is a solution.

TRY EXERCISE 43

EXAMPLE 6

Solve $3x - 1 \leq 2x - 5$ and then graph the solution.

SOLUTION   We have

$$3x - 1 \leq 2x - 5$$
$$3x - 1 + 1 \leq 2x - 5 + 1 \qquad \text{Adding 1 to both sides}$$
$$3x \leq 2x - 4 \qquad\qquad\qquad \text{Simplifying}$$
$$3x - 2x \leq 2x - 4 - 2x \qquad \text{Subtracting } 2x \text{ from both sides}$$
$$x \leq -4. \qquad\qquad\qquad\quad \text{Simplifying}$$

The graph is as follows:

The student should check that any number less than or equal to -4 is a solution. The solution set is $\{x \mid x \leq -4\}$, or $(-\infty, -4]$.

TRY EXERCISE 47

Solving Inequalities Using the Multiplication Principle

There is a multiplication principle for inequalities similar to that for equations, but it must be modified when multiplying both sides by a negative number. Consider the true inequality

$$3 < 7.$$

If we multiply both sides by a *positive* number—say, 2—we get another true inequality:

$$3 \cdot 2 < 7 \cdot 2, \quad \text{or} \quad 6 < 14. \qquad \text{TRUE}$$

If we multiply both sides by a negative number—say, -2—we get a *false* inequality:

$$3 \cdot (-2) < 7 \cdot (-2), \quad \text{or} \quad -6 < -14. \qquad \text{FALSE}$$

The fact that $6 < 14$ is true, but $-6 < -14$ is false, stems from the fact that the negative numbers, in a sense, *mirror* the positive numbers. Whereas 14 is to the *right* of 6, the number -14 is to the *left* of -6. Thus if we reverse the inequality symbol in $-6 < -14$, we get a true inequality:

$$-6 > -14. \qquad \text{TRUE}$$

> ### The Multiplication Principle for Inequalities
>
> For any real numbers a and b, and for any *positive* number c:
>
> $$a < b \quad \text{is equivalent to} \quad ac < bc, \quad \text{and}$$
> $$a > b \quad \text{is equivalent to} \quad ac > bc.$$
>
> For any real numbers a and b, and for any *negative* number c:
>
> $$a < b \quad \text{is equivalent to} \quad ac > bc, \quad \text{and}$$
> $$a > b \quad \text{is equivalent to} \quad ac < bc.$$
>
> Similar statements hold for $\leq$ and $\geq$.

> *CAUTION!* When multiplying or dividing both sides of an inequality by a negative number, don't forget to reverse the inequality symbol!

EXAMPLE 7   Solve and graph each inequality: **(a)** $\frac{1}{4}x < 7$; **(b)** $-2y \leq 18$.

SOLUTION

a) $\frac{1}{4}x < 7$

$\quad 4 \cdot \frac{1}{4}x < 4 \cdot 7$ Multiplying both sides by 4, the reciprocal of $\frac{1}{4}$

$\qquad\qquad\uparrow\text{\underline{}}$ The symbol stays the same, since 4 is positive.

$\quad\quad x < 28$ Simplifying

The solution set is $\{x \mid x < 28\}$, or $(-\infty, 28)$. The graph is shown at left.

b) $-2y \leq 18$

$\quad \dfrac{-2y}{-2} \underset{\uparrow}{\geq} \dfrac{18}{-2}$ Multiplying both sides by $-\frac{1}{2}$, or dividing both sides by -2

$\qquad\quad\text{\underline{}}$ *At this step*, we reverse the inequality, because $-\frac{1}{2}$ is negative.

$\quad\quad y \geq -9$ Simplifying

As a partial check, we substitute a number greater than -9, say -8, into the original inequality:

$$\frac{-2y \leq 18}{-2(-8) \mid 18}$$

$$16 \overset{?}{\leq} 18 \quad \text{TRUE} \qquad 16 \leq 18 \text{ is a true statement.}$$

The solution set is $\{y \mid y \geq -9\}$, or $[-9, \infty)$. The graph is shown at left.

> **TRY EXERCISE** 59

Using the Principles Together

We use the addition and multiplication principles together to solve inequalities much as we did when solving equations.

EXAMPLE 8   Solve: **(a)** $6 - 5y > 7$; **(b)** $2x - 9 < 7x + 1$.

SOLUTION

a) $\quad\quad 6 - 5y > 7$

$\quad -6 + 6 - 5y > -6 + 7$ Adding -6 to both sides

$\quad\quad\quad\quad -5y > 1$ Simplifying

$$-\tfrac{1}{5} \cdot (-5y) < -\tfrac{1}{5} \cdot 1 \qquad \text{Multiplying both sides by } -\tfrac{1}{5}, \text{ or dividing both sides by } -5$$

Remember to reverse the inequality symbol!

$$y < -\tfrac{1}{5} \qquad \text{Simplifying}$$

As a partial check, we substitute a number smaller than $-\tfrac{1}{5}$, say -1, into the original inequality:

$$\frac{6 - 5y > 7}{6 - 5(-1) \ \big|\ 7}$$
$$6 - (-5) \ \big|$$

$$11 \overset{?}{>} 7 \quad \text{TRUE} \qquad 11 > 7 \text{ is a true statement.}$$

The solution set is $\{y \,|\, y < -\tfrac{1}{5}\}$, or $(-\infty, -\tfrac{1}{5})$. We show the graph in the margin for reference.

b)

$$2x - 9 < 7x + 1$$
$$2x - 9 - 1 < 7x + 1 - 1 \qquad \text{Subtracting 1 from both sides}$$
$$2x - 10 < 7x \qquad \text{Simplifying}$$
$$2x - 10 - 2x < 7x - 2x \qquad \text{Subtracting } 2x \text{ from both sides}$$
$$-10 < 5x \qquad \text{Simplifying}$$
$$\frac{-10}{5} < \frac{5x}{5} \qquad \text{Dividing both sides by 5}$$
$$-2 < x \qquad \text{Simplifying}$$

The solution set is $\{x \,|\, -2 < x\}$, or $\{x \,|\, x > -2\}$, or $(-2, \infty)$.

TRY EXERCISE 69

All of the equation-solving techniques used in Sections 2.1 and 2.2 can be used with inequalities provided we remember to reverse the inequality symbol when multiplying or dividing both sides by a negative number.

EXAMPLE 9

Solve: **(a)** $16.3 - 7.2p \le -8.18$; **(b)** $3(x - 9) - 1 \le 2 - 5(x + 6)$.

SOLUTION

a) The greatest number of decimal places in any one number is *two*. Multiplying both sides by 100 will clear decimals. Then we proceed as before.

$$16.3 - 7.2p \le -8.18$$
$$100(16.3 - 7.2p) \le 100(-8.18) \qquad \text{Multiplying both sides by 100}$$
$$100(16.3) - 100(7.2p) \le 100(-8.18) \qquad \text{Using the distributive law}$$
$$1630 - 720p \le -818 \qquad \text{Simplifying}$$
$$-720p \le -818 - 1630 \qquad \text{Subtracting 1630 from both sides}$$
$$-720p \le -2448 \qquad \begin{array}{l}\text{Simplifying;}\\ -818 - 1630 = -2448\end{array}$$
$$p \ge \frac{-2448}{-720} \qquad \text{Dividing both sides by } -720$$

Remember to reverse the symbol!

$$p \ge 3.4$$

The solution set is $\{p \,|\, p \ge 3.4\}$, or $[3.4, \infty)$.

b) $3(x - 9) - 1 \leq 2 - 5(x + 6)$

$$3x - 27 - 1 \leq 2 - 5x - 30 \qquad \text{Using the distributive law to remove parentheses}$$

$$3x - 28 \leq -5x - 28 \qquad \text{Simplifying}$$

$$3x - 28 + 28 \leq -5x - 28 + 28 \qquad \text{Adding 28 to both sides}$$

$$3x \leq -5x$$

$$3x + 5x \leq -5x + 5x \qquad \text{Adding } 5x \text{ to both sides}$$

$$8x \leq 0$$

$$x \leq 0 \qquad \text{Dividing both sides by 8}$$

The solution set is $\{x \,|\, x \leq 0\}$, or $(-\infty, 0]$.

 TRY EXERCISE ▶ 83

-3 -2 -1 0

2.6   EXERCISE SET

For Extra Help
MyMathLab Math XL PRACTICE   WATCH   DOWNLOAD

↪ *Concept Reinforcement   Insert the symbol*
$<, >, \leq$, *or* $\geq$ *to make each pair of inequalities equivalent.*

1. $-5x \leq 30$; $x \;\rule{1em}{0.4pt}\; -6$ **2.** $-7t \geq 56$; $t \;\rule{1em}{0.4pt}\; -8$

3. $-2t > -14$; $t \;\rule{1em}{0.4pt}\; 7$ **4.** $-3x < -15$; $x \;\rule{1em}{0.4pt}\; 5$

Classify each pair of inequalities as "equivalent" or "not equivalent."

5. $x < -2$; $-2 > x$ **6.** $t > -1$; $-1 < t$

7. $-4x - 1 \leq 15$;   **8.** $-2t + 3 \geq 11$;
$\quad -4x \leq 16$ $\quad -2t \geq 14$

Determine whether each number is a solution of the given inequality.

9. $x > -4$

   a) 4   **b)** -6 **c)** -4

10. $t < 3$

   a) -3 **b)** 3   **c)** $2\frac{19}{20}$

11. $y \leq 19$

   a) 18.99   **b)** 19.01   **c)** 19

12. $n \geq -4$

   a) 0   **b)** -4.1 **c)** -3.9

13. $c \geq -7$

   a) 0   **b)** -5.4 **c)** 7.1

14. $a > 6$

   a) 6   **b)** -6.7 **c)** 0

15. $z < -3$

   a) 0   **b)** $-3\frac{1}{3}$ **c)** 1

16. $m \leq -2$

   a) $-1\frac{9}{10}$ **b)** 0   **c)** $-2\frac{1}{3}$

Graph on a number line.

17. $y < 2$ **18.** $x \leq 7$

19. $x \geq -1$ **20.** $t > -2$

21. $0 \leq t$ **22.** $1 \leq m$

23. $-5 \leq x < 2$

24. $-3 < x \leq 5$

25. $-4 < x < 0$

26. $0 \leq x \leq 5$

Graph each inequality, and write the solution set using both set-builder notation and interval notation.

27. $y < 6$ **28.** $x > 4$

29. $x \geq -4$ **30.** $t \leq 6$

31. $t > -3$ **32.** $y < -3$

33. $x \leq -7$ **34.** $x \geq -6$

Describe each graph using set-builder notation and interval notation.

35.

36.

37.

38.

39.

40.

41.

42.

Solve using the addition principle. Graph and write set-builder notation and interval notation for each answer.

43. $y + 6 > 9$

44. $x + 8 \leq -10$

45. $n - 6 < 11$

46. $n - 4 > -3$

47. $2x \leq x - 9$

48. $3x \leq 2x + 7$

49. $y + \frac{1}{3} \leq \frac{5}{6}$

50. $x + \frac{1}{4} \leq \frac{1}{2}$

51. $t - \frac{1}{8} > \frac{1}{2}$

52. $y - \frac{1}{3} > \frac{1}{4}$

53. $-9x + 17 > 17 - 8x$

54. $-8n + 12 > 12 - 7n$

Aha! **55.** $-23 < -t$

56. $19 < -x$

57. $10 - y \leq -12$

58. $3 - y \geq -6$

Solve using the multiplication principle. Graph and write set-builder notation and interval notation for each answer.

59. $4x < 28$

60. $3x \geq 24$

61. $-24 > 8t$

62. $-16x < -64$

63. $1.8 \geq -1.2n$

64. $9 \leq -2.5a$

65. $-2y \leq \frac{1}{5}$

66. $-2x \geq \frac{1}{5}$

67. $-\frac{8}{5} > 2x$

68. $-\frac{5}{8} < -10y$

Solve using the addition and multiplication principles.

69. $2 + 3x < 20$

70. $7 + 4y < 31$

71. $4t - 5 \leq 23$

72. $15x - 7 \leq -7$

73. $39 > 3 - 9x$

74. $5 > 5 - 7y$

75. $5 - 6y > 25$

76. $8 - 2y > 9$

77. $-3 < 8x + 7 - 7x$

78. $-5 < 9x + 8 - 8x$

79. $6 - 4y > 6 - 3y$

80. $7 - 8y > 5 - 7y$

81. $7 - 9y \leq 4 - 7y$

82. $6 - 13y \leq 4 - 12y$

83. $2.1x + 43.2 > 1.2 - 8.4x$

84. $0.96y - 0.79 \leq 0.21y + 0.46$

85. $1.7t + 8 - 1.62t < 0.4t - 0.32 + 8$

86. $0.7n - 15 + n \geq 2n - 8 - 0.4n$

87. $\frac{x}{3} + 4 \leq 1$

88. $\frac{2}{3} - \frac{x}{5} < \frac{4}{15}$

89. $3 < 5 - \frac{t}{7}$

90. $2 > 9 - \frac{x}{5}$

91. $4(2y - 3) \leq -44$

92. $3(2y - 3) > 21$

93. $8(2t + 1) > 4(7t + 7)$

94. $3(t - 2) \geq 9(t + 2)$

95. $3(r - 6) + 2 < 4(r + 2) - 21$

96. $5(t + 3) + 9 \geq 3(t - 2) - 10$

97. $\frac{4}{5}(3x + 4) \leq 20$

98. $\frac{2}{3}(2x - 1) \geq 10$

99. $\frac{2}{3}\left(\frac{7}{8} - 4x\right) - \frac{5}{8} < \frac{3}{8}$

100. $\frac{3}{4}\left(3x - \frac{1}{2}\right) - \frac{2}{3} < \frac{1}{3}$

101. Are the inequalities $x > -3$ and $x \geq -2$ equivalent? Why or why not?

102. Are the inequalities $t < -7$ and $t \leq -8$ equivalent? Why or why not?

Skill Review

Review simplifying expressions (Section 1.8).

Simplify. [1.8]

103. $5x - 2(3 - 6x)$

104. $8m - n - 3(2m + 5n)$

105. $x - 2[4y + 3(8 - x) - 1]$

106. $5 - 3t - 4[6 + 5(2t - 1) + t]$

107. $3[5(2a - b) + 1] - 5[4 - (a - b)]$

108. $9x - 2\{4 - 5[6 - 2(x + 1) - x]\}$

Synthesis

109. Explain how it is possible for the graph of an inequality to consist of just one number. (*Hint:* See Example 3c.)

110. The statements of the addition and multiplication principles begin with *conditions* set for the variables. Explain the conditions given for each principle.

Solve.

Aha! **111.** $x < x + 1$

112. $6[4 - 2(6 + 3t)] > 5[3(7 - t) - 4(8 + 2t)] - 20$

113. $27 - 4[2(4x - 3) + 7] \geq 2[4 - 2(3 - x)] - 3$

Solve for x.

114. $\frac{1}{2}(2x + 2b) > \frac{1}{3}(21 + 3b)$

115. $-(x + 5) \geq 4a - 5$

116. $y < ax + b$ (Assume $a < 0$.)

117. $y < ax + b$ (Assume $a > 0$.)

118. Graph the solutions of $|x| < 3$ on a number line.

Aha! **119.** Determine the solution set of $|x| > -3$.

120. Determine the solution set of $|x| < 0$.

CONNECTING the CONCEPTS

The procedure for solving inequalities is very similar to that used to solve equations. There are, however, two important differences.

- The multiplication principle for inequalities differs from the multiplication principle for equations: When we multiply or divide on both sides of an inequality by a *negative* number, we must *reverse* the direction of the inequality.

- The solution set of an equation like those we solved in this chapter typically consists of one number. The solution set of an inequality typically consists of a set of numbers and is written using set-builder notation.

Compare the following solutions.

Solve: $2 - 3x = x + 10$.

SOLUTION

$$2 - 3x = x + 10$$
$$-3x = x + 8 \qquad \text{Subtracting 2 from both sides}$$
$$-4x = 8 \qquad \text{Subtracting } x \text{ from both sides}$$
$$x = -2 \qquad \text{Dividing both sides by } -4$$

The solution is -2.

Solve: $2 - 3x > x + 10$.

SOLUTION

$$2 - 3x > x + 10$$
$$-3x > x + 8 \qquad \text{Subtracting 2 from both sides}$$
$$-4x > 8 \qquad \text{Subtracting } x \text{ from both sides}$$
$$x < -2 \qquad \text{Dividing both sides by } -4 \text{ and reversing the direction of the inequality symbol}$$

The solution is $\{x | x < -2\}$, or $(-\infty, -2)$.

MIXED REVIEW

Solve.

1. $x - 6 = 15$
2. $x - 6 \leq 15$
3. $3x = -18$
4. $3x > -18$
5. $-3x > -18$
6. $5x + 2 = 17$
7. $7 - 3x = 8$
8. $4y - 7 < 5$
9. $3 - t \geq 19$
10. $2 + 3n = 5n - 9$
11. $3 - 5a > a + 9$
12. $1.2x - 3.4 < 0.4x + 5.2$
13. $\frac{2}{3}(x + 5) \geq -4$
14. $\frac{n}{5} - 6 = 15$
15. $0.5x - 2.7 = 3x + 7.9$
16. $5(6 - t) = -45$
17. $8 - \frac{y}{3} \leq 7$
18. $\frac{1}{3}x - \frac{5}{6} = \frac{3}{2} - \frac{1}{6}x$
19. $-15 > 7 - 5x$
20. $10 \geq -2(a - 5)$

2.7 Solving Applications with Inequalities

Translating to Inequalities ▪ Solving Problems

The five steps for problem solving can be used for problems involving inequalities.

Translating to Inequalities

Before solving problems that involve inequalities, we list some important phrases to look for. Sample translations are listed as well.

Important Words	Sample Sentence	Translation
is at least	Ming walks at least 2 mi a day.	$m \geq 2$
is at most	At most 5 students dropped the course.	$n \leq 5$
cannot exceed	The width cannot exceed 40 ft.	$w \leq 40$
must exceed	The speed must exceed 15 mph.	$s > 15$
is less than	Kamal's weight is less than 120 lb.	$w < 120$
is more than	Boston is more than 200 mi away.	$d > 200$
is between	The film was between 90 and 100 min long.	$90 < t < 100$
minimum	Ned drank a minimum of 5 glasses of water a day.	$w \geq 5$
maximum	The maximum penalty is $100.	$p \leq 100$
no more than	Alan weighs no more than 90 lb.	$w \leq 90$
no less than	Mallory scored no less than 8.3.	$s \geq 8.3$

The following phrases deserve special attention.

Translating "at least" and "at most"

The quantity x is at least some amount q: $x \geq q$.

(If x is *at least* q, it cannot be less than q.)

The quantity x is at most some amount q: $x \leq q$.

(If x is *at most* q, it cannot be more than q.)

Solving Problems

EXAMPLE 1

Catering costs.   To cater a party, Curtis' Barbeque charges a $50 setup fee plus $15 per person. The cost of Hotel Pharmacy's end-of-season softball party cannot exceed $450. How many people can attend the party?

SOLUTION

1. **Familiarize.** Suppose that 20 people were to attend the party. The cost would then be $50 + $15 · 20, or $350. This shows that more than 20 people could attend without exceeding $450. Instead of making another guess, we let n = the number of people in attendance.

2. **Translate.** The cost of the party will be $50 for the setup fee plus $15 times the number of people attending. We can reword as follows:

Rewording:	The setup fee	plus	the cost of the meals	cannot exceed	$450.
Translating:	50	+	15 · n	≤	450

3. **Carry out.** We solve for n:

$$50 + 15n \leq 450$$
$$15n \leq 400 \qquad \text{Subtracting 50 from both sides}$$
$$n \leq \frac{400}{15} \qquad \text{Dividing both sides by 15}$$
$$n \leq 26\frac{2}{3}. \qquad \text{Simplifying}$$

4. **Check.** Although the solution set of the inequality is all numbers less than or equal to $26\frac{2}{3}$, since n represents the number of people in attendance, we round *down* to 26. If 26 people attend, the cost will be $50 + $15 · 26, or $440, and if 27 attend, the cost will exceed $450.

5. **State.** At most 26 people can attend the party.   TRY EXERCISE 23

CAUTION! Solutions of problems should always be checked using the original wording of the problem. In some cases, answers might need to be whole numbers or integers or rounded off in a particular direction.

Some applications with inequalities involve *averages,* or *means.* You are already familiar with the concept of averages from grades in courses that you have taken.

Average, or Mean

To find the **average**, or **mean**, of a set of numbers, add the numbers and then divide by the number of addends.

EXAMPLE 2

Financial aid.   Full-time students in a health-care education program can receive financial aid and employee benefits from Covenant Health System by working at Covenant while attending school and also agreeing to work there after graduation. Students who work an average of at least 16 hr per week receive extra pay and part-time employee benefits. For the first three weeks of September, Dina worked 20 hr, 12 hr, and 14 hr. How many hours must she work during the fourth week in order to average at least 16 hr per week for the month?

Source: Covenant Health Systems

SOLUTION

1. **Familiarize.** Suppose Dina works 10 hr during the fourth week. Her average for the month would be

$$\frac{20 \text{ hr} + 12 \text{ hr} + 14 \text{ hr} + 10 \text{ hr}}{4} = 14 \text{ hr.} \qquad \text{There are 4 addends, so we divide by 4.}$$

This shows that Dina must work more than 10 hr during the fourth week, if she is to average at least 16 hr of work per week. We let x represent the number of hours Dina works during the fourth week.

2. **Translate.** We reword the problem and translate as follows:

Rewording: The average number   should be
of hours worked   at least   16 hr.

Translating: $\dfrac{20 + 12 + 14 + x}{4} \qquad \geq \qquad 16$

3. **Carry out.** Because of the fraction, it is convenient to use the multiplication principle first:

$$\frac{20 + 12 + 14 + x}{4} \geq 16$$

$$4\left(\frac{20 + 12 + 14 + x}{4}\right) \geq 4 \cdot 16 \qquad \text{Multiplying both sides by 4}$$

$$20 + 12 + 14 + x \geq 64$$

$$46 + x \geq 64 \qquad \text{Simplifying}$$

$$x \geq 18. \qquad \text{Subtracting 46 from both sides}$$

4. **Check.** As a partial check, we show that if Dina works 18 hr, she will average at least 16 hr per week:

$$\frac{20 + 12 + 14 + 18}{4} = \frac{64}{4} = 16. \qquad \text{Note that 16 is at least 16.}$$

5. **State.** Dina will average at least 16 hr of work per week for September if she works at least 18 hr during the fourth week.

▸ **TRY EXERCISE** 27

Translating for Success

Translate each word problem to an equation or an inequality and select a correct translation from A–O.

1. Consecutive integers. The sum of two consecutive even integers is 102. Find the integers.

2. Salary increase. After Susanna earned a 5% raise, her new salary was $25,750. What was her former salary?

3. Dimensions of a rectangle. The length of a rectangle is 6 in. more than the width. The perimeter of the rectangle is 102 in. Find the length and the width.

4. Population. The population of Kelling Point is decreasing at a rate of 5% per year. The current population is 25,750. What was the population the previous year?

5. Reading assignment. Quinn has 6 days to complete a 150-page reading assignment. How many pages must he read the first day so that he has no more than 102 pages left to read on the 5 remaining days?

A. $0.05(25{,}750) = x$

B. $x + 2x = 102$

C. $2x + 2(x + 6) = 102$

D. $150 - x \leq 102$

E. $x - 0.05x = 25{,}750$

F. $x + (x + 2) = 102$

G. $x + (x + 6) > 102$

H. $x + 5x = 150$

I. $x + 0.05x = 25{,}750$

J. $x + (2x + 6) = 102$

K. $x + (x + 1) = 102$

L. $102 + x > 150$

M. $0.05x = 25{,}750$

N. $102 + 5x > 150$

O. $x + (x + 6) = 102$

Answers on page A-5

An additional, animated version of this activity appears in MyMathLab. To use MyMathLab, you need a course ID and a student access code. Contact your instructor for more information.

6. Numerical relationship. One number is 6 more than twice another. The sum of the numbers is 102. Find the numbers.

7. DVD collections. Together Mindy and Ken have 102 DVDs. If Ken has 6 more DVDs than Mindy, how many does each have?

8. Sales commissions. Kirk earns a commission of 5% on his sales. One year he earned commissions totaling $25,750. What were his total sales for the year?

9. Fencing. Jess has 102 ft of fencing that he plans to use to enclose two dog runs. The perimeter of one run is to be twice the perimeter of the other. Into what lengths should the fencing be cut?

10. Quiz scores. Lupe has a total of 102 points on the first 6 quizzes in her sociology class. How many total points must she earn on the 5 remaining quizzes in order to have more than 150 points for the semester?

↪ *Concept Reinforcement*   *In each of Exercises 1–8, match the sentence with one of the following:*

$$a < b; \quad a \le b; \quad b < a; \quad b \le a.$$

1. a is at least b.

2. a exceeds b.

3. a is at most b.

4. a is exceeded by b.

5. b is no more than a.

6. b is no less than a.

7. b is less than a.

8. b is more than a.

Translate to an inequality.

9. A number is less than 10.

10. A number is greater than or equal to 4.

11. The temperature is at most $-3°C$.

12. The average credit-card debt is more than $8000.

13. To rent a car, a driver must have a minimum of 5 yr driving experience.

14. The Barringdean Shopping Center is no more than 20 mi away.

15. The age of the Mayan altar exceeds 1200 yr.

16. The maximum safe exposure limit of formaldehyde is 2 parts per million.

17. Tania earns between $12 and $15 an hour.

18. Leslie's test score was at least 85.

19. Wind speeds were greater than 50 mph.

20. The costs of production of that software cannot exceed $12,500.

21. A room at Pine Tree Bed and Breakfast costs no more than $120 a night.

22. The cost of gasoline was at most $4 per gallon.

Use an inequality and the five-step process to solve each problem.

23. *Furnace repairs.*   RJ's Plumbing and Heating charges $55 plus $40 per hour for emergency service. Gary remembers being billed over $150 for an emergency call. How long was RJ's there?

24. *College tuition.*   Karen's financial aid stipulates that her tuition not exceed $1000. If her local community college charges a $35 registration fee plus $375 per course, what is the greatest number of courses for which Karen can register?

25. *Graduate school.*   An unconditional acceptance into the Master of Business Administration (MBA) program at Arkansas State University will be given to students whose GMAT score plus 200 times the undergraduate grade point average is at least 950. Robbin's GMAT score was 500. What must her grade point average be in order to be unconditionally accepted into the program?
Source: graduateschool.astate.edu

26. *Car payments.*   As a rule of thumb, debt payments (other than mortgages) should be less than 8% of a consumer's monthly gross income. Oliver makes $54,000 a year and has a $100 student-loan payment every month. What size car payment can he afford?
Source: money.cnn.com

27. *Quiz average.*   Rod's quiz grades are 73, 75, 89, and 91. What scores on a fifth quiz will make his average quiz grade at least 85?

28. *Nutrition.*   Following the guidelines of the U.S. Department of Agriculture, Dale tries to eat at least 5 half-cup servings of vegetables each day. For the first six days of one week, she had 4, 6, 7, 4, 6, and 4 servings. How many servings of vegetables should Dale eat on Saturday, in order to average at least 5 servings per day for the week?

29. *College course load.*   To remain on financial aid, Millie needs to complete an average of at least 7 credits per quarter each year. In the first three quarters of 2008, Millie completed 5, 7, and 8 credits. How many credits of course work must Millie complete in the fourth quarter if she is to remain on financial aid?

30. *Music lessons.* Band members at Colchester Middle School are expected to average at least 20 min of practice time per day. One week Monroe practiced 15 min, 28 min, 30 min, 0 min, 15 min, and 25 min. How long must he practice on the seventh day if he is to meet expectations?

31. *Baseball.* In order to qualify for a batting title, a major league baseball player must average at least 3.1 plate appearances per game. For the first nine games of the season, a player had 5, 1, 4, 2, 3, 4, 4, 3, and 2 plate appearances. How many plate appearances must the player have in the tenth game in order to average at least 3.1 per game?
Source: Major League Baseball

32. *Education.* The Mecklenberg County Public Schools stipulate that a standard school day will average at least $5\frac{1}{2}$ hr, excluding meal breaks. For the first four days of one school week, bad weather resulted in school days of 4 hr, $6\frac{1}{2}$ hr, $3\frac{1}{2}$ hr, and $6\frac{1}{2}$ hr. How long must the Friday school day be in order to average at least $5\frac{1}{2}$ hr for the week?
Source: www.meck.k12.va.us

33. *Perimeter of a triangle.* One side of a triangle is 2 cm shorter than the base. The other side is 3 cm longer than the base. What lengths of the base will allow the perimeter to be greater than 19 cm?

34. *Perimeter of a sign.* The perimeter of a rectangular sign is not to exceed 50 ft. The length is to be twice the width. What widths will meet these conditions?

35. *Well drilling.* All Seasons Well Drilling offers two plans. Under the "pay-as-you-go" plan, they charge $500 plus $8 a foot for a well of any depth. Under their "guaranteed-water" plan, they charge a flat fee of $4000 for a well that is guaranteed to provide adequate water for a household. For what depths would it save a customer money to use the pay-as-you-go plan?

36. *Cost of road service.* Rick's Automotive charges $50 plus $15 for each (15-min) unit of time when making a road call. Twin City Repair charges $70 plus $10 for each unit of time. Under what circumstances would it be more economical for a motorist to call Rick's?

37. *Insurance-covered repairs.* Most insurance companies will replace a vehicle if an estimated repair exceeds 80% of the "blue-book" value of the vehicle. Michele's insurance company paid $8500 for repairs to her Subaru after an accident. What can be concluded about the blue-book value of the car?

38. *Insurance-covered repairs.* Following an accident, Jeff's Ford pickup was replaced by his insurance company because the damage was so extensive. Before the damage, the blue-book value of the truck was $21,000. How much would it have cost to repair the truck? (See Exercise 37.)

39. *Sizes of packages.* The U.S. Postal Service defines a "package" as a parcel for which the sum of the length and the girth is less than 84 in. (Length is the longest side of a package and girth is the distance around the other two sides of the package.) A box has a fixed girth of 29 in. Determine (in terms of an inequality) those lengths for which the box is considered a "package."

Girth = 29 in.

L

40. *Sizes of envelopes.* Rhetoric Advertising is a direct-mail company. It determines that for a particular campaign, it can use any envelope with a fixed width of $3\frac{1}{2}$ in. and an area of at least $17\frac{1}{2}$ in². Determine (in terms of an inequality) those lengths that will satisfy the company constraints.

$3\frac{1}{2}$ in. $17\frac{1}{2}$ in²

L

41. *Body temperature.* A person is considered to be feverish when his or her temperature is higher than 98.6°F. The formula $F = \frac{9}{5}C + 32$ can be used to convert Celsius temperatures C to Fahrenheit temperatures F. For which Celsius temperatures is a person considered feverish?

42. *Gold temperatures.* Gold stays solid at Fahrenheit temperatures below 1945.4°. Determine (in terms of an inequality) those Celsius temperatures for which gold stays solid. Use the formula given in Exercise 41.

43. *Area of a triangular sign.* Zoning laws in Harrington prohibit displaying signs with areas exceeding 12 ft². If Flo's Marina is ordering a triangular sign with an 8-ft base, how tall can the sign be?

44. *Area of a triangular flag.* As part of an outdoor education course, Trisha needs to make a bright-colored triangular flag with an area of at least 3 ft². What heights can the triangle be if the base is $1\frac{1}{2}$ ft?

45. *Fat content in foods.* Reduced Fat Skippy® peanut butter contains 12 g of fat per serving. In order for a food to be labeled "reduced fat," it must have at least 25% less fat than the regular item. What can you conclude about the number of grams of fat in a serving of the regular Skippy peanut butter?
Source: Best Foods

46. *Fat content in foods.* Reduced Fat Chips Ahoy!® cookies contain 5 g of fat per serving. What can you conclude about the number of grams of fat in regular Chips Ahoy! cookies (see Exercise 45)?
Source: Nabisco Brands, Inc.

47. *Weight gain.* In the last weeks before the yearly Topsfield Weigh In, heavyweight pumpkins gain about 26 lb per day. Charlotte's heaviest pumpkin weighs 532 lb on September 5. For what dates will its weight exceed 818 lb?
Source: Based on a story in the *Burlington Free Press*

48. *Pond depth.* On July 1, Garrett's Pond was 25 ft deep. Since that date, the water level has dropped $\frac{2}{3}$ ft per week. For what dates will the water level not exceed 21 ft?

49. *Cell-phone budget.* Liam has budgeted $60 a month for his cell phone. For his service, he pays a monthly fee of $39.95, plus taxes of $6.65, plus 10¢ for each text message sent or received. How many text messages can he send or receive and not exceed his budget?

50. *Banquet costs.* The women's volleyball team can spend at most $700 for its awards banquet at a local restaurant. If the restaurant charges a $100 setup fee plus $24 per person, at most how many can attend?

51. *World records in the mile run.* The formula
$$R = -0.0065t + 4.3259$$
can be used to predict the world record, in minutes, for the 1-mi run t years after 1900. Determine (in terms of an inequality) those years for which the world record will be less than 3.6 min.
Source: Based on information from Information Please Database 2007, Pearson Education, Inc.

52. *Women's records in the women's 1500-m run.* The formula
$$R = -0.0026t + 4.0807$$
can be used to predict the world record, in minutes, for the 1500-m run t years after 1900. Determine (in terms of an inequality) those years for which the world record will be less than 3.8 min.
Source: Based on information from *Track and Field*

53. *Toll charges.*   The equation

$$y = 0.06x + 0.50$$

can be used to determine the approximate cost y, in dollars, of driving x miles on the Pennsylvania Turnpike. For what mileages x will the cost be at most $14?

54. *Price of a movie ticket.*   The average price of a movie ticket can be estimated by the equation

$$P = 0.169Y - 333.04,$$

where Y is the year and P is the average price, in dollars. For what years will the average price of a movie ticket be at least $7? (Include the year in which the $7 ticket first occurs.)
Source: National Association of Theatre Owners

55. If f represents Fran's age and t represents Todd's age, write a sentence that would translate to $t + 3 < f$.

56. Explain how the meanings of "Five more than a number" and "Five is more than a number" differ.

Skill Review

Review operations with real numbers (Sections 1.5–1.8).

Simplify.

57. $-2 + (-5) - 7$ [1.6]

58. $\dfrac{1}{2} \div \left(-\dfrac{3}{4}\right)$ [1.7]

59. $3 \cdot (-10) \cdot (-1) \cdot (-2)$ [1.7]

60. $-6.3 + (-4.8)$ [1.5]

61. $(3 - 7) - (4 - 8)$ [1.8]

62. $3 - 2 + 5 \cdot 10 \div 5^2 \cdot 2$ [1.8]

63. $\dfrac{-2 - (-6)}{8 - 10}$ [1.8]

64. $\dfrac{1 - (-7)}{-3 - 5}$ [1.8]

Synthesis

65. Write a problem for a classmate to solve. Devise the problem so the answer is "At most 18 passengers can go on the boat." Design the problem so that at least one number in the solution must be rounded down.

66. Write a problem for a classmate to solve. Devise the problem so the answer is "The Rothmans can drive 90 mi without exceeding their truck rental budget."

67. *Ski wax.*   Green ski wax works best between 5° and 15° Fahrenheit. Determine those Celsius temperatures for which green ski wax works best. (See Exercise 41.)

68. *Parking fees.*   Mack's Parking Garage charges $4.00 for the first hour and $2.50 for each additional hour. For how long has a car been parked when the charge exceeds $16.50?

Aha! **69.** The area of a square can be no more than 64 cm². What lengths of a side will allow this?

Aha! **70.** The sum of two consecutive odd integers is less than 100. What is the largest pair of such integers?

71. *Nutritional standards.*   In order for a food to be labeled "lowfat," it must have fewer than 3 g of fat per serving. Reduced-fat tortilla chips contain 60% less fat than regular nacho cheese tortilla chips, but still cannot be labeled lowfat. What can you conclude about the fat content of a serving of nacho cheese tortilla chips?

72. *Parking fees.*   When asked how much the parking charge is for a certain car (see Exercise 68), Mack replies, "between 14 and 24 dollars." For how long has the car been parked?

73. *Frequent buyer bonus.*   Alice's Books allows customers to select one free book for every 10 books purchased. The price of that book cannot exceed the average cost of the 10 books. Neoma has bought 9 books whose average cost is $12 per book. How much should her tenth book cost if she wants to select a $15 book for free?

74. *Grading.*   After 9 quizzes, Blythe's average is 84. Is it possible for Blythe to improve her average by two points with the next quiz? Why or why not?

75. *Discount card.*   Barnes & Noble offers a member card for $25 a year. This card entitles a customer to a 40% discount off list price on hardcover bestsellers, a 20% discount on adult hardcovers, and a 10% discount on other purchases. Describe two sets of circumstances for which an individual would save money by becoming a member.
Source: Barnes & Noble

Study Summary

KEY TERMS AND CONCEPTS	EXAMPLES

SECTION 2.1: SOLVING EQUATIONS

Equivalent equations share the same solution.

$3x - 1 = 10$, $3x = 11$, and $x = \dfrac{11}{3}$ are equivalent equations.

The Addition Principle for Equations

$a = b$ is equivalent to

$a + c = b + c.$

$x + 5 = -2$ is equivalent to

$x + 5 + (-5) = -2 + (-5)$ and to

$x = -7.$

The Multiplication Principle for Equations

$a = b$ is equivalent to $ac = bc,$

for $c \neq 0.$

$-\frac{1}{3}x = 7$ is equivalent to

$(-3)(-\frac{1}{3}x) = (-3)(7)$ and to

$x = -21.$

SECTION 2.2: USING THE PRINCIPLES TOGETHER

We can **clear fractions** by multiplying both sides of an equation by the least common multiple of the denominators in the equation.

Solve: $\frac{1}{2}x - \frac{1}{3} = \frac{1}{6}x + \frac{2}{3}.$

$6\left(\frac{1}{2}x - \frac{1}{3}\right) = 6\left(\frac{1}{6}x + \frac{2}{3}\right)$ Multiplying by 6, the least common denominator

$6 \cdot \frac{1}{2}x - 6 \cdot \frac{1}{3} = 6 \cdot \frac{1}{6}x + 6 \cdot \frac{2}{3}$ Using the distributive law

$3x - 2 = x + 4$ Simplifying

$2x = 6$ Subtracting x from and adding 2 to both sides

$x = 3$

We can **clear decimals** by multiplying both sides by a power of 10. If there is at most one decimal place in any one number, multiply by 10. If there are at most two decimal places, multiply by 100, and so on.

Solve: $3.6t - 1.5 = 2 - 0.8t.$

$10(3.6t - 1.5) = 10(2 - 0.8t)$ Multiplying both sides by 10 because the greatest number of decimal places is 1.

$36t - 15 = 20 - 8t$ Using the distributive law

$44t = 35$ Adding $8t$ and 15 to both sides

$t = \dfrac{35}{44}$ Dividing both sides by 44

SECTION 2.3: FORMULAS

A **formula** uses letters to show a relationship among two or more quantities. Formulas can be solved for a given letter using the addition and multiplication principles.

Solve: $x = \frac{2}{5}y + 7$ *for y.*

$x = \frac{2}{5}y + 7$ We are solving for y.

$x - 7 = \frac{2}{5}y$ Isolating the term containing y

$\frac{5}{2}(x - 7) = \frac{5}{2} \cdot \frac{2}{5}y$ Multiplying both sides by $\frac{5}{2}$

$\frac{5}{2}x - \frac{5}{2} \cdot 7 = 1 \cdot y$ Using the distributive law

$\frac{5}{2}x - \frac{35}{2} = y$ We have solved for y.

SECTION 2.4: APPLICATIONS WITH PERCENT

Percent Notation

$n\%$ means $\dfrac{n}{100}$, or $n \times \dfrac{1}{100}$, or $n \times 0.01$

$31\% = 0.31;$ $\frac{1}{8} = 0.125 = 12.5\%;$
$2.9\% = 0.029;$ $2.94 = 294\%$

Key Words in Percent Translations

"Of" translates to " $\cdot$ " or "$\times$"

"What" translates to a variable

"Is" or "Was" translates to "$=$"

"%" translates to "$\times \frac{1}{100}$" or "$\times 0.01$"

$$
\begin{array}{ccccc}
\underline{\text{What percent}} & \text{of} & 60 & \text{is} & 7.2? \\
\downarrow & & \downarrow & \downarrow & \downarrow \\
n & \cdot & 60 & = & 7.2
\end{array}
$$

$$n = \frac{7.2}{60}$$

$$n = 0.12$$

Thus, 7.2 is 12% of 60.

SECTION 2.5: PROBLEM SOLVING

Five Steps for Problem Solving in Algebra

1. *Familiarize* yourself with the problem.
2. *Translate* to mathematical language. (This often means writing an equation.)
3. *Carry out* some mathematical manipulation. (This often means *solving* an equation.)
4. *Check* your possible answer in the original problem.
5. *State* the answer clearly.

The perimeter of a rectangle is 70 cm. The width is 5 cm longer than half the length. Find the length and the width.

1. **Familiarize.** Look up, if necessary, the formula for the perimeter of a rectangle:

   $$P = 2l + 2w.$$

   We are looking for two values, the length and the width. We can describe the width in terms of the length:

   $$w = \tfrac{1}{2}l + 5.$$

2. **Translate.**

   $$
   \begin{array}{lcccccc}
   \textit{Rewording:} & \underline{\text{Twice the}} & & \underline{\text{twice the}} & & \underline{\text{the}} \\
    & \text{length} & \text{plus} & \text{width} & \text{is} & \text{perimeter.} \\
    & \downarrow & \downarrow & \downarrow & \downarrow & \downarrow \\
   \textit{Translating:} & 2l & + & 2\left(\tfrac{1}{2}l + 5\right) & = & 70
   \end{array}
   $$

3. **Carry out.** Solve the equation:

   $$
   \begin{aligned}
   2l + 2\left(\tfrac{1}{2}l + 5\right) &= 70 \\
   2l + l + 10 &= 70 && \text{\small Using the distributive law} \\
   3l + 10 &= 70 && \text{\small Combining like terms} \\
   3l &= 60 && \text{\small Subtracting 10 from both sides} \\
   l &= 20. && \text{\small Dividing both sides by 3}
   \end{aligned}
   $$

   If $l = 20$, then $w = \tfrac{1}{2}l + 5 = \tfrac{1}{2} \cdot 20 + 5 = 10 + 5 = 15$.

4. **Check.** The width should be 5 cm longer than half the length. Since half the length is 10 cm, and 15 cm is 5 cm longer, this statement checks. The perimeter should be 70 cm. Since $2l + 2w = 2(20) + 2(15) = 40 + 30 = 70$, this statement also checks.

5. **State.** The length is 20 cm and the width is 15 cm.

SECTION 2.6: SOLVING INEQUALITIES

An **inequality** is any sentence containing $<$, $>$, $\leq$, $\geq$, or $\neq$. Solution sets of inequalities can be **graphed** and written in **set-builder notation** or **interval notation**.

Interval Notation	*Set-builder Notation*	*Graph*
(a, b)	$\{x \mid a < x < b\}$	
$[a, b]$	$\{x \mid a \leq x \leq b\}$	
$[a, b)$	$\{x \mid a \leq x < b\}$	
$(a, b]$	$\{x \mid a < x \leq b\}$	
(a, ∞)	$\{x \mid a < x\}$	
$(-\infty, a)$	$\{x \mid x < a\}$	

The Addition Principle for Inequalities

For any real numbers a, b, and c,

$a < b$ is equivalent to $a + c < b + c$;
$a > b$ is equivalent to $a + c > b + c$.

Similar statements hold for $\leq$ and $\geq$.

$x + 3 \leq 5$ is equivalent to
$x + 3 - 3 \leq 5 - 3$ and to
$x \leq 2$.

The Multiplication Principle for Inequalities

For any real numbers a and b, and for any *positive* number c,

$a < b$ is equivalent to $ac < bc$;
$a > b$ is equivalent to $ac > bc$.

For any real numbers a and b, and for any *negative* number c,

$a < b$ is equivalent to $ac > bc$;
$a > b$ is equivalent to $ac < bc$.

Similar statements hold for $\leq$ and $\geq$.

$3x > 9$ is equivalent to
$\frac{1}{3} \cdot 3x > \frac{1}{3} \cdot 9$ The inequality symbol does not change because $\frac{1}{3}$ is positive.
$x > 3$.

$-3x > 9$ is equivalent to
$-\frac{1}{3} \cdot -3x < -\frac{1}{3} \cdot 9$ The inequality symbol is reversed because $-\frac{1}{3}$ is negative.
$x < -3$.

SECTION 2.7: SOLVING APPLICATIONS WITH INEQUALITIES

Many real-world problems can be solved by translating the problem to an inequality and applying the five-step problem-solving strategy.

Translate to an inequality.

The test score must exceed 85.	$s > 85$
At most 15 volunteers greeted visitors.	$v \leq 15$
Ona makes no more than \$100 a week.	$w \leq 100$
Herbs need at least 4 hr of sun a day.	$h \geq 4$

Review Exercises: Chapter 2

👈 *Concept Reinforcement*   *Classify each statement as either true or false.*

1. $5x - 4 = 2x$ and $3x = 4$ are equivalent equations. [2.1]

2. $5 - 2t < 9$ and $t > 6$ are equivalent inequalities. [2.6]

3. Some equations have no solution. [2.1]

4. Consecutive odd integers are 2 units apart. [2.5]

5. For any number a, $a \leq a$. [2.6]

6. The addition principle is always used before the multiplication principle. [2.2]

7. A 10% discount results in a sale price that is 90% of the original price. [2.4]

8. Often it is impossible to list all solutions of an inequality number by number. [2.6]

Solve. Label any contradictions or identities.

9. $x + 9 = -16$ [2.1]

10. $-8x = -56$ [2.1]

11. $-\dfrac{x}{5} = 13$ [2.1]

12. $-8 = n - 11$ [2.1]

13. $\frac{2}{5}t = -8$ [2.1]

14. $x - 0.1 = 1.01$ [2.1]

15. $-\frac{2}{3} + x = -\frac{1}{6}$ [2.1]

16. $4y + 11 = 5$ [2.2]

17. $5 - x = 13$ [2.2]

18. $3t + 7 = t - 1$ [2.2]

19. $7x - 6 = 25x$ [2.2]

20. $\frac{1}{4}x - \frac{5}{8} = \frac{3}{8}$ [2.2]

21. $14y = 23y - 17 - 9y$ [2.2]

22. $0.22y - 0.6 = 0.12y + 3 - 0.8y$ [2.2]

23. $\frac{1}{4}x - \frac{1}{8}x = 3 - \frac{1}{16}x$ [2.2]

24. $6(4 - n) = 18$ [2.2]

25. $4(5x - 7) = -56$ [2.2]

26. $8(x - 2) = 4(x - 4)$ [2.2]

27. $3(x - 4) + 2 = x + 2(x - 5)$ [2.2]

Solve each formula for the given letter. [2.3]

28. $C = \pi d$, for d

29. $V = \dfrac{1}{3}Bh$, for B

30. $5x - 2y = 10$, for y

31. $tx = ax + b$, for x

32. Find decimal notation: 1.2%. [2.4]

33. Find percent notation: $\frac{11}{25}$. [2.4]

34. What percent of 60 is 42? [2.4]

35. 49 is 35% of what number? [2.4]

Determine whether each number is a solution of $x \leq -5$. [2.6]

36. -3

37. -7

38. 4

Graph on a number line. [2.6]

39. $5x - 6 < 2x + 3$

40. $-2 < x \leq 5$

41. $t > 0$

Solve. Write the answers in set-builder notation and interval notation. [2.6]

42. $t + \frac{2}{3} \geq \frac{1}{6}$

43. $9x \geq 63$

44. $2 + 6y > 20$

45. $7 - 3y \geq 27 + 2y$

46. $3x + 5 < 2x - 6$

47. $-4y < 28$

48. $3 - 4x < 27$

49. $4 - 8x < 13 + 3x$

50. $13 \leq -\frac{2}{3}t + 5$

51. $7 \leq 1 - \frac{3}{4}x$

Solve.

52. In 2006, U.S. retailers lost a record $41.6 billion due to theft and fraud. Of this amount, $20 billion was due to employee theft. What percent of the total loss was employee theft? [2.4]
Source: www.wwaytv3.com

53. An 18-ft beam is cut into two pieces. One piece is 2 ft longer than the other. How long are the pieces? [2.5]

54. In 2004, a total of 103,000 students from China and Japan enrolled in U.S. colleges and universities. The number of Japanese students was 10,000 more than half the number of Chinese students. How many Chinese students and how many Japanese students enrolled in the United States? [2.5]
Source: Institute of International Education

55. The sum of two consecutive odd integers is 116. Find the integers. [2.5]

56. The perimeter of a rectangle is 56 cm. The width is 6 cm less than the length. Find the width and the length. [2.5]

57. After a 25% reduction, a picnic table is on sale for $120. What was the regular price? [2.4]

58. From 2000 to 2006, the number of U.S. wireless-phone subscribers increased by 114 percent to 233 million. How many subscribers were there in 2000? [2.4]
Source: Cellular Telecommunications and Internet Association

59. The measure of the second angle of a triangle is 50° more than that of the first. The measure of the third angle is 10° less than twice the first. Find the measures of the angles. [2.5]

60. The U.S. Centers for Disease Control recommends that for a typical 2000-calorie daily diet, no more than 65 g of fat be consumed. In the first three days of a four-day vacation, Teresa consumed 55 g, 80 g, and 70 g of fat. Determine how many grams of fat Teresa can consume on the fourth day if she is to average no more than 65 g of fat per day. [2.7]

61. *Blueprints.* To make copies of blueprints, Vantage Reprographics charges a $6 setup fee plus $4 per copy. Myra can spend no more than $65 for the copying. What number of copies will allow her to stay within budget? [2.7]

Synthesis

62. How does the multiplication principle for equations differ from the multiplication principle for inequalities? [2.1], [2.6]

63. Explain how checking the solutions of an equation differs from checking the solutions of an inequality. [2.1], [2.6]

64. A study of sixth- and seventh-graders in Boston revealed that, on average, the students spent 3 hr 20 min per day watching TV or playing video and computer games. This represents 108% more than the average time spent reading or doing homework. How much time each day was spent, on average, reading or doing homework? [2.4]
Source: Harvard School of Public Health

65. In June 2007, a team of Brazilian scientists exploring the Amazon measured its length as 65 mi longer than the Nile. If the combined length of both rivers is 8385 mi, how long is each river? [2.5]
Source: news.nationalgeographic.com

66. Kent purchased a book online at 25% off the retail price. The shipping charges were $4.95. If the amount due was $16.95, what was the retail price of the book? [2.4], [2.5]

Solve.

67. $2|n| + 4 = 50$ [1.4], [2.2]

68. $|3n| = 60$ [1.4], [2.1]

69. $y = 2a - ab + 3$, for a [2.3]

70. The Maryland Heart Center gives the following steps to calculate the number of fat grams needed daily by a moderately active woman. Write the steps as one formula relating the number of fat grams F to a woman's weight w, in pounds. [2.3]
  1. Calculate the total number of calories per day.
  ____ pounds × 12 calories = ____ total calories per day
  2. Take the total number of calories and multiply by 30 percent.
  ____ calories per day × 0.30 = ____ calories from fat per day.
  3. Take the number of calories from fat per day and divide by 9 (there are 9 calories per gram of fat).
  ____ calories from fat per day divided by 9 = ____ fat grams per day

Test: Chapter 2

CHAPTER **Test Prep** VIDEO CD *Step-by-step test solutions are found on the video CD in the front of this book.*

Solve. Label any contradictions or identities.

1. $t + 7 = 16$

2. $t - 3 = 12$

3. $6x = -18$

4. $-\frac{4}{7}x = -28$

5. $3t + 7 = 2t - 5$

6. $\frac{1}{2}x - \frac{3}{5} = \frac{2}{5}$

7. $8 - y = 16$

8. $4.2x + 3.5 = 1.2 - 2.5x$

9. $4(x + 2) = 36$

10. $\frac{5}{6}(3x + 1) = 20$

11. $13t - (5 - 2t) = 5(3t - 1)$

Solve. Write the answers in set-builder notation and interval notation.

12. $x + 6 > 1$

13. $14x + 9 > 13x - 4$

14. $-5y \geq 65$

15. $4y \leq -30$

16. $4n + 3 < -17$

17. $3 - 5x > 38$

18. $\frac{1}{2}t - \frac{1}{4} \leq \frac{3}{4}t$

19. $5 - 9x \geq 19 + 5x$

Solve each formula for the given letter.

20. $A = 2\pi rh$, for r

21. $w = \dfrac{P + l}{2}$, for l

22. Find decimal notation: 230%.

23. Find percent notation: 0.003.

24. What number is 18.5% of 80?

25. What percent of 75 is 33?

Graph on a number line.

26. $y < 4$

27. $-2 \leq x \leq 2$

Solve.

28. The perimeter of a rectangular calculator is 36 cm. The length is 4 cm greater than the width. Find the width and the length.

29. In 1948, Earl Shaffer became the first person to hike all 2100 mi of the Appalachian trail—from Springer Mountain, Georgia, to Mt. Katahdin, Maine. Shaffer repeated the feat 50 years later, and at age 79 became the oldest person to hike the entire trail. When Shaffer stood atop Big Walker Mountain, Virginia, he was three times as far from the northern end of the trail as from the southern end. At that point, how far was he from each end of the trail?

30. The perimeter of a triangle is 249 mm. If the sides are consecutive odd integers, find the length of each side.

31. By lowering the temperature of their electric hot-water heater from 140°F to 120°F, the Kellys' average electric bill dropped by 7% to $60.45. What was their electric bill before they lowered the temperature of their hot water?

32. *Mass transit.* Local light rail service in Denver, Colorado, costs $1.50 per trip (one way). A monthly pass costs $54. Gail is a student at Community College of Denver. Express as an inequality the number of trips per month that Gail should make if the pass is to save her money.
Source: rtd-denver.com

Synthesis

Solve.

33. $c = \dfrac{2cd}{a - d}$, for d

34. $3|w| - 8 = 37$

35. Translate to an inequality.

A plant marked "partial sun" needs at least 4 hr but no more than 6 hr of sun each day.
Source: www.yardsmarts.com

36. A concert promoter had a certain number of tickets to give away. Five people got the tickets. The first got one third of the tickets, the second got one fourth of the tickets, and the third got one fifth of the tickets. The fourth person got eight tickets, and there were five tickets left for the fifth person. Find the total number of tickets given away.

Simplify.

1. $18 + (-30)$ [1.5]

2. $\frac{1}{2} - \left(-\frac{1}{4}\right)$ [1.6]

3. $-1.2(3.5)$ [1.7]

4. $-5 \div \left(-\frac{1}{2}\right)$ [1.7]

5. $150 - 10^2 \div 25 \cdot 4$ [1.8]

6. $(150 - 10^2) \div (25 \cdot 4)$ [1.8]

Remove parentheses and simplify. [1.8]

7. $5x - (3x - 1)$

8. $2(t + 6) - 12t$

9. $3[4n - 5(2n - 1)] - 3(n - 7)$

10. Graph on a number line: $-\frac{5}{2}$. [1.4]

11. Find the absolute value: $|27|$. [1.4]

12. Factor: $12x + 18y + 30z$. [1.8]

Solve.

13. $12 = -2x$ [2.1]

14. $4x - 7 = 3x + 9$ [2.1]

15. $\frac{2}{3}t + 7 = 13$ [2.2]

16. $9(2a - 1) = 4$ [2.2]

17. $12 - 3(5x - 1) = x - 1$ [2.2]

18. $3(x + 1) - 2 = 8 - 5(x + 7)$ [2.2]

Solve each formula for the given letter. [2.3]

19. $\frac{1}{2}x = 2yz$, for z

20. $4x - 9y = 1$, for y

21. $an = p - rn$, for n

22. Find decimal notation: 183%. [2.4]

23. Find percent notation: $\frac{3}{8}$. [2.4]

24. Graph on a number line: $t > -\frac{5}{2}$. [2.6]

Solve. Write the answer in set-builder notation and interval notation. [2.6]

25. $4t + 10 \leq 2$

26. $8 - t > 5$

27. $4 < 10 - \dfrac{x}{5}$

28. $4(2n - 3) \leq 2(5n - 8)$

Solve.

29. The total attendance at NCAA basketball games during the 2006–2007 school year was 33 million. This was 31.25% less than the total attendance at NCAA football games during that year. What was the total attendance at NCAA football games during the 2006–2007 school year? [2.4]
Source: NCAA

30. On an average weekday, a full-time college student spends a total of 7.1 hr in educational activities and in leisure activities. The average student spends 0.7 hr more in leisure activities than in educational activities. On an average weekday, how many hours does a full-time college student spend on educational activities? [2.5]
Source: U.S. Bureau of Labor Statistics

31. The wavelength w, in meters per cycle, of a musical note is given by

$$w = \frac{r}{f},$$

where r is the speed of the sound, in meters per second, and f is the frequency, in cycles per second. The speed of sound in air is 344 m/sec. What is the wavelength of a note whose frequency in air is 24 cycles per second? [2.3]

32. A 24-ft ribbon is cut into two pieces. One piece is 6 ft longer than the other. How long are the pieces? [2.5]

33. Juanita has budgeted an average of $65 a month for entertainment. For the first five months of the year, she has spent $88, $15, $125, $50, and $60. How much can Juanita spend in the sixth month without exceeding her average budget? [2.7]

34. In 2006, about 17 million Americans had diabetes. The U.S. Centers for Disease Control predicts that by 2050, 50 million Americans may have the disease. By what percent would the number of Americans with diabetes increase? [2.4]

35. The second angle of a triangle is twice as large as the first. The third angle is 5° more than four times the first. Find the measure of the largest angle. [2.5]

36. The length of a rectangular frame is 53 cm. For what widths would the perimeter be greater than 160 cm? [2.7]

Synthesis

37. Simplify: $t - \{t - [3t - (2t - t) - t] - 4t\} - t.$ [1.8]

38. Solve: $3|n| + 10 = 25.$ [2.2]

39. Lindy sold her Fender acoustic guitar on eBay using i-soldit.com. The i-soldit location she used charges 35% of the first $500 of the selling price and 20% of the amount over $500. After these charges were deducted from the selling price, she received $745. For how much did her guitar sell? [2.4], [2.5]
Source: Based on information in *The Wall Street Journal*, 9/11/07

Introduction to Graphing

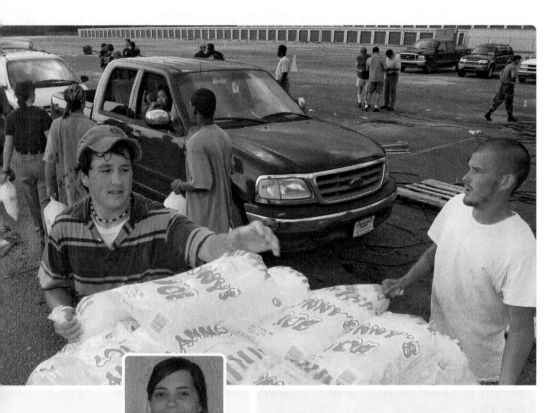

HEATHER HUTH
DIRECTOR OF VOLUNTEERS
New Orleans, Louisiana

We average about 750 volunteers a month who come to
Beacon of Hope to help us clean
New Orleans' neighborhoods. We
service 22 neighborhoods, so
I use math to figure out how
many volunteers to send to each
location, the quantity of
supplies each will need,
and how much time is required
to complete the task.

AN APPLICATION

An increasing number of college
students are donating time and energy
in volunteer service. The number of
college students volunteering grew
from 2.7 million in 2002 to 3.3 million
in 2005. Graph the given data and
estimate the number of college
students who volunteered in 2004, and
then predict the number of college
students who will volunteer in 2010.

Source: Corporation for National and
Community Service

This problem appears as Example 7 in
Section 3.7.

W e now begin our study of graphing. First we will examine graphs as they commonly appear in newspapers or magazines and develop some terminology. Following that, we will graph certain equations and study the connection between rate and slope. We will also learn how graphs can be used as a problem-solving tool in many applications.

Our work in this chapter centers on equations that contain two variables.

3.1   Reading Graphs, Plotting Points, and Scaling Graphs

Problem Solving with Bar, Circle, and Line Graphs   ■   Points and Ordered Pairs   ■
Numbering the Axes Appropriately

Today's print and electronic media make almost constant use of graphs. In this section, we consider problem solving with bar graphs, line graphs, and circle graphs. Then we examine graphs that use a coordinate system.

Problem Solving with Bar, Circle, and Line Graphs

A *bar graph* is a convenient way of showing comparisons. In every bar graph, certain categories, such as levels of education in the example below, are paired with certain numbers.

EXAMPLE   1

Lifetime earnings.   Getting a college degree usually means delaying the start of a career. As the bar graph below shows, this loss in earnings is more than made up over a worker's lifetime.

Source: U.S. Census Bureau

a) Keagan plans to get an associate's degree. How much can he expect to make in his lifetime?

b) Isabella would like to make at least $2 million in her lifetime. What level of education should she pursue?

SOLUTION

a) Since level of education is shown on the horizontal scale, we go to the top of the bar above the label "associate's degree." Then we move horizontally from the top of the bar to the vertical scale, which shows earnings. We read there that Keagan can expect to make about $1.6 million in his lifetime.

b) By moving up the vertical scale to $2 million and then moving horizontally, we see that the first bar to reach a height of $2 million or higher corresponds to a bachelor's degree. Thus Isabella should pursue a bachelor's, master's, doctoral, or professional degree in order to make at least $2 million in her lifetime.

 TRY EXERCISE 5

Circle graphs, or *pie charts,* are often used to show what percent of the whole each particular item in a group represents.

EXAMPLE 2   *Student aid.*   The circle graph below shows the sources for student aid in 2006 and the percentage of aid students received from each source. In that year, the total amount of aid distributed was $134.8 billion. About 5,387,000 students received a federal Pell grant. What was the average amount of the aid per recipient?

Source: Trends in Student Aid 2006, www.collegeboard.com

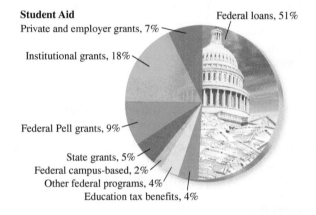

Student Aid
Private and employer grants, 7%
Federal loans, 51%
Institutional grants, 18%
Federal Pell grants, 9%
State grants, 5%
Federal campus-based, 2%
Other federal programs, 4%
Education tax benefits, 4%

SOLUTION

1. **Familiarize.** The problem involves percents, so if we were unsure of how to solve percent problems, we might review Section 2.4.

   The solution of this problem will involve two steps. We are told the total amount of student aid distributed. In order to find the average amount of a Pell grant, we must first calculate the total of all Pell grants and then divide by the number of students.

   We let $g =$ the average amount of a Pell grant in 2006.

2. **Translate.** From the circle graph, we see that federal Pell grants were 9% of the total amount of aid. The total amount distributed was $134.8 billion, or $134,800,000,000, so we have

Find the value of all Pell grants.

$$\text{the value of all Pell grants} = 0.09(134,800,000,000)$$
$$= 12,132,000,000.$$

Then we reword the problem and translate as follows:

Calculate the average amount of a Pell grant.

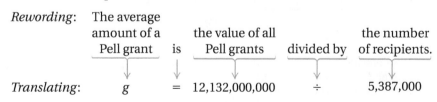

Rewording: The average amount of a Pell grant   is   the value of all Pell grants   divided by   the number of recipients.

Translating: g $=$ 12,132,000,000 $\div$ 5,387,000

3. **Carry out.** We solve the equation:

$$g = 12,132,000,000 \div 5,387,000$$
$$\approx 2252. \quad \text{Rounding to the nearest dollar}$$

4. **Check.** If each student received $2252, the total amount of aid distributed through Pell grants would be $2252 · 5,387,000, or $12,131,524,000. Since this is approximately 9% of the total student aid for 2006, our answer checks.

5. **State.** In 2006, the average Pell grant was $2252.　　　TRY EXERCISE 9

Exercise and pulse rate. The following *line graph* shows the relationship between a person's resting pulse rate and months of regular exercise.* Note that the symbol ⌇ is used to indicate that counting on the vertical scale begins at 50.

a) How many months of regular exercise are required to lower the pulse rate as much as possible?

b) How many months of regular exercise are needed to achieve a pulse rate of 65 beats per minute?

SOLUTION

a) The lowest point on the graph occurs above the number 6. Thus, after 6 months of regular exercise, the pulse rate is lowered as much as possible.

b) To determine how many months of exercise are needed to lower a person's resting pulse rate to 65, we locate 65 midway between 60 and 70 on the vertical scale. From that location, we move right until the line is reached. At that point, we move down to the horizontal scale and read the number of months required, as shown.

The pulse rate is 65 beats per minute after 3 months of regular exercise.

　　　TRY EXERCISE 17

*Data from *Body Clock* by Dr. Martin Hughes (New York: Facts on File, Inc.), p. 60.

EXAMPLE 3

TECHNOLOGY CONNECTION

The portion of the coordinate plane shown by a graphing calculator is called a **viewing window.** We indicate the **dimensions** of the window by setting a minimum *x*-value, a maximum *x*-value, a minimum *y*-value, and a maximum *y*-value. The **scale** by which we count must also be chosen. Window settings are often abbreviated in the form [L, R, B, T], with the letters representing **L**eft, **R**ight, **B**ottom, and **T**op endpoints. The window [−10, 10, −10, 10] is called the **standard viewing window.** On most graphing calculators, a standard viewing window can be set up using an option in the zoom menu.

　　To set up a [−100, 100, −5, 5] window, we press (WINDOW) and use the following settings. A scale of 10 for the *x*-axis is large enough for the marks on the *x*-axis to be distinct.

```
WINDOW
 Xmin=-100
 Xmax=100
 Xscl=10
 Ymin=-5
 Ymax=5
 Yscl=1
 Xres=1
```

　　When (GRAPH) is pressed, a graph extending from −100 to 100 along the *x*-axis (counted by 10's) and from −5 to 5 along the *y*-axis appears. When the arrow keys are pressed, a cursor can be

(continued)

moved, its coordinates appearing at the bottom of the window.

Set up the following viewing windows, choosing an appropriate scale for each axis. Then move the cursor and practice reading coordinates.

1. $[-10, 10, -10, 10]$
2. $[-5, 5, 0, 100]$
3. $[-1, 1, -0.1, 0.1]$

Points and Ordered Pairs

The line graph in Example 3 contains a collection of points. Each point pairs up a number of months of exercise with a pulse rate. To create such a graph, we **graph**, or **plot**, pairs of numbers on a plane. This is done using two perpendicular number lines called **axes** (pronounced "ak-sēz"; singular, **axis**). The point at which the axes cross is called the **origin**. Arrows on the axes indicate the positive directions.

Consider the pair $(3, 4)$. The numbers in such a pair are called **coordinates**. The **first coordinate** in this case is 3 and the **second coordinate** is 4.* To plot, or graph, $(3, 4)$, we start at the origin, move horizontally to the 3, move up vertically 4 units, and then make a "dot." Thus, $(3, 4)$ is located above 3 on the first axis and to the right of 4 on the second axis.

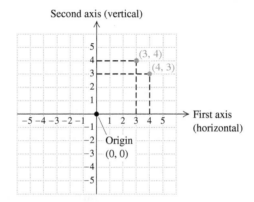

The point $(4, 3)$ is also plotted in the figure above. Note that $(3, 4)$ and $(4, 3)$ are different points. For this reason, coordinate pairs are called **ordered pairs**—the order in which the numbers appear is important.

EXAMPLE   4   Plot the point $(-3, 4)$.

SOLUTION   The first number, -3, is negative. Starting at the origin, we move 3 units in the negative horizontal direction (3 units to the left). The second number, 4, is positive, so we move 4 units in the positive vertical direction (up). The point $(-3, 4)$ is above -3 on the first axis and to the left of 4 on the second axis.

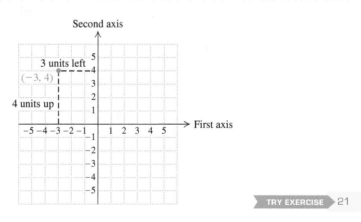

TRY EXERCISE   21

*The first coordinate is called the *abscissa* and the second coordinate is called the *ordinate*. The plane is called the *Cartesian coordinate plane* after the French mathematician René Descartes (1595–1650).

To find the coordinates of a point, we see how far to the right or left of the origin the point is and how far above or below the origin it is. Note that the coordinates of the origin itself are $(0, 0)$.

EXAMPLE   5

Find the coordinates of points *A, B, C, D, E, F,* and *G*.

STUDENT NOTES ⎯⎯⎯⎯⎯⎯

It is important that you remember that the first coordinate of an ordered pair is always represented on the horizontal axis. It is better to go slowly and plot points correctly than to go quickly and require more than one attempt.

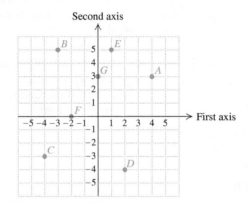

SOLUTION   Point *A* is 4 units to the right of the origin and 3 units above the origin. Its coordinates are $(4, 3)$. The coordinates of the other points are as follows:

   B: $(-3, 5)$;   *C*: $(-4, -3)$;   *D*: $(2, -4)$;

   E: $(1, 5)$;   *F*: $(-2, 0)$;   *G*: $(0, 3)$.   **TRY EXERCISE** ▸ 27

The variables *x* and *y* are commonly used when graphing on a plane. Coordinates of ordered pairs are often labeled

   (*x*-coordinate, *y*-coordinate).

The first, or horizontal, axis is labeled the *x*-axis, and the second, or vertical, axis is labeled the *y*-axis.

Numbering the Axes Appropriately

In Examples 4 and 5, each square on the grid shown is 1 unit long and 1 unit high: The **scale** of both the *x*-axis and the *y*-axis is 1. Often it is necessary to use a different scale on one or both of the axes.

EXAMPLE   6

Use a grid 10 squares wide and 10 squares high to plot $(-34, 450)$, $(48, 95)$, and $(10, -200)$.

SOLUTION   Since *x*-coordinates vary from a low of -34 to a high of 48, the 10 horizontal squares must span $48 - (-34)$, or 82 units. Because 82 is not a multiple of 10, we round *up* to the next multiple of 10, which is 90. Dividing 90 by 10, we find that if each square is 9 units wide (has a scale of 9), we could represent all the *x*-values. However, since it is more convenient to count by 10's, we will instead use a scale of 10. Starting at 0, we count backward to -40 and forward to 60.

This is how we will arrange the *x*-axis.

There is more than one correct way to cover the values from -34 to 48 using 10 increments. For instance, we could have counted from -60 to 90, using a scale

This is how we will arrange the y-axis.

of 15. In general, we try to use the smallest range and scale that will cover the given coordinates. Scales that are multiples of 2, 5, or 10 are especially convenient. It is essential that the numbering always begin at the origin.

Since we must be able to show y-values from -200 to 450, the 10 vertical squares must span $450 - (-200)$, or 650 units. For convenience, we round 650 *up* to 700 and then divide by 10: $700 \div 10 = 70$. Using 70 as the scale, we count *down* from 0 until we pass -200 and *up* from 0 until we pass 450, as shown at left.

Next, we combine our work with the x-values and the y-values to draw a graph in which the x-axis extends from -40 to 60 with a scale of 10 and the y-axis extends from -210 to 490 with a scale of 70. To correctly locate the axes on the grid, the two 0's must coincide where the axes cross. Finally, once the graph has been numbered, we plot the points as shown below.

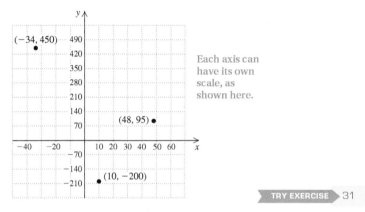

Each axis can have its own scale, as shown here.

TRY EXERCISE ▶ 31

The horizontal and vertical axes divide the plane into four regions, or **quadrants**, as indicated by Roman numerals in the following figure. Note that the point $(-4, 5)$ is in the second quadrant and the point $(5, -5)$ is in the fourth quadrant. The points $(3, 0)$ and $(0, 1)$ are on the axes and are not considered to be in any quadrant.

Second quadrant:
First coordinate negative, second coordinate positive:
$(-, +)$

First quadrant:
Both coordinates positive:
$(+, +)$

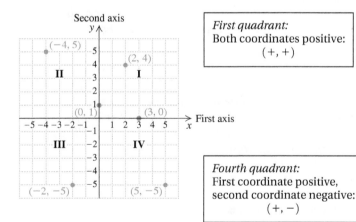

Third quadrant:
Both coordinates negative:
$(-, -)$

Fourth quadrant:
First coordinate positive, second coordinate negative:
$(+, -)$

3.1   EXERCISE SET

Concept Reinforcement   In each of Exercises 1–4, match the set of coordinates with the graph on the right that would be the best for plotting the points.

1. ____ $(-9, 3), (-2, -1), (4, 5)$

2. ____ $(-2, -1), (1, 5), (7, 3)$

3. ____ $(-2, -9), (2, 1), (4, -6)$

4. ____ $(-2, -1), (-9, 3), (-4, -6)$

a)

b)

c)

d)
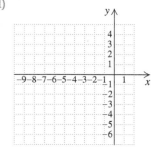

The **TRY EXERCISES** *for examples are indicated by a shaded block   on the exercise number. Complete step-by-step solutions for these exercises appear online at www.pearsonhighered.com/bittingerellenbogen.*

Driving under the influence.   A blood-alcohol level of 0.08% or higher makes driving illegal in the United States. This bar graph shows how many drinks a person of a certain weight would need to consume in 1 hr to achieve a blood-alcohol level of 0.08%. Note that a 12-oz beer, a 5-oz glass of wine, or a cocktail containing $1\frac{1}{2}$ oz of distilled liquor all count as one drink.
Source: Adapted from soberup.com and vsa.vassar.edu/~source/drugs/alcohol.html

Friends Don't Let Friends Drive Drunk

5. Approximately how many drinks would a 100-lb person have consumed in 1 hr to reach a blood-alcohol level of 0.08%?

6. Approximately how many drinks would a 160-lb person have consumed in 1 hr to reach a blood-alcohol level of 0.08%?

7. What can you conclude about the weight of someone who has consumed 3 drinks in 1 hr without reaching a blood-alcohol level of 0.08%?

8. What can you conclude about the weight of someone who has consumed 4 drinks in 1 hr without reaching a blood-alcohol level of 0.08%?

Student aid.   Use the information in Example 2 to answer Exercises 9–12.

9. In 2006, there were 13,334,170 full-time equivalent students in U.S. colleges and universities. What was the average federal loan per full-time equivalent student?

10. In 2006, there were 13,334,170 full-time equivalent students in U.S. colleges and universities. What was the average education tax benefit received per full-time equivalent student?

11. Approximately 8.6% of campus-based federal student aid is given to students in two-year public institutions. How much campus-based aid did students at two-year public institutions receive in 2006?

12. Approximately 17.7% of Pell grant dollars is given to students in for-profit institutions. How much did students in for-profit institutions receive in Pell grants in 2006?

Sorting solid waste.   Use the following pie chart to answer Exercises 13–16.

Sorting Solid Waste

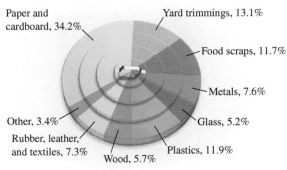

Paper and cardboard, 34.2%
Yard trimmings, 13.1%
Food scraps, 11.7%
Metals, 7.6%
Other, 3.4%
Glass, 5.2%
Rubber, leather, and textiles, 7.3%
Wood, 5.7%
Plastics, 11.9%

Source: Environmental Protection Agency

13. In 2005, Americans generated 245 million tons of waste. How much of the waste was plastic?

14. In 2005, the average American generated 4.5 lb of waste per day. How much of that was paper and cardboard?

15. Americans are recycling about 25.3% of all glass that is in the waste stream. How much glass did Americans recycle in 2005? (See Exercise 13.)

16. Americans are recycling about 61.9% of all yard trimmings. What amount of yard trimmings did the average American recycle per day in 2005? (Use the information in Exercise 14.)

Home video spending.   The line graph below shows U.S. consumer spending on home-video movies.

Home Video Spending

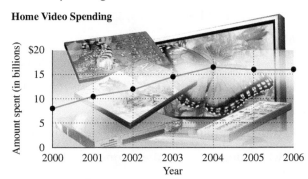

Amount spent (in billions)
Year

Source: Adams Media Research

17. Approximately how much was spent on home videos in 2002?

18. Approximately how much was spent on home videos in 2006?

19. In what year was approximately $10.5 billion spent on home videos?

20. In what year was approximately $14.5 billion spent on home videos?

Plot each group of points.

21. $(1, 2)$, $(-2, 3)$, $(4, -1)$, $(-5, -3)$, $(4, 0)$, $(0, -2)$

22. $(-2, -4)$, $(4, -3)$, $(5, 4)$, $(-1, 0)$, $(-4, 4)$, $(0, 5)$

23. $(4, 4)$, $(-2, 4)$, $(5, -3)$, $(-5, -5)$, $(0, 4)$, $(0, -4)$, $(-4, 0)$, $(0, 0)$

24. $(2, 5)$, $(-1, 3)$, $(3, -2)$, $(-2, -4)$, $(0, 0)$, $(0, -5)$, $(5, 0)$, $(-5, 0)$

25. *Text messaging.*   Listed below are estimates of the number of text messages sent in the United States. Make a line graph of the data.

Year	Monthly Text Messages (in millions)
2000	12
2001	34
2002	931
2003	1221
2004	2862
2005	7253
2006	8000 (estimated)

Source: CSCA

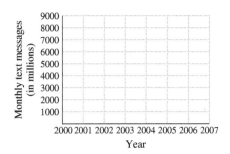

Monthly text messages (in millions)
Year

26. *Ozone layer.* Listed below are estimates of the ozone level. Make a line graph of the data, listing years on the horizontal scale.

Year	Ozone Level (in Dobson Units)
2000	287.1
2001	288.2
2002	285.8
2003	285.0
2004	281.2
2005	283.5

Source: johnstonsarchive.net

In Exercises 27–30, find the coordinates of points A, B, C, D, and E.

27.

28.

29.

30.

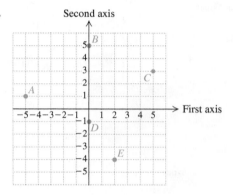

In Exercises 31–40, use a grid 10 squares wide and 10 squares high to plot the given coordinates. Choose your scale carefully. Scales may vary.

31. $(-75, 5), (-18, -2), (9, -4)$

32. $(-13, 3), (48, -1), (62, -4)$

33. $(-1, 83), (-5, -14), (5, 37)$

34. $(2, -79), (4, -25), (-4, 12)$

35. $(-10, -4), (-16, 7), (3, 15)$

36. $(5, -16), (-7, -4), (12, 3)$

37. $(-100, -5), (350, 20), (800, 37)$

38. $(750, -8), (-150, 17), (400, 32)$

39. $(-83, 491), (-124, -95), (54, -238)$

40. $(738, -89), (-49, -6), (-165, 53)$

In which quadrant is each point located?

41. $(7, -2)$ **42.** $(-1, -4)$ **43.** $(-4, -3)$

44. $(1, -5)$ **45.** $(2, 1)$ **46.** $(-4, 6)$

47. $(-4.9, 8.3)$ **48.** $(7.5, 2.9)$

49. In which quadrants are the first coordinates positive?

50. In which quadrants are the second coordinates negative?

51. In which quadrants do both coordinates have the same sign?

52. In which quadrants do the first and second coordinates have opposite signs?

53. The following graph was included in a mailing sent by Agway® to their oil customers in 2000. What information is missing from the graph and why is the graph misleading?

Residential Fuel Oil and Natural Gas Prices

Average fuel price in gallon equivalents spent in Northeast and Mid-Atlantic

- Oil prices
- Natural gas prices

Source: Energy Research Center, Inc.   *3/1/99–2/29/00

54. What do all points plotted on the vertical axis of a graph have in common?

Skill Review

To prepare for Section 3.2, review solving for a variable (Section 2.3).

Solve for y. [2.3]

55. $5y = 2x$

56. $2y = -3x$

57. $x - y = 8$

58. $2x + 5y = 10$

59. $2x + 3y = 5$

60. $5x - 8y = 1$

Synthesis

61. In an article about consumer spending on home videos (see the graph used for Exercise 17), the *Wall Street Journal* (9/2/06) stated that "the movie industry has hit a wall." To what were they referring?

62. Describe what the result would be if the first and second coordinates of every point in the following graph of an arrow were interchanged.

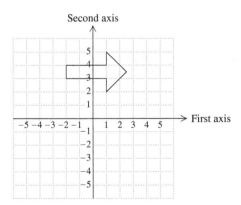

63. In which quadrant(s) could a point be located if its coordinates are opposites of each other?

64. In which quadrant(s) could a point be located if its coordinates are reciprocals of each other?

65. The points $(-1, 1)$, $(4, 1)$, and $(4, -5)$ are three vertices of a rectangle. Find the coordinates of the fourth vertex.

66. The pairs $(-2, -3)$, $(-1, 2)$, and $(4, -3)$ can serve as three (of four) vertices for three different parallelograms. Find the fourth vertex of each parallelogram.

67. Graph eight points such that the sum of the coordinates in each pair is 7. Answers may vary.

68. Find the perimeter of a rectangle if three of its vertices are $(5, -2)$, $(-3, -2)$, and $(-3, 3)$.

69. Find the area of a triangle whose vertices have coordinates $(0, 9)$, $(0, -4)$, and $(5, -4)$.

Coordinates on the globe. *Coordinates can also be used to describe the location on a sphere: 0° latitude is the equator and 0° longitude is a line from the North Pole to the South Pole through France and Algeria. In the figure shown here, hurricane Clara is at a point about 260 mi northwest of Bermuda near latitude 36.0° North, longitude 69.0° West.*

70. Approximate the latitude and the longitude of Bermuda.

71. Approximate the latitude and the longitude of Lake Okeechobee.

72. The graph accompanying Example 3 flattens out. Why do you think this occurs?

73. In the *Star Trek* science-fiction series, a three-dimensional coordinate system is used to locate objects in space. If the center of a planet is used as the origin, how many "quadrants" will exist? Why? If possible, sketch a three-dimensional coordinate system and label each "quadrant."

CORNER

You Sank My Battleship!

Focus: Graphing points; logical questioning
Time: 15–25 minutes
Group size: 3–5
Materials: Graph paper

In the game Battleship®, a player places a miniature ship on a grid that only that player can see. An opponent guesses at coordinates that might "hit" the "hidden" ship. The following activity is similar to this game.

ACTIVITY

1. Using only integers from −10 to 10 (inclusive), one group member should secretly record the coordinates of a point on a slip of paper. (This point is the hidden "battleship.")

2. The other group members can then ask up to 10 "yes/no" questions in an effort to determine the coordinates of the secret point. Be sure to phrase each question mathematically (for example, "Is the *x*-coordinate negative?")

3. The group member who selected the point should answer each question. On the basis of the answer given, another group member should cross out the points no longer under consideration. All group members should check that this is done correctly.

4. If the hidden point has not been determined after 10 questions have been answered, the secret coordinates should be revealed to all group members.

5. Repeat parts (1)–(4) until each group member has had the opportunity to select the hidden point and answer questions.

3.2   Graphing Linear Equations

Solutions of Equations ▪ Graphing Linear Equations ▪ Applications

We have seen how bar, line, and circle graphs can represent information. Now we begin to learn how graphs can be used to represent solutions of equations.

Solutions of Equations

When an equation contains two variables, solutions are ordered pairs in which each number in the pair replaces a letter in the equation. Unless stated otherwise, the first number in each pair replaces the variable that occurs first alphabetically.

EXAMPLE 1 Determine whether each of the following pairs is a solution of $4b - 3a = 22$: **(a)** $(2, 7)$; **(b)** $(1, 6)$.

SOLUTION

a) We substitute 2 for a and 7 for b (alphabetical order of variables):

$$\begin{array}{c|c} 4b - 3a = 22 & \\ \hline 4(7) - 3(2) & 22 \\ 28 - 6 & \\ 22 \stackrel{?}{=} 22 & \text{TRUE} \end{array}$$

Since $22 = 22$ is *true*, the pair $(2, 7)$ *is* a solution.

b) In this case, we replace a with 1 and b with 6:

$$\begin{array}{c|c} 4b - 3a = 22 & \\ \hline 4(6) - 3(1) & 22 \\ 24 - 3 & \\ 21 \stackrel{?}{=} 22 & \text{FALSE} \quad 21 \neq 22 \end{array}$$

Since $21 = 22$ is *false*, the pair $(1, 6)$ is *not* a solution.   **TRY EXERCISE** 7

EXAMPLE 2

Show that the pairs $(3, 7)$, $(0, 1)$, and $(-3, -5)$ are solutions of $y = 2x + 1$. Then graph the three points to determine another pair that is a solution.

SOLUTION   To show that a pair is a solution, we substitute, replacing x with the first coordinate and y with the second coordinate of each pair:

$$\begin{array}{c|c} y = 2x + 1 & \\ \hline 7 & 2 \cdot 3 + 1 \\ & 6 + 1 \\ 7 \stackrel{?}{=} 7 & \text{TRUE} \end{array} \qquad \begin{array}{c|c} y = 2x + 1 & \\ \hline 1 & 2 \cdot 0 + 1 \\ & 0 + 1 \\ 1 \stackrel{?}{=} 1 & \text{TRUE} \end{array} \qquad \begin{array}{c|c} y = 2x + 1 & \\ \hline -5 & 2(-3) + 1 \\ & -6 + 1 \\ -5 \stackrel{?}{=} -5 & \text{TRUE} \end{array}$$

In each of the three cases, the substitution results in a true equation. Thus the pairs $(3, 7)$, $(0, 1)$, and $(-3, -5)$ are all solutions. We graph them as shown at left.

Note that the three points appear to "line up." Will other points that line up with these points also represent solutions of $y = 2x + 1$? To find out, we use a ruler and draw a line passing through $(-3, -5)$, $(0, 1)$, and $(3, 7)$.

The line appears to pass through $(2, 5)$. Let's check to see if this pair is a solution of $y = 2x + 1$:

$$\begin{array}{c|c} y = 2x + 1 & \\ \hline 5 & 2 \cdot 2 + 1 \\ & 4 + 1 \\ 5 \stackrel{?}{=} 5 & \text{TRUE} \end{array}$$

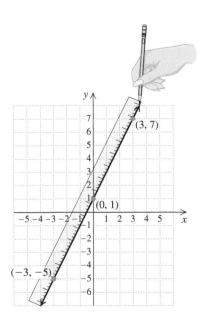

We see that $(2, 5)$ *is* a solution. You should perform a similar check for at least one other point that appears to be on the line.   **TRY EXERCISE** 13

Example 2 leads us to suspect that *any* point on the line passing through $(3, 7)$, $(0, 1)$, and $(-3, -5)$ represents a solution of $y = 2x + 1$. In fact, every solution of $y = 2x + 1$ is represented by a point on this line and every point on this line represents a solution. The line is called the **graph** of the equation.

Graphing Linear Equations

Equations like $y = 2x + 1$ or $4b - 3a = 22$ are said to be **linear** because the graph of each equation is a line. In general, any equation that can be written in the form $y = mx + b$ or $Ax + By = C$ (where $m, b, A, B,$ and C are constants and A and B are not both 0) is linear.

To *graph* an equation is to make a drawing that represents its solutions. Linear equations can be graphed as follows.

> **To Graph a Linear Equation**
> 1. Select a value for one coordinate and calculate the corresponding value of the other coordinate. Form an ordered pair. This pair is one solution of the equation.
> 2. Repeat step (1) to find a second ordered pair. A third ordered pair should be found to use as a check.
> 3. Plot the ordered pairs and draw a straight line passing through the points. The line represents all solutions of the equation.

EXAMPLE 3   Graph: $y = -3x + 1$.

SOLUTION   Since $y = -3x + 1$ is in the form $y = mx + b$, the equation is linear and the graph is a straight line. We select a convenient value for x, compute y, and form an ordered pair. Then we repeat the process for other choices of x.

If $x = 2$,   then $y = -3 \cdot 2 + 1 = -5$,   and $(2, -5)$ is a solution.
If $x = 0$,   then $y = -3 \cdot 0 + 1 = 1$,   and $(0, 1)$ is a solution.
If $x = -1$,   then $y = -3(-1) + 1 = 4$,   and $(-1, 4)$ is a solution.

Results are often listed in a table, as shown below. The points corresponding to each pair are then plotted.

$y = -3x + 1$

Calculate ordered pairs.

x	y	(x, y)
2	−5	$(2, -5)$
0	1	$(0, 1)$
−1	4	$(-1, 4)$

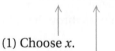

(1) Choose x.
(2) Compute y.
(3) Form the pair (x, y).

Plot the points.   (4) Plot the points.

Note that all three points line up. If they didn't, we would know that we had made a mistake, because the equation is linear. When only two points are plotted, an error is more difficult to detect.

Draw the graph.   Finally, we use a ruler or other straight-edge to draw a line. We add arrowheads to the ends of the line to indicate that it extends indefinitely beyond the edge of the grid drawn. Every point on the line represents a solution of $y = -3x + 1$.

TRY EXERCISE 21

EXAMPLE 4

Graph: $y = 2x - 3$.

SOLUTION   We select some convenient x-values and compute y-values.

If $x = 0$,   then $y = 2 \cdot 0 - 3 = -3$,   and $(0, -3)$ is a solution.

If $x = 1$,   then $y = 2 \cdot 1 - 3 = -1$,   and $(1, -1)$ is a solution.

If $x = 4$,   then $y = 2 \cdot 4 - 3 = 5$,   and $(4, 5)$ is a solution.

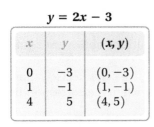

$y = 2x - 3$

x	y	(x, y)
0	−3	$(0, -3)$
1	−1	$(1, -1)$
4	5	$(4, 5)$

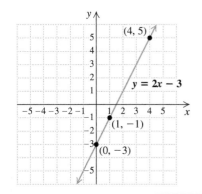

TRY EXERCISE 27

EXAMPLE 5

Graph: $4x + 2y = 12$.

SOLUTION   To form ordered pairs, we can replace either variable with a number and then calculate the other coordinate:

If $y = 0$, we have $4x + 2 \cdot 0 = 12$

$4x = 12$

$x = 3$,

so $(3, 0)$ is a solution.

If $x = 0$, we have $4 \cdot 0 + 2y = 12$

$2y = 12$

$y = 6$,

so $(0, 6)$ is a solution.

If $y = 2$, we have $4x + 2 \cdot 2 = 12$

$4x + 4 = 12$

$4x = 8$

$x = 2$,

so $(2, 2)$ is a solution.

$4x + 2y = 12$

x	y	(x, y)
3	0	$(3, 0)$
0	6	$(0, 6)$
2	2	$(2, 2)$

TRY EXERCISE 37

Note that in Examples 3 and 4 the variable y is isolated on one side of the equation. This generally simplifies calculations, so it is important to be able to solve for y before graphing.

EXAMPLE **6**   Graph $3y = 2x$ by first solving for y.

SOLUTION   To isolate y, we divide both sides by 3, or multiply both sides by $\frac{1}{3}$:

$$3y = 2x$$

$$\frac{1}{3} \cdot 3y = \frac{1}{3} \cdot 2x \qquad \text{Using the multiplication principle to multiply both sides by } \frac{1}{3}$$

$$\left. \begin{array}{l} 1y = \frac{2}{3} \cdot x \\ y = \frac{2}{3}x. \end{array} \right\} \quad \text{Simplifying}$$

Because all the equations above are equivalent, we can use $y = \frac{2}{3}x$ to draw the graph of $3y = 2x$.

To graph $y = \frac{2}{3}x$, we can select x-values that are multiples of 3. This will allow us to avoid fractions when the corresponding y-values are computed.

$$\left. \begin{array}{lll} \text{If } x = 3, & \text{then } y = \frac{2}{3} \cdot 3 = 2. \\ \text{If } x = -3, & \text{then } y = \frac{2}{3}(-3) = -2. \\ \text{If } x = 6, & \text{then } y = \frac{2}{3} \cdot 6 = 4. \end{array} \right\} \quad \begin{array}{l} \text{Note that when multiples of 3 are} \\ \text{substituted for } x, \text{ the } y\text{-coordinates} \\ \text{are not fractions.} \end{array}$$

The following table lists these solutions. Next, we plot the points and see that they form a line. Finally, we draw and label the line.

$$3y = 2x, \text{ or } y = \frac{2}{3}x$$

x	y	(x, y)
3	2	$(3, 2)$
-3	-2	$(-3, -2)$
6	4	$(6, 4)$

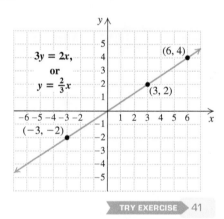

TRY EXERCISE   41

EXAMPLE **7**   Graph $x + 5y = -10$ by first solving for y.

SOLUTION   We have

$$x + 5y = -10$$

$$5y = -x - 10 \qquad \text{Adding } -x \text{ to both sides}$$

$$y = \frac{1}{5}(-x - 10) \qquad \text{Multiplying both sides by } \frac{1}{5}$$

$$y = -\frac{1}{5}x - 2. \qquad \text{Using the distributive law}$$

> *CAUTION!*   It is very important to multiply *both* $-x$ and -10 by $\frac{1}{5}$.

Thus, $x + 5y = -10$ is equivalent to $y = -\frac{1}{5}x - 2$. It is important to note that if we now choose x-values that are multiples of 5, we can avoid fractions when calculating the corresponding y-values.

$$\text{If } x = 5, \quad \text{then } y = -\frac{1}{5} \cdot 5 - 2 = -1 - 2 = -3.$$

$$\text{If } x = 0, \quad \text{then } y = -\frac{1}{5} \cdot 0 - 2 = 0 - 2 = -2.$$

$$\text{If } x = -5, \quad \text{then } y = -\frac{1}{5}(-5) - 2 = 1 - 2 = -1.$$

$$x + 5y = -10, \text{ or } y = -\frac{1}{5}x - 2$$

x	y	(x, y)
5	−3	$(5, -3)$
0	−2	$(0, -2)$
−5	−1	$(-5, -1)$

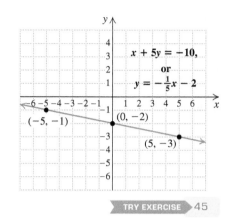

TRY EXERCISE 45

Applications

Linear equations appear in many real-life situations.

EXAMPLE 8   *Fuel efficiency.*   A typical tractor-trailer will move 18 tons of air per mile at 55 mph. Air resistance increases with speed, causing fuel efficiency to decrease at higher speeds. At highway speeds, a certain truck's fuel efficiency t, in miles per gallon (mpg), can be given by

$$t = -0.1s + 13.1,$$

where s is the speed of the truck, in miles per hour (mph). Graph the equation and then use the graph to estimate the fuel efficiency at 66 mph.

Source: Based on data from Kenworth Truck Co.

SOLUTION   We graph $t = -0.1s + 13.1$ by first selecting values for s and then calculating the associated values t. Since the equation is true for highway speeds, we use $s \geq 50$.

If $s = 50$,   then $t = -0.1(50) + 13.1 = 8.1$.
If $s = 60$,   then $t = -0.1(60) + 13.1 = 7.1$.
If $s = 70$,   then $t = -0.1(70) + 13.1 = 6.1$.

s	t
50	8.1
60	7.1
70	6.1

Because we are *selecting* values for s and *calculating* values for t, we represent s on the horizontal axis and t on the vertical axis. Counting by 5's horizontally, beginning at 50, and by 0.5 vertically, beginning at 4, will allow us to plot all three pairs, as shown below.

Speed (in miles per hour)

Since the three points line up, our calculations are probably correct. We draw a line, beginning at (50, 8.1). To estimate the fuel efficiency at 66 mph, we locate the point on the line that is above 66 and then find the value on the *t*-axis that corresponds to that point, as shown at left. The fuel efficiency at 66 mph is about 6.5 mpg.

TRY EXERCISE 49

CAUTION! When the coordinates of a point are read from a graph, as in Example 8, values should not be considered exact.

Many equations in two variables have graphs that are not straight lines. Three such graphs are shown below. As before, each graph represents the solutions of the given equation. Graphing calculators are especially helpful when drawing these *nonlinear* graphs. Nonlinear graphs are studied later in this text and in more advanced courses.

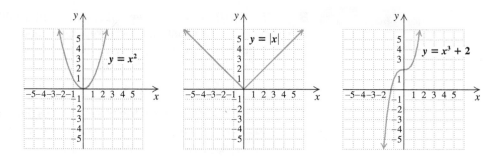

TECHNOLOGY CONNECTION

Most graphing calculators require that *y* be alone on one side before the equation is entered. For example, to graph $5y + 4x = 13$, we would first solve for *y*. The student can check that solving for *y* yields the equation $y = -\frac{4}{5}x + \frac{13}{5}$.

We press $\boxed{Y=}$, enter $-\frac{4}{5}x + \frac{13}{5}$ as Y1, and press $\boxed{GRAPH}$. The graph is shown here in the standard viewing window $[-10, 10, -10, 10]$.

Using a graphing calculator, graph each of the following. Select the "standard" $[-10, 10, -10, 10]$ window.

1. $y = -5x + 6.5$
2. $y = 3x + 4.5$
3. $7y - 4x = 22$
4. $5y + 11x = -20$
5. $2y - x^2 = 0$
6. $y + x^2 = 8$

🪝 *Concept Reinforcement*   *Classify each statement as either true or false.*

1. A linear equation in two variables has at most one solution.

2. Every solution of $y = 3x - 7$ is an ordered pair.

3. The graph of $y = 3x - 7$ represents all solutions of the equation.

4. If a point is on the graph of $y = 3x - 7$, the corresponding ordered pair is a solution of the equation.

5. To find a solution of $y = 3x - 7$, we can choose any value for x and calculate the corresponding value for y.

6. The graph of every equation is a straight line.

Determine whether each equation has the given ordered pair as a solution.

7. $y = 4x - 7$; $(2, 1)$

8. $y = 5x + 8$; $(0, 8)$

9. $3y + 4x = 19$; $(5, 1)$

10. $5x - 3y = 15$; $(0, 5)$

11. $4m - 5n = 7$; $(3, -1)$

12. $3q - 2p = -8$; $(1, -2)$

In Exercises 13–20, an equation and two ordered pairs are given. Show that each pair is a solution of the equation. Then graph the two pairs to determine another solution. Answers may vary.

13. $y = x + 3$; $(-1, 2), (4, 7)$

14. $y = x - 2$; $(3, 1), (-2, -4)$

15. $y = \frac{1}{2}x + 3$; $(4, 5), (-2, 2)$

16. $y = \frac{1}{2}x - 1$; $(6, 2), (0, -1)$

17. $y + 3x = 7$; $(2, 1), (4, -5)$

18. $2y + x = 5$; $(-1, 3), (7, -1)$

19. $4x - 2y = 10$; $(0, -5), (4, 3)$

20. $6x - 3y = 3$; $(1, 1), (-1, -3)$

Graph each equation.

21. $y = x + 1$

22. $y = x - 1$

23. $y = -x$

24. $y = x$

25. $y = 2x$

26. $y = -3x$

27. $y = 2x + 2$

28. $y = 3x - 2$

29. $y = -\frac{1}{2}x$

30. $y = \frac{1}{4}x$

31. $y = \frac{1}{3}x - 4$

32. $y = \frac{1}{2}x + 1$

33. $x + y = 4$

34. $x + y = -5$

35. $x - y = -2$

36. $y - x = 3$

37. $x + 2y = -6$

38. $x + 2y = 8$

39. $y = -\frac{2}{3}x + 4$

40. $y = \frac{3}{2}x + 1$

41. $4x = 3y$

42. $2x = 5y$

43. $5x - y = 0$

44. $3x - 5y = 0$

45. $6x - 3y = 9$

46. $8x - 4y = 12$

47. $6y + 2x = 8$

48. $8y + 2x = -4$

49. *Student aid.*   The average award a of federal student financial assistance per student is approximated by
$$a = 0.08t + 2.5,$$
where a is in thousands of dollars and t is the number of years since 1994. Graph the equation and use the graph to estimate the average amount of federal student aid per student in 2010.
Source: Based on data from U.S. Department of Education, Office of Postsecondary Education

50. *Value of a color copier.*   The value of Dupliographic's color copier is given by
$$v = -0.68t + 3.4,$$
where v is the value, in thousands of dollars, t years from the date of purchase. Graph the equation and use the graph to estimate the value of the copier after $2\frac{1}{2}$ yr.

51. *FedEx mailing costs.*   Recently, the cost c, in dollars, of shipping a FedEx Priority Overnight package weighing 1 lb or more a distance of 1001 to 1400 mi was given by
$$c = 3.1w + 29.07,$$
where w is the package's weight, in pounds. Graph the equation and use the graph to estimate the cost of shipping a $6\frac{1}{2}$-lb package.
Source: Based on data from FedEx.com

52. *Increasing life expectancy.*   A smoker is 15 times more likely to die of lung cancer than a nonsmoker. An ex-smoker who stopped smoking t years ago is

w times more likely to die of lung cancer than a nonsmoker, where

$$w = 15 - t.$$

Graph the equation and use the graph to estimate how much more likely it is for Sandy to die of lung cancer than Polly, if Polly never smoked and Sandy quit $2\frac{1}{2}$ yr ago.
Source: Data from *Body Clock* by Dr. Martin Hughes, p. 60. New York: Facts on File, Inc.

53. *Scrapbook pricing.*   The price *p*, in dollars, of an 8-in. by 8-in. assembled scrapbook is given by

$$p = 3.5n + 9,$$

where *n* is the number of pages in the scrapbook. Graph the equation and use the graph to estimate the price of a scrapbook containing 25 pages.
Source: www.scrapbooksplease.com

54. *Value of computer software.*   The value *v* of a shop-keeper's inventory software program, in hundreds of dollars, is given by

$$v = -\tfrac{3}{4}t + 6,$$

where *t* is the number of years since the shopkeeper first bought the program. Graph the equation and use the graph to estimate what the program is worth 4 yr after it was first purchased.

55. *Bottled water.*   The number of gallons of bottled water *w* consumed by the average American in one year is given by

$$w = 1.6t + 16.7,$$

where *t* is the number of years since 2000. Graph the equation and use the graph to predict the number of gallons consumed by the average American in 2010.
Source: Based on data from Beverage Marketing Corporation

56. *Record temperature drop.*   On January 22, 1943, the temperature *T*, in degrees Fahrenheit, in Spearfish, South Dakota, could be approximated by

$$T = -2m + 54,$$

where *m* is the number of minutes since 9:00 A.M. that morning. Graph the equation and use the graph to estimate the temperature at 9:15 A.M.
Source: Based on information from the National Oceanic Atmospheric Administration

57. *Cost of college.*   The cost *T*, in hundreds of dollars, of tuition and fees at many community colleges can be approximated by

$$T = \tfrac{5}{4}c + 2,$$

where *c* is the number of credits for which a student registers. Graph the equation and use the graph to

estimate the cost of tuition and fees when a student registers for 4 three-credit courses.

Bartonville Community College
Ferndell Hall

Tuition $125 / credit
Fees
Registration $85
Transcripts $55
Computer $45
Activities $15

Activities include: Math team, fencing, drama club

58. *Cost of college.*   The cost *C*, in thousands of dollars, of a year at a private four-year college (all expenses) can be approximated by

$$C = \tfrac{13}{10}t + 21,$$

where *t* is the number of years since 1995. Graph the equation and use the graph to predict the cost of a year at a private four-year college in 2012.
Source: Based on information in *Statistical Abstract of the United States*, 2007

59. The equations $3x + 4y = 8$ and $y = -\tfrac{3}{4}x + 2$ are equivalent. Which equation would be easier to graph and why?

60. Suppose that a linear equation is graphed by plotting three points and that the three points line up with each other. Does this *guarantee* that the equation is being correctly graphed? Why or why not?

Skill Review

Review solving equations and formulas (Sections 2.2 and 2.3).

Solve and check. [2.2]

61. $5x + 3 \cdot 0 = 12$

62. $3 \cdot 0 - 8y = 6$

63. $5x + 3(2 - x) = 12$

64. $3(y - 5) - 8y = 6$

Solve. [2.3]

65. $A = \dfrac{T + Q}{2}$, for *Q*

66. $pq + p = w$, for *p*

67. $Ax + By = C$, for *y*

68. $\dfrac{y - k}{m} = x - h$, for *y*

Synthesis

69. Janice consistently makes the mistake of plotting the *x*-coordinate of an ordered pair using the *y*-axis, and the *y*-coordinate using the *x*-axis. How will Janice's incorrect graph compare with the appropriate graph?

70. Explain how the graph in Example 8 can be used to determine the speed for which the fuel efficiency is 6 mpg.

71. *Bicycling.* Long Beach Island in New Jersey is a long, narrow, flat island. For exercise, Laura routinely bikes to the northern tip of the island and back. Because of the steady wind, she uses one gear going north and another for her return. Laura's bike has 21 gears and the sum of the two gears used on her ride is always 24. Write and graph an equation that represents the different pairings of gears that Laura uses. Note that there are no fraction gears on a bicycle.

In Exercises 72–75, try to find an equation for the graph shown.

72.

73.

74.

75.

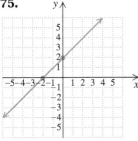

76. Translate to an equation:

   d dimes and *n* nickels total $1.75.

Then graph the equation and use the graph to determine three different combinations of dimes and nickels that total $1.75 (see also Exercise 90).

77. Translate to an equation:

   d $25 dinners and *l* $5 lunches total $225.

Then graph the equation and use the graph to determine three different combinations of lunches and dinners that total $225 (see also Exercise 90).

Use the suggested x-values $-3, -2, -1, 0, 1, 2,$ *and* 3 *to graph each equation.*

78. $y = |x|$

Aha! **79.** $y = -|x|$

Aha! **80.** $y = |x| - 2$

81. $y = x^2$

82. $y = x^2 + 1$

For Exercises 83–88, use a graphing calculator to graph the equation. Use a $[-10, 10, -10, 10]$ *window.*

83. $y = -2.8x + 3.5$

84. $y = 4.5x + 2.1$

85. $y = 2.8x - 3.5$

86. $y = -4.5x - 2.1$

87. $y = x^2 + 4x + 1$

88. $y = -x^2 + 4x - 7$

89. Example 8 discusses fuel efficiency. If fuel costs $3.50 a gallon, how much money will a truck driver save on a 500-mi trip by driving at 55 mph instead of 70 mph? How many gallons of fuel will be saved?

90. Study the graph of Exercises 76 and 77. Does *every* point on the graph represent a solution of the associated problem? Why or why not?

3.3   Graphing and Intercepts

Intercepts ▪ Using Intercepts to Graph ▪ Graphing Horizontal or Vertical Lines

Unless a line is horizontal or vertical, it will cross both axes. Often, finding the points where the axes are crossed gives us a quick way of graphing linear equations.

Intercepts

In Example 5 of Section 3.2, we graphed $4x + 2y = 12$ by plotting the points $(3, 0)$, $(0, 6)$, and $(2, 2)$ and then drawing the line.

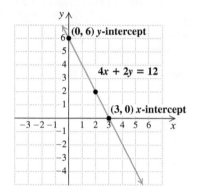

- The point at which a graph crosses the y-axis is called the **y-intercept**. In the figure above, the y-intercept is $(0, 6)$. The x-coordinate of a y-intercept is always 0.

- The point at which a graph crosses the x-axis is called the **x-intercept**. In the figure above, the x-intercept is $(3, 0)$. The y-coordinate of an x-intercept is always 0.

It is possible for the graph of a curve to have more than one y-intercept or more than one x-intercept.

EXAMPLE 1   For the graph shown below, **(a)** give the coordinates of any x-intercepts and **(b)** give the coordinates of any y-intercepts.

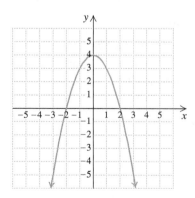

SOLUTION

a) The x-intercepts are the points at which the graph crosses the x-axis. For the graph shown, the x-intercepts are $(-2, 0)$ and $(2, 0)$.

b) The y-intercept is the point at which the graph crosses the y-axis. For the graph shown, the y-intercept is $(0, 4)$.

> TRY EXERCISE   7

Using Intercepts to Graph

It is important to know how to locate a graph's intercepts from the equation being graphed.

To Find Intercepts

To find the y-intercept(s) of an equation's graph, replace x with 0 and solve for y.

To find the x-intercept(s) of an equation's graph, replace y with 0 and solve for x.

EXAMPLE   2   Find the y-intercept and the x-intercept of the graph of $2x + 4y = 20$.

SOLUTION   To find the y-intercept, we let $x = 0$ and solve for y:

$$2 \cdot 0 + 4y = 20 \qquad \text{Replacing } x \text{ with } 0$$
$$4y = 20$$
$$y = 5.$$

Thus the y-intercept is $(0, 5)$.

To find the x-intercept, we let $y = 0$ and solve for x:

$$2x + 4 \cdot 0 = 20 \qquad \text{Replacing } y \text{ with } 0$$
$$2x = 20$$
$$x = 10.$$

Thus the x-intercept is $(10, 0)$.

> TRY EXERCISE   15

Since two points are sufficient to graph a line, intercepts can be used to graph linear equations.

EXAMPLE   3   Graph $2x + 4y = 20$ using intercepts.

SOLUTION   In Example 2, we showed that the y-intercept is $(0, 5)$ and the x-intercept is $(10, 0)$. Before drawing a line, we plot a third point as a check. We substitute any convenient value for x and solve for y.

If we let $x = 5$, then

$$2 \cdot 5 + 4y = 20 \qquad \text{Substituting 5 for } x$$
$$10 + 4y = 20$$
$$4y = 10 \qquad \text{Subtracting 10 from both sides}$$
$$y = \tfrac{10}{4}, \text{or } 2\tfrac{1}{2}. \qquad \text{Solving for } y$$

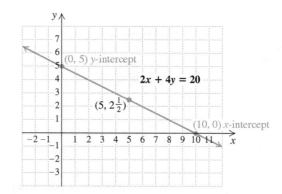

The point $\left(5, 2\tfrac{1}{2}\right)$ appears to line up with the intercepts, so our work is probably correct. To finish, we draw and label the line.

TRY EXERCISE ▶ 25

Note that when we solved for the y-intercept, we replaced x with 0 and simplified $2x + 4y = 20$ to $4y = 20$. Thus, to find the y-intercept, we can momentarily ignore the x-term and solve the remaining equation.

In a similar manner, when we solved for the x-intercept, we simplified $2x + 4y = 20$ to $2x = 20$. Thus, to find the x-intercept, we can momentarily ignore the y-term and then solve this remaining equation.

EXAMPLE 4   Graph $3x - 2y = 60$ using intercepts.

SOLUTION   To find the y-intercept, we let $x = 0$. This amounts to temporarily ignoring the x-term and then solving:

$$-2y = 60 \qquad \text{For } x = 0, \text{ we have } 3 \cdot 0 - 2y, \text{ or simply } -2y.$$
$$y = -30.$$

The y-intercept is $(0, -30)$.

To find the x-intercept, we let $y = 0$. This amounts to temporarily disregarding the y-term and then solving:

$$3x = 60 \qquad \text{For } y = 0, \text{ we have } 3x - 2 \cdot 0, \text{ or simply } 3x.$$
$$x = 20.$$

The x-intercept is $(20, 0)$.

To find a third point, we can replace x with 4 and solve for y:

$$3 \cdot 4 - 2y = 60 \qquad \text{Numbers other than 4 can be used for } x.$$
$$12 - 2y = 60$$
$$-2y = 48$$
$$y = -24. \qquad \text{This means that } (4, -24) \text{ is on the graph.}$$

In order for us to graph all three points, the y-axis of our graph must go down to at least -30 and the x-axis must go up to at least 20. Using a scale of 5 units per square allows us to display both intercepts and $(4, -24)$, as well as the origin.

The point $(4, -24)$ appears to line up with the intercepts, so we draw and label the line, as shown at left.

> TRY EXERCISE ▸ 45

TECHNOLOGY CONNECTION

When an equation has been entered into a graphing calculator, we may not be able to see both intercepts. For example, if $y = -0.8x + 17$ is graphed in the window $[-10, 10, -10, 10]$, neither intercept is visible.

$y_1 = -0.8x + 17$

To better view the intercepts, we can change the window dimensions or we can zoom out. The ZOOM feature allows us to reduce or magnify a graph or a portion

of a graph. Before zooming, the ZOOM *factors* must be set in the memory of the ZOOM key. If we zoom out with factors set at 5, both intercepts are visible but the axes are heavily drawn, as shown in the preceding figure.

This suggests that the *scales* of the axes should be changed. To do this, we use the WINDOW menu and set Xscl to 5 and Yscl to 5. The resulting graph has tick marks 5 units apart and clearly shows both intercepts. Other choices for Xscl and Yscl can also be made.

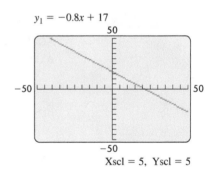

Graph each equation so that both intercepts can be easily viewed. Zoom or adjust the window settings so that tick marks can be clearly seen on both axes.

1. $y = -0.72x - 15$
2. $y - 2.13x = 27$
3. $5x + 6y = 84$
4. $2x - 7y = 150$
5. $19x - 17y = 200$
6. $6x + 5y = 159$

Graphing Horizontal or Vertical Lines

The equations graphed in Examples 3 and 4 are both in the form $Ax + By = C$. We have already stated that any equation in the form $Ax + By = C$ is linear, provided A and B are not both zero. What if A or B (but not both) is zero? We will find that when A is zero, there is no x-term and the graph is a horizontal line. We will also find that when B is zero, there is no y-term and the graph is a vertical line.

EXAMPLE   5

Graph: $y = 3$.

SOLUTION   We can regard the equation $y = 3$ as $0 \cdot x + y = 3$. No matter what number we choose for x, we find that y must be 3 if the equation is to be solved. Consider the following table.

STUDENT NOTES

Many students draw horizontal lines when they should be drawing vertical lines and vice versa. To avoid this mistake, first locate the correct number on the axis whose label is given. Thus, to graph $x = 2$, we locate 2 on the x-axis and then draw a line perpendicular to that axis at that point. Note that the graph of $x = 2$ on a plane is a line, whereas the graph of $x = 2$ on a number line is a point.

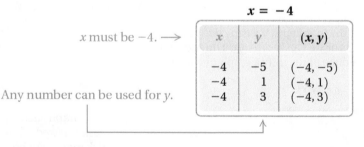

$y = 3$

Choose any number for x. →

x	y	(x, y)
-2	3	$(-2, 3)$
0	3	$(0, 3)$
4	3	$(4, 3)$

y must be 3.

All pairs will have 3 as the y-coordinate.

When we plot the ordered pairs $(-2, 3)$, $(0, 3)$, and $(4, 3)$ and connect the points, we obtain a horizontal line. Any ordered pair of the form $(x, 3)$ is a solution, so the line is parallel to the x-axis with y-intercept $(0, 3)$. Note that the graph of $y = 3$ has no x-intercept.

TRY EXERCISE   53

EXAMPLE   6

Graph: $x = -4$.

SOLUTION   We can regard the equation $x = -4$ as $x + 0 \cdot y = -4$. We make up a table with all -4's in the x-column.

$x = -4$

x must be -4. →

x	y	(x, y)
-4	-5	$(-4, -5)$
-4	1	$(-4, 1)$
-4	3	$(-4, 3)$

Any number can be used for y.

All pairs will have -4 as the x-coordinate.

When we plot the ordered pairs $(-4, -5)$, $(-4, 1)$, and $(-4, 3)$ and connect them, we obtain a vertical line. Any ordered pair of the form $(-4, y)$ is a solution. The line is parallel to the y-axis with x-intercept $(-4, 0)$. Note that the graph of $x = -4$ has no y-intercept.

TRY EXERCISE   55

Linear Equations in One Variable

The graph of $y = b$ is a horizontal line, with y-intercept $(0, b)$.

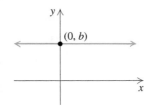

The graph of $x = a$ is a vertical line, with x-intercept $(a, 0)$.

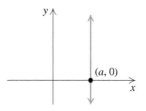

EXAMPLE **7**   Write an equation for each graph.

a)

b)

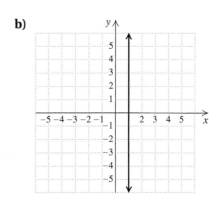

SOLUTION

a) Note that every point on the horizontal line passing through $(0, -2)$ has -2 as the y-coordinate. Thus the equation of the line is $y = -2$.

b) Note that every point on the vertical line passing through $(1, 0)$ has 1 as the x-coordinate. Thus the equation of the line is $x = 1$.   **TRY EXERCISE** 71

3.3   **EXERCISE SET**

For Extra Help
MyMathLab   Math XL PRACTICE   WATCH   DOWNLOAD

↪ *Concept Reinforcement* *In each of Exercises 1–6, match the phrase with the most appropriate choice from the column on the right.*

1. _____ A vertical line

2. _____ A horizontal line

3. _____ A y-intercept

4. _____ An x-intercept

5. _____ A third point as a check

6. _____ Use a scale of 10 units per square.

a) $2x + 5y = 100$

b) $(3, -2)$

c) $(1, 0)$

d) $(0, 2)$

e) $y = 3$

f) $x = -4$

For Exercises 7–14, list **(a)** *the coordinates of the y-intercept and* **(b)** *the coordinates of all x-intercepts.*

7.

8.

9.

10.

11.

12.

13.

14.

For Exercises 15–24, list (**a**) *the coordinates of any y-intercept and* (**b**) *the coordinates of any x-intercept. Do not graph.*

15. $3x + 5y = 15$

16. $2x + 7y = 14$

17. $9x - 2y = 36$

18. $10x - 3y = 60$

19. $-4x + 5y = 80$

20. $-5x + 6y = 100$

Aha! **21.** $x = 12$

22. $y = 10$

23. $y = -9$

24. $x = -5$

Find the intercepts. Then graph.

25. $3x + 5y = 15$ **26.** $2x + y = 6$

27. $x + 2y = 4$ **28.** $2x + 5y = 10$

29. $-x + 2y = 8$ **30.** $-x + 3y = 9$

31. $3x + y = 9$ **32.** $2x - y = 8$

33. $y = 2x - 6$ **34.** $y = -3x + 6$

35. $5x - 10 = 5y$ **36.** $3x - 9 = 3y$

37. $2x - 5y = 10$ **38.** $2x - 3y = 6$

39. $6x + 2y = 12$

40. $4x + 5y = 20$

41. $4x + 3y = 16$

42. $3x + 2y = 8$

43. $2x + 4y = 1$

44. $3x - 6y = 1$

45. $5x - 3y = 180$

46. $10x + 7y = 210$

47. $y = -30 + 3x$

48. $y = -40 + 5x$

49. $-4x = 20y + 80$

50. $60 = 20x - 3y$

51. $y - 3x = 0$

52. $x + 2y = 0$

Graph.

53. $y = 1$ **54.** $y = 4$

55. $x = 3$ **56.** $x = 6$

57. $y = -2$ **58.** $y = -4$

59. $x = -1$ **60.** $x = -6$

61. $y = -15$ **62.** $x = 20$

63. $y = 0$ **64.** $y = \frac{3}{2}$

65. $x = -\frac{5}{2}$ **66.** $x = 0$

67. $-4x = -100$

68. $12y = -360$

69. $35 + 7y = 0$

70. $-3x - 24 = 0$

Write an equation for each graph.

71.

72.

73.

74.

75.

76.

77. Explain in your own words why the graph of $y = 8$ is a horizontal line.

78. Explain in your own words why the graph of $x = -4$ is a vertical line.

Skill Review

Review translating to algebraic expressions (Section 1.1).

Translate to an algebraic expression. [1.1]

79. 7 less than d

80. 5 more than w

81. The sum of 7 and four times a number

82. The product of 3 and a number

83. Twice the sum of two numbers

84. Half of the sum of two numbers

Synthesis

85. Describe what the graph of $x + y = C$ will look like for any choice of C.

86. If the graph of a linear equation has one point that is both the x- and the y-intercepts, what is that point? Why?

87. Write an equation for the x-axis.

88. Write an equation of the line parallel to the x-axis and passing through $(3, 5)$.

89. Write an equation of the line parallel to the y-axis and passing through $(-2, 7)$.

90. Find the coordinates of the point of intersection of the graphs of $y = x$ and $y = 6$.

91. Find the coordinates of the point of intersection of the graphs of the equations $x = -3$ and $y = 4$.

92. Write an equation of the line shown in Exercise 7.

93. Write an equation of the line shown in Exercise 10.

94. Find the value of C such that the graph of $3x + C = 5y$ has an x-intercept of $(-4, 0)$.

95. Find the value of C such that the graph of $4x = C - 3y$ has a y-intercept of $(0, -8)$.

96. For A and B nonzero, the graphs of $Ax + D = C$ and $By + D = C$ will be parallel to an axis. Explain why.

97. Find the x-intercept of the graph of $Ax + D = C$.

In Exercises 98–103, find the intercepts of each equation algebraically. Then adjust the window and scale so that the intercepts can be checked graphically with no further window adjustments.

98. $3x + 2y = 50$

99. $2x - 7y = 80$

100. $y = 1.3x - 15$

101. $y = 0.2x - 9$

102. $25x - 20y = 1$

103. $50x + 25y = 1$

3.4   Rates

Rates of Change   ■   Visualizing Rates

Rates of Change

Because graphs make use of two axes, they allow us to visualize how two quantities change with respect to each other. A number accompanied by units is used to represent this type of change and is referred to as a *rate*.

> **Rate**
>
> A *rate* is a ratio that indicates how two quantities change with respect to each other.

Rates occur often in everyday life:

A business whose customer base grows by 1500 customers over a period of 2 yr has an average *growth rate* of $\frac{1500}{2}$, or 750, customers per year.

A vehicle traveling 260 mi in 4 hr is moving at a *rate* of $\frac{260}{4}$, or 65, mph (miles per hour).

A class of 25 students pays a total of $93.75 to visit a museum. The *rate* is $\frac{\$93.75}{25}$, or $3.75, per student.

> *CAUTION!*   To calculate a rate, it is important to keep track of the units being used.

EXAMPLE   1   On January 3, Alisha rented a Ford Focus with a full tank of gas and 9312 mi on the odometer. On January 7, she returned the car with 9630 mi on the odometer.* If the rental agency charged Alisha $108 for the rental and needed 12 gal of gas to fill up the gas tank, find the following rates.

a) The car's rate of gas consumption, in miles per gallon

b) The average cost of the rental, in dollars per day

c) The car's rate of travel, in miles per day

SOLUTION

a) The rate of gas consumption, in miles per gallon, is found by dividing the number of miles traveled by the number of gallons used for that amount of driving:

$$\text{Rate, in miles per gallon} = \frac{9630 \text{ mi} - 9312 \text{ mi}}{12 \text{ gal}}$$

The word "per" indicates division.

$$= \frac{318 \text{ mi}}{12 \text{ gal}}$$

$$= 26.5 \text{ mi/gal} \qquad \textit{Dividing}$$

$$= 26.5 \text{ miles per gallon.}$$

---

*For all problems concerning rentals, assume that the pickup time was later in the day than the return time so that no late fees were applied.

b) The average cost of the rental, in dollars per day, is found by dividing the cost of the rental by the number of days:

$$\text{Rate, in dollars per day} = \frac{108 \text{ dollars}}{4 \text{ days}} \qquad \begin{array}{l} \text{From January 3 to} \\ \text{January 7 is} \\ 7 - 3 = 4 \text{ days.} \end{array}$$

$$= 27 \text{ dollars/day}$$

$$= \$27 \text{ per day.}$$

c) The car's rate of travel, in miles per day, is found by dividing the number of miles traveled by the number of days:

$$\text{Rate, in miles per day} = \frac{318 \text{ mi}}{4 \text{ days}} \qquad \begin{array}{l} 9630 \text{ mi} - 9312 \text{ mi} = 318 \text{ mi;} \\ \text{From January 3 to January 7} \\ \text{is } 7 - 3 = 4 \text{ days.} \end{array}$$

$$= 79.5 \text{ mi/day}$$

$$= 79.5 \text{ mi per day.} \qquad \boxed{\text{TRY EXERCISE}} \; 7$$

> *CAUTION!* Units are a vital part of real-world problems. They must be considered in the translation of a problem and included in the answer to a problem.

Many problems involve a rate of travel, or *speed*. The **speed** of an object is found by dividing the distance traveled by the time required to travel that distance.

EXAMPLE 2

Transportation. An Atlantic City Express bus makes regular trips between Paramus and Atlantic City, New Jersey. At 6:00 P.M., the bus is at mileage marker 40 on the Garden State Parkway, and at 8:00 P.M. it is at marker 170. Find the average speed of the bus.

SOLUTION Speed is the distance traveled divided by the time spent traveling:

$$\text{Bus speed} = \frac{\text{Distance traveled}}{\text{Time spent traveling}}$$

$$= \frac{\text{Change in mileage}}{\text{Change in time}}$$

$$= \frac{130 \text{ mi}}{2 \text{ hr}} \qquad \begin{array}{l} 170 \text{ mi} - 40 \text{ mi} = 130 \text{ mi;} \\ 8:00 \text{ P.M.} - 6:00 \text{ P.M.} = 2 \text{ hr} \end{array}$$

$$= 65 \frac{\text{mi}}{\text{hr}}$$

$$= 65 \text{ miles per hour.} \qquad \begin{array}{l} \text{This } average \text{ speed does not} \\ \text{indicate by how much the bus speed} \\ \text{may vary along the route.} \end{array}$$

$$\boxed{\text{TRY EXERCISE}} \; 13$$

Visualizing Rates

Graphs allow us to visualize a rate of change. As a rule, the quantity listed in the numerator appears on the vertical axis and the quantity listed in the denominator appears on the horizontal axis.

EXAMPLE **3**   *Recycling.* Between 1991 and 2006, the amount of paper recycled in the United States increased at a rate of approximately 1.5 million tons per year. In 1991, approximately 31 million tons of paper was recycled. Draw a graph to represent this information.

Source: Based on information from American Forest and Paper Association

SOLUTION   To label the axes, note that the rate is given as 1.5 million tons per year, or

$$1.5 \text{ million } \frac{\text{tons}}{\text{yr}}.$$
←——Numerator: vertical axis
←——Denominator: horizontal axis

We list *Amount of paper recycled (in millions of tons)* on the vertical axis and *Year* on the horizontal axis. (See the figure on the left below.)

Next, we select a scale for each axis that allows us to plot the given information. If we count by increments of 10 million on the vertical axis, we can show 31 million tons for 1991 and increasing amounts for later years. On the horizontal axis, we count by increments of 2 years to make certain that both 1991 and 2006 are included. (See the figure in the middle below.)

Label the axes.

Select the scale.

Draw the graph.

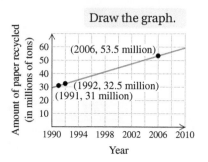

We now plot the point corresponding to (1991, 31 million). Then, to display the rate of growth, we move from that point to a second point that represents 1.5 million more tons 1 year later.

(1991,   31 million)   Beginning point

(1991 + 1,   31 million + 1.5 million)   1.5 million more tons, 1 year later

(1992,   32.5 million)   A second point on the graph

Similarly, we can find the coordinates for 2006. Since 2006 is 15 years after 1991, we add 15 to the year and 15(1.5 million) = 22.5 million to the amount.

(1991,   31 million)   Beginning point

(1991 + 15, 31 million + 22.5 million)   15(1.5) million more tons, 15 years later

(2006,   53.5 million)   A third point on the graph

After plotting the three points, we draw a line through them, as shown in the figure on the right above. This gives us the graph.   ▶ TRY EXERCISE ▶ 19

EXAMPLE **4**   *Banking.* Nadia prepared the following graph from data collected on a recent day at a branch bank.

a) What rate can be determined from the graph?

b) What is that rate?

SOLUTION

a) Because the vertical axis shows the number of transactions and the horizontal axis lists the time in hour-long increments, we can find the rate *Number of transactions per hour.*

b) The points (9:00, 75) and (11:00, 225) are both on the graph. This tells us that in the 2 hours between 9:00 and 11:00, there were 225 − 75 = 150 transactions. Thus the rate is

$$\frac{225 \text{ transactions} - 75 \text{ transactions}}{11{:}00 - 9{:}00} = \frac{150 \text{ transactions}}{2 \text{ hours}}$$

$$= 75 \text{ transactions per hour.}$$

Note that this is an *average* rate.

TRY EXERCISE 29

3.4 EXERCISE SET

For Extra Help MyMathLab Math XL PRACTICE WATCH DOWNLOAD

🔖 *Concept Reinforcement* *For Exercises 1–6, fill in the missing units for each rate.*

1. If Eva biked 100 miles in 5 hours, her average rate was 20 _____.

2. If it took Lauren 18 hours to read 6 chapters, her average rate was 3 _____.

3. If Denny's ticket cost $300 for a 150-mile flight, his average rate was 2 _____.

4. If Geoff planted 36 petunias along a 12-ft sidewalk, his average rate was 3 _____.

5. If Christi ran 8 errands in 40 minutes, her average rate was 5 _____.

6. If Ben made 8 cakes using 20 cups of flour, his average rate was $2\frac{1}{2}$ _____.

Solve. For Exercises 7–14, round answers to the nearest cent.

7. *Car rentals.* Late on June 5, Gaya rented a Ford Focus with a full tank of gas and 13,741 mi on the odometer. On June 8, she returned the car with 14,131 mi on the odometer. The rental agency charged Gaya $118 for the rental and needed 13 gal of gas to fill up the tank.

   a) Find the car's rate of gas consumption, in miles per gallon.

   b) Find the average cost of the rental, in dollars per day.

   c) Find the average rate of travel, in miles per day.

   d) Find the rental rate, in cents per mile.

8. *SUV rentals.*   On February 10, Oscar rented a Chevy Trailblazer with a full tank of gas and 13,091 mi on the odometer. On February 12, he returned the vehicle with 13,322 mi on the odometer. The rental agency charged $92 for the rental and needed 14 gal of gas to fill the tank.

   a) Find the SUV's rate of gas consumption, in miles per gallon.

   b) Find the average cost of the rental, in dollars per day.

   c) Find the average rate of travel, in miles per day.

   d) Find the rental rate, in cents per mile.

9. *Bicycle rentals.*   At 9:00, Jodi rented a mountain bike from The Bike Rack. She returned the bicycle at 11:00, after cycling 14 mi. Jodi paid $15 for the rental.

   a) Find Jodi's average speed, in miles per hour.

   b) Find the rental rate, in dollars per hour.

   c) Find the rental rate, in dollars per mile.

10. *Bicycle rentals.*   At 2:00, Braden rented a mountain bike from The Slick Rock Cyclery. He returned the bike at 5:00, after cycling 18 mi. Braden paid $12 for the rental.

   a) Find Braden's average speed, in miles per hour.

   b) Find the rental rate, in dollars per hour.

   c) Find the rental rate, in dollars per mile.

11. *Proofreading.*   Sergei began proofreading at 9:00 A.M., starting at the top of page 93. He worked until 2:00 P.M. that day and finished page 195. He billed the publishers $110 for the day's work.

   a) Find the rate of pay, in dollars per hour.

   b) Find the average proofreading rate, in number of pages per hour.

   c) Find the rate of pay, in dollars per page.

12. *Temporary help.*   A typist for Kelly Services reports to 3E's Properties for work at 10:00 A.M. and leaves at 6:00 P.M. after having typed from the end of page 8 to the end of page 50 of a proposal. 3E's pays $120 for the typist's services.

   a) Find the rate of pay, in dollars per hour.

   b) Find the average typing rate, in number of pages per hour.

   c) Find the rate of pay, in dollars per page.

13. *National debt.*   The U.S. federal budget debt was $5770 billion in 2001 and $8612 billion in 2006. Find the rate at which the debt was increasing.
   Source: U.S. Office of Management and Budget

14. *Four-year-college tuition.*   The average tuition at a public four-year college was $3983 in 2001 and $5948 in 2005. Find the rate at which tuition was increasing.
   Source: U.S. National Center for Education Statistics

15. *Elevators.*   At 2:38, Lara entered an elevator on the 34th floor of the Regency Hotel. At 2:40, she stepped off at the 5th floor.

   a) Find the elevator's average rate of travel, in number of floors per minute.

   b) Find the elevator's average rate of travel, in seconds per floor.

16. *Snow removal.*   By 1:00 P.M., Olivia had already shoveled 2 driveways, and by 6:00 P.M. that day, the number was up to 7.

   a) Find Olivia's average shoveling rate, in number of driveways per hour.

   b) Find Olivia's average shoveling rate, in hours per driveway.

17. *Mountaineering.*   The fastest ascent of Mt. Everest was accomplished by the Sherpa guide Pemba Dorje of Nepal in 2004. Pemba Dorje climbed from base camp, elevation 17,552 ft, to the summit, elevation 29,028 ft, in 8 hr 10 min.
   Source: *Guinness Book of World Records* 2006 Edition

   a) Find Pemba Dorje's average rate of ascent, in feet per minute.

   b) Find Pemba Dorje's average rate of ascent, in minutes per foot.

18. *Mountaineering.* As part of an ill-fated expedition to climb Mt. Everest in 1996, author Jon Krakauer departed "The Balcony," elevation 27,600 ft, at 7:00 A.M. and reached the summit, elevation 29,028 ft, at 1:25 P.M.
Source: Krakauer, Jon, *Into Thin Air, the Illustrated Edition.* New York: Random House, 1998

   a) Find Krakauer's average rate of ascent, in feet per minute.
   b) Find Krakauer's average rate of ascent, in minutes per foot.

In Exercises 19–28, draw a linear graph to represent the given information. Be sure to label and number the axes appropriately (see Example 3).

19. *Landfills.* In 2006, 35,700,000 tons of paper was deposited in landfills in the United States, and this figure was decreasing by 700,000 tons per year.
Source: Based on data from American Forest and Paper Association

20. *Health insurance.* In 2005, the average cost for health insurance for a family was about $11,000 and the figure was rising at a rate of about $1100 per year.
Source: Based on data from Kaiser/HRET Survey of Health Benefits

21. *Prescription drug sales.* In 2006, there were sales of approximately $11 billion of asthma drug products in the United States, and the figure was increasing at a rate of about $1.2 billion per year.
Source: *The Wall Street Journal,* 6/28/2007

22. *Violent crimes.* In 2004, there were approximately 21.1 violent crimes per 1000 population in the United States, and the figure was dropping at a rate of about 1.2 crimes per 1000 per year.
Source: U.S. Bureau of Justice Statistics

23. *Train travel.* At 3:00 P.M., the Boston–Washington Metroliner had traveled 230 mi and was cruising at a rate of 90 miles per hour.

24. *Plane travel.* At 4:00 P.M., the Seattle–Los Angeles shuttle had traveled 400 mi and was cruising at a rate of 300 miles per hour.

25. *Wages.* By 2:00 P.M., Diane had earned $50. She continued earning money at a rate of $15 per hour.

26. *Wages.* By 3:00 P.M., Arnie had earned $70. He continued earning money at a rate of $12 per hour.

27. *Telephone bills.* Roberta's phone bill was already $7.50 when she made a call for which she was charged at a rate of $0.10 per minute.

28. *Telephone bills.* At 3:00 P.M., Larry's phone bill was $6.50 and increasing at a rate of 7¢ per minute.

In Exercises 29–38, use the graph provided to calculate a rate of change in which the units of the horizontal axis are used in the denominator.

29. *Call center.* The following graph shows data from a technical assistance call center. At what rate are calls being handled?

30. *Hairdresser.* Eve's Custom Cuts has a graph displaying data from a recent day of work. At what rate does Eve work?

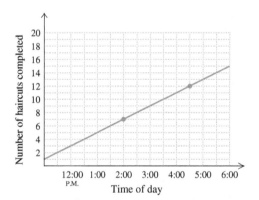

31. *Train travel.* The following graph shows data from a recent train ride from Chicago to St. Louis. At what rate did the train travel?

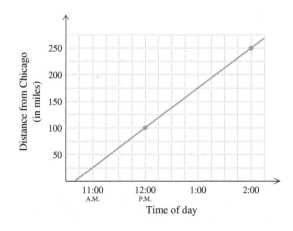

32. *Train travel.* The following graph shows data from a recent train ride from Denver to Kansas City. At what rate did the train travel?

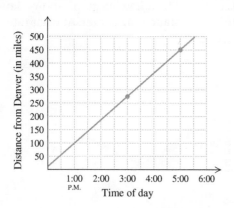

33. *Cost of a telephone call.* The following graph shows data from a recent phone call between the United States and the Netherlands. At what rate was the customer being billed?

34. *Cost of a telephone call.* The following graph shows data from a recent phone call between the United States and South Korea. At what rate was the customer being billed?

35. *Population.* The following graph shows data regarding the population of Youngstown,

Ohio. At what rate was the population changing?

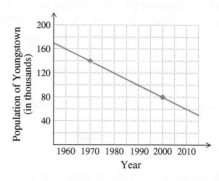

36. *Depreciation of an office machine.* Data regarding the value of a particular color copier is represented in the following graph. At what rate is the value changing?

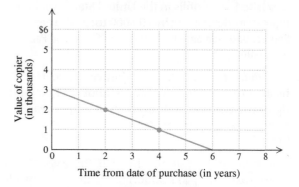

37. *Gas mileage.* The following graph shows data for a 2008 Toyota Prius driven on interstate highways. At what rate was the vehicle consuming gas?
Source: www.fueleconomy.gov

38. *Gas mileage.* The following graph shows data for a 2008 Chevy Malibu driven on city streets. At what rate was the vehicle consuming gas?
Source: Chevrolet

In each of Exercises 39–44, match the description with the most appropriate graph from the choices below. Scales are intentionally omitted. Assume that of the three sports listed, swimming is the slowest and biking is the fastest.

39. ____ Robin trains for triathlons by running, biking, and then swimming every Saturday.

40. ____ Gene trains for triathlons by biking, running, and then swimming every Sunday.

41. ____ Shirley trains for triathlons by swimming, biking, and then running every Sunday.

42. ____ Evan trains for triathlons by swimming, running, and then biking every Saturday.

43. ____ Angie trains for triathlons by biking, swimming, and then running every Sunday.

44. ____ Mick trains for triathlons by running, swimming, and then biking every Saturday.

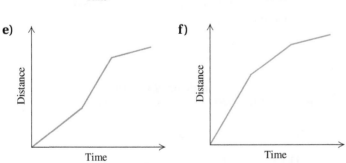

45. What does a negative rate of travel indicate? Explain.

46. Explain how to convert from kilometers per hour to meters per second.

Skill Review

To prepare for Section 3.5, review subtraction and order of operations (Sections 1.6 and 1.8).

Simplify.

47. $-2 - (-7)$ [1.6]

48. $-9 - (-3)$ [1.6]

49. $\dfrac{5 - (-4)}{-2 - 7}$ [1.8]

50. $\dfrac{8 - (-4)}{2 - 11}$ [1.8]

51. $\dfrac{-4 - 8}{11 - 2}$ [1.8]

52. $\dfrac{-5 - (-3)}{4 - 6}$ [1.8]

53. $\dfrac{-6 - (-6)}{-2 - 7}$ [1.8]

54. $\dfrac{-3 - 5}{-1 - (-1)}$ [1.8]

Synthesis

55. How would the graphs of Jon's and Jenny's total earnings compare in each of the following situations?

  a) Jon earns twice as much per hour as Jenny.

  b) Jon and Jenny earn the same hourly rate, but Jenny received a bonus for a cost-saving suggestion.

  c) Jon is paid by the hour, and Jenny is paid a weekly salary.

56. Write an exercise similar to those in Exercises 7–18 for a classmate to solve. Design the problem so that the solution is "The motorcycle's rate of gas consumption was 65 miles per gallon."

57. *Aviation.* A Boeing 737 climbs from sea level to a cruising altitude of 31,500 ft at a rate of 6300 ft/min. After cruising for 3 min, the jet is forced to land, descending at a rate of 3500 ft/min. Represent the flight with a graph in which altitude is measured on the vertical axis and time on the horizontal axis.

58. *Wages with commissions.* Each salesperson at Mike's Bikes is paid $140 a week plus 13% of all sales up to $2000, and then 20% on any sales in excess of $2000. Draw a graph in which sales are measured on the horizontal axis and wages on the vertical axis. Then use the graph to estimate the wages paid when a salesperson sells $2700 in merchandise in one week.

59. *Taxi fares.* The driver of a New York City Yellow Cab recently charged $2 plus 50¢ for each fifth of a mile traveled. Draw a graph that could be used to determine the cost of a fare.

60. *Gas mileage.* Suppose that a Kawasaki motorcycle travels three times as far as a Chevy Malibu on the same amount of gas (see Exercise 38). Draw a graph that reflects this information.

61. *Aviation.* Tim's F-16 jet is moving forward at a deck speed of 95 mph aboard an aircraft carrier that is traveling 39 mph in the same direction. How fast is the jet traveling, in minutes per mile, with respect to the sea?

62. *Navigation.* In 3 sec, Penny walks 24 ft, to the bow (front) of a tugboat. The boat is cruising at a rate of 5 ft/sec. What is Penny's rate of travel with respect to land?

63. *Running.* Anne ran from the 4-km mark to the 7-km mark of a 10-km race in 15.5 min. At this rate, how long would it take Anne to run a 5-mi race?

64. *Running.* Jerod ran from the 2-mi marker to the finish line of a 5-mi race in 25 min. At this rate, how long would it take Jerod to run a 10-km race?

65. Alex picks apples twice as fast as Ryan. By 4:30, Ryan had already picked 4 bushels of apples. Fifty minutes later, his total reached $5\frac{1}{2}$ bushels. Find Alex's picking rate. Give your answer in number of bushels per hour.

66. At 3:00 P.M., Catanya and Chad had already made 46 candles. By 5:00 P.M., the total reached 100 candles. Assuming a constant production rate, at what time did they make their 82nd candle?

COLLABORATIVE CORNER

Determining Depreciation Rates

Focus: Modeling, graphing, and rates

Time: 30 minutes

Group size: 3

Materials: Graph paper and straightedges

From the minute a new car is driven out of the dealership, it *depreciates*, or drops in value with the passing of time. The N.A.D.A. Official Used Car Guide is a periodic listing of the trade-in values of used cars. The data below are taken from two such reports from 2007.

ACTIVITY

1. Each group member should select a different one of the cars listed in the table below as his or her own. Assuming that the values are dropping linearly, each student should draw a line representing the trade-in value of his or her car. Draw all three lines on the same graph. Let the horizontal axis represent the time, in months, since January 2007, and let the vertical axis represent the trade-in value of each car. Decide as a group how many months or dollars each square should represent. Make the drawings as neat as possible.

2. At what *rate* is each car depreciating and how are the different rates illustrated in the graph of part (1)?

3. If one of the three cars had to be sold in January 2009, which one would your group sell and why? Compare answers with other groups.

Car	Trade-in Value in January 2007	Trade-in Value in June 2007
2005 Mustang V6 Coupe	$13,625	$13,125
2005 Nissan Sentra SE-R	$11,825	$11,000
2005 Volkswagen Jetta Sedan GL	$12,600	$11,425

3.5   Slope

Rate and Slope   ▪   Horizontal and Vertical Lines   ▪   Applications

In Section 3.4, we introduced *rate* as a method of measuring how two quantities change with respect to each other. In this section, we will discuss how rate can be related to the slope of a line.

Rate and Slope

Automated digitization machines use robotic arms to carefully turn pages of books so that they can take pictures of each page. Suppose that a large university library purchased a DL-1500 and an APT 1200. The DL-1500 digitizes 3 volumes of an encyclopedia every 2 hr. The APT 1200 digitizes 6 volumes of an encyclopedia every 5 hr. The following tables list the number of books digitized after various amounts of time for each machine.

Source: Based on information from Kirtas and 4DigitalBooks

DL-1500	
Hours Elapsed	**Books Digitized**
0	0
2	3
4	6
6	9
8	12

APT 1200	
Hours Elapsed	**Books Digitized**
0	0
5	6
10	12
15	18
20	24

We now graph the pairs of numbers listed in the tables, using the horizontal axis for the number of hours elapsed and the vertical axis for the number of books digitized.

DL-1500

APT 1200

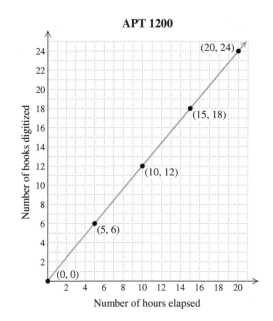

By comparing the number of books digitized by each machine over a specified period of time, we can compare the two rates. For example, the DL-1500 digitizes 3 books every 2 hr, so its *rate* is $3 \div 2 = \frac{3}{2}$ books per hour. Since the APT 1200 digitizes 6 books every 5 hr, its rate is $6 \div 5 = \frac{6}{5}$ books per hour. Note that the rate of the DL-1500 is greater so its graph is steeper.

The rates $\frac{3}{2}$ and $\frac{6}{5}$ can also be found using the coordinates of any two points that are on the line. For example, we can use the points $(6, 9)$ and $(8, 12)$ to find the digitization rate for the DL-1500. To do so, remember that these coordinates tell us that after 6 hr, 9 books have been digitized, and after 8 hr, 12 books have been digitized. In the 2 hr between the 6-hr and 8-hr points, $12 - 9$, or 3, books were digitized. Thus we have

$$\text{DL-1500 digitization rate} = \frac{\text{change in number of books digitized}}{\text{corresponding change in time}}$$

$$= \frac{12 - 9 \text{ books}}{8 - 6 \text{ hr}}$$

$$= \frac{3 \text{ books}}{2 \text{ hr}} = \frac{3}{2} \text{ books per hour.}$$

Because the line is straight, the same rate is found using *any* pair of points on the line. For example, using $(0, 0)$ and $(4, 6)$, we have

$$\text{DL-1500 digitization rate} = \frac{6 - 0 \text{ books}}{4 - 0 \text{ hr}} = \frac{6 \text{ books}}{4 \text{ hr}} = \frac{3}{2} \text{ books per hour.}$$

Note that the rate is always the vertical change divided by the corresponding horizontal change.

EXAMPLE   1   Use the graph of book digitization by the APT 1200 to find the rate at which books are digitized.

SOLUTION   We can use any two points on the line, such as $(15, 18)$ and $(20, 24)$:

$$\text{APT 1200 digitization rate} = \frac{\text{change in number of books digitized}}{\text{corresponding change in time}}$$

$$= \frac{24 - 18 \text{ books}}{20 - 15 \text{ hr}}$$

$$= \frac{6 \text{ books}}{5 \text{ hr}}$$

$$= \frac{6}{5} \text{ books per hour.}$$

As a check, we can use another pair of points, like $(0, 0)$ and $(10, 12)$:

$$\text{APT 1200 digitization rate} = \frac{12 - 0 \text{ books}}{10 - 0 \text{ hr}}$$

$$= \frac{12 \text{ books}}{10 \text{ hr}}$$

$$= \frac{6}{5} \text{ books per hour.}$$

TRY EXERCISE   11

When the axes of a graph are simply labeled x and y, the ratio of vertical change to horizontal change is the rate at which y is changing with respect to x. This ratio is a measure of a line's slant, or **slope**.

Consider a line passing through $(2, 3)$ and $(6, 5)$, as shown below. We find the ratio of vertical change, or *rise*, to horizontal change, or *run*, as follows:

$$\text{Ratio of vertical change to horizontal change} = \frac{\text{change in } y}{\text{change in } x} = \frac{\text{rise}}{\text{run}}$$

$$= \frac{5 - 3}{6 - 2}$$

$$= \frac{2}{4}, \text{ or } \frac{1}{2}.$$

Note that these calculations can be performed without viewing a graph.

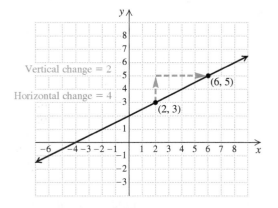

Thus the y-coordinates of points on this line increase at a rate of 2 units for every 4-unit increase in x, which is 1 unit for every 2-unit increase in x, or $\frac{1}{2}$ unit for every 1-unit increase in x. The slope of the line is $\frac{1}{2}$.

In the box below, the *subscripts* 1 and 2 are used to distinguish two arbitrary points, point 1 and point 2, from each other. The slightly lowered 1's and 2's are not exponents but are used to denote x-values (or y-values) that may differ from each other.

Slope

The *slope* of the line containing points (x_1, y_1) and (x_2, y_2) is given by

$$m = \frac{\text{change in } y}{\text{change in } x} = \frac{\text{rise}}{\text{run}} = \frac{y_2 - y_1}{x_2 - x_1}.$$

EXAMPLE **2** Graph the line containing the points $(-4, 3)$ and $(2, -6)$ and find the slope.

SOLUTION The graph is shown below. From $(-4, 3)$ to $(2, -6)$, the change in y, or rise, is $-6 - 3$, or -9. The change in x, or run, is $2 - (-4)$, or 6. Thus,

$$\text{Slope} = \frac{\text{change in } y}{\text{change in } x}$$

$$= \frac{\text{rise}}{\text{run}}$$

$$= \frac{-6 - 3}{2 - (-4)}$$

$$= \frac{-9}{6}$$

$$= -\frac{9}{6}, \text{ or } -\frac{3}{2}.$$

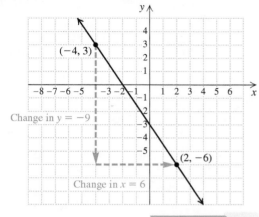

STUDENT NOTES

You may wonder which point should be regarded as (x_1, y_1) and which should be (x_2, y_2). To see that the math works out the same either way, perform both calculations on your own.

TRY EXERCISE 39

CAUTION! When we use the formula

$$m = \frac{y_2 - y_1}{x_2 - x_1},$$

it makes no difference which point is considered (x_1, y_1). What matters is that we subtract the y-coordinates in the same order that we subtract the x-coordinates.

To illustrate, we reverse *both* of the subtractions in Example 2. The slope is still $-\frac{3}{2}$:

$$\text{Slope} = \frac{\text{change in } y}{\text{change in } x} = \frac{3 - (-6)}{-4 - 2} = \frac{9}{-6} = -\frac{3}{2}.$$

As shown in the graphs below, a line with positive slope slants up from left to right, and a line with negative slope slants down from left to right. The larger the absolute value of the slope, the steeper the line.

$m = \frac{3}{7}$

$m = 2, \text{ or } \frac{2}{1}$

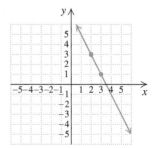

$m = -2, \text{ or } \frac{-2}{1}$

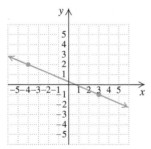

$m = -\frac{3}{7}$

Horizontal and Vertical Lines

What about the slope of a horizontal line or a vertical line?

EXAMPLE 3   Find the slope of the line $y = 4$.

SOLUTION   Consider the points $(2, 4)$ and $(-3, 4)$, which are on the line. The change in y, or the rise, is $4 - 4$, or 0. The change in x, or the run, is $-3 - 2$, or -5. Thus,

$$m = \frac{4 - 4}{-3 - 2}$$

$$= \frac{0}{-5}$$

$$= 0.$$

Any two points on a horizontal line have the same y-coordinate. Thus the change in y is 0, so the slope is 0.

TRY EXERCISE 55

A horizontal line has slope 0.

EXAMPLE 4   Find the slope of the line $x = -3$.

SOLUTION   Consider the points $(-3, 4)$ and $(-3, -2)$, which are on the line. The change in y, or the rise, is $-2 - 4$, or -6. The change in x, or the run, is $-3 - (-3)$, or 0. Thus,

$$m = \frac{-2 - 4}{-3 - (-3)}$$

$$= \frac{-6}{0}. \quad \text{(undefined)}$$

Since division by 0 is not defined, the slope of this line is not defined. The answer to a problem of this type is "The slope of this line is undefined."

TRY EXERCISE 57

The slope of a vertical line is undefined.

Applications

We have seen that slope has many real-world applications, ranging from car speed to production rate. Some applications use slope to measure steepness. For example, numbers like 2%, 3%, and 6% are often used to represent the **grade** of a road, a measure of a road's steepness. That is, since $3\% = \frac{3}{100}$, a 3% grade means that for every horizontal distance of 100 ft, the road rises or drops 3 ft. The concept of grade also occurs in skiing or snowboarding, where a 7% grade is considered very tame, but a 70% grade is considered steep.

EXAMPLE 5　　*Skiing.* Among the steepest skiable terrain in North America, the Headwall on Mount Washington, in New Hampshire, drops 720 ft over a horizontal distance of 900 ft. Find the grade of the Headwall.

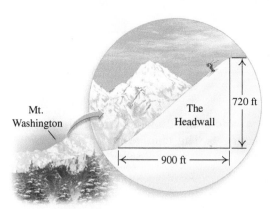

SOLUTION　The grade of the Headwall is its slope, expressed as a percent:

$$m = \frac{720}{900}$$
$$= \frac{8}{10}$$
$$= 80\%.$$

Grade is slope expressed as a percent.

TRY EXERCISE 63

Carpenters use slope when designing stairs, ramps, or roof pitches. Another application occurs in the engineering of a dam—the force or strength of a river depends on how much the river drops over a specified distance.

3.5　EXERCISE SET

For Extra Help　MyMathLab　MathXL PRACTICE　 WATCH　 DOWNLOAD

Concept Reinforcement　State whether each of the following rates is positive, negative, or zero.

1. The rate at which a teenager's height changes

2. The rate at which an elderly person's height changes

3. The rate at which a pond's water level changes during a drought

4. The rate at which a pond's water level changes during the rainy season

5. The rate at which a runner's distance from the starting point changes during a race

6. The rate at which a runner's distance from the finish line changes during a race

7. The rate at which the number of U.S. senators changes

8. The rate at which the number of people in attendance at a basketball game changes in the moments before the opening tipoff

9. The rate at which the number of people in attendance at a basketball game changes in the moments after the final buzzer sounds

10. The rate at which a person's I.Q. changes during his or her sleep

11. *Blogging.*   Find the rate at which a career blogger is paid.

Source: Based on information from Wired

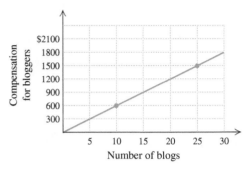

12. *Fitness.*   Find the rate at which a runner burns calories.

13. *Cell-phone prices.*   Find the rate of change in the average price of a new cell phone.

Source: Based on information from Market Reporter at PriceGrabber.com 2006

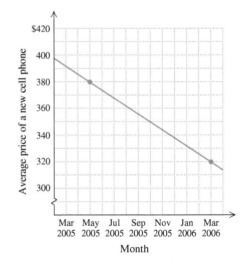

14. *Retail sales.*   Find the rate of change in the percentage of department stores' share of total retail sales.

Source: Based on information from the National Retail Federation

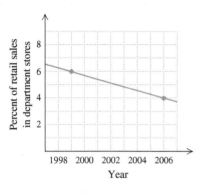

15. *College admission tests.*   Find the rate of change in SAT verbal scores with respect to family income.

Source: Based on 2004–2005 data from the National Center for Education Statistics

16. *Long-term care.*   Find the rate of change in Medicaid spending on long-term care.

Source: Based on data from Thomson Medstat, prepared by AARP Public Policy Institute

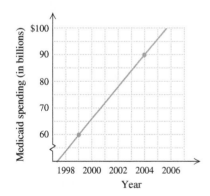

17. *Meteorology.*   Find the rate of change in the temperature in Spearfish, Montana, on January 22, 1943, as shown below.

Source: National Oceanic Atmospheric Administration

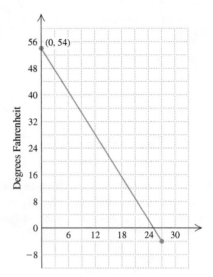

Number of minutes after 9 A.M.

18. Find the rate of change in the number of union-represented Ford employees.

Source: Ford Motor Co.

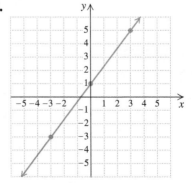

Find the slope, if it is defined, of each line. If the slope is undefined, state this.

19.

20.

21.

22.

23.

24.

28.

25.

29.

26.

30.

27.

31.

32.

33.

34.

35.

36.

37.

38.

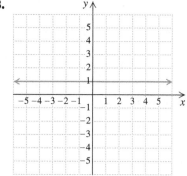

Find the slope of the line containing each given pair of points. If the slope is undefined, state this.

39. $(1, 3)$ and $(5, 8)$ **40.** $(1, 8)$ and $(6, 9)$

41. $(-2, 4)$ and $(3, 0)$ **42.** $(-4, 2)$ and $(2, -3)$

43. $(-4, 0)$ and $(5, 6)$ **44.** $(3, 0)$ and $(6, 9)$

45. $(0, 7)$ and $(-3, 10)$ **46.** $(0, 9)$ and $(-5, 0)$

47. $(-2, 3)$ and $(-6, 5)$ **48.** $(-1, 4)$ and $(5, -8)$

Aha! **49.** $\left(-2, \frac{1}{2}\right)$ and $\left(-5, \frac{1}{2}\right)$

50. $(-5, -1)$ and $(2, -3)$

51. $(5, -4)$ and $(2, -7)$

52. $(-10, 3)$ and $(-10, 4)$

53. $(6, -4)$ and $(6, 5)$

54. $(5, -2)$ and $(-4, -2)$

Find the slope of each line whose equation is given. If the slope is undefined, state this.

55. $y = 5$ **56.** $y = 13$

57. $x = -8$ **58.** $x = 18$

59. $x = 9$ **60.** $x = -7$

61. $y = -10$ **62.** $y = -4$

63. *Surveying.* Lick Skillet Road, near Boulder, Colorado, climbs 792 ft over a horizontal distance of 5280 ft. What is the grade of the road?

64. *Navigation.* Capital Rapids drops 54 ft vertically over a horizontal distance of 1080 ft. What is the slope of the rapids?

65. *Construction.* Part of New Valley rises 28 ft over a horizontal distance of 80 ft, and is too steep to build on. What is the slope of the land?

66. *Engineering.* At one point, Yellowstone's Beartooth Highway rises 315 ft over a horizontal distance of 4500 ft. Find the grade of the road.

67. *Carpentry.* Find the slope (or pitch) of the roof.

2 ft 5 in.

8 ft 2 in.

68. *Exercise.* Find the slope (or grade) of the treadmill.

0.4 ft

5 ft

69. *Bicycling.* To qualify as a rated climb on the Tour de France, a grade must average at least 4%. The ascent of Dooley Mountain, Oregon, part of the Elkhorn Classic, begins at 3500 ft and climbs to 5400 ft over a horizontal distance of 37,000 ft. What is the grade of the road? Would it qualify as a rated climb if it were part of the Tour de France?
Source: barkercityherald.com

70. *Construction.* Public buildings regularly include steps with 7-in. risers and 11-in. treads. Find the grade of such a stairway.

11 in.

7 in.

71. Explain why the order in which coordinates are subtracted to find slope does not matter so long as y-coordinates and x-coordinates are subtracted in the same order.

72. If one line has a slope of -3 and another has a slope of 2, which line is steeper? Why?

Skill Review

To prepare for Section 3.6, review solving a formula for a variable and graphing linear equations (Sections 2.3 and 3.2).

Solve. [2.3]

73. $ax + by = c$, for y **74.** $rx - mn = p$, for r

75. $ax - by = c$, for y **76.** $rs + nt = q$, for t

Graph. [3.2]

77. $8x + 6y = 24$ **78.** $3y = 4$

Synthesis

79. The points $(-4, -3)$, $(1, 4)$, $(4, 2)$, and $(-1, -5)$ are vertices of a quadrilateral. Use slopes to explain why the quadrilateral is a parallelogram.

80. Which is steeper and why: a ski slope that is $50°$ or one with a grade of 100%?

81. The plans below are for a skateboard "Fun Box". For the ramps labeled A, find the slope or grade.
Source: www.heckler.com

82. A line passes through $(4, -7)$ and never enters the first quadrant. What numbers could the line have for its slope?

83. A line passes through $(2, 5)$ and never enters the second quadrant. What numbers could the line have for its slope?

84. *Architecture.* Architects often use the equation $x + y = 18$ to determine the height y, in inches, of the riser of a step when the tread is x inches wide. Express the slope of stairs designed with this equation without using the variable y.

In Exercises 85 and 86, the slope of the line is $-\frac{2}{3}$, but the numbering on one axis is missing. How many units should each tick mark on that unnumbered axis represent?

85.

86.

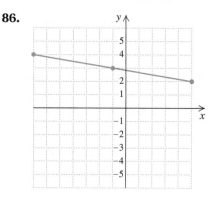

3.6 ## Slope–Intercept Form

Using the *y*-intercept and the Slope to Graph a Line ▪ Equations in Slope–Intercept Form ▪ Graphing and Slope–Intercept Form ▪ Parallel and Perpendicular Lines

If we know the slope and the *y*-intercept of a line, it is possible to graph the line. In this section, we will discover that a line's slope and *y*-intercept can be determined directly from the line's equation, provided the equation is written in a certain form.

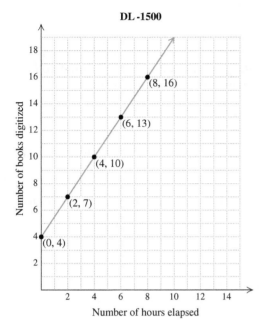

DL-1500

Number of books digitized

Number of hours elapsed

Using the *y*–intercept and the Slope to Graph a Line

Let's modify the book-digitization situation that first appeared in Section 3.5. Suppose that as the information technologist arrives, 4 books had already been digitized by the DL-1500. If the rate of $\frac{3}{2}$ books per hour remains in effect, the table and graph shown here can be made.

DL-1500	
Hours Elapsed	**Books Digitized**
0	4
2	7
4	10
6	13
8	16

To confirm that the digitization rate is still $\frac{3}{2}$, we calculate the slope. Recall that

$$\text{Slope} = \frac{\text{change in } y}{\text{change in } x} = \frac{\text{rise}}{\text{run}} = \frac{y_2 - y_1}{x_2 - x_1},$$

where (x_1, y_1) and (x_2, y_2) are any two points on the graphed line. Here we select $(0, 4)$ and $(2, 7)$:

$$\text{Slope} = \frac{\text{change in } y}{\text{change in } x} = \frac{7 - 4}{2 - 0} = \frac{3}{2}.$$

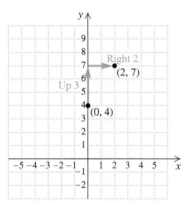

Knowing that the slope is $\frac{3}{2}$, we could have drawn the graph by plotting $(0, 4)$ and from there moving *up* 3 units and *to the right* 2 units. This would have located the point $(2, 7)$. Using $(0, 4)$ and $(2, 7)$, we can then draw the line. This is the method used in the next example.

EXAMPLE   1   Draw a line that has slope $\frac{1}{4}$ and *y*-intercept $(0, 2)$.

SOLUTION   We plot $(0, 2)$ and from there move *up* 1 unit and *to the right* 4 units. This locates the point $(4, 3)$. We plot $(4, 3)$ and draw a line passing through $(0, 2)$ and $(4, 3)$, as shown on the right below.

Plot the *y*-intercept.

Slope = $\frac{1}{4}$

Use the slope to plot a second point.

Draw the line.

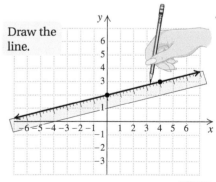

TRY EXERCISE   7

Equations in Slope–Intercept Form

It is possible to read the slope and the y-intercept of a line directly from its equation. Recall from Section 3.3 that to find the y-intercept of an equation's graph, we replace x with 0 and solve the resulting equation for y. For example, to find the y-intercept of the graph of $y = 2x + 3$, we replace x with 0 and solve as follows:

$$y = 2x + 3$$
$$= 2 \cdot 0 + 3 = 0 + 3 = 3. \qquad \text{The } y\text{-intercept is } (0, 3).$$

The y-intercept of the graph of $y = 2x + 3$ is $(0, 3)$. It can be similarly shown that the graph of $y = mx + b$ has the y-intercept $(0, b)$.

To calculate the slope of the graph of $y = 2x + 3$, we need two ordered pairs that are solutions of the equation. The y-intercept $(0, 3)$ is one pair; a second pair, $(1, 5)$, can be found by substituting 1 for x. We then have

$$\text{Slope} = \frac{\text{change in } y}{\text{change in } x} = \frac{5 - 3}{1 - 0} = \frac{2}{1} = 2.$$

Note that the slope, 2, is also the x-coefficient in $y = 2x + 3$. It can be similarly shown that the graph of any equation of the form $y = mx + b$ has slope m (see Exercise 79).

STUDENT NOTES ────────

An equation for a given line can be written in many different forms. Note that in the slope–intercept form, the equation is solved for y.

The Slope–Intercept Equation

The equation $y = mx + b$ is called the *slope–intercept equation*. The equation represents a line of slope m with y-intercept $(0, b)$.

The equation of any nonvertical line can be written in this form.

EXAMPLE 2   Find the slope and the y-intercept of each line whose equation is given.

a) $y = \frac{4}{5}x - 8$ **b)** $2x + y = 5$ **c)** $3x - 4y = 7$

SOLUTION

a) We rewrite $y = \frac{4}{5}x - 8$ as $y = \frac{4}{5}x + (-8)$. Now we simply read the slope and the y-intercept from the equation:

$$y = \tfrac{4}{5}x + (-8).$$

The slope is $\frac{4}{5}$. The y-intercept is $(0, -8)$.

b) We first solve for y to find an equivalent equation in the form $y = mx + b$:

$$2x + y = 5$$
$$y = -2x + 5. \qquad \text{Adding } -2x \text{ to both sides}$$

The slope is -2. The y-intercept is $(0, 5)$.

c) We rewrite the equation in the form $y = mx + b$:

$$3x - 4y = 7$$
$$-4y = -3x + 7 \qquad \text{Adding } -3x \text{ to both sides}$$
$$y = -\tfrac{1}{4}(-3x + 7) \qquad \text{Multiplying both sides by } -\tfrac{1}{4}$$
$$y = \tfrac{3}{4}x - \tfrac{7}{4}. \qquad \text{Using the distributive law}$$

The slope is $\frac{3}{4}$. The y-intercept is $\left(0, -\frac{7}{4}\right)$.

TRY EXERCISE 19

EXAMPLE 3   A line has slope $-\frac{12}{5}$ and y-intercept $(0, 11)$. Find an equation of the line.

SOLUTION   We use the slope–intercept equation, substituting $-\frac{12}{5}$ for m and 11 for b:

$$y = mx + b = -\frac{12}{5}x + 11.$$

The desired equation is $y = -\frac{12}{5}x + 11$.

▶ TRY EXERCISE 35

EXAMPLE 4   *Threatened species.*   A threatened species is a species that is likely to become endangered in the future. Determine an equation for the graph of threatened species in the Blue Mountains.

Source: Based on information from Sustainable Blue Mountains

SOLUTION   To write an equation for a line, we can use slope–intercept form, provided the slope and the y-intercept are known. From the graph, we see that $(0, 55)$ is the y-intercept. Looking closely, we see that the line passes through $(4, 70)$. We can either count squares on the graph or use the formula to calculate the slope:

$$m = \frac{\text{change in } y}{\text{change in } x} = \frac{70 - 55}{4 - 0} = \frac{15}{4}.$$

The desired equation is

$$y = \frac{15}{4}x + 55, \qquad \text{Using } \tfrac{15}{4} \text{ for } m \text{ and } 55 \text{ for } b$$

where y is the number of threatened species in the Blue Mountains x years after 2000.

▶ TRY EXERCISE 43

Graphing and Slope–Intercept Form

In Example 1, we drew a graph, knowing only the slope and the y-intercept. In Example 2, we determined the slope and the y-intercept of a line by examining its equation. We now combine the two procedures to develop a quick way to graph a linear equation.

EXAMPLE 5   Graph: **(a)** $y = \frac{3}{4}x + 5$; **(b)** $2x + 3y = 3$.

SOLUTION

a) From the equation $y = \frac{3}{4}x + 5$, we see that the slope of the graph is $\frac{3}{4}$ and the y-intercept is $(0, 5)$. We plot $(0, 5)$ and then consider the slope, $\frac{3}{4}$. Starting at $(0, 5)$, we plot a second point by moving *up* 3 units (since the numerator is *positive* and corresponds to the change in y) and *to the right* 4 units (since the denominator is *positive* and corresponds to the change in x). We reach a new point, $(4, 8)$.

Since $\frac{3}{4} = \frac{-3}{-4}$, we can again start at the *y*-intercept, $(0, 5)$, but move *down* 3 units (since the numerator is *negative* and corresponds to the change in *y*) and *to the left* 4 units (since the denominator is *negative* and corresponds to the change in *x*). We reach another point, $(-4, 2)$. Once two or three points have been plotted, the line representing all solutions of $y = \frac{3}{4}x + 5$ can be drawn.

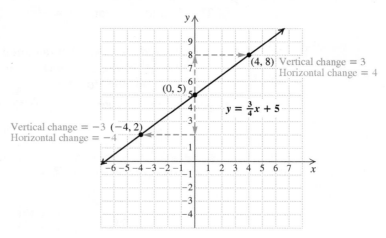

b) To graph $2x + 3y = 3$, we first rewrite it in slope–intercept form:

$$2x + 3y = 3$$
$$3y = -2x + 3 \qquad \text{Adding } -2x \text{ to both sides}$$
$$y = \tfrac{1}{3}(-2x + 3) \qquad \text{Multiplying both sides by } \tfrac{1}{3}$$
$$y = -\tfrac{2}{3}x + 1. \qquad \text{Using the distributive law}$$

To graph $y = -\frac{2}{3}x + 1$, we first plot the *y*-intercept, $(0, 1)$. We can think of the slope as $\frac{-2}{3}$. Starting at $(0, 1)$ and using the slope, we find a second point by moving *down* 2 units (since the numerator is *negative*) and *to the right* 3 units (since the denominator is *positive*). We plot the new point, $(3, -1)$. In a similar manner, we can move from the point $(3, -1)$ to locate a third point, $(6, -3)$. The line can then be drawn.

Since $-\frac{2}{3} = \frac{2}{-3}$, an alternative approach is to again plot $(0, 1)$, but this time move *up* 2 units (since the numerator is *positive*) and *to the left* 3 units (since the denominator is *negative*). This leads to another point on the graph, $(-3, 3)$.

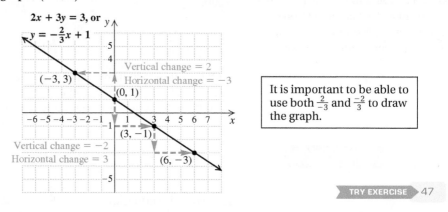

It is important to be able to use both $\frac{2}{-3}$ and $\frac{-2}{3}$ to draw the graph.

TRY EXERCISE 47

Slope–intercept form allows us to quickly determine the slope of a line by simply inspecting its equation. This can be especially helpful when attempting to decide whether two lines are parallel or perpendicular.

Parallel and Perpendicular Lines

Two lines are parallel if they lie in the same plane and do not intersect no matter how far they are extended. If two lines are vertical, they are parallel. How can we tell if nonvertical lines are parallel? The answer is simple: We look at their slopes.

> **Slope and Parallel Lines**
>
> Two lines are parallel if they have the same slope or if both lines are vertical.

EXAMPLE 6 Determine whether the graphs of $y = -3x + 4$ and $6x + 2y = -10$ are parallel.

SOLUTION We compare the slopes of the two lines to determine whether the graphs are parallel.

One of the two equations given is in slope–intercept form:

$$y = -3x + 4. \qquad \text{The slope is } -3 \text{ and the } y\text{-intercept is } (0, 4).$$

To find the slope of the other line, we need to rewrite the other equation in slope–intercept form:

$$6x + 2y = -10$$
$$2y = -6x - 10 \qquad \text{Adding } -6x \text{ to both sides}$$
$$y = -3x - 5. \qquad \text{The slope is } -3 \text{ and the } y\text{-intercept is } (0, -5).$$

Since both lines have slope -3 but different y-intercepts, the graphs are parallel. There is no need for us to actually graph either equation. TRY EXERCISE 63

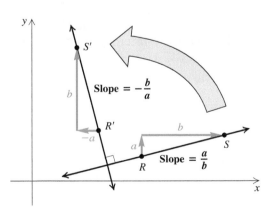

Two lines are perpendicular if they intersect at a right angle. If one line is vertical and another is horizontal, they are perpendicular. There are other instances in which two lines are perpendicular.

Consider a line $\overleftrightarrow{RS}$ as shown at left, with slope a/b. Then think of rotating the figure 90° to get a line $\overleftrightarrow{R'S'}$ perpendicular to $\overleftrightarrow{RS}$. For the new line, the rise and the run are interchanged, but the run is now negative. Thus the slope of the new line is $-b/a$. Let's multiply the slopes:

$$\frac{a}{b}\left(-\frac{b}{a}\right) = -1.$$

This can help us determine which lines are perpendicular.

> **Slope and Perpendicular Lines**
>
> Two lines are perpendicular if the product of their slopes is -1 or if one line is vertical and the other line is horizontal.

Thus, if one line has slope m ($m \neq 0$), the slope of a line perpendicular to it is $-1/m$. That is, we take the reciprocal of m ($m \neq 0$) and change the sign.

EXAMPLE 7   Determine whether the graphs of $2x + y = 8$ and $y = \frac{1}{2}x + 7$ are perpendicular.

SOLUTION   One of the two equations given is in slope–intercept form:

$y = \frac{1}{2}x + 7$.   The slope is $\frac{1}{2}$.

To find the slope of the other line, we rewrite the other equation in slope–intercept form:

$2x + y = 8$

$\qquad y = -2x + 8$.   Adding $-2x$ to both sides

The slope of the line is -2.

The lines are perpendicular if the product of their slopes is -1. Since

$$\frac{1}{2}(-2) = -1,$$

the graphs are perpendicular.   **TRY EXERCISE** 69

EXAMPLE 8   Write a slope–intercept equation for the line whose graph is described.

a) Parallel to the graph of $2x - 3y = 7$, with y-intercept $(0, -1)$

b) Perpendicular to the graph of $2x - 3y = 7$, with y-intercept $(0, -1)$

SOLUTION   We begin by determining the slope of the line represented by $2x - 3y = 7$:

$2x - 3y = 7$

$\qquad -3y = -2x + 7$ Adding $-2x$ to both sides

$\qquad\quad y = \frac{2}{3}x - \frac{7}{3}$.   Dividing both sides by -3

The slope is $\frac{2}{3}$.

a) A line parallel to the graph of $2x - 3y = 7$ has a slope of $\frac{2}{3}$. Since the y-intercept is $(0, -1)$, the slope–intercept equation is

$y = \frac{2}{3}x - 1$.   Substituting in $y = mx + b$

b) A line perpendicular to the graph of $2x - 3y = 7$ has a slope that is the opposite of the reciprocal of $\frac{2}{3}$, or $-\frac{3}{2}$. Since the y-intercept is $(0, -1)$, the slope–intercept equation is

$y = -\frac{3}{2}x - 1$.   Substituting in $y = mx + b$

TRY EXERCISE 75

3.6 EXERCISE SET

↪ *Concept Reinforcement* *In each of Exercises 1–6, match the phrase with the most appropriate choice from the column on the right.*

1. ____ The slope of the graph of $y = 3x - 2$
2. ____ The slope of the graph of $y = 2x - 3$
3. ____ The slope of the graph of $y = \frac{2}{3}x + 3$
4. ____ The y-intercept of the graph of $y = 2x - 3$
5. ____ The y-intercept of the graph of $y = 3x - 2$
6. ____ The y-intercept of the graph of $y = \frac{2}{3}x + \frac{3}{4}$

a) $\left(0, \frac{3}{4}\right)$

b) 2

c) $(0, -3)$

d) $\frac{2}{3}$

e) $(0, -2)$

f) 3

Draw a line that has the given slope and y-intercept.

7. Slope $\frac{2}{3}$; y-intercept $(0, 1)$

8. Slope $\frac{3}{5}$; y-intercept $(0, -1)$

9. Slope $\frac{5}{3}$; y-intercept $(0, -2)$

10. Slope $\frac{1}{2}$; y-intercept $(0, 0)$

11. Slope $-\frac{1}{3}$; y-intercept $(0, 5)$

12. Slope $-\frac{4}{5}$; y-intercept $(0, 6)$

13. Slope 2; y-intercept $(0, 0)$

14. Slope -2; y-intercept $(0, -3)$

15. Slope -3; y-intercept $(0, 2)$

16. Slope 3; y-intercept $(0, 4)$

Aha! 17. Slope 0; y-intercept $(0, -5)$

18. Slope 0; y-intercept $(0, 1)$

Find the slope and the y-intercept of each line whose equation is given.

19. $y = -\frac{2}{7}x + 5$

20. $y = -\frac{3}{8}x + 4$

21. $y = \frac{1}{3}x + 7$

22. $y = \frac{4}{5}x + 1$

23. $y = \frac{9}{5}x - 4$

24. $y = -\frac{9}{10}x - 5$

25. $-3x + y = 7$

26. $-4x + y = 7$

27. $4x + 2y = 8$

28. $3x + 4y = 12$

Aha! 29. $y = 3$

30. $y - 3 = 5$

31. $2x - 5y = -8$

32. $12x - 6y = 9$

33. $9x - 8y = 0$

34. $7x = 5y$

Find the slope–intercept equation for the line with the indicated slope and y-intercept.

35. Slope 5; y-intercept $(0, 7)$

36. Slope -4; y-intercept $\left(0, -\frac{3}{5}\right)$

37. Slope $\frac{7}{8}$; y-intercept $(0, -1)$

38. Slope $\frac{5}{7}$; y-intercept $(0, 4)$

39. Slope $-\frac{5}{3}$; y-intercept $(0, -8)$

40. Slope $\frac{3}{4}$; y-intercept $(0, -35)$

Aha! 41. Slope 0; y-intercept $\left(0, \frac{1}{3}\right)$

42. Slope 7; y-intercept $(0, 0)$

Determine an equation for each graph shown.

43.

U.S. Bottled Water Consumption

Number of gallons per person

Number of years since 2000

Based on information from the International Bottled Water Association

44.

Cost of an Overseas Calling-Card Telephone Call

Cost of telephone call

Number of minutes

Source: www.pennytalk.com

45.

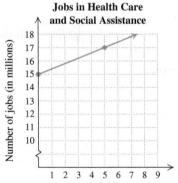

Jobs in Health Care and Social Assistance

Number of jobs (in millions)

Number of years since 2000

Source: U.S. Bureau of Labor Statistics

46.

Average Hourly Earnings in Accommodations and Food Services

Average hourly earnings

Number of years since 1995

Source: U.S. Bureau of Labor Statistics

Graph.

47. $y = \frac{2}{3}x + 2$ **48.** $y = -\frac{2}{3}x - 3$

49. $y = -\frac{2}{3}x + 3$ **50.** $y = \frac{2}{3}x - 2$

51. $y = \frac{3}{2}x + 3$ **52.** $y = \frac{3}{2}x - 2$

53. $y = -\frac{4}{3}x + 3$ **54.** $y = -\frac{3}{2}x - 2$

55. $2x + y = 1$ **56.** $3x + y = 2$

57. $3x + y = 0$ **58.** $2x + y = 0$

59. $4x + 5y = 15$ **60.** $2x + 3y = 9$

61. $x - 4y = 12$ **62.** $x + 5y = 20$

Determine whether each pair of equations represents parallel lines.

63. $y = \frac{3}{4}x + 6,$ **64.** $y = \frac{1}{3}x - 2,$
   $y = \frac{3}{4}x - 2$ $y = -\frac{1}{3}x + 1$

65. $y = 2x - 5,$ **66.** $y = -3x + 1,$
   $4x + 2y = 9$ $6x + 2y = 8$

67. $3x + 4y = 8,$ **68.** $3x = 5y - 2,$
   $7 - 12y = 9x$ $10y = 4 - 6x$

Determine whether each pair of equations represents perpendicular lines.

69. $y = 4x - 5,$ **70.** $2x - 5y = -3,$
   $4y = 8 - x$ $2x + 5y = 4$

71. $x - 2y = 5,$ **72.** $y = -x + 7,$
   $2x + 4y = 8$ $y - x = 3$

73. $2x + 3y = 1,$
$3x - 2y = 1$

74. $y = 5 - 3x,$
$3x - y = 8$

Write a slope–intercept equation of the line whose graph is described.

75. Parallel to the graph of $y = 5x - 7$; y-intercept $(0, 11)$

76. Parallel to the graph of $2x - y = 1$; y-intercept $(0, -3)$

77. Perpendicular to the graph of $2x + y = 0$; y-intercept $(0, 0)$

78. Perpendicular to the graph of $y = \frac{1}{3}x + 7$; y-intercept $(0, 5)$

Aha! **79.** Parallel to the graph of $y = x$; y-intercept $(0, 3)$

Aha! **80.** Perpendicular to the graph of $y = x$; y-intercept $(0, 0)$

81. Perpendicular to the graph of $x + y = 3$; y-intercept $(0, -4)$

82. Parallel to the graph of $3x + 2y = 5$; y-intercept $(0, -1)$

83. Can a horizontal line be graphed using the method of Example 5? Why or why not?

84. If two lines are perpendicular, does it follow that the lines have slopes that are negative reciprocals of each other? Why or why not?

Skill Review

To prepare for Section 3.7, review solving a formula for a variable and subtracting real numbers (Sections 1.6 and 2.3).

Solve. [2.3]

85. $y - k = m(x - h)$, for y

86. $y - 9 = -2(x + 4)$, for y

Simplify. [1.6]

87. $-10 - (-3)$

88. $8 - (-5)$

89. $-4 - 5$

90. $-6 - 5$

Synthesis

91. Explain how it is possible for an incorrect graph to be drawn, even after plotting three points that line up.

92. Which would you prefer, and why: graphing an equation of the form $y = mx + b$ or graphing an equation of the form $Ax + By = C$?

93. Show that the slope of the line given by $y = mx + b$ is m. (*Hint*: Substitute both 0 and 1 for x to find two pairs of coordinates. Then use the formula, Slope = change in y/change in x.)

94. Write an equation of the line with the same slope as the line given by $5x + 2y = 8$ and the same y-intercept as the line given by $3x - 7y = 10$.

95. Write an equation of the line parallel to the line given by $2x - 6y = 10$ and having the same y-intercept as the line given by $9x + 6y = 18$.

96. Write an equation of the line parallel to the line given by $3x - 2y = 8$ and having the same y-intercept as the line given by $2y + 3x = -4$.

97. Write an equation of the line perpendicular to the line given by $3x - 5y = 8$ and having the same y-intercept as the line given by $2x + 4y = 12$.

98. Write an equation of the line perpendicular to the line given by $2x + 3y = 7$ and having the same y-intercept as the line given by $5x + 2y = 10$.

99. Write an equation of the line perpendicular to the line given by $3x - 2y = 9$ and having the same y-intercept as the line given by $2x + 5y = 0$.

100. Write an equation of the line perpendicular to the line given by $2x + 5y = 6$ that passes through $(2, 6)$. (*Hint*: Draw a graph.)

CONNECTING the CONCEPTS

If any two points are plotted on a plane, there is only one line that will go through both points. Thus, if we know that the graph of an equation is a straight line, we need only find two points that are on that line. Then we can plot those points and draw the line that goes through them.

The different graphing methods discussed in this chapter present efficient ways of finding two points that are on the graph of the equation. Following is a general strategy for graphing linear equations.

1. Make sure that the equation is linear. Linear equations can always be written in the form $Ax + By = C$. (*A* or *B* may be 0.)
2. Graph the line. Use substitution to find two points on the line, or use a more efficient method based on the form of the equation.
3. Check the graph by finding another point that should be on the line and determining whether it does actually fall on the line.

Form of Equation	Graph
$x = a$	Draw a vertical line through $(a, 0)$.
$y = b$	Draw a horizontal line through $(0, b)$.
$y = mx + b$	Plot the *y*-intercept $(0, b)$. Start at the *y*-intercept and count off the rise and run using the slope *m* to find another point. Draw a line through the two points.
$Ax + By = C$	Determine the *x*- and *y*-intercepts $(a, 0)$ and $(0, b)$. Draw a line through the two points.

MIXED REVIEW

For each equation, (a) determine whether it is linear and (b) if it is linear, graph the line.

1. $x = 3$
2. $y = -2$
3. $y = \frac{1}{2}x + 3$
4. $4x + 3y = 12$
5. $y - 5 = x$
6. $x + y = -2$
7. $3xy = 6$
8. $2x = 3y$
9. $3 - y = 4$
10. $y = x^2 - 4$
11. $2y = 9x - 10$
12. $x + 8 = 7$
13. $2x - 6 = 3y$
14. $y - 2x = 4$
15. $2y - x = 4$
16. $y = \dfrac{1}{x}$
17. $x - 2y = 0$
18. $y = 4 - x$
19. $y = 4 + x$
20. $4x - 5y = 20$

3.7 Point–Slope Form

Writing Equations in Point–Slope Form ▪ Graphing and Point–Slope Form ▪ Estimations and Predictions Using Two Points

There are many applications in which a slope—or a rate of change—and an ordered pair are known. When the ordered pair is the y-intercept, an equation in slope–intercept form can be easily produced. When the ordered pair represents a point other than the y-intercept, a different form, known as *point–slope form*, is more convenient.

Writing Equations in Point–Slope Form

Consider a line with slope 2 passing through the point $(4, 1)$, as shown in the figure. In order for a point (x, y) to be on the line, the coordinates x and y must be solutions of the slope equation

$$\frac{y - 1}{x - 4} = 2. \qquad \text{If } (x, y) \text{ is not on the line, this equation will not be true.}$$

Take a moment to examine this equation. Pairs like $(5, 3)$ and $(3, -1)$ are on the line and are solutions, since

$$\frac{3 - 1}{5 - 4} = 2 \quad \text{and} \quad \frac{-1 - 1}{3 - 4} = 2.$$

When $x \neq 4$, then $x - 4 \neq 0$, and we can multiply on both sides of the slope equation by $x - 4$:

$$(x - 4) \cdot \frac{y - 1}{x - 4} = 2(x - 4)$$

$$y - 1 = 2(x - 4). \qquad \text{Removing a factor equal to 1: } \frac{x - 4}{x - 4} = 1$$

Every point on the line is a solution of this equation.

This is considered **point–slope form** for the line shown in the figure at left. A point–slope equation can be written any time a line's slope and a point on the line are known.

> ### The Point–Slope Equation
> The equation $y - y_1 = m(x - x_1)$ is called the *point–slope equation* for the line with slope m that contains the point (x_1, y_1).

Point–slope form is especially useful in more advanced mathematics courses, where problems similar to the following often arise.

EXAMPLE 1   Write a point–slope equation for the line with slope $\frac{1}{5}$ that contains the point $(7, 2)$.

SOLUTION   We substitute $\frac{1}{5}$ for m, 7 for x_1, and 2 for y_1:

$$y - y_1 = m(x - x_1) \qquad \text{Using the point–slope equation}$$

$$y - 2 = \tfrac{1}{5}(x - 7). \qquad \text{Substituting}$$

▸ TRY EXERCISE 13

EXAMPLE **2**   Write a point–slope equation for the line with slope $-\frac{4}{3}$ that contains the point $(1, -6)$.

SOLUTION   We substitute $-\frac{4}{3}$ for m, 1 for x_1, and -6 for y_1:

$$y - y_1 = m(x - x_1) \qquad \text{Using the point–slope equation}$$
$$y - (-6) = -\frac{4}{3}(x - 1). \qquad \text{Substituting}$$

> TRY EXERCISE   19

EXAMPLE **3**   Write the slope–intercept equation for the line with slope 2 that contains the point $(3, 1)$.

STUDENT NOTES

There are several forms in which a line's equation can be written. For instance, as shown in Example 3, $y - 1 = 2(x - 3), y - 1 = 2x - 6$, and $y = 2x - 5$ all are equations for the same line.

SOLUTION   There are two parts to this solution. First, we write an equation in point–slope form:

$$y - y_1 = m(x - x_1)$$
$$y - 1 = 2(x - 3). \qquad \text{Substituting} \qquad \boxed{\text{Write in point–slope form.}}$$

Next, we find an equivalent equation of the form $y = mx + b$:

$$y - 1 = 2(x - 3)$$
$$y - 1 = 2x - 6 \qquad \text{Using the distributive law} \qquad \boxed{\text{Write in slope–intercept form.}}$$
$$y = 2x - 5. \qquad \begin{array}{l}\text{Adding 1 to both sides to get}\\ \text{slope–intercept form}\end{array}$$

> TRY EXERCISE   27

EXAMPLE **4**   Consider the line given by the equation $8y = 7x - 24$.

a) Write the slope–intercept equation for a parallel line passing through $(-1, 2)$.

b) Write the slope–intercept equation for a perpendicular line passing through $(-1, 2)$.

TECHNOLOGY CONNECTION

To check that the graphs of $y = \frac{7}{8}x - 3$ and $y = -\frac{8}{7}x + \frac{6}{7}$ are perpendicular, we use the ZSQUARE option of the ZOOM menu to create a "squared" window. This corrects for distortion that would result from the units on the axes being of different lengths.

1. Show that the graphs of $y = \frac{3}{4}x + 2$ and $y = -\frac{4}{3}x - 1$ appear to be perpendicular.
2. Show that the graphs of $y = -\frac{2}{5}x - 4$ and $y = \frac{5}{2}x + 3$ appear to be perpendicular.
3. To see that this type of check is not foolproof, graph

    $$y = \frac{31}{40}x + 2$$
    and $y = -\frac{40}{30}x - 1$.

    Are the lines perpendicular? Why or why not?

SOLUTION   Both parts (a) and (b) require us to find the slope of the line given by $8y = 7x - 24$. To do so, we solve for y to find slope–intercept form:

$$8y = 7x - 24$$
$$y = \frac{7}{8}x - 3. \qquad \text{Multiplying both sides by } \frac{1}{8}$$
$$\qquad\qquad\qquad \text{The slope is } \frac{7}{8}.$$

a) The slope of any parallel line will be $\frac{7}{8}$. The point–slope equation yields

$$y - 2 = \frac{7}{8}[x - (-1)] \qquad \begin{array}{l}\text{Substituting } \frac{7}{8} \text{ for the slope and}\\ (-1, 2) \text{ for the point}\end{array}$$
$$y - 2 = \frac{7}{8}[x + 1]$$
$$y = \frac{7}{8}x + \frac{7}{8} + 2 \qquad \begin{array}{l}\text{Using the distributive law and}\\ \text{adding 2 to both sides}\end{array}$$
$$y = \frac{7}{8}x + \frac{23}{8}.$$

b) The slope of a perpendicular line is given by the opposite of the reciprocal of $\frac{7}{8}$, or $-\frac{8}{7}$. The point–slope equation yields

$$y - 2 = -\frac{8}{7}[x - (-1)] \qquad \begin{array}{l}\text{Substituting } -\frac{8}{7} \text{ for the slope and}\\ (-1, 2) \text{ for the point}\end{array}$$
$$y - 2 = -\frac{8}{7}[x + 1]$$
$$y = -\frac{8}{7}x - \frac{8}{7} + 2 \qquad \begin{array}{l}\text{Using the distributive law and}\\ \text{adding 2 to both sides}\end{array}$$
$$y = -\frac{8}{7}x + \frac{6}{7}.$$

> TRY EXERCISE   39

Graphing and Point–Slope Form

When we know a line's slope and a point that is on the line, we can draw the graph, much as we did in Section 3.6. For example, the information given in the statement of Example 3 is sufficient for drawing a graph.

EXAMPLE 5   Graph the line with slope 2 that passes through $(3, 1)$.

SOLUTION   We plot $(3, 1)$, move *up* 2 and *to the right* 1 $\left(\text{since } 2 = \frac{2}{1}\right)$, and draw the line.

Plot the point.

Use the slope to plot a second point.

Draw the line.

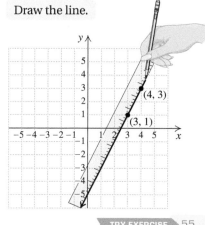

> TRY EXERCISE 55

EXAMPLE 6   Graph: $y - 2 = 3(x - 4)$.

SOLUTION   Since $y - 2 = 3(x - 4)$ is in point–slope form, we know that the line has slope 3, or $\frac{3}{1}$, and passes through the point $(4, 2)$. We plot $(4, 2)$ and then find a second point by moving *up* 3 units and *to the right* 1 unit. The line can then be drawn, as shown below.

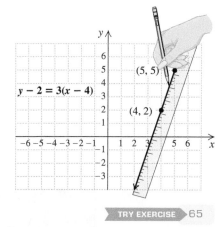

> TRY EXERCISE 65

EXAMPLE 7   Graph: $y + 4 = -\frac{5}{2}(x + 3)$.

SOLUTION   Once we have written the equation in point–slope form, $y - y_1 = m(x - x_1)$, we can proceed much as we did in Example 6. To find an equivalent equation in point–slope form, we subtract opposites instead of adding:

$$y + 4 = -\frac{5}{2}(x + 3)$$
$$y - (-4) = -\frac{5}{2}(x - (-3)).$$ Subtracting a negative instead of adding a positive. This is now in point–slope form.

From this last equation, $y - (-4) = -\frac{5}{2}(x - (-3))$, we see that the line passes through $(-3, -4)$ and has slope $-\frac{5}{2}$, or $\frac{5}{-2}$.

> TRY EXERCISE   61

Estimations and Predictions Using Two Points

We can estimate real-life quantities that are not already known by using two points with known coordinates. When the unknown point is located *between* the two points, this process is called **interpolation**. If a graph passing through the known points is *extended* to predict future values, the process is called **extrapolation**. In statistics, methods exist for using a set of several points to interpolate or extrapolate values using curves other than lines.

EXAMPLE   **8**   *Student volunteers.*   An increasing number of college students are donating time and energy in volunteer service. The number of college-student volunteers grew from 2.7 million in 2002 to 3.3 million in 2005.

Source: Corporation for National and Community Service

a) Graph the line passing through the given data points, letting $x =$ the number of years since 2000.

b) Determine an equation for the line and estimate the number of college students who volunteered in 2004.

c) Predict the number of college students who will volunteer in 2010.

SOLUTION

a) We first draw and label a horizontal axis to display the year and a vertical axis to display the number of college-student volunteers, in millions. Next, we number the axes, choosing scales that will include both the given values and the values to be estimated.

   Since $x =$ the number of years since 2000, we plot the points $(2, 2.7)$ and $(5, 3.3)$ and draw a line passing through both points.

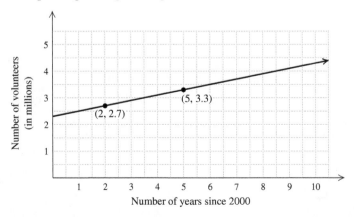

b) To find an equation for the line, we first calculate its slope:

$$m = \frac{\text{change in } y}{\text{change in } x} = \frac{3.3 - 2.7}{5 - 2} = \frac{0.6}{3} = 0.2.$$

The number of college-student volunteers increased at a rate of 0.2 million students per year. We can use either of the given points to write a point–slope equation for the line. Let's use $(2, 2.7)$ and then write an equivalent equation in slope–intercept form:

$y - 2.7 = 0.2(x - 2)$ This is a point–slope equation.

$y - 2.7 = 0.2x - 0.4$ Using the distributive law

$y = 0.2x + 2.3.$ Adding 2.7 to both sides. This is slope–intercept form.

To estimate the number of college-student volunteers in 2004, we substitute 4 for x in the slope–intercept equation:

$y = 0.2 \cdot 4 + 2.3 = 3.1.$

As the graph confirms, in 2004 there were about 3.1 million college-student volunteers.

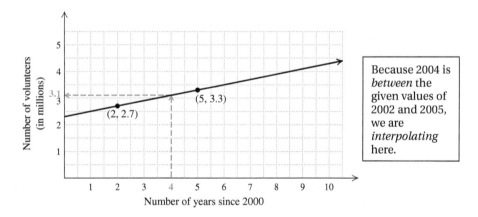

Because 2004 is *between* the given values of 2002 and 2005, we are *interpolating* here.

c) To predict the number of college-student volunteers in 2010, we again substitute for x in the slope–intercept equation:

$y = 0.2 \cdot 10 + 2.3 = 4.3.$ 2010 is 10 yr after 2000.

As we can see from the graph, if the trend continues, there will be about 4.3 million college-student volunteers in 2010.

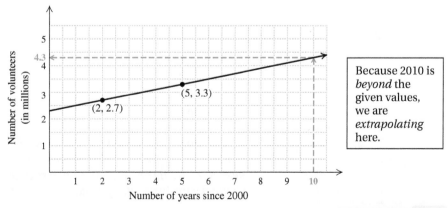

Because 2010 is *beyond* the given values, we are *extrapolating* here.

TRY EXERCISE ▶ 71

Visualizing for Success

A

B

C

D

E

F

G

H

I

J

Match each equation with its graph.

1. $y = x + 4$

2. $y = 2x$

3. $y = 3$

4. $x = 3$

5. $y = -\frac{1}{2}x$

6. $2x - 3y = 6$

7. $y = -3x - 2$

8. $3x + 2y = 6$

9. $y - 3 = 2(x - 1)$

10. $y + 2 = \frac{1}{2}(x + 1)$

Answers on page A-13

An additional, animated version of this activity appears in MyMathLab. To use MyMathLab, you need a course ID and a student access code. Contact your instructor for more information.

↪ *Concept Reinforcement* In each of Exercises 1–8, match the given information about a line with the appropriate equation from the column on the right.

1. ____ Slope 5; includes (2, 3)

2. ____ Slope 5; includes (3, 2)

3. ____ Slope −5; includes (2, 3)

4. ____ Slope −5; includes (3, 2)

5. ____ Slope −5; includes (−2, −3)

6. ____ Slope 5; includes (−2, −3)

7. ____ Slope −5; includes (−3, −2)

8. ____ Slope 5; includes (−3, −2)

a) $y + 3 = 5(x + 2)$

b) $y - 2 = 5(x - 3)$

c) $y + 2 = 5(x + 3)$

d) $y - 3 = -5(x - 2)$

e) $y + 3 = -5(x + 2)$

f) $y + 2 = -5(x + 3)$

g) $y - 3 = 5(x - 2)$

h) $y - 2 = -5(x - 3)$

In each of Exercises 9–12, match the graph with the appropriate equation from the column on the right.

9.

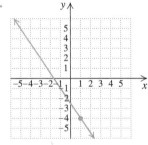

a) $y - 4 = -\frac{3}{2}(x + 1)$

b) $y - 4 = \frac{3}{2}(x + 1)$

c) $y + 4 = -\frac{3}{2}(x - 1)$

d) $y + 4 = \frac{3}{2}(x - 1)$

10.

11.

12.

Write a point–slope equation for the line with the given slope that contains the given point.

13. $m = 3$; $(1, 6)$ 14. $m = 2$; $(3, 7)$

15. $m = \frac{3}{5}$; $(2, 8)$ 16. $m = \frac{2}{3}$; $(4, 1)$

17. $m = -4$; $(3, 1)$ 18. $m = -5$; $(6, 2)$

19. $m = \frac{3}{2}$; $(5, -4)$ 20. $m = -\frac{4}{3}$; $(7, -1)$

21. $m = -\frac{5}{4}$; $(-2, 6)$ 22. $m = \frac{7}{2}$; $(-3, 4)$

23. $m = -2$; $(-4, -1)$ 24. $m = -3$; $(-2, -5)$

25. $m = 1$; $(-2, 8)$ 26. $m = -1$; $(-3, 6)$

Write the slope–intercept equation for the line with the given slope that contains the given point.

27. $m = 4$; $(3, 5)$ 28. $m = 3$; $(6, 2)$

29. $m = \frac{7}{4}$; $(4, -2)$ 30. $m = \frac{8}{3}$; $(3, -4)$

31. $m = -2$; $(-3, 7)$ 32. $m = -3$; $(-2, 1)$

33. $m = -4$; $(-2, -1)$ 34. $m = -5$; $(-1, -4)$

35. $m = \frac{2}{3}$; $(5, 6)$ 36. $m = \frac{3}{2}$; $(7, 4)$

Aha! 37. $m = -\frac{5}{6}$; $(0, 4)$ 38. $m = -\frac{3}{4}$; $(0, 5)$

Write an equation of the line containing the specified point and parallel to the indicated line.

39. $(2, 5)$, $x - 2y = 3$

40. $(1, 4)$, $3x + y = 5$

Aha! **41.** $(0, -5)$, $y = 4x + 3$

42. $(0, 2)$, $y = x - 11$

43. $(-2, -3)$, $2x + 3y = -7$

44. $(-7, 0)$, $5x + 2y = 6$

45. $(5, -4)$, $x = 2$

46. $(-3, 6)$, $y = 7$

Write an equation of the line containing the specified point and perpendicular to the indicated line.

47. $(3, 1)$, $2x - 3y = 4$

48. $(6, 0)$, $5x + 4y = 1$

49. $(-4, 2)$, $x + y = 6$

50. $(-2, -5)$, $x - 2y = 3$

Aha! **51.** $(0, 6)$, $2x - 5 = y$

52. $(0, -7)$, $4x + 3 = y$

53. $(-3, 7)$, $y = 5$

54. $(4, -2)$, $x = 1$

55. Graph the line with slope $\frac{4}{3}$ that passes through the point $(1, 2)$.

56. Graph the line with slope $\frac{2}{5}$ that passes through the point $(3, 4)$.

57. Graph the line with slope $-\frac{3}{4}$ that passes through the point $(2, 5)$.

58. Graph the line with slope $-\frac{3}{2}$ that passes through the point $(1, 4)$.

Graph.

59. $y - 5 = \frac{1}{3}(x - 2)$ **60.** $y - 2 = \frac{1}{2}(x - 1)$

61. $y - 1 = -\frac{1}{4}(x - 3)$ **62.** $y - 1 = -\frac{1}{2}(x - 3)$

63. $y + 2 = \frac{2}{3}(x - 1)$ **64.** $y - 1 = \frac{3}{4}(x + 5)$

65. $y + 4 = 3(x + 1)$

66. $y + 3 = 2(x + 1)$

67. $y - 4 = -2(x + 1)$

68. $y + 3 = -1(x - 4)$

69. $y + 1 = -\frac{3}{5}(x - 2)$

70. $y - 2 = -\frac{2}{3}(x + 1)$

In Exercises 71–78, graph the given data and determine an equation for the related line (as in Example 8). Then use the equation to answer parts (a) and (b).

71. *Birth rate among teenagers.* The birth rate among teenagers, measured in births per 1000 females age 15–19, fell steadily from 62.1 in 1991 to 41.1 in 2007.
Source: National Center for Health Statistics

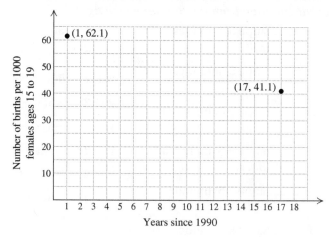

a) Calculate the birth rate among teenagers in 1999.
b) Predict the birth rate among teenagers in 2008.

72. *Food-stamp program participation.* Participation in the U.S. food-stamp program grew from approximately 17.1 million people in 2000 to approximately 23 million in 2004.
Source: U.S. Department of Agriculture

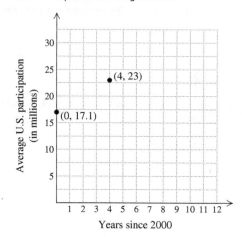

a) Calculate the number of participants in 2001.
b) Predict the number of participants in 2010.

73. *Cigarette smoking.* The percentage of people age 25–44 who smoke has changed from 14.2% in 2001 to 10.8% in 2004.
Source: Office on Smoking and Health, National Center for Chronic Disease Prevention and Health Promotion
a) Calculate the percentage of people age 25–44 who smoked in 2002.
b) Predict the percentage of people age 25–44 who will smoke in 2010.

74. *Cigarette smoking.* The percentage of people age 18–24 who smoke has dropped from 5.2% in 2001 to 3.4% in 2004.
Source: Office on Smoking and Health, National Center for Chronic Disease Prevention and Health Promotion

a) Calculate the percentage of people age 18–24 who smoked in 2003.

b) Estimate the percentage of people age 18–24 who smoked in 2008.

75. *College enrollment.* U.S. college enrollment has grown from approximately 14.3 million in 1995 to 17.4 million in 2005.
Source: National Center for Education Statistics

a) Calculate the U.S. college enrollment for 2002.

b) Predict the U.S. college enrollment for 2010.

76. *High school enrollment.* U.S. high school enrollment has changed from approximately 13.7 million in 1995 to 16.3 million in 2005.
Source: National Center for Education Statistics

a) Calculate the U.S. high school enrollment for 2002.

b) Predict the U.S. high school enrollment for 2010.

77. *Aging population.* The number of U.S. residents over the age of 65 was approximately 31 million in 1990 and 36.3 million in 2004.
Source: U.S. Census Bureau

Aha! **a)** Calculate the number of U.S. residents over the age of 65 in 1997.

b) Predict the number of U.S. residents over the age of 65 in 2010.

78. *Urban population.* The percentage of the U.S. population that resides in metropolitan areas increased from about 78% in 1980 to about 83% in 2006.

a) Calculate the percentage of the U.S. population residing in metropolitan areas in 1992.

b) Predict the percentage of the U.S. population residing in metropolitan areas in 2012.

Write the slope–intercept equation for the line containing the given pair of points.

79. $(2, 3)$ and $(4, 1)$

80 $(6, 8)$ and $(3, 5)$

81. $(-3, 1)$ and $(3, 5)$

82. $(-3, 4)$ and $(3, 1)$

83. $(5, 0)$ and $(0, -2)$

84. $(-2, 0)$ and $(0, 3)$

85. $(-4, -1)$ and $(1, 9)$

86. $(-3, 5)$ and $(-1, -3)$

87. Can equations for horizontal or vertical lines be written in point–slope form? Why or why not?

88. Describe a situation in which it is easier to graph the equation of a line in point–slope form than in slope–intercept form.

Skill Review

Review exponential notation and order of operations (Section 1.8).

Simplify. [1.8]

89. $(-5)^3$

90. $(-2)^6$

91. -2^6

92. $3 \cdot 2^4 - 5 \cdot 2^3$

93. $2 - (3 - 2^2) + 10 \div 2 \cdot 5$

94. $(5 - 7)^2(3 - 2 \cdot 2)$

Synthesis

95. Describe a procedure that can be used to write the slope–intercept equation for any nonvertical line passing through two given points.

96. Any nonvertical line has many equations in point–slope form, but only one in slope–intercept form. Why is this?

Graph.

Aha! **97.** $y - 3 = 0(x - 52)$

98. $y + 4 = 0(x + 93)$

Write the slope–intercept equation for each line shown.

99.

100.

101.

102.

Aha! **103.** Write an equation of the line parallel to the line given by $y = 3 - 4x$ that passes through $(0, 7)$.

104. Write the slope–intercept equation of the line that has the same y-intercept as the line $x - 3y = 6$ and contains the point $(5, -1)$.

105. Write the slope–intercept equation of the line that contains the point $(-1, 5)$ and is parallel to the line passing through $(2, 7)$ and $(-1, -3)$.

106. Write the slope–intercept equation of the line that has x-intercept $(-2, 0)$ and is parallel to $4x - 8y = 12$.

Another form of a linear equation is the double-intercept *form:* $\dfrac{x}{a} + \dfrac{y}{b} = 1$. *From this form, we can read the* x-intercept $(a, 0)$ *and the* y-intercept $(0, b)$ *directly.*

107. Find the x-intercept and the y-intercept of the graph of the line given by $\dfrac{x}{2} + \dfrac{y}{5} = 1$.

108. Find the x-intercept and the y-intercept of the graph of the line given by $\dfrac{x}{10} - \dfrac{y}{3} = 1$.

109. Write the equation $4y - 3x = 12$ in double-intercept form and find the intercepts.

110. Write the equation $6x + 5y = 30$ in double-intercept form and find the intercepts.

111. Why is slope–intercept form more useful than point–slope form when using a graphing calculator? How can point–slope form be modified so that it is more easily used with graphing calculators?

CONNECTING the CONCEPTS

Any line can be described by a number of equivalent equations. We write the equation in the form that is most useful for us. For example, all four of the equations below describe the given line.

$2x - 3y = -6;$

$y = \frac{2}{3}x + 2;$

$y - 4 = \frac{2}{3}(x - 3);$

$2x + 6 = 3y$

Form of a Linear Equation	Example	Uses
Standard form: $Ax + By = C$	$2x - 3y = -6$	Finding x- and y-intercepts; Graphing using intercepts
Slope–intercept form: $y = mx + b$	$y = \dfrac{2}{3}x + 2$	Finding slope and y-intercept; Graphing using slope and y-intercept; Writing an equation given slope and y-intercept
Point–slope form: $y - y_1 = m(x - x_1)$	$y - 4 = \dfrac{2}{3}(x - 3)$	Finding slope and a point on the line; Graphing using slope and a point on the line; Writing an equation given slope and a point on the line

MIXED REVIEW

Tell whether each equation is in standard form, slope–intercept form, point–slope form, or none of these.

1. $y = -\frac{1}{2}x - 7$

2. $5x - 8y = 10$

3. $x = y + 2$

4. $\frac{1}{2}x + \frac{1}{3}y = 5$

5. $y - 2 = 5(x + 1)$

6. $3y + 7 = x$

Write each equation in standard form.

7. $2x = 5y + 10$

8. $x = y + 2$

9. $y = 2x + 7$

10. $y = -\frac{1}{2}x + 3$

11. $y - 2 = 3(x + 7)$

12. $x - 7 = 11$

Write each equation in slope–intercept form.

13. $2x - 7y = 8$

14. $y + 5 = -(x + 3)$

15. $8x = y + 3$

16. $6x + 10y = 30$

17. $9y = 5 - 8x$

18. $x - y = 3x + y$

19. $2 - 3y = 5y + 6$

20. $3(x - 4) = 6(y - 2)$

Study Summary

KEY TERMS AND CONCEPTS	EXAMPLES

SECTION 3.1: READING GRAPHS, PLOTTING POINTS, AND SCALING GRAPHS

Ordered pairs, like $(-3, 2)$ or $(4, 3)$, can be **plotted** or **graphed** using a **coordinate system** that uses two **axes**, which are most often labeled x and y. The axes intersect at the **origin**, $(0, 0)$, and divide a plane into four **quadrants**.

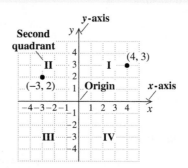

SECTION 3.2: GRAPHING LINEAR EQUATIONS

To **graph** an equation means to make a drawing that represents all of its solutions.

A **linear equation**, such as $y = 2x - 7$ or $2x + 3y = 12$, has a graph that is a straight line.

Any linear equation can be graphed by finding two ordered pairs that are solutions of the equation, plotting the corresponding points, and drawing a line through those points. Plotting a third point serves as a check.

x	y	(x, y)
1	2	$(1, 2)$
0	-1	$(0, -1)$
-1	-4	$(-1, -4)$

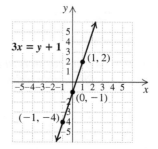

SECTION 3.3: GRAPHING AND INTERCEPTS

Intercepts
To find a y-intercept $(0, b)$, let $x = 0$ and solve for y.

To find an x-intercept $(a, 0)$, let $y = 0$ and solve for x.

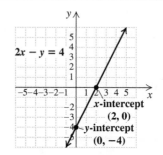

Horizontal Lines
The slope of a horizontal line is 0.
The graph of $y = b$ is a horizontal line, with y-intercept $(0, b)$.

Vertical Lines
The slope of a vertical line is undefined.
The graph of $x = a$ is a vertical line, with x-intercept $(a, 0)$.

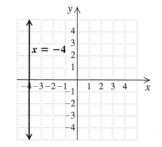

SECTION 3.4: RATES

A **rate** is a ratio that indicates how two quantities change with respect to each other.

Lara had \$1500 in her savings account at the beginning of February, and \$2400 at the beginning of May. Find the rate at which Lara is saving.

$$\text{Savings rate} = \frac{\text{Amount saved}}{\text{Number of months}}$$

$$= \frac{\$2400 - \$1500}{3 \text{ months}}$$

$$= \frac{\$900}{3 \text{ months}} = \$300 \text{ per month}$$

SECTION 3.5: SLOPE

Slope

$$\text{Slope} = m = \frac{\text{change in } y}{\text{change in } x}$$

$$= \frac{\text{rise}}{\text{run}} = \frac{y_2 - y_1}{x_2 - x_1}$$

The slope of the line containing the points $(-1, -4)$ and $(2, -6)$ is

$$m = \frac{-6 - (-4)}{2 - (-1)} = \frac{-2}{3} = -\frac{2}{3}.$$

A line with positive slope slants up from left to right.

A line with negative slope slants down from left to right.

The slope of a horizontal line is 0.

The slope of a vertical line is undefined.

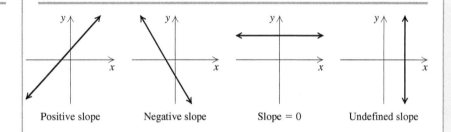

Positive slope   Negative slope   Slope $= 0$ Undefined slope

SECTION 3.6: SLOPE–INTERCEPT FORM

Slope–Intercept Form

$$y = mx + b$$

The slope of the line is m.
The y-intercept of the line is $(0, b)$.

For the line given by $y = \frac{2}{3}x - 8$:

The slope is $\frac{2}{3}$ and the y-intercept is $(0, -8)$.

To graph a line written in slope–intercept form, plot the y-intercept and count off the slope.

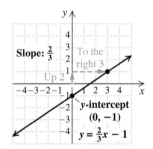

Parallel and Perpendicular Lines

Two lines are parallel if they have the same slope or if both are vertical.

Determine whether the graphs of $y = \frac{2}{3}x - 5$ and $3y - 2x = 7$ are parallel.

$$y = \frac{2}{3}x - 5 \qquad 3y - 2x = 7$$

The slope is $\frac{2}{3}$. $3y = 2x + 7$

$$y = \frac{2}{3}x + \frac{7}{3}$$

The slope is $\frac{2}{3}$.

Since the slopes are the same, the graphs are parallel.

Two lines are perpendicular if the product of their slopes is -1 or if one line is vertical and the other line is horizontal.

Determine whether the graphs of $y = \frac{2}{3}x - 5$ and $2y + 3x = 1$ are perpendicular.

$$y = \tfrac{2}{3}x - 5 \qquad\qquad 2y + 3x = 1$$

The slope is $\frac{2}{3}$. $\qquad\qquad 2y = -3x + 1$

$$y = -\tfrac{3}{2}x + \tfrac{1}{2}$$

The slope is $-\frac{3}{2}$.

Since $\frac{2}{3}\left(-\frac{3}{2}\right) = -1$, the graphs are perpendicular.

SECTION 3.7: POINT–SLOPE FORM

Point–Slope Form

$$y - y_1 = m(x - x_1)$$

The slope of the line is m.
The line passes through (x_1, y_1).

Write a point–slope equation for the line with slope -2 that contains the point $(3, -5)$.

$$y - y_1 = m(x - x_1)$$
$$y - (-5) = -2(x - 3)$$

Review Exercises: Chapter 3

⤹ Concept Reinforcement   *Classify each statement as either true or false.*

1. Not every ordered pair lies in one of the four quadrants. [3.1]

2. The equation of a vertical line cannot be written in slope–intercept form. [3.6]

3. Equations for lines written in slope–intercept form appear in the form $Ax + By = C$. [3.6]

4. Every horizontal line has an x-intercept. [3.3]

5. A line's slope is a measure of rate. [3.5]

6. A positive rate of ascent means that an airplane is flying increasingly higher above the earth. [3.4]

7. Any two points on a line can be used to determine the line's slope. [3.5]

8. Knowing a line's slope is enough to write the equation of the line. [3.6]

9. Knowing two points on a line is enough to write the equation of the line. [3.7]

10. Parallel lines that are not vertical have the same slope. [3.6]

The following circle graph shows the percentage of online searches done in July 2006 that were performed by a particular search engine. [3.1]
Source: NetRatings for SearchEngineWatch.com

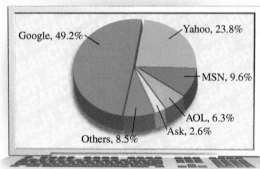

Online Searches

Google, 49.2%
Yahoo, 23.8%
MSN, 9.6%
AOL, 6.3%
Ask, 2.6%
Others, 8.5%

11. There were 5.6 billion searches done by home and business Internet users in July 2006. How many searches were done using Yahoo?

12. About 55% of the online searches done by Waterworks Graphics are image searches. In July 2006, Waterworks employees did 4200 online searches. If their search engine use is typical, how many image searches did they do using Google?

Plot each point. [3.1]

13. $(5, -1)$ **14.** $(2, 3)$ **15.** $(-4, 0)$

In which quadrant is each point located? [3.1]

16. $(-8, -7)$ **17.** $(15.3, -13.8)$ **18.** $\left(-\frac{1}{2}, \frac{1}{10}\right)$

Find the coordinates of each point in the figure. [3.1]

19. *A* **20.** *B* **21.** *C*

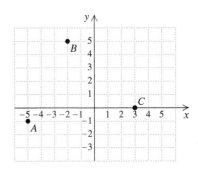

22. Use a grid 10 squares wide and 10 squares high to plot $(-65, -2)$, $(-10, 6)$, and $(25, 7)$. Choose the scale carefully. [3.1]

23. Determine whether the equation $y = 2x + 7$ has *each* ordered pair as a solution: **(a)** $(3, 1)$; **(b)** $(-3, 1)$. [3.2]

24. Show that the ordered pairs $(0, -3)$ and $(2, 1)$ are solutions of the equation $2x - y = 3$. Then use the graph of the two points to determine another solution. Answers may vary. [3.2]

Graph.

25. $y = x - 5$ [3.2] **26.** $y = -\frac{1}{4}x$ [3.2]

27. $y = -x + 4$ [3.2] **28.** $4x + y = 3$ [3.2]

29. $4x + 5 = 3$ [3.3] **30.** $5x - 2y = 10$ [3.3]

31. *TV viewing.* The average number of daily viewers v, in millions, of ABC's soap opera "General Hospital" is given by $v = -\frac{1}{4}t + 9$, where t is the number of years since 2000. Graph the equation and use the graph to predict the average number of daily viewers of "General Hospital" in 2008. [3.2]
Source: Nielsen Media Research

32. At 4:00 P.M., Jesse's Honda Civic was at mile marker 17 of Interstate 290 in Chicago. At 4:45 P.M., Jesse was at mile marker 23. [3.4]

a) Find Jesse's driving rate, in number of miles per minute.
b) Find Jesse's driving rate, in number of minutes per mile.

33. *Gas mileage.* The following graph shows data for a Ford Explorer driven on city streets. At what rate was the vehicle consuming gas? [3.4]

Find the slope of each line. [3.5]

34. **35.**

36.

Find the slope of the line containing the given pair of points. If it is undefined, state this. [3.5]

37. $(-2, 5)$ and $(3, -1)$

38. $(6, 5)$ and $(-2, 5)$

39. $(-3, 0)$ and $(-3, 5)$

40. $(-8.3, 4.6)$ and $(-9.9, 1.4)$

41. *Architecture.* To meet federal standards, a wheelchair ramp cannot rise more than 1 ft over a horizontal distance of 12 ft. Express this slope as a grade. [3.5]

1 ft

12 ft

42. Find the x-intercept and the y-intercept of the line given by $5x - 8y = 80$. [3.3]

43. Find the slope and the y-intercept of the line given by $3x + 5y = 45$. [3.6]

Determine whether each pair of lines is parallel, perpendicular, or neither. [3.6]

44. $y + 5 = -x,$
$x - y = 2$

45. $3x - 5 = 7y,$
$7y - 3x = 7$

46. Write the slope–intercept equation of the line with slope $\frac{3}{8}$ and y-intercept $(0, 7)$. [3.6]

47. Write a point–slope equation for the line with slope $-\frac{1}{3}$ that contains the point $(-2, 9)$. [3.7]

48. The average tuition at a public two-year college was $1359 in 2001 and $1847 in 2005. Graph the data and determine an equation for the related line. Then **(a)** calculate the average tuition at a public two-year college in 2004 and **(b)** predict the average tuition at a public two-year college in 2012. [3.7]
Source: U.S. National Center for Education Statistics

49. Write the slope–intercept equation for the line with slope 5 that contains the point $(3, -10)$. [3.7]

50. Write the slope–intercept equation for the line that is perpendicular to the line $3x - 5y = 9$ and that contains the point $(2, -5)$ [3.7]

Graph.

51. $y = \frac{2}{3}x - 5$ [3.6]

52. $2x + y = 4$ [3.3]

53. $y = 6$ [3.3]

54. $x = -2$ [3.3]

55. $y + 2 = -\frac{1}{2}(x - 3)$ [3.7]

Synthesis

56. Can two perpendicular lines share the same y-intercept? Why or why not? [3.3]

57. Is it possible for a graph to have only one intercept? Why or why not? [3.3]

58. Find the value of m in $y = mx + 3$ such that $(-2, 5)$ is on the graph. [3.2]

59. Find the value of b in $y = -5x + b$ such that $(3, 4)$ is on the graph. [3.2]

60. Find the area and the perimeter of a rectangle for which $(-2, 2)$, $(7, 2)$, and $(7, -3)$ are three of the vertices. [3.1]

61. Find three solutions of $y = 4 - |x|$. [3.2]

Test: Chapter 3

CHAPTER Test Prep VIDEO CD   *Step-by-step test solutions are found on the video CD in the front of this book.*

Volunteering. The following pie chart shows the types of organizations in which college students volunteer.
Source: Corporation for National and Community Service

Volunteering by College Students, 2005

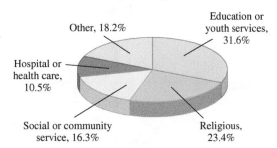

Other, 18.2%

Hospital or health care, 10.5%

Social or community service, 16.3%

Education or youth services, 31.6%

Religious, 23.4%

1. At Rolling Hills College, 25% of the 1200 students volunteer. If their choice of organizations is typical, how many students will volunteer in education or youth services?

2. At Valley University, $\frac{1}{3}$ of the 3900 students volunteer. If their choice of organizations is typical, how many students will volunteer in hospital or health-care services?

In which quadrant is each point located?

3. $(-2, -10)$

4. $(-1.6, 2.3)$

Find the coordinates of each point in the figure.

5. *A*

6. *B*

7. *C*

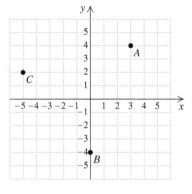

Graph.

8. $y = 2x - 1$

9. $2x - 4y = -8$

10. $y + 1 = 6$

11. $y = \frac{3}{4}x$

12. $2x - y = 3$

13. $x = -1$

Find the slope of the line containing each pair of points. If it is undefined, state this.

14. $(3, -2)$ and $(4, 3)$

15. $(-5, 6)$ and $(-1, -3)$

16. $(4, 7)$ and $(4, -8)$

17. *Running.*   Jon reached the 3-km mark of a race at 2:15 P.M. and the 6-km mark at 2:24 P.M. What is his running rate?

18. At one point Filbert Street, the steepest street in San Francisco, drops 63 ft over a horizontal distance of 200 ft. Find the road grade.

19. Find the *x*-intercept and the *y*-intercept of the line given by $5x - y = 30$.

20. Find the slope and the *y*-intercept of the line given by $y - 8x = 10$.

21. Write the slope–intercept equation of the line with slope $-\frac{1}{3}$ and *y*-intercept $(0, -11)$.

Determine without graphing whether each pair of lines is parallel, perpendicular, or neither.

22. $4y + 2 = 3x,$
$-3x + 4y = -12$

23. $y = -2x + 5,$
$2y - x = 6$

24. Write the slope–intercept equation of the line that is perpendicular to the line $2x - 5y = 8$ and that contains the point $(-3, 2)$.

25. *Aerobic exercise.*   A person's target heart rate is the number of beats per minute that brings the most aerobic benefit to his or her heart. The target heart rate for a 20-year-old is 150 beats per minute; for a 60-year-old, it is 120 beats per minute.

   a) Graph the data and determine an equation for the related line. Let a = age and r = target heart rate, in number of beats per minute.

   b) Calculate the target heart rate for a 36-year-old.

Graph.

26. $y = \frac{1}{4}x - 2$

27. $y + 4 = -\frac{1}{2}(x - 3)$

Synthesis

28. Write an equation of the line that is parallel to the graph of $2x - 5y = 6$ and has the same *y*-intercept as the graph of $3x + y = 9$.

29. A diagonal of a square connects the points $(-3, -1)$ and $(2, 4)$. Find the area and the perimeter of the square.

30. List the coordinates of three other points that are on the same line as $(-2, 14)$ and $(17, -5)$. Answers may vary.

Cumulative Review: Chapters 1–3

1. Evaluate $\dfrac{x}{5y}$ for $x = 70$ and $y = 2$. [1.1]

2. Multiply: $6(2a - b + 3)$. [1.2]

3. Factor: $8x - 4y + 4$. [1.2]

4. Find the prime factorization of 54. [1.3]

5. Find decimal notation: $-\frac{3}{20}$. [1.4]

6. Find the absolute value: $|-37|$. [1.4]

7. Find the opposite of $-\frac{1}{10}$. [1.6]

8. Find the reciprocal of $-\frac{1}{10}$. [1.7]

9. Find decimal notation: 36.7%. [2.4]

Simplify.

10. $\frac{3}{5} - \frac{5}{12}$ [1.3]

11. $3.4 + (-0.8)$ [1.5]

12. $(-2)(-1.4)(2.6)$ [1.7]

13. $\frac{3}{8} \div \left(-\frac{9}{10}\right)$ [1.7]

14. $1 - [32 \div (4 + 2^2)]$ [1.8]

15. $-5 + 16 \div 2 \cdot 4$ [1.8]

16. $y - (3y + 7)$ [1.8]

17. $3(x - 1) - 2[x - (2x + 7)]$ [1.8]

Solve.

18. $2.7 = 5.3 + x$ [2.1]

19. $\frac{5}{3}x = -45$ [2.1]

20. $3x - 7 = 41$ [2.2]

21. $\dfrac{3}{4} = \dfrac{-n}{8}$ [2.1]

22. $14 - 5x = 2x$ [2.2]

23. $3(5 - x) = 2(3x + 4)$ [2.2]

24. $\frac{1}{4}x - \frac{2}{3} = \frac{3}{4} + \frac{1}{3}x$ [2.2]

25. $y + 5 - 3y = 5y - 9$ [2.2]

26. $x - 28 < 20 - 2x$ [2.6]

27. $2(x + 2) \geq 5(2x + 3)$ [2.6]

28. Solve $A = 2\pi rh + \pi r^2$ for h. [2.3]

29. In which quadrant is the point $(3, -1)$ located? [3.1]

30. Graph on a number line: $-1 < x \leq 2$. [2.6]

31. Use a grid 10 squares wide and 10 squares high to plot $(-150, -40)$, $(40, -7)$, and $(0, 6)$. Choose the scale carefully. [3.1]

Graph.

32. $x = 3$ [3.3]

33. $2x - 5y = 10$ [3.3]

34. $y = -2x + 1$ [3.2]

35. $y = \frac{2}{3}x$ [3.2]

36. $y = -\frac{3}{4}x + 2$ [3.6]

37. $2y - 5 = 3$ [3.3]

Find the coordinates of the x- and y-intercepts. Do not graph.

38. $2x - 7y = 21$ [3.3]

39. $y = 4x + 5$ [3.3]

40. Find the slope and the y-intercept of the line given by $3x - y = 2$. [3.6]

41. Find the slope of the line containing the points $(-4, 1)$ and $(2, -1)$. [3.5]

42. Write an equation of the line with slope $\frac{2}{7}$ and y-intercept $(0, -4)$. [3.6]

43. Write a point–slope equation of the line with slope $-\frac{3}{8}$ that contains the point $(-6, 4)$. [3.7]

44. Write the slope–intercept form of the equation in Exercise 43. [3.6]

45. Determine an equation for the following graph. [3.6], [3.7]

Solve.

46. U.S. bicycle sales rose from 15 million in 1995 to 20 million in 2005. Find the rate of change of bicycle sales. [3.4]
Sources: National Bicycle Dealers Association; U.S. Department of Transportation

47. A 150-lb person will burn 240 calories per hour when riding a bicycle at 6 mph. The same person will burn 410 calories per hour when cycling at 12 mph. [3.7]
Source: American Heart Association

  a) Graph the data and determine an equation for the related line. Let r = the rate at which the person is cycling and c = the number of calories burned per hour.

  b) Use the equation of part (a) to estimate the number of calories burned per hour by a 150-lb person cycling at 10 mph.

48. Americans spent an estimated $238 billion on home remodeling in 2006. This was $\frac{17}{15}$ of the amount spent on remodeling in 2005. How much was spent on remodeling in 2005? [2.5]
Source: National Association of Home Builders' Remodelers Council

49. In 2005, the mean earnings of individuals with a high school diploma was $29,448. This was about 54% of the mean earnings of those with a bachelor's degree. What were the mean earnings of individuals with a bachelor's degree in 2005? [2.4]
Source: U.S. Census Bureau

50. Recently there were 132 million Americans with either O-positive or O-negative blood. Those with O-positive blood outnumbered those with O-negative blood by 90 million. How many Americans had O-negative blood? [2.5]
Source: American Red Cross

51. Tina paid $126 for a cordless drill, including a 5% sales tax. How much did the drill itself cost? [2.4]

52. A 143-m wire is cut into three pieces. The second is 3 m longer than the first. The third is four fifths as long as the first. How long is each piece? [2.5]

53. In order to qualify for availability pay, a criminal investigator must average at least 2 hr of unscheduled duty per workday. For the first four days of one week, Alayna worked 1, 0, 3, and 2 extra hours. How many extra hours must she work on Friday in order to qualify for availability pay? [2.7]
Source: U.S. Department of Justice

Synthesis

54. Anya's salary at the end of a year is $26,780. This reflects a 4% salary increase in February and then a 3% cost-of-living adjustment in June. What was her salary at the beginning of the year? [2.4]

Solve. If no solution exists, state this.

55. $4|x| - 13 = 3$ [1.4], [2.2]

56. $4(x + 2) = 9(x - 2) + 16$ [2.2]

57. $2(x + 3) + 4 = 0$ [2.2]

58. $\dfrac{2 + 5x}{4} = \dfrac{11}{28} + \dfrac{8x + 3}{7}$ [2.2]

59. $5(7 + x) = (x + 6)5$ [2.2]

60. Solve $p = \dfrac{2}{m + Q}$ for Q. [2.3]

61. The points $(-3, 0)$, $(0, 7)$, $(3, 0)$, and $(0, -7)$ are vertices of a parallelogram. Find four equations of lines that intersect to form the parallelogram. [3.6]

4

Systems of Equations in Two Variables

Where Are the Wide, Open Spaces?

Some of America's National Parks are crowded with visitors, while in others it is easy to find solitude. As the accompanying graph shows, the number of visits to Gates of the Arctic National Park is increasing and the number to North Cascades National Park is decreasing. In Example 6 of Section 4.1, we will estimate the year in which the number of visits to both parks will be the same.

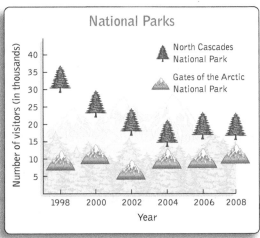

4.1 Systems of Equations and Graphing
VISUALIZING FOR SUCCESS

4.2 Systems of Equations and Substitution

4.3 Systems of Equations and Elimination
MID-CHAPTER REVIEW

4.4 More Applications Using Systems

4.5 Solving Equations by Graphing
STUDY SUMMARY
REVIEW EXERCISES • CHAPTER TEST

Taken from *Elementary and Intermediate Algebra: Graphs and Models,* Fourth Edition by: Marvin L. Bitinger, David J. Ellenbogen, and Barbara L. Johnson

In fields ranging from business to zoology, problems arise that are most easily solved using a *system of equations*. In this chapter, we solve systems and applications using graphing and two algebraic methods. The graphing method is then applied to the solution of equations.

4.1 Systems of Equations and Graphing

- Solutions of Systems

- Solving Systems of Equations by Graphing

- Models

l, or $w + 44$

w

STUDY TIP

Speak Up

Feel free to ask questions in class at appropriate times. Most instructors welcome questions and encourage students to ask them. Other students in your class probably have the same questions you do.

SOLUTIONS OF SYSTEMS

A **system of equations** is a set of two or more equations, in two or more variables, for which we seek a common solution. It is often easier to translate real-world situations to a system of two equations that use two variables, or unknowns, than it is to represent the situation with one equation using one variable. For example, the following problem can be represented by two equations using two unknowns:

> The perimeter of an NBA basketball court is 288 ft. The length is 44 ft longer than the width. Find the dimensions of the court.
> **Source:** National Basketball Association

If we let w = the width of the court, in feet, and l = the length of the court, in feet, the problem translates to the following system of equations:

$$2l + 2w = 288, \qquad \text{The perimeter is 288.}$$
$$l = w + 44. \qquad \text{The length is 44 more than the width.}$$

A solution of this system will be a length and a width that make *both* equations true, often written as an ordered pair of the form (l, w). Note that variables are listed in alphabetical order within an ordered pair unless stated otherwise.

EXAMPLE 1   Consider the system from above:

$$2l + 2w = 288,$$
$$l = w + 44.$$

Determine whether each pair is a solution of the system: **(a)** $(94, 50)$; **(b)** $(90, 46)$.

SOLUTION

a) Unless stated otherwise, we use alphabetical order of the variables. Thus we replace l with 94 and w with 50.

$$
\begin{array}{c|c}
2l + 2w = 288 & \\
\hline
2 \cdot 94 + 2 \cdot 50 & 288 \\
188 + 100 & \\
288 \stackrel{?}{=} 288 & \text{TRUE}
\end{array}
\qquad
\begin{array}{c|c}
l = w + 44 & \\
\hline
94 & 50 + 44 \\
94 \stackrel{?}{=} 94 & \text{TRUE}
\end{array}
$$

Since $(94, 50)$ checks in *both* equations, it is a solution of the system.

b) We substitute 90 for *l* and 46 for *w*:

$$
\begin{array}{c|c}
2l + 2w = 288 & \\
\hline
2 \cdot 90 + 2 \cdot 46 & 288 \\
180 + 92 & \\
& 272 \stackrel{?}{=} 288 \quad \text{FALSE}
\end{array}
\qquad
\begin{array}{c|c}
l = w + 44 & \\
\hline
90 & 46 + 44 \\
90 \stackrel{?}{=} 90 & \quad \text{TRUE}
\end{array}
$$

Since $(90, 46)$ is not a solution of *both* equations, it is not a solution of the system.

⬛ Try Exercise 9.

A solution of a system of two equations in two variables is an ordered pair of numbers that makes both equations true. The numbers in the ordered pair correspond to the variables in alphabetical order.

In Example 1, we demonstrated that $(94, 50)$ is a solution of the system, but we did not show how the pair $(94, 50)$ was found. One way to find such a solution uses graphs.

SOLVING SYSTEMS OF EQUATIONS BY GRAPHING

Recall that the graph of an equation is a drawing that represents its solution set. Each point on the graph corresponds to an ordered pair that is a solution of the equation. By graphing two equations using one set of axes, we can identify a solution of both equations by looking for a point of intersection.

EXAMPLE 2   Solve this system of equations by graphing:

$$x + y = 7,$$
$$y = 3x - 1.$$

SOLUTION   We graph the equations using any method studied earlier. The equation $x + y = 7$ can be graphed easily using the intercepts, $(0, 7)$ and $(7, 0)$. The equation $y = 3x - 1$ is in slope–intercept form, so it can be graphed by plotting its *y*-intercept, $(0, -1)$, and "counting off" a slope of 3.

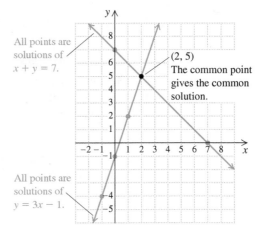

All points are solutions of $x + y = 7$.

$(2, 5)$
The common point gives the common solution.

All points are solutions of $y = 3x - 1$.

The "apparent" solution of the system, $(2, 5)$, should be checked in both equations. Note that the solution is an ordered pair in the form (x, y).

Check:

$$\frac{x + y = 7}{2 + 5 \mid 7}$$
$$7 \overset{?}{=} 7 \quad \text{TRUE}$$

$$\frac{y = 3x - 1}{5 \mid 3 \cdot 2 - 1}$$
$$5 \overset{?}{=} 5 \quad \text{TRUE}$$

Since it checks in both equations, $(2, 5)$ is a solution of the system.

Try Exercise 17.

Point of Intersection

Often a graphing calculator provides a more accurate solution than graphs drawn by hand. We can trace along the graph of one of the functions to find the coordinates of the point of intersection. Most graphing calculators can find the point of intersection directly using an INTERSECT feature.

To find the point of intersection of two graphs, press (CALC) and choose the INTERSECT option. The questions FIRST CURVE? and SECOND CURVE? are used to identify the graphs with which we are concerned. Position the cursor on each graph, in turn, and press **ENTER**, using the up and down arrow keys, if necessary, to move to another graph.

The calculator then asks a third question, GUESS?. Since graphs may intersect at more than one point, we must visually identify the point of intersection in which we are interested and indicate the general location of that point. Enter a guess either by moving the cursor near the point of intersection and pressing **ENTER** or by typing a guess and pressing **ENTER**. The calculator then returns the coordinates of the point of intersection. At this point, the calculator variables X and Y contain the coordinates of the point of intersection. These values can be used to check an answer, and often they can be converted to fraction notation from the home screen using the FRAC option of the MATH MATH menu.

Your Turn

1. Enter the equations $y_1 = 2x - 3$ and $y_2 = 4 - x$. Press (ZOOM) (6) to graph them in a standard viewing window.
2. Press (CALC) (5) to choose the INTERSECT option.
3. Choose the curves. If these two equations are the only ones entered, simply press **ENTER** **ENTER**.
4. Make a guess by moving the cursor close to the point of intersection and pressing **ENTER**.
5. The coordinates of the point of intersection are written in decimal form. Return to the home screen and convert both X and Y to fraction notation. $X = \frac{7}{3}, Y = \frac{5}{3}$

Most pairs of lines have exactly one point in common. We will soon see, however, that this is not always the case.

EXAMPLE 3 Solve graphically:

$$y - x = 1,$$
$$y + x = 3.$$

SOLUTION

BY HAND	WITH A GRAPHING CALCULATOR

BY HAND

All ordered pairs from line L_1 in the graph below are solutions of the first equation. All ordered pairs from line L_2 are solutions of the second equation. The point of intersection has coordinates that make *both* equations true. Apparently, $(1, 2)$ is the solution. Graphing is not always accurate, so solving by graphing may yield approximate answers. Our check below shows that $(1, 2)$ is indeed the solution.

Graph both equations.

Look for any points in common.

Check.

Check:

$$\begin{array}{c|c} y - x = 1 \\ \hline 2 - 1 & 1 \\ 1 \stackrel{?}{=} 1 & \text{TRUE} \end{array}$$

$$\begin{array}{c|c} y + x = 3 \\ \hline 2 + 1 & 3 \\ 3 \stackrel{?}{=} 3 & \text{TRUE} \end{array}$$

WITH A GRAPHING CALCULATOR

We first solve each equation for y:

$$y - x = 1 \qquad\qquad y + x = 3$$
$$y = x + 1; \qquad\qquad y = 3 - x.$$

Then we enter and graph $y_1 = x + 1$ and $y_2 = 3 - x$.

After selecting the INTERSECT option, we choose the two *curves* and enter a guess. The coordinates of the point of intersection then appear at the bottom of the screen.

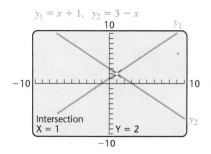

Since, in the calculator, X now has the value 1 and Y has the value 2, we can check from the home screen. The solution is $(1, 2)$.

Try Exercise 19.

EXAMPLE 4 Solve each system graphically.

a) $y = -3x + 5,$
       $y = -3x - 2$

b) $3y - 2x = 6,$
        $-12y + 8x = -24$

SOLUTION

a) We graph the equations. The lines have the same slope, -3, and different y-intercepts, so they are parallel. There is no point at which they cross, so the system has no solution.

$$y = -3x + 5,$$
$$y = -3x - 2$$

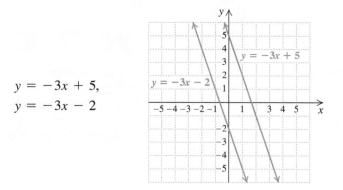

What happens when we try to solve this system using a graphing calculator? As shown at left, the graphs appear to be parallel. (This must be verified algebraically by confirming that they have the same slope.) When we attempt to find the intersection using the INTERSECT feature, we get an error message.

$y_1 = -3x + 5, \quad y_2 = -3x - 2$

b) We graph the equations and find that the same line is drawn twice. Thus any solution of one equation is a solution of the other. Each equation has an infinite number of solutions, so the system itself has an infinite number of solutions. We check one solution, $(0, 2)$, which is the y-intercept of each equation.

Student Notes

Although the system in Example 4(b) is true for an infinite number of ordered pairs, those pairs must be of a certain form. Only pairs that are solutions of $3y - 2x = 6$ or $-12y + 8x = -24$ are solutions of the system. It is incorrect to think that *all* ordered pairs are solutions.

$$3y - 2x = 6,$$
$$-12y + 8x = -24$$

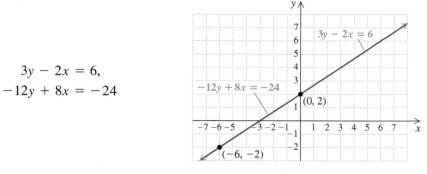

Check:

$$\begin{array}{c|c} 3y - 2x = 6 \\ \hline 3(2) - 2(0) & 6 \\ 6 - 0 & \\ 6 \overset{?}{=} 6 & \text{TRUE} \end{array}$$

$$\begin{array}{c|c} -12y + 8x = -24 \\ \hline -12(2) + 8(0) & -24 \\ -24 + 0 & \\ -24 \overset{?}{=} -24 & \text{TRUE} \end{array}$$

You can check that $(-6, -2)$ is another solution of both equations. In fact, any pair that is a solution of one equation is a solution of the other equation as well. Thus the solution set is

$$\{(x, y) \mid 3y - 2x = 6\}$$

or, in words, "the set of all pairs (x, y) for which $3y - 2x = 6$." Since the two equations are equivalent, we could have written instead

$$\{(x, y) \mid -12y + 8x = -24\}.$$

If we attempt to find the intersection of the graphs of the equations in this system using INTERSECT, the graphing calculator will return as the intersection whatever point we choose as the guess. This is a point of intersection, as is any other point on the graph of the lines.

Try Exercise 33.

When we graph a system of two linear equations in two variables, one of the following three outcomes will occur.

1. The lines have one point in common, and that point is the only solution of the system (see Example 3). Any system that has at least one solution is said to be **consistent.**

2. The lines are parallel, with no point in common, and the system has no solution (see Example 4a). This type of system is called **inconsistent.**

3. The lines coincide, sharing the same graph. Because every solution of one equation is a solution of the other, the system has an infinite number of solutions (see Example 4b). Since it has a solution, this type of system is also consistent.

When one equation in a system can be obtained by multiplying both sides of another equation by a constant, the two equations are said to be **dependent.** Thus the equations in Example 4(b) are dependent, but those in Examples 3 and 4(a) are **independent.** For systems of three or more equations, the definitions of dependent and independent must be slightly modified.

Connecting the Concepts

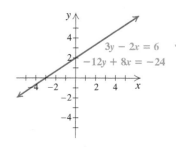

Graphs intersect at one point.

The system

$$y - x = 1,$$
$$y + x = 3$$

is *consistent* and has one solution.

Since neither equation is a multiple of the other, the equations are *independent.*

Graphs are parallel.

The system

$$y = -3x - 2,$$
$$y = -3x + 5$$

is *inconsistent* because there is no solution.

Since neither equation is a multiple of the other, the equations are *independent.*

Equations have the same graph.

The system

$$3y - 2x = 6,$$
$$-12y + 8x = -24$$

is *consistent* and has an infinite number of solutions.

Since one equation is a multiple of the other, the equations are *dependent.*

Graphing calculators are especially useful when equations contain fractions or decimals or when the coordinates of the intersection are not integers.

EXAMPLE 5 Solve graphically:

$$3.45x + 4.21y = 8.39,$$
$$7.12x - 5.43y = 6.18.$$

SOLUTION First, we solve for y in each equation:

$3.45x + 4.21y = 8.39$

$\qquad 4.21y = 8.39 - 3.45x$ Subtracting $3.45x$ from both sides

$\qquad\qquad y = (8.39 - 3.45x)/4.21;$ Dividing both sides by 4.21. This can also be written $y = 8.39/4.21 - 3.45x/4.21$.

$7.12x - 5.43y = 6.18$

$\qquad -5.43y = 6.18 - 7.12x$ Subtracting $7.12x$ from both sides

$\qquad\qquad y = (6.18 - 7.12x)/(-5.43).$ Dividing both sides by -5.43

It is not necessary to simplify further. We have the system

$$y = (8.39 - 3.45x)/4.21,$$
$$y = (6.18 - 7.12x)/(-5.43).$$

Next, we enter both equations and graph using the same viewing window. By using the INTERSECT feature in the CALC menu, we see that, to the nearest hundredth, the solution is $(1.47, 0.79)$. Note that the coordinates found by the calculator are approximations.

$y_1 = (8.39 - 3.45x)/4.21,$
$y_2 = (6.18 - 7.12x)/(-5.43)$

Intersection
X = 1.4694603   Y = .78868457

Try Exercise 37.

MODELS

EXAMPLE 6 National Parks. The Gates of the Arctic National Park is growing in popularity while the North Cascades National Park is attracting fewer visitors. Use the data in the table below to predict when the number of visitors to the two parks will be the same.

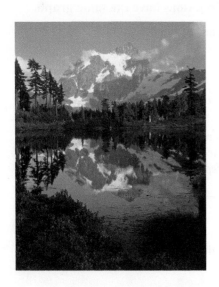

Year	Number of Visitors to Gates of the Arctic National Park (in thousands)	Number of Visitors to North Cascades National Park (in thousands)
1996	6.4	27.9
1998	8.3	32.8
2000	11.3	25.7
2002	6.6	20.7
2004	10.3	16.9
2006	10.0	19.2
2008	11.4	18.7

Source: National Parks Service

SOLUTION We enter the number of years after 1996 as L1, the number of visitors to Gates of the Arctic as L2, and the number of visitors to North Cascades as L3. A good choice of a viewing window is $[0, 15, 0, 40]$, with Xscl = 5 and Yscl = 5.

We graph the data, using a box as the mark for Gates of the Arctic and a plus sign as the mark for North Cascades. Although neither set of data is exactly linear, a line is still a good model of each set for purposes of estimation and prediction.

Xscl = 5, Yscl = 5

LinReg(ax+b) L1,
L2, Y1

LinReg(ax+b) L1,
L3, Y2

The figures at left show the commands used to find the linear regression lines for the data. The line for Gates of the Arctic, using lists L1 and L2, is stored as Y1. The line for North Cascades, using lists L1 and L3, is stored as Y2.

The screen on the left below gives us the two equations. Rounding the coefficients to four decimal places gives

$$y_1 = 0.3107x + 7.3214 \quad \text{and} \quad y_2 = -1.1357x + 29.9429.$$

Xscl = 5, Yscl = 5

We graph the equations (using the rounded coefficients) along with the data and determine the coordinates of the point of intersection. The x-coordinate of the point of intersection must be within the window dimensions, so we extend the window, as shown on the right above. The point of intersection is approximately $(15.6, 12.2)$. Since x represents the number of years after 1996, this tells us that approximately 15.6 years after 1996, both parks will have about 12.2 thousand visitors. Rounding, we state that there will be the same number of visitors to the parks in about 2012.

Try Exercise 47.

Graphing is helpful when solving systems because it allows us to "see" the solution. It can also be used with systems of nonlinear equations, and in many applications, it provides a satisfactory answer. However, often we cannot get a precise solution of a system using graphing. In Sections 4.2 and 4.3, we will develop two algebraic methods of solving systems that will produce exact answers.

A

Visualizing for Success

F

B

Match each equation or system of equations with its graph.

1. $x + y = 2,$
   $x - y = 2$

2. $y = \frac{1}{3}x - 5$

3. $4x - 2y = -8$

4. $2x + y = 1,$
   $x + 2y = 1$

5. $8y + 32 = 0$

6. $y = -x + 4$

7. $\frac{2}{3}x + y = 4$

8. $x = 4,$
   $y = 3$

9. $y = \frac{1}{2}x + 3,$
   $2y - x = 6$

10. $y = -x + 5,$
    $y = 3 - x$

Answers on page A-16

An additional, animated version of this activity appears in MyMathLab. To use MyMathLab, you need a course ID and a student access code. Contact your instructor for more information.

G

H

I

C

D

E

J

4.1 Exercise Set

Concept Reinforcement   Classify each of the following statements as either true or false.

1. Solutions of systems of equations in two variables are ordered pairs.

2. Every system of equations has at least one solution.

3. It is possible for a system of equations to have an infinite number of solutions.

4. The graphs of the equations in a system of two equations may coincide.

5. The graphs of the equations in a system of two equations could be parallel lines.

6. Any system of equations that has at most one solution is said to be consistent.

7. Any system of equations that has more than one solution is said to be inconsistent.

8. The equations $x + y = 5$ and $2(x + y) = 2(5)$ are dependent.

Determine whether the ordered pair is a solution of the given system of equations. Remember to use alphabetical order of variables.

9. $(1, 2)$; $4x - y = 2,$
    $10x - 3y = 4$

10. $(4, 0)$; $2x + 7y = 8,$
    $x - 9y = 4$

11. $(-5, 1)$; $x + 5y = 0,$
    $y = 2x + 9$

12. $(-1, -2)$; $x + 3y = -7,$
    $3x - 2y = 12$

13. $(0, -5)$; $x - y = 5,$
    $y = 3x - 5$

14. $(5, 2)$; $a + b = 7,$
    $2a - 8 = b$

Aha! 15. $(3, 1)$; $3x + 4y = 13,$
    $6x + 8y = 26$

16. $(4, -2)$; $-3x - 2y = -8,$
    $8 = 3x + 2y$

Solve each system graphically. Be sure to check your solution. If a system has an infinite number of solutions, use set-builder notation to write the solution set. If a system has no solution, state this. Where appropriate, round to the nearest hundredth.

17. $x - y = 3,$
    $x + y = 5$

18. $x + y = 4,$
    $x - y = 2$

19. $3x + y = 5,$
    $x - 2y = 4$

20. $2x - y = 4,$
    $5x - y = 13$

21. $4y = x + 8,$
    $3x - 2y = 6$

22. $4x - y = 9,$
    $x - 3y = 16$

23. $x = y - 1,$
    $2x = 3y$

24. $a = 1 + b,$
    $b = 5 - 2a$

25. $x = -3,$
    $y = 2$

26. $x = 4,$
    $y = -5$

27. $t + 2s = -1,$
    $s = t + 10$

28. $b + 2a = 2,$
    $a = -3 - b$

29. $2b + a = 11,$
    $a - b = 5$

30. $y = -\frac{1}{3}x - 1,$
    $4x - 3y = 18$

31. $y = -\frac{1}{4}x + 1,$
    $2y = x - 4$

32. $6x - 2y = 2,$
    $9x - 3y = 1$

33. $y - x = 5,$
    $2x - 2y = 10$

34. $y = -x - 1,$
    $4x - 3y = 24$

35. $y = 3 - x,$
    $2x + 2y = 6$

36. $2x - 3y = 6,$
    $3y - 2x = -6$

37. $y = -5.43x + 10.89,$
    $y = 6.29x - 7.04$

38. $y = 123.52x + 89.32,$
    $y = -89.22x + 33.76$

39. $2.6x - 1.1y = 4,$
    $1.32y = 3.12x - 5.04$

40. $2.18x + 7.81y = 13.78,$
    $5.79x - 3.45y = 8.94$

41. $0.2x - y = 17.5,$
    $2y - 10.6x = 30$

42. $1.9x = 4.8y + 1.7,$
$12.92x + 23.8 = 32.64y$

43. For the systems in the odd-numbered exercises 17–41, which are consistent?

44. For the systems in the even-numbered exercises 18–42, which are consistent?

45. For the systems in the odd-numbered exercises 17–41, which contain dependent equations?

46. For the systems in the even-numbered exercises 18–42, which contain dependent equations?

47. *College Faculty.* The number of part-time faculty in institutions of higher learning is growing rapidly. The table below lists the number of full-time faculty and the number of part-time faculty for various years. Use linear regression to fit a line to each set of data, and use those equations to predict the year in which the number of part-time faculty and the number of full-time faculty will be the same.

Year	Number of Full-time Faculty (in thousands)	Number of Part-time Faculty (in thousands)
1980	450	236
1985	459	256
1991	536	291
1995	551	381
1999	591	437
2005	676	615

Source: U.S. National Center for Education Statistics

48. *Milk Cows.* The number of milk cows in Vermont has decreased since 2004, while the number in Colorado has increased, as shown in the table below. Use linear regression to fit a line to each set of data, and use those equations to predict the year in which the number of milk cows in the two states will be the same.

Year	Number of Milk Cows in Vermont (in thousands)	Number of Milk Cows in Colorado (in thousands)
2004	145	102
2005	143	104
2006	141	110
2007	140	118
2008	140	128

Source: U.S. Department of Agriculture

49. *Financial Advisers.* Financial advisers are leaving major national firms and setting up their own businesses, as shown in the table below. Use linear regression to fit a line to each set of data, and use those equations to predict the year in which there will be the same number of independent financial advisers as there are those in major national firms.

Year	Number of Independent Financial Advisers (in thousands)	Number of Financial Advisers with National Firms (in thousands)
2004	21	60
2005	23	62
2006	25	59
2007	28	57
2008	32	55

Source: Based on information from Cerulli Associates

50. *Recycling.* In the United States, the amount of waste being recovered is slowly catching up to the amount of waste being discarded, as shown in the table below. Use linear regression to fit a line to each set of data, and use those equations to predict the year in which the amount of waste recycled will equal the amount discarded.

Year	Amount of Waste Recovered (in pounds per person per day)	Amount of Waste Discarded (in pounds per person per day)
1980	0.35	3.24
1990	0.73	3.12
2000	1.35	2.64
2008	1.50	2.43

Source: U.S. Environmental Protection Agency

51. Suppose that the equations in a system of two linear equations are dependent. Does it follow that the system is consistent? Why or why not?

52. Why is slope–intercept form especially useful when solving systems of equations by graphing?

SKILL REVIEW

To prepare for Section 4.2, review solving equations and formulas.

Solve.

53. $2(4x - 3) - 7x = 9$

54. $6y - 3(5 - 2y) = 4$

55. $4x - 5x = 8x - 9 + 11x$

56. $8x - 2(5 - x) = 7x + 3$

Solve.

57. $3x + 4y = 7$, for y

58. $2x - 5y = 9$, for y

SYNTHESIS

Advertising Media. For Exercises 59 and 60, consider the graph below showing the U.S. market share for various advertising media.

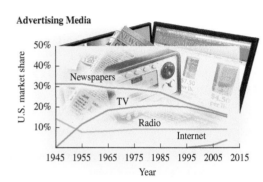

Advertising Media

Source: *The Wall Street Journal,* 12/30/07

TW **59.** At what point in time could it have been said that no medium was third in market share? Explain.

TW **60.** Will the Internet advertising market share ever exceed that of radio? TV? newspapers? If so, when? Explain your answers.

61. For each of the following conditions, write a system of equations.

   a) $(5, 1)$ is a solution.

   b) There is no solution.

   c) There is an infinite number of solutions.

62. A system of linear equations has $(1, -1)$ and $(-2, 3)$ as solutions. Determine:

   a) a third point that is a solution, and

   b) how many solutions there are.

63. The solution of the following system is $(4, -5)$. Find A and B.

$$Ax - 6y = 13,$$
$$x - By = -8.$$

Solve graphically.

64. $y = |x|$,
$$x + 4y = 15$$

65. $x - y = 0$,
$$y = x^2$$

In Exercises 66–69, match each system with the appropriate graph from the selections given.

a)

b)

c)

d)

66. $x = 4y$,
$3x - 5y = 7$

67. $2x - 8 = 4y$,
$x - 2y = 4$

68. $8x + 5y = 20$,
$4x - 3y = 6$

69. $x = 3y - 4$,
$2x + 1 = 6y$

70. *Copying Costs.* Aaron occasionally goes to an office store with small copying jobs. He can purchase a "copy card" for $20 that will entitle him to 500 copies, or he can simply pay 6¢ per page.

   a) Create cost equations for each method of paying for a number (up to 500) of copies.

   b) Graph both cost equations on the same set of axes.

   c) Use the graph to determine how many copies Aaron must make if the card is to be more economical.

71. *Computers.* In 2004, about 46 million notebook PCs were shipped worldwide, and that number was growing at a rate of $22\frac{2}{3}$ million per year. There were 140 million desktop PCs shipped worldwide in 2004, and that number was growing at a rate of 4 million per year.
Source: iSuppli

   a) Write two equations that can be used to predict n, the number of notebook PCs and desktop PCs, in millions, shipped t years after 2004.

   b) Use a graphing calculator to determine the year in which the numbers of notebook PCs and desktop PCs were the same.

 Try Exercise Answers: Section 4.1

9. Yes **17.** $(4, 1)$ **19.** $(2, -1)$ **33.** No solution
37. Approximately $(1.53, 2.58)$
47. Full-time faculty: $y = 9.0524x + 430.6778$; part-time faculty: $y = 14.7175x + 185.3643$; y is in thousands and x is the number of years after 1980; in about 2023

4.2 Systems of Equations and Substitution

- The Substitution Method

- Solving for the Variable First

- Problem Solving

Near the end of Section 4.1, we mentioned that graphing can be an imprecise method for solving systems. In this section and the next, we develop *algebraic* methods of finding exact solutions.

THE SUBSTITUTION METHOD

One algebraic method for solving systems, the **substitution method,** relies on having a variable isolated.

EXAMPLE 1 Solve the system

$$x + y = 7, \qquad (1)$$
$$y = 3x - 1. \qquad (2)$$

We have numbered the equations (1) and (2) for easy reference.

SOLUTION Equation (2) says that y and $3x - 1$ name the same number. Thus we can substitute $3x - 1$ for y in equation (1):

$$x + y = 7 \qquad \text{Equation (1)}$$
$$x + (3x - 1) = 7. \qquad \text{Substituting } 3x - 1 \text{ for } y$$

This last equation has only one variable, for which we now solve:

$$x + (3x - 1) = 7$$
$$4x - 1 = 7 \qquad \text{Removing parentheses and combining like terms}$$
$$4x = 8 \qquad \text{Adding 1 to both sides}$$
$$x = 2. \qquad \text{Dividing both sides by 4}$$

We have found the x-value of the solution. To find the y-value, we return to the original pair of equations. Substituting into either equation will give us the y-value. We choose equation (1):

$$x + y = 7 \qquad \text{Equation (1)}$$
$$2 + y = 7 \qquad \text{Substituting 2 for } x$$
$$y = 5. \qquad \text{Subtracting 2 from both sides}$$

We now have the ordered pair $(2, 5)$. A check assures us that it is the solution.

$$\begin{array}{c|c} x + y = 7 \\ \hline 2 + 5 \ | \ 7 \\ 7 \overset{?}{=} 7 \quad \text{TRUE} \end{array} \qquad \begin{array}{c|c} y = 3x - 1 \\ \hline 5 \ | \ 3 \cdot 2 - 1 \\ 5 \overset{?}{=} 5 \qquad \text{TRUE} \end{array}$$

Since $(2, 5)$ checks, it is the solution. For this particular system, we can also check by examining the graph from Example 2 in Section 4.1, as shown at left.

Try Exercise 5.

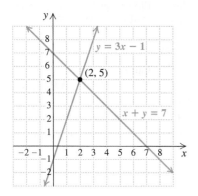

> **CAUTION!** A solution of a system of equations in two variables is an ordered *pair* of numbers. Once you have solved for one variable, don't forget the other. A common mistake is to solve for only one variable.

EXAMPLE 2   Solve:

$$x = 3 - 2y, \qquad (1) \qquad \text{\small{\textit{x} and 3 − 2\textit{y} name the same number.}}$$
$$y - 3x = 5. \qquad (2)$$

SOLUTION   We substitute $3 - 2y$ for x in the second equation:

$$y - 3x = 5 \qquad \text{\small Equation (2)}$$
$$y - 3(3 - 2y) = 5. \qquad \text{\small Substituting 3 − 2\textit{y} for \textit{x}, making sure}$$
$$\text{\small to use parentheses}$$

Now we solve for y:

$$y - 9 + 6y = 5 \qquad \text{\small Using the distributive law}$$
$$7y - 9 = 5$$
$$7y = 14 \qquad \text{\small Solving for \textit{y}}$$
$$y = 2.$$

Next, we substitute 2 for y in equation (1) of the original system:

$$x = 3 - 2y \qquad \text{\small Equation (1)}$$
$$x = 3 - 2 \cdot 2 \qquad \text{\small Substituting 2 for \textit{y}}$$
$$x = -1. \qquad \text{\small Simplifying}$$

We check the ordered pair $(-1, 2)$.

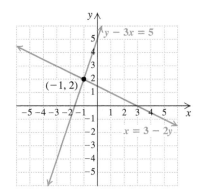

Check:

$$
\begin{array}{c|c}
\multicolumn{2}{c}{x = 3 - 2y} \\
\hline
-1 & 3 - 2 \cdot 2 \\
 & 3 - 4 \\
\hline
\multicolumn{2}{c}{-1 \overset{?}{=} -1 \quad \text{\small TRUE}}
\end{array}
\qquad
\begin{array}{c|c}
\multicolumn{2}{c}{y - 3x = 5} \\
\hline
2 - 3(-1) & 5 \\
2 + 3 & \\
\hline
\multicolumn{2}{c}{5 \overset{?}{=} 5 \quad \text{\small TRUE}}
\end{array}
$$

The pair $(-1, 2)$ is the solution. A graph is shown at left as another check.

Try Exercise 9.

SOLVING FOR THE VARIABLE FIRST

Sometimes neither equation has a variable alone on one side. In that case, we solve one equation for one of the variables and then proceed as before.

EXAMPLE 3   Solve:

$$x - 2y = 6, \qquad (1)$$
$$3x + 2y = 4. \qquad (2)$$

SOLUTION   We can solve either equation for either variable. Since the coefficient of x is 1 in equation (1), it is easier to solve that equation for x:

> Solve for x in terms of y.

$$x - 2y = 6 \qquad \text{\small Equation (1)}$$
$$x = 6 + 2y. \qquad (3) \qquad \text{\small Adding 2\textit{y} to both sides}$$

We substitute $6 + 2y$ for x in equation (2) of the original pair and solve for y:

> Substitute.

$$3x + 2y = 4 \qquad \text{\small Equation (2)}$$
$$3(6 + 2y) + 2y = 4 \qquad \text{\small Substituting 6 + 2\textit{y} for \textit{x}}$$

Remember to use parentheses when you substitute.

$18 + 6y + 2y = 4$ Using the distributive law

$18 + 8y = 4$ Combining like terms

$8y = -14$ Subtracting 18 from both sides

$y = \frac{-14}{8} = -\frac{7}{4}.$ Dividing both sides by 8

Find the value of y.

To find x, we can substitute $-\frac{7}{4}$ for y in equation (1), (2), or (3). Because it is generally easier to use an equation that has already been solved for a specific variable, we decide to use equation (3):

Substitute.

Find the value of x.

$$x = 6 + 2y$$
$$x = 6 + 2\left(-\frac{7}{4}\right)$$
$$x = 6 - \frac{7}{2} = \frac{12}{2} - \frac{7}{2} = \frac{5}{2}.$$

We check the ordered pair $\left(\frac{5}{2}, -\frac{7}{4}\right)$.

Check:

$$\begin{array}{c|c} x - 2y = 6 \\ \hline \frac{5}{2} - 2\left(-\frac{7}{4}\right) & 6 \\ \frac{5}{2} + \frac{7}{2} & \\ \frac{12}{2} & \\ 6 \overset{?}{=} 6 & \text{TRUE} \end{array}$$

$$\begin{array}{c|c} 3x + 2y = 4 \\ \hline 3 \cdot \frac{5}{2} + 2\left(-\frac{7}{4}\right) & 4 \\ \frac{15}{2} - \frac{7}{2} & \\ \frac{8}{2} & \\ 4 \overset{?}{=} 4 & \text{TRUE} \end{array}$$

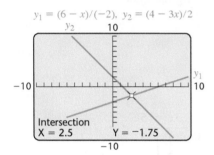

$y_1 = (6 - x)/(-2),\ y_2 = (4 - 3x)/2$

Intersection
X = 2.5   Y = −1.75

To check using a graphing calculator, we must first solve each equation for y. When we do so, equation (1) becomes $y = (6 - x)/(-2)$ and equation (2) becomes $y = (4 - 3x)/2$. The graph at left confirms the solution. Since $\left(\frac{5}{2}, -\frac{7}{4}\right)$ checks, it is the solution.

Try Exercise 19.

Some systems have no solution and some have an infinite number of solutions.

EXAMPLE 4   Solve each system.

a) $y = \frac{5}{2}x + 4,$ (1)
  $y = \frac{5}{2}x - 3$ (2)

b) $2y = 6x + 4,$ (1)
  $y = 3x + 2$ (2)

SOLUTION

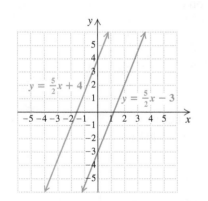

$y = \frac{5}{2}x + 4$

$y = \frac{5}{2}x - 3$

a) Since the lines have the same slope, $\frac{5}{2}$, and different y-intercepts, they are parallel. Let's see what happens if we try to solve this system by substituting $\frac{5}{2}x - 3$ for y in the first equation:

$$y = \frac{5}{2}x + 4 \qquad \text{Equation (1)}$$
$$\frac{5}{2}x - 3 = \frac{5}{2}x + 4 \qquad \text{Substituting } \frac{5}{2}x - 3 \text{ for } y$$
$$-3 = 4. \qquad \text{Subtracting } \frac{5}{2}x \text{ from both sides}$$

When we subtract $\frac{5}{2}x$ from both sides, we obtain a *false* equation, or contradiction. In such a case, when solving algebraically leads to a false equation, we state that the system has no solution and thus is inconsistent.

b) If we use substitution to solve the system, we can substitute $3x + 2$ for y in equation (1):

$$2y = 6x + 4 \qquad \text{Equation (1)}$$
$$2(3x + 2) = 6x + 4 \qquad \text{Substituting } 3x + 2 \text{ for } y$$
$$6x + 4 = 6x + 4.$$

This last equation is true for *any* choice of x, indicating that for any choice of x, a solution can be found. When the algebraic solution of a system of two equations leads to an identity—that is, an equation that is true for all real numbers—any pair that is a solution of equation (1) is also a solution of equation (2). The equations are dependent and the solution set is infinite:

$$\{(x, y) \mid y = 3x + 2\}, \quad \text{or equivalently,} \quad \{(x, y) \mid 2y = 6x + 4\}.$$

Try Exercises 15 and 21.

To Solve a System Using Substitution

1. Solve for a variable in either one of the equations if neither equation already has a variable isolated.
2. Using the result of step (1), substitute in the *other* equation for the variable isolated in step (1).
3. Solve the equation from step (2).
4. Substitute the solution from step (3) into one of the other equations to solve for the other variable.
5. Check that the ordered pair resulting from steps (3) and (4) checks in both of the original equations.

PROBLEM SOLVING

Now let's use the substitution method in problem solving.

EXAMPLE 5   Supplementary Angles.   Two angles are supplementary. One angle measures 30° more than twice the other. Find the measures of the two angles.

SOLUTION

1. **Familiarize.** Recall that two angles are supplementary if the sum of their measures is 180°. We could try to guess a solution, but instead we make a drawing and translate. We let x and y represent the measures of the two angles.
2. **Translate.** Since we are told that the angles are supplementary, one equation is

$$x + y = 180. \qquad (1)$$

The second sentence can be rephrased and translated as follows:

Rewording: One angle   is   30° more than two times the other.

Translating: y $=$ $2x + 30$ (2)

We now have a system of two equations in two unknowns:

$$x + y = 180, \qquad (1)$$
$$y = 2x + 30. \qquad (2)$$

3. **Carry out.** We substitute $2x + 30$ for y in equation (1):

$$
\begin{aligned}
x + y &= 180 &&\text{Equation (1)}\\
x + (2x + 30) &= 180 &&\text{Substituting}\\
3x + 30 &= 180\\
3x &= 150 &&\text{Subtracting 30 from both sides}\\
x &= 50. &&\text{Dividing both sides by 3}
\end{aligned}
$$

Supplementary angles

Substituting 50 for x in equation (1) then gives us

$$x + y = 180 \qquad \text{Equation (1)}$$
$$50 + y = 180 \qquad \text{Substituting 50 for } x$$
$$y = 130.$$

4. **Check.** If one angle is 50° and the other is 130°, then the sum of the measures is 180°. Thus the angles are supplementary. If 30° is added to twice the measure of the smaller angle, we have $2 \cdot 50° + 30°$, or 130°, which is the measure of the other angle. The numbers check.

5. **State.** One angle measures 50° and the other 130°.

Try Exercise 43.

4.2 Exercise Set

FOR EXTRA HELP   *MyMathLab* Math XL
                                       PRACTICE   WATCH DOWNLOAD READ REVIEW

Concept Reinforcement *Classify each of the following statements as either true or false.*

1. When using the substitution method, we must solve for the variables in alphabetical order.

2. The substitution method often requires us to first solve for a variable, much as we did when solving for a letter in a formula.

3. When solving a system of equations algebraically leads to a false equation, the system has no solution.

4. When solving a system of two equations algebraically leads to an equation that is always true, the system has an infinite number of solutions.

Solve each system using the substitution method. If a system has an infinite number of solutions, use set-builder notation to write the solution set. If a system has no solution, state this.

5. $x + y = 5,$
$\quad y = x + 3$

6. $x + y = 9,$
$\quad x = y + 1$

7. $\quad x = y + 1,$
$x + 2y = 4$

8. $\quad y = x - 3,$
$3x + y = 5$

9. $\quad y = 2x - 5,$
$3y - x = 5$

10. $\quad y = 2x + 1,$
$x + y = 4$

11. $\quad a = -4b,$
$a + 5b = 5$

12. $\quad r = -3s,$
$r + 4s = 10$

13. $2x + 3y = 8,$
$\quad x = y - 6$

14. $\quad x = y - 8,$
$3x + 2y = 1$

15. $\quad x = 2y + 1,$
$3x - 6y = 2$

16. $\quad y = 3x - 1,$
$6x - 2y = 2$

17. $s + t = -4,$
$s - t = 2$

18. $x - y = 2,$
$x + y = -2$

19. $x - y = 5,$
$x + 2y = 7$

20. $y - 2x = -6,$
$2y - x = 5$

21. $x - 2y = 7,$
$3x - 21 = 6y$

22. $x - 4y = 3,$
$2x - 6 = 8y$

23. $\quad y = 2x + 5,$
$-2y = -4x - 10$

24. $\quad y = -2x + 3,$
$3y = -6x + 9$

25. $2x + 3y = -2,$
$2x - y = 9$

26. $x + 2y = 10,$
$3x + 4y = 8$

27. $\quad a - b = 6,$
$3a - 4b = 18$

28. $\quad 3a + 2b = 2,$
$-2a + b = 8$

29. $\quad s = \frac{1}{2}r,$
$3r - 4s = 10$

30. $\quad x = \frac{1}{2}y,$
$2x + y = 12$

31. $8x + 2y = 6,$
$\quad y = 3 - 4x$

32. $x - 3y = 7,$
$-4x + 12y = 28$

33. $x - 2y = 5,$
$2y - 3x = 1$

34. $x - 3y = -1,$
$5y - 2x = 4$

Aha! 35. $2x - y = 0,$
$2x - y = -2$

36. $5x = y - 3,$
$5x = y + 5$

Solve using a system of equations.

37. The sum of two numbers is 83. One number is 5 more than the other. Find the numbers.

38. The sum of two numbers is 76. One number is 2 more than the other. Find the numbers.

39. Find two numbers for which the sum is 93 and the difference is 9.

40. Find two numbers for which the sum is 76 and the difference is 12.

41. The difference between two numbers is 16. Three times the larger number is seven times the smaller. What are the numbers?

42. The difference between two numbers is 18. Twice the smaller number plus three times the larger is 74. What are the numbers?

43. *Supplementary Angles.* Two angles are supplementary. One angle is 15° more than twice the other. Find the measure of each angle.

44. *Supplementary Angles.* Two angles are supplementary. One angle is 8° less than three times the other. Find the measure of each angle.

45. *Complementary Angles.* Two angles are complementary. Their difference is 18°. Find the measure of each angle. (*Complementary angles* are angles for which the sum is 90°.)

Complementary angles

46. *Complementary Angles.* Two angles are complementary. One angle is 42° more than one-half the other. Find the measure of each angle.

47. *Poster Dimensions.* Morrison ordered a poster printed from his prize-winning photograph. The poster had a perimeter of 100 in., and the length was 6 in. more than the width. Find the length and the width.

48. *Two-by-Four.* The perimeter of a cross section of a "two-by-four" piece of lumber is 10 in. The length is 2 in. longer than the width. Find the actual dimensions of the cross section of a two-by-four.

Two-by-four   *P* = 10 in.

49. *Dimensions of Colorado.* The state of Colorado is roughly in the shape of a rectangle whose perimeter is 1300 mi. The width is 110 mi less than the length. Find the length and the width.

50. *Dimensions of Wyoming.* The state of Wyoming is in the shape of a rectangle with a perimeter of 1280 mi. The width is 90 mi less than the length. Find the length and the width.

51. *Soccer.* The perimeter of a soccer field is 280 yd. The width is 5 yd more than half the length. Find the length and the width.

52. *Racquetball.* A regulation racquetball court has a perimeter of 120 ft, with a length that is twice the width. Find the length and the width of a court.

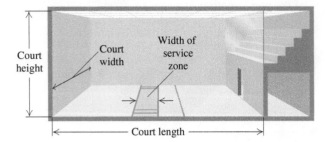

Court height

Court width

Width of service zone

Court length

53. *Racquetball.* The height of the front wall of a standard racquetball court is four times the width of the service zone (see the figure). Together, these measurements total 25 ft. Find the height and the width.

54. *Lacrosse.* The perimeter of a lacrosse field is 340 yd. The length is 10 yd less than twice the width. Find the length and the width.

TW **55.** Briley solves every system of two equations (in x and y) by first solving for y in the first equation and then substituting into the second equation. Is he using the best approach? Why or why not?

TW **56.** Describe two advantages of the substitution method over the graphing method for solving systems of equations.

SKILL REVIEW

To prepare for Section 4.3, review simplifying algebraic expressions.

Simplify.

57. $2(5x + 3y) - 3(5x + 3y)$

58. $5(2x + 3y) - 3(7x + 5y)$

59. $4(5x + 6y) - 5(4x + 7y)$

60. $2(7x + 5 - 3y) - 7(2x + 5)$

61. $2(5x - 3y) - 5(2x + y)$

62. $4(2x + 3y) + 3(5x - 4y)$

SYNTHESIS

TW **63.** Hilary can tell by inspection that the system
$$x = 2y - 1,$$
$$x = 2y + 3$$
has no solution. How can she tell?

TW **64.** Under what circumstances can a system of equations be solved more easily by graphing than by substitution?

Solve by the substitution method.

65. $\frac{1}{6}(a + b) = 1,$

$\frac{1}{4}(a - b) = 2$

66. $\frac{x}{5} - \frac{y}{2} = 3,$

$\frac{x}{4} + \frac{3y}{4} = 1$

67. $y + 5.97 = 2.35x,$

$2.14y - x = 4.88$

68. $a + 4.2b = 25.1,$

$9a - 1.8b = 39.78$

69. *Age at Marriage.* Trudy is 20 years younger than Dennis. She feels that she needs to be 7 more than half of Dennis's age before they can marry. What is the youngest age at which Trudy can marry Dennis and honor this requirement?

Exercises 70 and 71 contain systems of three equations in three variables. A solution is an ordered triple of the form (x, y, z). *Use the substitution method to solve.*

70. $x + y + z = 4,$

$x - 2y - z = 1,$

$y = -1$

71. $x + y + z = 180,$

$x = z - 70,$

$2y - z = 0$

72. *Softball.* The perimeter of a softball diamond is two-thirds of the perimeter of a baseball diamond. Together, the two perimeters measure 200 yd. Find the distance between the bases in each sport.

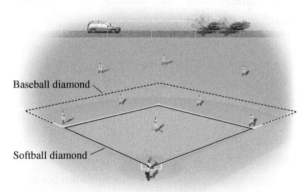

Baseball diamond

Softball diamond

TW **73.** Solve Example 3 by first solving for $2y$ in equation (1) and then substituting for $2y$ in equation (2). Is this method easier than the procedure used in Example 3? Why or why not?

74. Write a system of two linear equations that can be solved more quickly—but still precisely—by a graphing calculator than by substitution. Time yourself using both methods to solve the system.

Try Exercise Answers: Section 4.2

5. $(1, 4)$ **9.** $(4, 3)$ **15.** No solution

19. $\left(\frac{17}{3}, \frac{2}{3}\right)$ **21.** $\{(x, y) | x - 2y = 7\}$ **43.** $55°, 125°$

4.3   Systems of Equations and Elimination

■ Solving by the
  Elimination Method

■ Problem Solving

Although substitution can be used to solve any system of two equations, another method, *elimination,* is simpler to use for many problems.

SOLVING BY THE ELIMINATION METHOD

The **elimination method** for solving systems of equations makes use of the addition principle.

EXAMPLE 1   Solve the system

$$2x + 3y = 13, \quad (1)$$
$$4x - 3y = 17. \quad (2)$$

SOLUTION   According to equation (2), $4x - 3y$ and 17 are the same number. Thus we can add $4x - 3y$ to the left side of equation (1) and 17 to the right side:

$$
\begin{array}{ll}
2x + 3y = 13 & (1) \\
4x - 3y = 17 & (2) \\
\hline
6x + 0y = 30. & \text{Adding. Note that } y \text{ has been "eliminated."}
\end{array}
$$

The resulting equation has just one variable:

$$6x = 30.$$

Dividing both sides of this equation by 6, we find that $x = 5$.
    Next, we substitute 5 for x in either of the original equations:

$$
\begin{array}{ll}
2x + 3y = 13 & \text{Equation (1)} \\
2(5) + 3y = 13 & \text{Substituting 5 for } x \\
10 + 3y = 13 & \\
3y = 3 & \\
y = 1. & \text{Solving for } y
\end{array}
$$

We check the ordered pair (5, 1). The graph shown at left also serves as a check.

$$
\begin{array}{c}
Check: \\
\\
\end{array}
\quad
\begin{array}{c|c}
2x + 3y = 13 & \\
\hline
2(5) + 3(1) & 13 \\
10 + 3 & \\
13 \overset{?}{=} 13 & \text{TRUE}
\end{array}
\quad
\begin{array}{c|c}
4x - 3y = 17 & \\
\hline
4(5) - 3(1) & 17 \\
20 - 3 & \\
17 \overset{?}{=} 17 & \text{TRUE}
\end{array}
$$

Since (5, 1) checks in both equations, it is the solution.

Try Exercise 5.

    Adding in Example 1 eliminated the variable y because two terms, $-3y$ in equation (2) and $3y$ in equation (1), are opposites. Most systems have no pair of terms that are opposites. We can create such a pair of terms by multiplying one or both of the equations by appropriate numbers.

EXAMPLE 2   Solve:

$$2x + 3y = 8, \quad (1)$$
$$x + 3y = 7. \quad (2)$$

SOLUTION   Adding these equations as they now appear will not eliminate a variable. However, if the $3y$ were $-3y$ in one equation, we could eliminate y. We multiply both sides of equation (2) by -1 to find an equivalent equation that contains $-3y$, and then add:

$$
\begin{aligned}
2x + 3y &= 8 && \text{Equation (1)} \\
-x - 3y &= -7 && \text{Multiplying both sides of equation (2) by } -1 \\
\hline
x &= 1. && \text{Adding}
\end{aligned}
$$

Next, we substitute 1 for x in either of the original equations:

$$
\begin{aligned}
x + 3y &= 7 && \text{Equation (2)} \\
1 + 3y &= 7 && \text{Substituting 1 for } x \\
3y &= 6 \\
y &= 2.
\end{aligned}
$$
Solving for y

We can check the ordered pair $(1, 2)$. The graph shown at left is also a check.

Check:

$$
\begin{array}{c|c}
2x + 3y = 8 & \\
\hline
2(1) + 3(2) & 8 \\
2 + 6 & \\
8 \overset{?}{=} 8 & \text{TRUE}
\end{array}
\qquad
\begin{array}{c|c}
x + 3y = 7 & \\
\hline
1 + 3(2) & 7 \\
1 + 6 & \\
7 \overset{?}{=} 7 & \text{TRUE}
\end{array}
$$

Since $(1, 2)$ checks in both equations, it is the solution.

Try Exercise 17.

When deciding which variable to eliminate, we inspect the coefficients in both equations. If one coefficient is a multiple of the coefficient of the same variable in the other equation, that is the easiest variable to eliminate.

EXAMPLE 3   Solve:

$$
\begin{aligned}
3x + 6y &= -6, && (1) \\
5x - 2y &= 14. && (2)
\end{aligned}
$$

SOLUTION   No terms are opposites, but if both sides of equation (2) are multiplied by 3 (or if both sides of equation (1) are multiplied by $\frac{1}{3}$), the coefficients of y will be opposites. Note that 6 is the LCM of 2 and 6:

$$
\begin{aligned}
3x + 6y &= -6 && \text{Equation (1)} \\
15x - 6y &= 42 && \text{Multiplying both sides of equation (2) by 3} \\
\hline
18x &= 36 && \text{Adding} \\
x &= 2. && \text{Solving for } x
\end{aligned}
$$

We then substitute 2 for x in either equation (1) or equation (2):

$$
\begin{aligned}
3(2) + 6y &= -6 && \text{Substituting 2 for } x \text{ in equation (1)} \\
6 + 6y &= -6 \\
6y &= -12 \\
y &= -2.
\end{aligned}
$$
Solving for y

We leave it to the student to confirm that $(2, -2)$ checks and is the solution. The graph at left also serves as a check.

Try Exercise 21.

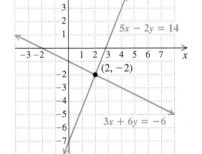

Sometimes both equations must be multiplied to find the least common multiple of two coefficients.

EXAMPLE 4 Solve:

$$3y + 1 + 2x = 0, \quad (1)$$
$$5x = 7 - 4y. \quad (2)$$

SOLUTION It is often helpful to write both equations in the form $Ax + By = C$ before attempting to eliminate a variable:

$$2x + 3y = -1, \quad (3) \qquad \text{Subtracting 1 from both sides and rearranging the terms of the first equation}$$

$$5x + 4y = 7. \quad (4) \qquad \text{Adding } 4y \text{ to both sides of equation (2)}$$

Since neither coefficient of x is a multiple of the other and neither coefficient of y is a multiple of the other, we use the multiplication principle with *both* equations. Note that we can eliminate the x-term by multiplying both sides of equation (3) by 5 and both sides of equation (4) by -2:

Multiply to get terms that are opposites.

$$\begin{array}{rl} 10x + 15y = & -5 \qquad \text{Multiplying both sides of equation (3) by 5} \\ -10x - 8y = & -14 \qquad \text{Multiplying both sides of equation (4) by } -2 \\ \hline 7y = & -19 \qquad \text{Adding} \\ y = & \frac{-19}{7} = -\frac{19}{7}. \qquad \text{Dividing by 7} \end{array}$$

Solve for one variable.

We substitute $-\frac{19}{7}$ for y in equation (3):

Substitute.

$$\begin{aligned} 2x + 3y &= -1 & \text{Equation (3)} \\ 2x + 3\left(-\tfrac{19}{7}\right) &= -1 & \text{Substituting } -\tfrac{19}{7} \text{ for } y \\ 2x - \tfrac{57}{7} &= -1 \\ 2x &= -1 + \tfrac{57}{7} & \text{Adding } \tfrac{57}{7} \text{ to both sides} \\ 2x &= -\tfrac{7}{7} + \tfrac{57}{7} = \tfrac{50}{7} \\ x &= \tfrac{50}{7} \cdot \tfrac{1}{2} = \tfrac{25}{7}. & \text{Solving for } x \end{aligned}$$

Solve for the other variable.

We check the ordered pair $\left(\tfrac{25}{7}, -\tfrac{19}{7}\right)$.

Check in both equations.

Check:

$$\begin{array}{c|c} 3y + 1 + 2x = 0 \\ \hline 3\left(-\tfrac{19}{7}\right) + 1 + 2\left(\tfrac{25}{7}\right) & 0 \\ -\tfrac{57}{7} + \tfrac{7}{7} + \tfrac{50}{7} \\ & 0 \overset{?}{=} 0 \quad \text{TRUE} \end{array} \qquad \begin{array}{c|c} 5x = 7 - 4y \\ \hline 5\left(\tfrac{25}{7}\right) & 7 - 4\left(-\tfrac{19}{7}\right) \\ \tfrac{125}{7} & \tfrac{49}{7} + \tfrac{76}{7} \\ \tfrac{125}{7} \overset{?}{=} \tfrac{125}{7} & \text{TRUE} \end{array}$$

State the solution as an ordered pair.

The solution is $\left(\tfrac{25}{7}, -\tfrac{19}{7}\right)$.

Try Exercise 33.

Next, we consider a system with no solution and see what happens when the elimination method is used.

EXAMPLE 5 Solve:

$$y - 3x = 2, \quad (1)$$
$$y - 3x = 1. \quad (2)$$

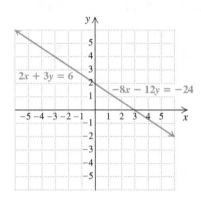

SOLUTION To eliminate y, we multiply both sides of equation (2) by -1. Then we add:

$$
\begin{array}{rl}
y - 3x = & 2 \\
\underline{-y + 3x = -1} & \qquad \text{Multiplying both sides of equation (2) by } -1 \\
0 = & 1. \qquad \text{Adding}
\end{array}
$$

Note that in eliminating y, we eliminated x as well. The resulting equation, $0 = 1$, is false for any pair (x, y), so there is *no solution*.

Try Exercise 23.

Sometimes there is an infinite number of solutions.

EXAMPLE 6 Solve:

$$
\begin{array}{rl}
2x + 3y = 6, & \qquad (1) \\
-8x - 12y = -24. & \qquad (2)
\end{array}
$$

SOLUTION To eliminate x, we multiply both sides of equation (1) by 4 and then add the two equations:

$$
\begin{array}{rl}
8x + 12y = & 24 \qquad \text{Multiplying both sides of equation (1) by 4} \\
\underline{-8x - 12y = -24} & \\
0 = & 0. \qquad \text{Adding}
\end{array}
$$

Again, we have eliminated *both* variables. The resulting equation, $0 = 0$, is always true, indicating that the equations are dependent. Such a system has an infinite solution set:

$$\{(x, y) \mid 2x + 3y = 6\}, \quad \text{or equivalently,} \quad \{(x, y) \mid -8x - 12y = -24\}.$$

Try Exercise 15.

When decimals or fractions appear, we can first multiply to clear them. Then we proceed as before.

EXAMPLE 7 Solve:

$$
\begin{array}{rl}
\frac{1}{2}x + \frac{3}{4}y = 2, & \qquad (1) \\
x + 3y = 7. & \qquad (2)
\end{array}
$$

SOLUTION The number 4 is the LCD for equation (1). Thus we multiply both sides of equation (1) by 4 to clear fractions:

$$
\begin{array}{rl}
4\left(\frac{1}{2}x + \frac{3}{4}y\right) = 4 \cdot 2 & \qquad \text{Multiplying both sides of equation (1) by 4} \\
4 \cdot \frac{1}{2}x + 4 \cdot \frac{3}{4}y = 8 & \qquad \text{Using the distributive law} \\
2x + 3y = 8.
\end{array}
$$

The resulting system is

$$
\begin{array}{rl}
2x + 3y = 8, & \qquad \text{This equation is equivalent to equation (1).} \\
x + 3y = 7.
\end{array}
$$

As we saw in Example 2, the solution of this system is $(1, 2)$.

Try Exercise 35.

PROBLEM SOLVING

We now use the elimination method to solve a problem.

EXAMPLE 8 Birthday Parties. Anne plans to give a birthday party for her 5-year-old daughter at either Karate World or Fitness King. Karate World charges a $60 setup fee plus $10 per child for the party. Fitness King charges a $40 setup fee plus $12 per child. For how many children will the party prices be the same?

SOLUTION

1. **Familiarize.** Let's make and check a guess of 8 children. The two party prices would be:

   Karate World: $60 + $10(8) = $60 + $80 = $140;
   Fitness King: $40 + $12(8) = $40 + $96 = $136.

   We see that our guess is close, but that the prices are not exactly equal. From the check, we can see how equations can be written to model the situation. We let n = the number of children and p = the price of the party.

2. **Translate.** We reword the problem and translate.

Rewording:	Karate World price	is	setup fee	plus	$10	times	the number of children.
Translating:	p	$=$	60	$+$	10	$\cdot$	n

Rewording:	Fitness King price	is	setup fee	plus	$12	times	the number of children.
Translating:	p	$=$	40	$+$	12	$\cdot$	n

   We now have the system of equations

   $$p = 60 + 10n,$$
   $$p = 40 + 12n.$$

3. **Carry out.** We use elimination to solve the system.

   $$\begin{array}{rl} p = & 60 + 10n \\ -p = & -40 - 12n \\ \hline 0 = & 20 - 2n \end{array}$$ Multiplying by -1

   Adding to eliminate p

   We can now solve for n:

   $$0 = 20 - 2n$$
   $$2n = 20$$
   $$n = 10.$$

4. **Check.** We compare the prices for 10 children:

   Karate World: $60 + $10(10) = $60 + $100 = $160;
   Fitness King: $40 + $12(10) = $40 + $120 = $160.

   The prices are the same.

5. **State.** The prices are the same for a party of 10 children.

Try Exercise 39.

4.3 Exercise Set

Concept Reinforcement   *Classify each of the following statements as either true or false.*

1. The elimination method is never easier to use than the substitution method.

2. The elimination method works especially well when the coefficients of one variable are opposites of each other.

3. When the elimination method yields an equation that is always true, there is an infinite number of solutions.

4. When the elimination method yields an equation that is never true, the system has no solution.

Solve using the elimination method. If a system has an infinite number of solutions, use set-builder notation to write the solution set. If a system has no solution, state this.

5. $x - y = 6,$
   $x + y = 12$

6. $x + y = 3,$
   $x - y = 7$

7. $x + y = 6,$
   $-x + 3y = -2$

8. $x + y = 6,$
   $-x + 2y = 15$

9. $4x - y = 1,$
   $3x + y = 13$

10. $3x - y = 9,$
    $2x + y = 6$

11. $5a + 4b = 7,$
    $-5a + b = 8$

12. $7c + 4d = 16,$
    $c - 4d = -4$

13. $8x - 5y = -9,$
    $3x + 5y = -2$

14. $3a - 3b = -15,$
    $-3a - 3b = -3$

15. $3a - 6b = 8,$
    $-3a + 6b = -8$

16. $8x + 3y = 4,$
    $-8x - 3y = -4$

17. $-x - y = 8,$
    $2x - y = -1$

18. $x + y = -7,$
    $3x + y = -9$

19. $x + 3y = 19,$
    $x - y = -1$

20. $3x - y = 8,$
    $x + 2y = 5$

21. $8x - 3y = -6,$
    $5x + 6y = 75$

22. $x - y = 3,$
    $2x - 3y = -1$

23. $2w - 3z = -1,$
    $-4w + 6z = 5$

24. $7p + 5q = 2,$
    $8p - 9q = 17$

25. $4a + 6b = -1,$
    $a - 3b = 2$

26. $x + 9y = 1,$
    $2x - 6y = 10$

27. $3y = x,$
    $5x + 14 = y$

28. $5a = 2b,$
    $2a + 11 = 3b$

29. $4x - 10y = 13,$
    $-2x + 5y = 8$

30. $2p + 5w = 9,$
    $3p - 2w = 4$

31. $8n + 6 - 3m = 0,$
    $32 = m - n$

32. $6x - 8 + y = 0,$
    $11 = 3y - 8x$

33. $3x + 5y = 4,$
    $-2x + 3y = 10$

34. $2x + y = 13,$
    $4x + 2y = 23$

35. $0.06x + 0.05y = 0.07,$
    $0.4x - 0.3y = 1.1$

36. $x - \frac{3}{2}y = 13,$
    $\frac{3}{2}x - y = 17$

37. $x + \frac{9}{2}y = \frac{15}{4},$
    $\frac{9}{10}x - y = \frac{9}{20}$

38. $1.8x - 2y = 0.9,$
    $0.04x + 0.18y = 0.15$

Solve.

39. *Car Rentals.*   The University of Oklahoma School of Drama can rent a cargo van for $27 per day plus 22¢ per mile or a pickup truck for $29 per day plus 17¢ per mile. For what mileage is the cost the same?
Source: fleetservices.ou.edu

40. *RV Rentals.*   Stoltzfus RV rents a Class A recreational vehicle (RV) for $1545 for one week plus 20¢ per mile. Martin RV rents a similar RV for $1183 for one week plus 30¢ per mile. For what mileage is the cost the same?
Sources: Stoltzfus RV; Martin RV

41. *Complementary Angles.*   Two angles are complementary. The difference of the angle measures is 38°. Find the measure of each angle.

42. *Complementary Angles.*   Two angles are complementary. The difference of the angle measures is 86°. Find the measure of each angle.

43. *Phone Rates.*   Elke makes frequent calls from the United States to Austria. She is choosing between a PowerNet Global plan that costs $1.99 per month plus 43¢ per minute and an AT&T plan that costs $3.99 per month plus 28¢ per minute. For what number of minutes will the two plans cost the same?
Sources: AT&T; PNG

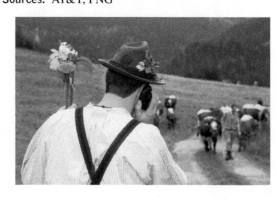

44. *Phone Rates.* Recently, AT&T offered the One Rate 5¢ Nationwide Advantage Plan for $5.00 per month plus 5¢ per minute. AT&T also offered the Value Card Plus Plan for $1.95 per month plus 15¢ per minute. For what number of minutes per month will the two plans cost the same?
Source: AT&T

45. *Supplementary Angles.* Two angles are supplementary. The difference of the angle measures is 68°. Find the measure of each angle.

46. *Supplementary Angles.* Two angles are supplementary. The difference of the angle measures is 90°. Find the measure of each angle.

47. *Planting Grapes.* South Wind Vineyards uses 820 acres to plant Chardonnay and Riesling grapes. The vintner knows the profits will be greatest by planting 140 more acres of Chardonnay than Riesling. How many acres of each type of grape should be planted?

48. *Baking.* Maple Branch Bakers sells 175 loaves of bread each day—some white and the rest whole-wheat. Because of a regular order from a local sandwich shop, Maple Branch consistently bakes 9 more loaves of white bread than whole-wheat. How many loaves of each type of bread do they bake?

49. *Framing.* Anu has 18 ft of molding from which he needs to make a rectangular frame. Because of the dimensions of the mirror being framed, the frame must be twice as long as it is wide. What should the dimensions of the frame be?

50. *Gardening.* Patrice has 108 ft of fencing for a rectangular garden. If the garden's length is to be $1\frac{1}{2}$ times its width, what should the garden's dimensions be?

TW 51. Describe a method that could be used for writing a system that contains dependent equations.

TW 52. Describe a method that could be used for writing an inconsistent system of equations.

SKILL REVIEW

To prepare for Section 4.4, review percent notation.

Convert to decimal notation.

53. 12.2%

54. 0.5%

Solve.

55. What percent of 65 is 26?

56. What number is 17% of 18?

Translate to an algebraic expression.

57. 12% of the number of liters

58. 10.5% of the number of pounds

SYNTHESIS

TW 59. If a system has an infinite number of solutions, does it follow that *any* ordered pair is a solution? Why or why not?

TW 60. Explain how the multiplication and addition principles are used in this section. Then count the number of times that these principles are used in Example 4.

Solve using substitution, elimination, or graphing.

61. $x + y = 7,$
$3(y - x) = 9$

62. $y = 3x + 4,$
$3 + y = 2(y - x)$

63. $2(5a - 5b) = 10,$
$-5(2a + 6b) = 10$

64. $0.05x + y = 4,$
$\dfrac{x}{2} + \dfrac{y}{3} = 1\dfrac{1}{3}$

Aha! 65. $y = -\dfrac{2}{7}x + 3,$
$y = \dfrac{4}{5}x + 3$

66. $y = \dfrac{2}{5}x - 7,$
$y = \dfrac{2}{5}x + 4$

Solve for x and y.

67. $y = ax + b,$
$y = x + c$

68. $ax + by + c = 0,$
$ax + cy + b = 0$

69. *Math in History.* Several ancient Chinese books included problems that can be solved by translating to systems of equations. *Arithmetical Rules in Nine Sections* is a book of 246 problems compiled by a Chinese mathematician, Chang Tsang, who died in 152 B.C. One of the problems is: Suppose there are a number of rabbits and pheasants confined in a cage. In all, there are 35 heads and 94 feet. How many rabbits and how many pheasants are there? Solve the problem.

70. *Age.* Miguel's age is 20% of his mother's age. Twenty years from now, Miguel's age will be 52% of his mother's age. How old are Miguel and his mother now?

71. *Age.* If 5 is added to a man's age and the total is divided by 5, the result will be his daughter's age. Five years ago, the man's age was eight times his daughter's age. Find their present ages.

72. *Dimensions of a Triangle.* When the base of a triangle is increased by 1 ft and the height is increased by 2 ft, the height changes from being two-thirds of the base to being four-fifths of the base. Find the original dimensions of the triangle

Try Exercise Answers: Section 4.3
5. (9, 3) **15.** $\{(a, b) \mid 3a - 6b = 8\}$ **17.** $(-3, -5)$
21. (3, 10) **23.** No solution **33.** $(-2, 2)$
35. $(2, -1)$ **39.** 40 mi

Mid-Chapter Review

We now have three different methods for solving systems of equations. Each method has certain strengths and weaknesses, as outlined below.

Method	Strengths	Weaknesses
Graphical	Solutions are displayed visually. Can be used with any system that can be graphed.	For some systems, only approximate solutions can be found graphically. The graph drawn may not be large enough to show the solution.
Substitution	Yields exact solutions. Easy to use when a variable has a coefficient of 1.	Introduces extensive computations with fractions when solving more complicated systems. Solutions are not displayed graphically.
Elimination	Yields exact solutions. Easy to use when fractions or decimals appear in the system. The preferred method for systems of 3 or more equations in 3 or more variables. (See Chapter 11.)	Solutions are not displayed graphically.

GUIDED SOLUTIONS

Solve. [4.2], [4.3]

1. $2x - 3y = 5,$
$\quad y = x - 1$

Solution

$$2x - 3\left(\boxed{}\right) = 5 \qquad \text{Substituting } x - 1 \text{ for } y$$

$$2x - \boxed{} + \boxed{} = 5 \qquad \text{Using the distributive law}$$

$$\boxed{} + 3 = 5 \qquad \text{Combining like terms}$$

$$-x = \boxed{} \qquad \text{Subtracting 3 from both sides}$$

$$x = \boxed{} \qquad \text{Dividing both sides by } -1$$

$$y = x - 1$$

$$y = \boxed{} - 1 \qquad \text{Substituting}$$

$$y = \boxed{}$$

The solution is $\left(\boxed{}, \boxed{}\right)$.

2. $2x - 5y = 1,$
$\quad x + 5y = 8$

Solution

$$2x - 5y = 1$$
$$x + 5y = 8$$
$$\overline{\boxed{} = \boxed{}}$$
$$x = \boxed{}$$

$$x + 5y = 8$$
$$\boxed{} + 5y = 8 \qquad \text{Substituting}$$
$$5y = \boxed{}$$
$$y = \boxed{}$$

The solution is $\left(\boxed{}, \boxed{}\right)$.

MIXED REVIEW

Solve using the best method.

1. $x = y,$
$\quad x + y = 2$

2. $x + y = 10,$
$\quad x - y = 8$

3. $y = \frac{1}{2}x + 1,$
$\quad y = 2x - 5$

4. $y = 2x - 3,$
$\quad x + y = 12$

5. $x = 5,$
$\quad y = 10$

6. $3x + 5y = 8,$
$\quad 3x - 5y = 4$

7. $2x - y = 1,$
$\quad 2y - 4x = 3$

8. $x = 2 - y,$
$\quad 3x + 3y = 6$

9. $x + 2y = 3,$
   $3x = 4 - y$

10. $9x + 8y = 0,$
   $11x - 7y = 0$

11. $10x + 20y = 40,$
   $x - \ \ y = 7$

12. $y = \frac{5}{3}x + 7,$
   $y = \frac{5}{3}x - 8$

13. $2x - 5y = 1,$
   $3x + 2y = 11$

14. $\dfrac{x}{2} + \dfrac{y}{3} = \dfrac{2}{3},$
   $\dfrac{x}{5} + \dfrac{5y}{2} = \dfrac{1}{4}$

15. $1.1x - 0.3y = 0.8,$
   $2.3x + 0.3y = 2.6$

16. $y = -3,$
   $x = 11$

17. $x - 2y = 5,$
   $3x - 15 = 6y$

18. $12x - 19y = 13,$
   $8x + 19y = 7$

19. $0.2x + 0.7y = 1.2,$
   $0.3x - 0.1y = 2.7$

20. $\frac{1}{4}x = \frac{1}{3}y,$
   $\frac{1}{2}x - \frac{1}{15}y = 2$

4.4 More Applications Using Systems

- **Total-Value Problems**

- **Mixture Problems**

- **Motion Problems**

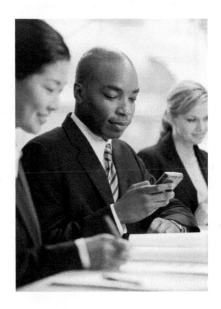

The five steps for problem solving and the methods for solving systems of equations can be used in a variety of applications.

EXAMPLE 1   Text Messaging.   In 2008, the average wireless subscriber sent or received a total of 561 calls and text messages each month. The number of text messages was 153 more than the number of calls. How many calls and how many text messages were sent or received each month?
Source: Nielsen Telecom Practice Group

SOLUTION

1. **Familiarize.** We let c = the number of calls and t = the number of text messages sent or received monthly. Since we have two unknowns, we look for two relationships to translate.

2. **Translate.** There are two statements to translate. First, we know the total number of calls and text messages:

Rewording: The number of calls   plus   the number of text messages   was   561.

Translating: c $+$ t $=$ 561

   We also know how many more text messages there were than calls:

Rewording: The number of text messages   was   153 more than the number of calls.

Translating: t $=$ $c + 153$

   We have now translated the problem to a system of equations:

   $c + t = 561,$
   $t = c + 153.$

3. **Carry out.** We solve the system of equations both algebraically and graphically.

ALGEBRAIC APPROACH	GRAPHICAL APPROACH

ALGEBRAIC APPROACH

Since one equation already has a variable isolated, let's use the substitution method:

$$c + t = 561$$

$$c + (c + 153) = 561 \qquad \text{Substituting } c + 153 \text{ for } t$$

$$2c + 153 = 561 \qquad \text{Combining like terms}$$

$$2c = 408 \qquad \text{Subtracting 153 from both sides}$$

$$c = 204. \qquad \text{Dividing both sides by 2}$$

Next, using either of the original equations, we substitute and solve for t:

$$t = c + 153$$

$$t = 204 + 153$$

$$t = 357.$$

We have $c = 204, t = 357$.

GRAPHICAL APPROACH

First, we let $x = c$ and $y = t$ and substitute. Then we graph $y_1 = 561 - x$ and $y_2 = x + 153$. Since the total number of calls and text messages is 561, we choose a viewing window of $[0, 600, 0, 600]$, with Xscl = 50 and Yscl = 50.

$y_1 = 561 - x, \ y_2 = x + 153$

Intersection
X = 204 Y = 357
Xscl = 50, Yscl = 50

We have a solution of $(204, 357)$.

4. **Check.** Checking using the wording in the original problem, we see that the total number of calls and text messages is $204 + 357$, or 561. Also, the number of text messages, 357, is 153 more than the number of calls: $357 - 204 = 153$. The numbers check.

5. **State.** There were 204 calls and 357 text messages sent or received monthly.

Try Exercise 1.

TOTAL-VALUE PROBLEMS

EXAMPLE 2 Purchasing. Recently the Riley Recreation Center purchased 120 stamps for $40.80. If the stamps were a combination of 28¢ postcard stamps and 44¢ first-class stamps, how many of each type were bought?

SOLUTION

1. **Familiarize.** To familiarize ourselves with this problem, let's guess that the center bought 60 stamps at 28¢ each and 60 stamps at 44¢ each. The total cost would then be

$$60 \cdot \$0.28 + 60 \cdot \$0.44 = \$16.80 + \$26.40, \text{ or } \$43.20.$$

Since $\$43.20 \neq \$40.80$, our guess is incorrect. We let $p =$ the number of postcard stamps and $f =$ the number of first-class stamps purchased.

2. **Translate.** Since a total of 120 stamps was purchased, we have

$$p + f = 120.$$

To find a second equation, we reword some information, focusing on the amount of money paid:

Rewording: The money paid for postcard stamps plus the money paid for first-class stamps totaled $40.80.

Translating: $p \cdot 0.28$ + $f \cdot 0.44$ = 40.80

Note that we changed all the money units to dollars.

Presenting the information in a table can be helpful.

	Postcard Stamps	First-Class Stamps	Total
Cost per Stamp	$0.28	$0.44	
Number of Stamps	p	f	120 $\longrightarrow p + f = 120$
Amount Paid	$0.28p$	$0.44f$	40.80 $\longrightarrow 0.28p + 0.44f = 40.80$

We have translated to a system of equations:

$$p + f = 120, \qquad (1)$$
$$0.28p + 0.44f = 40.80. \qquad (2)$$

3. Carry out. We now solve the system of equations

$$p + f = 120, \qquad (1)$$
$$28p + 44f = 4080. \qquad (2) \qquad \text{Working in cents rather than dollars}$$

ALGEBRAIC APPROACH

Because both equations are in the form $Ax + By = C$, let's use the elimination method to solve the system. We can eliminate p by multiplying both sides of equation (1) by -28 and adding them to the corresponding sides of equation (2):

$$
\begin{array}{ll}
-28p - 28f = -3360 & \text{Multiplying both sides} \\
 & \text{of equation (1) by } -28 \\
\underline{28p + 44f = 4080} & \\
16f = 720 & \text{Adding} \\
f = 45. & \text{Solving for } f
\end{array}
$$

To find p, we substitute 45 for f in equation (1) and then solve for p:

$$
\begin{array}{ll}
p + f = 120 & \text{Equation (1)} \\
p + 45 = 120 & \text{Substituting 45 for } f \\
p = 75. & \text{Solving for } p
\end{array}
$$

We obtain $(45, 75)$, or $f = 45$, $p = 75$.

GRAPHICAL APPROACH

We replace f with x and p with y and solve for y:

$$
\begin{array}{ll}
y + x = 120 & \text{Solving for } y \text{ in equation (1)} \\
y = 120 - x
\end{array}
$$

and

$$
\begin{array}{ll}
28y + 44x = 4080 & \text{Solving for } y \text{ in equation (2)} \\
28y = 4080 - 44x \\
y = (4080 - 44x)/28.
\end{array}
$$

Since the number of each kind of stamp is between 0 and 120, an appropriate viewing window is $[0, 120, 0, 120]$.

$y_1 = 120 - x,$
$y_2 = (4080 - 44x)/28$

Intersection
X = 45   Y = 75

Xscl = 10, Yscl = 10

The point of intersection is $(45, 75)$. Since f was replaced with x and p with y, we have $f = 45$, $p = 75$.

It is very important that you clearly label precisely what each variable represents. Not only will this help you write equations, but it will also allow you to write solutions correctly.

4. **Check.** We check in the original problem. Recall that f is the number of first-class stamps and p the number of postcard stamps.

Number of stamps: $f + p = 45 + 75 = 120$

Cost of first-class stamps: $\$0.44f = 0.44 \times 45 = \$19.80$

Cost of postcard stamps: $\$0.28p = 0.28 \times 75 = \$21.00$

$$\text{Total} = \$40.80$$

The numbers check.

5. **State.** The center bought 45 first-class stamps and 75 postcard stamps.

Try Exercise 9.

    Example 2 involves two types of items (first-class stamps and postcard stamps), the quantity of each type bought, and the total value of the items. We refer to this type of problem as a *total-value problem.*

MIXTURE PROBLEMS

EXAMPLE 3   Blending Teas.   Tea Pots n Treasures sells loose Oolong tea for $2.15 per ounce. Donna mixed Oolong tea with shaved almonds that sell for $0.95 per ounce to create the Market Street Oolong blend that sells for $1.85 per ounce. One week, she made 300 oz of Market Street Oolong. How much tea and how much shaved almonds did Donna use?

SOLUTION

1. **Familiarize.** This problem is similar to Example 2. Since we know the price per ounce of the blend, we can find the total value of the blend by multiplying 300 ounces times $1.85 per ounce. We let l = the number of ounces of Oolong tea and a = the number of ounces of shaved almonds.

2. **Translate.** Since a 300-oz batch is being made, we must have

$$l + a = 300.$$

To find a second equation, note that the total value of the 300-oz blend must match the combined value of the separate ingredients:

Rewording: The value of the Oolong tea   plus   the value of the almonds   is   the value of the Market Street blend.

Translating: $l \cdot \$2.15$ + $a \cdot \$0.95$ = $300 \cdot \$1.85$

These equations can also be obtained from a table.

	Oolong Tea	Almonds	Market Street Blend	
Number of Ounces	l	a	300	$\longrightarrow \, l + a = 300$
Price per Ounce	$2.15	$0.95	$1.85	
Value of Tea	$2.15l$	$0.95a$	$300 \cdot \$1.85$, or $555	$\longrightarrow \, 2.15l + 0.95a = 555$

Clearing decimals in the second equation, we have $215l + 95a = 55{,}500$. We have translated to a system of equations:

$$l + a = 300, \quad (1)$$
$$215l + 95a = 55{,}500. \quad (2)$$

3. **Carry out.** We solve the system both algebraically and graphically.

ALGEBRAIC APPROACH	GRAPHICAL APPROACH

ALGEBRAIC APPROACH

We can solve using substitution. When equation (1) is solved for l, we have $l = 300 - a$. Substituting $300 - a$ for l in equation (2), we find a:

$215(300 - a) + 95a = 55{,}500$ Substituting

$64{,}500 - 215a + 95a = 55{,}500$ Using the distributive law

$-120a = -9000$ Combining like terms; subtracting 64,500 from both sides

$a = 75$.   Dividing both sides by -120

We have $a = 75$ and, from equation (1) above, $l + a = 300$. Thus, $l = 225$.

GRAPHICAL APPROACH

We replace a with x and l with y and solve for y, which gives us the system of equations

$$y = 300 - x,$$
$$y = (55{,}500 - 95x)/215.$$

We choose the viewing window $[0, 300, 0, 300]$, graph the equations, and find the point of intersection.

$y_1 = 300 - x,$
$y_2 = (55500 - 95x)/215$

Intersection
X = 75   Y = 225

Xscl = 50, Yscl = 50

The point of intersection is $(75, 225)$. Since a was replaced with x and l with y, we have $a = 75, l = 225$.

4. **Check.** Combining 225 oz of Oolong tea and 75 oz of almonds will give a 300-oz blend. The value of 225 oz of Oolong is $225(\$2.15)$, or $\$483.75$. The value of 75 oz of almonds is $75(\$0.95)$, or $\$71.25$. Thus the combined value of the blend is $\$483.75 + \$71.25$, or $\$555$. A 300-oz blend priced at $\$1.85$ per ounce would also be worth $\$555$, so our answer checks.

5. **State.** The Market Street blend was made by combining 225 oz of Oolong tea and 75 oz of almonds.

Try Exercise 21.

EXAMPLE 4   Student Loans.   Rani's student loans totaled $\$9600$. Part was a PLUS loan made at 3.28% interest and the rest was a Perkins loan made at 5% interest. After one year, Rani's loans accumulated $\$402.60$ in interest. What was the original amount of each loan?

SOLUTION

1. **Familiarize.** We begin with a guess. If $7000 was borrowed at 3.28% and $2600 was borrowed at 5%, the two loans would total $9600. The interest would then be 0.0328($7000), or $229.60, and 0.05($2600), or $130, for a total of only $359.60 in interest. Our guess was wrong, but checking the guess familiarized us with the problem. More than $2600 was borrowed at the higher rate.

2. **Translate.** We let l = the amount of the PLUS loan and k = the amount of the Perkins loan. Next, we organize a table in which the entries in each column come from the formula for simple interest:

$$Principal \cdot Rate \cdot Time = Interest.$$

	PLUS Loan	Perkins Loan	Total	
Principal	l	k	$9600	→ $l + k = 9600$
Rate of Interest	3.28%	5%		
Time	1 year	1 year		
Interest	0.0328l	0.05k	$402.60	→ $0.0328l + 0.05k = 402.60$

The total amount borrowed is found in the first row of the table:

$$l + k = 9600.$$

A second equation, representing the accumulated interest, can be found in the last row:

$$0.0328l + 0.05k = 402.60, \quad \text{or} \quad 328l + 500k = 4,026,000. \quad \text{Clearing decimals}$$

3. **Carry out.** The system can be solved by elimination:

$$l + k = 9600 \xrightarrow{\text{Multiplying both sides by } -500} -500l - 500k = -4,800,000$$
$$328l + 500k = 4,026,000 \qquad\qquad\qquad\qquad 328l + 500k = 4,026,000$$
$$\overline{\qquad\qquad -172l = -774,000}$$

$$l + k = 9600 \longleftarrow l = 4500$$
$$4500 + k = 9600$$
$$k = 5100.$$

We find that $l = 4500$ and $k = 5100$.

4. **Check.** The total amount borrowed is $4500 + $5100, or $9600. The interest on $4500 at 3.28% for 1 year is 0.0328($4500), or $147.60. The interest on $5100 at 5% for 1 year is 0.05($5100), or $255. The total amount of interest is $147.60 + $255, or $402.60, so the numbers check.

5. **State.** The PLUS loan was for $4500 and the Perkins loan was for $5100.

Try Exercise 27.

> **Problem-Solving Tip**
>
> When solving a problem, see if it is patterned or modeled after a problem that you have already solved.

Before proceeding to Example 5, briefly scan Examples 2–4 for similarities. Note that in each case, one of the equations in the system is a simple sum while the other equation represents a sum of products. Example 5 continues this pattern.

EXAMPLE 5 Mixing Fertilizers. Nature's Green Gardening, Inc., carries two brands of fertilizer containing nitrogen and water. "Gentle Grow" is 3% nitrogen and "Sun Saver" is 8% nitrogen. Nature's Green needs to combine the two types of solutions into a 90-L mixture that is 6% nitrogen. How much of each brand should be used?

SOLUTION

1. **Familiarize.** We make a drawing and note that we must consider not only the size of the mixture, but also its strength. Let's make a guess to gain familiarity with the problem.

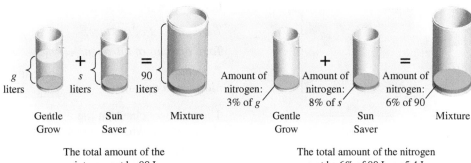

| The total amount of the mixture must be 90 L. | The total amount of the nitrogen must be 6% of 90 L, or 5.4 L. |

Suppose that 40 L of Gentle Grow and 50 L of Sun Saver are mixed. The resulting mixture will be the right size, 90 L, but will it be the right strength? To find out, note that 40 L of Gentle Grow would contribute $0.03(40) = 1.2$ L of nitrogen to the mixture while 50 L of Sun Saver would contribute $0.08(50) = 4$ L of nitrogen to the mixture. The total amount of nitrogen in the mixture would then be $1.2 + 4$, or 5.2 L. But we want 6% of 90, or 5.4 L, to be nitrogen. Our guess of 40 L and 50 L is close but incorrect. Checking our guess has familiarized us with the problem.

2. **Translate.** Let g = the number of liters of Gentle Grow and s = the number of liters of Sun Saver. The information can be organized in a table.

	Gentle Grow	Sun Saver	Mixture	
Number of Liters	g	s	90	$\rightarrow g + s = 90$
Percent of Nitrogen	3%	8%	6%	
Amount of Nitrogen	$0.03g$	$0.08s$	0.06×90, or 5.4 liters	$\rightarrow 0.03g + 0.08s = 5.4$

If we add g and s in the first row, we get one equation. It represents the total amount of mixture: $g + s = 90$.

If we add the amounts of nitrogen listed in the third row, we get a second equation. This equation represents the amount of nitrogen in the mixture: $0.03g + 0.08s = 5.4$.

After clearing decimals, we have translated the problem to the system

$$g + s = 90, \qquad (1)$$
$$3g + 8s = 540. \qquad (2)$$

3. Carry out. We use the elimination method to solve the system:

$$-3g - 3s = -270 \qquad \text{Multiplying both sides of equation (1) by } -3$$
$$\underline{3g + 8s = 540}$$
$$5s = 270 \qquad \text{Adding}$$
$$s = 54; \qquad \text{Solving for } s$$
$$g + 54 = 90 \qquad \text{Substituting into equation (1)}$$
$$g = 36. \qquad \text{Solving for } g$$

4. Check. Remember, g is the number of liters of Gentle Grow and s is the number of liters of Sun Saver.

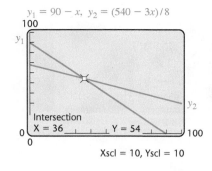

$$y_1 = 90 - x, \ y_2 = (540 - 3x)/8$$

Intersection
X = 36   Y = 54

Xscl = 10, Yscl = 10

Total amount of mixture: $\qquad\qquad\qquad\qquad g + s = 36 + 54 = 90$

Total amount of nitrogen: $\qquad$ 3% of 36 + 8% of $54 = 1.08 + 4.32 = 5.4$

Percentage of nitrogen in mixture: $\qquad \dfrac{\text{Total amount of nitrogen}}{\text{Total amount of mixture}} = \dfrac{5.4}{90} = 6\%$

The numbers check in the original problem. We can also check graphically, as shown at left, where x replaces g and y replaces s.

5. State. Nature's Green Gardening should mix 36 L of Gentle Grow with 54 L of Sun Saver.

Try Exercise 25.

MOTION PROBLEMS

When a problem deals with distance, speed (rate), and time, recall the following.

Distance, Rate, and Time Equations If r represents rate, t represents time, and d represents distance, then

$$d = rt, \qquad r = \frac{d}{t}, \quad \text{and} \quad t = \frac{d}{r}.$$

Be sure to remember at least one of these equations. The others can be obtained by multiplying or dividing on both sides as needed.

EXAMPLE 6 Train Travel. A Vermont Railways freight train, loaded with logs, leaves Boston, heading to Washington, D.C., at a speed of 60 km/h. Two hours later, an Amtrak® Metroliner leaves Boston, bound for Washington, D.C., on a parallel track at 90 km/h. At what point will the Metroliner catch up to the freight train?

SOLUTION

1. Familiarize. Let's make a guess and check to see if it is correct. Suppose the trains meet after traveling 180 km. We can calculate the time for each train.

	Distance	Rate	Time
Freight train	180 km	60 km/h	$\frac{180}{60} = 3$ hr
Metroliner	180 km	90 km/h	$\frac{180}{90} = 2$ hr

We see that the distance cannot be 180 km, since the difference in travel times for the trains is *not* 2 hr. Although our guess is wrong, we can use a similar chart to organize the information in this problem.

The distance at which the trains meet is unknown, but we do know that the trains will have traveled the same distance when they meet. We let d = this distance.

The time that the trains are running is also unknown, but we do know that the freight train has a 2-hr head start. Thus if we let t = the number of hours that the freight train is running before they meet, then $t - 2$ is the number of hours that the Metroliner runs before catching up to the freight train.

60 km/h
d kilometers
t hours

90 km/h
d kilometers
$t - 2$ hours

Trains meet here

2. **Translate.** We can organize the information in a chart. The formula *Distance* = *Rate · Time* guides our choice of rows and columns.

	Distance	Rate	Time
Freight Train	d	60	t
Metroliner	d	90	$t - 2$

$d = 60t$

$d = 90(t - 2)$

Using *Distance* = *Rate · Time* twice, we get two equations:

$$d = 60t, \qquad (1)$$
$$d = 90(t - 2). \qquad (2)$$

3. **Carry out.** We solve the system both algebraically and graphically.

ALGEBRAIC APPROACH

We solve the system using the substitution method:

$60t = 90(t - 2)$ Substituting $60t$ for d in equation (2)

$60t = 90t - 180$ Using the distributive law

$-30t = -180$

$t = 6.$

The time for the freight train is 6 hr, which means that the time for the Metroliner is $6 - 2$, or 4 hr. Remember that it is distance, not time, that the problem asked for. Thus for $t = 6$, we have $d = 60 \cdot 6 = 360$ km.

GRAPHICAL APPROACH

We replace d with y and t with x. Since y = distance and x = time, we use a viewing window of $[0, 10, 0, 500]$. We graph $y_1 = 60x$ and $y_2 = 90(x - 2)$ and find the point of intersection, $(6, 360)$.

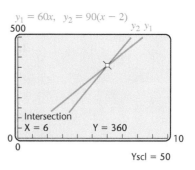

$y_1 = 60x$, $y_2 = 90(x - 2)$

Intersection
X = 6   Y = 360

Yscl = 50

The problem asks for the distance that the trains travel. Recalling that y = distance, we see that the distance that both trains travel is 360 km.

Student Notes

Always be careful to answer the question asked in the problem. In Example 6, the problem asks for distance, not time. Answering "6 hr" would be incorrect.

4. **Check.** At 60 km/h, the freight train will travel 60 · 6, or 360 km, in 6 hr. At 90 km/h, the Metroliner will travel 90 · (6 − 2) = 360 km in 4 hr. The numbers check.

5. **State.** The Metroliner will catch up to the freight train at a point 360 km from Boston.

Try Exercise 35.

EXAMPLE 7   Jet Travel.   A Boeing 747-400 jet flies 4 hr west with a 60-mph tailwind. Returning *against* the wind takes 5 hr. Find the speed of the jet with no wind.

SOLUTION

1. **Familiarize.** We imagine the situation and make a drawing. Note that the wind *speeds up* the jet on the outbound flight but *slows down* the jet on the return flight.

Let's make a guess of the jet's speed if there were no wind. Note that the distances traveled each way must be the same.

Speed with no wind:	400 mph
Speed with the wind:	400 + 60 = 460 mph
Speed against the wind:	400 − 60 = 340 mph
Distance with the wind:	460 · 4 = 1840 mi
Distance against the wind:	340 · 5 = 1700 mi

Since the distances are not the same, our guess of 400 mph is incorrect.

We let r = the speed, in miles per hour, of the jet in still air. Then $r + 60$ = the jet's speed with the wind and $r − 60$ = the jet's speed against the wind. We also let d = the distance traveled, in miles.

2. **Translate.** The information can be organized in a chart. The distances traveled are the same, so we use *Distance = Rate* (or *Speed*) *· Time*. Each row of the chart gives an equation.

	Distance	Rate	Time	
With Wind	d	$r + 60$	4	$d = (r + 60)4$
Against Wind	d	$r − 60$	5	$d = (r − 60)5$

The two equations constitute a system:

$$d = (r + 60)4, \quad (1)$$
$$d = (r - 60)5. \quad (2)$$

3. Carry out. We solve the system using substitution:

$(r - 60)5 = (r + 60)4$ Substituting $(r - 60)5$ for d in equation (1)

$5r - 300 = 4r + 240$ Using the distributive law

$r = 540.$ Solving for r

4. Check. When $r = 540$, the speed with the wind is $540 + 60 = 600$ mph, and the speed against the wind is $540 - 60 = 480$ mph. The distance with the wind, $600 \cdot 4 = 2400$ mi, matches the distance into the wind, $480 \cdot 5 = 2400$ mi, so we have a check.

5. State. The speed of the jet with no wind is 540 mph.

Try Exercise 37.

Tips for Solving Motion Problems

1. Draw a diagram using an arrow or arrows to represent distance and the direction of each object in motion.
2. Organize the information in a chart.
3. Look for times, distances, or rates that are the same. These often can lead to an equation.
4. Translating to a system of equations allows for the use of two variables.
5. Always make sure that you have answered the question asked.

4.4 Exercise Set

FOR EXTRA HELP   MyMathLab

1. *Endangered Species.* In 2009, there were 1010 endangered plant and animal species in the United States. There were 192 more endangered plant species than animal species. How many plant species and how many animal species were considered endangered in 2009?
Source: U.S. Fish and Wildlife Service

2. *e-mail Usage.* In 2007, the average e-mail user sent 578 personal and business e-mails each week. The number of personal e-mails was 30 fewer than the number of business e-mails. How many of each type were sent each week?
Source: *JupiterResearch*

3. *Social Networking.* In April 2009, Facebook and MySpace together had an estimated 160 million unique users. Facebook had 8 million fewer users than twice the number of users MySpace had that same month. How many unique users did each online social network have in April 2009?
Source: www.insidefacebook.com

4. *Snowmen.* The tallest snowman ever recorded—really a snow *woman* named Olympia—was built by residents of Bethel, Maine, and surrounding towns. Her body and head together made up her total record height of 122 ft. The body was 2 ft longer than 14 times the height of the head. What were the separate heights of Olympia's head and body?

Source: Based on information from *Guinness World Records* 2010

5. *Geometry.* Two angles are supplementary. One angle is 3° less than twice the other. Find the measures of the angles.

Supplementary angles

6. *Geometry.* Two angles are complementary. The sum of the measures of the first angle and half the second angle is 64°. Find the measures of the angles.

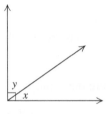

Complementary angles

7. *College Credits.* Each course at Mt. Regis College is worth either 3 or 4 credits. The members of the men's swim team are taking a total of 48 courses that are worth a total of 155 credits. How many 3-credit courses and how many 4-credit courses are being taken?

8. *College Credits.* Each course at Pease County Community College is worth either 3 or 4 credits. The members of the women's golf team are taking a total of 27 courses that are worth a total of 89 credits. How many 3-credit courses and how many 4-credit courses are being taken?

9. *Returnable Bottles.* As part of a fundraiser, the Cobble Hill Daycare collected 430 returnable bottles and cans, some worth 5 cents each and the rest worth 10 cents each. If the total value of the cans and bottles was $26.20, how many 5-cent bottles or cans and how many 10-cent bottles or cans were collected?

10. *Retail Sales.* Cool Treats sold 60 ice cream cones. Single-dip cones sold for $2.50 each and double-dip cones for $4.15 each. In all, $179.70 was taken in for the cones. How many of each size cone were sold?

11. *Yellowstone Park Admissions.* Entering Yellowstone National Park costs $25 for a car and $20 for a motorcycle. One June day, 5950 cars or motorcycles

enter and pay a total of $137,625. How many motorcycles entered on that day?

Source: National Park Service, U.S. Department of the Interior

12. *Zoo Admissions.* During the summer months, the Bronx Zoo charges $15 for adults and $11 for children. One July day, a total of $11,920 was collected from 960 adults and children. How many adult admissions were there?

Source: Bronx Zoo

13. *Printing.* King Street Printing recently charged 1.9¢ per sheet of paper, but 2.4¢ per sheet for paper made of recycled fibers. Darren's bill for 150 sheets of paper was $3.41. How many sheets of each type were used?

14. *Photocopying.* Quick Copy recently charged 6¢ per page for copying pages that can be machine-fed and 18¢ per page for copying pages that must be hand-placed on the copier. If Lea's bill for 90 copies was $9.24, how many copies of each type were made?

15. *Jewelry Design.* In order to make a necklace, Alicia purchased 80 beads for a total of $39 (excluding tax). Some of the beads were sterling silver beads that cost 40¢ each and the rest were gemstone beads that cost 65¢ each. How many of each type of bead did Alicia buy?

16. *Vehicles.* 2 Your Door is purchasing new hybrid SUVs for its delivery fleet. On order are 35 Mercury Mariner and Ford Escape hybrids. Each Mercury Mariner costs $29,000, and each Ford Escape costs $32,000. If the total price is $1,042,000, how many of each did they order?

17. *Sales.* Office Depot® recently sold a black Epson® T069120-S ink cartridge for $16.99 and a black HP C4902AN cartridge for $25.99. At the start of a recent fall semester, a total of 50 of these cartridges was sold for a total of $984.50. How many of each type were purchased?

18. *Office Supplies.* Hancock County Social Services is preparing materials for a seminar. They purchase a combination of 80 large and small binders. The large binders cost $8.49 each and the small ones cost

$5.99 each. If the total cost of the binders was $544.20, how many of each size were purchased?

Aha! **19.** *Blending Coffees.*   The Roasted Bean charges $13.00 per pound for Fair Trade Organic Mexican coffee and $11.00 per pound for Fair Trade Organic Peruvian coffee. How much of each type should be used to make a 28-lb blend that sells for $12.00 per pound?

20. *Mixed Nuts.*   Oh Nuts! sells pistachio kernels for $6.50 per pound and almonds for $8.00 per pound. How much of each type should be used to make a 50-lb mixture that sells for $7.40 per pound?

21. *Blending Spices.*   Spice of Life sells ground sumac for $1.35 per ounce and ground thyme for $1.85 per ounce. Aman wants to make a 20-oz Zahtar seasoning blend using the two spices that sells for $1.65 per ounce. How much of each spice should Aman use?

22. *Blending Coffees.*   The Gathering Grounds charges $10.00 per pound for Columbian Supreme coffee and $12.00 per pound for Columbian Supreme decaffeinated coffee. The Lanosgas buy some of each to make their own partially-decaffeinated blend. If they pay $53 for a 5-lb blend, how much of each did they purchase?

23. *Acid Mixtures.*   Jerome's experiment requires him to mix a 50%-acid solution with an 80%-acid solution to create 200 mL of a 68%-acid solution. How much 50%-acid solution and how much 80%-acid solution should he use? Complete the following table as part of the *Translate* step.

Type of Solution	50%-Acid	80%-Acid	68%-Acid Mix
Amount of Solution	x	y	
Percent Acid	50%		68%
Amount of Acid in Solution		$0.8y$	

24. *Ink Remover.*   Etch Clean Graphics uses one cleanser that is 25% acid and a second that is 50% acid. How many liters of each should be mixed to get 30 L of a solution that is 40% acid?

25. *Catering.*   Cati's Catering is planning an office reception. The office administrator has requested a candy mixture that is 25% chocolate. Cati has available mixtures that are either 50% chocolate or 10% chocolate. How much of each type should be mixed to get a 20-lb mixture that is 25% chocolate?

26. *Livestock Feed.*   Soybean meal is 16% protein and corn meal is 9% protein. How many pounds of each should be mixed to get a 350-lb mixture that is 12% protein?

27. *Student Loans.*   Asel's two student loans totaled $12,000. One of her loans was at 6.5% simple interest and the other at 7.2%. After one year, Asel owed $811.50 in interest. What was the amount of each loan?

28. *Investments.*   A self-employed contractor nearing retirement made two investments totaling $15,000. In one year, these investments yielded $1023 in simple interest. Part of the money was invested at 6% and the rest at 7.5%. How much was invested at each rate?

29. *Automotive Maintenance.*   "Steady State" antifreeze is 18% alcohol and "Even Flow" is 10% alcohol. How many liters of each should be mixed to get 20 L of a mixture that is 15% alcohol?

30. *Chemistry.*   E-Chem Testing has a solution that is 80% base and another that is 30% base. A technician needs 150 L of a solution that is 62% base. The 150 L will be prepared by mixing the two solutions on hand. How much of each should be used?

31. *Octane Ratings.* The octane rating of a gasoline is a measure of the amount of isooctane in the gas. Manufacturers recommend using 93-octane gasoline on retuned motors. How much 87-octane gas and 95-octane gas should Yousef mix in order to make 10 gal of 93-octane gas for his retuned Ford F-150?
Source: Champlain Electric and Petroleum Equipment

32. *Octane Ratings.* Subaru recommends 91-octane gasoline for the 2008 Legacy 3.0 R. How much 87-octane gas and 93-octane gas should Kelsey mix in order to make 12 gal of 91-octane gas for her Legacy?
Sources: Champlain Electric and Petroleum Equipment; Dean Team Ballwin

33. *Food Science.* The bar graph below shows the milk fat percentages in three dairy products. How many pounds each of whole milk and cream should be mixed to form 200 lb of milk for cream cheese?

Milk Fat

34. *Food Science.* How much lowfat milk (1% fat) and how much whole milk (4% fat) should be mixed to make 5 gal of reduced fat milk (2% fat)?

35. *Train Travel.* A train leaves Danville Union and travels north at a speed of 75 km/h. Two hours later, an express train leaves on a parallel track and travels north at 125 km/h. How far from the station will they meet?

36. *Car Travel.* Two cars leave Salt Lake City, traveling in opposite directions. One car travels at a speed of 80 km/h and the other at 96 km/h. In how many hours will they be 528 km apart?

37. *Canoeing.* Kahla paddled for 4 hr with a 6-km/h current to reach a campsite. The return trip against the same current took 10 hr. Find the speed of Kahla's canoe in still water.

38. *Boating.* Cody's motorboat took 3 hr to make a trip downstream with a 6-mph current. The return trip against the same current took 5 hr. Find the speed of the boat in still water.

39. *Point of No Return.* A plane flying the 3458-mi trip from New York City to London has a 50-mph tailwind. The flight's *point of no return* is the point at which the flight time required to return to New York is the same as the time required to continue to London. If the speed of the plane in still air is 360 mph, how far is New York from the point of no return?

40. *Point of No Return.* A plane is flying the 2553-mi trip from Los Angeles to Honolulu into a 60-mph headwind. If the speed of the plane in still air is 310 mph, how far from Los Angeles is the plane's point of no return? (See Exercise 39.)

41. *Basketball Scoring.* Wilt Chamberlain once scored a record 100 points on a combination of 64 foul shots (each worth one point) and two-pointers. How many shots of each type did he make?

42. *Basketball Scoring.* LeBron James recently scored 34 points on a combination of 21 foul shots and two-pointers. How many shots of each type did he make?

43. *Phone Rates.* Kim makes frequent calls from the United States to Korea. Her calling plan costs $3.99 per month plus 9¢ per minute for calls made to a landline and 15¢ per minute for calls made to a wireless number. One month her bill was $58.89. If she talked for a total of 400 min, how many minutes were to a landline and how many minutes to a wireless number?
Source: wireless.att.com

44. *Radio Airplay.* Roscoe must play 12 commercials during his 1-hr radio show. Each commercial is either 30 sec or 60 sec long. If the total commercial time during that hour is 10 min, how many commercials of each type does Roscoe play?

45. *Making Change.* Monica makes a $9.25 purchase at the bookstore with a $20 bill. The store has no bills and gives her the change in quarters and fifty-cent pieces. There are 30 coins in all. How many of each kind are there?

46. *Money Exchange.* Sabina goes to a bank and gets change for a $50 bill consisting of all $5 bills and $1 bills. There are 22 bills in all. How many of each kind are there?

TW **47.** In what ways are Examples 3 and 4 similar? In what sense are their systems of equations similar?

TW **48.** Write at least three study tips of your own for someone beginning this exercise set.

SKILL REVIEW

To prepare for Section 4.5, review graphing equations and functions.

Graph.

49. $y = 2x - 3$

50. $y = -\frac{1}{3}x + 4$

51. $y = 2$

52. $y = -4$

53. $f(x) = -\frac{2}{3}x + 1$

54. $g(x) = 5x - 2$

SYNTHESIS

TW **55.** Suppose that in Example 3 you are asked only for the amount of almonds needed for the Market Street Blend. Would the method of solving the problem change? Why or why not?

TW **56.** Write a problem similar to Example 2 for a classmate to solve. Design the problem so that the solution is "The florist sold 14 hanging plants and 9 flats of petunias."

57. *Metal Alloys.* In order for a metal to be labeled "sterling silver," the silver alloy must contain at least 92.5% pure silver. Mitchell has 32 oz of coin silver, which is 90% pure silver. How much pure silver must he add to the coin silver in order to have a sterling-silver alloy?

Source: Hardy, R. Allen, *The Jewelry Repair Manual.* Courier Dover Publications, 1996, p. 271.

58. *Recycled Paper.* Unable to purchase 60 reams of paper that contains 20% post-consumer fiber, the Naylor School bought paper that was either 0% post-consumer fiber or 30% post-consumer fiber. How many reams of each should be purchased in order to use the same amount of post-consumer fiber as if the 20% post-consumer fiber paper were available?

59. *Automotive Maintenance.* The radiator in Michelle's car contains 6.3 L of antifreeze and water. This mixture is 30% antifreeze. How much of this mixture should she drain and replace with pure antifreeze so that there will be a mixture of 50% antifreeze?

60. *Exercise.* Cindi jogs and walks to school each day. She averages 4 km/h walking and 8 km/h jogging. From home to school is 6 km and Cindi makes the trip in 1 hr. How far does she jog in a trip?

61. *Book Sales.* *American Economic History* can be purchased as a three-volume set for $88 or each volume can be purchased separately for $39. An economics class spent $1641 for 51 volumes. How many three-volume sets were ordered?

Source: National History Day, www.nhd.org.

62. The tens digit of a two-digit positive integer is 2 more than three times the units digit. If the digits are interchanged, the new number is 13 less than half the given number. Find the given integer. (*Hint:* Let x = the tens-place digit and y = the units-place digit; then $10x + y$ is the number.)

63. *Wood Stains.* Williams' Custom Flooring has 0.5 gal of stain that is 20% brown and 80% neutral. A customer orders 1.5 gal of a stain that is 60% brown and 40% neutral. How much pure brown stain and how much neutral stain should be added to the original 0.5 gal in order to make up the order? (This problem was suggested by Professor Chris Burditt of Yountville, California.)

64. *Train Travel.* A train leaves Union Station for Central Station, 216 km away, at 9 A.M. One hour later, a train leaves Central Station for Union Station. They meet at noon. If the second train had started at 9 A.M. and the first train at 10:30 A.M., they would still have met at noon. Find the speed of each train.

65. *Fuel Economy.* Grady's station wagon gets 18 miles per gallon (mpg) in city driving and 24 mpg in highway driving. The car is driven 465 mi on 23 gal of gasoline. How many miles were driven in the city and how many were driven on the highway?

66. *Biochemistry.* Industrial biochemists routinely use a machine to mix a buffer of 10% acetone by adding 100% acetone to water. One day, instead of adding 5 L of acetone to create a vat of buffer, a machine added 10 L. How much additional water was needed to bring the concentration down to 10%?

67. Recently, Staples® charged $5.99 for a 2-count pack of Bic® Round Stic Grip mechanical pencils and $7.49 for a 12-count pack of Bic® Matic Grip mechanical pencils. Wiese Accounting purchased 138 of these two types of mechanical pencils for a total of $157.26. How many packs of each did they buy?

▓ Try Exercise Answers: Section 4.4

1. Plant species: 601; animal species: 409 **9.** 5-cent bottles or cans: 336; 10-cent bottles or cans: 94 **21.** Sumac: 8 oz; thyme: 12 oz **25.** 50% chocolate: 7.5 lb; 10% chocolate: 12.5 lb **27.** $7500 at 6.5%; $4500 at 7.2% **35.** 375 km **37.** 14 km/h

Collaborative Corner

How Many Two's? How Many Three's?

Focus: Systems of linear equations
Time: 20 minutes
Group Size: 3

The box score at right, from the 2010 NBA All-Star game, contains information on how many field goals (worth either 2 or 3 points) and free throws (worth 1 point) each player attempted and made. For example, the line "James 10-22 4-4 25" means that the East's LeBron James made 10 field goals out of 22 attempts and 4 free throws out of 4 attempts, for a total of 25 points.

ACTIVITY

1. Work as a group to develop a system of two equations in two unknowns that can be used to determine how many 2-pointers and how many 3-pointers were made by the West.

2. Each group member should solve the system from part (1) in a different way: one person algebraically, one person by making a table and methodically checking all combinations of 2- and

3-pointers, and one person by guesswork. Compare answers when this has been completed.

3. Determine, as a group, how many 2- and 3-pointers the East made.

East (141)
James 10–22 4–4 25, Garnett 2–4 0–0 4, Howard 7–10 2–3 17, Johnson 4–8 0–0 10, Wade 12–16 4–6 28, Pierce 3–6 0–0 8, Bosh 9–16 5–7 23, Rondo 2–3 0–0 4, Wallace 1–3 0–0 2, Lee 2–3 0–0 4, Rose 4–8 0–0 8, Horford 4–5 0–1 8
Totals 60–104 15–21 141

West (139)
Duncan 1–4 1–2 3, Nowitzki 8–15 6–6 22, Stoudemire 5–10 2–2 12, Anthony 13–22 0–1 27, Nash 2–4 0–0 4, Gasol 5–9 3–3 13, Billups 6–11 0–0 17, Williams 6–11 0–0 14, Durant 7–14 0–0 15, Randolph 4–10 0–0 8, Kaman 2–4 0–0 4, Kidd 0–1 0–0 0
Totals 59–115 12–14 139

East   37 39 42 23 — 141
West   34 35 40 30 — 139

4.5 Solving Equations by Graphing

- Solving Equations Graphically: The Intersect Method

- Solving Equations Graphically: The Zero Method

- Applications

Recall that to *solve* an equation means to find all the replacements for the variable that make the equation true. We have seen how to solve algebraically; we now use a graphical method to solve.

SOLVING EQUATIONS GRAPHICALLY: THE INTERSECT METHOD

To see how solutions of equations are related to graphs, consider the graphs of the functions given by $f(x) = 2x + 5$ and $g(x) = -3$. The graphs intersect at $(-4, -3)$. At that point,

$$f(-4) = -3 \quad \text{and}$$
$$g(-4) = -3.$$

Thus,

$$f(x) = g(x) \quad \text{when } x = -4;$$
$$2x + 5 = -3 \quad \text{when } x = -4.$$

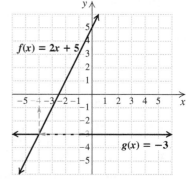

The solution of $2x + 5 = -3$ is -4, which is the x-coordinate of the point of intersection of the graphs of f and g.

EXAMPLE 1 Solve graphically: $\frac{1}{2}x + 3 = 2$.

SOLUTION First, we define $f(x)$ and $g(x)$. If $f(x) = \frac{1}{2}x + 3$ and $g(x) = 2$, then the equation becomes

$$\frac{1}{2}x + 3 = 2$$
$$f(x) = g(x). \quad \text{Substituting}$$

We graph both functions. The intersection appears to be $(-2, 2)$, so the solution is apparently -2.

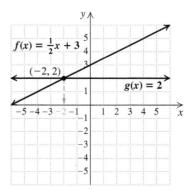

Check:

$$\frac{1}{2}x + 3 = 2$$

$\frac{1}{2}(-2) + 3$	2
$-1 + 3$	
$2 \overset{?}{=} 2$	TRUE

The solution is -2.

▌ Try Exercise 7.

Connecting the Concepts

Although graphical solutions of systems and equations look similar, different solutions are read from the graph. The solution of a system of equations is an ordered pair. The solution of a linear equation in one variable is a single number.

Solving a system of equations

$$y = x - 3,$$
$$y = 3x - 5$$

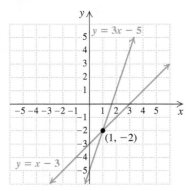

The solution of the system is $(1, -2)$.

Solving an equation

$$x - 3 = 3x - 5$$

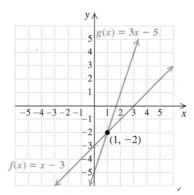

The solution of the equation is 1.

EXAMPLE 2 Solve: $-\frac{3}{4}x + 6 = 2x - 1$.

ALGEBRAIC APPROACH

We have

$$-\frac{3}{4}x + 6 = 2x - 1$$

$$-\frac{3}{4}x + 6 - 6 = 2x - 1 - 6 \qquad \text{Subtracting 6 from both sides}$$

$$-\frac{3}{4}x = 2x - 7 \qquad \text{Simplifying}$$

$$-\frac{3}{4}x - 2x = 2x - 7 - 2x \qquad \text{Subtracting } 2x \text{ from both sides}$$

$$-\frac{3}{4}x - \frac{8}{4}x = -7 \qquad \text{Simplifying}$$

$$-\frac{11}{4}x = -7 \qquad \text{Combining like terms}$$

$$-\frac{4}{11}\left(-\frac{11}{4}x\right) = -\frac{4}{11}(-7) \qquad \text{Multiplying both sides by } -\frac{4}{11}$$

$$x = \frac{28}{11}. \qquad \text{Simplifying}$$

Check:

$$\begin{array}{c|c} \multicolumn{2}{c}{-\frac{3}{4}x + 6 = 2x - 1} \\ \hline -\frac{3}{4}\left(\frac{28}{11}\right) + 6 & 2\left(\frac{28}{11}\right) - 1 \\ -\frac{21}{11} + \frac{66}{11} & \frac{56}{11} - \frac{11}{11} \\ \frac{45}{11} \overset{?}{=} & \frac{45}{11} \end{array}$$ TRUE

The solution is $\frac{28}{11}$.

GRAPHICAL APPROACH

We graph $f(x) = -\frac{3}{4}x + 6$ and $g(x) = 2x - 1$. It appears that the lines intersect at $(2.5, 4)$.

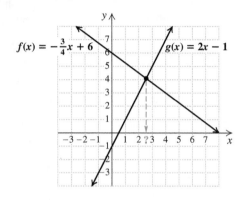

Check:

$$\begin{array}{c|c} \multicolumn{2}{c}{-\frac{3}{4}x + 6 = 2x - 1} \\ \hline -\frac{3}{4}(2.5) + 6 & 2(2.5) - 1 \\ -1.875 + 6 & 5 - 1 \\ 4.125 \overset{?}{=} & 4 \end{array}$$ FALSE

Our check shows that 2.5 is *not* the solution. To find the exact solution graphically, we need a method that will determine coordinates more precisely.

Try Exercise 37.

CAUTION! When using a hand-drawn graph to solve an equation, it is important to use graph paper and to work as neatly as possible. Use a straight-edge when drawing lines and be sure to erase any mistakes completely.

We can use the INTERSECT option of the CALC menu on a graphing calculator to find the point of intersection.

EXAMPLE 3 Solve using a graphing calculator: $-\frac{3}{4}x + 6 = 2x - 1$.

SOLUTION In Example 2, we saw that the graphs of $f(x) = -\frac{3}{4}x + 6$ and $g(x) = 2x - 1$ intersect near the point $(2.5, 4)$. Using a calculator, we now graph $y_1 = -\frac{3}{4}x + 6$ and $y_2 = 2x - 1$ and use the INTERSECT feature.

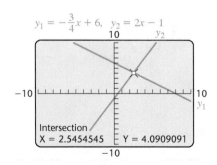

It appears from the screen above that the solution is 2.5454545. To check, we evaluate both sides of the equation $-\frac{3}{4}x + 6 = 2x - 1$ for this value of x. We evaluate Y1(X) and Y2(X) from the home screen, as shown on the left below. Converting X to fraction notation will give an exact solution. From the screen on the right below, we see that $\frac{28}{11}$ is the solution of the equation.

Y₁(X)	
	4.090909091
Y₂(X)	
	4.090909091

X ▸ Frac	
	28/11

▌ Try Exercise 41.

SOLVING EQUATIONS GRAPHICALLY: THE ZERO METHOD

When we are solving an equation graphically, it can be challenging to determine a portion of the x, y-coordinate plane that contains the point of intersection. The Zero method makes that determination easier because we are interested only in the point at which a graph crosses the x-axis.

To solve an equation using the Zero method, we use the addition principle to get zero on one side of the equation. Then we look for the intersection of the line and the x-axis, or the x-intercept of the graph. If using function notation, we look for the *zero* of the function, or the input x that makes the output zero.

Zero of a Function   A zero of a function is an input whose corresponding output is 0. If a is a zero of the function f, then $f(a) = 0$.

The y-coordinate of a point is 0 when the point is on the x-axis. Thus a zero of a function is the x-coordinate of any point at which its graph crosses or touches the x-axis.

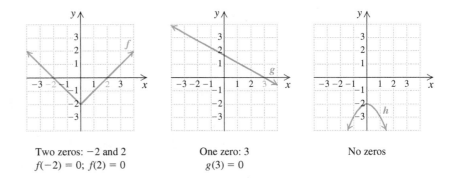

Two zeros: -2 and 2   One zero: 3   No zeros
$f(-2) = 0$; $f(2) = 0$ $g(3) = 0$

— *Zeros of a Function*

We can determine any zeros of a function using the ZERO option in the CALC menu of a graphing calculator. After graphing the function and choosing the ZERO option, we will be prompted for a Left Bound, a Right Bound, and a Guess. Since there may be more than one zero of a function, the left and right bounds indicate which zero we are currently finding. We examine the graph to find any places where it appears that the graph touches or crosses the x-axis, and then find those x-values one at a time. By using the arrow keys or entering a value on

(continued)

the keypad, we choose an x-value less than the zero for the left bound, an x-value more than the zero for the right bound, and a value close to the zero for the Guess.

Your Turn

1. Find the zero of $f(x) = 4.5 - 0.81x$. Enter $y_1 = 4.5 - 0.81x$ and graph using a standard viewing window.   The zero should appear to be about 5.

2. Press CALC 2. Press 3 ENTER 8 ENTER to choose a Left Bound of 3 and a Right Bound of 8. Then press 5 ENTER to enter a Guess of 5.   The zero is 5.5555556.

3. From the home screen, press X,T,θ,n MATH 1 ENTER to convert the solution to a fraction. $\frac{50}{9}$

EXAMPLE 4   Find the zeros of the function given by $f(x) = \frac{2}{3}x + 5$.

ALGEBRAIC APPROACH

We want to find any x-values for which $f(x) = 0$, so we substitute 0 for $f(x)$ and solve:

$$f(x) = \tfrac{2}{3}x + 5$$
$$0 = \tfrac{2}{3}x + 5 \qquad \text{Substituting 0 for } f(x)$$
$$-\tfrac{2}{3}x = 5 \qquad \text{Subtracting } -\tfrac{2}{3}x \text{ from both sides}$$
$$\left(-\tfrac{3}{2}\right)\left(-\tfrac{2}{3}x\right) = \left(-\tfrac{3}{2}\right)(5) \qquad \text{Multiplying by the reciprocal of } -\tfrac{2}{3}$$
$$x = -\tfrac{15}{2}. \qquad \text{Simplifying}$$

The zero of the function is $-\frac{15}{2}$, or -7.5.

GRAPHICAL APPROACH

We graph the function. There appears to be one zero of the function, approximately -7.

We press CALC 2 to choose the ZERO option of the CALC menu. We then choose -10 for a Left Bound, -5 for a Right Bound, and -7 for a Guess. The zero of the function is -7.5.

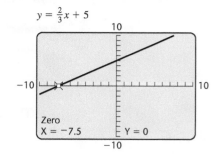

$y = \tfrac{2}{3}x + 5$

Zero
X = -7.5   Y = 0

Try Exercise 25.

Note that the answer to Example 4 is a value for x. A zero of a function is an x-value, not a function value or an ordered pair.

EXAMPLE 5   Solve graphically, using the Zero method: $2x - 5 = 4x - 11$.

SOLUTION   We first get 0 on one side of the equation:

$$2x - 5 = 4x - 11$$
$$-2x - 5 = -11 \qquad \text{Subtracting } 4x \text{ from both sides}$$
$$-2x + 6 = 0. \qquad \text{Adding 11 to both sides}$$

We then graph $f(x) = -2x + 6$, and find the x-intercept of the graph, as shown at left.

The x-intercept of the graph appears to be $(3, 0)$. We check 3 in the original equation.

Check:
$$\begin{array}{c|c} 2x - 5 = 4x - 11 \\ \hline 2 \cdot 3 - 5 & 4 \cdot 3 - 11 \\ 6 - 5 & 12 - 11 \\ 1 \overset{?}{=} 1 & \text{TRUE} \end{array}$$

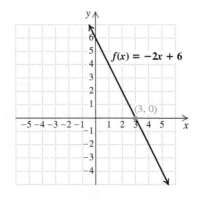

$f(x) = -2x + 6$

$(3, 0)$

The solution is 3.

Try Exercise 31.

EXAMPLE 6   Solve $3 - 8x = 5 - 7x$ using both the Intersect method and the Zero method.

GRAPHICAL APPROACH: INTERSECT METHOD	GRAPHICAL APPROACH: ZERO METHOD

We graph $y_1 = 3 - 8x$ and $y_2 = 5 - 7x$ and determine the coordinates of any point of intersection.

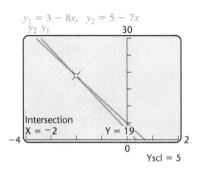

The point of intersection is $(-2, 19)$.
The solution is -2.

We first get zero on one side of the equation:

$$3 - 8x = 5 - 7x$$
$$-2 - 8x = -7x \qquad \text{Subtracting 5 from both sides}$$
$$-2 - x = 0. \qquad \text{Adding } 7x \text{ to both sides}$$

Then we graph $y = -2 - x$ and use the ZERO option to determine the x-intercept of the graph.

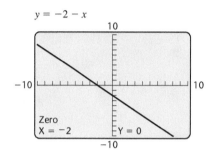

The solution is the first coordinate of the x-intercept, or -2.

Try Exercise 39.

APPLICATIONS

EXAMPLE 7   Photo-Book Prices.   A medium wire-bound photo book from iPhoto costs $10 for the book and 20 pages. Each additional page costs $0.50. Formulate and graph a mathematical model for the price. Then use the model to estimate the size of a book for which the price is $18.00.
Source: www.apple.com

SOLUTION

1. **Familiarize.** For a 20-page book, the price is $10. How much would a 26-page book cost? The price is $10 plus the cost for the additional 6 pages:

$$\$10 + 6(\$0.50) = \$10 + \$3 = \$13.$$

This can be generalized in a model if we let $P(x)$ represent the price of the book, in dollars, for a book with x pages more than the 20 included in the price.

2. **Translate.** We reword and translate as follows:

Rewording:	The total price	is	the price of the 20-page book	plus	$0.50 per additional page.
Translating:	$P(x)$	$=$	10	$+$	$0.50x$

3. **Carry out.** To estimate the size of a book for which the price is $18.00, we are estimating the solution of

$$0.50x + 10 = 18. \qquad \text{Replacing } P(x) \text{ with } 18$$

We do this by graphing $P(x) = 0.50x + 10$ and $y = 18$ and looking for the point of intersection. On a graphing calculator, we let $y_1 = 0.5x + 10$ and $y_2 = 18$ and adjust the window dimensions to include the point of intersection. We find a point of intersection at $(16, 18)$.

Thus we estimate that an $18.00 book will have 16 additional pages, or a total of 36 pages.

4. Check. For a book with 36 pages, the price is $10 plus $0.50 for each page over 20. Since $36 - 20 = 16$, the price will be

$$\$10 + 16(\$0.50) = \$10 + \$8 = \$18.$$

Our estimate turns out to be the exact answer.

5. State. A photo book that costs $18 has 36 pages.

⬛ Try Exercise 43.

4.5 Exercise Set

FOR EXTRA HELP   *MyMathLab*   Math XL WATCH DOWNLOAD READ REVIEW

↪ *Concept Reinforcement* *Exercises 1–6 refer to the graph below. Match each description with the appropriate answer from the column on the right.*

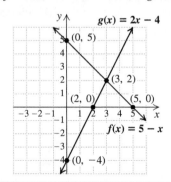

1. The solution of $5 - x = 2x - 4$ a) $(0, -4)$

2. The zero of g b) $(5, 0)$

3. The solution of $5 - x = 0$ c) $(3, 2)$

4. The x-intercept of the graph of f d) 2

5. The y-intercept of the graph of g e) 3

6. The solution of   f) 5
$$\begin{aligned} y &= 5 - x, \\ y &= 2x - 4 \end{aligned}$$

Estimate the solution of each equation from the associated graph.

7. $2x - 1 = -5$

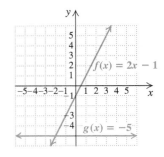

8. $\frac{1}{2}x + 1 = 3$

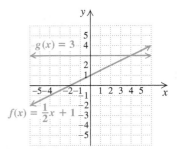

9. $2x + 3 = x - 1$

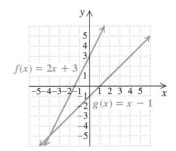

10. $2 - x = 3x - 2$

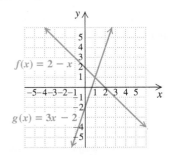

11. $\frac{1}{2}x + 3 = x - 1$

12. $2x - \frac{1}{2} = x + \frac{5}{2}$

13. $f(x) = g(x)$

14. $f(x) = g(x)$

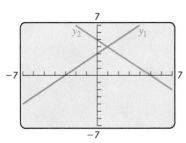

15. Estimate the value of x for which $y_1 = y_2$.

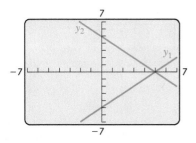

16. Estimate the value of x for which $y_1 = y_2$.

In Exercises 17–30, determine the zeros, if any, of each function.

17.

18.

19.

20.

21.

22.

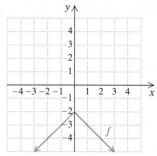

23. $f(x) = x - 5$ **24.** $f(x) = x + 3$

25. $f(x) = \frac{1}{2}x + 10$ **26.** $f(x) = \frac{2}{3}x - 6$

27. $f(x) = 2.7 - x$ **28.** $f(x) = 0.5 - x$

29. $f(x) = 3x + 7$ **30.** $f(x) = 5x - 8$

Solve graphically.

31. $x - 3 = 4$ **32.** $x + 4 = 6$

33. $2x + 1 = 7$ **34.** $3x - 5 = 1$

35. $\frac{1}{3}x - 2 = 1$ **36.** $\frac{1}{2}x + 3 = -1$

37. $x + 3 = 5 - x$ **38.** $x - 7 = 3x - 3$

39. $5 - \frac{1}{2}x = x - 4$ **40.** $3 - x = \frac{1}{2}x - 3$

41. $2x - 1 = -x + 3$ **42.** $-3x + 4 = 3x - 4$

Use a graph to estimate the solution in each of the following. Be sure to use graph paper and a straightedge if graphing by hand.

43. *Health Care.* Under a particular Anthem health-insurance plan, an individual pays the first $5000 of hospitalization charges each year plus 30% of all charges in excess of $5000. In 2010, Gerry's only hospitalization was for rotator cuff surgery. By approximately how much did Gerry's hospital bill exceed $5000, if the surgery ended up costing him $6350?
Source: www.ehealthinsurance.com

44. *Cable TV.* Gina's new TV service costs $200 for the hardware plus $35 per month for the service. After how many months has she spent $480 for cable TV?

45. *Cell-Phone Charges.* Skytone Calling charges $100 for a Smart phone and $35 per month under its economy plan. Estimate the time required for the total cost to reach $275.

46. *Cell-Phone Charges.* The Cellular Connection charges $80 for a Smart phone and $40 per month under its economy plan. Estimate the time required for the total cost to reach $240.

47. *Parking Fees.*   Karla's Parking charges $3.00 to park plus 50¢ for each 15-min unit of time. Estimate how long someone can park for $7.50.*

48. *Cost of a Road Call.*   Dave's Foreign Auto Village charges $50 for a road call plus $15 for each 15-min unit of time. Estimate the time required for a road call that cost $140.*

49. *Cost of a FedEx Delivery.*   In 2010, for Standard delivery to the closest zone of packages weighing from 100 to 499 lb, FedEx charged $130 plus $1.30 for each pound over 100. Estimate the weight of a package that cost $325 to ship.
Source: www.fedex.com

50. *Copying Costs.*   For each copy of a research paper, a university copy center charged $2.25 for a spiral binding and 8¢ for each page that was a double-sided copy. Estimate the number of pages in a spiral-bound research paper that cost $8.25 per copy. Assume that every page in the report was a double-sided copy.

TW **51.** Explain the difference between finding $f(0)$ and finding the zeros of f.

TW **52.** Darnell used a graphical method to solve $2x - 3 = x + 4$. He stated that the solution was $(7, 11)$. Can this answer be correct? What mistake do you think Darnell is making?

SKILL REVIEW

Review exponential notation and order of operations. Simplify.

53. $(-5)^3$

54. $(-2)^6$

55. -2^6

56. $3 \cdot 2^4 - 5 \cdot 2^3$

57. $2 - (3 - 2^2) + 10 \div 2 \cdot 5$

58. $(5 - 7)^2(3 - 2 \cdot 2)$

---

*More precise, nonlinear models of Exercises 47 and 48 appear in Exercises 69 and 70, respectively.

SYNTHESIS

TW **59.** Explain why, when we are solving an equation graphically, the *x*-coordinate of the point of intersection gives the solution of the equation.

TW **60.** Explain the difference between "solving by graphing" and "graphing the solution set."

Estimate the solution(s) from the associated graph.

61. $f(x) = g(x)$

62. $f(x) = g(x)$

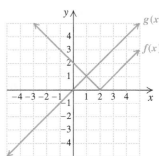

Solve graphically. Be sure to check.

63. $2x = |x + 1|$ **64.** $x - 1 = |4 - 2x|$

65. $\frac{1}{2}x = 3 - |x|$ **66.** $2 - |x| = 1 - 3x$

67. $x^2 = x + 2$ **68.** $x^2 = x$

69. (Refer to Exercise 47.) It costs as much to park at Karla's for 16 min as it does for 29 min. Thus the linear graph drawn in the solution of Exercise 47 is not a precise representation of the situation. Draw a graph with a series of "steps" that more accurately reflects the situation.

70. (Refer to Exercise 48.) A 32-min road call with Dave's costs the same as a 44-min road call. Thus the linear graph drawn in the solution of Exercise 48 is not a precise representation of the situation. Draw a graph with a series of "steps" that more accurately reflects the situation.

Try Exercise Answers: Section 4.5
7. −2 **25.** −20 **31.** 7 **37.** 1 **39.** 6 **41.** $1\frac{1}{3}$ **43.** $9500, or $4500 over $5000

Study Summary

KEY TERMS AND CONCEPTS	EXAMPLES	PRACTICE EXERCISES

SECTION 4.1: SYSTEMS OF EQUATIONS AND GRAPHING

A solution of a **system of two equations** is an ordered pair that makes both equations true. The intersection of the graphs of the equations gives the solution of the system.

A **consistent** system has at least one solution; an **inconsistent** system has no solution.

When one equation in a system of two equations is a nonzero multiple of the other, the equations are **dependent** and there is an infinite number of solutions. Otherwise, the equations are **independent.**

$$x + y = 3,$$
$$y = x - 1$$

The graphs intersect at $(2, 1)$.
The solution is $(2, 1)$.
The system is consistent.
The equations are independent.

$$x + y = 3,$$
$$x + y = 1$$

The graphs do not intersect.
There is no solution.
The system is inconsistent.
The equations are independent.

$$x + y = 3,$$
$$2x + 2y = 6$$

The graphs are the same.
The solution set is
$\{(x, y) \mid x + y = 3\}$.
The system is consistent.
The equations are dependent.

1. Solve by graphing:
$$x - y = 3,$$
$$y = 2x - 5.$$

SECTION 4.2: SYSTEMS OF EQUATIONS AND SUBSTITUTION

To use the **substitution method,** we solve one equation for a variable and substitute that expression for that variable in the other equation.

Solve:
$$2x + 3y = 8,$$
$$x = y + 1.$$

Substitute and solve for y:
$$2(y + 1) + 3y = 8$$
$$2y + 2 + 3y = 8$$
$$y = \frac{6}{5}.$$

Substitute and solve for x:
$$x = y + 1$$
$$x = \frac{6}{5} + 1$$
$$x = \frac{11}{5}.$$

The solution is $\left(\frac{11}{5}, \frac{6}{5}\right)$.

2. Solve by substitution:
$$x = 3y - 2,$$
$$y - x = 1.$$

SECTION 4.3: SYSTEMS OF EQUATIONS AND ELIMINATION

To use the **elimination method,** we add to eliminate a variable.

Solve:
$$4x - 2y = 6,$$
$$3x + y = 7.$$

3. Solve by elimination:
$$2x - y = 5,$$
$$x + 3y = 1.$$

Eliminate y and solve for x:

$$4x - 2y = 6$$
$$\underline{6x + 2y = 14}$$
$$10x \qquad = 20$$
$$x = 2.$$

Substitute and solve for y:

$$3x + y = 7$$
$$3 \cdot 2 + y = 7$$
$$y = 1.$$

The solution is $(2, 1)$.

SECTION 4.4: MORE APPLICATIONS USING SYSTEMS

Total-value, mixture, and **motion problems** often translate directly to systems of equations.

Motion problems use one of the following relationships:

$$d = rt, \quad r = \frac{d}{t}, \quad t = \frac{d}{r}.$$

Simple-interest problems use the formula

Principal · Rate · Time
= Interest.

Total Value

Recently the Riley Recreation Center purchased 120 stamps for $40.80. If the stamps were a combination of 28¢ postcard stamps and 44¢ first-class stamps, how many of each type were bought? (See Example 2 on pp. 256–258 for a solution.)

Mixture

Nature's Green Gardening, Inc., carries two brands of fertilizer containing nitrogen and water. "Gentle Grow" is 3% nitrogen and "Sun Saver" is 8% nitrogen. Nature's Green needs to combine the two types of solutions into a 90-L mixture that is 6% nitrogen. How much of each brand should be used? (See Example 5 on pp. 305–306 for a solution.)

Motion

A Boeing 747-400 jet flies 4 hr west with a 60-mph tailwind. Returning against the wind takes 5 hr. Find the speed of the jet with no wind. (See Example 7 on pp. 308–309 for a solution.)

4. Barlow's Office Supply charges $17.49 for a box of Roller Grip™ pens and $16.49 for a box of eGEL™ pens. If Letsonville Community College purchased 120 such boxes for $2010.80, how many boxes of each type did they purchase?

5. An industrial cleaning solution that is 40% nitric acid is added to a solution that is 15% nitric acid in order to create 2 L of a solution that is 25% nitric acid. How much 40%-acid and how much 15%-acid should be used?

6. Ruth paddled for $1\frac{1}{2}$ hr with a 2-mph current to view a rock formation. The return trip against the same current took $2\frac{1}{2}$ hr. Find the speed of Ruth's canoe in still water.

SECTION 4.5: SOLVING EQUATIONS BY GRAPHING

A **zero** of a function is an input x such that $f(x) = 0$. Graphically, it is the x-coordinate of an x-intercept of the graph of f.

The x-intercept is $(-2, 0)$.
The zero of f is -2 because $f(-2) = 0$.

7. Find the zero of the function given by $f(x) = 8x - 1$.

Equations can be solved graphically using either the **Intersect** method or the **Zero** method.

Solve graphically: $x + 1 = 2x - 3$.

Intersect Method

Graph $y = x + 1$
and $y = 2x - 3$.

Zero Method

$$x + 1 = 2x - 3$$
$$0 = x - 4$$

Graph $y = x - 4$.

The solution is 4.

The solution is 4.

8. Solve graphically:

$$x - 3 = 5x + 1.$$

Review Exercises 4

🖋 *Concept Reinforcement.* *Complete each of the following sentences.*

1. The system

$$5x + 3y = 7,$$
$$y = 2x + 1$$

is most easily solved using the _____ method. [4.2]

2. The system

$$-2x + 3y = 8,$$
$$2x + 2y = 7$$

is most easily solved using the _____ method. [4.3]

3. Of the methods used to solve systems of equations, the _____ method may yield only approximate solutions. [4.1]

4. When one equation in a system is a multiple of another equation in that system, the equations are said to be _____. [4.1]

5. A system for which there is no solution is said to be _____. [4.1]

6. When we are using an algebraic method to solve a system of equations, obtaining a _____ tells us that the system is inconsistent. [4.2]

7. When we are graphing to solve a system of two equations, if there is no solution, the lines will be _____. [4.1]

8. If $f(10) = 0$, 10 is a _____ of f. [4.5]

9. The numbers in an ordered pair that is a solution of a system correspond to the variables in _____ order. [4.1]

10. When we are solving an equation graphically, the solution is the _____ of the point of intersection of the graphs. [4.5]

For Exercises 11–19, if a system has an infinite number of solutions, use set-builder notation to write the solution set. If a system has no solution, state this.

Solve graphically. [4.1]

11. $y = x - 3,$
    $y = \frac{1}{4}x$

12. $16x - 7y = 25,$
    $8x + 3y = 19$

Solve using the substitution method. [4.2]

13. $x - y = 8,$
    $y = 3x + 2$

14. $y = x + 2,$
    $y - x = 8$

15. $x - 3y = -2,$
    $7y - 4x = 6$

Solve using the elimination method. [4.3]

16. $2x - 5y = 11,$
    $y - 2x = 5$

17. $4x - 7y = 18,$
    $9x + 14y = 40$

18. $3x - 5y = 9,$
    $5x - 3y = -1$

19. $1.5x - 3 = -2y,$
    $3x + 4y = 6$

Solve.

20. *Architecture.*   The rectangular ground floor of the John Hancock building has a perimeter of 860 ft. The length is 100 ft more than the width. Find the length and the width. [4.2]

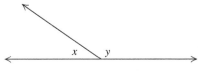

$x + 100$

x

21. A nontoxic floor wax can be made from lemon juice and food-grade linseed oil. The amount of oil should be twice the amount of lemon juice. How much of each ingredient is needed to make 32 oz of floor wax? (The mix should be spread with a rag and buffed when dry.) [4.4]

22. *Music Lessons.*   Jillian charges $25 for a private guitar lesson and $18 for a group guitar lesson. One day in August, Jillian earned $265 from 12 students. How many students of each type did Jillian teach? [4.4]

23. *Geometry.*   Two angles are supplementary. One angle is 7° less than 10 times the other. Find the measures of the angles. [4.2]

x y

Supplementary angles

24. A freight train leaves Houston at midnight traveling north at a speed of 44 mph. One hour later, a passenger train, going 55 mph, travels north from Houston on a parallel track. How many hours will the passenger train travel before it overtakes the freight train? [4.4]

25. D'Andre wants 14 L of fruit punch that is 10% juice. At the store, he finds punch that is 15% juice and punch that is 8% juice. How much of each should he purchase? [4.4]

26. *Printing.*   Using some pages that hold 1300 words per page and others that hold 1850 words per page, a typesetter is able to completely fill 12 pages with an 18,350-word document. How many pages of each kind were used? [4.4]

27. Use the graph below to solve $x - 1 = 2x + 1$. [4.5]

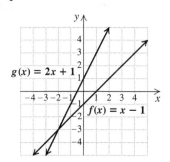

$g(x) = 2x + 1$

$f(x) = x - 1$

28. Use the graph in Exercise 27 to determine any zeros of f. [4.5]

29. Determine any zeros of $f(x) = 4 - 7x$. [4.5]

30. Solve graphically: $3x - 2 = x + 4$. [4.5]

SYNTHESIS

TW 31. Explain why any solution of a system of equations is a point of intersection of the graphs of each equation in the system. [4.1]

TW 32. Explain the difference between solving a system of equations graphically and solving an equation graphically. [4.1], [4.5]

33. Solve graphically:
$$y = x + 2,$$
$$y = x^2 + 2. \quad [4.1]$$

34. The solution of the following system is $(6, 2)$. Find C and D.
$$2x - Dy = 6,$$
$$Cx + 4y = 14 \quad [4.1]$$

35. For a two-digit number, the sum of the ones digit and the tens digit is 6. When the digits are reversed, the new number is 18 more than the original number. Find the original number. [4.4]

36. A sales representative agrees to a 1-year compensation package of $42,000 plus a computer. After 7 months, the sales representative leaves the company and receives a prorated compensation package consisting of the computer and $23,750. What was the value of the computer? [4.4]

Chapter Test 4

For Exercises 1–9, if a system has an infinite number of solutions, use set-builder notation to write the solution set. If a system has no solution, state this.

Solve by graphing.

1. $2x + y = 8,$
$\quad y - x = 2$

2. $2y - x = 7,$
$\quad 2x - 4y = 4$

Solve using the substitution method.

3. $x + 3y = -8,$
$\quad 4x - 3y = 23$

4. $2x + 4y = -6,$
$\quad y = 3x - 9$

5. $x = 5y - 10,$
$\quad 15y = 3x + 30$

Solve using the elimination method.

6. $3x - y = 7,$
$\quad x + y = 1$

7. $4y + 2x = 18,$
$\quad 3x + 6y = 26$

8. $4x - 6y = 3,$
$\quad 6x - 4y = -3$

9. $4x + 5y = 5,$
$\quad 6x + 7y = 7$

Solve.

10. *Perimeter of a Garden.*   Hassam is designing a rectangular garden with a perimeter of 66 ft. The length of the garden is 1 ft longer than three times the width. Find the dimensions of the garden.

11. *Geometry.*   Two angles are complementary. The sum of the measures of the first angle and half the second angle is 64°. Find the measures of the angles.

Complementary angles

12. In 2007, Nintendo Co. sold three times as many Wii game machines in Japan as Sony Corp. sold PlayStation 3 consoles. Together, they sold 4.84 million game machines in Japan. How many of each were sold?
Source: Bloomberg.com

13. *Books.*   The Friends of the Greenfield Public Library charge $1.75 for used hardbacks and 75¢ for used paperbacks. Keith purchased a total of 23 books for $28.25. How many books of each type did he buy?

14. Pepperidge Farm® Goldfish is a snack food for which 40% of its calories come from fat. Rold Gold® Pretzels receive 9% of their calories from fat. How many grams of each would be needed to make 620 g of a snack mix for which 15% of the calories are from fat?

15. *Boating.*   Kylie's motorboat took 3 hr to make a trip downstream on a river flowing at 5 mph. The return trip against the same current took 5 hr. Find the speed of the boat in still water.

16. *Coin Value.*   A collection of quarters and nickels is worth $1.25. There are 13 coins in all. How many of each are there?

17. Solve graphically: $2x - 5 = 3x - 3$.

18. Determine any zeros of the function given by $f(x) = \frac{1}{2}x - 5$.

SYNTHESIS

Solve.

19. $3(x - y) = 4 + x,$
$\qquad\quad x = 5y + 2$

20. $\frac{3}{2}x - y = 24,$
$\quad 2x + \frac{3}{2}y = 15$

21. You are in line at a ticket window. There are 2 more people ahead of you in line than there are behind you. In the entire line, there are three times as many people as there are behind you. How many are in the line?

22. The graph of the function $f(x) = mx + b$ contains the points $(-1, 3)$ and $(-2, -4)$. Find m and b.

Polynomials

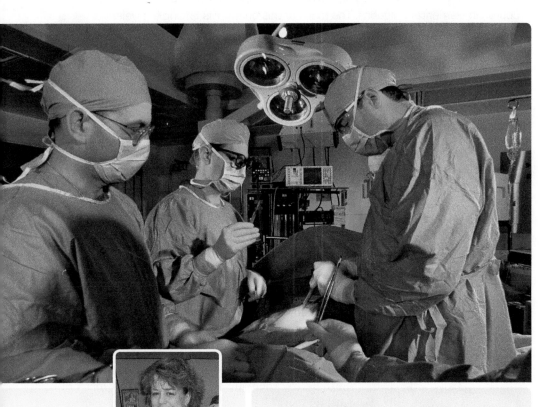

SHELLEY ZOMAK
TRANSPLANT COORDINATOR
(NURSE)
Pittsburgh, Pennsylvania

It is very important that a transplant recipient take the medications prescribed to maintain a determined blood concentration of the drug. As a transplant coordinator, I use math to educate patients on the correct dosing of medications, since the doctor's orders do not always match the pills available from the pharmacy. Some medications need to be adjusted more frequently on the basis of the patient's weight.

AN APPLICATION

Often a patient needing a kidney transplant has a willing kidney donor who does not match the patient medically. A kidney-paired donation matches donor–recipient pairs. Two kidney transplants are performed simultaneously, with each patient receiving the kidney of a stranger. The number k of such "kidney swaps" t years after 2003 can be approximated by

$$k = 14.3t^3 - 56t^2 + 57.7t + 19.$$

Estimate the number of kidney-paired donations in 2006.

Source: Based on data from United Network for Organ Sharing

This problem appears as Exercise 69 in Section 5.3.

Taken from *Elementary and Intermediate Algebra: Concepts and Applications, Fifth Edition* by: Marvin L. Bitinger, David J. Ellenbogen, and Barbara L. Johnson

A lgebraic expressions such as $16t^2$, $5a^2 - 3ab$, and $3x^2 - 7x + 5$ are called polynomials. Polynomials occur frequently in applications and appear in most branches of mathematics. Thus learning to add, subtract, multiply, and divide polynomials is an important part of nearly every course in elementary algebra. The focus of this chapter is finding equivalent expressions, not solving equations.

5.1   Exponents and Their Properties

Multiplying Powers with Like Bases   ■   Dividing Powers with Like Bases   ■   Zero as an Exponent   ■
Raising a Power to a Power   ■   Raising a Product or a Quotient to a Power

In Section 5.3, we begin our study of polynomials. Before doing so, however, we must develop some rules for working with exponents.

Multiplying Powers with Like Bases

Recall from Section 1.8 that an expression like a^3 means $a \cdot a \cdot a$. We can use this fact to find the product of two expressions that have the same base:

$$a^3 \cdot a^2 = (a \cdot a \cdot a)(a \cdot a)$$ There are three factors in a^3 and two factors in a^2.

$$a^3 \cdot a^2 = a \cdot a \cdot a \cdot a \cdot a$$ Using an associative law
$$a^3 \cdot a^2 = a^5.$$

Note that the exponent in a^5 is the sum of the exponents in $a^3 \cdot a^2$. That is, $3 + 2 = 5$. Similarly,

$$b^4 \cdot b^3 = (b \cdot b \cdot b \cdot b)(b \cdot b \cdot b)$$
$$b^4 \cdot b^3 = b^7, \quad \text{where } 4 + 3 = 7.$$

Adding the exponents gives the correct result.

STUDENT NOTES ————

There are several rules for manipulating exponents in this section. One way to remember them all is to replace variables with numbers (other than 1) and see what the results suggest. For example, multiplying $2^2 \cdot 2^3$ and examining the result is a fine way of reminding yourself that $a^m \cdot a^n = a^{m+n}$.

> **The Product Rule**
>
> For any number a and any positive integers m and n,
>
> $$a^m \cdot a^n = a^{m+n}.$$
>
> (To multiply powers with the same base, keep the base and add the exponents.)

EXAMPLE 1   Multiply and simplify each of the following. (Here "simplify" means express the product as one base to a power whenever possible.)

a) $2^3 \cdot 2^8$

b) $5^3 \cdot 5^8 \cdot 5^1$

c) $(r + s)^7(r + s)^6$

d) $(a^3 b^2)(a^3 b^5)$

SOLUTION

a) $2^3 \cdot 2^8 = 2^{3+8}$ Adding exponents: $a^m \cdot a^n = a^{m+n}$

$= 2^{11}$

> CAUTION!   The base is unchanged: $2^3 \cdot 2^8 \neq 4^{11}$.

b) $5^3 \cdot 5^8 \cdot 5^1 = 5^{3+8+1}$ Adding exponents

$= 5^{12}$

> CAUTION! $5^{12} \neq 5 \cdot 12$.

c) $(r + s)^7(r + s)^6 = (r + s)^{7+6}$ The base here is $r + s$.

$= (r + s)^{13}$

> CAUTION! $(r + s)^{13} \neq r^{13} + s^{13}$.

d) $(a^3b^2)(a^3b^5) = a^3b^2a^3b^5$ Using an associative law

$= a^3a^3b^2b^5$ Using a commutative law

$= a^6b^7$ Adding exponents   TRY EXERCISE 15

Dividing Powers with Like Bases

Recall that any expression that is divided or multiplied by 1 is unchanged. This, together with the fact that anything (besides 0) divided by itself is 1, can lead to a rule for division:

$$\frac{a^5}{a^2} = \frac{a \cdot a \cdot a \cdot a \cdot a}{a \cdot a}$$

$$\frac{a^5}{a^2} = \frac{a \cdot a \cdot a}{1} \cdot \frac{a \cdot a}{a \cdot a}$$

$$\frac{a^5}{a^2} = \frac{a \cdot a \cdot a}{1} \cdot 1$$

$$\frac{a^5}{a^2} = a \cdot a \cdot a = a^3.$$

Note that the exponent in a^3 is the difference of the exponents in a^5/a^2. Similarly,

$$\frac{x^4}{x^3} = \frac{x \cdot x \cdot x \cdot x}{x \cdot x \cdot x} = \frac{x}{1} \cdot \frac{x \cdot x \cdot x}{x \cdot x \cdot x} = \frac{x}{1} \cdot 1 = x = x^1.$$

Subtracting the exponents gives the correct result.

> ### The Quotient Rule
>
> For any nonzero number a and any positive integers m and n for which $m > n$,
>
> $$\frac{a^m}{a^n} = a^{m-n}.$$
>
> (To divide powers with the same base, subtract the exponent of the denominator from the exponent of the numerator.)

EXAMPLE 2   Divide and simplify. (Here "simplify" means express the quotient as one base to a power whenever possible.)

a) $\dfrac{x^8}{x^2}$ **b)** $\dfrac{7^9}{7^4}$ **c)** $\dfrac{(5a)^{12}}{(5a)^4}$ **d)** $\dfrac{4p^5q^7}{6p^2q}$

SOLUTION

a) $\dfrac{x^8}{x^2} = x^{8-2}$ Subtracting exponents: $\dfrac{a^m}{a^n} = a^{m-n}$

   $= x^6$

b) $\dfrac{7^9}{7^4} = 7^{9-4}$

   $= 7^5$

> CAUTION! The base is unchanged:
>
> $$\dfrac{7^9}{7^4} \neq 1^5.$$

c) $\dfrac{(5a)^{12}}{(5a)^4} = (5a)^{12-4} = (5a)^8$ The base here is $5a$.

d) $\dfrac{4p^5q^7}{6p^2q} = \dfrac{4}{6} \cdot \dfrac{p^5}{p^2} \cdot \dfrac{q^7}{q^1}$ Note that the 4 and 6 are factors, not exponents!

   $= \dfrac{2}{3} \cdot p^{5-2} \cdot q^{7-1} = \dfrac{2}{3}p^3q^6$ Using the quotient rule twice; simplifying   TRY EXERCISE ▸ 33

Zero as an Exponent

The quotient rule can be used to help determine what 0 should mean when it appears as an exponent. Consider a^4/a^4, where a is nonzero. Since the numerator and the denominator are the same,

$$\frac{a^4}{a^4} = 1.$$

On the other hand, using the quotient rule would give us

$$\frac{a^4}{a^4} = a^{4-4} = a^0.$$ Subtracting exponents

Since $a^0 = a^4/a^4 = 1$, this suggests that $a^0 = 1$ for any nonzero value of a.

> ### The Exponent Zero
>
> For any real number a, with $a \neq 0$,
>
> $$a^0 = 1.$$
>
> (Any nonzero number raised to the 0 power is 1.)

Note that in the above box, 0^0 is not defined. For this text, we will assume that expressions like a^m do not represent 0^0.

EXAMPLE 3   Simplify: **(a)** 1948^0; **(b)** $(-9)^0$; **(c)** $(3x)^0$; **(d)** $3x^0$; **(e)** $(-1)9^0$; **(f)** -9^0.

SOLUTION

a) $1948^0 = 1$ Any nonzero number raised to the 0 power is 1.

b) $(-9)^0 = 1$ Any nonzero number raised to the 0 power is 1. The base here is -9.

c) $(3x)^0 = 1$, for any $x \neq 0$.   The parentheses indicate that the base is $3x$.

d) Since $3x^0$ means $3 \cdot x^0$, the base is x. Recall that simplifying exponential expressions is done before multiplication in the rules for order of operations:

$$3x^0 = 3 \cdot 1 = 3, \quad \text{for any } x \neq 0.$$

e) $(-1)9^0 = (-1)1 = -1$ The base here is 9.

f) -9^0 is read "the opposite of 9^0" and is equivalent to $(-1)9^0$:

$$-9^0 = (-1)9^0 = (-1)1 = -1.$$

Note from parts (b), (e), and (f) that $-9^0 = (-1)9^0$ and $-9^0 \neq (-9)^0$.

> TRY EXERCISE ▶ 49

CAUTION! $-9^0 \neq (-9)^0$, and, in general, $-a^n \neq (-a)^n$.

Raising a Power to a Power

Consider an expression like $(7^2)^4$:

$$(7^2)^4 = (7^2)(7^2)(7^2)(7^2)$$ There are four factors of 7^2.

$$(7^2)^4 = (7 \cdot 7)(7 \cdot 7)(7 \cdot 7)(7 \cdot 7)$$ We could also use the product rule.

$$(7^2)^4 = 7 \cdot 7 \cdot 7 \cdot 7 \cdot 7 \cdot 7 \cdot 7 \cdot 7$$ Using an associative law

$$(7^2)^4 = 7^8.$$

Note that the exponent in 7^8 is the product of the exponents in $(7^2)^4$. Similarly,

$$(y^5)^3 = y^5 \cdot y^5 \cdot y^5$$ There are three factors of y^5.

$$(y^5)^3 = (y \cdot y \cdot y \cdot y \cdot y)(y \cdot y \cdot y \cdot y \cdot y)(y \cdot y \cdot y \cdot y \cdot y)$$

$$(y^5)^3 = y^{15}.$$

Once again, we get the same result if we multiply exponents:

$$(y^5)^3 = y^{5 \cdot 3} = y^{15}.$$

The Power Rule

For any number a and any whole numbers m and n,

$$(a^m)^n = a^{mn}.$$

(To raise a power to a power, multiply the exponents and leave the base unchanged.)

Remember that for this text we assume that 0^0 is not considered.

EXAMPLE   4   Simplify: **(a)** $(3^5)^4$; **(b)** $(m^2)^5$.

SOLUTION

a) $(3^5)^4 = 3^{5 \cdot 4}$ Multiplying exponents: $(a^m)^n = a^{mn}$

$\qquad = 3^{20}$

b) $(m^2)^5 = m^{2 \cdot 5}$

$\qquad = m^{10}$

> TRY EXERCISE ▶ 57

Raising a Product or a Quotient to a Power

When an expression inside parentheses is raised to a power, the inside expression is the base. Let's compare $2a^3$ and $(2a)^3$:

$2a^3 = 2 \cdot a \cdot a \cdot a;$ The base is a.

$(2a)^3 = (2a)(2a)(2a)$ The base is $2a$.

$(2a)^3 = (2 \cdot 2 \cdot 2)(a \cdot a \cdot a)$

$(2a)^3 = 2^3 a^3$

$(2a)^3 = 8a^3.$

We see that $2a^3$ and $(2a)^3$ are *not* equivalent. Note too that $(2a)^3$ can be simplified by cubing each factor in $2a$. This leads to the following rule for raising a product to a power.

> ### Raising a Product to a Power
>
> For any numbers a and b and any whole number n,
>
> $$(ab)^n = a^n b^n.$$
>
> (To raise a product to a power, raise each factor to that power.)

EXAMPLE 5

Simplify: **(a)** $(4a)^3$; **(b)** $(-5x^4)^2$; **(c)** $(a^7 b)^2 (a^3 b^4)$.

SOLUTION

a) $(4a)^3 = 4^3 a^3 = 64a^3$ Raising each factor to the third power and simplifying

b) $(-5x^4)^2 = (-5)^2 (x^4)^2$ Raising each factor to the second power Parentheses are important here.

$\qquad\qquad = 25x^8$ Simplifying $(-5)^2$ and using the power rule

c) $(a^7 b)^2 (a^3 b^4) = (a^7)^2 b^2 a^3 b^4$ Raising a product to a power

$\qquad\qquad\qquad = a^{14} b^2 a^3 b^4$ Multiplying exponents

$\qquad\qquad\qquad = a^{17} b^6$ Adding exponents   TRY EXERCISE 63

> *CAUTION!*   The rule $(ab)^n = a^n b^n$ applies only to *products* raised to a power, not to sums or differences. For example, $(3 + 4)^2 \neq 3^2 + 4^2$ since $49 \neq 9 + 16$. Similarly, $(5x)^2 = 5^2 \cdot x^2$, but $(5 + x)^2 \neq 5^2 + x^2$.

There is a similar rule for raising a quotient to a power.

> ### Raising a Quotient to a Power
>
> For any numbers a and b, $b \neq 0$, and any whole number n,
>
> $$\left(\frac{a}{b}\right)^n = \frac{a^n}{b^n}.$$
>
> (To raise a quotient to a power, raise the numerator to the power and divide by the denominator to the power.)

EXAMPLE 6   Simplify: **(a)** $\left(\dfrac{x}{5}\right)^2$; **(b)** $\left(\dfrac{5}{a^4}\right)^3$; **(c)** $\left(\dfrac{3a^4}{b^3}\right)^2$.

SOLUTION

a) $\left(\dfrac{x}{5}\right)^2 = \dfrac{x^2}{5^2} = \dfrac{x^2}{25}$ Squaring the numerator and the denominator

b) $\left(\dfrac{5}{a^4}\right)^3 = \dfrac{5^3}{(a^4)^3}$ Raising a quotient to a power

$\qquad = \dfrac{125}{a^{4\cdot 3}} = \dfrac{125}{a^{12}}$ Using the power rule and simplifying

c) $\left(\dfrac{3a^4}{b^3}\right)^2 = \dfrac{(3a^4)^2}{(b^3)^2}$ Raising a quotient to a power

$\qquad = \dfrac{3^2(a^4)^2}{b^{3\cdot 2}} = \dfrac{9a^8}{b^6}$ Raising a product to a power and using the power rule

> **TRY EXERCISE** 75

In the following summary of definitions and rules, we assume that no denominators are 0 and that 0^0 is not considered.

> ### Definitions and Properties of Exponents
>
> For any whole numbers m and n,
>
> | | |
> |---|---|
> | 1 as an exponent: | $a^1 = a$ |
> | 0 as an exponent: | $a^0 = 1$ |
> | The Product Rule: | $a^m \cdot a^n = a^{m+n}$ |
> | The Quotient Rule: | $\dfrac{a^m}{a^n} = a^{m-n}$ |
> | The Power Rule: | $(a^m)^n = a^{mn}$ |
> | Raising a product to a power: | $(ab)^n = a^n b^n$ |
> | Raising a quotient to a power: | $\left(\dfrac{a}{b}\right)^n = \dfrac{a^n}{b^n}$ |

5.1   **EXERCISE SET**

For Extra Help

🖐 *Concept Reinforcement*   *In each of Exercises 1–8, complete the sentence using the most appropriate phrase from the column on the right.*

1. To raise a product to a power, ____

2. To raise a quotient to a power, ____

3. To raise a power to a power, ____

4. To divide powers with the same base, ____

5. Any nonzero number raised to the 0 power____

6. To multiply powers with the same base, ____

7. To square a fraction, ____

8. To square a product, ____

a) keep the base and add the exponents.

b) multiply the exponents and leave the base unchanged.

c) square the numerator and square the denominator.

d) square each factor.

e) raise each factor to that power.

f) raise the numerator to the power and divide by the denominator to the power.

g) is one.

h) subtract the exponent of the denominator from the exponent of the numerator.

Identify the base and the exponent in each expression.

9. $(2x)^5$

10. $(x + 1)^0$

11. $2x^3$

12. $-y^6$

13. $\left(\dfrac{4}{y}\right)^7$

14. $(-5x)^4$

Simplify. Assume that no denominator is 0 and that 0^0 is not considered.

15. $d^3 \cdot d^{10}$

16. $8^4 \cdot 8^3$

17. $a^6 \cdot a$

18. $y^7 \cdot y^9$

19. $6^5 \cdot 6^{10}$

20. $t^0 \cdot t^{16}$

21. $(3y)^4(3y)^8$

22. $(2t)^8(2t)^{17}$

23. $(8n)(8n)^9$

24. $(5p)^0(5p)^1$

25. $(a^2b^7)(a^3b^2)$

26. $(m - 3)^4(m - 3)^5$

27. $(x + 3)^5(x + 3)^8$

28. $(a^8b^3)(a^4b)$

29. $r^3 \cdot r^7 \cdot r^0$

30. $s^4 \cdot s^5 \cdot s^2$

31. $(mn^5)(m^3n^4)$

32. $(a^3b)(ab)^4$

33. $\dfrac{7^5}{7^2}$

34. $\dfrac{4^7}{4^3}$

35. $\dfrac{t^8}{t}$

36. $\dfrac{x^7}{x}$

37. $\dfrac{(5a)^7}{(5a)^6}$

38. $\dfrac{(3m)^9}{(3m)^8}$

Aha! 39. $\dfrac{(x + y)^8}{(x + y)^8}$

40. $\dfrac{(9x)^{10}}{(9x)^2}$

41. $\dfrac{(r + s)^{12}}{(r + s)^4}$

42. $\dfrac{(a - b)^4}{(a - b)^3}$

43. $\dfrac{12d^9}{15d^2}$

44. $\dfrac{10n^7}{15n^3}$

45. $\dfrac{8a^9b^7}{2a^2b}$

46. $\dfrac{12r^{10}s^7}{4r^2s}$

47. $\dfrac{x^{12}y^9}{x^0y^2}$

48. $\dfrac{a^{10}b^{12}}{a^2b^0}$

Simplify.

49. t^0 when $t = 15$

50. y^0 when $y = 38$

51. $5x^0$ when $x = -22$

52. $7m^0$ when $m = 1.7$

53. $7^0 + 4^0$

54. $(8 + 5)^0$

55. $(-3)^1 - (-3)^0$

56. $(-4)^0 - (-4)^1$

Simplify. Assume that no denominator is 0 and that 0^0 is not considered.

57. $(x^3)^{11}$

58. $(a^5)^8$

59. $(5^8)^4$

60. $(2^5)^2$

61. $(t^{20})^4$

62. $(x^{25})^6$

63. $(10x)^2$

64. $(5a)^2$

65. $(-2a)^3$

66. $(-3x)^3$

67. $(-5n^7)^2$

68. $(-4m^4)^2$

69. $(a^2b)^7$

70. $(xy^4)^9$

71. $(r^5t)^3(r^2t^8)$

72. $(a^4b^6)(a^2b)^5$

73. $(2x^5)^3(3x^4)$

74. $(5x^3)^2(2x^7)$

75. $\left(\dfrac{x}{5}\right)^3$

76. $\left(\dfrac{2}{a}\right)^4$

77. $\left(\dfrac{7}{6n}\right)^2$

78. $\left(\dfrac{4x}{3}\right)^3$

79. $\left(\dfrac{a^3}{b^8}\right)^6$

80. $\left(\dfrac{x^5}{y^2}\right)^7$

81. $\left(\dfrac{x^2y}{z^3}\right)^4$

82. $\left(\dfrac{a^4}{b^2c}\right)^5$

83. $\left(\dfrac{a^3}{-2b^5}\right)^4$

84. $\left(\dfrac{x^5}{-3y^3}\right)^4$

85. $\left(\dfrac{5x^7y}{-2z^4}\right)^3$

86. $\left(\dfrac{-4p^5}{3m^2n^3}\right)^3$

Aha! **87.** $\left(\dfrac{4x^3y^5}{3z^7}\right)^0$

88. $\left(\dfrac{5a^7}{2b^5c}\right)^0$

89. Explain in your own words why $-5^2 \neq (-5)^2$.

90. Under what circumstances should exponents be added?

Skill Review

To prepare for Section 5.2, review operations with integers (Sections 1.5–1.7).

Perform the indicated operations.

91. $-10 - 14$ [1.6]

92. $-3(5)$ [1.7]

93. $-16 + 5$ [1.5]

94. $12 - (-4)$ [1.6]

95. $-3 + (-11)$ [1.5]

96. $-8 - (-12)$ [1.6]

Synthesis

97. Under what conditions does a^n represent a negative number? Why?

98. Using the quotient rule, explain why 9^0 is 1.

99. Suppose that the width of a square is three times the width of a second square. How do the areas of the squares compare? Why?

100. Suppose that the width of a cube is twice the width of a second cube. How do the volumes of the cubes compare? Why?

Find a value of the variable that shows that the two expressions are not *equivalent. Answers may vary.*

101. $3x^2$; $(3x)^2$

102. $(a + 5)^2$; $a^2 + 5^2$

103. $\dfrac{t^6}{t^2}$; t^3

104. $\dfrac{a + 7}{7}$; a

Simplify.

105. $y^{4x} \cdot y^{2x}$

106. $a^{10k} \div a^{2k}$

107. $\dfrac{x^{5t}(x^t)^2}{(x^{3t})^2}$

108. $\dfrac{\left(\frac{1}{2}\right)^3\left(\frac{2}{3}\right)^4}{\left(\frac{5}{6}\right)^3}$

109. Solve for x:

$$\frac{t^{26}}{t^x} = t^x.$$

Replace ■ *with* $>$, $<$, *or* $=$ *to write a true sentence.*

110. 3^5 ■ 3^4

111. 4^2 ■ 4^3

112. 4^3 ■ 5^3

113. 4^3 ■ 3^4

114. 9^7 ■ 3^{13}

115. 25^8 ■ 125^5

Use the fact that $10^3 \approx 2^{10}$ to estimate each of the following powers of 2. Then compute the power of 2 with a calculator and find the difference between the exact value and the approximation.

116. 2^{14}

117. 2^{22}

118. 2^{26}

119. 2^{31}

In computer science, 1 KB of memory refers to 1 kilobyte, or 1×10^3 bytes, of memory. This is really an approximation of 1×2^{10} bytes (since computer memory actually uses powers of 2).

120. The TI-84 Plus graphing calculator has 480 KB of "FLASH ROM." How many bytes is this?

121. The TI-84 Plus Silver Edition graphing calculator has 1.5 MB (megabytes) of FLASH ROM, where 1 MB is 1000 KB (see Exercise 120). How many bytes of FLASH ROM does this calculator have?

5.2   Negative Exponents and Scientific Notation

Negative Integers as Exponents   ▪   Scientific Notation   ▪
Multiplying and Dividing Using Scientific Notation

We now attach a meaning to negative exponents. Once we understand both positive exponents and negative exponents, we can study a method for writing numbers known as *scientific notation*.

Negative Integers as Exponents

Let's define negative exponents so that the rules that apply to whole-number exponents will hold for all integer exponents. To do so, consider a^{-5} and the rule for adding exponents:

$$a^{-5} = a^{-5} \cdot 1 \qquad \text{Using the identity property of 1}$$

$$= \frac{a^{-5}}{1} \cdot \frac{a^5}{a^5} \qquad \text{Writing 1 as } \frac{a^5}{a^5} \text{ and } a^{-5} \text{ as } \frac{a^{-5}}{1}$$

$$= \frac{a^{-5+5}}{a^5} \qquad \text{Adding exponents}$$

$$= \frac{1}{a^5}. \qquad -5 + 5 = 0 \text{ and } a^0 = 1$$

This leads to our definition of negative exponents.

Negative Exponents

For any real number a that is nonzero and any integer n,

$$a^{-n} = \frac{1}{a^n}.$$

(The numbers a^{-n} and a^n are reciprocals of each other.)

EXAMPLE 1   Express using positive exponents and, if possible, simplify.

a) m^{-3} 　　　　**b)** 4^{-2} 　　　　**c)** $(-3)^{-2}$ 　　　　**d)** ab^{-1}

SOLUTION

a) $m^{-3} = \dfrac{1}{m^3}$ 　　　　　　　　　m^{-3} is the reciprocal of m^3.

b) $4^{-2} = \dfrac{1}{4^2} = \dfrac{1}{16}$ 　　　　　4^{-2} is the reciprocal of 4^2. Note that $4^{-2} \neq 4(-2)$.

c) $(-3)^{-2} = \dfrac{1}{(-3)^2} = \dfrac{1}{(-3)(-3)} = \dfrac{1}{9}$ 　　$(-3)^{-2}$ is the reciprocal of $(-3)^2$. Note that $(-3)^{-2} \neq -\dfrac{1}{3^2}$.

d) $ab^{-1} = a\left(\dfrac{1}{b^1}\right) = a\left(\dfrac{1}{b}\right) = \dfrac{a}{b}$ 　　b^{-1} is the reciprocal of b^1. Note that the base is b, not ab.

TRY EXERCISE 5

> CAUTION!   A negative exponent does not, in itself, indicate that an expression is negative. As shown in Example 1,
>
> $$4^{-2} \neq 4(-2) \quad \text{and} \quad (-3)^{-2} \neq -\frac{1}{3^2}.$$

The following is another way to illustrate why negative exponents are defined as they are.

On this side, we divide by 5 at each step.		On this side, the exponents decrease by 1.
	$125 = 5^3$	
	$25 = 5^2$	
	$5 = 5^1$	
	$1 = 5^0$	
	$\dfrac{1}{5} = 5^?$	
	$\dfrac{1}{25} = 5^?$	

To continue the pattern, it follows that

$$\frac{1}{5} = \frac{1}{5^1} = 5^{-1}, \qquad \frac{1}{25} = \frac{1}{5^2} = 5^{-2}, \quad \text{and, in general,} \quad \frac{1}{a^n} = a^{-n}.$$

EXAMPLE 2   Express $\dfrac{1}{x^7}$ using negative exponents.

SOLUTION   We know that $\dfrac{1}{a^n} = a^{-n}.$ Thus,

$$\frac{1}{x^7} = x^{-7}.$$

> TRY EXERCISE 25

The rules for powers still hold when exponents are negative.

EXAMPLE 3   Simplify. Do not use negative exponents in the answer.

a) $t^5 \cdot t^{-2}$ **b)** $(5x^2y^{-3})^4$ **c)** $\dfrac{x^{-4}}{x^{-5}}$

d) $\dfrac{1}{t^{-5}}$ **e)** $\dfrac{s^{-3}}{t^{-5}}$ **f)** $\dfrac{-10x^{-3}y}{5x^2y^5}$

SOLUTION

a) $t^5 \cdot t^{-2} = t^{5+(-2)} = t^3$ Adding exponents

b) $(5x^2y^{-3})^4 = 5^4(x^2)^4(y^{-3})^4$ Raising each factor to the fourth power

$$= 625x^8y^{-12} = \frac{625x^8}{y^{12}}$$

c) $\dfrac{x^{-4}}{x^{-5}} = x^{-4-(-5)} = x^1 = x$ We subtract exponents even if the exponent in the denominator is negative.

d) Since $\dfrac{1}{a^n} = a^{-n},$ we have $\dfrac{1}{t^{-5}} = t^{-(-5)} = t^5.$

e) $\dfrac{s^{-3}}{t^{-5}} = s^{-3} \cdot \dfrac{1}{t^{-5}}$

$$= \frac{1}{s^3} \cdot t^5 = \frac{t^5}{s^3}$$ Using the result from part (d) above

f) $\dfrac{-10x^{-3}y}{5x^2y^5} = \dfrac{-10}{5} \cdot \dfrac{x^{-3}}{x^2} \cdot \dfrac{y^1}{y^5}$ Note that the -10 and 5 are factors.

$\qquad\qquad = -2 \cdot x^{-3-2} \cdot y^{1-5}$ Using the quotient rule twice; simplifying

$\qquad\qquad = -2x^{-5}y^{-4} = \dfrac{-2}{x^5y^4}$

> **TRY EXERCISE** 33

The result from Example 3(e) can be generalized.

Factors and Negative Exponents

For any nonzero real numbers a and b and any integers m and n,

$$\frac{a^{-n}}{b^{-m}} = \frac{b^m}{a^n}.$$

(A factor can be moved to the other side of the fraction bar if the sign of the exponent is changed.)

EXAMPLE **4**   Simplify: $\dfrac{-15x^{-7}}{5y^2z^{-4}}$.

SOLUTION   We can move the factors x^{-7} and z^{-4} to the other side of the fraction bar if we change the sign of each exponent:

$$\frac{-15x^{-7}}{5y^2z^{-4}} = \frac{-15}{5} \cdot \frac{x^{-7}}{y^2z^{-4}}$$ We can simply divide the constant factors.

$$= -3 \cdot \frac{z^4}{y^2x^7}$$

$$= \frac{-3z^4}{x^7y^2}.$$

> **TRY EXERCISE** 55

Another way to change the sign of the exponent is to take the reciprocal of the base. To understand why this is true, note that

$$\left(\frac{s}{t}\right)^{-5} = \frac{s^{-5}}{t^{-5}} = \frac{t^5}{s^5} = \left(\frac{t}{s}\right)^5.$$

This often provides the easiest way to simplify an expression containing a negative exponent.

Reciprocals and Negative Exponents

For any nonzero real numbers a and b and any integer n,

$$\left(\frac{a}{b}\right)^{-n} = \left(\frac{b}{a}\right)^n.$$

(Any base to a power is equal to the reciprocal of the base raised to the opposite power.)

EXAMPLE 5

Simplify: $\left(\dfrac{x^4}{2y}\right)^{-3}$.

SOLUTION

$$\left(\frac{x^4}{2y}\right)^{-3} = \left(\frac{2y}{x^4}\right)^{3}$$ Taking the reciprocal of the base and changing the sign of the exponent

$$= \frac{(2y)^3}{(x^4)^3}$$ Raising a quotient to a power by raising both the numerator and the denominator to the power

$$= \frac{2^3 y^3}{x^{12}}$$ Raising a product to a power; using the power rule in the denominator

$$= \frac{8y^3}{x^{12}}$$ Cubing 2

TRY EXERCISE 73

Scientific Notation

When we are working with the very large numbers or very small numbers that frequently occur in science, **scientific notation** provides a useful way of writing them. The following are examples of scientific notation.

The mass of the earth:

6.0×10^{24} kilograms (kg) = 6,000,000,000,000,000,000,000,000 kg

The mass of a hydrogen atom:

1.7×10^{-24} g = 0.0000000000000000000000017 g

Scientific Notation

Scientific notation for a number is an expression of the type

$$N \times 10^m,$$

where N is at least 1 but less than 10 (that is, $1 \le N < 10$), N is expressed in decimal notation, and m is an integer.

STUDENT NOTES

Definitions are usually written as concisely as possible, so that every phrase included is important. The definition for scientific notation states that $1 \le N < 10$. Thus, 2.68×10^5 is written in scientific notation, but 26.8×10^5 and 0.268×10^5 are *not* written in scientific notation.

Converting from scientific notation to decimal notation involves multiplying by a power of 10. Consider the following.

Scientific Notation	Multiplication	Decimal Notation
4.52×10^2	4.52×100	452.
4.52×10^1	4.52×10	45.2
4.52×10^0	4.52×1	4.52
4.52×10^{-1}	4.52×0.1	0.452
4.52×10^{-2}	4.52×0.01	0.0452

Note that when m, the power of 10, is positive, the decimal point moves right m places in decimal notation. When m is negative, the decimal point moves left $|m|$ places. We generally try to perform this multiplication mentally.

EXAMPLE 6   Convert to decimal notation: **(a)** 7.893×10^5; **(b)** 4.7×10^{-8}.

SOLUTION

a) Since the exponent is positive, the decimal point moves to the right:

7.89300. $7.893 \times 10^5 = 789,300$ The decimal point moves to the
⌣⌣⌣   right 5 places.
5 places

b) Since the exponent is negative, the decimal point moves to the left:

0.00000004.7 $4.7 \times 10^{-8} = 0.000000047$ The decimal point
⌣⌣⌣   moves to the left 8 places.
8 places

TRY EXERCISE ▸ 85

To convert from decimal notation to scientific notation, this procedure is reversed.

EXAMPLE 7   Write in scientific notation: **(a)** 83,000; **(b)** 0.0327.

SOLUTION

a) We need to find m such that $83,000 = 8.3 \times 10^m$. To change 8.3 to 83,000 requires moving the decimal point 4 places to the right. This can be accomplished by multiplying by 10^4. Thus,

$$83,000 = 8.3 \times 10^4. \qquad \text{This is scientific notation.}$$

b) We need to find m such that $0.0327 = 3.27 \times 10^m$. To change 3.27 to 0.0327 requires moving the decimal point 2 places to the left. This can be accomplished by multiplying by 10^{-2}. Thus,

$$0.0327 = 3.27 \times 10^{-2}. \qquad \text{This is scientific notation.}$$

TRY EXERCISE ▸ 93

Conversions to and from scientific notation are often made mentally. Remember that positive exponents are used to represent large numbers and negative exponents are used to represent small numbers between 0 and 1.

Multiplying and Dividing Using Scientific Notation

Products and quotients of numbers written in scientific notation are found using the rules for exponents.

EXAMPLE 8   Simplify.

a) $(1.8 \times 10^9) \cdot (2.3 \times 10^{-4})$

b) $(3.41 \times 10^5) \div (1.1 \times 10^{-3})$

SOLUTION

a) $(1.8 \times 10^9) \cdot (2.3 \times 10^{-4})$

$\qquad = 1.8 \times 2.3 \times 10^9 \times 10^{-4}$ Using the associative and commutative laws

$\qquad = 4.14 \times 10^{9+(-4)}$ Adding exponents

$\qquad = 4.14 \times 10^5$

b) $(3.41 \times 10^5) \div (1.1 \times 10^{-3})$

$$= \frac{3.41 \times 10^5}{1.1 \times 10^{-3}}$$

$$= \frac{3.41}{1.1} \times \frac{10^5}{10^{-3}}$$

$$= 3.1 \times 10^{5-(-3)} \qquad \text{Subtracting exponents}$$

$$= 3.1 \times 10^8$$

> **TRY EXERCISE** 103

When a problem is stated using scientific notation, we generally use scientific notation for the answer. This often requires an additional conversion.

EXAMPLE   9   Simplify.

a) $(3.1 \times 10^5) \cdot (4.5 \times 10^{-3})$ **b)** $(7.2 \times 10^{-7}) \div (8.0 \times 10^6)$

SOLUTION

a) We have

$$(3.1 \times 10^5) \cdot (4.5 \times 10^{-3}) = 3.1 \times 4.5 \times 10^5 \times 10^{-3}$$
$$= 13.95 \times 10^2.$$

Our answer is not yet in scientific notation because 13.95 is not between 1 and 10. We convert to scientific notation as follows:

$$13.95 \times 10^2 = 1.395 \times 10^1 \times 10^2 \qquad \text{Substituting } 1.395 \times 10^1 \text{ for } 13.95$$
$$= 1.395 \times 10^3. \qquad \text{Adding exponents}$$

b) $(7.2 \times 10^{-7}) \div (8.0 \times 10^6) = \dfrac{7.2 \times 10^{-7}}{8.0 \times 10^6} = \dfrac{7.2}{8.0} \times \dfrac{10^{-7}}{10^6}$

$$= 0.9 \times 10^{-13}$$

$$= 9.0 \times 10^{-1} \times 10^{-13} \qquad \text{Substituting } 9.0 \times 10^{-1} \text{ for } 0.9$$

$$= 9.0 \times 10^{-14} \qquad \text{Adding exponents}$$

> **TRY EXERCISE** 111

TECHNOLOGY CONNECTION

A key labeled $\boxed{10^x}$, $\boxed{\wedge}$, or $\boxed{EE}$ is used to enter scientific notation into a calculator. Sometimes this is a secondary function, meaning that another key—often labeled SHIFT or **2ND** —must be pressed first.

To check Example 8(a), we press

1.8 $\boxed{EE}$ 9 $\boxed{\times}$ 2.3 $\boxed{EE}$ $\boxed{(-)}$ 4.

When we then press $\boxed{=}$ or **ENTER**, the result 4.14E5 appears. This represents 4.14×10^5. On many calculators, the MODE Sci must be selected in order to display scientific notation.

```
1.8E9*2.3E-4
                4.14E5
```

On some calculators, this appears as

or

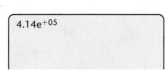

Calculate each of the following.

1. $(3.8 \times 10^9) \cdot (4.5 \times 10^7)$
2. $(2.9 \times 10^{-8}) \div (5.4 \times 10^6)$
3. $(9.2 \times 10^7) \div (2.5 \times 10^{-9})$

⟶ *Concept Reinforcement Match each expression with an equivalent expression from the column on the right.*

1. ____ $\left(\dfrac{x^3}{y^2}\right)^{-2}$

a) $\dfrac{y^6}{x^9}$

2. ____ $\left(\dfrac{y^2}{x^3}\right)^{-2}$

b) $\dfrac{x^9}{y^6}$

3. ____ $\left(\dfrac{y^{-2}}{x^{-3}}\right)^{-3}$

c) $\dfrac{y^4}{x^6}$

4. ____ $\left(\dfrac{x^{-3}}{y^{-2}}\right)^{-3}$

d) $\dfrac{x^6}{y^4}$

Express using positive exponents. Then, if possible, simplify.

5. 2^{-3}

6. 10^{-5}

7. $(-2)^{-6}$

8. $(-3)^{-4}$

9. t^{-9}

10. x^{-7}

11. xy^{-2}

12. $a^{-3}b$

13. $r^{-5}t$

14. xy^{-9}

15. $\dfrac{1}{a^{-8}}$

16. $\dfrac{1}{z^{-6}}$

17. 7^{-1}

18. 3^{-1}

19. $\left(\dfrac{3}{5}\right)^{-2}$

20. $\left(\dfrac{3}{4}\right)^{-2}$

21. $\left(\dfrac{x}{2}\right)^{-5}$

22. $\left(\dfrac{a}{2}\right)^{-4}$

23. $\left(\dfrac{s}{t}\right)^{-7}$

24. $\left(\dfrac{r}{v}\right)^{-5}$

Express using negative exponents.

25. $\dfrac{1}{9^2}$

26. $\dfrac{1}{5^2}$

27. $\dfrac{1}{y^3}$

28. $\dfrac{1}{t^4}$

29. $\dfrac{1}{5}$

30. $\dfrac{1}{8}$

31. $\dfrac{1}{t}$

32. $\dfrac{1}{m}$

Simplify. Do not use negative exponents in the answer.

33. $2^{-5} \cdot 2^8$

34. $5^{-8} \cdot 5^{10}$

35. $x^{-3} \cdot x^{-9}$

36. $x^{-4} \cdot x^{-7}$

37. $t^{-3} \cdot t$

38. $y^{-5} \cdot y$

39. $(n^{-5})^3$

40. $(m^{-5})^{10}$

41. $(t^{-3})^{-6}$

42. $(a^{-4})^{-7}$

43. $(t^4)^{-3}$

44. $(x^4)^{-5}$

45. $(mn)^{-7}$

46. $(ab)^{-9}$

47. $(3x^{-4})^2$

48. $(2a^{-5})^3$

49. $(5r^{-4}t^3)^2$

50. $(4x^5y^{-6})^3$

51. $\dfrac{t^{12}}{t^{-2}}$

52. $\dfrac{x^7}{x^{-2}}$

53. $\dfrac{y^{-7}}{y^{-3}}$

54. $\dfrac{z^{-6}}{z^{-2}}$

55. $\dfrac{15y^{-7}}{3y^{-10}}$

56. $\dfrac{-12a^{-5}}{2a^{-8}}$

57. $\dfrac{2x^6}{x}$

58. $\dfrac{3x}{x^{-1}}$

59. $\dfrac{-15a^{-7}}{10b^{-9}}$

60. $\dfrac{12x^{-6}}{8y^{-10}}$

Aha! 61. $\dfrac{t^{-7}}{t^{-7}}$

62. $\dfrac{a^{-5}}{b^{-7}}$

63. $\dfrac{8x^{-3}}{y^{-7}z^{-1}}$

64. $\dfrac{10a^{-1}}{b^{-7}c^{-3}}$

65. $\dfrac{3t^4}{s^{-2}u^{-4}}$

66. $\dfrac{5x^{-8}}{y^{-3}z^2}$

67. $(x^4y^5)^{-3}$

68. $(t^5x^3)^{-4}$

69. $(3m^{-5}n^{-3})^{-2}$

70. $(2y^{-4}z^{-2})^{-3}$

71. $(a^{-5}b^7c^{-2})(a^{-3}b^{-2}c^6)$

72. $(x^3y^{-4}z^{-5})(x^{-4}y^{-2}z^9)$

73. $\left(\dfrac{a^4}{3}\right)^{-2}$

74. $\left(\dfrac{y^2}{2}\right)^{-2}$

75. $\left(\dfrac{m^{-1}}{n^{-4}}\right)^3$

76. $\left(\dfrac{x^2y}{z^{-5}}\right)^3$

77. $\left(\dfrac{2a^2}{3b^4}\right)^{-3}$

78. $\left(\dfrac{a^2b}{2d^3}\right)^{-5}$

Aha! 79. $\left(\dfrac{5x^{-2}}{3y^{-2}z}\right)^0$

80. $\left(\dfrac{4a^3b^{-2}}{5c^{-3}}\right)^1$

81. $\dfrac{-6a^3b^{-5}}{-3a^7b^{-8}}$

82. $\dfrac{12x^{-2}y^4}{-3xy^{-7}}$

83. $\dfrac{10x^{-4}yz^7}{8x^7y^{-3}z^{-3}}$

84. $\dfrac{9a^6b^{-4}c^7}{27a^{-4}b^5c^9}$

Convert to decimal notation.

85. 4.92×10^3

86. 8.13×10^4

87. 8.92×10^{-3}

88. 7.26×10^{-4}

89. 9.04×10^8

90. 1.35×10^7

91. 3.497×10^{-6}

92. 9.043×10^{-3}

Convert to scientific notation.

93. 36,000,000

94. 27,400

95. 0.00583

96. 0.0814

97. 78,000,000,000

98. 3,700,000,000,000

99. 0.000000527

100. 0.0000506

101. 0.000001032

102. 0.00000008

Multiply or divide, and write scientific notation for the result.

103. $(3 \times 10^5)(2 \times 10^8)$

104. $(3.1 \times 10^7)(2.1 \times 10^{-4})$

105. $(3.8 \times 10^9)(6.5 \times 10^{-2})$

106. $(7.1 \times 10^{-7})(8.6 \times 10^{-5})$

107. $(8.7 \times 10^{-12})(4.5 \times 10^{-5})$

108. $(4.7 \times 10^5)(6.2 \times 10^{-12})$

109. $\dfrac{8.5 \times 10^8}{3.4 \times 10^{-5}}$

110. $\dfrac{5.6 \times 10^{-2}}{2.5 \times 10^5}$

111. $(4.0 \times 10^3) \div (8.0 \times 10^8)$

112. $(1.5 \times 10^{-3}) \div (1.6 \times 10^{-6})$

113. $\dfrac{7.5 \times 10^{-9}}{2.5 \times 10^{12}}$

114. $\dfrac{3.0 \times 10^{-2}}{6.0 \times 10^{10}}$

115. Without performing actual computations, explain why 3^{-29} is smaller than 2^{-29}.

116. Explain why each of the following is not scientific notation:

$$12.6 \times 10^8;$$
$$4.8 \times 10^{1.7};$$
$$0.207 \times 10^{-5}.$$

Skill Review

To prepare for Section 5.3, review combining like terms and evaluating expressions (Sections 1.6 and 1.8).

Combine like terms. [1.6]

117. $9x + 2y - x - 2y$

118. $5a - 7b - 8a + b$

119. $-3x + (-2) - 5 - (-x)$

120. $2 - t - 3t - r - 7$

Evaluate. [1.8]

121. $4 + x^3$, for $x = 10$

122. $-x^2 - 5x + 3$, for $x = -2$

Synthesis

123. Explain what requirements must be met in order for x^{-n} to represent a negative integer.

124. Explain why scientific notation cannot be used without an understanding of the rules for exponents.

125. Write the reciprocal of 1.25×10^{-6} in scientific notation.

126. Write the reciprocal of 2.5×10^9 in scientific notation.

127. Write $8^{-3} \cdot 32 \div 16^2$ as a power of 2.

128. Write $81^3 \div 27 \cdot 9^2$ as a power of 3.

Simplify each of the following. Use a calculator only where indicated.

Aha! **129.** $\dfrac{125^{-4}(25^2)^4}{125}$

130. $(13^{-12})^2 \cdot 13^{25}$

131. $[(5^{-3})^2]^{-1}$

132. $5^0 - 5^{-1}$

133. $3^{-1} + 4^{-1}$

134. $\dfrac{4.2 \times 10^8[(2.5 \times 10^{-5}) \div (5.0 \times 10^{-9})]}{3.0 \times 10^{-12}}$

135. $\dfrac{27^{-2}(81^2)^3}{9^8}$

136. $\dfrac{7.4 \times 10^{29}}{(5.4 \times 10^{-6})(2.8 \times 10^8)}$

137. $\dfrac{5.8 \times 10^{17}}{(4.0 \times 10^{-13})(2.3 \times 10^4)}$

138. $\dfrac{(7.8 \times 10^7)(8.4 \times 10^{23})}{2.1 \times 10^{-12}}$

139. $\dfrac{(2.5 \times 10^{-8})(6.1 \times 10^{-11})}{1.28 \times 10^{-3}}$

140. Determine whether each of the following is true for all pairs of integers m and n and all positive numbers x and y.

  a) $x^m \cdot y^n = (xy)^{mn}$

  b) $x^m \cdot y^m = (xy)^{2m}$

  c) $(x - y)^m = x^m - y^m$

Solve. Write scientific notation for each answer.

141. *Ecology.*   In one year, a large tree can remove from the air the same amount of carbon dioxide produced by a car traveling 500 mi. If New York City contains approximately 600,000 trees, how many miles of car traffic can those trees clean in a year?
Sources: Colorado Tree Coalition; New York City Department of Parks and Recreations

142. *Computer technology.*   One gigabit is about 1 billion bits of information. In 2007, Intel Corp. began making silicon modulators that can encode data onto a beam of light at a rate of 40 gigabits per second. If 25 of these communication lasers are packed on a single chip, how many bits per second could that chip encode?
Source: The Wall Street Journal, 7/25/2007

143. *Hotel management.*   The new Four Seasons Hotel in Seattle contains 110,000 ft^2 of condominium space. If these condos sold for about $2100 per ft^2, how much money did the hotel make selling the condominiums?
Source: seattletimes.nwsource.com

144. *Coral reefs.*   There are 10 million bacteria per square centimeter of coral in a coral reef. The coral reefs near the Hawaiian Islands cover 14,000 km^2. How many bacteria are there in Hawaii's coral reefs?
Sources: livescience.com; U.S. Geological Survey

145. *Hospital care.*   In 2005, 115 million patients visited emergency rooms in the United States. If the average visit lasted 3.3 hr, how many minutes in all did people spend in emergency rooms in 2005?
Source: The Indianapolis Star, 7/25/07

CONNECTING the CONCEPTS

The following properties of exponents hold for all integers m and n, assuming that no denominator is 0 and that 0^0 is not considered.

Definitions and Properties of Exponents

The following summary assumes that no denominators are 0 and that 0^0 is not considered. For any integers m and n,

1 as an exponent:	$a^1 = a$
0 as an exponent:	$a^0 = 1$
Negative exponents:	$a^{-n} = \dfrac{1}{a^n},$
	$\dfrac{a^{-n}}{b^{-m}} = \dfrac{b^m}{a^n},$
	$\left(\dfrac{a}{b}\right)^{-n} = \left(\dfrac{b}{a}\right)^n$
The Product Rule:	$a^m \cdot a^n = a^{m+n}$
The Quotient Rule:	$\dfrac{a^m}{a^n} = a^{m-n}$
The Power Rule:	$(a^m)^n = a^{mn}$
Raising a product to a power:	$(ab)^n = a^n b^n$
Raising a quotient to a power:	$\left(\dfrac{a}{b}\right)^n = \dfrac{a^n}{b^n}$

MIXED REVIEW

Simplify. Do not use negative exponents in the answer.

1. $x^4 x^{10}$

2. $x^{-4} x^{-10}$

3. $\dfrac{x^{-4}}{x^{10}}$

4. $\dfrac{x^4}{x^{-10}}$

5. $(x^{-4})^{-10}$

6. $(x^4)^{10}$

7. $\dfrac{1}{c^{-8}}$

8. c^{-8}

9. $(2x^3 y)^4$

10. $(2x^3 y)^{-4}$

11. $(3xy^{-1}z^5)^0$

12. $(a^2 b)(a^3 b^{-1})$

13. $\left(\dfrac{a^3}{b^4}\right)^5$

14. $\left(\dfrac{a^3}{b^4}\right)^{-5}$

15. $\dfrac{30x^4 y^3}{12xy^7}$

16. $\dfrac{12ab^{-8}}{14a^{-1}b^{-3}}$

17. $\dfrac{7p^{-5}}{xt^{-6}}$

18. $\left(\dfrac{3a^{-1}}{4b^{-3}}\right)^{-2}$

19. $(2p^2 q^4)(3pq^5)^2$

20. $(2xy^{-1})^{-1}(3x^2 y^{-3})^2$

5.3   Polynomials

Terms ▪ Types of Polynomials ▪ Degree and Coefficients ▪ Combining Like Terms ▪ Evaluating Polynomials and Applications

We now examine an important algebraic expression known as a *polynomial*. Certain polynomials have appeared earlier in this text so you already have some experience working with them.

STUDY SKILLS ——————

A Text Is Not Light Reading

Do not expect a math text to read like a magazine or novel. On one hand, most assigned readings in a math text consist of only a few pages. On the other hand, every sentence and word is important and should make sense. If they don't, ask for help as soon as possible.

Terms

At this point, we have seen a variety of algebraic expressions like

$$3a^2b^4, \quad 2l + 2w, \quad \text{and} \quad 5x^2 + x - 2.$$

Within these expressions, $3a^2b^4$, $2l$, $2w$, $5x^2$, x, and -2 are examples of *terms*. A **term** (see p. 17) can be a number (like -2), a variable (like x), a product of numbers and/or variables (like $3a^2b^4$, $2l$, $2w$, or $5x^2$), or a quotient of numbers and/or variables (like $7/t$ or $(a^2b^3)/(4c)$).*

Types of Polynomials

If a term is a product of constants and/or variables, it is called a **monomial**. Note that a term, but not a monomial, can include division by a variable. A **polynomial** is a monomial or a sum of monomials.

Examples of monomials: $7, \quad t, \quad 2l, \quad 2w, \quad 5x^3y, \quad \frac{3}{7}a^5$

Examples of polynomials: $4x + 7, \quad \frac{2}{3}t^2, \quad 6a + 7, \quad -5n^2 + m - 1, \quad 42r^5,$
$x, \quad 0$

When a polynomial is written as a sum of monomials, each monomial is called a *term of the polynomial.*

EXAMPLE 1   Identify the terms of the polynomial $3t^4 - 5t^6 - 4t + 2$.

SOLUTION   The terms are $3t^4$, $-5t^6$, $-4t$, and 2. We can see this by rewriting all subtractions as additions of opposites:

$$3t^4 - 5t^6 - 4t + 2 = 3t^4 + (-5t^6) + (-4t) + 2.$$

These are the terms of the polynomial.

TRY EXERCISE ▸ 9

A polynomial that is composed of two terms is called a **binomial**, whereas those composed of three terms are called **trinomials**. Polynomials with four or more terms have no special name.

——————

*Later in this text, expressions like $5x^{3/2}$ and $2a^{-7}b$ will be discussed. Such expressions are also considered terms.

Monomials	Binomials	Trinomials	No Special Name
$4x^2$	$2x + 4$	$3t^3 + 4t + 7$	$4x^3 - 5x^2 + xy - 8$
9	$3a^5 + 6bc$	$6x^7 - 8z^2 + 4$	$z^5 + 2z^4 - z^3 + 7z + 3$
$-7a^{19}b^5$	$-9x^7 - 6$	$4x^2 - 6x - \frac{1}{2}$	$4x^6 - 3x^5 + x^4 - x^3 + 2x - 1$

The following algebraic expressions are *not* polynomials:

$$(1)\ \frac{x+3}{x-4}, \quad (2)\ 5x^3 - 2x^2 + \frac{1}{x}, \quad (3)\ \frac{1}{x^3 - 2}.$$

Expressions (1) and (3) are not polynomials because they represent quotients, not sums. Expression (2) is not a polynomial because $1/x$ is not a monomial.

Degree and Coefficients

The **degree of a term of a polynomial** is the number of variable factors in that term. Thus the degree of $7t^2$ is 2 because $7t^2$ has two variable factors: $7t^2 = 7 \cdot t \cdot t$. We will revisit the meaning of degree in Section 5.7 when polynomials in several variables are examined.

EXAMPLE 2   Determine the degree of each term: (a) $8x^4$; (b) $3x$; (c) 7.

SOLUTION

a) The degree of $8x^4$ is 4. x^4 represents 4 variable factors: $x \cdot x \cdot x \cdot x$.
b) The degree of $3x$ is 1.   There is 1 variable factor.
c) The degree of 7 is 0.   There is no variable factor.

The degree of a constant polynomial, as in Example 2(c), is 0 since there are no variable factors. There is an exception to this statement, however. Since $0 = 0x = 0x^2 = 0x^3$ and so on, we say that the polynomial 0 has *no* degree.

The part of a term that is a constant factor is the **coefficient** of that term. Thus the coefficient of $3x$ is 3, and the coefficient for the term 7 is simply 7.

EXAMPLE 3   Identify the coefficient of each term in the polynomial

$$4x^3 - 7x^2y + x - 8.$$

SOLUTION

The coefficient of $4x^3$ is 4.
The coefficient of $-7x^2y$ is -7.
The coefficient of the third term is 1, since $x = 1x$.
The coefficient of -8 is simply -8.   **TRY EXERCISE** 13

The **leading term** of a polynomial is the term of highest degree. Its coefficient is called the **leading coefficient** and its degree is referred to as the **degree of the polynomial**. To see how this terminology is used, consider the polynomial

$$3x^2 - 8x^3 + 5x^4 + 7x - 6.$$

The *terms* are $3x^2$, $-8x^3$, $5x^4$, $7x$, and -6.
The *coefficients* are   3, -8,   5,   7,   and -6.
The *degree of each term* is   2,   3,   4,   1,   and 0.
The *leading term* is $5x^4$ and the *leading coefficient* is 5.
The *degree of the polynomial* is 4.

Combining Like Terms

Recall from Section 1.8 that *like*, or *similar*, *terms* are either constant terms or terms containing the same variable(s) raised to the same power(s). To simplify certain polynomials, we can often *combine*, or *collect*, like terms.

EXAMPLE **4**

Identify the like terms in $4x^3 + 5x - 7x^2 + 2x^3 + x^2$.

SOLUTION

Like terms: $4x^3$ and $2x^3$ Same variable and exponent

Like terms: $-7x^2$ and x^2 Same variable and exponent

EXAMPLE **5**

Write an equivalent expression by combining like terms.

a) $2x^3 + 6x^3$ **b)** $5x^2 + 7 + 2x^4 - 6x^2 - 11 - 2x^4$

c) $7a^3 - 5a^2 + 9a^3 + a^2$ **d)** $\frac{2}{3}x^4 - x^3 - \frac{1}{6}x^4 + \frac{2}{5}x^3 - \frac{3}{10}x^3$

STUDENT NOTES

Remember that when we combine like terms, we are not solving equations, but are forming equivalent expressions.

SOLUTION

a) $2x^3 + 6x^3 = (2 + 6)x^3$ Using the distributive law

               $= 8x^3$

b) $5x^2 + 7 + 2x^4 - 6x^2 - 11 - 2x^4$

     $= 5x^2 - 6x^2 + 2x^4 - 2x^4 + 7 - 11$

     $= (5 - 6)x^2 + (2 - 2)x^4 + (7 - 11)$ ⎫

     $= -1x^2 + 0x^4 + (-4)$ ⎬   These steps are often done mentally.

     $= -x^2 - 4$ ⎭

c) $7a^3 - 5a^2 + 9a^3 + a^2 = 7a^3 - 5a^2 + 9a^3 + 1a^2$ $a^2 = 1 \cdot a^2 = 1a^2$

                        $= 16a^3 - 4a^2$

d) $\frac{2}{3}x^4 - x^3 - \frac{1}{6}x^4 + \frac{2}{5}x^3 - \frac{3}{10}x^3 = \left(\frac{2}{3} - \frac{1}{6}\right)x^4 + \left(-1 + \frac{2}{5} - \frac{3}{10}\right)x^3$

                                 $= \left(\frac{4}{6} - \frac{1}{6}\right)x^4 + \left(-\frac{10}{10} + \frac{4}{10} - \frac{3}{10}\right)x^3$

                                 $= \frac{3}{6}x^4 - \frac{9}{10}x^3$

                                 $= \frac{1}{2}x^4 - \frac{9}{10}x^3$ There are no similar terms, so we are done.

TRY EXERCISE 41

Note in Example 5 that the solutions are written so that the term of highest degree appears first, followed by the term of next highest degree, and so on. This is known as **descending order** and is the form in which answers will normally appear.

Evaluating Polynomials and Applications

When each variable in a polynomial is replaced with a number, the polynomial then represents a number, or *value*, that can be calculated using the rules for order of operations.

EXAMPLE **6**

Evaluate $-x^2 + 3x + 9$ for $x = -2$.

SOLUTION   For $x = -2$, we have

Substitute. $-x^2 + 3x + 9 = -(-2)^2 + 3(-2) + 9$ The negative sign in front of x^2 remains.

                        $= -(4) + 3(-2) + 9$

Simplify. $= -4 + (-6) + 9$

                        $= -10 + 9 = -1.$

TRY EXERCISE 51

EXAMPLE 7

Games in a sports league. In a sports league of *n* teams in which each team plays every other team twice, the total number of games to be played is given by the polynomial

$$n^2 - n.$$

A girls' soccer league has 10 teams. How many games are played if each team plays every other team twice?

SOLUTION   We evaluate the polynomial for $n = 10$:

$$n^2 - n = 10^2 - 10$$
$$= 100 - 10 = 90.$$

The league plays 90 games. **TRY EXERCISE** 61

EXAMPLE 8

Vehicle miles traveled. The average annual number of vehicle miles traveled per vehicle (VMT), in thousands, for a driver of age *a* can be approximated by the polynomial

$$-0.003a^2 + 0.2a + 8.6.$$

Find the VMT per vehicle for a 20-year-old driver.

Source: Based on information from the Energy Information Administration

SOLUTION   To find the VMT per vehicle for a 20-year-old driver, we evaluate the polynomial for $a = 20$:

$$-0.003a^2 + 0.2a + 8.6 = -0.003(20)^2 + 0.2(20) + 8.6$$
$$= -0.003 \cdot 400 + 4 + 8.6$$
$$= -1.2 + 4 + 8.6$$
$$= 11.4.$$

The average annual number of VMT per vehicle by a 20-year-old driver is 11.4 thousand, or 11,400. **TRY EXERCISE** 65

Sometimes, a graph can be used to estimate the value of a polynomial visually.

EXAMPLE 9

Vehicle miles traveled. In the following graph, the polynomial from Example 8 has been graphed by evaluating it for several choices of *a*. Use the graph to estimate the number of vehicle miles traveled each year, per vehicle, by a 30-year-old driver.

TECHNOLOGY CONNECTION

One way to evaluate a polynomial is to use the TRACE key. For example, to evaluate $-0.003a^2 + 0.2a + 8.6$ in Example 9 for $a = 30$, we can enter the polynomial as $y = -0.003x^2 + 0.2x + 8.6$. We then use TRACE and enter an *x*-value of 30.

(continued)

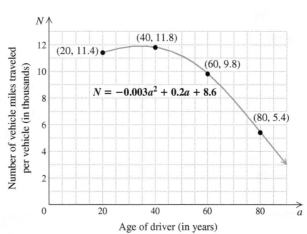

The value of the polynomial appears as y, and the cursor automatically appears at $(30, 11.9)$. The Value option of the CALC menu works in a similar way.

$y = -0.003x^2 + 0.2x + 8.6$

Xscl = 10, Yscl = 2

1. Use TRACE or CALC Value to find the value of $-0.003a^2 + 0.2a + 8.6$ for $a = 60$.

SOLUTION   To estimate the number of vehicle miles traveled by a 30-year-old driver, we locate 30 on the horizontal axis. From there, we move vertically until we meet the curve at some point. From that point, we move horizontally to the N-axis.

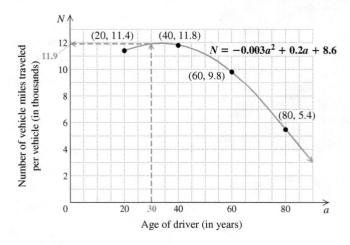

The average number of vehicle miles traveled each year, per vehicle, by a 30-year-old driver is 11.9 thousand, or 11,900. (For $a = 30$, the value of $-0.003a^2 + 0.2a + 8.6$ is approximately 11.9.)

TRY EXERCISE 71

5.3   EXERCISE SET

🔖 *Concept Reinforcement*   *In each of Exercises 1–8, match the description with the most appropriate algebraic expression from the column on the right.*

1. ____ A polynomial with four terms

2. ____ A polynomial with 7 as its leading coefficient

3. ____ A trinomial written in descending order

4. ____ A polynomial with degree 5

5. ____ A binomial with degree 7

6. ____ A monomial of degree 0

7. ____ An expression with two terms that is not a binomial

8. ____ An expression with three terms that is not a trinomial

a) $8x^3 + \dfrac{2}{x^2}$

b) $5x^4 + 3x^3 - 4x + 7$

c) $\dfrac{3}{x} - 6x^2 + 9$

d) $8t - 4t^5$

e) 5

f) $6x^2 + 7x^4 - 2x^3$

g) $4t - 2t^7$

h) $3t^2 + 4t + 7$

Identify the terms of each polynomial.

9. $8x^3 - 11x^2 + 6x + 1$

10. $5a^3 + 4a^2 - a - 7$

11. $-t^6 - 3t^3 + 9t - 4$

12. $n^5 - 4n^3 + 2n - 8$

Determine the coefficient and the degree of each term in each polynomial.

13. $8x^4 + 2x$

14. $9a^3 - 4a^2$

15. $9t^2 - 3t + 4$

16. $7x^4 + 5x - 3$

17. $6a^5 + 9a + a^3$

18. $4t^8 - t + 6t^5$

19. $x^4 - x^3 + 4x - 3$

20. $2a^5 + a^2 + 8a + 10$

For each of the following polynomials, **(a)** *list the degree of each term;* **(b)** *determine the leading term and the leading coefficient; and* **(c)** *determine the degree of the polynomial.*

21. $5t + t^3 + 8t^4$

22. $1 + 6n + 4n^2$

23. $3a^2 - 7 + 2a^4$

24. $9x^4 + x^2 + x^7 - 12$

25. $8 + 6x^2 - 3x - x^5$

26. $9a - a^4 + 3 + 2a^3$

27. Complete the following table for the polynomial
$7x^2 + 8x^5 - 4x^3 + 6 - \frac{1}{2}x^4$.

Term	Coefficient	Degree of the Term	Degree of the Polynomial
		5	
$-\frac{1}{2}x^4$			
	-4		
		2	
	6		

28. Complete the following table for the polynomial
$-3x^4 + 6x^3 - 2x^2 + 8x + 7$.

Term	Coefficient	Degree of the Term	Degree of the Polynomial
	-3		
$6x^3$			
		2	
		1	
	7		

Classify each polynomial as a monomial, a binomial, a trinomial, or a polynomial with no special name.

29. $x^2 - 23x + 17$

30. $-9x^2$

31. $x^3 - 7x + 2x^2 - 4$

32. $t^3 + 4$

33. $y + 8$

34. $3x^8 + 12x^3 - 9$

35. 17

36. $2x^4 - 7x^3 + x^2 + x - 6$

Combine like terms. Write all answers in descending order.

37. $5n^2 + n + 6n^2$

38. $5a + 7a^2 + 3a$

39. $3a^4 - 2a + 2a + a^4$

40. $9b^5 + 3b^2 - 2b^5 - 3b^2$

41. $7x^3 - 11x + 5x + x^2$

42. $3x^4 - 7x + x^4 - 2x$

43. $4b^3 + 5b + 7b^3 + b^2 - 6b$

44. $6x^2 + 2x^4 - 2x^2 - x^4 - 4x^2 + x$

45. $10x^2 + 2x^3 - 3x^3 - 4x^2 - 6x^2 - x^4$

46. $12t^6 - t^3 + 8t^6 + 4t^3 - t^7 - 3t^3$

47. $\frac{1}{5}x^4 + 7 - 2x^2 + 3 - \frac{2}{15}x^4 + 2x^2$

48. $\frac{1}{6}x^3 + 3x^2 - \frac{1}{3}x^3 + 7 + x^2 - 10$

49. $8.3a^2 + 3.7a - 8 - 9.4a^2 + 1.6a + 0.5$

50. $1.4y^3 + 2.9 - 7.7y - 1.3y - 4.1 + 9.6y^3$

Evaluate each polynomial for $x = 3$ and for $x = -3$.

51. $-4x + 9$

52. $-6x + 5$

53. $2x^2 - 3x + 7$

54. $4x^2 - 6x + 9$

55. $-3x^3 + 7x^2 - 4x - 8$

56. $-2x^3 - 3x^2 + 4x + 2$

57. $2x^4 - \frac{1}{9}x^3$

58. $\frac{1}{3}x^4 - 2x^3$

59. $-x - x^2 - x^3$

60. $-x^2 - 3x^3 - x^4$

Back-to-college expenses. The amount of money, in billions of dollars, spent on shoes for college can be estimated by the polynomial

$$0.4t + 1.13,$$

where t is the number of years since 2004.
Source: Based on data from the National Retail Federation

61. Estimate the amount spent on shoes for college in 2006.

62. Estimate the amount spent on shoes for college in 2010.

63. *Skydiving.* During the first 13 sec of a jump, the number of feet that a skydiver falls in *t* seconds is approximated by the polynomial

$$11.12t^2.$$

Approximately how far has a skydiver fallen 10 sec after having jumped from a plane?

$11.12\,t^2$

64. *Skydiving.* For jumps that exceed 13 sec, the polynomial $173t - 369$ can be used to approximate the distance, in feet, that a skydiver has fallen in t seconds. Approximately how far has a skydiver fallen 20 sec after having jumped from a plane?

Circumference. *The circumference of a circle of radius r is given by the polynomial $2\pi r$, where π is an irrational number. For an approximation of π, use 3.14.*

65. Find the circumference of a circle with radius 10 cm.

66. Find the circumference of a circle with radius 5 ft.

Area of a circle. *The area of a circle of radius r is given by the polynomial πr^2. Use 3.14 as an approximation for π.*

67. Find the area of a circle with radius 7 m.

68. Find the area of a circle with radius 6 ft.

Kidney transplants. *Often a patient needing a kidney transplant has a willing kidney donor who does not match the patient medically. A kidney-paired donation matches donor–recipient pairs. Two kidney transplants are performed simultaneously, with each patient receiving the kidney of a stranger. The number k of such "kidney swaps" t years after 2003 can be approximated by*

$$k = 14.3t^3 - 56t^2 + 57.7t + 19.$$

Use the following graph for Exercises 69 and 70.
Source: Based on data from United Network for Organ Sharing

69. Estimate the number of kidney-paired donations in 2006.

70. Estimate the number of kidney-paired donations in 2004.

Memorizing words. *Participants in a psychology experiment were able to memorize an average of M words in t minutes, where $M = -0.001t^3 + 0.1t^2$. Use the following graph for Exercises 71–74.*

71. Estimate the number of words memorized after 10 min.

72. Estimate the number of words memorized after 14 min.

73. Find the approximate value of M for $t = 8$.

74. Find the approximate value of M for $t = 12$.

Body mass index. *The body mass index, or BMI, is one measure of a person's health. The average BMI B for males of age x, where x is between 2 and 20, is approximated by*

$$B = -0.003x^3 + 0.13x^2 - 1.2x + 18.6.$$

Use the following graph for Exercises 75 and 76.
Source: Based on information from the National Center for Health Statistics

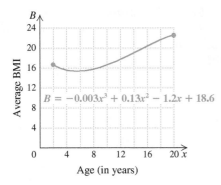

$B = -0.003x^3 + 0.13x^2 - 1.2x + 18.6$

Age (in years)

75. Approximate the average BMI for 4-year-old males; for 14-year-old males.

76. Approximate the average BMI for 10-year-old males; for 16-year-old males.

77. Explain how it is possible for a term to not be a monomial.

78. Is it possible to evaluate polynomials without understanding the rules for order of operations? Why or why not?

Skill Review

To prepare for Section 5.4, review simplifying expressions containing parentheses (Section 1.8).

Simplify. [1.8]

79. $2x + 5 - (x + 8)$ **80.** $3x - 7 - (5x - 1)$

81. $4a + 3 - (-2a + 6)$ **82.** $\frac{1}{2}t - \frac{1}{4} - \left(\frac{3}{2}t + \frac{3}{4}\right)$

83. $4t^4 + 8t - (5t^4 - 9t)$

84. $0.1a^2 + 5 - (-0.3a^2 + a - 6)$

Synthesis

85. Suppose that the coefficients of a polynomial are all integers and the polynomial is evaluated for some integer. Must the value of the polynomial then also be an integer? Why or why not?

86. Is it easier to evaluate a polynomial before or after like terms have been combined? Why?

87. Construct a polynomial in x (meaning that x is the variable) of degree 5 with four terms, with coefficients that are consecutive even integers. Write in descending order.

Revenue, cost, and profit.   Gigabytes Electronics is selling a new type of computer monitor. Total revenue is the total amount of money taken in and total cost is the total amount paid for producing the items. The firm estimates that for the monitor's first year, revenue from the sale of x monitors is

$$250x - 0.5x^2 \text{ dollars,}$$

and the total cost is given by

$$4000 + 0.6x^2 \text{ dollars.}$$

Profit is the difference between revenue and cost.

88. Find the profit when 20 monitors are produced and sold.

89. Find the profit when 30 monitors are produced and sold.

Simplify.

90. $\frac{9}{2}x^8 + \frac{1}{9}x^2 + \frac{1}{2}x^9 + \frac{9}{2}x + \frac{9}{2}x^9 + \frac{8}{9}x^2 + \frac{1}{2}x - \frac{1}{2}x^8$

91. $(3x^2)^3 + 4x^2 \cdot 4x^4 - x^4(2x)^2 + ((2x)^2)^3 - 100x^2(x^2)^2$

92. A polynomial in x has degree 3. The coefficient of x^2 is 3 less than the coefficient of x^3. The coefficient of x is three times the coefficient of x^2. The remaining constant is 2 more than the coefficient of x^3. The sum of the coefficients is -4. Find the polynomial.

93. Use the graph for Exercises 75 and 76 to determine the ages for which the average BMI is 16.

94. *Path of the Olympic arrow.*   The Olympic flame at the 1992 Summer Olympics was lit by a flaming arrow. As the arrow moved d meters horizontally from the archer, its height h, in meters, was approximated by the polynomial

$$-0.0064d^2 + 0.8d + 2.$$

Complete the table for the choices of d given. Then plot the points and draw a graph representing the path of the arrow.

d	$-0.0064d^2 + 0.8d + 2$
0	
30	
60	
90	
120	

▦ *Semester averages.* *Professor Sakima calculates a student's average for her course using*

$$A = 0.3q + 0.4t + 0.2f + 0.1h,$$

with q, t, f, and h representing a student's quiz average, test average, final exam score, and homework average, respectively. In Exercises 95 and 96, find the given student's course average rounded to the nearest tenth.

95. Galina: quizzes: 60, 85, 72, 91; final exam: 84; tests: 89, 93, 90; homework: 88

96. Nigel: quizzes: 95, 99, 72, 79; final exam: 91; tests: 68, 76, 92; homework: 86

In Exercises 97 and 98, complete the table for the given choices of t. Then plot the points and connect them with a smooth curve representing the graph of the polynomial.

97.

t	$-t^2 + 10t - 18$
3	
4	
5	
6	
7	

98.

t	$-t^2 + 6t - 4$
1	
2	
3	
4	
5	

5.4   Addition and Subtraction of Polynomials

Addition of Polynomials ▪ Opposites of Polynomials ▪ Subtraction of Polynomials ▪ Problem Solving

Addition of Polynomials

To add two polynomials, we write a plus sign between them and combine like terms.

EXAMPLE **1**   Write an equivalent expression by adding.

a) $(-5x^3 + 6x - 1) + (4x^3 + 3x^2 + 2)$

b) $\left(\frac{2}{3}x^4 + 3x^2 - 7x + \frac{1}{2}\right) + \left(-\frac{1}{3}x^4 + 5x^3 - 3x^2 + 3x - \frac{1}{2}\right)$

SOLUTION

a) $(-5x^3 + 6x - 1) + (4x^3 + 3x^2 + 2)$

$= -5x^3 + 6x - 1 + 4x^3 + 3x^2 + 2$ Writing without parentheses

$= -5x^3 + 4x^3 + 3x^2 + 6x - 1 + 2$ Using the commutative and associative laws to write like terms together

$= (-5 + 4)x^3 + 3x^2 + 6x + (-1 + 2)$ Combining like terms; using the distributive law

$= -x^3 + 3x^2 + 6x + 1$ Note that $-1x^3 = -x^3$.

b) $\left(\frac{2}{3}x^4 + 3x^2 - 7x + \frac{1}{2}\right) + \left(-\frac{1}{3}x^4 + 5x^3 - 3x^2 + 3x - \frac{1}{2}\right)$

$= \left(\frac{2}{3} - \frac{1}{3}\right)x^4 + 5x^3 + (3 - 3)x^2 + (-7 + 3)x + \left(\frac{1}{2} - \frac{1}{2}\right)$ Combining
like terms

$= \frac{1}{3}x^4 + 5x^3 - 4x$

> **TRY EXERCISE** 9

After some practice, polynomial addition is often performed mentally.

EXAMPLE 2

Add: $(2 - 3x + x^2) + (-5 + 7x - 3x^2 + x^3)$.

SOLUTION   We have

$(2 - 3x + x^2) + (-5 + 7x - 3x^2 + x^3)$

$= (2 - 5) + (-3 + 7)x + (1 - 3)x^2 + x^3$ You might do this
step mentally.

$= -3 + 4x - 2x^2 + x^3.$ Then you would write only this.

> **TRY EXERCISE** 17

In the polynomials of the last example, the terms are arranged according to degree, from least to greatest. Such an arrangement is called *ascending order.* As a rule, answers are written in ascending order when the polynomials in the original problem are given in ascending order. If the polynomials in the original problem are given in descending order, the answer is usually written in descending order.

We can also add polynomials by writing like terms in columns. Sometimes this makes like terms easier to see.

EXAMPLE 3

Add: $9x^5 - 2x^3 + 6x^2 + 3$ and $5x^4 - 7x^2 + 6$ and $3x^6 - 5x^5 + x^2 + 5$.

SOLUTION   We arrange the polynomials with like terms in columns.

$$
\begin{array}{l}
9x^5 \qquad\quad\ - 2x^3 + 6x^2 +\ \ 3 \\
\qquad\quad 5x^4 \qquad\quad - 7x^2 +\ \ 6 \qquad \text{We leave spaces for missing terms.} \\
\underline{3x^6 - 5x^5 \qquad\qquad\quad\ + 1x^2 +\ \ 5} \qquad \text{Writing } x^2 \text{ as } 1x^2 \\
3x^6 + 4x^5 + 5x^4 - 2x^3 \qquad\quad + 14 \qquad \text{Adding}
\end{array}
$$

The answer is $3x^6 + 4x^5 + 5x^4 - 2x^3 + 14$.

> **TRY EXERCISE** 23

Opposites of Polynomials

In Section 1.8, we used the property of -1 to show that the opposite of a sum is the sum of the opposites. This idea can be extended.

The Opposite of a Polynomial

To find an equivalent polynomial for the *opposite*, or *additive inverse,* of a polynomial, change the sign of every term. This is the same as multiplying the polynomial by -1.

EXAMPLE 4

Write two equivalent expressions for the opposite of $4x^5 - 7x^3 - 8x + \frac{5}{6}$.

SOLUTION

i) $-\left(4x^5 - 7x^3 - 8x + \frac{5}{6}\right)$ This is one representation of the opposite of $4x^5 - 7x^3 - 8x + \frac{5}{6}$.

ii) $-4x^5 + 7x^3 + 8x - \frac{5}{6}$ Changing the sign of every term

Thus, $-\left(4x^5 - 7x^3 - 8x + \frac{5}{6}\right)$ and $-4x^5 + 7x^3 + 8x - \frac{5}{6}$ are equivalent. Both expressions represent the opposite of $4x^5 - 7x^3 - 8x + \frac{5}{6}$. **TRY EXERCISE** 27

EXAMPLE 5

Simplify: $-\left(-7x^4 - \frac{5}{9}x^3 + 8x^2 - x + 67\right)$.

SOLUTION   We have

$$-\left(-7x^4 - \frac{5}{9}x^3 + 8x^2 - x + 67\right) = 7x^4 + \frac{5}{9}x^3 - 8x^2 + x - 67.$$

The same result can be found by multiplying by -1:

$$-\left(-7x^4 - \frac{5}{9}x^3 + 8x^2 - x + 67\right)$$
$$= -1(-7x^4) + (-1)\left(-\frac{5}{9}x^3\right) + (-1)(8x^2) + (-1)(-x) + (-1)67$$
$$= 7x^4 + \frac{5}{9}x^3 - 8x^2 + x - 67.$$ **TRY EXERCISE** 31

Subtraction of Polynomials

We can now subtract one polynomial from another by adding the opposite of the polynomial being subtracted.

EXAMPLE 6

Write an equivalent expression by subtracting.

a) $(9x^5 + x^3 - 2x^2 + 4) - (-2x^5 + x^4 - 4x^3 - 3x^2)$
b) $(7x^5 + x^3 - 9x) - (3x^5 - 4x^3 + 5)$

SOLUTION

a) $(9x^5 + x^3 - 2x^2 + 4) - (-2x^5 + x^4 - 4x^3 - 3x^2)$
$= 9x^5 + x^3 - 2x^2 + 4 + 2x^5 - x^4 + 4x^3 + 3x^2$ Adding the opposite
$= 11x^5 - x^4 + 5x^3 + x^2 + 4$ Combining like terms

b) $(7x^5 + x^3 - 9x) - (3x^5 - 4x^3 + 5)$
$= 7x^5 + x^3 - 9x + (-3x^5) + 4x^3 - 5$ Adding the opposite
$= 7x^5 + x^3 - 9x - 3x^5 + 4x^3 - 5$ Try to go directly to this step.
$= 4x^5 + 5x^3 - 9x - 5$ Combining like terms **TRY EXERCISE** 39

To subtract using columns, we first replace the coefficients in the polynomial being subtracted with their opposites. We then add as before.

EXAMPLE 7

Write in columns and subtract: $(5x^2 - 3x + 6) - (9x^2 - 5x - 3)$.

SOLUTION

i) $5x^2 - 3x + 6$ Writing similar terms in columns
   $-(9x^2 - 5x - 3)$

ii) $5x^2 - 3x + 6$ Changing signs and removing parentheses
   $-9x^2 + 5x + 3$

iii) $5x^2 - 3x + 6$
   $-9x^2 + 5x + 3$
   $-4x^2 + 2x + 9$ Adding **TRY EXERCISE** 53

If you can do so without error, you can arrange the polynomials in columns, mentally find the opposite of each term being subtracted, and write the answer. Lining up like terms is important and may require leaving some blank space.

EXAMPLE 8   Write in columns and subtract: $(x^3 + x^2 - 12) - (-2x^3 + x^2 - 3x + 6)$.

SOLUTION   We have

$$
\begin{array}{r}
x^3 + x^2 \qquad\ - 12 \qquad \text{Leaving a blank space for the missing term}\\
\underline{-(-2x^3 + x^2 - 3x + \ 6)}\\
3x^3 \qquad\quad + 3x - 18
\end{array}
$$

TRY EXERCISE ▶ 55

> *CAUTION!*   Be sure to subtract every term of the polynomial being subtracted when using columns.

Problem Solving

EXAMPLE 9   Find a polynomial for the sum of the areas of rectangles A, B, C, and D.

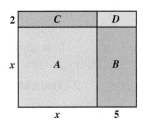

SOLUTION

1. **Familiarize.** Recall that the area of a rectangle is the product of its length and width.

2. **Translate.** We translate the problem to mathematical language. The sum of the areas is a sum of products. We find each product and then add:

   Area of A plus   area of B plus   area of C plus   area of D

   $x \cdot x$ $+$ $5x$ $+$ $2x$ $+$ $2 \cdot 5.$

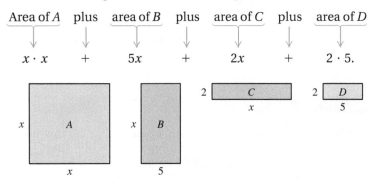

3. **Carry out.** We simplify $x \cdot x$ and $2 \cdot 5$ and combine like terms:

   $$x^2 + 5x + 2x + 10 = x^2 + 7x + 10.$$

4. **Check.** A partial check is to replace x with a number, say 3. Then we evaluate $x^2 + 7x + 10$ and compare that result with an alternative calculation:

   $$3^2 + 7 \cdot 3 + 10 = 9 + 21 + 10 = 40.$$

   When we substitute 3 for x and calculate the total area by regarding the figure as one large rectangle, we should also get 40:

   Total area $= (x + 5)(x + 2) = (3 + 5)(3 + 2) = 8 \cdot 5 = 40.$

Our check is only partial, since it is possible for an incorrect answer to equal 40 when evaluated for $x = 3$. This would be unlikely, especially if a second choice of x, say $x = 5$, also checks. We leave that check to the student.

5. **State.** A polynomial for the sum of the areas is $x^2 + 7x + 10$.

> **TRY EXERCISE** 61

EXAMPLE 10 A 16-ft wide round fountain is built in a square city park that measures x ft by x ft. Find a polynomial for the remaining area of the park.

SOLUTION

1. **Familiarize.** We make a drawing of the square park and the circular fountain, and let x represent the length of a side of the park.

The area of a square is given by $A = s^2$, and the area of a circle is given by $A = \pi r^2$. Note that a circle with a diameter of 16 ft has a radius of 8 ft.

2. **Translate.** We reword the problem and translate as follows.

Rewording: Area of park   minus   area of fountain   is   area left over.

Translating: x ft $\cdot$ x ft $-$ $\pi \cdot 8$ ft $\cdot 8$ ft $=$ Area left over

3. **Carry out.** We carry out the multiplication:

$$x^2 \text{ ft}^2 - 64\pi \text{ ft}^2 = \text{Area left over.}$$

4. **Check.** As a partial check, note that the units in the answer are square feet (ft^2), a measure of area, as expected.

5. **State.** The remaining area of the park is $(x^2 - 64\pi) \text{ ft}^2$.   > **TRY EXERCISE** 69

TECHNOLOGY CONNECTION

To check polynomial addition or subtraction, we can let $y_1 =$ the expression before the addition or subtraction has been performed and $y_2 =$ the simplified sum or difference. If the addition or subtraction is correct, y_1 will equal y_2 and $y_2 - y_1$ will be 0. We enter $y_2 - y_1$ as y_3, using **VARS**. Below is a check of Example 6(b) in which

$$y_1 = (7x^5 + x^3 - 9x) - (3x^5 - 4x^3 + 5),$$
$$y_2 = 4x^5 + 5x^3 - 9x - 5,$$

and

$$y_3 = y_2 - y_1.$$

We graph only y_3. If indeed y_1 and y_2 are equivalent, then y_3 should equal 0. This means its graph should coincide with the x-axis. The TRACE or TABLE features can confirm

that y_3 is always 0, or we can select y_3 to be drawn bold at the $\boxed{Y=}$ window.

$y_3 = y_2 - y_1$

```
                    10




-10  |_|_|_|_|_|_|_|_|_|_|_|_|_|_|_|_|_|_|  10
                    ⋈

     X = 2.5531915   Y = 0
                   -10
```

1. Use a graphing calculator to check Examples 1, 2, and 6.

| 5.4 | EXERCISE SET | |

Concept Reinforcement *For Exercises 1–4, replace ▪ with the correct expression or operation sign.*

1. $(3x^2 + 2) + (6x^2 + 7) = (3 + 6)$ ▪ $+ (2 + 7)$

2. $(5t - 6) + (4t + 3) = (5 + 4)t + ($ ▪ $+ 3)$

3. $(9x^3 - x^2) - (3x^3 + x^2) = 9x^3 - x^2 - 3x^3$ ▪ x^2 ▪

4. $(-2n^3 + 5) - (n^2 - 2) = -2n^3 + 5 - n^2$ ▪ 2

Add.

5. $(3x + 2) + (x + 7)$

6. $(x + 1) + (12x + 10)$

7. $(2t + 7) + (-8t + 1)$

8. $(4t - 3) + (-11t + 2)$

9. $(x^2 + 6x + 3) + (-4x^2 - 5)$

10. $(x^2 - 5x + 4) + (8x - 9)$

11. $(7t^2 - 3t - 6) + (2t^2 + 4t + 9)$

12. $(8a^2 + 4a - 7) + (6a^2 - 3a - 1)$

13. $(4m^3 - 7m^2 + m - 5) + (4m^3 + 7m^2 - 4m - 2)$

14. $(5n^3 - n^2 + 4n + 11) + (2n^3 - 4n^2 + n - 11)$

15. $(3 + 6a + 7a^2 + a^3) + (4 + 7a - 8a^2 + 6a^3)$

16. $(7 + 4t - 5t^2 + 6t^3) + (2 + t + 6t^2 - 4t^3)$

17. $(3x^6 + 2x^4 - x^3 + 5x) + (-x^6 + 3x^3 - 4x^2 + 7x^4)$

18. $(4x^5 - 6x^3 - 9x + 1) + (3x^4 + 6x^3 + 9x^2 + x)$

19. $\left(\frac{3}{5}x^4 + \frac{1}{2}x^3 - \frac{2}{3}x + 3\right) + \left(\frac{2}{5}x^4 - \frac{1}{4}x^3 - \frac{3}{4}x^2 - \frac{1}{6}x\right)$

20. $\left(\frac{1}{3}x^9 + \frac{1}{5}x^5 - \frac{1}{2}x^2 + 7\right) + \left(-\frac{1}{5}x^9 + \frac{1}{4}x^4 - \frac{3}{5}x^5\right)$

21. $(5.3t^2 - 6.4t - 9.1) + (4.2t^3 - 1.8t^2 + 7.3)$

22. $(4.9a^3 + 3.2a^2 - 5.1a) + (2.1a^2 - 3.7a + 4.6)$

23. $-4x^3 + 8x^2 + 3x - 2$
    $ - 4x^2 + 3x + 2$

24. $-3x^4 + 6x^2 + 2x - 4$
    $ - 3x^2 + 2x + 4$

25. $0.05x^4 + 0.12x^3 - 0.5x^2$
    $ - 0.02x^3 + 0.02x^2 + 2x$
    $1.5x^4 + 0.01x^2 + 0.15$
    $ 0.25x^3 + 0.85$
    $-0.25x^4 + 10x^2 - 0.04$

26. $0.15x^4 + 0.10x^3 - 0.9x^2$
    $ - 0.01x^3 + 0.01x^2 + x$
    $1.25x^4 + 0.11x^2 + 0.01$
    $ 0.27x^3 + 0.99$
    $-0.35x^4 + 15x^2 - 0.03$

Write two equivalent expressions for the opposite of each polynomial, as in Example 4.

27. $-3t^3 + 4t^2 - 7$

28. $-x^3 - 5x^2 + 2x$

29. $x^4 - 8x^3 + 6x$

30. $5a^3 + 2a - 17$

Simplify.

31. $-(9x - 10)$

32. $-(-5x + 8)$

33. $-(3a^4 - 5a^2 + 1.2)$

34. $-(-6a^3 + 0.2a^2 - 7)$

35. $-\left(-4x^4 + 6x^2 + \frac{3}{4}x - 8\right)$

36. $-\left(3x^5 - 2x^3 - \frac{3}{5}x^2 + 16\right)$

Subtract.

37. $(3x + 1) - (5x + 8)$

38. $(7x + 3) - (3x + 2)$

39. $(-9t + 12) - (t^2 + 3t - 1)$

40. $(a^2 - 3a - 2) - (2a^2 - 6a - 2)$

41. $(4a^2 + a - 7) - (3 - 8a^3 - 4a^2)$

42. $(-4x^2 + 2x) - (-5x^2 + 2x^3 + 3)$

43. $(1.2x^3 + 4.5x^2 - 3.8x) - (-3.4x^3 - 4.7x^2 + 23)$

44. $(0.5x^4 - 0.6x^2 + 0.7) - (2.3x^4 + 1.8x - 3.9)$

Aha! **45.** $(7x^3 - 2x^2 + 6) - (6 - 2x^2 + 7x^3)$

46. $(8x^5 + 3x^4 + x - 1) - (8x^5 + 3x^4 - 1)$

47. $(3 + 5a + 3a^2 - a^3) - (2 + 4a - 9a^2 + 2a^3)$

48. $(7 + t - 5t^2 + 2t^3) - (1 + 2t - 4t^2 + 5t^3)$

49. $\left(\frac{5}{8}x^3 - \frac{1}{4}x - \frac{1}{3}\right) - \left(-\frac{1}{2}x^3 + \frac{1}{4}x - \frac{1}{3}\right)$

50. $\left(\frac{1}{5}x^3 + 2x^2 - \frac{3}{10}\right) - \left(-\frac{2}{5}x^3 + 2x^2 + \frac{7}{1000}\right)$

51. $(0.07t^3 - 0.03t^2 + 0.01t) - (0.02t^3 + 0.04t^2 - 1)$

52. $(0.9a^3 + 0.2a - 5) - (0.7a^4 - 0.3a - 0.1)$

53. $x^3 + 3x^2 + 1$
  $\underline{-(x^3 +\ \ x^2 - 5)}$

54. $x^2 + 5x + 6$
  $\underline{-(x^2 + 2x + 1)}$

55. $4x^4 - 2x^3$
  $\underline{-(7x^4 + 6x^3 + 7x^2)}$

56. $5x^4 + 6x^3 - 9x^2$
  $\underline{-(-6x^4\qquad\ \ + x^2)}$

57. Solve.

   a) Find a polynomial for the sum of the areas of the rectangles shown in the figure.

   b) Find the sum of the areas when $x = 5$ and $x = 7$.

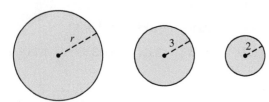

58. Solve. Leave the answers in terms of π.

   a) Find a polynomial for the sum of the areas of the circles shown in the figure.

   b) Find the sum of the areas when $r = 5$ and $r = 11.3$.

Find a polynomial for the perimeter of each figure in Exercises 59 and 60.

59.

60.

Find two algebraic expressions for the area of each figure. First, regard the figure as one large rectangle, and then regard the figure as a sum of four smaller rectangles.

61.

62.

63.

64.

Find a polynomial for the shaded area of each figure.

65.

66.

67.

68.

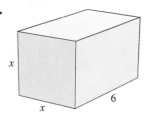

69. A 2-ft by 6-ft bath enclosure is installed in a new bathroom measuring x ft by x ft. Find a polynomial for the remaining floor area.

70. A 5-ft by 7-ft Jacuzzi™ is installed on an outdoor deck measuring y ft by y ft. Find a polynomial for the remaining area of the deck.

71. A 12-ft wide round patio is laid in a garden measuring z ft by z ft. Find a polynomial for the remaining area of the garden.

72. A 10-ft wide round water trampoline is floating in a pool measuring x ft by x ft. Find a polynomial for the remaining surface area of the pool.

73. A 12-m by 12-m mat includes a circle of diameter d meters for wrestling. Find a polynomial for the area of the mat outside the wrestling circle.

74. A 2-m by 3-m rug is spread inside a tepee that has a diameter of x meters. Find a polynomial for the area of the tepee's floor that is not covered.

75. Explain why parentheses are used in the statement of the solution of Example 10: $(x^2 - 64\pi)$ ft^2.

76. Is the sum of two trinomials always a trinomial? Why or why not?

Skill Review

To prepare for Section 5.5, review multiplying using the distributive law and multiplying with exponential notation (Sections 1.8 and 4.1).

Simplify.

77. $2(x^2 - x + 3)$ [1.8]

78. $-5(3x^2 - 2x - 7)$ [1.8]

79. $x^2 \cdot x^6$ [5.1]

80. $y^6 \cdot y$ [5.1]

81. $2n \cdot n^2$ [5.1]

82. $-6n^4 \cdot n^8$ [5.1]

Synthesis

83. What can be concluded about two polynomials whose sum is zero?

84. Which, if any, of the commutative, associative, and distributive laws are needed for adding polynomials? Why?

Simplify.

85. $(6t^2 - 7t) + (3t^2 - 4t + 5) - (9t - 6)$

86. $(3x^2 - 4x + 6) - (-2x^2 + 4) + (-5x - 3)$

87. $4(x^2 - x + 3) - 2(2x^2 + x - 1)$

88. $3(2y^2 - y - 1) - (6y^2 - 3y - 3)$

89. $(345.099x^3 - 6.178x) - (94.508x^3 - 8.99x)$

Find a polynomial for the surface area of the right rectangular solid.

90.

91.

92.

93.

94. Find a polynomial for the total length of all edges in the figure appearing in Exercise 93.

95. Find a polynomial for the total length of all edges in the figure appearing in Exercise 90.

96. *Total profit.* Hadley Electronics is marketing a new digital camera. Total revenue is the total amount of money taken in. The firm determines that when it sells x cameras, its total revenue is given by

$$R = 175x - 0.4x^2.$$

Total cost is the total cost of producing x cameras. Hadley Electronics determines that the total cost of producing x cameras is given by

$$C = 5000 + 0.6x^2.$$

The total profit P is

(Total Revenue) − (Total Cost) = $R - C$.

a) Find a polynomial for total profit.
b) What is the total profit on the production and sale of 75 cameras?
c) What is the total profit on the production and sale of 120 cameras?

97. Does replacing each occurrence of the variable x in $4x^7 - 6x^3 + 2x$ with its opposite result in the opposite of the polynomial? Why or why not?

5.5 Multiplication of Polynomials

Multiplying Monomials ▪ Multiplying a Monomial and a Polynomial ▪ Multiplying Any Two Polynomials ▪ Checking by Evaluating

We now multiply polynomials using techniques based largely on the distributive, associative, and commutative laws and the rules for exponents.

Multiplying Monomials

Consider $(3x)(4x)$. We multiply as follows:

$$
\begin{aligned}
(3x)(4x) &= 3 \cdot x \cdot 4 \cdot x && \text{Using an associative law}\\
&= 3 \cdot 4 \cdot x \cdot x && \text{Using a commutative law}\\
&= (3 \cdot 4) \cdot x \cdot x && \text{Using an associative law}\\
&= 12x^2.
\end{aligned}
$$

> **To Multiply Monomials**
>
> To find an equivalent expression for the product of two monomials, multiply the coefficients and then multiply the variables using the product rule for exponents.

EXAMPLE 1

Multiply to form an equivalent expression.

a) $(5x)(6x)$

b) $(-a)(3a)$

c) $(7x^5)(-4x^3)$

SOLUTION

a) $(5x)(6x) = (5 \cdot 6)(x \cdot x)$ Multiplying the coefficients; multiplying the variables

$\qquad\qquad\quad = 30x^2$ Simplifying

b) $(-a)(3a) = (-1a)(3a)$ Writing $-a$ as $-1a$ can ease calculations.

$\qquad\qquad\quad = (-1 \cdot 3)(a \cdot a)$ Using an associative law and a commutative law

$\qquad\qquad\quad = -3a^2$

c) $(7x^5)(-4x^3) = 7(-4)(x^5 \cdot x^3)$

$\qquad\qquad\qquad = -28x^{5+3}$ $\left.\vphantom{\begin{aligned}&\\&\end{aligned}}\right\}$ Using the product rule for exponents

$\qquad\qquad\qquad = -28x^8$

TRY EXERCISE 13

After some practice, you can try writing only the answer.

Multiplying a Monomial and a Polynomial

To find an equivalent expression for the product of a monomial, such as $5x$, and a polynomial, such as $2x^2 - 3x + 4$, we use the distributive law.

EXAMPLE   2   Multiply: **(a)** $x(x + 3)$; **(b)** $5x(2x^2 - 3x + 4)$.

SOLUTION

a) $x(x + 3) = x \cdot x + x \cdot 3$ Using the distributive law

$\qquad\quad = x^2 + 3x$

b) $5x(2x^2 - 3x + 4) = (5x)(2x^2) - (5x)(3x) + (5x)(4)$ Using the
                                                                   distributive law

$\qquad\qquad\qquad\qquad = 10x^3 - 15x^2 + 20x$ Performing the three
                                                       multiplications

TRY EXERCISE   29

The product in Example 2(a) can be visualized as the area of a rectangle with width x and length $x + 3$.

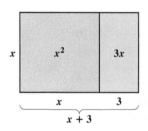

Note that the total area can be expressed as $x(x + 3)$ or, by adding the two smaller areas, $x^2 + 3x$.

The Product of a Monomial and a Polynomial

To multiply a monomial and a polynomial, multiply each term of the polynomial by the monomial.

Try to do this mentally, when possible. Remember that we multiply coefficients and, when the bases match, add exponents.

EXAMPLE   3   Multiply: $2x^2(x^3 - 7x^2 + 10x - 4)$.

SOLUTION

$\qquad\qquad\qquad$ *Think:* $\underbrace{2x^2 \cdot x^3} - \underbrace{2x^2 \cdot 7x^2} + \underbrace{2x^2 \cdot 10x} - \underbrace{2x^2 \cdot 4}$

$2x^2(x^3 - 7x^2 + 10x - 4) = 2x^5 \quad - \quad 14x^4 \quad + \quad 20x^3 \quad - \quad 8x^2$

TRY EXERCISE   31

Multiplying Any Two Polynomials

Before considering the product of *any* two polynomials, let's look at products when both polynomials are binomials.

To find an equivalent expression for the product of two binomials, we again begin by using the distributive law. This time, however, it is a *binomial* rather than a monomial that is being distributed.

EXAMPLE 4   Multiply each pair of binomials.

a) $x + 5$ and $x + 4$ **b)** $4x - 3$ and $x - 2$

SOLUTION

a) $(x + 5)\ (x + 4) = (x + 5)\ x +\ (x + 5)\ 4$ Using the distributive law

$\qquad\qquad\quad = x(x + 5) + 4(x + 5)$ Using the commutative law for multiplication

$\qquad\qquad\quad = x \cdot x + x \cdot 5 + 4 \cdot x + 4 \cdot 5$ Using the distributive law (twice)

$\qquad\qquad\quad = x^2 + 5x + 4x + 20$ Multiplying the monomials

$\qquad\qquad\quad = x^2 + 9x + 20$ Combining like terms

b) $(4x - 3)\ (x - 2) = (4x - 3)\ x -\ (4x - 3)\ 2$ Using the distributive law

$\qquad\qquad\quad = x(4x - 3) - 2(4x - 3)$ Using the commutative law for multiplication. This step is often omitted.

$\qquad\qquad\quad = x \cdot 4x - x \cdot 3 - 2 \cdot 4x - 2(-3)$ Using the distributive law (twice)

$\qquad\qquad\quad = 4x^2 - 3x - 8x + 6$ Multiplying the monomials

$\qquad\qquad\quad = 4x^2 - 11x + 6$ Combining like terms

TRY EXERCISE 37

To visualize the product in Example 4(a), consider a rectangle of length $x + 5$ and width $x + 4$, as shown here.

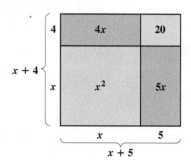

The total area can be expressed as $(x + 5)(x + 4)$ or, by adding the four smaller areas, $x^2 + 5x + 4x + 20$.

Let's consider the product of a binomial and a trinomial. Again we make repeated use of the distributive law.

EXAMPLE 5   Multiply: $(x^2 + 2x - 3)(x + 4)$.

SOLUTION

$$(x^2 + 2x - 3)\ (x + 4)$$

$$= (x^2 + 2x - 3)\ x + \ (x^2 + 2x - 3)\ 4 \qquad \text{Using the distributive law}$$

$$= x(x^2 + 2x - 3) + 4(x^2 + 2x - 3) \qquad \text{Using the commutative law}$$

$$= x \cdot x^2 + x \cdot 2x - x \cdot 3 + 4 \cdot x^2 + 4 \cdot 2x - 4 \cdot 3 \qquad \text{Using the distributive law (twice)}$$

$$= x^3 + 2x^2 - 3x + 4x^2 + 8x - 12 \qquad \text{Multiplying the monomials}$$

$$= x^3 + 6x^2 + 5x - 12 \qquad \text{Combining like terms}$$

TRY EXERCISE 57

Perhaps you have discovered the following in the preceding examples.

The Product of Two Polynomials

To multiply two polynomials P and Q, select one of the polynomials, say P. Then multiply each term of P by every term of Q and combine like terms.

To use columns for long multiplication, multiply each term in the top row by every term in the bottom row. We write like terms in columns, and then add the results. Such multiplication is like multiplying with whole numbers.

$$
\begin{array}{r}
321 \\
\times\ 12 \\
\hline
642 \\
321 \\
\hline
3852
\end{array}
\qquad
\begin{array}{r}
300 + 20 + 1 \\
\times \qquad 10 + 2 \\
\hline
600 + 40 + 2 \\
3000 + 200 + 10 \\
\hline
3000 + 800 + 50 + 2
\end{array}
$$

Multiplying the top row by 2
Multiplying the top row by 10
Adding

EXAMPLE 6   Multiply: $(5x^4 - 2x^2 + 3x)(x^2 + 2x)$.

SOLUTION

$$
\begin{array}{r}
5x^4 \qquad - 2x^2 + 3x \ \Big\} \\
x^2 + 2x \ \ \\
\hline
10x^5 \qquad - 4x^3 + 6x^2 \\
5x^6 \qquad - 2x^4 + 3x^3 \\
\hline
5x^6 + 10x^5 - 2x^4 - x^3 + 6x^2
\end{array}
$$

Note that each polynomial is written in descending order, and space is left for missing terms.

Multiplying the top row by $2x$

Multiplying the top row by x^2

Combining like terms

Line up like terms in columns.

TRY EXERCISE 61

With practice, you will be able to skip some steps. Sometimes we multiply horizontally, while still aligning like terms as we write the product.

EXAMPLE **7** Multiply: $(2x^3 + 3x^2 - 4x + 6)(3x + 5)$.

SOLUTION

Multiplying by $3x$

$$(2x^3 + 3x^2 - 4x + 6)(3x + 5) = 6x^4 + 9x^3 - 12x^2 + 18x$$
$$+ 10x^3 + 15x^2 - 20x + 30$$

Multiplying by 5

$$= 6x^4 + 19x^3 + 3x^2 - 2x + 30$$

TRY EXERCISE 65

Checking by Evaluating

How can we be certain that our multiplication (or addition or subtraction) of polynomials is correct? One check is to simply review our calculations. A different type of check, used in Example 9 of Section 5.4, makes use of the fact that equivalent expressions have the same value when evaluated for the same replacement. Thus a quick, partial, check of Example 7 can be made by selecting a convenient replacement for x (say, 1) and comparing the values of the expressions $(2x^3 + 3x^2 - 4x + 6)(3x + 5)$ and $6x^4 + 19x^3 + 3x^2 - 2x + 30$:

$$(2x^3 + 3x^2 - 4x + 6)(3x + 5) = (2 \cdot 1^3 + 3 \cdot 1^2 - 4 \cdot 1 + 6)(3 \cdot 1 + 5)$$
$$= (2 + 3 - 4 + 6)(3 + 5)$$
$$= 7 \cdot 8 = 56;$$

$$6x^4 + 19x^3 + 3x^2 - 2x + 30 = 6 \cdot 1^4 + 19 \cdot 1^3 + 3 \cdot 1^2 - 2 \cdot 1 + 30$$
$$= 6 + 19 + 3 - 2 + 30$$
$$= 28 - 2 + 30 = 56.$$

Since the value of both expressions is 56, the multiplication in Example 7 is very likely correct.

It is possible, by chance, for two expressions that are not equivalent to share the same value when evaluated. For this reason, checking by evaluating is only a partial check. Consult your instructor for the checking approach that he or she prefers.

TECHNOLOGY CONNECTION

Tables can also be used to check polynomial multiplication. To illustrate, we can check Example 7 by entering $y_1 = (2x^3 + 3x^2 - 4x + 6)(3x + 5)$ and $y_2 = 6x^4 + 19x^3 + 3x^2 - 2x + 30$.

When TABLE is then pressed, we are shown two columns of values—one for y_1 and one for y_2. If our multiplication was correct, the columns of values will match.

X	Y1	Y2
−3	36	36
−2	−10	−10
−1	22	22
0	30	30
1	56	56
2	286	286
3	1050	1050

X = −3

1. Form a table and scroll up and down to check Example 6.
2. Check Example 7 using the method discussed in Section 5.4: Let

$$y_1 = (2x^3 + 3x^2 - 4x + 6)(3x + 5),$$
$$y_2 = 6x^4 + 19x^3 + 3x^2 - 2x + 30,$$

and

$$y_3 = y_2 - y_1.$$

Then check that y_3 is always 0.

↪ *Concept Reinforcement* *In each of Exercises 1–6, match the expression with the correct result from the column on the right. Choices may be used more than once.*

1. ____ $3x^2 \cdot 2x^4$ a) $6x^8$

2. ____ $3x^8 + 5x^8$ b) $8x^6$

3. ____ $4x^3 \cdot 2x^5$ c) $6x^6$

4. ____ $3x^5 \cdot 2x^3$ d) $8x^8$

5. ____ $4x^6 + 2x^6$

6. ____ $4x^4 \cdot 2x^2$

Multiply.

7. $(3x^5)7$ 8. $2x^3 \cdot 11$

9. $(-x^3)(x^4)$ 10. $(-x^2)(-x)$

11. $(-x^6)(-x^2)$ 12. $(-x^5)(x^3)$

13. $4t^2(9t^2)$ 14. $(6a^8)(3a^2)$

15. $(0.3x^3)(-0.4x^6)$ 16. $(-0.1x^6)(0.2x^4)$

17. $\left(-\frac{1}{4}x^4\right)\left(\frac{1}{5}x^8\right)$ 18. $\left(-\frac{1}{5}x^3\right)\left(-\frac{1}{3}x\right)$

19. $(-5n^3)(-1)$ 20. $19t^2 \cdot 0$

21. $11x^5(-4x^5)$ 22. $12x^3(-5x^3)$

23. $(-4y^5)(6y^2)(-3y^3)$ 24. $7x^2(-2x^3)(2x^6)$

25. $5x(4x + 1)$ 26. $3x(2x - 7)$

27. $(a - 9)3a$ 28. $(a - 7)4a$

29. $x^2(x^3 + 1)$ 30. $-2x^3(x^2 - 1)$

31. $-3n(2n^2 - 8n + 1)$

32. $4n(3n^3 - 4n^2 - 5n + 10)$

33. $-5t^2(3t + 6)$ 34. $7t^2(2t + 1)$

35. $\frac{2}{3}a^4\left(6a^5 - 12a^3 - \frac{5}{8}\right)$ 36. $\frac{3}{4}t^5\left(8t^6 - 12t^4 + \frac{12}{7}\right)$

37. $(x + 3)(x + 4)$ 38. $(x + 7)(x + 3)$

39. $(t + 7)(t - 3)$ 40. $(t - 4)(t + 3)$

41. $(a - 0.6)(a - 0.7)$ 42. $(a - 0.4)(a - 0.8)$

43. $(x + 3)(x - 3)$ 44. $(x + 6)(x - 6)$

45. $(4 - x)(7 - 2x)$ 46. $(5 + x)(5 + 2x)$

47. $\left(t + \frac{3}{2}\right)\left(t + \frac{4}{3}\right)$ 48. $\left(a - \frac{2}{5}\right)\left(a + \frac{5}{2}\right)$

49. $\left(\frac{1}{4}a + 2\right)\left(\frac{3}{4}a - 1\right)$ 50. $\left(\frac{2}{5}t - 1\right)\left(\frac{3}{5}t + 1\right)$

Draw and label rectangles similar to those following Examples 2 and 4 to illustrate each product.

51. $x(x + 5)$ 52. $x(x + 2)$

53. $(x + 1)(x + 2)$ 54. $(x + 3)(x + 1)$

55. $(x + 5)(x + 3)$ 56. $(x + 4)(x + 6)$

Multiply and check.

57. $(x^2 - x + 3)(x + 1)$

58. $(x^2 + x - 7)(x + 2)$

59. $(2a + 5)(a^2 - 3a + 2)$

60. $(3t - 4)(t^2 - 5t + 1)$

61. $(y^2 - 7)(3y^4 + y + 2)$

62. $(a^2 + 4)(5a^3 - 3a - 1)$

Aha! 63. $(3x + 2)(7x + 4x + 1)$

64. $(4x - 5x - 3)(1 + 2x^2)$

65. $(x^2 + 5x - 1)(x^2 - x + 3)$

66. $(x^2 - 3x + 2)(x^2 + x + 1)$

67. $\left(5t^2 - t + \frac{1}{2}\right)(2t^2 + t - 4)$

68. $(2t^2 - 5t - 4)\left(3t^2 - t + \frac{1}{2}\right)$

69. $(x + 1)(x^3 + 7x^2 + 5x + 4)$

70. $(x + 2)(x^3 + 5x^2 + 9x + 3)$

71. Is it possible to understand polynomial multiplication without understanding the distributive law? Why or why not?

72. The polynomials

$$(a + b + c + d) \quad \text{and} \quad (r + s + m + p)$$

are multiplied. Without performing the multiplication, determine how many terms the product will contain. Provide a justification for your answer.

Skill Review

Review simplifying expressions using the rules for order of operations (Section 1.8).

Simplify. [1.8]

73. $(9 - 3)(9 + 3) + 3^2 - 9^2$

74. $(7 + 2)(7 - 2) + 2^2 - 7^2$

75. $5 + \dfrac{7 + 4 + 2 \cdot 5}{7}$

76. $11 - \dfrac{2 + 6 \cdot 3 + 4}{6}$

77. $(4 + 3 \cdot 5 + 5) \div 3 \cdot 4$

78. $(2 + 2 \cdot 7 + 4) \div 2 \cdot 5$

Synthesis

79. Under what conditions will the product of two binomials be a trinomial?

80. How can the following figure be used to show that $(x + 3)^2 \neq x^2 + 9$?

Find a polynomial for the shaded area of each figure.

81.

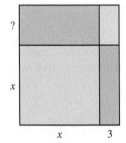

14y − 5

3y

6y   3y + 5

82.

21t + 8

3t − 4

4t   2t

For each figure, determine what the missing number must be in order for the figure to have the given area.

83. Area is $x^2 + 8x + 15$

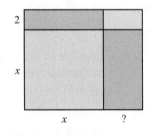

?

x

x   3

84. Area is $x^2 + 7x + 10$

2

x

x   ?

85. A box with a square bottom and no top is to be made from a 12-in.–square piece of cardboard. Squares with side x are cut out of the corners and the sides are folded up. Find the polynomials for the volume and the outside surface area of the box.

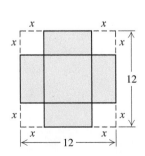

86. Find a polynomial for the volume of the solid shown below.

(x + 2) m

x m

x m   7 m

5 m

6 m

87. An open wooden box is a cube with side x cm. The box, including its bottom, is made of wood that is 1 cm thick. Find a polynomial for the interior volume of the cube.

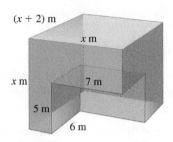

1 cm

x cm

x cm   x cm

88. A side of a cube is $(x + 2)$ cm long. Find a polynomial for the volume of the cube.

89. A rectangular garden is twice as long as it is wide and is surrounded by a sidewalk that is 4 ft wide (see the figure below). The area of the sidewalk is 256 ft². Find the dimensions of the garden.

← 4 ft →

Compute and simplify.

90. $(x + 3)(x + 6) + (x + 3)(x + 6)$

Aha! **91.** $(x - 2)(x - 7) - (x - 7)(x - 2)$

92. $(x + 5)^2 - (x - 3)^2$

93. $(x + 2)(x + 4)(x - 5)$

94. $(x - 3)^3$

Aha! **95.** Extend the pattern and simplify

$$(x - a)(x - b)(x - c)(x - d)\cdots(x - z).$$

96. Use a graphing calculator to check your answers to Exercises 25, 45, and 57. Use graphs, tables, or both, as directed by your instructor.

COLLABORATIVE

CORNER

Slick Tricks with Algebra

Focus: Polynomial multiplication

Time: 15 minutes

Group size: 2

Consider the following dialogue.

Jinny: Cal, let me do a number trick with you. Think of a number between 1 and 7. I'll have you perform some manipulations to this number, you'll tell me the result, and I'll tell me your number.

Cal: OK. I've thought of a number.

Jinny: Good. Write it down so I can't see it. Now double it, and then subtract x from the result.

Cal: Hey, this is algebra!

Jinny: I know. Now square your binomial. After you're through squaring, subtract x^2.

Cal: How did you know I had an x^2? I *thought* this was rigged!

Jinny: It is. Now divide each of the remaining terms by 4 and tell me either your constant term

or your x-term. I'll tell you the other term and the number you chose.

Cal: OK. The constant term is 16.

Jinny: Then the other term is $-4x$ and the number you chose was 4.

Cal: You're right! How did you do it?

ACTIVITY

1. Each group member should follow Jinny's instructions. Then determine how Jinny determined Cal's number and the other term.

2. Suppose that, at the end, Cal told Jinny the x-term. How would Jinny have determined Cal's number and the other term?

3. Would Jinny's "trick" work with *any* real number? Why do you think she specified numbers between 1 and 7?

5.6 Special Products

Products of Two Binomials ▪ Multiplying Sums and Differences of Two Terms ▪ Squaring Binomials ▪ Multiplications of Various Types

We can observe patterns in the products of two binomials. These patterns allow us to compute such products quickly.

Products of Two Binomials

In Section 5.5, we found the product $(x + 5)(x + 4)$ by using the distributive law a total of three times (see p. 322). Note that each term in $x + 5$ is multiplied by each term in $x + 4$. To shorten our work, we can go right to this step:

$$\begin{aligned}(x + 5)(x + 4) &= x \cdot x + x \cdot 4 + 5 \cdot x + 5 \cdot 4 \\ &= x^2 + 4x + 5x + 20 \\ &= x^2 + 9x + 20.\end{aligned}$$

Note that $x \cdot x$ is found by multiplying the *First* terms of each binomial, $x \cdot 4$ is found by multiplying the *Outer* terms of the two binomials, $5 \cdot x$ is the product of the *Inner* terms of the two binomials, and $5 \cdot 4$ is the product of the *Last* terms of each binomial:

$$\underbrace{\text{First}}_{} \quad \underbrace{\text{Outer}}_{} \quad \underbrace{\text{Inner}}_{} \quad \underbrace{\text{Last}}_{}$$
$$\text{terms} \quad \text{terms} \quad \text{terms} \quad \text{terms}$$

$$(x + 5)(x + 4) = x \cdot x + 4 \cdot x + 5 \cdot x + 5 \cdot 4.$$

To remember this shortcut for multiplying, we use the initials **FOIL**.

The FOIL Method

To multiply two binomials, $A + B$ and $C + D$, multiply the First terms AC, the Outer terms AD, the Inner terms BC, and then the Last terms BD. Then combine like terms, if possible.

$$(A + B)(C + D) = AC + AD + BC + BD$$

1. Multiply First terms: AC.
2. Multiply Outer terms: AD.
3. Multiply Inner terms: BC.
4. Multiply Last terms: BD.

$$\downarrow$$
$$\text{FOIL}$$

Because addition is commutative, the individual multiplications can be performed in any order. Both FLOI and FIOL yield the same result as FOIL, but FOIL is most easily remembered and most widely used.

EXAMPLE **1** Form an equivalent expression by multiplying: $(x + 8)(x^2 + 5)$.

SOLUTION

$$(x + 8)(x^2 + 5) = x^3 + 5x + 8x^2 + 40 \qquad \text{There are no like terms.}$$
$$= x^3 + 8x^2 + 5x + 40 \qquad \text{Writing in descending order}$$

TRY EXERCISE 5

After multiplying, remember to combine any like terms.

EXAMPLE **2** Multiply to form an equivalent expression.

a) $(x + 7)(x + 4)$ **b)** $(y + 3)(y - 2)$
c) $(4t^3 + 5t)(3t^2 - 2)$ **d)** $(3 - 4x)(7 - 5x^3)$

SOLUTION

a) $(x + 7)(x + 4) = x^2 + 4x + 7x + 28 \qquad \text{Using FOIL}$
$$= x^2 + 11x + 28 \qquad \text{Combining like terms}$$

b) $(y + 3)(y - 2) = y^2 - 2y + 3y - 6$
$$= y^2 + y - 6$$

c) $(4t^3 + 5t)(3t^2 - 2) = 12t^5 - 8t^3 + 15t^3 - 10t$

> Remember to add exponents when multiplying terms with the same base.

$$= 12t^5 + 7t^3 - 10t$$

d) $(3 - 4x)(7 - 5x^3) = 21 - 15x^3 - 28x + 20x^4$

$$= 21 - 28x - 15x^3 + 20x^4$$

> In general, if the original binomials are written in *ascending* order, the answer is also written that way.

TRY EXERCISE 9

Multiplying Sums and Differences of Two Terms

Consider the product of the sum and the difference of the same two terms, such as

$$(x + 5)(x - 5).$$

Since this is the product of two binomials, we can use FOIL. In doing so, we find that the "outer" and "inner" products are opposites:

a) $(x + 5)(x - 5) = x^2 - 5x + 5x - 25$

$$= x^2 - 25;$$

b) $(3a - 2)(3a + 2) = 9a^2 + 6a - 6a - 4$

$$= 9a^2 - 4;$$

> The "outer" and "inner" terms "drop out." Their sum is zero.

c) $\left(x^3 + \frac{2}{7}\right)\left(x^3 - \frac{2}{7}\right) = x^6 - \frac{2}{7}x^3 + \frac{2}{7}x^3 - \frac{4}{49}$

$$= x^6 - \frac{4}{49}.$$

Because opposites always add to zero, for products like $(x + 5)(x - 5)$ we can use a shortcut that is faster than FOIL.

The Product of a Sum and a Difference

The product of the sum and the difference of the same two terms is the square of the first term minus the square of the second term:

$$(A + B)(A - B) = \underbrace{A^2 - B^2}.$$

This is called a *difference of squares*.

EXAMPLE 3 Multiply.

a) $(x + 4)(x - 4)$

b) $(5 + 2w)(5 - 2w)$

c) $(3a^4 - 5)(3a^4 + 5)$

SOLUTION

$$(A + B)(A - B) = A^2 - B^2$$

a) $(x + 4)(x - 4) = x^2 - 4^2$

> Saying the words can help: "The square of the first term, x^2, minus the square of the second, 4^2"

$$= x^2 - 16$$ Simplifying

b) $(5 + 2w)(5 - 2w) = 5^2 - (2w)^2$

$\qquad\qquad\qquad\quad = 25 - 4w^2$ Squaring both 5 and $2w$

c) $(3a^4 - 5)(3a^4 + 5) = (3a^4)^2 - 5^2$

$\qquad\qquad\qquad\qquad = 9a^8 - 25$ Remember to multiply exponents when raising a power to a power.

TRY EXERCISE ▷ 41

Squaring Binomials

Consider the square of a binomial, such as $(x + 3)^2$. This can be expressed as $(x + 3)(x + 3)$. Since this is the product of two binomials, we can use FOIL. But again, this product occurs so often that a faster method has been developed. Look for a pattern in the following:

a) $(x + 3)^2 = (x + 3)(x + 3)$

$\qquad\qquad = x^2 + 3x + 3x + 9$

$\qquad\qquad = x^2 + 6x + 9;$

b) $(5 - 3p)^2 = (5 - 3p)(5 - 3p)$

$\qquad\qquad\quad = 25 - 15p - 15p + 9p^2$

$\qquad\qquad\quad = 25 - 30p + 9p^2;$

c) $(a^3 - 7)^2 = (a^3 - 7)(a^3 - 7)$

$\qquad\qquad\quad = a^6 - 7a^3 - 7a^3 + 49$

$\qquad\qquad\quad = a^6 - 14a^3 + 49.$

Perhaps you noticed that in each product the "outer" product and the "inner" product are identical. The other two terms, the "first" product and the "last" product, are squares.

The Square of a Binomial

The square of a binomial is the square of the first term, plus twice the product of the two terms, plus the square of the last term:

$$(A + B)^2 = A^2 + 2AB + B^2; \atop (A - B)^2 = A^2 - 2AB + B^2.$$

These are called *perfect-square trinomials.**

EXAMPLE 4   Write an equivalent expression for each square of a binomial.

a) $(x + 7)^2$
c) $(3a + 0.4)^2$

b) $(t - 5)^2$
d) $(5x - 3x^4)^2$

SOLUTION

$$(A + B)^2 = A^2 + 2 \cdot A \cdot B + B^2$$

a) $(x + 7)^2 = x^2 + 2 \cdot x \cdot 7 + 7^2$ Saying the words can help: "The square of the first term, x^2, plus twice the product of the terms, $2 \cdot 7x$, plus the square of the second term, 7^2"

$\qquad\qquad\quad = x^2 + 14x + 49$

---

*Another name for these is *trinomial squares.*

b) $(t - 5)^2 = t^2 - 2 \cdot t \cdot 5 + 5^2$
$$= t^2 - 10t + 25$$

c) $(3a + 0.4)^2 = (3a)^2 + 2 \cdot 3a \cdot 0.4 + 0.4^2$
$$= 9a^2 + 2.4a + 0.16$$

d) $(5x - 3x^4)^2 = (5x)^2 - 2 \cdot 5x \cdot 3x^4 + (3x^4)^2$
$$= 25x^2 - 30x^5 + 9x^8 \quad \text{Using the rules for exponents}$$

> **TRY EXERCISE** 57

CAUTION!   Although the square of a product is the product of the squares, the square of a sum is *not* the sum of the squares. That is, $(AB)^2 = A^2B^2$, but

The term $2AB$ is missing.

$$(A + B)^2 \neq A^2 + B^2.$$

To confirm this inequality, note that

$$(7 + 5)^2 = 12^2 = 144,$$

whereas

$$7^2 + 5^2 = 49 + 25 = 74, \quad \text{and} \quad 74 \neq 144.$$

Geometrically, $(A + B)^2$ can be viewed as the area of a square with sides of length $A + B$:

$$(A + B)(A + B) = (A + B)^2.$$

This is equal to the sum of the areas of the four smaller regions:

$$A^2 + AB + AB + B^2 = A^2 + 2AB + B^2.$$

Thus,

$$(A + B)^2 = A^2 + 2AB + B^2.$$

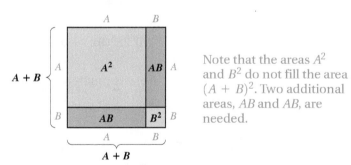

Note that the areas A^2 and B^2 do not fill the area $(A + B)^2$. Two additional areas, AB and AB, are needed.

Multiplications of Various Types

Recognizing patterns often helps when new problems are encountered. To simplify a new multiplication problem, always examine what type of product it is so that the best method for finding that product can be used. To do this, ask yourself questions similar to the following.

Multiplying Two Polynomials

1. Is the multiplication the product of a monomial and a polynomial? If so, multiply each term of the polynomial by the monomial.
2. Is the multiplication the product of two binomials? If so:

   a) Is it the product of the sum and the difference of the *same* two terms? If so, use the pattern
   $$(A + B)(A - B) = A^2 - B^2.$$

   b) Is the product the square of a binomial? If so, use the pattern
   $$(A + B)(A + B) = (A + B)^2 = A^2 + 2AB + B^2,$$
   or
   $$(A - B)(A - B) = (A - B)^2 = A^2 - 2AB + B^2.$$

   c) If neither (a) nor (b) applies, use FOIL.

3. Is the multiplication the product of two polynomials other than those above? If so, multiply each term of one by every term of the other. Use columns if you wish.

EXAMPLE 5   Multiply.

a) $(x + 3)(x - 3)$ b) $(t + 7)(t - 5)$
c) $(x + 7)(x + 7)$ d) $2x^3(9x^2 + x - 7)$
e) $(p + 3)(p^2 + 2p - 1)$ f) $\left(3x - \frac{1}{4}\right)^2$

SOLUTION

a) $(x + 3)(x - 3) = x^2 - 9$ This is the product of the sum and the difference of the same two terms.

b) $(t + 7)(t - 5) = t^2 - 5t + 7t - 35$ Using FOIL
$$= t^2 + 2t - 35$$

c) $(x + 7)(x + 7) = x^2 + 14x + 49$ This is the square of a binomial, $(x + 7)^2$.

d) $2x^3(9x^2 + x - 7) = 18x^5 + 2x^4 - 14x^3$ Multiplying each term of the trinomial by the monomial

e) We multiply each term of $p^2 + 2p - 1$ by every term of $p + 3$:
$$(p + 3)(p^2 + 2p - 1) = p^3 + 2p^2 - p \qquad \text{Multiplying by } p$$
$$+ 3p^2 + 6p - 3 \qquad \text{Multiplying by 3}$$
$$= p^3 + 5p^2 + 5p - 3.$$

f) $\left(3x - \frac{1}{4}\right)^2 = 9x^2 - 2(3x)\left(\frac{1}{4}\right) + \frac{1}{16}$ Squaring a binomial
$$= 9x^2 - \frac{3}{2}x + \frac{1}{16}$$

TRY EXERCISE 69

1

2

3

4

5

Visualizing for Success

In each of Exercises 1–10, find two algebraic expressions for the shaded area of the figure from the list below.

A. $9 - 4x^2$

B. $x^2 - (x - 6)^2$

C. $(x + 3)(x - 3)$

D. $10^2 + 2^2$

E. $8x + 15$

F. $(x + 5)(x + 3) - x^2$

G. $x^2 - 6x + 9$

H. $(3 - 2x)^2 + 4x(3 - 2x)$

I. $(x + 3)^2$

J. $(5x + 3)^2 - 25x^2$

K. $(5 - 2x)^2 + 4x(5 - 2x)$

L. $x^2 - 9$

M. 104

N. $x^2 - 15$

O. $12x - 36$

P. $30x + 9$

Q. $(x - 5)(x - 3) + 3(x - 5) + 5(x - 3)$

R. $(x - 3)^2$

S. $25 - 4x^2$

T. $x^2 + 6x + 9$

Answers on page A-19

An additional, animated version of this activity appears in MyMathLab. To use MyMathLab, you need a course ID and a student access code. Contact your instructor for more information.

6

7

8

9

10

5.6 EXERCISE SET

↪ *Concept Reinforcement* *Classify each statement as either true or false.*

1. FOIL is simply a memory device for finding the product of two binomials.

2. The square of a binomial cannot be found using FOIL.

3. Once FOIL is used, it is always possible to combine like terms.

4. The square of $A + B$ is not the sum of the squares of A and B.

Multiply.

5. $(x^2 + 2)(x + 3)$

6. $(x - 5)(x^2 - 6)$

7. $(t^4 - 2)(t + 7)$

8. $(n^3 + 8)(n - 4)$

9. $(y + 2)(y - 3)$

10. $(a + 2)(a + 2)$

11. $(3x + 2)(3x + 5)$

12. $(4x + 1)(2x + 7)$

13. $(5x - 3)(x + 4)$

14. $(4x - 5)(4x + 5)$

15. $(3 - 2t)(5 - t)$

16. $(7 - a)(4 - 3a)$

17. $(x^2 + 3)(x^2 - 7)$

18. $(x^2 + 2)(x^2 - 8)$

19. $\left(p - \frac{1}{4}\right)\left(p + \frac{1}{4}\right)$

20. $\left(q + \frac{3}{4}\right)\left(q + \frac{3}{4}\right)$

21. $(x - 0.3)(x - 0.3)$

22. $(x - 0.1)(x + 0.1)$

23. $(-3n + 2)(n + 7)$

24. $(-m + 5)(2m - 9)$

25. $(x + 10)(x + 10)$

26. $(x + 12)(x + 12)$

27. $(1 - 3t)(1 + 5t^2)$

28. $(1 + 2t)(1 - 3t^2)$

29. $(x^2 + 3)(x^3 - 1)$

30. $(x^4 - 3)(2x + 1)$

31. $(3x^2 - 2)(x^4 - 2)$

32. $(x^{10} + 3)(x^{10} - 3)$

33. $(2t^3 + 5)(2t^3 + 5)$

34. $(5t^2 + 1)(2t^2 + 3)$

35. $(8x^3 + 5)(x^2 + 2)$

36. $(5 - 4x^5)(5 + 4x^5)$

37. $(10x^2 + 3)(10x^2 - 3)$

38. $(7x - 2)(2x - 7)$

Multiply. Try to recognize the type of product before multiplying.

39. $(x + 8)(x - 8)$

40. $(x + 1)(x - 1)$

41. $(2x + 1)(2x - 1)$

42. $(4n + 7)(4n - 7)$

43. $(5m^2 + 4)(5m^2 - 4)$

44. $(3x^4 + 2)(3x^4 - 2)$

45. $(9a^3 + 1)(9a^3 - 1)$

46. $(t^2 - 0.2)(t^2 + 0.2)$

47. $(x^4 + 0.1)(x^4 - 0.1)$

48. $(a^3 + 5)(a^3 - 5)$

49. $\left(t - \frac{3}{4}\right)\left(t + \frac{3}{4}\right)$

50. $\left(m - \frac{2}{3}\right)\left(m + \frac{2}{3}\right)$

51. $(x + 3)^2$

52. $(2x - 1)^2$

53. $(7x^3 - 1)^2$

54. $(5x^3 + 2)^2$

55. $\left(a - \frac{2}{5}\right)^2$

56. $\left(t - \frac{1}{5}\right)^2$

57. $(t^4 + 3)^2$

58. $(a^3 + 6)^2$

59. $(2 - 3x^4)^2$

60. $(5 - 2t^3)^2$

61. $(5 + 6t^2)^2$

62. $(3p^2 - p)^2$

63. $(7x - 0.3)^2$

64. $(4a - 0.6)^2$

65. $7n^3(2n^2 - 1)$

66. $5m^3(4 - 3m^2)$

67. $(a - 3)(a^2 + 2a - 4)$

68. $(x^2 - 5)(x^2 + x - 1)$

69. $(7 - 3x^4)(7 - 3x^4)$

70. $(x - 4x^3)^2$

71. $5x(x^2 + 6x - 2)$

72. $6x(-x^5 + 6x^2 + 9)$

73. $(q^5 + 1)(q^5 - 1)$

74. $(p^4 + 2)(p^4 - 2)$

75. $3t^2(5t^3 - t^2 + t)$

76. $-5x^3(x^2 + 8x - 9)$

77. $(6x^4 - 3x)^2$

78. $(8a^3 + 5)(8a^3 - 5)$

79. $(9a + 0.4)(2a^3 + 0.5)$

80. $(2a - 0.7)(8a^3 - 0.5)$

81. $\left(\frac{1}{5} - 6x^4\right)\left(\frac{1}{5} + 6x^4\right)$

82. $\left(3 + \frac{1}{2}t^5\right)\left(3 + \frac{1}{2}t^5\right)$

83. $(a + 1)(a^2 - a + 1)$

84. $(x - 5)(x^2 + 5x + 25)$

Find the total area of all shaded rectangles.

85.

86.

87.

88.

89.

90.

91.

92.

93.

94.

95.

96.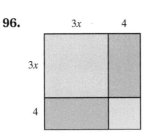

Draw and label rectangles similar to those in Exercises 85–96 to illustrate each of the following.

97. $(x + 5)^2$

98. $(x + 8)^2$

99. $(t + 9)^2$

100. $(a + 12)^2$

101. $(3 + x)^2$

102. $(7 + t)^2$

103. Kristi feels that since she can find the product of any two binomials using FOIL, she needn't study the other special products. What advice would you give her?

104. Under what conditions is the product of two binomials a binomial?

Skill Review

Review problem solving and solving a formula for a variable (Sections 2.3 and 2.5).

Solve. [2.5]

105. *Energy use.* Under typical use, a refrigerator, a freezer, and a washing machine together use 297 kilowatt-hours per month (kWh/mo). A refrigerator uses 21 times as much energy as a washing machine, and a freezer uses 11 times as much energy as a washing machine. How much energy is used by each appliance?

106. *Advertising.* North American advertisers spent $9.4 billion on search-engine marketing in 2006. This was a 62% increase over the amount spent in 2005. How much was spent in 2005?
Source: Search Engine Marketing Professional Organization

Solve. [2.3]

107. $5xy = 8$, for y

108. $3ab = c$, for a

109. $ax - by = c$, for x

110. $ax - by = c$, for y

Synthesis

111. By writing $19 \cdot 21$ as $(20 - 1)(20 + 1)$, Justin can find the product mentally. How do you think he does this?

112. The product $(A + B)^2$ can be regarded as the sum of the areas of four regions (as shown following Example 4). How might one visually represent $(A + B)^3$? Why?

Multiply.

Aha! **113.** $(4x^2 + 9)(2x + 3)(2x - 3)$

114. $(9a^2 + 1)(3a - 1)(3a + 1)$

Aha! **115.** $(3t - 2)^2(3t + 2)^2$

116. $(5a + 1)^2(5a - 1)^2$

117. $(t^3 - 1)^4(t^3 + 1)^4$

 118. $(32.41x + 5.37)^2$

Calculate as the difference of squares.

119. 18×22 [*Hint:* $(20 - 2)(20 + 2)$.]

120. 93×107

Solve.

121. $(x + 2)(x - 5) = (x + 1)(x - 3)$

122. $(2x + 5)(x - 4) = (x + 5)(2x - 4)$

Find a polynomial for the total shaded area in each figure.

123.

124.

125.

126. Find $(10 - 2x)^2$ by subtracting the white areas from 10^2.

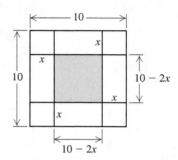

127. Find $(y - 2)^2$ by subtracting the white areas from y^2.

128. Find three consecutive integers for which the sum of the squares is 65 more than three times the square of the smallest integer.

129. Use a graphing calculator and the method developed on p. 258 to check your answers to Exercises 22, 47, and 83.

CONNECTING ⬍ the CONCEPTS

When writing equivalent polynomial expressions, look first at the operation that you are asked to perform.

Operation	Procedure	Examples
Addition	Combine like terms.	$(2x^3 + 3x^2 - 5x - 7) + (9x^3 - 11x + 8)$ $= \underbrace{2x^3 + 9x^3} + 3x^2 \underbrace{- 5x - 11x} \underbrace{- 7 + 8}$ $= \quad 11x^3 \quad + 3x^2 \quad -16x \quad + 1$
Subtraction	Add the opposite of the polynomial being subtracted.	$(9x^4 - 3x^2 + x - 7) - (4x^3 - 8x^2 - 9x + 11)$ $= 9x^4 - 3x^2 + x - 7 + (-4x^3 + 8x^2 + 9x - 11)$ $= 9x^4 - 3x^2 + x - 7 - 4x^3 + 8x^2 + 9x - 11$ $= 9x^4 - 4x^3 + 5x^2 + 10x - 18$
Multiplication	Multiply each term of one polynomial by every term of the other.	$(x^2 - 5x)(3x^4 - 7x^3 + 1)$ $= x^2(3x^4 - 7x^3 + 1) - 5x(3x^4 - 7x^3 + 1)$ $= 3x^6 - 7x^5 + x^2 - 15x^5 + 35x^4 - 5x$ $= 3x^6 - 22x^5 + 35x^4 + x^2 - 5x$
	Special products: $(A + B)(A - B) = A^2 - B^2;$ $(A + B)^2 = A^2 + 2AB + B^2;$ $(A - B)^2 = A^2 - 2AB + B^2;$ $(A + B)(C + D)$ $\quad = AC + AD + BC + BD$	$(x + 5)(x - 5) = x^2 - 25;$ $(2x + 3)^2 = (2x)^2 + 2(2x)(3) + (3)^2 = 4x^2 + 12x + 9;$ $(x^2 - 1)^2 = (x^2)^2 - 2(x^2)(1) + (1)^2 = x^4 - 2x^2 + 1;$ $(x^2 + 3)(x - 2) = x^2(x) + x^2(-2) + 3(x) + 3(-2)$ $\quad = x^3 - 2x^2 + 3x - 6$

MIXED REVIEW

Identify the operation to be performed. Then simplify to form an equivalent expression.

1. $(3x^2 - 2x + 6) + (5x - 3)$

2. $(9x + 6) - (3x - 7)$

3. $6x^3(8x^2 - 7)$

4. $(3x + 2)(2x - 1)$

5. $(9x^3 - 7x + 3) - (5x^2 - 10)$

6. $(2x + 1)(x^2 + x - 3)$

7. $(9x + 1)(9x - 1)$

8. $(8x^3 + 5x) + (9x^4 - 6x^3 - 10x)$

Perform the indicated operation to form an equivalent expression.

9. $(4x^2 - x - 7) - (10x^2 - 3x + 5)$

10. $(3x + 8)(3x + 7)$

11. $8x^5(5x^4 - 6x^3 + 2)$

12. $(t^9 + 3t^6 - 8t^2) + (5t^7 - 3t^6 + 8t^2)$

13. $(2m - 1)^2$

14. $(x - 1)(x^2 + x + 1)$

15. $(5x^3 - 6x^2 - 2x) + (6x^2 + 2x + 3)$

16. $(c + 3)(c - 3)$

17. $(4y^3 + 7)^2$

18. $(3a^4 - 9a^3 - 7) - (4a^3 + 13a^2 - 3)$

19. $(4t^2 - 5)(4t^2 + 5)$

20. $(a^4 + 3)(a^4 - 8)$

5.7   Polynomials in Several Variables

Evaluating Polynomials ▪ Like Terms and Degree ▪ Addition and Subtraction ▪ Multiplication

Thus far, the polynomials that we have studied have had only one variable. Polynomials such as

$$5x + x^2y - 3y + 7, \qquad 9ab^2c - 2a^3b^2 + 8a^2b^3, \quad \text{and} \quad 4m^2 - 9n^2$$

contain two or more variables. In this section, we will add, subtract, multiply, and evaluate such **polynomials in several variables**.

Evaluating Polynomials

To evaluate a polynomial in two or more variables, we substitute numbers for the variables. Then we compute, using the rules for order of operations.

EXAMPLE 1   Evaluate the polynomial $4 + 3x + xy^2 + 8x^3y^3$ for $x = -2$ and $y = 5$.

SOLUTION   We substitute -2 for x and 5 for y:

$$4 + 3x + xy^2 + 8x^3y^3 = 4 + 3(-2) + (-2) \cdot 5^2 + 8(-2)^3 \cdot 5^3$$
$$= 4 - 6 - 50 - 8000 = -8052.$$

> TRY EXERCISE 9

EXAMPLE 2   *Surface area of a right circular cylinder.*   The surface area of a right circular cylinder is given by the polynomial

$$2\pi rh + 2\pi r^2,$$

where h is the height and r is the radius of the base. A 12-oz can has a height of 4.7 in. and a radius of 1.2 in. Approximate its surface area to the nearest tenth of a square inch.

SOLUTION   We evaluate the polynomial for $h = 4.7$ in. and $r = 1.2$ in. If 3.14 is used to approximate π, we have

$$2\pi rh + 2\pi r^2 \approx 2(3.14)(1.2 \text{ in.})(4.7 \text{ in.}) + 2(3.14)(1.2 \text{ in.})^2$$
$$\approx 2(3.14)(1.2 \text{ in.})(4.7 \text{ in.}) + 2(3.14)(1.44 \text{ in}^2)$$
$$\approx 35.4192 \text{ in}^2 + 9.0432 \text{ in}^2 \approx 44.4624 \text{ in}^2.$$

If the π key of a calculator is used, we have

$$2\pi rh + 2\pi r^2 \approx 2(3.141592654)(1.2 \text{ in.})(4.7 \text{ in.})$$
$$+ 2(3.141592654)(1.2 \text{ in.})^2$$
$$\approx 44.48495197 \text{ in}^2.$$

Note that the unit in the answer (square inches) is a unit of area. The surface area is about 44.5 in^2 (square inches).

> TRY EXERCISE 13

Like Terms and Degree

Recall that the degree of a monomial is the number of variable factors in the term. For example, the degree of $5x^2$ is 2 because there are two variable factors in $5 \cdot x \cdot x$. Similarly, the degree of $5a^2b^4$ is 6 because there are 6 variable factors in $5 \cdot a \cdot a \cdot b \cdot b \cdot b \cdot b$. Note that 6 can be found by adding the exponents 2 and 4.

As we learned in Section 5.3, the degree of a polynomial is the degree of the term of highest degree.

EXAMPLE 3   Identify the coefficient and the degree of each term and the degree of the polynomial

$$9x^2y^3 - 14xy^2z^3 + xy + 4y + 5x^2 + 7.$$

SOLUTION

Term	Coefficient	Degree	Degree of the Polynomial
$9x^2y^3$	9	5	
$-14xy^2z^3$	−14	6	6
xy	1	2	
$4y$	4	1	
$5x^2$	5	2	
7	7	0	

TRY EXERCISE 21

STUDY SKILLS

Use Your Voice

Don't be hesitant to ask questions in class at appropriate times. Most instructors welcome questions and encourage students to ask them. Other students probably have the same questions you do, so asking questions can help others as well as you.

Note in Example 3 that although both xy and $5x^2$ have degree 2, they are *not* like terms. *Like*, or *similar, terms* either have exactly the same variables with exactly the same exponents or are constants. For example,

$8a^4b^7$ and $5b^7a^4$ are like terms

and

-17 and 3 are like terms,

but

$-2x^2y$ and $9xy^2$ are *not* like terms.

As always, combining like terms is based on the distributive law.

EXAMPLE 4   Combine like terms to form equivalent expressions.

a) $9x^2y + 3xy^2 - 5x^2y - xy^2$

b) $7ab - 5ab^2 + 3ab^2 + 6a^3 + 9ab - 11a^3 + b - 1$

SOLUTION

a) $9x^2y + 3xy^2 - 5x^2y - xy^2 = (9 - 5)x^2y + (3 - 1)xy^2$

$\qquad\qquad\qquad\qquad\qquad = 4x^2y + 2xy^2$ Try to go directly to this step.

b) $7ab - 5ab^2 + 3ab^2 + 6a^3 + 9ab - 11a^3 + b - 1$

$\qquad = -5a^3 - 2ab^2 + 16ab + b - 1$ We choose to write descending powers of a. Other, equivalent, forms can also be used.

TRY EXERCISE 25

Addition and Subtraction

The procedure used for adding polynomials in one variable is used to add polynomials in several variables.

EXAMPLE 5

Add.

a) $(-5x^3 + 3y - 5y^2) + (8x^3 + 4x^2 + 7y^2)$

b) $(5ab^2 - 4a^2b + 5a^3 + 2) + (3ab^2 - 2a^2b + 3a^3b - 5)$

SOLUTION

a) $(-5x^3 + 3y - 5y^2) + (8x^3 + 4x^2 + 7y^2)$

$\qquad = (-5 + 8)x^3 + 4x^2 + 3y + (-5 + 7)y^2$ Try to do this step mentally.

$\qquad = 3x^3 + 4x^2 + 3y + 2y^2$

b) $(5ab^2 - 4a^2b + 5a^3 + 2) + (3ab^2 - 2a^2b + 3a^3b - 5)$

$\qquad = 8ab^2 - 6a^2b + 5a^3 + 3a^3b - 3$

TRY EXERCISE 33

When subtracting a polynomial, remember to find the opposite of each term in that polynomial and then add.

EXAMPLE 6

Subtract: $(4x^2y + x^3y^2 + 3x^2y^3 + 6y) - (4x^2y - 6x^3y^2 + x^2y^2 - 5y)$.

SOLUTION

$$(4x^2y + x^3y^2 + 3x^2y^3 + 6y) - (4x^2y - 6x^3y^2 + x^2y^2 - 5y)$$

$\qquad = 4x^2y + x^3y^2 + 3x^2y^3 + 6y - 4x^2y + 6x^3y^2 - x^2y^2 + 5y$

$\qquad = 7x^3y^2 + 3x^2y^3 - x^2y^2 + 11y$ Combining like terms

TRY EXERCISE 35

Multiplication

To multiply polynomials in several variables, multiply each term of one polynomial by every term of the other, just as we did in Sections 5.5 and 5.6.

EXAMPLE 7

Multiply: $(3x^2y - 2xy + 3y)(xy + 2y)$.

SOLUTION

$$3x^2y - 2xy + 3y$$

$$\underline{\qquad\qquad xy + 2y}$$

$$\qquad 6x^2y^2 - 4xy^2 + 6y^2 \qquad \text{Multiplying by } 2y$$

$$\underline{3x^3y^2 - 2x^2y^2 + 3xy^2 \qquad\qquad} \text{Multiplying by } xy$$

$$3x^3y^2 + 4x^2y^2 - \ xy^2 + 6y^2 \qquad \text{Adding}$$

TRY EXERCISE 51

The special products discussed in Section 5.6 can speed up our work.

EXAMPLE 8

Multiply.

a) $(p + 5q)(2p - 3q)$ **b)** $(3x + 2y)^2$

c) $(a^3 - 7a^2b)^2$ **d)** $(3x^2y + 2y)(3x^2y - 2y)$

e) $(-2x^3y^2 + 5t)(2x^3y^2 + 5t)$ **f)** $(2x + 3 - 2y)(2x + 3 + 2y)$

SOLUTION

$$\quad\quad\quad\quad\quad\text{F}\quad\quad\text{O}\quad\quad\text{I}\quad\quad\text{L}$$

a) $(p + 5q)(2p - 3q) = 2p^2 - 3pq + 10pq - 15q^2$

$$= 2p^2 + 7pq - 15q^2 \quad \text{Combining like terms}$$

$$(A + B)^2 = A^2 + 2 \cdot A \cdot B + B^2$$
$$\downarrow \quad \downarrow \quad\quad \downarrow \quad\quad \downarrow \downarrow \downarrow \quad\quad \downarrow$$

b) $(3x + 2y)^2 = (3x)^2 + 2(3x)(2y) + (2y)^2 \quad \text{Using the pattern for squaring a binomial}$

$$= 9x^2 + 12xy + 4y^2$$

$$(A - B)^2 = A^2 - 2 \cdot A \cdot B + B^2$$
$$\downarrow \quad \downarrow \quad\quad \downarrow \quad\quad \downarrow \downarrow \downarrow \quad\quad \downarrow$$

c) $(a^3 - 7a^2b)^2 = (a^3)^2 - 2(a^3)(7a^2b) + (7a^2b)^2 \quad \text{Squaring a binomial}$

$$= a^6 - 14a^5b + 49a^4b^2 \quad \text{Using the rules for exponents}$$

$$(A + B)(A - B) = A^2 - B^2$$
$$\downarrow \quad \downarrow \quad \downarrow \quad \downarrow \quad\quad \downarrow \quad \downarrow$$

d) $(3x^2y + 2y)(3x^2y - 2y) = (3x^2y)^2 - (2y)^2 \quad \text{Using the pattern for multiplying the sum and the difference of two terms}$

$$= 9x^4y^2 - 4y^2 \quad \text{Using the rules for exponents}$$

e) $(-2x^3y^2 + 5t)(2x^3y^2 + 5t) = (5t - 2x^3y^2)(5t + 2x^3y^2) \quad \text{Using the commutative law for addition twice}$

$$= (5t)^2 - (2x^3y^2)^2 \quad \text{Multiplying the sum and the difference of the same two terms}$$

$$= 25t^2 - 4x^6y^4$$

$$(A - B)(A + B) = A^2 - B^2$$
$$\downarrow \quad \downarrow \quad \downarrow \quad \downarrow \quad\quad \downarrow \quad \downarrow$$

f) $(2x + 3 - 2y)(2x + 3 + 2y) = (2x + 3)^2 - (2y)^2 \quad \text{Multiplying a sum and a difference}$

$$= 4x^2 + 12x + 9 - 4y^2 \quad \text{Squaring a binomial}$$

> TRY EXERCISE 57

TECHNOLOGY CONNECTION

One way to evaluate the polynomial in Example 1 for $x = -2$ and $y = 5$ is to store -2 to X and 5 to Y and enter the polynomial.

```
-2 → X
                    -2
5 → Y
                     5
4+3X+XY²+8X^3Y^3
                  -8052
■
```

Evaluate.

1. $3x^2 - 2y^2 + 4xy + x$,
for $x = -6$ and $y = 2.3$
2. $a^2b^2 - 8c^2 + 4abc + 9a$,
for $a = 11$, $b = 15$, and $c = -7$

In Example 8, we recognized patterns that might elude some students, particularly in parts (e) and (f). In part (e), we *can* use FOIL, and in part (f), we *can* use long multiplication, but doing so is much slower. By carefully inspecting a problem before "jumping in," we can save ourselves considerable work. At least one instructor refers to this as "working smart" instead of "working hard."*

---

*Thanks to Pauline Kirkpatrick of Wharton County Junior College for this language.

5.7 EXERCISE SET

For Extra Help
MyMathLab   Math XL PRACTICE   WATCH   DOWNLOAD

🔖 *Concept Reinforcement* *Each of the expressions in Exercises 1–8 can be regarded as either* (**a**) *the square of a binomial,* (**b**) *the product of the sum and the difference of the same two terms, or* (**c**) *neither of the above. Select the appropriate choice for each expression.*

1. $(3x + 5y)^2$

2. $(4x - 9y)(4x + 9y)$

3. $(5a + 6b)(-6b + 5a)$

4. $(4a - 3b)(4a - 3b)$

5. $(r - 3s)(5r + 3s)$

6. $(2x - 7y)(7y - 2x)$

7. $(4x - 9y)(4x - 9y)$

8. $(2r + 9t)^2$

Evaluate each polynomial for x = 5 and y = −2.

9. $x^2 - 2y^2 + 3xy$

10. $x^2 + 5y^2 - 4xy$

Evaluate each polynomial for x = 2, y = −3, and z = −4.

11. $xy^2z - z$

12. $xy - x^2z + yz^2$

Lung capacity. *The polynomial*

$$0.041h - 0.018A - 2.69$$

can be used to estimate the lung capacity, in liters, of a female with height h, in centimeters, and age A, in years.

13. Find the lung capacity of a 20-year-old woman who is 160 cm tall.

14. Find the lung capacity of a 40-year-old woman who is 165 cm tall.

15. *Female caloric needs.* The number of calories needed each day by a moderately active woman who weighs w pounds, is h inches tall, and is a years old can be estimated by the polynomial

    $$917 + 6w + 6h - 6a.$$

    Rachel is moderately active, weighs 125 lb, is 64 in. tall, and is 27 yr old. What are her daily caloric needs?
    Source: Parker, M., *She Does Math.* Mathematical Association of America

16. *Male caloric needs.* The number of calories needed each day by a moderately active man who weighs w kilograms, is h centimeters tall, and is a years old can be estimated by the polynomial

    $$19.18w + 7h - 9.52a + 92.4.$$

    One of the authors of this text is moderately active, weighs 87 kg, is 185 cm tall, and is 59 yr old. What are his daily caloric needs?
    Source: Parker, M., *She Does Math.* Mathematical Association of America

Surface area of a silo. *A silo is a structure that is shaped like a right circular cylinder with a half sphere on top. The surface area of a silo of height h and radius r (including the area of the base) is given by the polynomial* $2\pi rh + \pi r^2$.

17. A coffee grinder is shaped like a silo, with a height of 7 in. and a radius of $1\frac{1}{2}$ in. Find the surface area of the coffee grinder. Use 3.14 for π.

18. A $1\frac{1}{2}$-oz bottle of roll-on deodorant has a height of 4 in. and a radius of $\frac{3}{4}$ in. Find the surface area of the bottle if the bottle is shaped like a silo. Use 3.14 for π.

Altitude of a launched object. *The altitude of an object, in meters, is given by the polynomial*

$$h + vt - 4.9t^2,$$

where h is the height, in meters, at which the launch occurs, v is the initial upward speed (or velocity), in meters per second, and t is the number of seconds for which the object is airborne.

19. A bocce ball is thrown upward with an initial speed of 18 m/sec by a person atop the Leaning Tower of Pisa, which is 50 m above the ground. How high will the ball be 2 sec after it has been thrown?

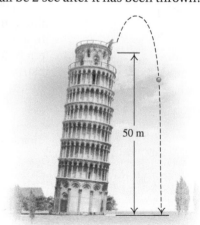

50 m

20. A golf ball is launched upward with an initial speed of 30 m/sec by a golfer atop the Washington Monument, which is 160 m above the ground. How high above the ground will the ball be after 3 sec?

Identify the coefficient and the degree of each term of each polynomial. Then find the degree of each polynomial.

21. $3x^2y - 5xy + 2y^2 - 11$

22. $xy^3 + 7x^3y^2 - 6xy^4 + 2$

23. $7 - abc + a^2b + 9ab^2$

24. $3p - pq - 7p^2q^3 - 8pq^6$

Combine like terms.

25. $3r + s - r - 7s$

26. $9a + b - 8a - 5b$

27. $5xy^2 - 2x^2y + x + 3x^2$

28. $m^3 + 2m^2n - 3m^2 + 3mn^2$

29. $6u^2v - 9uv^2 + 3vu^2 - 2v^2u + 11u^2$

30. $3x^2 + 6xy + 3y^2 - 5x^2 - 10xy$

31. $5a^2c - 2ab^2 + a^2b - 3ab^2 + a^2c - 2ab^2$

32. $3s^2t + r^2t - 9ts^2 - st^2 + 5t^2s - 7tr^2$

Add or subtract, as indicated.

33. $(6x^2 - 2xy + y^2) + (5x^2 - 8xy - 2y^2)$

34. $(7r^3 + rs - 5r^2) - (2r^3 - 3rs + r^2)$

35. $(3a^4 - 5ab + 6ab^2) - (9a^4 + 3ab - ab^2)$

36. $(2r^2t - 5rt + rt^2) - (7r^2t + rt - 5rt^2)$

Aha! **37.** $(5r^2 - 4rt + t^2) + (-6r^2 - 5rt - t^2) + (-5r^2 + 4rt - t^2)$

38. $(2x^2 - 3xy + y^2) + (-4x^2 - 6xy - y^2) + (4x^2 + 6xy + y^2)$

39. $(x^3 - y^3) - (-2x^3 + x^2y - xy^2 + 2y^3)$

40. $(a^3 + b^3) - (-5a^3 + 2a^2b - ab^2 + 3b^3)$

41. $(2y^4x^3 - 3y^3x) + (5y^4x^3 - y^3x) - (9y^4x^3 - y^3x)$

42. $(5a^2b - 7ab^2) - (3a^2b + ab^2) + (a^2b - 2ab^2)$

43. Subtract $7x + 3y$ from the sum of $4x + 5y$ and $-5x + 6y$.

44. Subtract $5a + 2b$ from the sum of $2a + b$ and $3a - 4b$.

Multiply.

45. $(4c - d)(3c + 2d)$

46. $(5x + y)(2x - 3y)$

47. $(xy - 1)(xy + 5)$

48. $(ab + 3)(ab - 5)$

49. $(2a - b)(2a + b)$

50. $(a - 3b)(a + 3b)$

51. $(5rt - 2)(4rt - 3)$

52. $(3xy - 1)(4xy + 2)$

53. $(m^3n + 8)(m^3n - 6)$

54. $(9 - u^2v^2)(2 - u^2v^2)$

55. $(6x - 2y)(5x - 3y)$

56. $(7a - 6b)(5a + 4b)$

57. $(pq + 0.1)(-pq + 0.1)$

58. $(rt + 0.2)(-rt + 0.2)$

59. $(x + h)^2$

60. $(a - r)^2$

61. $(4a - 5b)^2$

62. $(2x + 5y)^2$

63. $(ab + cd^2)(ab - cd^2)$

64. $(p^3 - 5q)(p^3 + 5q)$

65. $(2xy + x^2y + 3)(xy + y^2)$

66. $(5cd - c^2 - d^2)(2c - c^2d)$

Aha! **67.** $(a + b - c)(a + b + c)$

68. $(x + y + 2z)(x + y - 2z)$

69. $[a + b + c][a - (b + c)]$

70. $(a + b + c)(a - b - c)$

Find the total area of each shaded area.

71.

72.

73.

74.

75.

76.
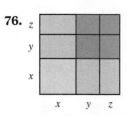

89.
$$5x^3 - 2x^2 + 1$$
$$-(5x^3 - 15x^2)$$

90.
$$2x^2 + 5x - 3$$
$$-(2x^2 + 6x)$$

77.

78.

Synthesis

91. The concept of "leading term" was intentionally not discussed in this section. Why?

92. Explain how it is possible for the sum of two trinomials in several variables to be a binomial in one variable.

Draw and label rectangles similar to those in Exercises 71, 72, 75, and 76 to illustrate each product.

79. $(r + s)(u + v)$

80. $(m + r)(n + v)$

81. $(a + b + c)(a + d + f)$

82. $(r + s + t)^2$

83. Is it possible for a polynomial in 4 variables to have a degree less than 4? Why or why not?

84. A fourth-degree monomial is multiplied by a third-degree monomial. What is the degree of the product? Explain your reasoning.

Skill Review

To prepare for Section 5.8, review subtraction of polynomials using columns (Section 5.4).

Subtract. [5.4]

85.
$$x^2 - 3x - 7$$
$$-(\quad 5x - 3)$$

86.
$$2x^3 \quad - x + 3$$
$$-(\quad x^2 \quad - 1)$$

87.
$$3x^2 + x + 5$$
$$-(3x^2 + 3x)$$

88.
$$4x^3 - 3x^2 + x$$
$$-(4x^3 - 8x^2)$$

Find a polynomial for the shaded area. (Leave results in terms of π where appropriate.)

93.

94.

95.

96.

97. Find a polynomial for the total volume of the figure shown.

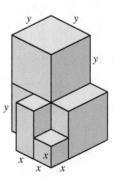

98. Find the shaded area in this figure using each of the approaches given below. Then check that both answers match.

a) Find the shaded area by subtracting the area of the unshaded square from the total area of the figure.

b) Find the shaded area by adding the areas of the three shaded rectangles.

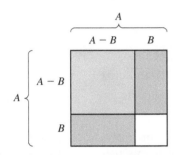

Find a polynomial for the surface area of each solid object shown. (Leave results in terms of π.)

99.   **100.**

101. The observatory at Danville University is shaped like a silo that is 40 ft high and 30 ft wide (see Exercise 17). The Heavenly Bodies Astronomy Club is to paint the exterior of the observatory using paint that covers 250 ft² per gallon. How many gallons should they purchase? Explain your reasoning.

102. Multiply: $(x + a)(x - b)(x - a)(x + b)$.

The computer application Excel allows values for cells in a spreadsheet to be calculated from values in other cells. For example, if the cell C1 *contains the formula*

$$= A1 + 2 * B1,$$

the value in C1 *will be the sum of the value in* A1 *and twice the value in* B1. *This formula is a polynomial in the two variables* A1 *and* B1.

103. The cell D4 contains the formula

$$= 2 * A4 + 3 * B4.$$

What is the value in D4 if the value in A4 is 5 and the value in B4 is 10?

104. The cell D6 contains the formula

$$= A1 - 0.2 * B1 + 0.3 * C1.$$

What is the value in D6 if the value in A1 is 10, the value in B1 is -3, and the value in C1 is 30?

105. *Interest compounded annually.* An amount of money *P* that is invested at the yearly interest rate *r* grows to the amount $P(1 + r)^t$ after *t* years. Find a polynomial that can be used to determine the amount to which *P* will grow after 2 yr.

106. *Yearly depreciation.* An investment *P* that drops in value at the yearly rate *r* drops in value to

$$P(1 - r)^t$$

after *t* years. Find a polynomial that can be used to determine the value to which *P* has dropped after 2 yr.

107. Suppose that $10,400 is invested at 8.5% compounded annually. How much is in the account at the end of 5 yr? (See Exercise 105.)

108. A $90,000 investment in computer hardware is depreciating at a yearly rate of 12.5%. How much is the investment worth after 4 yr? (See Exercise 106.)

COLLABORATIVE CORNER

Finding the Magic Number

Focus: Evaluating polynomials in several variables

Time: 15–25 minutes

Group size: 3

Materials: A coin for each person

When a team nears the end of its schedule in first place, fans begin to discuss the team's "magic number." A team's magic number is the combined number of wins by that team and losses by the second-place team that guarantee the leading team a first-place finish. For example, if the Cubs' magic number is 3 over the Reds, any combination of Cubs wins and Reds losses that totals 3 will guarantee a first-place finish for the Cubs. A team's magic number is computed using the polynomial

$$G - P - L + 1,$$

where G is the length of the season, in games, P is the number of games that the leading team has played, and L is the total number of games that the second-place team has lost minus the total number of games that the leading team has lost.

ACTIVITY

1. The standings below are from a fictitious league. Each group should calculate the Jaguars' magic number with respect to the Catamounts as well as the Jaguars' magic number with respect to the Wildcats.

(Assume that the schedule is 162 games long.)

	W	L
Jaguars	92	64
Catamounts	90	66
Wildcats	89	66

2. Each group member should play the role of one of the teams, using coin tosses to simulate the remaining games. If a group member correctly predicts the side (heads or tails) that comes up, the coin toss represents a win for that team. Should the other side appear, the toss represents a loss. Assume that these games are against other (unlisted) teams in the league. Each group member should perform three coin tosses and then update the standings.

3. Recalculate the two magic numbers, using the updated standings from part (2).

4. Slowly—one coin toss at a time—play out the remainder of the season. Record all wins and losses, update the standings, and recalculate the magic numbers each time all three group members have completed a round of coin tosses.

5. Examine the work in part (4) and explain why a magic number of 0 indicates that a team has been eliminated from contention.

5.8   Division of Polynomials

Dividing by a Monomial   ▪   Dividing by a Binomial

In this section, we study division of polynomials. We will find that polynomial division is similar to division in arithmetic.

Dividing by a Monomial

We first consider division by a monomial. When dividing a monomial by a monomial, we use the quotient rule of Section 5.1 to subtract exponents when bases are the same. For example,

$$\frac{15x^{10}}{3x^4} = 5x^{10-4}$$
$$= 5x^6$$

> **CAUTION!** The coefficients are divided but the exponents are subtracted.

and

$$\frac{42a^2b^5}{-3ab^2} = \frac{42}{-3}a^{2-1}b^{5-2}$$ Recall that $a^m/a^n = a^{m-n}$.
$$= -14ab^3.$$

To divide a polynomial by a monomial, we note that since

$$\frac{A}{C} + \frac{B}{C} = \frac{A+B}{C},$$

it follows that

$$\frac{A+B}{C} = \frac{A}{C} + \frac{B}{C}.$$ Switching the left side and the right side of the equation

This is actually how we perform divisions like $86 \div 2$. Although we might simply write

$$\frac{86}{2} = 43,$$

we are really saying

$$\frac{80+6}{2} = \frac{80}{2} + \frac{6}{2} = 40 + 3.$$

Similarly, to divide a polynomial by a monomial, we divide each term by the monomial:

$$\frac{80x^5 + 6x^7}{2x^3} = \frac{80x^5}{2x^3} + \frac{6x^7}{2x^3}$$
$$= \frac{80}{2}x^{5-3} + \frac{6}{2}x^{7-3}$$ Dividing coefficients and subtracting exponents
$$= 40x^2 + 3x^4.$$

EXAMPLE 1   Divide $x^4 + 15x^3 - 6x^2$ by $3x$.

SOLUTION   We divide each term of $x^4 + 15x^3 - 6x^2$ by $3x$:

$$\frac{x^4 + 15x^3 - 6x^2}{3x} = \frac{x^4}{3x} + \frac{15x^3}{3x} - \frac{6x^2}{3x}$$
$$= \frac{1}{3}x^{4-1} + \frac{15}{3}x^{3-1} - \frac{6}{3}x^{2-1}$$ Dividing coefficients and subtracting exponents
$$= \frac{1}{3}x^3 + 5x^2 - 2x.$$ This is the quotient.

To check, we multiply our answer by $3x$, using the distributive law:

$$3x\left(\frac{1}{3}x^3 + 5x^2 - 2x\right) = 3x \cdot \frac{1}{3}x^3 + 3x \cdot 5x^2 - 3x \cdot 2x$$

$$= x^4 + 15x^3 - 6x^2.$$

This is the polynomial that was being divided, so our answer, $\frac{1}{3}x^3 + 5x^2 - 2x$, checks.

> **TRY EXERCISE** 5

EXAMPLE 2   Divide and check: $(10a^5b^4 - 2a^3b^2 + 6a^2b) \div (-2a^2b)$.

SOLUTION   We have

$$\frac{10a^5b^4 - 2a^3b^2 + 6a^2b}{-2a^2b} = \frac{10a^5b^4}{-2a^2b} - \frac{2a^3b^2}{-2a^2b} + \frac{6a^2b}{-2a^2b}$$

We divide coefficients and subtract exponents.

$$= -\frac{10}{2}a^{5-2}b^{4-1} - \left(-\frac{2}{2}\right)a^{3-2}b^{2-1} + \left(-\frac{6}{2}\right)$$

$$= -5a^3b^3 + ab - 3.$$

Check: $-2a^2b(-5a^3b^3 + ab - 3)$

$$= -2a^2b(-5a^3b^3) + (-2a^2b)(ab) + (-2a^2b)(-3)$$

$$= 10a^5b^4 - 2a^3b^2 + 6a^2b$$

Our answer, $-5a^3b^3 + ab - 3$, checks.

> **TRY EXERCISE** 7

Dividing by a Binomial

The divisors in Examples 1 and 2 have just one term. For divisors with more than one term, we use long division, much as we do in arithmetic. Polynomials are written in descending order and any missing terms in the dividend are written in, using 0 for the coefficients.

EXAMPLE 3   Divide $x^2 + 5x + 6$ by $x + 3$.

SOLUTION   We begin by dividing x^2 by x:

Divide the first term, x^2, by the first term in the divisor: $x^2/x = x$. Ignore the term 3 for the moment.

$$
\begin{array}{r}
x \\
x + 3 \overline{\smash{)}\ x^2 + 5x + 6} \\
-(x^2 + 3x) \\
\hline
2x.
\end{array}
$$

Multiply $x + 3$ by x, using the distributive law.

Subtract both x^2 and $3x$: $x^2 + 5x - (x^2 + 3x) = 2x$.

Now we "bring down" the next term—in this case, 6. The current remainder, $2x + 6$, now becomes the focus of our division. We divide $2x$ by x.

STUDENT NOTES

Long division of polynomials offers many opportunities to make errors. Rather than have one small mistake throw off all your work, we recommend that you double-check each step of your work as you move forward.

$$\begin{array}{r} x\ +2 \leftarrow \\ x+3\overline{)x^2+5x+6} \\ \underline{-(x^2+3x)} \\ 2x+6 \end{array}$$

Divide $2x$ by x: $2x/x = 2$.

$$\underline{-(2x+6)} \leftarrow \text{Multiply 2 by the divisor, } x+3, \text{ using the}$$
distributive law.

$$0 \leftarrow \text{Subtract } (2x+6)-(2x+6)=0.$$

The quotient is $x + 2$. The notation R 0 indicates a remainder of 0, although a remainder of 0 is generally not listed in an answer.

Check: To check, we multiply the quotient by the divisor and add any remainder to see if we get the dividend:

$$\underset{\text{Divisor}}{(x+3)}\ \underset{\text{Quotient}}{(x+2)}\ +\ \underset{\text{Remainder}}{0}\ =\ \underset{\text{Dividend}}{x^2+5x+6}.$$

Our answer, $x + 2$, checks.

TRY EXERCISE 17

EXAMPLE **4**   Divide: $(2x^2 + 5x - 1) \div (2x - 1)$.

SOLUTION   We begin by dividing $2x^2$ by $2x$:

Divide the first term by the first term: $2x^2/(2x) = x$.

$$\begin{array}{r} x \leftarrow \\ 2x-1\overline{)2x^2+5x-1} \\ \underline{-(2x^2-\ x)} \leftarrow \\ 6x \leftarrow \end{array}$$

Multiply $2x - 1$ by x.

Subtract by changing signs and adding: $(2x^2 + 5x) - (2x^2 - x) = 6x.$

CAUTION! Write the parentheses around the polynomial being subtracted to remind you to subtract all its terms.

Now, we bring down the -1 and divide $6x - 1$ by $2x - 1$.

$$\begin{array}{r} x\ +3 \leftarrow \\ 2x-1\overline{)2x^2+5x-1} \\ \underline{-(2x^2-\ x)} \\ 6x-1 \end{array}$$

Divide $6x$ by $2x$: $6x/(2x) = 3$.

$$\underline{-(6x-3)} \leftarrow \text{Multiply 3 by the divisor, } 2x-1.$$

$$2 \leftarrow \text{Subtract. Note that } -1-(-3)=-1+3=2.$$

The answer is $x + 3$ with R 2.

Another way to write $x + 3$ R 2 is as

$$\underset{\text{Quotient}}{x+3}+\frac{2}{2x-1}. \quad \leftarrow \text{Remainder}$$
$$\uparrow\text{Divisor}$$

(This is the way answers will be given at the back of the book.)

Check: To check, we multiply the divisor by the quotient and add the remainder:

$$(2x-1)(x+3)+2 = 2x^2+5x-3+2$$
$$= 2x^2+5x-1. \quad \text{Our answer checks.}$$

TRY EXERCISE 29

Our division procedure ends when the degree of the remainder is less than that of the divisor. Check that this was indeed the case in Example 4.

EXAMPLE 5   Divide each of the following.

a) $(x^3 + 1) \div (x + 1)$ **b)** $(x^4 - 3x^2 + 4x - 3) \div (x^2 - 5)$

SOLUTION

a)
$$
\begin{array}{r}
x^2 - x + 1 \\
x + 1\overline{)x^3 + 0x^2 + 0x + 1} \quad \longleftarrow \text{Writing in the missing terms}\\
\underline{-(x^3 + x^2)} \\
-x^2 + 0x \quad \longleftarrow \text{Subtracting } x^3 + x^2 \text{ from } x^3 + 0x^2 \text{ and}\\
\underline{-(-x^2 - x)} \quad \text{bringing down the } 0x\\
x + 1 \quad \longleftarrow \text{Subtracting } -x^2 - x \text{ from } -x^2 + 0x \text{ and}\\
\underline{-(x + 1)} \quad \text{bringing down the } 1\\
0
\end{array}
$$

The answer is $x^2 - x + 1$.

Check: $(x + 1)(x^2 - x + 1) = x^3 - x^2 + x + x^2 - x + 1$
$$= x^3 + 1.$$

b)
$$
\begin{array}{r}
x^2 + 2 \\
x^2 - 5\overline{)x^4 + 0x^3 - 3x^2 + 4x - 3} \quad \text{Writing in the missing term}\\
\underline{-(x^4 - 5x^2)}\\
2x^2 + 4x - 3 \quad \longleftarrow \text{Subtracting } x^4 - 5x^2 \text{ from}\\
\underline{-(2x^2 - 10)} \quad x^4 - 3x^2 \text{ and bringing down } 4x - 3\\
4x + 7 \quad \longleftarrow \text{Subtracting } 2x^2 - 10 \text{ from}\\
2x^2 + 4x - 3
\end{array}
$$

Since the remainder, $4x + 7$, is of lower degree than the divisor, the division process stops. The answer is

$$x^2 + 2 + \frac{4x + 7}{x^2 - 5}.$$

Check: $(x^2 - 5)(x^2 + 2) + 4x + 7 = x^4 + 2x^2 - 5x^2 - 10 + 4x + 7$
$$= x^4 - 3x^2 + 4x - 3.$$

TRY EXERCISE 35

5.8   **EXERCISE SET**

For Extra Help

 MyMathLab   MathXL PRACTICE   WATCH   DOWNLOAD

Divide and check.

1. $\dfrac{40x^6 - 25x^3}{5}$

2. $\dfrac{16a^5 - 24a^2}{8}$

3. $\dfrac{u - 2u^2 + u^7}{u}$

4. $\dfrac{50x^5 - 7x^4 + 2x}{x}$

5. $(18t^3 - 24t^2 + 6t) \div (3t)$

6. $(20t^3 - 15t^2 + 30t) \div (5t)$

7. $(42x^5 - 36x^3 + 9x^2) \div (6x^2)$

8. $(24x^6 + 18x^4 + 8x^3) \div (4x^3)$

9. $(32t^5 + 16t^4 - 8t^3) \div (-8t^3)$

10. $(36t^6 - 27t^5 - 9t^2) \div (-9t^2)$

11. $\dfrac{8x^2 - 10x + 1}{2x}$

12. $\dfrac{9x^2 + 3x - 2}{3x}$

13. $\dfrac{5x^3y + 10x^5y^2 + 15x^2y}{5x^2y}$

14. $\dfrac{12a^3b^2 + 4a^4b^5 + 16ab^2}{4ab^2}$

15. $\dfrac{9r^2s^2 + 3r^2s - 6rs^2}{-3rs}$

16. $\dfrac{4x^4y - 8x^6y^2 + 12x^8y^6}{4x^4y}$

17. $(x^2 - 8x + 12) \div (x - 2)$

18. $(x^2 + 2x - 15) \div (x + 5)$

19. $(t^2 - 10t - 20) \div (t - 5)$

20. $(t^2 + 8t - 15) \div (t + 4)$

21. $(2x^2 + 11x - 5) \div (x + 6)$

22. $(3x^2 - 2x - 13) \div (x - 2)$

23. $\dfrac{t^3 + 27}{t + 3}$ **24.** $\dfrac{a^3 + 8}{a + 2}$

25. $\dfrac{a^2 - 21}{a - 5}$ **26.** $\dfrac{t^2 - 13}{t - 4}$

27. $(5x^2 - 16x) \div (5x - 1)$

28. $(3x^2 - 7x + 1) \div (3x - 1)$

29. $(6a^2 + 17a + 8) \div (2a + 5)$

30. $(10a^2 + 19a + 9) \div (2a + 3)$

31. $\dfrac{2t^3 - 9t^2 + 11t - 3}{2t - 3}$

32. $\dfrac{8t^3 - 22t^2 - 5t + 12}{4t + 3}$

33. $(x^3 - x^2 + x - 1) \div (x - 1)$

34. $(t^3 - t^2 + t - 1) \div (t + 1)$

35. $(t^4 + 4t^2 + 3t - 6) \div (t^2 + 5)$

36. $(t^4 - 2t^2 + 4t - 5) \div (t^2 - 3)$

37. $(6x^4 - 3x^2 + x - 4) \div (2x^2 + 1)$

38. $(4x^4 - 4x^2 - 3) \div (2x^2 - 3)$

39. How is the distributive law used when dividing a polynomial by a binomial?

40. On an assignment, Emmy Lou *incorrectly* writes
$$\frac{12x^3 - 6x}{3x} = 4x^2 - 6x.$$

What mistake do you think she is making and how might you convince her that a mistake has been made?

Skill Review

Review graphing linear equations (Chapter 3).

Graph.

41. $3x - 4y = 12$ [3.3]   **42.** $y = -\frac{2}{3}x + 4$ [3.6]

43. $3y - 2 = 7$ [3.3]   **44.** $8x = 4y$ [3.2]

45. Find the slope of the line containing the points $(3, 2)$ and $(-7, 5)$. [3.5]

46. Find the slope and the *y*-intercept of the line given by $2y = 8x + 7$. [3.6]

47. Find the slope–intercept form of the line with slope -5 and *y*-intercept $(0, -10)$. [3.6]

48. Find the slope–intercept form of the line containing the points $(6, 3)$ and $(-2, -7)$. [3.7]

Synthesis

49. Explain how to form trinomials for which division by $x - 5$ results in a remainder of 3.

50. Under what circumstances will the quotient of two binomials have more than two terms?

Divide.

51. $(10x^{9k} - 32x^{6k} + 28x^{3k}) \div (2x^{3k})$

52. $(45a^{8k} + 30a^{6k} - 60a^{4k}) \div (3a^{2k})$

53. $(6t^{3h} + 13t^{2h} - 4t^h - 15) \div (2t^h + 3)$

54. $(x^4 + a^2) \div (x + a)$

55. $(5a^3 + 8a^2 - 23a - 1) \div (5a^2 - 7a - 2)$

56. $(15y^3 - 30y + 7 - 19y^2) \div (3y^2 - 2 - 5y)$

57. Divide the sum of $4x^5 - 14x^3 - x^2 + 3$ and $2x^5 + 3x^4 + x^3 - 3x^2 + 5x$ by $3x^3 - 2x - 1$.

58. Divide $5x^7 - 3x^4 + 2x^2 - 10x + 2$ by the sum of $(x - 3)^2$ and $5x - 8$.

If the remainder is 0 when one polynomial is divided by another, the divisor is a factor of the dividend. Find the value(s) of c for which $x - 1$ is a factor of each polynomial.

59. $x^2 - 4x + c$

60. $2x^2 - 3cx - 8$

61. $c^2x^2 + 2cx + 1$

Study Summary

KEY TERMS AND CONCEPTS	EXAMPLES

SECTION 5.1: EXPONENTS AND THEIR PROPERTIES

(Assume that no denominators are 0 and that 0^0 is not considered.)

For any integers m and n:

1 as an exponent:	$a^1 = a$	$3^1 = 3$
0 as an exponent:	$a^0 = 1$	$3^0 = 1$
The Product Rule:	$a^m \cdot a^n = a^{m+n}$	$3^5 \cdot 3^9 = 3^{5+9} = 3^{14}$
The Quotient Rule:	$\dfrac{a^m}{a^n} = a^{m-n}$	$\dfrac{3^7}{3} = 3^{7-1} = 3^6$
The Power Rule:	$(a^m)^n = a^{mn}$	$(3^4)^2 = 3^{4 \cdot 2} = 3^8$
Raising a product to a power:	$(ab)^n = a^n b^n$	$(3x^5)^4 = 3^4(x^5)^4 = 81x^{20}$
Raising a quotient to a power:	$\left(\dfrac{a}{b}\right)^n = \dfrac{a^n}{b^n}$	$\left(\dfrac{3}{x}\right)^6 = \dfrac{3^6}{x^6}$

SECTION 5.2: NEGATIVE EXPONENTS AND SCIENTIFIC NOTATION

$a^{-n} = \dfrac{1}{a^n}$;

$\dfrac{a^{-n}}{b^{-m}} = \dfrac{b^m}{a^n}$;

$\left(\dfrac{a}{b}\right)^{-n} = \left(\dfrac{b}{a}\right)^n$

$3^{-2} = \dfrac{1}{3^2} = \dfrac{1}{9}$;

$\dfrac{3^{-7}}{x^{-5}} = \dfrac{x^5}{3^7}$;

$\left(\dfrac{3}{x}\right)^{-2} = \left(\dfrac{x}{3}\right)^2$

Scientific notation is given by $N \times 10^m$, where m is an integer, N is in decimal notation, and $1 \le N < 10$.

$4100 = 4.1 \times 10^3$;

$5 \times 10^{-3} = 0.005$

SECTION 5.3: POLYNOMIALS

A **polynomial** is a monomial or a sum of monomials.

When a polynomial is written as a sum of monomials, each monomial is a **term** of the polynomial.

The **degree of a term** of a polynomial is the number of variable factors in that term.

The **coefficient** of a term is the part of the term that is a constant factor.

The **leading term** of a polynomial is the term of highest degree.

The **leading coefficient** is the coefficient of the leading term.

The **degree of the polynomial** is the degree of the leading term.

Polynomial: $10x - x^3 - \frac{1}{2}x^2 + 3x^5 + 7$

Term	$10x$	$-x^3$	$-\frac{1}{2}x^2$	$3x^5$	7
Degree of term	1	3	2	5	0
Coefficient of term	10	-1	$-\frac{1}{2}$	3	7
Leading term	$3x^5$				
Leading coefficient	3				
Degree of polynomial	5				

A **monomial** has one term.

A **binomial** has two terms.

A **trinomial** has three terms.

Monomial (one term): $4x^3$

Binomial (two terms): $x^2 - 5$

Trinomial (three terms): $3t^3 + 2t - 10$

Like terms, or **similar terms**, are either constant terms or terms containing the same variable(s) raised to the same power(s). These can be **combined** within a polynomial.

Combine like terms: $3y^4 + 6y^2 - 7 - y^4 - 6y^2 + 8$.

$$3y^4 + 6y^2 - 7 - y^4 - 6y^2 + 8 = \underbrace{3y^4 - y^4} + \underbrace{6y^2 - 6y^2} \underbrace{- 7 + 8}$$
$$= 2y^4 \quad + \quad 0 \quad + 1$$
$$= 2y^4 + 1$$

To **evaluate** a polynomial, replace the variable with a number. The **value** is calculated using the rules for order of operations.

Evaluate $t^3 - 2t^2 - 5t + 1$ *for* $t = -2$.
$$t^3 - 2t^2 - 5t + 1 = (-2)^3 - 2(-2)^2 - 5(-2) + 1$$
$$= -8 - 2(4) - (-10) + 1$$
$$= -8 - 8 + 10 + 1$$
$$= -5$$

SECTION 5.4: ADDITION AND SUBTRACTION OF POLYNOMIALS

Add polynomials by combining like terms.

$(2x^2 - 3x + 7) + (5x^3 + 3x - 9)$
$$= 2x^2 + (-3x) + 7 + 5x^3 + 3x + (-9)$$
$$= 5x^3 + 2x^2 - 2$$

Subtract polynomials by adding the opposite of the polynomial being subtracted.

$(2x^2 - 3x + 7) - (5x^3 + 3x - 9)$
$$= 2x^2 - 3x + 7 + (-5x^3 - 3x + 9)$$
$$= 2x^2 - 3x + 7 - 5x^3 - 3x + 9$$
$$= -5x^3 + 2x^2 - 6x + 16$$

SECTION 5.5: MULTIPLICATION OF POLYNOMIALS

Multiply polynomials by multiplying each term of one polynomial by each term of the other.

$(x + 2)(x^2 - x - 1)$
$$= x \cdot x^2 - x \cdot x - x \cdot 1 + 2 \cdot x^2 - 2 \cdot x - 2 \cdot 1$$
$$= x^3 - x^2 - x + 2x^2 - 2x - 2$$
$$= x^3 + x^2 - 3x - 2$$

SECTION 5.6: SPECIAL PRODUCTS

FOIL (First, Outer, Inner, Last):

$(A + B)(C + D) = AC + AD + BC + BD$

$(x + 3)(x - 2) = x^2 - 2x + 3x - 6$
$$= x^2 + x - 6$$

The product of a sum and a difference:
$$(A + B)(A - B) = A^2 - B^2$$
$A^2 - B^2$ is called a **difference of squares**.

$(t^3 + 5)(t^3 - 5) = (t^3)^2 - 5^2$
$$= t^6 - 25$$

The square of a binomial:

$$(A + B)^2 = A^2 + 2AB + B^2;$$
$$(A - B)^2 = A^2 - 2AB + B^2$$

$A^2 + 2AB + B^2$ and $A^2 - 2AB + B^2$ are called **perfect-square trinomials**.

$$(5x + 3)^2 = (5x)^2 + 2(5x)(3) + 3^2 = 25x^2 + 30x + 9;$$
$$(5x - 3)^2 = (5x)^2 - 2(5x)(3) + 3^2 = 25x^2 - 30x + 9$$

SECTION 5.7: POLYNOMIALS IN SEVERAL VARIABLES

To **evaluate** a polynomial, replace each variable with a number and simplify.

Evaluate $4 - 3xy + x^2y$ *for* $x = 5$ *and* $y = -1$.

$$\begin{aligned} 4 - 3xy + x^2y &= 4 - 3(5)(-1) + (5)^2(-1) \\ &= 4 - (-15) + (-25) \\ &= -6 \end{aligned}$$

The **degree** of a term is the number of variables in the term or the sum of the exponents of the variables.

The degree of $-19x^3yz^2$ is 6.

Add, subtract, and multiply polynomials in several variables in the same way as polynomials in one variable.

$$(3xy^2 - 4x^2y + 5xy) + (xy - 6x^2y) = 3xy^2 - 10x^2y + 6xy;$$
$$(3xy^2 - 4x^2y + 5xy) - (xy - 6x^2y) = 3xy^2 + 2x^2y + 4xy;$$
$$(2a^2b + 3a)(5a^2b - a) = 10a^4b^2 + 13a^3b - 3a^2$$

SECTION 5.8: DIVISION OF POLYNOMIALS

To divide a polynomial by a monomial, divide each term by the monomial. Divide coefficients and subtract exponents.

$$\frac{3t^5 - 6t^4 + 4t^2 + 9t}{3t} = \frac{3t^5}{3t} - \frac{6t^4}{3t} + \frac{4t^2}{3t} + \frac{9t}{3t}$$
$$= t^4 - 2t^3 + \tfrac{4}{3}t + 3$$

To divide a polynomial by a binomial, use long division.

Divide: $(x^2 + 5x - 2) \div (x - 3)$.

$$\begin{array}{r} x + 8 \\ x - 3 \overline{)\, x^2 + 5x - 2} \\ \underline{-(x^2 - 3x)} \\ 8x - 2 \\ \underline{-(8x - 24)} \\ 22 \end{array}$$

$$(x^2 + 5x - 2) \div (x - 3) = x + 8 + \frac{22}{x - 3}$$

Review Exercises: Chapter 5

➤ *Concept Reinforcement* *Classify each statement as either true or false.*

1. When two polynomials that are written in descending order are added, the result is generally written in descending order. [5.4]

2. The product of the sum and the difference of the same two terms is a difference of squares. [5.6]

3. When a binomial is squared, the result is a perfect-square trinomial. [5.6]

4. FOIL can be used whenever two polynomials are being multiplied. [5.6]

5. The degree of a polynomial cannot exceed the value of the polynomial's leading coefficient. [5.3]

6. Scientific notation is used only for extremely large numbers. [5.2]

7. FOIL can be used with polynomials in several variables. [5.7]

8. A positive number raised to a negative exponent can never represent a negative number. [5.2]

Simplify. [5.1]

9. $n^3 \cdot n^8 \cdot n$

10. $(7x)^8 \cdot (7x)^2$

11. $t^6 \cdot t^0$

12. $\dfrac{4^5}{4^2}$

13. $\dfrac{(a+b)^4}{(a+b)^4}$

14. $\dfrac{-18c^9d^3}{2c^5d}$

15. $(-2xy^2)^3$

16. $(2x^3)(-3x)^2$

17. $(a^2b)(ab)^5$

18. $\left(\dfrac{2t^5}{3s^4}\right)^2$

19. Express using a positive exponent: 8^{-6}. [5.2]

20. Express using a negative exponent: $\dfrac{1}{a^9}$. [5.2]

Simplify. Do not use negative exponents in the answer. [5.2]

21. $4^5 \cdot 4^{-7}$

22. $\dfrac{6a^{-5}b}{3a^8b^{-8}}$

23. $(w^3)^{-5}$

24. $(2x^{-3}y)^{-2}$

25. $\left(\dfrac{2x}{y}\right)^{-3}$

26. Convert to decimal notation: 4.7×10^8. [5.2]

27. Convert to scientific notation: 0.0000109. [5.2]

Multiply or divide and write scientific notation for the result. [5.2]

28. $(3.8 \times 10^4)(5.5 \times 10^{-1})$

29. $\dfrac{1.28 \times 10^{-8}}{2.5 \times 10^{-4}}$

Identify the terms of each polynomial. [5.3]

30. $8x^2 - x + \frac{2}{3}$

31. $-4y^5 + 7y^2 - 3y - 2$

List the coefficients of the terms in each polynomial. [5.3]

32. $9x^2 - x + 7$

33. $7n^4 - \frac{5}{6}n^2 - 4n + 10$

For each polynomial, (a) *list the degree of each term;* (b) *determine the leading term and the leading coefficient; and* (c) *determine the degree of the polynomial.* [5.3]

34. $4t^2 + 6 + 15t^5$

35. $-2x^5 + 7 - 3x^2 + x$

Classify each polynomial as a monomial, a binomial, a trinomial, or a polynomial with no special name. [5.3]

36. $4x^3 - 5x + 3$

37. $4 - 9t^3 - 7t^4 + 10t^2$

38. $7y^2$

Combine like terms and write in descending order. [5.3]

39. $3x - x^2 + 4x$

40. $\frac{3}{4}x^3 + 4x^2 - x^3 + 7$

41. $-4t^3 + 2t + 4t^3 + 8 - t - 9$

42. $-a + \frac{1}{3} + 20a^5 - 1 - 6a^5 - 2a^2$

Evaluate each polynomial for $x = -2$. [5.3]

43. $9x - 6$

44. $x^2 - 3x + 6$

Add or subtract. [5.4]

45. $(8x^4 - x^3 + x - 4) + (x^5 + 7x^3 - 3x - 5)$

46. $(5a^5 - 2a^3 - 9a^2) + (2a^5 + a^3) + (-a^5 - 3a^2)$

47. $(y^2 + 8y - 7) - (4y^2 - 10)$

48. $(3x^5 - 4x^4 + 2x^2 + 3) -$
    $(2x^5 - 4x^4 + 3x^3 + 4x^2 - 5)$

49. $\begin{aligned} -\tfrac{3}{4}x^4 + \tfrac{1}{2}x^3 \qquad\qquad\quad + \tfrac{7}{8} \\ -\tfrac{1}{4}x^3 - \quad x^2 - \tfrac{7}{4}x \qquad \\ \underline{+\tfrac{3}{2}x^4 \qquad\qquad + \tfrac{2}{3}x^2 \qquad\quad - \tfrac{1}{2}} \end{aligned}$

50. $\begin{aligned} 2x^5 \qquad - \quad x^3 \qquad\quad + x + 3 \\ \underline{-(3x^5 - x^4 + 4x^3 + 2x^2 - x + 3)} \end{aligned}$

51. The length of a rectangle is 3 m greater than its width.

$w + 3$

w

a) Find a polynomial for the perimeter. [5.4]
b) Find a polynomial for the area. [5.5]

Multiply.

52. $5x^2(-6x^3)$ [5.5]

53. $(7x + 1)^2$ [5.6]

54. $(a - 7)(a + 4)$ [5.6]

55. $(d - 8)(d + 8)$ [5.6]

56. $(4x^2 - 5x + 1)(3x - 2)$ [5.5]

57. $(x - 8)^2$ [5.6]

58. $3t^2(5t^3 - 2t^2 + 4t)$ [5.5]

59. $(2a + 9)(2a - 9)$ [5.6]

60. $(x - 0.8)(x - 0.5)$ [5.6]

61. $(x^4 - 2x + 3)(x^3 + x - 1)$ [5.5]

62. $(4y^3 - 5)^2$ [5.6]

63. $(2t^2 + 3)(t^2 - 7)$ [5.6]

64. $\left(a - \frac{1}{2}\right)\left(a + \frac{2}{3}\right)$ [5.6]

65. $(-7 + 2n)(7 + 2n)$ [5.6]

66. Evaluate $2 - 5xy + y^2 - 4xy^3 + x^6$ for $x = -1$ and $y = 2$. [5.7]

Identify the coefficient and the degree of each term of each polynomial. Then find the degree of each polynomial. [5.7]

67. $x^5y - 7xy + 9x^2 - 8$

68. $a^3b^8c^2 - c^{22} + a^5c^{10}$

Combine like terms. [5.7]

69. $u + 3v - 5u + v - 7$

70. $6m^3 + 3m^2n + 4mn^2 + m^2n - 5mn^2$

Add or subtract. [5.7]

71. $(4a^2 - 10ab - b^2) + (-2a^2 - 6ab + b^2)$

72. $(6x^3y^2 - 4x^2y - 6x) - (-5x^3y^2 + 4x^2y + 6x^2 - 6)$

Multiply. [5.7]

73. $(2x + 5y)(x - 3y)$

74. $(5ab - cd^2)^2$

75. Find a polynomial for the shaded area. [5.7]

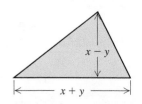

$x - y$

$x + y$

Divide. [5.8]

76. $(3y^5 - y^2 + 12y) \div (3y)$

77. $(6x^3 - 5x^2 - 13x + 13) \div (2x + 3)$

78. $\dfrac{t^4 + t^3 + 2t^2 - t - 3}{t + 1}$

Synthesis

79. Explain why $5x^3$ and $(5x)^3$ are not equivalent expressions. [5.1]

80. A binomial is squared and the result, written in descending order, is $x^2 - 6x + 9$. Is it possible to determine what binomial was squared? Why or why not? [5.6]

81. Determine, without performing the multiplications, the degree of each product. [5.5]
a) $(x^5 - 6x^2 + 3)(x^4 + 3x^3 + 7)$
b) $(x^7 - 4)^4$

82. Simplify:
$$(-3x^5 \cdot 3x^3 - x^6(2x)^2 + (3x^4)^2 + (2x^2)^4 - 20x^2(x^3)^2)^2.$$ [5.1], [5.3]

83. A polynomial has degree 4. The x^2-term is missing. The coefficient of x^4 is two times the coefficient of x^3. The coefficient of x is 3 less than the coefficient of x^4. The remaining coefficient is 7 less than the coefficient of x. The sum of the coefficients is 15. Find the polynomial. [5.3]

Aha! **84.** Multiply: $[(x - 5) - 4x^3][(x - 5) + 4x^3]$. [5.6]

85. Solve: $(x - 7)(x + 10) = (x - 4)(x - 6)$. [2.2], [5.6]

86. *Blood donors.* Every 4–6 weeks, Jordan donates 1.14×10^6 cubic millimeters (two pints) of whole blood, from which platelets are removed and the blood returned to the body. In one cubic millimeter of blood, there are about 2×10^5 platelets. Approximate the number of platelets in Jordan's typical donation. [5.2]

Test: Chapter 5

Test Prep VIDEO CD

Step-by-step test solutions are found on the video CD in the front of this book.

Simplify.

1. $x^7 \cdot x \cdot x^5$

2. $\dfrac{3^8}{3^7}$

3. $\dfrac{(3m)^4}{(3m)^4}$

4. $(t^5)^9$

5. $(5x^4y)(-2x^5y)^3$

6. $\dfrac{24a^7b^4}{20a^2b}$

7. Express using a positive exponent: y^{-7}.

8. Express using a negative exponent: $\dfrac{1}{5^6}$.

Simplify.

9. $t^{-4} \cdot t^{-5}$

10. $\dfrac{9x^3y^2}{3x^8y^{-3}}$

11. $(2a^3b^{-1})^{-4}$

12. $\left(\dfrac{ab}{c}\right)^{-3}$

13. Convert to scientific notation: 3,060,000,000.

14. Convert to decimal notation: 5×10^{-8}.

Multiply or divide and write scientific notation for the result.

15. $\dfrac{5.6 \times 10^6}{3.2 \times 10^{-11}}$

16. $(2.4 \times 10^5)(5.4 \times 10^{16})$

17. Classify $4x^2y - 7y^3$ as a monomial, a binomial, a trinomial, or a polynomial with no special name.

18. Identify the coefficient of each term of the polynomial:

$3x^5 - x + \frac{1}{9}$.

19. Determine the degree of each term, the leading term and the leading coefficient, and the degree of the polynomial:

$2t^3 - t + 7t^5 + 4$.

20. Evaluate $x^2 + 5x - 1$ for $x = -3$.

Combine like terms and write in descending order.

21. $4a^2 - 6 + a^2$

22. $y^2 - 3y - y + \frac{3}{4}y^2$

23. $3 - x^2 + 8x + 5x^2 - 6x - 2x + 4x^3$

Add or subtract.

24. $(3x^5 + 5x^3 - 5x^2 - 3) + (x^5 + x^4 - 3x^2 + 2x - 4)$

25. $\left(x^4 + \frac{2}{3}x + 5\right) + \left(4x^4 + 5x^2 + \frac{1}{3}x\right)$

26. $(5a^4 + 3a^3 - a^2 - 2a - 1) - (7a^4 - a^2 - a + 6)$

27. $(t^3 - 0.3t^2 - 20) - (t^4 - 1.5t^3 + 0.3t^2 - 11)$

Multiply.

28. $-2x^2(3x^2 - 3x - 5)$

29. $\left(x - \frac{1}{3}\right)^2$

30. $(5t - 7)(5t + 7)$

31. $(3b + 5)(2b - 1)$

32. $(x^6 - 4)(x^8 + 4)$

33. $(8 - y)(6 + 5y)$

34. $(2x + 1)(3x^2 - 5x - 3)$

35. $(8a^3 + 3)^2$

36. Evaluate $2x^2y - 3y^2$ for $x = -3$ and $y = 2$.

37. Combine like terms:

$2x^3y - y^3 + xy^3 + 8 - 6x^3y - x^2y^2 + 11$.

38. Subtract:

$(8a^2b^2 - ab + b^3) - (-6ab^2 - 7ab - ab^3 + 5b^3)$.

39. Multiply: $(3x^5 - y)(3x^5 + y)$.

Divide.

40. $(12x^4 + 9x^3 - 15x^2) \div (3x^2)$

41. $(6x^3 - 8x^2 - 14x + 13) \div (3x + 2)$

Synthesis

42. The height of a box is 1 less than its length, and the length is 2 more than its width. Express the volume in terms of the length.

43. Solve: $x^2 + (x - 7)(x + 4) = 2(x - 6)^2$.

44. Simplify: $2^{-1} - 4^{-1}$.

45. Every day about 12.4 billion spam e-mails are sent. If each spam e-mail wastes 4 sec, how many hours are wasted each day due to spam?
Source: spam-filter-review.toptenreviews.com

1. Evaluate $\dfrac{2x + y}{5}$ for $x = 12$ and $y = 6$. [1.1]

2. Evaluate $5x^2y - xy + y^2$ for $x = -1$ and $y = -2$. [5.7]

Simplify.

3. $\frac{1}{15} - \frac{2}{9}$ [1.3]

4. $2 - [10 - (5 + 12 \div 2^2 \cdot 3)]$ [1.8]

5. $2y - (y - 7) + 3$ [1.8]

6. $t^4 \cdot t^7 \cdot t$ [5.1]

7. $\dfrac{-100x^6y^8}{25xy^5}$ [5.1]

8. $(2a^2b)(5ab^3)^2$ [5.1]

9. Factor: $10a - 6b + 12$. [1.2]

10. Find the absolute value: $\left|\dfrac{11}{16}\right|$. [1.4]

11. Determine the degree of the polynomial
$-x^4 + 5x^3 + 3x^6 - 1$. [5.3]

12. Combine like terms and write in descending order:
$-\frac{1}{2}t^3 + 3t^2 + \frac{3}{4}t^3 + 0.1 - 8t^2 - 0.45$. [5.3]

13. In which quadrant is $(-2, 5)$ located? [3.1]

14. Graph on a number line: $x > -1$. [2.6]

Graph.

15. $3y + 2x = 0$ [3.2]

16. $3y - 2x = 12$ [3.3]

17. $3y = 2$ [3.3]

18. $3y = 2x + 9$ [3.6]

19. Find the slope and the y-intercept of the line given by $y = \frac{1}{10}x + \frac{3}{8}$. [3.6]

20. Find the slope of the line containing the points $(2, 3)$ and $(-6, 8)$. [3.5]

21. Write an equation of the line with slope $-\frac{2}{3}$ and y-intercept $(0, -10)$. [3.6]

22. Find the coordinates of the x- and y-intercepts of the graph of $2x + 5y = 8$. Do not graph. [3.3]

Solve.

23. $\frac{1}{6}n = -\frac{2}{3}$ [2.1]

24. $3 - 5x = 0$ [2.2]

25. $5y + 7 = 8y - 1$ [2.2]

26. $0.4t - 0.5 = 8.3$ [2.2]

27. $5(3 - x) = 2 + 7(x - 1)$ [2.2]

28. $2 - (x - 7) = 8 - 4(x + 5)$ [2.2]

29. $-\frac{1}{2}t \le 4$ [2.6]

30. $3x - 5 > 9x - 8$ [2.6]

31. Solve $c = \dfrac{5pq}{2t}$ for t. [2.3]

Add or subtract.

32. $(2u^2v - uv^2 + uv) + (3u^2 - v^2u + 5vu^2)$ [5.7]

33. $(3x^3 - 2x^2 + 6x) - (x^2 - 6x + 7)$ [5.4]

34. $(2x^5 - x^4 - x) - (x^5 - x^4 + x)$ [5.4]

Multiply.

35. $10(2a - 3b + 7)$ [1.2]

36. $8x^3(-2x^2 - 6x + 7)$ [5.5]

37. $(3a + 7)(2a - 1)$ [5.6]

38. $(x - 2)(x^2 + x - 5)$ [5.5]

39. $(4t^2 + 3)^2$ [5.6]

40. $\left(\frac{1}{2}x + 1\right)\left(\frac{1}{2}x - 1\right)$ [5.6]

41. $(2r^2 + s)(3r^2 - 4s)$ [5.7]

42. Divide: $(x^2 - x + 3) \div (x - 1)$. [5.8]

Simplify. Do not use negative exponents in the answer. [5.2]

43. 7^{-10}

44. $x^{-8} \cdot x$

45. $\left(\dfrac{4s}{3t^{-5}}\right)^{-2}$

46. $(3x^{-7}y^{-2})^{-1}$

Solve.

47. In 2007, Europe and the United States together had installed wind turbines capable of producing about 60 thousand megawatts of electricity. Europe's wind-turbine capacity was four times that of the United States. What was Europe's wind-turbine capacity in 2007? [2.5]
Source: BP Statistical Review of World Energy, 2007

48. In the first four months of 2007, U.S. electric utilities used coal to generate 644 megawatt hours of electricity. This was 49.6% of the total amount of electricity generated. How much electricity was generated in the first four months of 2007? [2.4]
Source: U.S. Energy Information Administration

49. Antonio's energy-efficient washer and dryer use a total of 70 kilowatt hours (kWh) of electricity each month. The dryer uses 10 more than twice as many kilowatt hours as the washer. How many kilowatt hours does each appliance use in a month? [2.5]

50. A typical two-person household will use 195 kWh of electricity each month to heat water. The usage increases to 315 kWh per month for a four-person household. [3.7]
Source: Lee County Electric Cooperative

  a) Graph the data and determine an equation for the related line. Let w represent the number of kilowatt hours used each month and n represent the number of people in a household.

  b) Use the equation of part (a) to estimate the number of kilowatt hours used each month by a five-person household.

51. Abrianna's contract specifies that she cannot work more than 40 hr per week. For the first 4 days of one week, she worked 8, 10, 7, and 9 hr. How many hours can she work on the fifth day without violating her contract? [2.7]

52. In 2006, Brazil owed about $240 billion in external debt. This amount was $\frac{3}{2}$ of Russia's debt. How much did Russia owe in 2006? [2.5]

53. In 2006, the average GPA of incoming freshmen at the University of South Carolina was 3.73. This was a 3.6% increase over the average GPA in 2001. What was the average GPA in 2001? [2.4]
Source: *The Wall Street Journal*, 11/10/06

54. U.S. retail losses due to crime have increased from $26 billion in 1998 to $38 billion in 2005. Find the rate of change of retail losses due to crime. [3.4]
Source: University of Florida

Synthesis

Solve. If no solution exists, state this.

55. $3x - 2(x + 6) = 4(x - 3)$ [2.2]

56. $x - (2x - 1) = 3x - 4(x + 1) + 10$ [2.2]

57. $(x - 2)(x + 3) = (4 - x)^2$ [2.2], [5.6]

58. Find the equation of a line with the same slope as $y = \frac{1}{2}x - 7$ and the same y-intercept as $2y = 5x + 8$. [3.6]

Simplify.

59. $7^{-1} + 8^0$ [5.2]

60. $-2x^5(x^7) + (x^3)^4 - (4x^5)^2(-x^2)$ [5.1], [5.3]

Polynomials and Factoring

CHRIS GJERSVIK
PRINCIPAL NETWORK ENGINEER
Upper Saddle River, New Jersey

The math skills we use in net-working–telecommunications help us in so many ways. For instance, we use math when planning the budgets for a computer network or phone system and when determining capacity of a network. We need to accurately size network circuits so they have enough bandwidth to carry phone calls, Internet access, streaming video, e-mail, and other such applications. Finally, we use math when we need to analyze network traffic and break it down into its most basic form, which uses the binary numeral system.

AN APPLICATION

The number N, in millions, of broadband cable and DSL subscribers in the United States t years after 1998 can be approximated by

$$N = 0.3t^2 + 0.6t.$$

When will there be 36 million broadband cable and DSL subscribers?

Source: Based on information from Leichtman Research Group

This problem appears as Exercise 19 in Section 6.8.

n Chapter 1, we learned that *factoring* is multiplying reversed. Thus factoring polynomials requires a solid command of the multiplication methods learned in Chapter 5. Factoring is an important skill that will be used to solve equations and simplify other types of expressions found later in the study of algebra.

In Sections 6.1–6.6, we factor polynomials to find equivalent expressions that are products. In Sections 6.7 and 6.8, we use factoring to solve equations, including those that arise from real-world problems.

6.1 Introduction to Factoring

Factoring Monomials ▪ Factoring When Terms Have a Common Factor ▪ Factoring by Grouping ▪ Checking by Evaluating

Just as a number like 15 can be factored as $3 \cdot 5$, a polynomial like $x^2 + 7x$ can be factored as $x(x + 7)$. In both cases, we ask ourselves, "What was multiplied to obtain the given result?" The situation is much like a popular television game show in which an "answer" is given and participants must find the "question" to which the answer corresponds.

> **Factoring**
>
> To *factor* a polynomial is to find an equivalent expression that is a product. An equivalent expression of this type is called a *factorization* of the polynomial.

Factoring Monomials

To factor a monomial, we find two monomials whose product is equivalent to the original monomial. For example, $20x^2$ can be factored as $2 \cdot 10x^2$, $4x \cdot 5x$, or $10x \cdot 2x$, as well as several other ways. To check, we multiply.

EXAMPLE 1 Find three factorizations of $15x^3$.

SOLUTION

a) $15x^3 = (3 \cdot 5)(x \cdot x^2)$ Thinking of how 15 and x^3 can be factored

$= (3x)(5x^2)$ The factors are $3x$ and $5x^2$. *Check:* $3x \cdot 5x^2 = 15x^3$.

b) $15x^3 = (3 \cdot 5)(x^2 \cdot x)$

$= (3x^2)(5x)$ The factors are $3x^2$ and $5x$. *Check:* $3x^2 \cdot 5x = 15x^3$.

c) $15x^3 = ((-5)(-3))x^3$

$= (-5)(-3x^3)$ The factors are -5 and $-3x^3$.
Check: $(-5)(-3x^3) = 15x^3$.

$(3x)(5x^2)$, $(3x^2)(5x)$, and $(-5)(-3x^3)$ are all factorizations of $15x^3$. Other factorizations exist as well.

▶ TRY EXERCISE 9

Recall from Section 1.2 that the word "factor" can be a verb or a noun, depending on the context in which it appears.

Factoring When Terms Have a Common Factor

To multiply a polynomial of two or more terms by a monomial, we use the distributive law: $a(b + c) = ab + ac$. To factor a polynomial with two or more terms of the form $ab + ac$, we use the distributive law with the sides of the equation switched: $ab + ac = a(b + c)$.

Multiply   *Factor*

$3(x + 2y - z)$ $3x + 6y - 3z$

$\quad = 3 \cdot x + 3 \cdot 2y - 3 \cdot z$ $\quad = 3 \cdot x + 3 \cdot 2y - 3 \cdot z$

$\quad = 3x + 6y - 3z$ $\quad = 3(x + 2y - z)$

In the factorization on the right, note that since 3 appears as a factor of $3x$, $6y$, and $-3z$, it is a *common factor* for all the terms of the trinomial $3x + 6y - 3z$.

When we factor, we are forming an equivalent expression that is a product.

EXAMPLE 2   Factor to form an equivalent expression: $10y + 15$.

SOLUTION   We write the prime factorization of both terms to determine any common factors:

The prime factorization of $10y$ is $2 \cdot 5 \cdot y$;

The prime factorization of 15 is $3 \cdot 5$.   } 5 is a common factor.

We "factor out" the common factor 5 using the distributive law:

> We can always check a factorization by multiplying.

$10y + 15 = 5 \cdot 2y + 5 \cdot 3$ Try to do this step mentally.

$\qquad\qquad = 5(2y + 3)$.   Using the distributive law

Check: $5(2y + 3) = 5 \cdot 2y + 5 \cdot 3 = 10y + 15$.

The factorization of $10y + 15$ is $5(2y + 3)$.   **TRY EXERCISE** 15

We generally factor out the *largest* common factor.

EXAMPLE 3   Factor: $8a - 12$.

SOLUTION   Lining up common factors in columns can help us determine the largest common factor:

The prime factorization of $8a$ is $2 \cdot 2 \cdot 2 \cdot \quad a$;

The prime factorization of 12 is $2 \cdot 2 \cdot \quad 3$.

Since both factorizations include two factors of 2, the largest common factor is $2 \cdot 2$, or 4:

$8a - 12 = 4 \cdot 2a - 4 \cdot 3$ 4 is a factor of $8a$ and of 12.

$8a - 12 = 4(2a - 3)$.   Try to go directly to this step.

Check: $4(2a - 3) = 4 \cdot 2a - 4 \cdot 3 = 8a - 12$, as expected.

The factorization of $8a - 12$ is $4(2a - 3)$.   **TRY EXERCISE** 17

> *CAUTION!* $2 \cdot 2 \cdot 2a - 2 \cdot 2 \cdot 3$ is a factorization of the *terms* of $8a - 12$ but not of the polynomial itself. The factorization of $8a - 12$ is $4(2a - 3)$.

A common factor may contain a variable.

EXAMPLE **4**   Factor: $24x^5 + 30x^2$.

SOLUTION

The prime factorization of $24x^5$ is $2 \cdot 2 \cdot 2 \cdot 3 \cdot \quad x \cdot x \cdot x \cdot x \cdot x.$
The prime factorization of $30x^2$ is $2 \cdot \quad\quad 3 \cdot 5 \cdot x \cdot x.$

The largest common factor is $2 \cdot 3 \cdot x \cdot x$, or $6x^2$. ←

$$24x^5 + 30x^2 = 6x^2 \cdot 4x^3 + 6x^2 \cdot 5 \qquad \text{Factoring each term}$$
$$= 6x^2(4x^3 + 5) \qquad\quad \text{Factoring out } 6x^2$$

Check: $6x^2(4x^3 + 5) = 6x^2 \cdot 4x^3 + 6x^2 \cdot 5 = 24x^5 + 30x^2$, as expected.

The factorization of $24x^5 + 30x^2$ is $6x^2(4x^3 + 5)$.   **TRY EXERCISE** 27

The largest common factor of a polynomial is the largest common factor of the coefficients times the largest common factor of the variable(s) in all the terms. Suppose in Example 4 that you did not recognize the *largest* common factor, and removed only part of it, as follows:

$$24x^5 + 30x^2 = 2x^2 \cdot 12x^3 + 2x^2 \cdot 15 \qquad 2x^2 \text{ is a common factor.}$$
$$= 2x^2(12x^3 + 15). \qquad\quad 12x^3 + 15 \text{ itself contains a}$$
$$\qquad\qquad\qquad\qquad\qquad\qquad \text{common factor.}$$

Note that $12x^3 + 15$ still has a common factor, 3. To find the largest common factor, continue factoring out common factors, as follows, until no more exist:

$$24x^5 + 30x^2 = 2x^2[3(4x^3 + 5)] \qquad \text{Factoring } 12x^3 + 15. \text{ Remember to rewrite}$$
$$\qquad\qquad\qquad\qquad\qquad\qquad \text{the first common factor, } 2x^2.$$
$$= 6x^2(4x^3 + 5). \qquad \text{Using an associative law; } 2x^2 \cdot 3 = 6x^2$$

Since $4x^3 + 5$ cannot be factored any further, we say that we have factored *completely*. When we are directed simply to factor, it is understood that we should always factor completely.

EXAMPLE **5**   Factor: $12x^5 - 15x^4 + 27x^3$.

SOLUTION

The prime factorization of $12x^5$ is $2 \cdot 2 \cdot 3 \cdot \quad\quad\quad x \cdot x \cdot x \cdot x \cdot x.$
The prime factorization of $15x^4$ is $\quad\quad 3 \cdot \quad\quad 5 \cdot x \cdot x \cdot x \cdot x.$
The prime factorization of $27x^3$ is $\quad\quad 3 \cdot 3 \cdot 3 \cdot \quad x \cdot x \cdot x.$

The largest common factor is $3 \cdot x \cdot x \cdot x$, or $3x^3$. ←

$$12x^5 - 15x^4 + 27x^3 = 3x^3 \cdot 4x^2 - 3x^3 \cdot 5x + 3x^3 \cdot 9$$
$$= 3x^3(4x^2 - 5x + 9)$$

Since $4x^2 - 5x + 9$ has no common factor, we are done, except for a check:

$$3x^3(4x^2 - 5x + 9) = 3x^3 \cdot 4x^2 - 3x^3 \cdot 5x + 3x^3 \cdot 9$$
$$= 12x^5 - 15x^4 + 27x^3,$$

as expected. The factorization of $12x^5 - 15x^4 + 27x^3$ is $3x^3(4x^2 - 5x + 9)$.

TRY EXERCISE 31

Note in Examples 4 and 5 that the *largest* common variable factor is the *smallest* power of x in the original polynomial.

With practice, we can determine the largest common factor without writing the prime factorization of each term. Then, to factor, we write the largest common factor and parentheses and then fill in the parentheses. It is customary for the leading coefficient of the polynomial inside the parentheses to be positive.

EXAMPLE 6

Factor: **(a)** $8r^3s^2 + 16rs^3$; **(b)** $-3xy + 6xz - 3x$.

SOLUTION

a) $8r^3s^2 + 16rs^3 = 8rs^2(r^2 + 2s)$ Try to go directly to this step.

The largest common factor is $8rs^2$. ←
$$\begin{cases} 8r^3s^2 = 2 \cdot 2 \cdot 2 \cdot \quad r \cdot r^2 \cdot s^2 \\ 16rs^3 = 2 \cdot 2 \cdot 2 \cdot 2 \cdot r \cdot \quad s^2 \cdot s \end{cases}$$

Check: $8rs^2(r^2 + 2s) = 8r^3s^2 + 16rs^3$.

STUDENT NOTES

The 1 in $(y - 2z + 1)$ plays an important role in Example 6(b). If left out of the factorization, the term $-3x$ would not appear in the check.

b) $-3xy + 6xz - 3x = -3x(y - 2z + 1)$ Note that either $-3x$ or $3x$ can be the largest common factor.

We generally factor out a negative when the first coefficient is negative. The way we factor can depend on the situation in which we are working. We might also factor as follows:

$$-3xy + 6xz - 3x = 3x(-y + 2z - 1).$$

The checks are left to the student.

▶ **TRY EXERCISE** 35

In some texts, the largest common factor is referred to as the *greatest* common factor. We have avoided this language because, as shown in Example 6(b), the largest common factor may represent a negative value that is actually *less* than other common factors.

┌───┐
│ **Tips for Factoring**   │
│   **1.** Factor out the largest common factor, if one exists. │
│   **2.** The common factor multiplies a polynomial with the same number │
│   of terms as the original polynomial.   │
│   **3.** Factoring can always be checked by multiplying. Multiplication │
│   should yield the original polynomial.   │
└───┘

Factoring by Grouping

Sometimes algebraic expressions contain a common factor with two or more terms.

EXAMPLE 7

Factor: $x^2(x + 1) + 2(x + 1)$.

SOLUTION   The binomial $x + 1$ is a factor of both $x^2(x + 1)$ and $2(x + 1)$. Thus, $x + 1$ is a common factor:

$$x^2(x + 1) + 2(x + 1) = (x + 1)x^2 + (x + 1)2$$ Using a commutative law twice. Try to do this step mentally.

$$= (x + 1)(x^2 + 2).$$ Factoring out the common factor, $x + 1$

To check, we could simply reverse the above steps.
The factorization is $(x + 1)(x^2 + 2)$.

▶ **TRY EXERCISE** 37

In Example 7, the common binomial factor was clearly visible. How do we find such a factor in a polynomial like $5x^3 - x^2 + 15x - 3$? Although there is no factor, other than 1, common to all four terms, $5x^3 - x^2$ and $15x - 3$ can be grouped and factored separately:

$$5x^3 - x^2 = x^2(5x - 1) \quad \text{and} \quad 15x - 3 = 3(5x - 1).$$

Note that $5x^3 - x^2$ and $15x - 3$ share a common factor, $5x - 1$. This means that the original polynomial, $5x^3 - x^2 + 15x - 3$, can be factored:

$$5x^3 - x^2 + 15x - 3 = (5x^3 - x^2) + (15x - 3) \qquad \text{Each binomial has a common factor.}$$

$$= x^2(5x - 1) + 3(5x - 1) \qquad \text{Factoring each binomial}$$

$$= (5x - 1)(x^2 + 3). \qquad \text{Factoring out the common factor, } 5x - 1$$

Check: $(5x - 1)(x^2 + 3) = 5x \cdot x^2 + 5x \cdot 3 - 1 \cdot x^2 - 1 \cdot 3$

$$= 5x^3 - x^2 + 15x - 3.$$

If a polynomial can be split into groups of terms and the groups share a common factor, then the original polynomial can be factored. This method, known as **factoring by grouping**, can be tried on any polynomial with four or more terms.

EXAMPLE   8   Factor by grouping.

a) $2x^3 + 8x^2 + x + 4$ 　　　　　　　　　　**b)** $8x^4 + 6x - 28x^3 - 21$

SOLUTION

a) $2x^3 + 8x^2 + x + 4 = (2x^3 + 8x^2) + (x + 4)$

$$= 2x^2(x + 4) + 1(x + 4) \qquad \text{Factoring } 2x^3 + 8x^2 \text{ to find a common binomial factor. Writing the 1 helps with the next step.}$$

$$= (x + 4)(2x^2 + 1) \qquad \text{Factoring out the common factor, } x + 4. \text{ The 1 is essential in the factor } 2x^2 + 1.$$

CAUTION!　Be sure to include the term 1. The check below shows why it is essential.

Check: $(x + 4)(2x^2 + 1) = x \cdot 2x^2 + x \cdot 1 + 4 \cdot 2x^2 + 4 \cdot 1$ 　　Using FOIL

$$= 2x^3 + x + 8x^2 + 4$$

$$= 2x^3 + 8x^2 + x + 4. \qquad \text{Using a commutative law}$$

The factorization is $(x + 4)(2x^2 + 1)$.

b) We have a choice of either

$$8x^4 + 6x - 28x^3 - 21 = (8x^4 + 6x) + (-28x^3 - 21)$$
$$= 2x(4x^3 + 3) + 7(-4x^3 - 3) \leftarrow \text{No common factor}$$

or

$$8x^4 + 6x - 28x^3 - 21 = (8x^4 + 6x) + (-28x^3 - 21)$$
$$= 2x(4x^3 + 3) + (-7)(4x^3 + 3). \leftarrow \text{Common factor}$$

Because of the common factor $4x^3 + 3$, we choose the latter:

$$8x^4 + 6x - 28x^3 - 21 = 2x(4x^3 + 3) + (-7)(4x^3 + 3)$$
$$= (4x^3 + 3)(2x + (-7)) \qquad \text{Try to do this step mentally.}$$
$$= (4x^3 + 3)(2x - 7). \qquad \text{The common factor } 4x^3 + 3 \text{ was factored out.}$$

Check: $(4x^3 + 3)(2x - 7) = 8x^4 - 28x^3 + 6x - 21$
$$= 8x^4 + 6x - 28x^3 - 21. \qquad \text{This is the original polynomial.}$$

The factorization is $(4x^3 + 3)(2x - 7)$.

TRY EXERCISE 43

Although factoring by grouping can be useful, some polynomials, like $x^3 + x^2 + 2x - 2$, cannot be factored this way. Factoring polynomials of this type is beyond the scope of this text.

Checking by Evaluating

One way to check a factorization is to multiply. A second type of check, discussed toward the end of Section 5.5, uses the fact that equivalent expressions have the same value when evaluated for the same replacement. Thus a quick, partial check of Example 8(a) can be made by using a convenient replacement for x (say, 1) and evaluating both $2x^3 + 8x^2 + x + 4$ and $(x + 4)(2x^2 + 1)$:

$$2 \cdot 1^3 + 8 \cdot 1^2 + 1 + 4 = 2 + 8 + 1 + 4$$
$$= 15;$$
$$(1 + 4)(2 \cdot 1^2 + 1) = 5 \cdot 3$$
$$= 15.$$

Since the value of both expressions is the same, the factorization is probably correct.

Keep in mind the possibility that two expressions that are not equivalent may share the same value when evaluated at a certain value. Because of this, unless several values are used (at least one more than the degree of the polynomial, it turns out), evaluating offers only a partial check. Consult with your instructor before making extensive use of this type of check.

TECHNOLOGY CONNECTION

A partial check of a factorization can be performed using a table or a graph. To check Example 8(a), we let

$$y_1 = 2x^3 + 8x^2 + x + 4 \quad \text{and} \quad y_2 = (x + 4)(2x^2 + 1).$$

Then we set up a table in AUTO mode (see p. 88). If the factorization is correct, the values of y_1 and y_2 will be the same regardless of the table settings used.

ΔTBL = 1

X	Y₁	Y₂
0	4	4
1	15	15
2	54	54
3	133	133
4	264	264
5	459	459
6	730	730

X = 0

We can also graph $y_1 = 2x^3 + 8x^2 + x + 4$ and $y_2 = (x + 4)(2x^2 + 1)$. If the graphs appear to coincide, the factorization is probably correct. The TRACE feature can be used to confirm this.

$$y_1 = 2x^3 + 8x^2 + x + 4,$$
$$y_2 = (x + 4)(2x^2 + 1)$$

Yscl = 2

Use a table or a graph to determine whether each factorization is correct.

1. $x^2 - 7x - 8 = (x - 8)(x + 1)$
2. $4x^2 - 5x - 6 = (4x + 3)(x - 2)$
3. $5x^2 + 17x - 12 = (5x + 3)(x - 4)$
4. $10x^2 + 37x + 7 = (5x - 1)(2x + 7)$
5. $12x^2 - 17x - 5 = (6x + 1)(2x - 5)$
6. $12x^2 - 17x - 5 = (4x + 1)(3x - 5)$
7. $x^2 - 4 = (x - 2)(x - 2)$
8. $x^2 - 4 = (x + 2)(x - 2)$

6.1 EXERCISE SET

Concept Reinforcement *In each of Exercises 1–8, match the phrase with the most appropriate choice from the column on the right.*

1. ____ A factorization of $35a^2b$

2. ____ A factor of $35a^2b$

3. ____ A common factor of $5x + 10$ and $4x + 8$

4. ____ A factorization of $3x^4 - 9x^2$

5. ____ A factorization of $9x^4 - 3x^2$

6. ____ A common factor of $2x + 10$ and $4x + 8$

7. ____ A factor of $3a + 6a^2$

8. ____ A factorization of $3a + 6a^2$

a) $3a(1 + 2a)$

b) $x + 2$

c) $3x^2(3x^2 - 1)$

d) $1 + 2a$

e) $3x^2(x^2 - 3)$

f) $5a^2$

g) 2

h) $7a \cdot 5ab$

Find three factorizations for each monomial. Answers may vary.

9. $14x^3$
10. $22x^3$
11. $-15a^4$
12. $-8t^5$
13. $25t^5$
14. $9a^4$

Factor. Remember to use the largest common factor and to check by multiplying. Factor out a negative factor if the first coefficient is negative.

15. $8x + 24$
16. $10x + 50$
17. $6x - 30$
18. $7x - 21$
19. $2x^2 + 2x - 8$
20. $6x^2 + 3x - 15$
21. $3t^2 + t$
22. $2t^2 + t$
23. $-5y^2 - 10y$
24. $-4y^2 - 12y$
25. $x^3 + 6x^2$
26. $5x^4 - x^2$

27. $16a^4 - 24a^2$

28. $25a^5 + 10a^3$

29. $-6t^6 + 9t^4 - 4t^2$

30. $-10t^5 + 15t^4 + 9t^3$

31. $6x^8 + 12x^6 - 24x^4 + 30x^2$

32. $10x^4 - 30x^3 - 50x - 20$

33. $x^5y^5 + x^4y^3 + x^3y^3 - x^2y^2$

34. $x^9y^6 - x^7y^5 + x^4y^4 + x^3y^3$

35. $-35a^3b^4 + 10a^2b^3 - 15a^3b^2$

36. $-21r^5t^4 - 14r^4t^6 + 21r^3t^6$

Factor.

37. $n(n - 6) + 3(n - 6)$

38. $b(b + 5) + 3(b + 5)$

39. $x^2(x + 3) - 7(x + 3)$

40. $3z^2(2z + 9) + (2z + 9)$

41. $y^2(2y - 9) + (2y - 9)$

42. $x^2(x - 7) - 3(x - 7)$

Factor by grouping, if possible, and check.

43. $x^3 + 2x^2 + 5x + 10$

44. $z^3 + 3z^2 + 7z + 21$

45. $5a^3 + 15a^2 + 2a + 6$

46. $3a^3 + 2a^2 + 6a + 4$

47. $9n^3 - 6n^2 + 3n - 2$

48. $10x^3 - 25x^2 + 2x - 5$

49. $4t^3 - 20t^2 + 3t - 15$

50. $8a^3 - 2a^2 + 12a - 3$

51. $7x^3 + 5x^2 - 21x - 15$

52. $5x^3 + 4x^2 - 10x - 8$

53. $6a^3 + 7a^2 + 6a + 7$

54. $7t^3 - 5t^2 + 7t - 5$

55. $2x^3 + 12x^2 - 5x - 30$

56. $x^3 - x^2 - 2x + 5$

57. $p^3 + p^2 - 3p + 10$

58. $w^3 + 7w^2 + 4w + 28$

59. $y^3 + 8y^2 - 2y - 16$

60. $3x^3 + 18x^2 - 5x - 25$

61. $2x^3 - 8x^2 - 9x + 36$

62. $20g^3 - 4g^2 - 25g + 5$

63. In answering a factoring problem, Taylor says the largest common factor is $-5x^2$ and Madison says the largest common factor is $5x^2$. Can they both be correct? Why or why not?

64. Write a two-sentence paragraph in which the word "factor" is used at least once as a noun and once as a verb.

Skill Review

To prepare for Section 6.2, review multiplying binomials using FOIL (Section 5.6).

Multiply. [5.6]

65. $(x + 2)(x + 7)$

66. $(x - 2)(x - 7)$

67. $(x + 2)(x - 7)$

68. $(x - 2)(x + 7)$

69. $(a - 1)(a - 3)$

70. $(t + 3)(t + 5)$

71. $(t - 5)(t + 10)$

72. $(a + 4)(a - 6)$

Synthesis

73. Azrah recognizes that evaluating provides only a partial check of her factoring. Because of this, she often performs a second check with a different replacement value. Is this a good idea? Why or why not?

74. Holly factors $12x^2y - 18xy^2$ as $6xy \cdot 2x - 6xy \cdot 3y$. Is this the factorization of the polynomial? Why or why not?

Factor, if possible.

75. $4x^5 + 6x^2 + 6x^3 + 9$

76. $x^6 + x^2 + x^4 + 1$

77. $2x^4 + 2x^3 - 4x^2 - 4x$

78. $x^3 + x^2 - 2x + 2$

Aha! **79.** $5x^5 - 5x^4 + x^3 - x^2 + 3x - 3$

Aha! **80.** $ax^2 + 2ax + 3a + x^2 + 2x + 3$

81. Write a trinomial of degree 7 for which $8x^2y^3$ is the largest common factor. Answers may vary.

6.2 Factoring Trinomials of the Type $x^2 + bx + c$

When the Constant Term Is Positive ▪ When the Constant Term Is Negative ▪
Prime Polynomials

We now learn how to factor trinomials like

$$x^2 + 5x + 4 \quad \text{or} \quad x^2 + 3x - 10,$$

for which no common factor exists and the leading coefficient is 1. Recall that when factoring, we are writing an equivalent expression that is a product. For these trinomials, the factors will be binomials.

As preparation for the factoring that follows, compare the following multiplications:

$$\begin{array}{cccc} \text{F} & \text{O} & \text{I} & \text{L} \\ \downarrow & \downarrow & \downarrow & \downarrow \end{array}$$

$$(x + 2)(x + 5) = x^2 + 5x + 2x + 2 \cdot 5$$
$$= x^2 + 7x + 10;$$

$$(x - 2)(x - 5) = x^2 - 5x - 2x + (-2)(-5)$$
$$= x^2 - 7x + 10;$$

$$(x + 3)(x - 7) = x^2 - 7x + 3x + 3(-7)$$
$$= x^2 - 4x - 21;$$

$$(x - 3)(x + 7) = x^2 + 7x - 3x + (-3)7$$
$$= x^2 + 4x - 21.$$

Note that for all four products:

- The product of the two binomials is a trinomial.
- The coefficient of x in the trinomial is the sum of the constant terms in the binomials.
- The constant term in the trinomial is the product of the constant terms in the binomials.

These observations lead to a method for factoring certain trinomials. We first consider trinomials that have a positive constant term, just as in the first two multiplications above.

When the Constant Term Is Positive

To factor a polynomial like $x^2 + 7x + 10$, we think of FOIL in reverse. The x^2 resulted from x times x, which suggests that the first term of each binomial factor is x. Next, we look for numbers p and q such that

$$x^2 + 7x + 10 = (x + p)(x + q).$$

To get the middle term and the last term of the trinomial, we need two numbers, p and q, whose product is 10 and whose sum is 7. Those numbers are 2 and 5. Thus the factorization is

$$(x + 2)(x + 5).$$

Check: $(x + 2)(x + 5) = x^2 + 5x + 2x + 10$
$$= x^2 + 7x + 10.$$

STUDENT NOTES

One way to approach finding the numbers p and q is to think of filling in a diamond:

Since $2 \cdot 5 = 10$ and $2 + 5 = 7$, the numbers we want are 2 and 5.

EXAMPLE 1

A GEOMETRIC APPROACH TO EXAMPLE 1

In Section 5.5, we saw that the product of two binomials can be regarded as the sum of the areas of four rectangles (see p. 322). Thus we can regard the factoring of $x^2 + 5x + 6$ as a search for p and q so that the sum of areas A, B, C, and D is $x^2 + 5x + 6$.

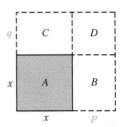

Note that area D is simply the product of p and q. In order for area D to be 6, p and q must be either 1 and 6 or 2 and 3. We illustrate both below.

When p and q are 1 and 6, the total area is $x^2 + 7x + 6$, but when p and q are 2 and 3, as shown on the right, the total area is $x^2 + 5x + 6$, as desired. Thus the factorization of $x^2 + 5x + 6$ is $(x + 2)(x + 3)$.

Factor to form an equivalent expression: $x^2 + 5x + 6$.

SOLUTION   Think of FOIL in reverse. The first term of each factor is x:

$$(x + \quad)(x + \quad).$$

To complete the factorization, we need a constant term for each binomial. The constants must have a product of 6 and a sum of 5. We list some pairs of numbers that multiply to 6 and then check the sum of each pair of factors.

Pairs of Factors of 6	Sums of Factors
1, 6	7
2, 3	5 ← The numbers we seek are 2 and 3.
−1, −6	−7
−2, −3	−5

Every pair has a product of 6. *One* pair has a sum of 5.

Since

$$2 \cdot 3 = 6 \quad \text{and} \quad 2 + 3 = 5,$$

the factorization of $x^2 + 5x + 6$ is $(x + 2)(x + 3)$.

Check: $(x + 2)(x + 3) = x^2 + 3x + 2x + 6$
$$= x^2 + 5x + 6.$$

Thus, $(x + 2)(x + 3)$ is a product that is equivalent to $x^2 + 5x + 6$.

Note that since 5 and 6 are both positive, when factoring $x^2 + 5x + 6$ we need not consider negative factors of 6. Note too that changing the signs of the factors changes only the sign of the sum (see the table above).

TRY EXERCISE 7

At the beginning of this section, we considered the multiplication $(x - 2)(x - 5)$. For this product, the resulting trinomial, $x^2 - 7x + 10$, has a positive constant term but a negative coefficient of x. This is because the *product* of two negative numbers is always positive, whereas the *sum* of two negative numbers is always negative.

To Factor $x^2 + bx + c$ When c Is Positive

When the constant term c of a trinomial is positive, look for two numbers with the same sign. Select pairs of numbers with the sign of b, the coefficient of the middle term.

$$x^2 - 7x + 10 = (x - 2)(x - 5);$$

$$x^2 + 7x + 10 = (x + 2)(x + 5)$$

EXAMPLE **2**   Factor: $y^2 - 8y + 12$.

SOLUTION   Since the constant term is positive and the coefficient of the middle term is negative, we look for a factorization of 12 in which both factors are negative. Their sum must be -8.

STUDENT NOTES

It is important to be able to list *all* the pairs of factors of a number. See Example 1 on p. 21 for an organized approach for listing pairs of factors.

Pairs of Factors of 12	Sums of Factors
$-1, -12$	-13
$-2, \;\; -6$	-8 ← We need a sum of -8.
$-3, \;\; -4$	-7

The numbers we need are -2 and -6.

The factorization of $y^2 - 8y + 12$ is $(y - 2)(y - 6)$. The check is left to the student.

TRY EXERCISE   13

When the Constant Term Is Negative

As we saw in two of the multiplications at the start of this section, the product of two binomials can have a negative constant term:

$$(x + 3)(x - 7) = x^2 - 4x - 21$$

and

$$(x - 3)(x + 7) = x^2 + 4x - 21.$$

It is important to note that when the signs of the constants in the binomials are reversed, only the sign of the middle term of the trinomial changes.

EXAMPLE **3**   Factor: $x^2 - 8x - 20$.

SOLUTION   The constant term, -20, must be expressed as the product of a negative number and a positive number. Since the sum of these two numbers must be negative (specifically, -8), the negative number must have the greater absolute value.

Pairs of Factors of -20	Sums of Factors
$1, -20$	-19
$2, -10$	-8 ← The numbers we need are 2 and -10.
$4, \;\; -5$	-1
$5, \;\; -4$	1
$10, -2$	8
$20, \;\; -1$	19

Because in these three pairs, the positive number has the greater absolute value, these sums are all positive. For this problem, these pairs can be eliminated even before calculating the sum.

The numbers that we are looking for are 2 and -10.

Check: $(x + 2)(x - 10) = x^2 - 10x + 2x - 20$
$$= x^2 - 8x - 20.$$

The factorization of $x^2 - 8x - 20$ is $(x + 2)(x - 10)$.

TRY EXERCISE   21

> **To Factor $x^2 + bx + c$ When c Is Negative**
>
> When the constant term c of a trinomial is negative, look for a positive number and a negative number that multiply to c. Select pairs of numbers for which the number with the larger absolute value has the same sign as b, the coefficient of the middle term.
>
> $$x^2 - 4x - 21 = (x + 3)(x - 7);$$
>
> $$x^2 + 4x - 21 = (x - 3)(x + 7)$$

EXAMPLE 4

Factor: $t^2 - 24 + 5t$.

SOLUTION   It helps to first write the trinomial in descending order: $t^2 + 5t - 24$. The factorization of the constant term, -24, must have one factor positive and one factor negative. The sum must be 5, so the positive factor must have the larger absolute value. Thus we consider only pairs of factors in which the positive factor has the larger absolute value.

Pairs of Factors of -24	Sums of Factors	
$-1, 24$	23	
$-2, 12$	10	
$-3,\ 8$	5 $\leftarrow$	—— The numbers we need are
$-4,\ 6$	2	-3 and 8.

The factorization is $(t - 3)(t + 8)$. The check is left to the student.

TRY EXERCISE 23

Polynomials in two or more variables, such as $a^2 + 4ab - 21b^2$, are factored in a similar manner.

EXAMPLE 5

Factor: $a^2 + 4ab - 21b^2$.

SOLUTION   It may help to write the trinomial in the equivalent form

$$a^2 + 4ba - 21b^2.$$

We now regard $-21b^2$ as the "constant" term and $4b$ as the "coefficient" of a. Then we try to express $-21b^2$ as a product of two factors whose sum is $4b$. Those factors are $-3b$ and $7b$.

Check: $(a - 3b)(a + 7b) = a^2 + 7ab - 3ba - 21b^2$
$$= a^2 + 4ab - 21b^2.$$

The factorization of $a^2 + 4ab - 21b^2$ is $(a - 3b)(a + 7b)$.

TRY EXERCISE 55

Prime Polynomials

EXAMPLE   6

Factor: $x^2 - x + 5$.

SOLUTION   Since 5 has very few factors, we can easily check all possibilities.

Pairs of Factors of 5	Sums of Factors
5, 1	6
−5, −1	−6

Since there are no factors whose sum is −1, the polynomial is *not* factorable into binomials.

TRY EXERCISE ▶ 37

In this text, a polynomial like $x^2 - x + 5$ that cannot be factored further is said to be **prime**. In more advanced courses, other types of numbers are considered. There, polynomials like $x^2 - x + 5$ can be factored and are not considered prime.

Often factoring requires two or more steps. Remember, when told to factor, we should *factor completely*. This means that the final factorization should contain only prime polynomials.

EXAMPLE   7

Factor: $-2x^3 + 20x^2 - 50x$.

SOLUTION   *Always* look first for a common factor. Since the leading coefficient is negative, we begin by factoring out $-2x$:

$$-2x^3 + 20x^2 - 50x = -2x(x^2 - 10x + 25).$$

STUDENT NOTES

Whenever a new set of parentheses is created while factoring, check the expression inside the parentheses to see if it can be factored further.

Now consider $x^2 - 10x + 25$. Since the constant term is positive and the coefficient of the middle term is negative, we look for a factorization of 25 in which both factors are negative. Their sum must be −10.

Pairs of Factors of 25	Sums of Factors
−25, −1	−26
−5, −5	−10 ←

The numbers we need are −5 and −5.

The factorization of $x^2 - 10x + 25$ is $(x - 5)(x - 5)$, or $(x - 5)^2$.

CAUTION!   When factoring involves more than one step, be careful to write out the *entire* factorization.

Check: $-2x(x - 5)(x - 5) = -2x[x^2 - 10x + 25]$ Multiplying binomials
$$= -2x^3 + 20x^2 - 50x.$$ Using the distributive law

The factorization of $-2x^3 + 20x^2 - 50x$ is $-2x(x - 5)(x - 5)$, or $-2x(x - 5)^2$.

TRY EXERCISE ▶ 27

Once any common factors have been factored out, the following summary can be used to factor $x^2 + bx + c$.

> To Factor $x^2 + bx + c$
>
> **1.** Find a pair of factors that have *c* as their product and *b* as their sum.
>
> **a)** If *c* is positive, both factors will have the same sign as *b*.
> **b)** If *c* is negative, one factor will be positive and the other will be negative. Select the factors such that the factor with the larger absolute value has the same sign as *b*.
>
> **2.** Check by multiplying.

Note that each polynomial has a unique factorization (except for the order in which the factors are written).

6.2 EXERCISE SET

↪ *Concept Reinforcement* *For Exercises 1–6, assume that a polynomial of the form $x^2 + bx + c$ can be factored as $(x + p)(x + q)$. Complete each sentence by replacing each blank with either "positive" or "negative."*

1. If *b* is positive and *c* is positive, then *p* will be _____ and *q* will be _____.

2. If *b* is negative and *c* is positive, then *p* will be _____ and *q* will be _____.

3. If *p* is negative and *q* is negative, then *b* must be _____ and *c* must be _____.

4. If *p* is positive and *q* is positive, then *b* must be _____ and *c* must be _____.

5. If *b*, *c*, and *p* are all negative, then *q* must be _____.

6. If *b* and *c* are negative and *p* is positive, then *q* must be _____.

Factor completely. Remember to look first for a common factor. Check by multiplying. If a polynomial is prime, state this.

7. $x^2 + 8x + 16$

8. $x^2 + 9x + 20$

9. $x^2 + 11x + 10$

10. $y^2 + 8y + 7$

11. $x^2 + 10x + 21$

12. $x^2 + 6x + 9$

13. $t^2 - 9t + 14$

14. $a^2 - 9a + 20$

15. $b^2 - 5b + 4$

16. $x^2 - 10x + 25$

17. $a^2 - 7a + 12$

18. $z^2 - 8z + 7$

19. $d^2 - 7d + 10$

20. $x^2 - 8x + 15$

21. $x^2 - 2x - 15$

22. $x^2 - x - 42$

23. $x^2 + 2x - 15$

24. $x^2 + x - 42$

25. $2x^2 - 14x - 36$

26. $3y^2 - 9y - 84$

27. $-x^3 + 6x^2 + 16x$

28. $-x^3 + x^2 + 42x$

29. $4y - 45 + y^2$

30. $7x - 60 + x^2$

31. $x^2 - 72 + 6x$

32. $-2x - 99 + x^2$

33. $-5b^2 - 35b + 150$

34. $-c^4 - c^3 + 56c^2$

35. $x^5 - x^4 - 2x^3$

36. $2a^2 - 4a - 70$

37. $x^2 + 5x + 10$

38. $x^2 + 11x + 18$

39. $32 + 12t + t^2$

40. $y^2 - y + 1$

41. $x^2 + 20x + 99$

42. $x^2 + 20x + 100$

43. $3x^3 - 63x^2 - 300x$

44. $2x^3 - 40x^2 + 192x$

45. $-2x^2 + 42x + 144$

56. $-4x^2 - 40x - 100$

47. $y^2 - 20y + 96$

48. $144 - 25t + t^2$

49. $-a^6 - 9a^5 + 90a^4$

50. $-a^4 - a^3 + 132a^2$

51. $t^2 + \frac{2}{3}t + \frac{1}{9}$

52. $x^2 - \frac{2}{5}x + \frac{1}{25}$

53. $11 + w^2 - 4w$

54. $6 + p^2 + 2p$

55. $p^2 - 7pq + 10q^2$

56. $a^2 - 2ab - 3b^2$

57. $m^2 + 5mn + 5n^2$

58. $x^2 - 11xy + 24y^2$

59. $s^2 - 4st - 12t^2$

60. $b^2 + 8bc - 20c^2$

61. $6a^{10} + 30a^9 - 84a^8$

62. $5a^8 - 20a^7 - 25a^6$

63. Without multiplying $(x - 17)(x - 18)$, explain why it cannot possibly be a factorization of $x^2 + 35x + 306$.

64. Shari factors $x^3 - 8x^2 + 15x$ as $(x^2 - 5x)(x - 3)$. Is she wrong? Why or why not? What advice would you offer?

Skill Review

To prepare for Section 6.3, review multiplying binomials using FOIL (Section 5.6).

Multiply. [5.6]

65. $(2x + 3)(3x + 4)$

66. $(2x + 3)(3x - 4)$

67. $(2x - 3)(3x + 4)$

68. $(2x - 3)(3x - 4)$

69. $(5x - 1)(x - 7)$

70. $(x + 6)(3x - 5)$

Synthesis

71. When searching for a factorization, why do we list pairs of numbers with the correct *product* instead of pairs of numbers with the correct *sum*?

72. When factoring $x^2 + bx + c$ with a large value of c, Riley begins by writing out the prime factorization of c. What is the advantage of doing this?

73. Find all integers b for which $a^2 + ba - 50$ can be factored.

74. Find all integers m for which $y^2 + my + 50$ can be factored.

Factor completely.

75. $y^2 - 0.2y - 0.08$

76. $x^2 + \frac{1}{2}x - \frac{3}{16}$

77. $-\frac{1}{3}a^3 + \frac{1}{3}a^2 + 2a$

78. $-a^7 + \frac{25}{7}a^5 + \frac{30}{7}a^6$

79. $x^{2m} + 11x^m + 28$

80. $-t^{2n} + 7t^n - 10$

Aha! **81.** $(a + 1)x^2 + (a + 1)3x + (a + 1)2$

82. $ax^2 - 5x^2 + 8ax - 40x - (a - 5)9$ (*Hint:* See Exercise 81.)

83. Find the volume of a cube if its surface area is $6x^2 + 36x + 54$ square meters.

Find a polynomial in factored form for the shaded area in each figure. (Use π in your answers where appropriate.)

84.

85.

86.

87.

88.

89.

90. A census taker asks a woman, "How many children do you have?"

"Three," she answers.

"What are their ages?"

She responds, "The product of their ages is 36. The sum of their ages is the house number next door."

The math-savvy census taker walks next door, reads the house number, appears puzzled, and returns to the woman, asking, "Is there something you forgot to tell me?"

"Oh yes," says the woman. "I'm sorry. The oldest child is at the park."

The census taker records the three ages, thanks the woman for her time, and leaves.

How old is each child? Explain how you reached this conclusion. (*Hint:* Consider factorizations.)

Source: Adapted from Anita Harnadek, *Classroom Quickies.* Pacific Grove, CA: Critical Thinking Press and Software

CORNER

Visualizing Factoring

Focus: Visualizing factoring
Time: 20–30 minutes
Group size: 3
Materials: Graph paper and scissors

The product $(x + 2)(x + 3)$ can be regarded as the area of a rectangle with width $x + 2$ and length $x + 3$. Similarly, factoring a polynomial like $x^2 + 5x + 6$ can be thought of as determining the length and the width of a rectangle that has area $x^2 + 5x + 6$. This is the approach used below.

ACTIVITY

1. **a)** To factor $x^2 + 11x + 10$ geometrically, the group needs to cut out shapes like those below to represent x^2, $11x$, and 10. This can be done by either tracing the figures below or by selecting a value for x, say 4, and using the squares on the graph paper to cut out the following:

   x^2:   Using the value selected for x, cut out a square that is x units on each side.
   $11x$: Using the value selected for x, cut out a rectangle that is 1 unit wide and x units long. Repeat this to form 11 such strips.
   10:    Cut out two rectangles with whole-number dimensions and an area of 10. One should be 2 units by 5 units and the other 1 unit by 10 units.

   b) The group, working together, should then attempt to use one of the two rectangles with area 10, along with all of the other shapes, to piece together one large rectangle. Only one of the rectangles with area 10 will work.

   c) From the large rectangle formed in part (b), use the length and the width to determine the factorization of $x^2 + 11x + 10$. Where do the dimensions of the rectangle representing 10 appear in the factorization?

2. Repeat step (1) above, but this time use the other rectangle with area 10, and use only 7 of the 11 strips, along with the x^2-shape. Piece together the shapes to form one large rectangle. What factorization do the dimensions of this rectangle suggest?

3. Cut out rectangles with area 12 and use the above approach to factor $x^2 + 8x + 12$. What dimensions should be used for the rectangle with area 12?

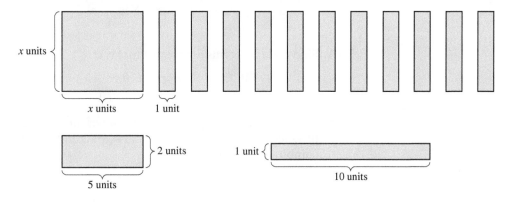

6.3   Factoring Trinomials of the Type $ax^2 + bx + c$

Factoring with FOIL ▪ The Grouping Method

In Section 6.2, we learned a FOIL-based method for factoring trinomials of the type $x^2 + bx + c$. Now we learn to factor trinomials in which the leading, or x^2, coefficient is not 1. First we will use another FOIL-based method and then we will use an alternative method that involves factoring by grouping. Use the method that you prefer or the one recommended by your instructor.

Factoring with FOIL

Before factoring trinomials of the type $ax^2 + bx + c$, consider the following:

$$\overset{\text{F}\quad\text{O}\quad\text{I}\quad\text{L}}{(2x + 5)(3x + 4)} = 6x^2 + 8x + 15x + 20$$

$$= 6x^2 + \quad 23x \quad + 20.$$

To factor $6x^2 + 23x + 20$, we could reverse the multiplication and look for two binomials whose product is this trinomial. We see from the multiplication above that:

- the product of the First terms must be $6x^2$;
- the product of the Outer terms plus the product of the Inner terms must be $23x$; and
- the product of the Last terms must be 20.

How can such a factorization be found without first seeing the corresponding multiplication? Our first approach relies on trial and error and FOIL.

To Factor $ax^2 + bx + c$ Using FOIL

1. Make certain that all common factors have been removed. If any remain, factor out the largest common factor.
2. Find two First terms whose product is ax^2:

$$(\ x + \ )(\ x + \ ) = ax^2 + bx + c.$$
$$\underset{\text{FOIL}}{\underline{\qquad\qquad}}$$

3. Find two Last terms whose product is c:

$$(\ x + \ )(\ x + \ ) = ax^2 + bx + c.$$
$$\underset{\text{FOIL}}{\underline{\qquad\qquad\qquad}}$$

4. Check by multiplying to see if the sum of the Outer and Inner products is bx. If necessary, repeat steps 2 and 3 until the correct combination is found.

$$(\ x + \ )(\ x + \ ) = ax^2 + bx + c.$$
$$\underset{\text{FOIL}}{\underline{\qquad\text{O}\qquad}}$$

If no correct combination exists, state that the polynomial is prime.

EXAMPLE   **1**   Factor: $3x^2 - 10x - 8$.

SOLUTION

1. First, check for a common factor. In this case, there is none (other than 1 or −1).
2. Find two **F**irst terms whose product is $3x^2$.
   The only possibilities for the **F**irst terms are $3x$ and x:

   $$(3x + \quad)(x + \quad).$$

3. Find two **L**ast terms whose product is −8. There are four pairs of factors of −8 and each can be listed in two ways:

   $$\begin{array}{ccc}
   -1, \quad 8 & & 8, -1 \\
   1, -8 & \text{and} & -8, \quad 1 \\
   -2, \quad 4 & & 4, -2 \\
   2, -4 & & -4, \quad 2.
   \end{array}$$

   Important! Since the First terms are not identical, we must consider the pairs of factors in both orders.

4. Knowing that all **F**irst and **L**ast products will check, systematically inspect the **O**uter and **I**nner products resulting from steps (2) and (3). Look for the combination in which the sum of the products is the middle term, $-10x$. Our search ends as soon as the correct combination is found. If none exists, we state that the polynomial is prime.

Pair of Factors	Corresponding Trial	Product	
−1, 8	$(3x - 1)(x + 8)$	$3x^2 + 24x - x - 8$ $= 3x^2 + 23x - 8$	Wrong middle term
1, −8	$(3x + 1)(x - 8)$	$3x^2 - 24x + x - 8$ $= 3x^2 - 23x - 8$	Wrong middle term
−2, 4	$(3x - 2)(x + 4)$	$3x^2 + 12x - 2x - 8$ $= 3x^2 + 10x - 8$	Wrong middle term
2, −4	$(3x + 2)(x - 4)$	$3x^2 - 12x + 2x - 8$ $= 3x^2 - 10x - 8$	Correct middle term!
8, −1	$(3x + 8)(x - 1)$	$3x^2 - 3x + 8x - 8$ $= 3x^2 + 5x - 8$	Wrong middle term
−8, 1	$(3x - 8)(x + 1)$	$3x^2 + 3x - 8x - 8$ $= 3x^2 - 5x - 8$	Wrong middle term
4, −2	$(3x + 4)(x - 2)$	$3x^2 - 6x + 4x - 8$ $= 3x^2 - 2x - 8$	Wrong middle term
−4, 2	$(3x - 4)(x + 2)$	$3x^2 + 6x - 4x - 8$ $= 3x^2 + 2x - 8$	Wrong middle term

The correct factorization is $(3x + 2)(x - 4)$.

TRY EXERCISE 5

Two observations can be made from Example 1. First, we listed all possible trials even though we generally stop after finding the correct factorization. We did this to show that **each trial differs only in the middle term of the product**. Second, note that as in Section 6.2, **only the sign of the middle term changes when the signs in the binomials are reversed**.

EXAMPLE 2   Factor: $10x^2 + 37x + 7$.

SOLUTION

1. There is no factor (other than 1 or -1) common to all three terms.

2. Because $10x^2$ factors as $10x \cdot x$ or $5x \cdot 2x$, we have two possibilities:

$$(10x +\ \ )(x +\ \ ) \quad \text{or} \quad (5x +\ \ )(2x +\ \ ).$$

3. There are two pairs of factors of 7 and each can be listed in two ways:

$$\begin{matrix} 1, & 7 \\ -1, & -7 \end{matrix} \quad \text{and} \quad \begin{matrix} 7, & 1 \\ -7, & -1. \end{matrix}$$

4. Look for **O**uter and **I**nner products for which the sum is the middle term. Because all coefficients in $10x^2 + 37x + 7$ are positive, we need consider only those combinations involving positive factors of 7.

Trial	*Product*	
$(10x + 1)(x + 7)$	$10x^2 + 70x + 1x + 7$	
	$= 10x^2 + 71x + 7$	Wrong middle term
$(10x + 7)(x + 1)$	$10x^2 + 10x + 7x + 7$	
	$= 10x^2 + 17x + 7$	Wrong middle term
$(5x + 7)(2x + 1)$	$10x^2 + 5x + 14x + 7$	
	$= 10x^2 + 19x + 7$	Wrong middle term
$(5x + 1)(2x + 7)$	$10x^2 + 35x + 2x + 7$	
	$= 10x^2 + 37x + 7$	Correct middle term!

The correct factorization is $(5x + 1)(2x + 7)$.

> **TRY EXERCISE** 9

A GEOMETRIC APPROACH TO EXAMPLE 2

The factoring of $10x^2 + 37x + 7$ can be regarded as a search for r and s so that the sum of areas A, B, C, and D is $10x^2 + 37x + 7$.

Because A must be $10x^2$, the product rs must be 10. Only when r is 2 and s is 5 will the sum of areas B and C be $37x$ (see below).

EXAMPLE 3   Factor: $24x^3 - 76x^2 + 40x$.

SOLUTION

1. First, we factor out the largest common factor, $4x$:

$$4x(6x^2 - 19x + 10).$$

2. Next, we factor $6x^2 - 19x + 10$. Since $6x^2$ can be factored as $3x \cdot 2x$ or $6x \cdot x$, we have two possibilities:

$$(3x +\ \ )(2x +\ \ ) \quad \text{or} \quad (6x +\ \ )(x +\ \ ).$$

3. There are four pairs of factors of 10 and each can be listed in two ways:

$$\begin{matrix} 1, & 10 \\ -1, & -10 \\ 2, & 5 \\ -2, & -5 \end{matrix} \quad \text{and} \quad \begin{matrix} 10, & 1 \\ -10, & -1 \\ 5, & 2 \\ -5, & -2. \end{matrix}$$

4. The two possibilities from step (2) and the eight possibilities from step (3) give $2 \cdot 8$, or 16 possibilities for factorizations. With careful consideration,

we can eliminate some possibilities without multiplying. Since the sign of the middle term, $-19x$, is negative, but the sign of the last term, 10, is positive, the two factors of 10 must both be negative. This means only four pairings from step (3) need be considered. We first try these factors with $(3x + \quad)(2x + \quad)$, looking for **O**uter and **I**nner products for which the sum is $-19x$. If none gives the correct factorization, then we will consider $(6x + \quad)(x + \quad)$.

Trial	*Product*	
$(3x - 1)(2x - 10)$	$6x^2 - 30x - 2x + 10$	
	$= 6x^2 - 32x + 10$	Wrong middle term
$(3x - 10)(2x - 1)$	$6x^2 - 3x - 20x + 10$	
	$= 6x^2 - 23x + 10$	Wrong middle term
$(3x - 2)(2x - 5)$	$6x^2 - 15x - 4x + 10$	
	$= 6x^2 - 19x + 10$	Correct middle term!
$(3x - 5)(2x - 2)$	$6x^2 - 6x - 10x + 10$	
	$= 6x^2 - 16x + 10$	Wrong middle term

Since we have a correct factorization, we need not consider

$$(6x + \quad)(x + \quad).$$

Look again at the possibility $(3x - 5)(2x - 2)$. Without multiplying, we can reject such a possibility. To see why, note that

$$(3x - 5)(2x - 2) = (3x - 5)2(x - 1).$$

The expression $2x - 2$ has a common factor, 2. But we removed the *largest* common factor in step (1). If $2x - 2$ were one of the factors, then 2 would be *another* common factor in addition to the original, $4x$. Thus, $(2x - 2)$ cannot be part of the factorization of $6x^2 - 19x + 10$. Similar reasoning can be used to reject $(3x - 1)(2x - 10)$ as a possible factorization.

Once the largest common factor is factored out, none of the remaining factors can have a common factor.

The factorization of $6x^2 - 19x + 10$ is $(3x - 2)(2x - 5)$, but do not forget the common factor! The factorization of $24x^3 - 76x^2 + 40x$ is

$$4x(3x - 2)(2x - 5).$$

> TRY EXERCISE ▸ 15

STUDENT NOTES ───────

Keep your work organized so that you can see what you have already considered. For example, when factoring $6x^2 - 19x + 10$, we can list all possibilities and cross out those in which a common factor appears:

$(3x - 1)(2x - 10)$
$(3x - 10)(2x - 1)$
$(3x - 2)(2x - 5)$
$(3x - 5)(2x - 2)$
$(6x - 1)(x - 10)$
$(6x - 10)(x - 1)$
$(6x - 2)(x - 5)$
$(6x - 5)(x - 2)$

By being organized and not erasing, we can see that there are only four possible factorizations.
─────────────────────

Tips for Factoring $ax^2 + bx + c$

To factor $ax^2 + bx + c\,(a > 0)$:

- Make sure that any common factor has been factored out.
- Once the largest common factor has been factored out of the original trinomial, no binomial factor can contain a common factor (other than 1 or -1).
- If c is positive, then the signs in both binomial factors must match the sign of b.
- Reversing the signs in the binomials reverses the sign of the middle term of their product.
- Organize your work so that you can keep track of which possibilities you have checked.
- Remember to include the largest common factor—if there is one—in the final factorization.
- Always check by multiplying.

EXAMPLE 4

Factor: $10x + 8 - 3x^2$.

SOLUTION   An important problem-solving strategy is to find a way to make new problems look like problems we already know how to solve. The factoring tips above apply only to trinomials of the form $ax^2 + bx + c$, with $a > 0$. This leads us to rewrite $10x + 8 - 3x^2$ in descending order:

$$10x + 8 - 3x^2 = -3x^2 + 10x + 8.$$ Using the commutative law to write descending order

Although $-3x^2 + 10x + 8$ looks similar to the trinomials we have factored, the tips above require a positive leading coefficient. This can be found by factoring out -1:

$$-3x^2 + 10x + 8 = -1(3x^2 - 10x - 8)$$ Factoring out -1 changes the signs of the coefficients.

$$= -1(3x + 2)(x - 4).$$ Using the result from Example 1

The factorization of $10x + 8 - 3x^2$ is $-1(3x + 2)(x - 4)$.   **TRY EXERCISE** 31

EXAMPLE 5

Factor: $6r^2 - 13rs - 28s^2$.

SOLUTION   In order for the product of the first terms to be $6r^2$ and the product of the last terms to be $-28s^2$, the binomial factors will be of the form

$$(\ r + \ s)(\ r + \ s).$$

We verify that no common factor exists and then examine the first term, $6r^2$. There are two possibilities:

$$(2r + \ )(3r + \ ) \quad \text{or} \quad (6r + \ )(r + \ ).$$

The last term, $-28s^2$, has the following pairs of factors:

$$
\begin{array}{llcll}
s, & -28s & & -28s, & s \\
-s, & 28s & & 28s, & -s \\
2s, & -14s & & -14s, & 2s \\
-2s, & 14s & \text{and} & 14s, & -2s \\
4s, & -7s & & -7s, & 4s \\
-4s, & 7s & & 7s, & -4s.
\end{array}
$$

Note that listing the pairs of factors of $-28s^2$ is just like listing the pairs of factors of -28, except that each factor also contains a factor of s.

Some trials, like $(2r + 28s)(3r - s)$ and $(2r + 14s)(3r - 2s)$, cannot be correct because both $(2r + 28s)$ and $(2r + 14s)$ contain a common factor, 2. We try $(2r + 7s)(3r - 4s)$:

$$(2r + 7s)(3r - 4s) = 6r^2 - 8rs + 21rs - 28s^2$$
$$= 6r^2 + 13rs - 28s^2.$$

Our trial is incorrect, but only because of the sign of the middle term. To correctly factor $6r^2 - 13rs - 28s^2$, we simply change the signs in the binomials:

$$(2r - 7s)(3r + 4s) = 6r^2 + 8rs - 21rs - 28s^2$$
$$= 6r^2 - 13rs - 28s^2.$$

The correct factorization of $6r^2 - 13rs - 28s^2$ is $(2r - 7s)(3r + 4s)$.

TRY EXERCISE 67

The Grouping Method

Another method of factoring trinomials of the type $ax^2 + bx + c$ is known as the *grouping method.* The grouping method relies on rewriting $ax^2 + bx + c$ in the form $ax^2 + px + qx + c$ and then factoring by grouping. To develop this method, consider the following*:

$$(2x + 5)(3x + 4) = 2x \cdot 3x + 2x \cdot 4 + 5 \cdot 3x + 5 \cdot 4 \qquad \text{Using FOIL}$$
$$= 2 \cdot 3 \cdot x^2 + 2 \cdot 4x + 5 \cdot 3x + 5 \cdot 4$$
$$= 2 \cdot 3 \cdot x^2 + (2 \cdot 4 + 5 \cdot 3)x + 5 \cdot 4$$

$$\underset{\underset{a}{\downarrow}}{\uparrow} \qquad\qquad \underset{\underset{b}{\downarrow}}{\uparrow} \qquad\qquad \underset{\underset{c}{\downarrow}}{\uparrow}$$

$$= 6x^2 \quad + \quad 23x \quad + \quad 20.$$

Note that reversing these steps shows that $6x^2 + 23x + 20$ can be rewritten as $6x^2 + 8x + 15x + 20$ and then factored by grouping. Note that the numbers that add to b (in this case, $2 \cdot 4$ and $5 \cdot 3$) also multiply to ac (in this case, $2 \cdot 3 \cdot 5 \cdot 4$).

To Factor $ax^2 + bx + c$, Using the Grouping Method

1. Factor out the largest common factor, if one exists.
2. Multiply the leading coefficient a and the constant c.
3. Find a pair of factors of ac whose sum is b.
4. Rewrite the middle term, bx, as a sum or a difference using the factors found in step (3).
5. Factor by grouping.
6. Include any common factor from step (1) and check by multiplying.

EXAMPLE   6   Factor: $3x^2 - 10x - 8$.

SOLUTION

1. First, we note that there is no common factor (other than 1 or -1).

2. We multiply the leading coefficient, 3, and the constant, -8:

   $$3(-8) = -24.$$

3. We next look for a factorization of -24 in which the sum of the factors is the coefficient of the middle term, -10.

Pairs of Factors of -24	Sums of Factors
1, -24	-23
-1, 24	23
2, -12	-10
-2, 12	10
3, -8	-5
-3, 8	5
4, -6	-2
-4, 6	2

$\leftarrow$ — $2 + (-12) = -10$

We normally stop listing pairs of factors once we have found the one we are after.

---

*This discussion was inspired by a lecture given by Irene Doo at Austin Community College.

4. Next, we express the middle term as a sum or a difference using the factors found in step (3):

$$-10x = 2x - 12x.$$

5. We now factor by grouping as follows:

$$3x^2 - 10x - 8 = 3x^2 + 2x - 12x - 8 \qquad \text{Substituting } 2x - 12x \\ \text{for } -10x. \text{ We could also} \\ \text{use } -12x + 2x.$$

$$= x(3x + 2) - 4(3x + 2) \qquad \text{Factoring by grouping;} \\ \text{see Section 6.1}$$

$$= (3x + 2)(x - 4). \qquad \text{Factoring out the common} \\ \text{factor, } 3x + 2$$

6. *Check:* $(3x + 2)(x - 4) = 3x^2 - 12x + 2x - 8 = 3x^2 - 10x - 8.$

The factorization of $3x^2 - 10x - 8$ is $(3x + 2)(x - 4)$.   **TRY EXERCISE** 51

EXAMPLE 7   Factor: $8x^3 + 22x^2 - 6x$.

SOLUTION

1. We factor out the largest common factor, $2x$:

$$8x^3 + 22x^2 - 6x = 2x(4x^2 + 11x - 3).$$

2. To factor $4x^2 + 11x - 3$ by grouping, we multiply the leading coefficient, 4, and the constant term, -3:

$$4(-3) = -12.$$

3. We next look for factors of -12 that add to 11.

Pairs of Factors of -12	Sums of Factors
1, -12	-11
-1, 12	11 ←
.	.
.	.
.	.

Since $-1 + 12 = 11$, there is no need to list other pairs of factors.

4. We then rewrite the $11x$ in $4x^2 + 11x - 3$ using

$$11x = -1x + 12x, \quad \text{or} \quad 11x = 12x - 1x.$$

5. Next, we factor by grouping:

$$4x^2 + 11x - 3 = 4x^2 - 1x + 12x - 3 \qquad \text{Rewriting the middle} \\ \text{term; } 12x - 1x \text{ could also} \\ \text{be used.}$$

$$= x(4x - 1) + 3(4x - 1) \qquad \text{Factoring by grouping.} \\ \text{Note the common factor,} \\ 4x - 1.$$

$$= (4x - 1)(x + 3). \qquad \text{Factoring out the} \\ \text{common factor}$$

6. The factorization of $4x^2 + 11x - 3$ is $(4x - 1)(x + 3)$. But don't forget the common factor, $2x$. The factorization of the original trinomial is

$$2x(4x - 1)(x + 3).$$ **TRY EXERCISE** 57

6.3   **EXERCISE SET**

↪ *Concept Reinforcement*   *In each of Exercises 1–4, match the polynomial with the correct factorization from the column on the right.*

1. ____ $12x^2 + 16x - 3$ a) $(7x - 1)(2x + 3)$

2. ____ $14x^2 + 19x - 3$ b) $(6x + 1)(2x - 3)$

3. ____ $14x^2 - 19x - 3$ c) $(6x - 1)(2x + 3)$

4. ____ $12x^2 - 16x - 3$ d) $(7x + 1)(2x - 3)$

Factor completely. If a polynomial is prime, state this.

5. $2x^2 + 7x - 4$ 6. $3x^2 + x - 4$

7. $3x^2 - 17x - 6$ 8. $5x^2 - 19x - 4$

9. $4t^2 + 12t + 5$ 10. $6t^2 + 17t + 7$

11. $15a^2 - 14a + 3$ 12. $10a^2 - 11a + 3$

13. $6x^2 + 17x + 12$ 14. $6x^2 + 19x + 10$

15. $6x^2 - 10x - 4$ 16. $5t^3 - 21t^2 + 18t$

17. $7t^3 + 15t^2 + 2t$ 18. $15t^2 + 20t - 75$

19. $10 - 23x + 12x^2$ 20. $-20 + 31x - 12x^2$

21. $-35x^2 - 34x - 8$ 22. $28x^2 + 38x - 6$

23. $4 + 6t^2 - 13t$ 24. $9 + 8t^2 - 18t$

25. $25x^2 + 40x + 16$ 26. $49t^2 + 42t + 9$

27. $20y^2 + 59y - 3$ 28. $25a^2 - 23a - 2$

29. $14x^2 + 73x + 45$ 30. $35x^2 - 57x - 44$

31. $-2x^2 + 15 + x$ 32. $2t^2 - 19 - 6t$

33. $-6x^2 - 33x - 15$ 34. $-12x^2 - 28x + 24$

35. $10a^2 - 8a - 18$ 36. $20y^2 - 25y + 5$

37. $12x^2 + 68x - 24$ 38. $6x^2 + 21x + 15$

39. $4x + 1 + 3x^2$ 40. $-9 + 18x^2 + 21x$

Factor. Use factoring by grouping even though it would seem reasonable to first combine like terms.

41. $x^2 + 3x - 2x - 6$ 42. $x^2 + 4x - 2x - 8$

43. $8t^2 - 6t - 28t + 21$

44. $35t^2 - 40t + 21t - 24$

45. $6x^2 + 4x + 15x + 10$ 46. $3x^2 - 2x + 3x - 2$

47. $2y^2 + 8y - y - 4$ 48. $7n^2 + 35n - n - 5$

49. $6a^2 - 8a - 3a + 4$ 50. $10a^2 - 4a - 5a + 2$

Factor completely. If a polynomial is prime, state this.

51. $16t^2 + 23t + 7$ 52. $9t^2 + 14t + 5$

53. $-9x^2 - 18x - 5$ 54. $-16x^2 - 32x - 7$

55. $10x^2 + 30x - 70$ 56. $10a^2 + 25a - 15$

57. $18x^3 + 21x^2 - 9x$ 58. $6x^3 - 4x^2 - 10x$

59. $89x + 64 + 25x^2$ 60. $47 - 42y + 9y^2$

61. $168x^3 + 45x^2 + 3x$

62. $144x^5 - 168x^4 + 48x^3$

63. $-14t^4 + 19t^3 + 3t^2$

64. $-70a^4 + 68a^3 - 16a^2$

65. $132y + 32y^2 - 54$ 66. $220y + 60y^2 - 225$

67. $2a^2 - 5ab + 2b^2$ 68. $3p^2 - 16pq - 12q^2$

69. $8s^2 + 22st + 14t^2$ 70. $10s^2 + 4st - 6t^2$

71. $27x^2 - 72xy + 48y^2$

72. $-30a^2 - 87ab - 30b^2$

73. $-24a^2 + 34ab - 12b^2$ 74. $15a^2 - 5ab - 20b^2$

75. $19x^3 - 3x^2 + 14x^4$ 76. $10x^5 - 2x^4 + 22x^3$

77. $18a^7 + 8a^6 + 9a^8$ 78. $40a^8 + 16a^7 + 25a^9$

 79. Asked to factor $2x^2 - 18x + 36$, Kay *incorrectly* answers
$$2x^2 - 18x + 36 = 2(x^2 + 9x + 18)$$
$$= 2(x + 3)(x + 6).$$
If this were a 10-point quiz question, how many points would you take off? Why?

 80. Asked to factor $4x^2 + 28x + 48$, Herb *incorrectly* answers
$$4x^2 + 28x + 48 = (2x + 6)(2x + 8)$$
$$= 2(x + 3)(x + 4).$$
If this were a 10-point quiz question, how many points would you take off? Why?

Skill Review

To prepare for Section 6.4, review the special products in Section 5.6.

Multiply. [5.6]

81. $(x - 2)^2$ 82. $(x + 2)^2$

83. $(x + 2)(x - 2)$ 84. $(5t - 3)^2$

85. $(4a + 1)^2$

86. $(2n + 7)(2n - 7)$

87. $(3c - 10)^2$

88. $(1 - 5a)^2$

89. $(8n + 3)(8n - 3)$

90. $(9 - y)(9 + y)$

95. $9a^2b^3 + 25ab^2 + 16$

96. $-9t^{10} - 12t^5 - 4$

97. $16t^{10} - 8t^5 + 1$

98. $9a^2b^2 - 15ab - 2$

99. $-15x^{2m} + 26x^m - 8$

Synthesis

100. $-20x^{2n} - 16x^n - 3$

91. Explain how you would prove to a fellow student that a given trinomial is prime.

101. $3a^{6n} - 2a^{3n} - 1$

102. $a^{2n+1} - 2a^{n+1} + a$

92. For the trinomial $ax^2 + bx + c$, suppose that a is the product of three different prime factors and c is the product of another two prime factors. How many possible factorizations (like those in Example 1) exist? Explain how you determined your answer.

103. $7(t - 3)^{2n} + 5(t - 3)^n - 2$

104. $3(a + 1)^{n+1}(a + 3)^2 - 5(a + 1)^n(a + 3)^3$

Factor. If a polynomial is prime, state this.

93. $18x^2y^2 - 3xy - 10$

94. $8x^2y^3 + 10xy^2 + 2y$

CONNECTING ↕ the CONCEPTS

In Sections 6.1–6.3, we have considered factoring out a common factor, factoring by grouping, and factoring with FOIL. The following is a good strategy to follow when you encounter a mixed set of factoring problems.

1. Factor out any common factor.
2. Try factoring by grouping for polynomials with four terms.
3. Try factoring with FOIL for trinomials. If the leading coefficient of the trinomial is not 1, you may instead try factoring by grouping.

Polynomial	Number of Terms	Factorization
$12y^5 - 6y^4 + 30y^2$	3	There is a common factor: $6y^2$. $12y^5 - 6y^4 + 30y^2 = 6y^2(2y^3 - y^2 + 5)$. The trinomial in the parentheses cannot be factored further.
$t^4 - 5t^3 - 3t + 15$	4	There is no common factor. We factor by grouping. $t^4 - 5t^3 - 3t + 15 = t^3(t - 5) - 3(t - 5)$ $= (t - 5)(t^3 - 3)$
$-4x^4 + 4x^3 + 80x^2$	3	There is a common factor: $-4x^2$. $-4x^4 + 4x^3 + 80x^2 = -4x^2(x^2 - x - 20)$ The trinomial in the parentheses can be factored: $-4x^4 + 4x^3 + 80x^2 = -4x^2(x^2 - x - 20)$ $= -4x^2(x + 4)(x - 5)$.
$10n^2 - 17n + 3$	3	There is no common factor. We factor with FOIL or by grouping. $10n^2 - 17n + 3 = (2n - 3)(5n - 1)$

MIXED REVIEW

Factor completely. If a polynomial is prime, state this.

1. $6x^5 - 18x^2$

2. $x^2 + 10x + 16$

3. $2x^2 + 13x - 7$

4. $x^3 + 3x^2 + 2x + 6$

5. $5x^2 + 40x - 100$

6. $x^2 - 2x - 5$

7. $7x^2y - 21xy - 28y$

8. $15a^4 - 27a^2b^2 + 21a^2b$

9. $b^2 - 14b + 49$

10. $12x^2 - x - 1$

11. $c^3 + c^2 - 4c - 4$

12. $2x^2 + 30x - 200$

13. $t^2 + t - 10$

14. $15d^2 - 30d + 75$

15. $15p^2 + 16pq + 4q^2$

16. $-2t^3 - 10t^2 - 12t$

17. $x^2 + 4x - 77$

18. $10c^2 + 20c + 10$

19. $5 + 3x - 2x^2$

20. $2m^3n - 10m^2n - 6mn + 30n$

6.4 Factoring Perfect-Square Trinomials and Differences of Squares

Recognizing Perfect-Square Trinomials ▪ Factoring Perfect-Square Trinomials ▪ Recognizing Differences of Squares ▪ Factoring Differences of Squares ▪ Factoring Completely

In Section 5.6, we studied special products of certain binomials. Reversing these rules provides shortcuts for factoring certain polynomials.

Recognizing Perfect-Square Trinomials

Some trinomials are squares of binomials. For example, $x^2 + 10x + 25$ is the square of the binomial $x + 5$, because

$$(x + 5)^2 = x^2 + 2 \cdot x \cdot 5 + 5^2 = x^2 + 10x + 25.$$

A trinomial that is the square of a binomial is called a **perfect-square trinomial**.
    In Section 5.6, we considered squaring binomials as a special-product rule:

$$(A + B)^2 = A^2 + 2AB + B^2;$$
$$(A - B)^2 = A^2 - 2AB + B^2.$$

Reading the right-hand sides first, we can use these equations to factor perfect-square trinomials. Note that in order for a trinomial to be the square of a binomial, it must have the following:

1. Two terms, A^2 and B^2, must be squares, such as

    $4, \quad x^2, \quad 81m^2, \quad 16t^2.$

2. Neither A^2 nor B^2 is being subtracted.

3. The remaining term is either $2 \cdot A \cdot B$ or $-2 \cdot A \cdot B$, where A and B are the square roots of A^2 and B^2.

STUDENT NOTES

If you're not already quick to recognize the squares that represent $1^2, 2^2, 3^2, \ldots, 12^2$, this would be a good time to memorize these numbers.

STUDY SKILLS

Fill in Your Blanks

Don't hesitate to write out any missing steps that you'd like to see included. For instance, in Example 1(c), we state (in red) that $16x^2$ is a square. To solidify your understanding, you may want to write $4x \cdot 4x = 16x^2$ in the margin of your text.

Determine whether each of the following is a perfect-square trinomial.

a) $x^2 + 6x + 9$ **b)** $t^2 - 8t - 9$ **c)** $16x^2 + 49 - 56x$

SOLUTION

a) To see if $x^2 + 6x + 9$ is a perfect-square trinomial, note that:

   1. Two terms, x^2 and 9, are squares.

   2. Neither x^2 nor 9 is being subtracted.

   3. The remaining term, $6x$, is $2 \cdot x \cdot 3$, where x and 3 are the square roots of x^2 and 9.

Thus, $x^2 + 6x + 9$ *is* a perfect-square trinomial.

b) To see if $t^2 - 8t - 9$ is a perfect-square trinomial, note that:

   1. Both t^2 and 9, are squares. But:

   2. Since 9 is being subtracted, $t^2 - 8t - 9$ *is not* a perfect-square trinomial.

c) To see if $16x^2 + 49 - 56x$ is a perfect-square trinomial, it helps to first write it in descending order:

$$16x^2 - 56x + 49.$$

Next, note that:

   1. Two terms, $16x^2$ and 49, are squares.

   2. There is no minus sign before $16x^2$ or 49.

   3. Twice the product of the square roots, $2 \cdot 4x \cdot 7$, is $56x$. The remaining term, $-56x$, is the opposite of this product.

Thus, $16x^2 + 49 - 56x$ *is* a perfect-square trinomial.   **TRY EXERCISE** 11

Factoring Perfect-Square Trinomials

Either of the factoring methods discussed in Section 6.3 can be used to factor perfect-square trinomials, but a faster method is to recognize the following patterns.

> ### Factoring a Perfect-Square Trinomial
> $$A^2 + 2AB + B^2 = (A + B)^2; \qquad A^2 - 2AB + B^2 = (A - B)^2$$

Each factorization uses the square roots of the squared terms and the sign of the remaining term. To verify these equations, you should compute $(A + B)(A + B)$ and $(A - B)(A - B)$.

Factor: **(a)** $x^2 + 6x + 9$; **(b)** $t^2 + 49 - 14t$; **(c)** $16x^2 - 40x + 25$.

SOLUTION

a) $x^2 + 6x + 9 = x^2 + 2 \cdot x \cdot 3 + 3^2 = (x + 3)^2$ The sign of the middle term is positive.

$$A^2 + 2 \; A \; B + B^2 = (A + B)^2$$

b) $t^2 + 49 - 14t = t^2 - 14t + 49$ Using a commutative law to write in descending order

$$= t^2 - 2 \cdot t \cdot 7 + 7^2 = (t - 7)^2$$

$$A^2 - 2 \; A \; B + B^2 = (A - B)^2$$

c) $16x^2 - 40x + 25 = (4x)^2 - 2 \cdot 4x \cdot 5 + 5^2 = (4x - 5)^2$ Recall that $(4x)^2 = 16x^2$.

$A^2 - 2 A B + B^2 = (A - B)^2$ **TRY EXERCISE** 19

Polynomials in more than one variable can also be perfect-square trinomials.

EXAMPLE 3

Factor: $4p^2 - 12pq + 9q^2$.

SOLUTION   We have

$$4p^2 - 12pq + 9q^2 = (2p)^2 - 2(2p)(3q) + (3q)^2 \qquad \text{Recognizing the perfect-square trinomial}$$

$$= (2p - 3q)^2. \qquad \text{The sign of the middle term is negative.}$$

Check: $(2p - 3q)(2p - 3q) = 4p^2 - 12pq + 9q^2$.

The factorization is $(2p - 3q)^2$.   **TRY EXERCISE** 43

EXAMPLE 4

Factor: $-75m^3 - 60m^2 - 12m$.

SOLUTION   *Always* look first for a common factor. This time there is one. We factor out $-3m$ so that the leading coefficient of the polynomial inside the parentheses is positive:

Factor out the common factor.

$$-75m^3 - 60m^2 - 12m = -3m[25m^2 + 20m + 4]$$

$$= -3m[(5m)^2 + 2(5m)(2) + 2^2] \qquad \text{Recognizing the perfect-square trinomial. Try to do this mentally.}$$

Factor the perfect-square trinomial.

$$= -3m(5m + 2)^2.$$

Check: $-3m(5m + 2)^2 = -3m(5m + 2)(5m + 2)$

$$= -3m(25m^2 + 20m + 4)$$

$$= -75m^3 - 60m^2 - 12m.$$

The factorization is $-3m(5m + 2)^2$.   **TRY EXERCISE** 31

Recognizing Differences of Squares

Some binomials represent the difference of two squares. For example, the binomial $16x^2 - 9$ is a difference of two expressions, $16x^2$ and 9, that are squares. To see this, note that $16x^2 = (4x)^2$ and $9 = 3^2$.

Any expression, like $16x^2 - 9$, that can be written in the form $A^2 - B^2$ is called a **difference of squares**. Note that in order for a binomial to be a difference of squares, it must have the following.

1. There must be two expressions, both squares, such as

$$25, \quad t^2, \quad 4x^2, \quad 1, \quad x^6, \quad 49y^8, \quad 100x^2y^2.$$

2. The terms in the binomial must have different signs.

Note that in order for an expression to be a square, its coefficient must be a perfect square and the power(s) of the variable(s) must be even.

EXAMPLE 5

Determine whether each of the following is a difference of squares.

a) $9x^2 - 64$ **b)** $25 - t^3$ **c)** $-4x^{10} + 36$

SOLUTION

a) To see if $9x^2 - 64$ is a difference of squares, note that:

   1. The first expression is a square: $9x^2 = (3x)^2$.
      The second expression is a square: $64 = 8^2$.
   2. The terms have different signs.

   Thus, $9x^2 - 64$ is a difference of squares, $(3x)^2 - 8^2$.

b) To see if $25 - t^3$ is a difference of squares, note that:

   1. The expression t^3 is not a square.

   Thus, $25 - t^3$ is not a difference of squares.

c) To see if $-4x^{10} + 36$ is a difference of squares, note that:

   1. The expressions $4x^{10}$ and 36 are squares: $4x^{10} = (2x^5)^2$ and $36 = 6^2$.
   2. The terms have different signs.

   Thus, $-4x^{10} + 36$ is a difference of squares, $6^2 - (2x^5)^2$. It is often useful to rewrite $-4x^{10} + 36$ in the equivalent form $36 - 4x^{10}$.   **TRY EXERCISE** 51

Factoring Differences of Squares

To factor a difference of squares, we reverse a pattern from Section 5.6.

> ### Factoring a Difference of Squares
> $A^2 - B^2 = (A + B)(A - B)$

   Once we have identified the expressions that are playing the roles of A and B, the factorization can be written directly. To verify this equation, simply multiply $(A + B)(A - B)$.

EXAMPLE 6

Factor: **(a)** $x^2 - 4$; **(b)** $1 - 9p^2$; **(c)** $s^6 - 16t^{10}$; **(d)** $50x^2 - 8x^8$.

SOLUTION

a) $x^2 - 4 = x^2 - 2^2 = (x + 2)(x - 2)$

$$A^2 - B^2 = (A + B)(A - B)$$

b) $1 - 9p^2 = 1^2 - (3p)^2 = (1 + 3p)(1 - 3p)$

$$A^2 - B^2 = (A + B)(A - B)$$

c) $s^6 - 16t^{10} = (s^3)^2 - (4t^5)^2$ Using the rules for powers

$$A^2 - B^2$$

$$= (s^3 + 4t^5)(s^3 - 4t^5)$$ Try to go directly to this step.

$$(A + B)(A - B)$$

d) *Always* look first for a common factor. This time there is one, $2x^2$:

Factor out the common factor.

$$50x^2 - 8x^8 = 2x^2(25 - 4x^6)$$
$$= 2x^2[5^2 - (2x^3)^2] \quad \text{Recognizing } A^2 - B^2.$$
$$\text{Try to do this mentally.}$$

Factor the difference of squares.

$$= 2x^2(5 + 2x^3)(5 - 2x^3).$$

Check: $2x^2(5 + 2x^3)(5 - 2x^3) = 2x^2(25 - 4x^6)$
$$= 50x^2 - 8x^8.$$

The factorization of $50x^2 - 8x^8$ is $2x^2(5 + 2x^3)(5 - 2x^3)$.

> TRY EXERCISE 57

> *CAUTION!* Note in Example 6 that a difference of squares is *not* the square of the difference; that is,
>
> $$A^2 - B^2 \neq (A - B)^2. \quad \text{To see this, note that}$$
> $$(A - B)^2 = A^2 - 2AB + B^2.$$

Factoring Completely

Sometimes, as in Examples 4 and 6(d), a *complete* factorization requires two or more steps. Factoring is complete when no factor can be factored further.

EXAMPLE 7 Factor: $y^4 - 16$.

SOLUTION We have

Factor a difference of squares.

$$y^4 - 16 = (y^2)^2 - 4^2 \quad \text{Recognizing } A^2 - B^2$$
$$= (y^2 + 4)(y^2 - 4) \quad \text{Note that } y^2 - 4 \text{ is not prime.}$$

Factor another difference of squares.

$$= (y^2 + 4)(y + 2)(y - 2). \quad \text{Note that } y^2 - 4 \text{ is itself a difference of squares.}$$

Check: $(y^2 + 4)(y + 2)(y - 2) = (y^2 + 4)(y^2 - 4)$
$$= y^4 - 16.$$

The factorization is $(y^2 + 4)(y + 2)(y - 2)$.

> TRY EXERCISE 79

Note in Example 7 that the factor $y^2 + 4$ is a *sum* of squares that cannot be factored further.

> *CAUTION!* There is no general formula for factoring a sum of squares. In particular,
>
> $$A^2 + B^2 \neq (A + B)^2.$$

As you proceed through the exercises, these suggestions may prove helpful.

> **Tips for Factoring**
> 1. Always look first for a common factor! If there is one, factor it out.
> 2. Be alert for perfect-square trinomials and for binomials that are differences of squares. Once recognized, they can be factored without trial and error.
> 3. Always factor completely.
> 4. Check by multiplying.

6.4 EXERCISE SET

For Extra Help

↪ *Concept Reinforcement* *Identify each of the following as a perfect-square trinomial, a difference of squares, a prime polynomial, or none of these.*

1. $4x^2 + 49$
2. $x^2 - 64$
3. $t^2 - 100$
4. $x^2 - 5x + 4$
5. $9x^2 + 6x + 1$
6. $a^2 - 8a + 16$
7. $2t^2 + 10t + 6$
8. $-25x^2 - 9$
9. $16t^2 - 25$
10. $4r^2 + 20r + 25$

Determine whether each of the following is a perfect-square trinomial.

11. $x^2 + 18x + 81$
12. $x^2 - 16x + 64$
13. $x^2 - 10x - 25$
14. $x^2 - 14x - 49$
15. $x^2 - 3x + 9$
16. $x^2 + 4x + 4$
17. $9x^2 + 25 - 30x$
18. $36x^2 + 16 - 24x$

Factor completely. Remember to look first for a common factor and to check by multiplying. If a polynomial is prime, state this.

19. $x^2 + 16x + 64$
20. $x^2 + 10x + 25$
21. $x^2 - 10x + 25$
22. $x^2 - 16x + 64$
23. $5p^2 + 20p + 20$
24. $3p^2 - 12p + 12$
25. $1 - 2t + t^2$
26. $1 + t^2 + 2t$
27. $18x^2 + 12x + 2$
28. $25x^2 + 10x + 1$
29. $49 - 56y + 16y^2$
30. $75 - 60m + 12m^2$
31. $-x^5 + 18x^4 - 81x^3$
32. $-2x^2 + 40x - 200$
33. $2n^3 + 40n^2 + 200n$
34. $x^3 + 24x^2 + 144x$

35. $20x^2 + 100x + 125$
36. $27m^2 - 36m + 12$
37. $49 - 42x + 9x^2$
38. $64 - 112x + 49x^2$
39. $16x^2 + 24x + 9$
40. $2a^2 + 28a + 98$
41. $2 + 20x + 50x^2$
42. $9x^2 + 30x + 25$
43. $9p^2 + 12pq + 4q^2$
44. $x^2 - 3xy + 9y^2$
45. $a^2 - 12ab + 49b^2$
46. $25m^2 - 20mn + 4n^2$
47. $-64m^2 - 16mn - n^2$
48. $-81p^2 + 18pq - q^2$
49. $-32s^2 + 80st - 50t^2$
50. $-36a^2 - 96ab - 64b^2$

Determine whether each of the following is a difference of squares.

51. $x^2 - 100$
52. $x^2 + 49$
53. $n^4 + 1$
54. $n^4 - 81$
55. $-1 + 64t^2$
56. $-12 + 25t^2$

Factor completely. Remember to look first for a common factor. If a polynomial is prime, state this.

57. $x^2 - 25$
58. $x^2 - 36$
59. $p^2 - 9$
60. $q^2 + 1$
61. $-49 + t^2$
62. $-64 + m^2$
63. $6a^2 - 24$
64. $x^2 - 8x + 16$
65. $49x^2 - 14x + 1$
66. $3t^2 - 3$
67. $200 - 2t^2$
68. $98 - 8w^2$

69. $-80a^2 + 45$

70. $25x^2 - 4$

71. $5t^2 - 80$

72. $-4t^2 + 64$

73. $8x^2 - 162$

74. $24x^2 - 54$

75. $36x - 49x^3$

76. $16x - 81x^3$

77. $49a^4 - 20$

78. $25a^4 - 9$

79. $t^4 - 1$

80. $x^4 - 16$

81. $-3x^3 + 24x^2 - 48x$

82. $-2a^4 + 36a^3 - 162a^2$

83. $75t^3 - 27t$

84. $80s^4 - 45s^2$

85. $a^8 - 2a^7 + a^6$

86. $x^8 - 8x^7 + 16x^6$

87. $10a^2 - 10b^2$

88. $6p^2 - 6q^2$

89. $16x^4 - y^4$

90. $98x^2 - 32y^2$

91. $18t^2 - 8s^2$

92. $a^4 - 81b^4$

93. Explain in your own words how to determine whether a polynomial is a perfect-square trinomial.

94. Explain in your own words how to determine whether a polynomial is a difference of squares.

Skill Review

To prepare for Section 6.5, review the product and power rules for exponents and multiplication of polynomials (Sections 5.1 and 5.5).

Simplify. [5.1]

95. $(2x^2y^4)^3$

96. $(-5x^2y)^3$

Multiply. [5.5]

97. $(x + 1)(x + 1)(x + 1)$

98. $(x - 1)^3$

99. $(p + q)^3$

100. $(p - q)^3$

Synthesis

101. Leon concludes that since $x^2 - 9 = (x - 3)(x + 3)$, it must follow that $x^2 + 9 = (x + 3)(x - 3)$. What mistake(s) is he making?

102. Write directions that would enable someone to construct a polynomial that contains a perfect-square trinomial, a difference of squares, and a common factor.

Factor completely. If a polynomial is prime, state this.

103. $x^8 - 2^8$

104. $3x^2 - \frac{1}{3}$

105. $18x^3 - \frac{8}{25}x$

106. $0.81t - t^3$

107. $(y - 5)^4 - z^8$

108. $x^2 - \left(\dfrac{1}{x}\right)^2$

109. $-x^4 + 8x^2 + 9$

110. $-16x^4 + 96x^2 - 144$

Aha! **111.** $(y + 3)^2 + 2(y + 3) + 1$

112. $49(x + 1)^2 - 42(x + 1) + 9$

113. $27p^3 - 45p^2 - 75p + 125$

114. $a^{2n} - 49b^{2n}$

115. $81 - b^{4k}$

116. $9b^{2n} + 12b^n + 4$

117. Subtract $(x^2 + 1)^2$ from $x^2(x + 1)^2$.

Factor by grouping. Look for a grouping of three terms that is a perfect-square trinomial.

118. $t^2 + 4t + 4 - 25$

119. $y^2 + 6y + 9 - x^2 - 8x - 16$

Find c such that each polynomial is the square of a binomial.

120. $cy^2 + 6y + 1$

121. $cy^2 - 24y + 9$

122. Find the value of a if $x^2 + a^2x + a^2$ factors into $(x + a)^2$.

123. Show that the difference of the squares of two consecutive integers is the sum of the integers. (*Hint*: Use x for the smaller number.)

6.5   Factoring Sums or Differences of Cubes

Formulas for Factoring Sums or Differences of Cubes   ■   Using the Formulas

Formulas for Factoring Sums or Differences of Cubes

We have seen that a difference of two squares can always be factored, but a *sum* of two squares is usually prime. The situation is different with cubes: The difference *or sum* of two cubes can always be factored. To see this, consider the following products:

$$(A + B)(A^2 - AB + B^2) = A(A^2 - AB + B^2) + B(A^2 - AB + B^2)$$
$$= A^3 - A^2B + AB^2 + A^2B - AB^2 + B^3$$
$$= A^3 + B^3 \quad \text{Combining like terms}$$

and

$$(A - B)(A^2 + AB + B^2) = A(A^2 + AB + B^2) - B(A^2 + AB + B^2)$$
$$= A^3 + A^2B + AB^2 - A^2B - AB^2 - B^3$$
$$= A^3 - B^3. \quad \text{Combining like terms}$$

These products allow us to factor a sum or a difference of two cubes. Observe how the location of the $+$ and $-$ signs changes.

> **Factoring a Sum or a Difference of Two Cubes**
> $$A^3 + B^3 = (A + B)(A^2 - AB + B^2);$$
> $$A^3 - B^3 = (A - B)(A^2 + AB + B^2)$$

Using the Formulas

Remembering this list of cubes may prove helpful when factoring.

N	0.2	0.1	0	1	2	3	4	5	6
N^3	0.008	0.001	0	1	8	27	64	125	216

We say that 2 is the *cube root* of 8, that 3 is the cube root of 27, and so on.

EXAMPLE   1   Write an equivalent expression by factoring: $x^3 + 27$.

SOLUTION   We first observe that

$$x^3 + 27 = x^3 + 3^3. \quad \text{This is a sum of cubes.}$$

Next, in one set of parentheses, we write the first cube root, x, plus the second cube root, 3:

$$(x + 3)(\qquad).$$

To get the other factor, we think of $x + 3$ and do the following:

Square the first term: x^2.
Multiply the terms and then change the sign: $-3x$.
Square the second term: 3^2, or 9.

$$(x + 3)(x^2 - 3x + 9).$$

Check: $(x + 3)(x^2 - 3x + 9) = x^3 - 3x^2 + 9x + 3x^2 - 9x + 27$
$$= x^3 + 27. \quad \text{Combining like terms}$$

Thus, $x^3 + 27 = (x + 3)(x^2 - 3x + 9)$.

> **TRY EXERCISE** ▸ 13

In Example 2, you will see that the pattern used to write the trinomial factor in Example 1 can be used when factoring a *difference* of two cubes as well.

EXAMPLE 2

Factor.

a) $125x^3 - y^3$
b) $m^6 + 64$
c) $128y^7 - 250x^6y$
d) $r^6 - s^6$

SOLUTION

a) We have
$$125x^3 - y^3 = (5x)^3 - y^3. \quad \text{This is a difference of cubes.}$$

In one set of parentheses, we write the cube root of the first term, $5x$, minus the cube root of the second term, y:

$$(5x - y)(\quad). \quad \text{This can be regarded as } 5x \text{ } plus \text{ the cube root of}$$
$$(-y)^3, \text{since } -y^3 = (-y)^3.$$

STUDENT NOTES

If you think of $A^3 - B^3$ as $A^3 + (-B)^3$, it is then sufficient to remember only the pattern for factoring a sum of two cubes. Be sure to simplify your result if you do this.

To get the other factor, we think of $5x + y$ and do the following:

Square the first term: $(5x)^2$, or $25x^2$.
Multiply the terms and then change the sign: $5xy$.
Square the second term: $(-y)^2 = y^2$.

$$(5x - y)(25x^2 + 5xy + y^2).$$

Check:
$$(5x - y)(25x^2 + 5xy + y^2) = 125x^3 + 25x^2y + 5xy^2 - 25x^2y - 5xy^2 - y^3$$
$$= 125x^3 - y^3. \quad \text{Combining like terms}$$

Thus, $125x^3 - y^3 = (5x - y)(25x^2 + 5xy + y^2)$.

b) We have
$$m^6 + 64 = (m^2)^3 + 4^3. \quad \text{Rewriting as a sum of quantities cubed}$$

Next, we reuse the pattern used in Example 1:
$$A^3 \ + \ B^3 = (A \ + \ B)(\ A^2 \ - \ A \cdot B + B^2)$$

$$(m^2)^3 + 4^3 = (m^2 + 4)((m^2)^2 - m^2 \cdot 4 + 4^2)$$
$$= (m^2 + 4)(m^4 - 4m^2 + 16). \quad \text{The check is left to the student.}$$

c) We have

$$128y^7 - 250x^6y = 2y(64y^6 - 125x^6)$$ Remember: *Always* look for a common factor.

$$= 2y[(4y^2)^3 - (5x^2)^3].$$ Rewriting as a difference of quantities cubed

To factor $(4y^2)^3 - (5x^2)^3$, we reuse the pattern in part (a) above:

$$A^3 \quad - \quad B^3 \quad = (A \quad - \quad B)(\quad A^2 \quad + \quad A \cdot B \quad + \quad B^2)$$
$$\downarrow \qquad\qquad \downarrow$$
$$(4y^2)^3 - (5x^2)^3 = (4y^2 - 5x^2)((4y^2)^2 + 4y^2 \cdot 5x^2 + (5x^2)^2)$$
$$= (4y^2 - 5x^2)(16y^4 + 20x^2y^2 + 25x^4).$$

The check is left to the student. We have

$$128y^7 - 250x^6y = 2y(4y^2 - 5x^2)(16y^4 + 20x^2y^2 + 25x^4).$$

d) We have

$$r^6 - s^6 = (r^3)^2 - (s^3)^2$$
$$= (r^3 + s^3)(r^3 - s^3)$$ Factoring a difference of two *squares*
$$= (r + s)(r^2 - rs + s^2)(r - s)(r^2 + rs + s^2).$$ Factoring the sum and the difference of two cubes

To check, read the steps in reverse order and inspect the multiplication.

> **TRY EXERCISES** 31 and 41

In Example 2(d), suppose we first factored $r^6 - s^6$ as a difference of two cubes:

$$(r^2)^3 - (s^2)^3 = (r^2 - s^2)(r^4 + r^2s^2 + s^4)$$
$$= (r + s)(r - s)(r^4 + r^2s^2 + s^4).$$

In this case, we might have missed some factors; $r^4 + r^2s^2 + s^4$ can be factored as $(r^2 - rs + s^2)(r^2 + rs + s^2)$, but we probably would never have suspected that such a factorization exists. Given a choice, it is generally better to factor as a difference of squares before factoring as a sum or a difference of cubes.

Useful Factoring Facts

Sum of cubes: $A^3 + B^3 = (A + B)(A^2 - AB + B^2)$

Difference of cubes: $A^3 - B^3 = (A - B)(A^2 + AB + B^2)$

Difference of squares: $A^2 - B^2 = (A + B)(A - B)$

There is no formula for factoring a sum of two squares.

🖐 *Concept Reinforcement* *Classify each binomial as either a sum of cubes, a difference of cubes, a difference of squares, or none of these.*

1. $x^3 - 1$

2. $8 + t^3$

3. $9x^4 - 25$

4. $9x^2 + 25$

5. $1000t^3 + 1$

6. $x^3y^3 - 27z^3$

7. $25x^2 + 8x$

8. $100y^8 - 25x^4$

9. $s^{21} - t^{15}$

10. $14x^3 - 2x$

Factor completely.

11. $x^3 - 64$

12. $t^3 - 27$

13. $z^3 + 1$

14. $x^3 + 8$

15. $t^3 - 1000$

16. $m^3 + 125$

17. $27x^3 + 1$

18. $8a^3 + 1$

19. $64 - 125x^3$

20. $27 - 8t^3$

21. $x^3 - y^3$

22. $y^3 - z^3$

23. $a^3 + \frac{1}{8}$

24. $x^3 + \frac{1}{27}$

25. $8t^3 - 8$

26. $2y^3 - 128$

27. $54x^3 + 2$

28. $8a^3 + 1000$

29. $rs^4 + 64rs$

30. $ab^5 + 1000ab^2$

31. $5x^3 - 40z^3$

32. $2y^3 - 54z^3$

33. $y^3 - \frac{1}{1000}$

34. $x^3 - \frac{1}{8}$

35. $x^3 + 0.001$

36. $y^3 + 0.125$

37. $64x^6 - 8t^6$

38. $125c^6 - 8d^6$

39. $54y^4 - 128y$

40. $3z^5 - 3z^2$

41. $z^6 - 1$

42. $t^6 + 1$

43. $t^6 + 64y^6$

44. $p^6 - q^6$

45. $x^{12} - y^3z^{12}$

46. $a^9 + b^{12}c^{15}$

🖎 47. How could you use factoring to convince someone that $x^3 + y^3 \neq (x + y)^3$?

🖎 48. Is the following statement true or false and why? If A^3 and B^3 have a common factor, then A and B have a common factor.

Skill Review

Review graphing linear equations (Chapter 3).

49. Find the slope of the line containing the points $(-2, -5)$ and $(3, -6)$. [3.5]

50. Find the slope of the line given by $y - 3 = \frac{1}{4}x$. [3.6]

Graph.

51. $2x - 5y = 10$ [3.3]

52. $-5x = 10$ [3.3]

53. $y = \frac{2}{3}x - 1$ [3.6]

54. $y - 2 = -2(x + 4)$ [3.7]

Synthesis

🖎 55. Explain how the geometric model below can be used to verify the formula for factoring $a^3 - b^3$.

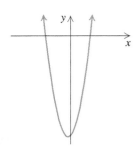

🖎 56. Explain how someone could construct a binomial that is both a difference of two cubes and a difference of two squares.

Factor.

57. $x^{6a} - y^{3b}$

58. $2x^{3a} + 16y^{3b}$

Aha! 59. $(x + 5)^3 + (x - 5)^3$

60. $\frac{1}{16}x^{3a} + \frac{1}{2}y^{6a}z^{9b}$

61. $5x^3y^6 - \frac{5}{8}$

62. $x^3 - (x + y)^3$

63. $x^{6a} - (x^{2a} + 1)^3$

64. $(x^{2a} - 1)^3 - x^{6a}$

65. $t^4 - 8t^3 - t + 8$

6.6 Factoring: A General Strategy

Choosing the Right Method

Thus far, each section in this chapter has examined one or two different methods for factoring polynomials. In practice, when the need for factoring a polynomial arises, we must decide on our own which method to use. Regardless of the polynomial with which we are faced, the guidelines listed below can always be used.

To Factor a Polynomial

    A. Always look for a common factor first. If there is one, factor out the largest common factor. Be sure to include it in your final answer.

    B. Then look at the number of terms.

    Two terms: Try factoring as a difference of squares first: $A^2 - B^2 = (A + B)(A - B)$. Next, try factoring as a sum or a difference of cubes: $A^3 + B^3 = (A + B)(A^2 - AB + B^2)$ and $A^3 - B^3 = (A - B)(A^2 + AB + B^2)$.

    Three terms: If the trinomial is a perfect-square trinomial, factor accordingly: $A^2 + 2AB + B^2 = (A + B)^2$ or $A^2 - 2AB + B^2 = (A - B)^2$. If it is not a perfect-square trinomial, try using FOIL or grouping.

    Four terms: Try factoring by grouping.

    C. Always *factor completely*. When a factor can itself be factored, be sure to factor it. Remember that some polynomials, like $x^2 + 9$, are prime.

    D. Check by multiplying.

Choosing the Right Method

EXAMPLE **1** Factor: $5t^4 - 80$.

SOLUTION

A. We look for a common factor:

$$5t^4 - 80 = 5(t^4 - 16). \quad \text{5 is the largest common factor.}$$

B. The factor $t^4 - 16$ is a difference of squares: $(t^2)^2 - 4^2$. We factor it, being careful to rewrite the 5 from step (A):

$$5t^4 - 80 = 5(t^2 + 4)(t^2 - 4). \quad t^4 - 16 = (t^2 + 4)(t^2 - 4)$$

C. Since $t^2 - 4$ is a difference of squares, we continue factoring:

$$5t^4 - 80 = 5(t^2 + 4)(t^2 - 4) = 5(t^2 + 4)(t - 2)(t + 2).$$

This is a sum of squares, which cannot be factored.

D. *Check:* $5(t^2 + 4)(t - 2)(t + 2) = 5(t^2 + 4)(t^2 - 4)$
$$= 5(t^4 - 16) = 5t^4 - 80.$$

The factorization is $5(t^2 + 4)(t - 2)(t + 2)$.

TRY EXERCISE 5

EXAMPLE 2

Factor: $2x^3 + 10x^2 + x + 5$.

SOLUTION

A. We look for a common factor. There is none.

B. Because there are four terms, we try factoring by grouping:

$$2x^3 + 10x^2 + x + 5$$
$$= (2x^3 + 10x^2) + (x + 5) \qquad \text{Separating into two binomials}$$
$$= 2x^2(x + 5) + 1(x + 5) \qquad \text{Factoring out the largest common factor from each binomial. The 1 serves as an aid.}$$

$$= (x + 5)(2x^2 + 1). \qquad \text{Factoring out the common factor, } x + 5$$

C. Nothing can be factored further, so we have factored completely.

D. *Check:* $(x + 5)(2x^2 + 1) = 2x^3 + x + 10x^2 + 5$
$$= 2x^3 + 10x^2 + x + 5.$$

The factorization is $(x + 5)(2x^2 + 1)$.   **TRY EXERCISE** 13

EXAMPLE 3

Factor: $-n^5 + 2n^4 + 35n^3$.

SOLUTION

A. We note that there is a common factor, $-n^3$:

$$-n^5 + 2n^4 + 35n^3 = -n^3(n^2 - 2n - 35).$$

B. The factor $n^2 - 2n - 35$ is not a perfect-square trinomial. We factor it using trial and error:

$$-n^5 + 2n^4 + 35n^3 = -n^3(n^2 - 2n - 35)$$
$$= -n^3(n - 7)(n + 5).$$

C. Nothing can be factored further, so we have factored completely.

D. *Check:* $-n^3(n - 7)(n + 5) = -n^3(n^2 - 2n - 35)$
$$= -n^5 + 2n^4 + 35n^3.$$

The factorization is $-n^3(n - 7)(n + 5)$.   **TRY EXERCISE** 21

EXAMPLE 4

Factor: $x^2 - 20x + 100$.

SOLUTION

A. We look first for a common factor. There is none.

B. This polynomial is a perfect-square trinomial. We factor it accordingly:

$$x^2 - 20x + 100 = x^2 - 2 \cdot x \cdot 10 + 10^2 \qquad \text{Try to do this step mentally.}$$
$$= (x - 10)^2.$$

C. Nothing can be factored further, so we have factored completely.

D. *Check:* $(x - 10)(x - 10) = x^2 - 20x + 100.$

The factorization is $(x - 10)(x - 10)$, or $(x - 10)^2$.   **TRY EXERCISE** 7

EXAMPLE   5

Factor: $6x^2y^4 - 21x^3y^5 + 3x^2y^6$.

SOLUTION

A. We first factor out the largest common factor, $3x^2y^4$:

$$6x^2y^4 - 21x^3y^5 + 3x^2y^6 = 3x^2y^4(2 - 7xy + y^2).$$

B. The constant term in $2 - 7xy + y^2$ is not a square, so we do not have a perfect-square trinomial. Note that x appears only in $-7xy$. The product of a form like $(1 - y)(2 - y)$ has no x in the middle term. Thus, $2 - 7xy + y^2$ cannot be factored.

C. Nothing can be factored further, so we have factored completely.

D. *Check:* $3x^2y^4(2 - 7xy + y^2) = 6x^2y^4 - 21x^3y^5 + 3x^2y^6$.

The factorization is $3x^2y^4(2 - 7xy + y^2)$.   ▸ TRY EXERCISE 33

EXAMPLE   6

Factor: $x^6 - 64$.

SOLUTION

A. We look first for a common factor. There is none (other than 1 or -1).

B. There are two terms, a difference of squares: $(x^3)^2 - (8)^2$. We factor:

$$x^6 - 64 = (x^3 + 8)(x^3 - 8).$$ Note that $x^6 = (x^3)^2$.

C. One factor is a sum of two cubes, and the other factor is a difference of two cubes. We factor both:

$$x^6 - 64 = (x + 2)(x^2 - 2x + 4)(x - 2)(x^2 + 2x + 4).$$

The factorization is complete because no factor can be factored further.

D. *Check:* $(x + 2)(x^2 - 2x + 4)(x - 2)(x^2 + 2x + 4) = (x^3 + 8)(x^3 - 8)$
$$= x^6 - 64.$$

The factorization is $(x + 2)(x^2 - 2x + 4)(x - 2)(x^2 + 2x + 4)$.

▸ TRY EXERCISE 31

EXAMPLE   7

Factor: $-25m^2 - 20mn - 4n^2$.

SOLUTION

A. We look first for a common factor. Since all the terms are negative, we factor out a -1:

$$-25m^2 - 20mn - 4n^2 = -1(25m^2 + 20mn + 4n^2).$$

B. There are three terms in the parentheses. Note that the first term and the last term are squares: $25m^2 = (5m)^2$ and $4n^2 = (2n)^2$. We see that twice the product of $5m$ and $2n$ is the middle term,

$$2 \cdot 5m \cdot 2n = 20mn,$$

so the trinomial is a perfect square. To factor, we write a binomial squared:

$$-25m^2 - 20mn - 4n^2 = -1(25m^2 + 20mn + 4n^2)$$
$$= -1(5m + 2n)^2.$$

C. Nothing can be factored further, so we have factored completely.

D. *Check:* $-1(5m + 2n)^2 = -1(25m^2 + 20mn + 4n^2)$
$$= -25m^2 - 20mn - 4n^2.$$

The factorization is $-1(5m + 2n)^2$, or $-(5m + 2n)^2$.   ▸ TRY EXERCISE 59

EXAMPLE **8**   Factor: $x^2y^2 + 7xy + 12$.

SOLUTION

A. We look first for a common factor. There is none.

B. Since only one term is a square, we do not have a perfect-square trinomial. We use trial and error, thinking of the product xy as a single variable:

$$(xy + \quad)(xy + \quad).$$

We factor the last term, 12. All the signs are positive, so we consider only positive factors. Possibilities are 1, 12 and 2, 6 and 3, 4. The pair 3, 4 gives a sum of 7 for the coefficient of the middle term. Thus,

$$x^2y^2 + 7xy + 12 = (xy + 3)(xy + 4).$$

C. Nothing can be factored further, so we have factored completely.

D. *Check:* $(xy + 3)(xy + 4) = x^2y^2 + 7xy + 12$.

The factorization is $(xy + 3)(xy + 4)$.

> **TRY EXERCISE** 61

Compare the variables appearing in Example 7 with those in Example 8. Note that if the leading term contains one variable and a different variable is in the last term, as in Example 7, each binomial contains two variable terms. When two variables appear in the leading term and no variables appear in the last term, as in Example 8, each binomial contains one term that has two variables and one term that is a constant.

EXAMPLE **9**   Factor: $a^4 - 16b^4$.

SOLUTION

A. We look first for a common factor. There is none.

B. There are two terms. Since $a^4 = (a^2)^2$ and $16b^4 = (4b^2)^2$, we see that we have a difference of squares. Thus,

$$a^4 - 16b^4 = (a^2 + 4b^2)(a^2 - 4b^2).$$

C. The factor $(a^2 - 4b^2)$ is itself a difference of squares. Thus,

$$a^4 - 16b^4 = (a^2 + 4b^2)(a + 2b)(a - 2b). \qquad \text{Factoring } a^2 - 4b^2$$

D. *Check:* $(a^2 + 4b^2)(a + 2b)(a - 2b) = (a^2 + 4b^2)(a^2 - 4b^2)$
$$= a^4 - 16b^4.$$

The factorization is $(a^2 + 4b^2)(a + 2b)(a - 2b)$.

> **TRY EXERCISE** 53

6.6   EXERCISE SET

For Extra Help   *MyMathLab*   Math XL PRACTICE   WATCH   DOWNLOAD

✎ *Concept Reinforcement* *In each of Exercises 1–4, complete the sentence.*

1. As a first step when factoring polynomials, always check for a _____.

2. When factoring a trinomial, if two terms are not squares, it cannot be a _____.

3. If a polynomial has four terms and no common factor, it may be possible to factor by _____.

4. It is always possible to check a factorization by _____.

Factor completely. If a polynomial is prime, state this.

5. $5a^2 - 125$

6. $10c^2 - 810$

7. $y^2 + 49 - 14y$

8. $a^2 + 25 + 10a$

9. $3t^2 + 16t + 21$

10. $8t^2 + 31t - 4$

11. $x^3 + 18x^2 + 81x$

12. $x^3 - 24x^2 + 144x$

13. $x^3 - 5x^2 - 25x + 125$

14. $x^3 + 3x^2 - 4x - 12$

15. $27t^3 - 3t$

16. $98t^2 - 18$

17. $9x^3 + 12x^2 - 45x$

18. $20x^3 - 4x^2 - 72x$

19. $t^2 + 25$

20. $4x^2 + 20x - 144$

21. $6y^2 + 18y - 240$

22. $4n^2 + 81$

23. $-2a^6 + 8a^5 - 8a^4$

24. $-x^5 - 14x^4 - 49x^3$

25. $5x^5 - 80x$

26. $4x^4 - 64$

27. $t^4 - 9$

28. $9 + t^8$

29. $-x^6 + 2x^5 - 7x^4$

30. $-x^5 + 4x^4 - 3x^3$

31. $x^3 - y^3$

32. $8t^3 + 1$

33. $ax^2 + ay^2$

34. $12n^2 + 24n^3$

35. $2\pi rh + 2\pi r^2$

36. $4\pi r^2 + 2\pi r$

Aha! **37.** $(a + b)5a + (a + b)3b$

38. $5c(a^3 + b) - (a^3 + b)$

39. $x^2 + x + xy + y$

40. $n^2 + 2n + np + 2p$

41. $a^2 - 2a - ay + 2y$

42. $2x^2 - 4x + xz - 2z$

43. $3x^2 + 13xy - 10y^2$

44. $-x^2 - y^2 - 2xy$

45. $8m^3n - 32m^2n^2 + 24mn$

46. $a^2 - 7a - 6$

47. $4b^2 + a^2 - 4ab$

48. $7p^4 - 7q^4$

49. $16x^2 + 24xy + 9y^2$

50. $6a^2b^3 + 12a^3b^2 - 3a^4b^2$

51. $m^2 - 5m + 8$

52. $25z^2 + 10zy + y^2$

53. $a^4b^4 - 16$

54. $a^5 - 4a^4b - 5a^3b^2$

55. $80cd^2 - 36c^2d + 4c^3$

56. $2p^2 + pq + q^2$

57. $64t^6 - 1$

58. $m^6 - 1$

59. $-12 - x^2y^2 - 8xy$

60. $m^2n^2 - 4mn - 32$

61. $5p^2q^2 + 25pq - 30$

62. $a^4b^3 + 2a^3b^2 - 15a^2b$

63. $54a^4 + 16ab^3$

64. $54x^3y - 250y^4$

65. $x^6 + x^5y - 2x^4y^2$

66. $2s^6t^2 + 10s^3t^3 + 12t^4$

67. $36a^2 - 15a + \frac{25}{16}$

68. $a^2 + 2a^2bc + a^2b^2c^2$

69. $\frac{1}{81}x^2 - \frac{8}{27}x + \frac{16}{9}$

70. $\frac{1}{4}a^2 + \frac{1}{3}ab + \frac{1}{9}b^2$

71. $1 - 16x^{12}y^{12}$

72. $b^4a - 81a^5$

73. $4a^2b^2 + 12ab + 9$

74. $9c^2 + 6cd + d^2$

75. $z^4 + 6z^3 - 6z^2 - 36z$

76. $t^5 - 2t^4 + 5t^3 - 10t^2$

77. Kelly factored $16 - 8x + x^2$ as $(x - 4)^2$, while Tony factored it as $(4 - x)^2$. Are they both correct? Why or why not?

78. Describe in your own words or draw a diagram representing a strategy for factoring polynomials.

Skill Review

To prepare for Section 6.7, review solving equations (Section 2.2).

Solve. [2.2]

79. $8x - 9 = 0$

80. $3x + 5 = 0$

81. $2x + 7 = 0$

82. $4x - 1 = 0$

83. $3 - x = 0$

84. $22 - 2x = 0$

85. $2x - 5 = 8x + 1$

86. $3(x - 1) = 9 - x$

Synthesis

87. There are third-degree polynomials in x that we are not yet able to factor, despite the fact that they are not prime. Explain how such a polynomial could be created.

88. Describe a method that could be used to find a binomial of degree 16 that can be expressed as the product of prime binomial factors.

Factor.

89. $-(x^5 + 7x^3 - 18x)$

90. $18 + a^3 - 9a - 2a^2$

91. $-x^4 + 7x^2 + 18$

92. $-3a^4 + 15a^2 - 12$

Aha! **93.** $y^2(y + 1) - 4y(y + 1) - 21(y + 1)$

94. $y^2(y - 1) - 2y(y - 1) + (y - 1)$

96. $(y + 4)^2 + 2x(y + 4) + x^2$

96. $6(x - 1)^2 + 7y(x - 1) - 3y^2$

97. $2(a + 3)^4 - (a + 3)^3(b - 2) - (a + 3)^2(b - 2)^2$

98. $5(t - 1)^5 - 6(t - 1)^4(s - 1) + (t - 1)^3(s - 1)^2$

99. $49x^4 + 14x^2 + 1 - 25x^6$

CORNER

Matching Factorizations*

Focus: Factoring

Time: 20 minutes

Group size: Begin with the entire class. If there is an odd number of students, the instructor should participate.

Materials: Prepared sheets of paper, pins or tape. On half of the sheets, the instructor writes a polynomial. On the remaining sheets, the instructor writes the factorization of those polynomials. The polynomials and factorizations should be similar; for example,

$$x^2 - 2x - 8, \quad (x - 2)(x - 4),$$
$$x^2 - 6x + 8, \quad (x - 1)(x - 8),$$
$$x^2 - 9x + 8, \quad (x + 2)(x - 4).$$

ACTIVITY

1. As class members enter the room, the instructor pins or tapes either a polynomial

or a factorization to the back of each student. Class members are told only whether their sheet of paper contains a polynomial or a factorization.

2. After all students are wearing a sheet of paper, they should mingle with one another, attempting to match up their factorization with the appropriate polynomial or vice versa. They may ask questions of one another that relate to factoring and polynomials. Answers to the questions should be yes or no. For example, a legitimate question might be "Is my last term negative?" or "Do my factors have opposite signs?"

3. The game is over when all factorization/polynomial pairs have "found" one another.

—————————————
*Thanks to Jann MacInnes of Florida Community College at Jacksonville–Kent Campus for suggesting this activity.

6.7   Solving Polynomial Equations by Factoring

The Principle of Zero Products ■ Factoring to Solve Equations

When we factor a polynomial, we are forming an *equivalent expression*. We now use our factoring skills to *solve equations*. We already know how to solve linear equations like $x + 2 = 7$ and $2x = 9$. The equations we will learn to solve in this section contain a variable raised to a power greater than 1 and will usually have more than one solution.

Whenever two polynomials are set equal to each other, we have a *polynomial equation*. The degree of a polynomial equation is the same as the highest degree of any term in the equation. Second-degree equations like $4t^2 - 9 = 0$ and $x^2 + 6x + 5 = 0$ are called **quadratic equations**.

Quadratic Equation

A *quadratic equation* is an equation equivalent to one of the form

$$ax^2 + bx + c = 0,$$

where a, b, and c are constants, with $a \neq 0$.

In order to solve quadratic equations, we need to develop a new principle.

The Principle of Zero Products

Suppose we are told that the product of two numbers is 6. On the basis of this information, it is impossible to know the value of either number—the product could be $2 \cdot 3$, $6 \cdot 1$, $12 \cdot \frac{1}{2}$, and so on. However, if we are told that the product of two numbers is 0, we know that at least one of the two factors must itself be 0. For example, if $(x + 3)(x - 2) = 0$, we can conclude that either $x + 3$ is 0 or $x - 2$ is 0.

The Principle of Zero Products

An equation $AB = 0$ is true if and only if $A = 0$ or $B = 0$, or both.
(A product is 0 if and only if at least one factor is 0.)

EXAMPLE **1**

Solve: $(x + 3)(x - 2) = 0$.

SOLUTION We are looking for all values of x that will make the equation true. The equation tells us that the product of $x + 3$ and $x - 2$ is 0. In order for the product to be 0, at least one factor must be 0. Thus we look for any value of x for which $x + 3 = 0$, as well as any value of x for which $x - 2 = 0$, that is, either

$$x + 3 = 0 \quad or \quad x - 2 = 0. \qquad \text{Using the principle of zero products. There are two equations to solve.}$$

We solve each equation:

$$x + 3 = 0 \quad or \quad x - 2 = 0$$
$$x = -3 \quad or \quad x = 2.$$

Both -3 and 2 should be checked in the original equation.

Check: For -3:

$$\frac{(x + 3)(x - 2) = 0}{(-3 + 3)(-3 - 2) \,\big|\, 0}$$

The factor $x + 3$ is 0 when $x = -3$. $\longrightarrow 0(-5)$

$$0 \overset{?}{=} 0 \quad \text{TRUE}$$

For 2:

$$\frac{(x + 3)(x - 2) = 0}{(2 + 3)(2 - 2) \,\big|\, 0}$$

$5(0) \longleftarrow$ The factor $x - 2$ is 0 when $x = 2$.

$$0 \overset{?}{=} 0 \quad \text{TRUE}$$

The solutions are -3 and 2.

TRY EXERCISE 5

When we are using the principle of zero products, the word "or" is meant to emphasize that any one of the factors could be the one that represents 0.

EXAMPLE **2**

Solve: $3(5x + 1)(x - 7) = 0$.

SOLUTION The factors in this equation are 3, $5x + 1$, and $x - 7$. Since the factor 3 is constant, the only way in which $3(5x + 1)(x - 7)$ can be 0 is for one of the other factors to be 0, that is,

$$5x + 1 = 0 \quad or \quad x - 7 = 0 \qquad \text{Using the principle of zero products}$$
$$5x = -1 \quad or \qquad x = 7 \qquad \text{Solving the two equations separately}$$
$$x = -\tfrac{1}{5} \quad or \qquad x = 7. \qquad 5x + 1 = 0 \text{ when } x = -\tfrac{1}{5}; x - 7 = 0 \text{ when } x = 7$$

STUDY SKILLS

Identify the Highlights

If you haven't already tried one, consider using a highlighter as you read. By highlighting sentences or phrases that you find especially important, you will make it easier to review important material in the future. Be sure to keep your highlighter available when you study.

Check:

For $-\frac{1}{5}$:

$$
\begin{array}{c|c}
\multicolumn{2}{c}{3(5x + 1)(x - 7) = 0} \\
\hline
3\left(5\left(-\frac{1}{5}\right) + 1\right)\left(-\frac{1}{5} - 7\right) & 0 \\
3(-1 + 1)\left(-7\frac{1}{5}\right) & \\
3(0)\left(-7\frac{1}{5}\right) & \\
0 \stackrel{?}{=} 0 & \text{TRUE}
\end{array}
$$

For 7:

$$
\begin{array}{c|c}
\multicolumn{2}{c}{3(5x + 1)(x - 7) = 0} \\
\hline
3(5(7) + 1)(7 - 7) & 0 \\
3(35 + 1)0 & \\
0 \stackrel{?}{=} 0 & \text{TRUE}
\end{array}
$$

The solutions are $-\frac{1}{5}$ and 7.

TRY EXERCISE ▶ 9

The constant factor 3 in Example 2 is never 0 and is not a solution of the equation. However, a variable factor such as x or t *can* equal 0, and must be considered when using the principle of zero products.

EXAMPLE 3

Solve: $7t(t - 5) = 0$.

SOLUTION   We have

$$7 \cdot t(t - 5) = 0 \qquad \text{The factors are 7, } t, \text{ and } t - 5.$$
$$t = 0 \quad or \quad t - 5 = 0 \qquad \text{Using the principle of zero products}$$
$$t = 0 \quad or \qquad t = 5. \qquad \text{Solving. Note that the constant factor, 7, is never 0.}$$

The solutions are 0 and 5. The check is left to the student.

TRY EXERCISE ▶ 15

Factoring to Solve Equations

By factoring and using the principle of zero products, we can now solve a variety of quadratic equations.

EXAMPLE 4

Solve: $x^2 + 5x + 6 = 0$.

SOLUTION   This equation differs from those solved in Chapter 2. There are no like terms to combine, and there is a squared term. We first factor the polynomial. Then we use the principle of zero products:

$$x^2 + 5x + 6 = 0$$
$$(x + 2)(x + 3) = 0 \qquad \text{Factoring}$$
$$x + 2 = 0 \quad or \quad x + 3 = 0 \qquad \text{Using the principle of zero products}$$
$$x = -2 \quad or \qquad x = -3.$$

Check:

For -2:

$$
\begin{array}{c|c}
\multicolumn{2}{c}{x^2 + 5x + 6 = 0} \\
\hline
(-2)^2 + 5(-2) + 6 & 0 \\
4 - 10 + 6 & \\
-6 + 6 & \\
0 \stackrel{?}{=} 0 & \text{TRUE}
\end{array}
$$

For -3:

$$
\begin{array}{c|c}
\multicolumn{2}{c}{x^2 + 5x + 6 = 0} \\
\hline
(-3)^2 + 5(-3) + 6 & 0 \\
9 - 15 + 6 & \\
-6 + 6 & \\
0 \stackrel{?}{=} 0 & \text{TRUE}
\end{array}
$$

The solutions are -2 and -3.

TRY EXERCISE ▶ 21

The principle of zero products applies even when there is a common factor.

EXAMPLE **5**

Solve: $x^2 + 7x = 0$.

SOLUTION   Although there is no constant term, because of the x^2-term, the equation is still quadratic. The methods of Chapter 2 are not sufficient, so we try factoring:

$$x^2 + 7x = 0$$
$$x(x + 7) = 0 \qquad \text{Factoring out the largest common factor, } x$$
$$x = 0 \quad or \quad x + 7 = 0 \qquad \text{Using the principle of zero products}$$
$$x = 0 \quad or \qquad x = -7.$$

The solutions are 0 and -7. The check is left to the student.

TRY EXERCISE 27

STUDENT NOTES

Checking for a common factor is an important step that is often overlooked. In Example 5, the equation must be factored. If we "divide both sides by x," we will not find the solution 0.

> *CAUTION!*   We *must* have 0 on one side of the equation before the principle of zero products can be used. Get all nonzero terms on one side and 0 on the other.

EXAMPLE **6**

Solve: **(a)** $x^2 - 8x = -16$; **(b)** $4t^2 = 25$.

SOLUTION

a) We first add 16 to get 0 on one side:

$$x^2 - 8x = -16$$
$$x^2 - 8x + 16 = 0 \qquad \text{Adding 16 to both sides to get 0 on one side}$$
$$(x - 4)(x - 4) = 0 \qquad \text{Factoring}$$
$$x - 4 = 0 \quad or \quad x - 4 = 0 \qquad \text{Using the principle of zero products}$$
$$x = 4 \quad or \qquad x = 4.$$

There is only one solution, 4. The check is left to the student.

b) We have

$$4t^2 = 25$$
$$4t^2 - 25 = 0 \qquad \text{Subtracting 25 from both sides to get 0 on one side}$$
$$(2t - 5)(2t + 5) = 0 \qquad \text{Factoring a difference of squares}$$
$$\left. \begin{array}{l} 2t - 5 = 0 \quad or \quad 2t + 5 = 0 \\ \quad 2t = 5 \quad or \qquad 2t = -5 \\ \qquad t = \tfrac{5}{2} \quad or \qquad\quad t = -\tfrac{5}{2}. \end{array} \right\} \quad \begin{array}{l}\text{Solving the two equations} \\ \text{separately}\end{array}$$

The solutions are $\tfrac{5}{2}$ and $-\tfrac{5}{2}$. The check is left to the student.

TRY EXERCISE 41

When solving quadratic equations by factoring, remember that a factorization is not useful unless 0 is on the other side of the equation.

EXAMPLE **7**

Solve: $(x + 3)(2x - 1) = 9$.

SOLUTION   Be careful with an equation like this! Since we need 0 on one side, we first multiply out the product on the left and then subtract 9 from both sides.

$$(x + 3)(2x - 1) = 9$$ This is not a product equal to 0.

$$2x^2 + 5x - 3 = 9$$ Multiplying on the left

$$2x^2 + 5x - 3 - 9 = 9 - 9$$ Subtracting 9 from both sides to get 0 on one side

$$2x^2 + 5x - 12 = 0$$ Combining like terms

$$(2x - 3)(x + 4) = 0$$ Factoring. Now we have a product equal to 0.

$$2x - 3 = 0 \quad or \quad x + 4 = 0$$ Using the principle of zero products

$$2x = 3 \quad or \qquad x = -4$$

$$x = \tfrac{3}{2} \quad or \qquad x = -4$$

Check: For $\tfrac{3}{2}$:

$$\frac{(x + 3)(2x - 1) = 9}{\left(\tfrac{3}{2} + 3\right)\left(2 \cdot \tfrac{3}{2} - 1\right) \,\Big|\, 9}$$
$$\left(\tfrac{9}{2}\right)(2) \,\Big|$$
$$9 \overset{?}{=} 9 \quad \text{TRUE}$$

For -4:

$$\frac{(x + 3)(2x - 1) = 9}{(-4 + 3)(2(-4)-1) \,\Big|\, 9}$$
$$(-1)(-9) \,\Big|$$
$$9 \overset{?}{=} 9 \quad \text{TRUE}$$

The solutions are $\tfrac{3}{2}$ and -4.

▶ TRY EXERCISE 43

We can use the principle of zero products to solve polynomials with degree greater than 2, if they can be factored.

EXAMPLE 8 Solve: $3x^3 - 30x = 9x^2$.

SOLUTION We have

$$3x^3 - 30x = 9x^2$$

$$3x^3 - 9x^2 - 30x = 0$$ Getting 0 on one side and writing in descending order

$$3x(x^2 - 3x - 10) = 0$$ Factoring out a common factor

$$3x(x + 2)(x - 5) = 0$$ Factoring the trinomial

$$3x = 0 \quad or \quad x + 2 = 0 \quad or \quad x - 5 = 0$$ Using the principle of zero products

$$x = 0 \quad or \qquad x = -2 \quad or \qquad x = 5.$$

Check:

$$\frac{3x^3 - 30x = 9x^2}{3 \cdot 0^3 - 30 \cdot 0 \,\Big|\, 9 \cdot 0^2}$$
$$0 - 0 \,\Big|\, 9 \cdot 0$$
$$0 \overset{?}{=} 0 \quad \text{TRUE}$$

$$\frac{3x^3 - 30x = 9x^2}{3(-2)^3 - 30(-2) \,\Big|\, 9(-2)^2}$$
$$3(-8) + 60 \,\Big|\, 9 \cdot 4$$
$$-24 + 60 \,\Big|\, 36$$
$$36 \overset{?}{=} 36 \quad \text{TRUE}$$

$$\frac{3x^3 - 30x = 9x^2}{3 \cdot 5^3 - 30 \cdot 5 \,\Big|\, 9 \cdot 5^2}$$
$$3 \cdot 125 - 150 \,\Big|\, 9 \cdot 25$$
$$375 - 150 \,\Big|\, 225$$
$$225 \overset{?}{=} 225 \quad \text{TRUE}$$

The solutions are 0, -2, and 5.

▶ TRY EXERCISE 53

ALGEBRAIC–GRAPHICAL CONNECTION

When graphing equations in Chapter 3, we found the x-intercept by replacing y with 0 and solving for x. This procedure is also used to find the x-intercepts when graphing equations of the form $y = ax^2 + bx + c$. We consider them briefly here from the standpoint of finding x-intercepts. The graphs are shaped as shown. Note that each x-intercept represents a solution of $ax^2 + bx + c = 0$.

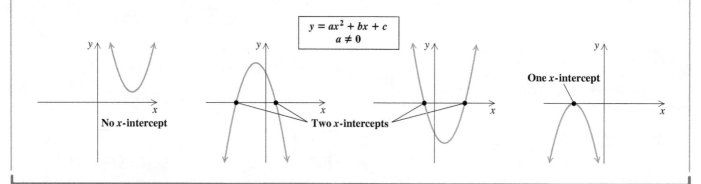

EXAMPLE 9   Find the x-intercepts for the graph of the equation shown. (The grid is intentionally not included.)

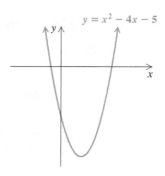

$$y = x^2 - 4x - 5$$

SOLUTION   To find the x-intercepts, we let $y = 0$ and solve for x:

$$0 = x^2 - 4x - 5 \qquad \text{Substituting 0 for } y$$
$$0 = (x - 5)(x + 1) \qquad \text{Factoring}$$
$$x - 5 = 0 \quad \text{or} \quad x + 1 = 0 \qquad \text{Using the principle of zero products}$$
$$x = 5 \quad \text{or} \qquad x = -1. \qquad \text{Solving for } x$$

The x-intercepts are $(5, 0)$ and $(-1, 0)$.

TRY EXERCISE 61

TECHNOLOGY CONNECTION

A graphing calculator allows us to solve polynomial equations even when an equation cannot be solved by factoring. For example, to solve $x^2 - 3x - 5 = 0$, we can let $y_1 = x^2 - 3x - 5$ and $y_2 = 0$. Selecting a bold line type to the left of y_2 in the ⬭Y=⬭ window makes the line easier to see. Using the INTERSECT option of the CALC menu, we select the two graphs in which we are interested, along with a guess. The graphing calculator displays the point of intersection.

An alternative method uses only y_1 and the ZERO option of the CALC menu. This option requires you to enter an x-value to the left of each x-intercept as a LEFT BOUND. An x-value to the right of the x-intercept is then entered as a RIGHT BOUND. Finally, a GUESS value between the two bounds is entered and the x-intercept, or ZERO, is displayed.

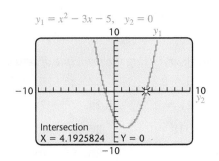

Use a graphing calculator to find the solutions, if they exist, accurate to two decimal places.

1. $x^2 + 4x - 3 = 0$
2. $x^2 - 5x - 2 = 0$
3. $x^2 + 13.54x + 40.95 = 0$
4. $x^2 - 4.43x + 6.32 = 0$
5. $1.235x^2 - 3.409x = 0$

6.7 EXERCISE SET

🔖 *Concept Reinforcement* *For each of Exercises 1–4, match the phrase with the most appropriate choice from the column on the right.*

1. _____ The name of equations of the type $ax^2 + bx + c = 0$, with $a \neq 0$

2. _____ The maximum number of solutions of quadratic equations

3. _____ The idea that $A \cdot B = 0$ if and only if $A = 0$ or $B = 0$

4. _____ The number that a product must equal before the principle of zero products is used

a) 2

b) 0

c) Quadratic

d) The principle of zero products

Solve using the principle of zero products.

5. $(x + 2)(x + 9) = 0$

6. $(x + 3)(x + 10) = 0$

7. $(2t - 3)(t + 6) = 0$

8. $(5t - 8)(t - 1) = 0$

9. $4(7x - 1)(10x - 3) = 0$

10. $6(4x - 3)(2x + 9) = 0$

11. $x(x - 7) = 0$

12. $x(x + 2) = 0$

13. $\left(\frac{2}{3}x - \frac{12}{11}\right)\left(\frac{7}{4}x - \frac{1}{12}\right) = 0$

14. $\left(\frac{1}{9} - 3x\right)\left(\frac{1}{5} + 2x\right) = 0$

15. $6n(3n + 8) = 0$

16. $10n(4n - 5) = 0$

17. $(20 - 0.4x)(7 - 0.1x) = 0$

18. $(1 - 0.05x)(1 - 0.3x) = 0$

19. $(3x - 2)(x + 5)(x - 1) = 0$

20. $(2x + 1)(x + 3)(x - 5) = 0$

Solve by factoring and using the principle of zero products.

21. $x^2 - 7x + 6 = 0$ **22.** $x^2 - 6x + 5 = 0$

23. $x^2 + 4x - 21 = 0$ **24.** $x^2 - 7x - 18 = 0$

25. $n^2 + 11n + 18 = 0$ **26.** $n^2 + 8n + 15 = 0$

27. $x^2 - 10x = 0$ **28.** $x^2 + 8x = 0$

29. $6t + t^2 = 0$ **30.** $3t - t^2 = 0$

31. $x^2 - 36 = 0$ **32.** $x^2 - 100 = 0$

33. $4t^2 = 49$ **34.** $9t^2 = 25$

35. $0 = 25 + x^2 + 10x$ **36.** $0 = 6x + x^2 + 9$

37. $64 + x^2 = 16x$ **38.** $x^2 + 1 = 2x$

39. $4t^2 = 8t$ **40.** $12t = 3t^2$

41. $4y^2 = 7y + 15$ **42.** $12y^2 - 5y = 2$

43. $(x - 7)(x + 1) = -16$

44. $(x + 2)(x - 7) = -18$

45. $15z^2 + 7 = 20z + 7$

46. $14z^2 - 3 = 21z - 3$

47. $36m^2 - 9 = 40$

48. $81x^2 - 5 = 20$

49. $(x + 3)(3x + 5) = 7$

50. $(x - 1)(5x + 4) = 2$

51. $3x^2 - 2x = 9 - 8x$

52. $x^2 - 2x = 18 + 5x$

53. $x^2(2x - 1) = 3x$

54. $x^2 = x(10 - 3x^2)$

55. $(2x - 5)(3x^2 + 29x + 56) = 0$

56. $(4x + 9)(15x^2 - 7x - 2) = 0$

57. Use this graph to solve $x^2 - 3x - 4 = 0$.

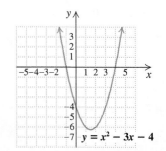

58. Use this graph to solve $x^2 + x - 6 = 0$.

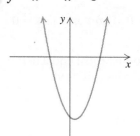

59. Use this graph to solve $-x^2 - x + 6 = 0$.

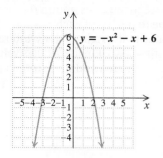

60. Use this graph to solve $-x^2 + 2x + 3 = 0$.

Find the x-intercepts for the graph of each equation. Grids are intentionally not included.

61. $y = x^2 - x - 6$ **62.** $y = x^2 + 3x - 4$

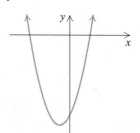

63. $y = x^2 + 2x - 8$ **64.** $y = x^2 - 2x - 15$

65. $y = 2x^2 + 3x - 9$

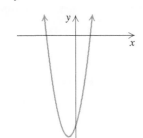

66. $y = 2x^2 + x - 10$

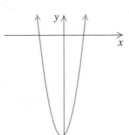

67. The equation $x^2 + 1 = 0$ has no real-number solutions. What implications does this have for the graph of $y = x^2 + 1$?

68. What is the difference between a quadratic polynomial and a quadratic equation?

Skill Review

To prepare for Section 6.8, review solving problems using the five-step strategy (Section 2.5).

Translate to an algebraic expression. [1.1]

69. The square of the sum of two numbers

70. The sum of the squares of two numbers

71. The product of two consecutive integers

Solve. [2.5]

72. In 2005, shoppers spent $22.8 billion on gifts for Mother's Day and for Father's Day combined. They spent $4.8 billion more for Mother's Day than for Father's Day. How much did shoppers spend for each holiday?
Source: National Retail Federation

73. The first angle of a triangle is four times as large as the second. The measure of the third angle is 30° less than that of the second. How large are the angles?

74. A rectangular table top is twice as long as it is wide. The perimeter of the table is 192 in. What are the dimensions of the table?

Synthesis

75. What is wrong with solving $x^2 = 3x$ by dividing both sides of the equation by x?

76. When the principle of zero products is used to solve a quadratic equation, will there always be two different solutions? Why or why not?

77. Find an equation with integer coefficients that has the given numbers as solutions. For example, 3 and -2 are solutions to $x^2 - x - 6 = 0$.
  a) $-4, 5$ **b)** $-1, 7$ **c)** $\frac{1}{4}, 3$
  d) $\frac{1}{2}, \frac{1}{3}$ **e)** $\frac{2}{3}, \frac{3}{4}$ **f)** $-1, 2, 3$

Solve.

78. $16(x - 1) = x(x + 8)$

79. $a(9 + a) = 4(2a + 5)$

80. $(t - 5)^2 = 2(5 - t)$

81. $-x^2 + \frac{9}{25} = 0$

82. $a^2 = \frac{49}{100}$

Aha! **83.** $(t + 1)^2 = 9$

84. $\frac{27}{25} x^2 = \frac{1}{3}$

85. For each equation on the left, find an equivalent equation on the right.
  a) $x^2 + 10x - 2 = 0$ $4x^2 + 8x + 36 = 0$
  b) $(x - 6)(x + 3) = 0$ $(2x + 8)(2x - 5) = 0$
  c) $5x^2 - 5 = 0$ $9x^2 - 12x + 24 = 0$
  d) $(2x - 5)(x + 4) = 0$ $(x + 1)(5x - 5) = 0$
  e) $x^2 + 2x + 9 = 0$ $x^2 - 3x - 18 = 0$
  f) $3x^2 - 4x + 8 = 0$ $2x^2 + 20x - 4 = 0$

86. Explain how to construct an equation that has seven solutions.

87. Explain how the graph in Exercise 59 can be used to visualize the solutions of
$$-x^2 - x + 6 = 4.$$

Use a graphing calculator to find the solutions of each equation. Round solutions to the nearest hundredth.

88. $-x^2 + 0.63x + 0.22 = 0$

89. $x^2 - 9.10x + 15.77 = 0$

90. $6.4x^2 - 8.45x - 94.06 = 0$

91. $x^2 + 13.74x + 42.00 = 0$

92. $0.84x^2 - 2.30x = 0$

93. $1.23x^2 + 4.63x = 0$

94. $x^2 + 1.80x - 5.69 = 0$

CONNECTING the CONCEPTS

Recall that an *equation* is a statement that two *expressions* are equal. When we simplify expressions, combine expressions, and form equivalent expressions, each result is an expression. When we are asked to solve an equation, the result is one or more numbers. Remember to read the directions to an exercise carefully so you do not attempt to "solve" an expression.

MIXED REVIEW

For Exercises 1–6, tell whether each is an example of an expression or an equation.

1. $x^2 - 25$

2. $x^2 - 25 = 0$

3. $x^2 + 2x = 5$

4. $(x + 3)(2x - 1)$

5. $x(x + 3) - 2(2x - 7) - (x - 5)$

6. $x = 10$

7. Add the expressions:
$$(2x^3 - 5x + 1) + (x^2 - 3x - 1).$$

8. Subtract the expressions:
$$(x^2 - x - 5) - (3x^2 - x + 6).$$

9. Solve the equation: $t^2 - 100 = 0$.

10. Multiply the expressions: $(3a - 2)(2a - 5)$.

11. Factor the expression: $n^2 - 10n + 9$.

12. Solve the equation: $x^2 + 16 = 10x$.

13. Solve: $4t^2 + 20t + 25 = 0$.

14. Add: $(3x^3 - 5x + 1) + (4x^3 + 7x - 8)$.

15. Factor: $16x^2 - 81$.

16. Solve: $y^2 - 5y - 24 = 0$.

17. Subtract: $(a^2 - 2) - (5a^2 + a + 9)$.

18. Factor: $18x^4 - 24x^3 + 20x^2$.

19. Solve: $3x^2 + 5x + 2 = 0$.

20. Multiply: $4x^2(2x^3 - 5x^2 + 3)$.

6.8   Solving Applications

Applications   ▪   The Pythagorean Theorem

Applications

We can use the five-step problem-solving process and our new methods of solving quadratic equations to solve new types of problems.

EXAMPLE 1

Race numbers.   Terry and Jody each entered a boat in the Lakeport Race. The racing numbers of their boats were consecutive numbers, the product of which was 156. Find the numbers.

SOLUTION

1. **Familiarize.** Consecutive numbers are one apart, like 49 and 50. Let $x =$ the first boat number; then $x + 1 =$ the next boat number.

2. **Translate.** We reword the problem before translating:

Rewording:	The first boat number	times	the next boat number	is	156.
Translating:	x	$\cdot$	$(x + 1)$	$=$	156

3. **Carry out.** We solve the equation as follows:

$$x(x + 1) = 156$$
$$x^2 + x = 156 \qquad \text{Multiplying}$$
$$x^2 + x - 156 = 0 \qquad \text{Subtracting 156 to get 0 on one side}$$
$$(x - 12)(x + 13) = 0 \qquad \text{Factoring}$$
$$x - 12 = 0 \quad or \quad x + 13 = 0 \qquad \text{Using the principle of zero products}$$
$$x = 12 \quad or \qquad x = -13. \qquad \text{Solving each equation}$$

4. **Check.** The solutions of the equation are 12 and -13. Since race numbers are not negative, -13 must be rejected. On the other hand, if x is 12, then $x + 1$ is 13 and $12 \cdot 13 = 156$. Thus the solution 12 checks.

5. **State.** The boat numbers for Terry and Jody were 12 and 13.

> TRY EXERCISE 5

EXAMPLE 2

Manufacturing.   Wooden Work, Ltd., builds cutting boards that are twice as long as they are wide. The most popular board that Wooden Work makes has an area of 800 cm². What are the dimensions of the board?

SOLUTION

1. **Familiarize.** We first make a drawing. Recall that the area of any rectangle is Length · Width. We let $x =$ the width of the board, in centimeters. The length is then $2x$, since the board is twice as long as it is wide.

$2x$ $\qquad$ x

2. **Translate.** We reword and translate as follows:

Rewording: The area of the rectangle is 800 cm^2.

Translating: $2x \cdot x = 800$

3. **Carry out.** We solve the equation as follows:

$$2x \cdot x = 800$$
$$2x^2 = 800$$

$2x^2 - 800 = 0$ Subtracting 800 to get 0 on one side of the equation

$2(x^2 - 400) = 0$ Factoring out a common factor of 2

$2(x - 20)(x + 20) = 0$ Factoring a difference of squares

$(x - 20)(x + 20) = 0$ Dividing both sides by 2

$x - 20 = 0$ *or* $x + 20 = 0$ Using the principle of zero products

$x = 20$ *or* $x = -20.$ Solving each equation

4. **Check.** The solutions of the equation are 20 and −20. Since the width must be positive, −20 cannot be a solution. To check 20 cm, we note that if the width is 20 cm, then the length is $2 \cdot 20$ cm $= 40$ cm and the area is 20 cm $\cdot$ 40 cm $= 800 \text{ cm}^2$. Thus the solution 20 checks.

5. **State.** The cutting board is 20 cm wide and 40 cm long.   **TRY EXERCISE**   9

EXAMPLE   **3**   *Dimensions of a leaf.*   Each leaf of one particular *Philodendron* species is approximately a triangle. A typical leaf has an area of 320 in^2. If the leaf is 12 in. longer than it is wide, find the length and the width of the leaf.

SOLUTION

1. **Familiarize.** The formula for the area of a triangle is Area $= \frac{1}{2} \cdot$ (base) $\cdot$ (height). We let $b =$ the width, in inches, of the triangle's base and $b + 12 =$ the height, in inches.

2. **Translate.** We reword and translate as follows:

Rewording: The area of the leaf is 320 in^2.

Translating: $\frac{1}{2} \cdot b(b + 12) = 320$

3. Carry out. We solve the equation as follows:

$$\tfrac{1}{2} \cdot b \cdot (b + 12) = 320$$

$$\tfrac{1}{2}(b^2 + 12b) = 320 \qquad \text{Multiplying}$$

$$b^2 + 12b = 640 \qquad \text{Multiplying by 2 to clear fractions}$$

$$b^2 + 12b - 640 = 0 \qquad \text{Subtracting 640 to get 0 on one side}$$

$$(b + 32)(b - 20) = 0 \qquad \text{Factoring}$$

$$b + 32 = 0 \quad or \quad b - 20 = 0 \qquad \text{Using the principle of zero products}$$

$$b = -32 \quad or \qquad b = 20.$$

4. Check. The width must be positive, so -32 cannot be a solution. Suppose the base is 20 in. The height would be $20 + 12$, or 32 in., and the area $\tfrac{1}{2}(20)(32)$, or 320 in². These numbers check in the original problem.

5. State. The leaf is 32 in. long and 20 in. wide.   ▶ TRY EXERCISE ▶ 13

EXAMPLE **4**   *Medicine.* For certain people suffering an extreme allergic reaction, the drug epinephrine (adrenaline) is sometimes prescribed. The number of micrograms N of epinephrine in an adult's bloodstream t minutes after 250 micrograms have been injected can be approximated by

$$-10t^2 + 100t = N.$$

How long after an injection will there be about 210 micrograms of epinephrine in the bloodstream?

Source: Based on information in Chohan, Naina, Rita M. Doyle, and Patricia Nayle (eds.), *Nursing Handbook*, 21st ed. Springhouse, PA: Springhouse Corporation, 2001

SOLUTION

1. Familiarize. To familiarize ourselves with this problem, we could calculate N for different choices of t. We leave this for the student. Note that there may be two solutions, one on each side of the time at which the drug's effect peaks.

2. Translate. To find the length of time after injection when 210 micrograms are in the bloodstream, we replace N with 210 in the formula above:

$$-10t^2 + 100t = 210. \qquad \text{Substituting 210 for } N. \text{ This is now an equation in one variable.}$$

3. Carry out. We solve the equation as follows:

$$-10t^2 + 100t = 210$$

$$-10t^2 + 100t - 210 = 0 \qquad \text{Subtracting 210 from both sides to get 0 on one side}$$

$$-10(t^2 - 10t + 21) = 0 \qquad \text{Factoring out the largest common factor, } -10$$

$$-10(t - 3)(t - 7) = 0 \qquad \text{Factoring}$$

$$t - 3 = 0 \quad or \quad t - 7 = 0 \qquad \text{Using the principle of zero products}$$

$$t = 3 \quad or \qquad t = 7.$$

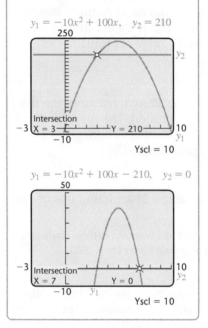

TECHNOLOGY CONNECTION

As a visual check for Example 4, we can either let $y_1 = -10x^2 + 100x$ and $y_2 = 210$, or let $y_1 = -10x^2 + 100x - 210$ and $y_2 = 0$. In either case, the points of intersection occur at $x = 3$ and $x = 7$, as shown.

4. **Check.** Since $-10 \cdot 3^2 + 100 \cdot 3 = -90 + 300 = 210$, the number 3 checks. Since $-10 \cdot 7^2 + 100 \cdot 7 = -490 + 700 = 210$, the number 7 also checks.

5. **State.** There will be 210 micrograms of epinephrine in the bloodstream approximately 3 minutes and 7 minutes after injection.

TRY EXERCISE 17

The Pythagorean Theorem

The following problems involve the Pythagorean theorem, which relates the lengths of the sides of a *right* triangle. A triangle is a **right triangle** if it has a 90°, or *right*, angle. The side opposite the 90° angle is called the **hypotenuse**. The other sides are called **legs**.

The Pythagorean Theorem

In any right triangle, if a and b are the lengths of the legs and c is the length of the hypotenuse, then

$$a^2 + b^2 = c^2, \quad \text{or}$$

$$(\text{Leg})^2 + (\text{Other leg})^2 = (\text{Hypotenuse})^2.$$

The equation $a^2 + b^2 = c^2$ is called the **Pythagorean equation.***

The Pythagorean theorem is named for the Greek mathematician Pythagoras (569?–500? B.C.). We can think of this relationship as adding areas.

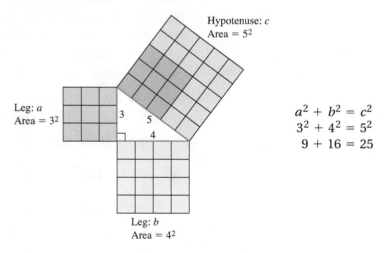

$$a^2 + b^2 = c^2$$
$$3^2 + 4^2 = 5^2$$
$$9 + 16 = 25$$

If we know the lengths of any two sides of a right triangle, we can use the Pythagorean equation to determine the length of the third side.

*The *converse* of the Pythagorean theorem is also true. That is, if $a^2 + b^2 = c^2$, then the triangle is a right triangle.

EXAMPLE 5   *Travel.* A zipline canopy tour in Alaska includes a cable that slopes downward from a height of 135 ft to a height of 100 ft. The trees that the cable connects are 120 ft apart. Find the minimum length of the cable.

SOLUTION

1. **Familiarize.** We first make a drawing or visualize the situation. The difference in height between the platforms is 35 ft. Note that the cable must have some extra length to allow for the rider's movement, but we will approximate its length as the hypotenuse of a right triangle, as shown.

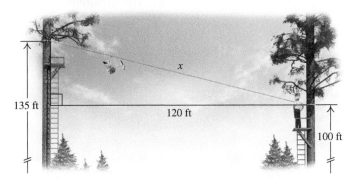

2. **Translate.** Since a right triangle is formed, we can use the Pythagorean theorem:

$$a^2 + b^2 = c^2$$
$$35^2 + 120^2 = x^2. \qquad \text{Substituting}$$

3. **Carry out.** We solve the equation as follows:

$$1225 + 14{,}400 = x^2 \qquad \text{Squaring 35 and 120}$$
$$15{,}625 = x^2 \qquad \text{Adding}$$
$$0 = x^2 - 15{,}625 \qquad \text{Subtracting 15,625 from both sides}$$
$$0 = (x + 125)(x - 125) \qquad \text{Note that } 15{,}625 = 125^2. \text{ A calculator would be helpful here.}$$
$$x + 125 = 0 \quad or \quad x - 125 = 0 \qquad \text{Using the principle of zero products}$$
$$x = -125 \quad or \qquad x = 125.$$

4. **Check.** Since the length of the cable must be positive, -125 is not a solution. If the length is 125 ft, we have $35^2 + 120^2 = 1225 + 14{,}400 = 15{,}625$, which is 125^2. Thus the solution 125 checks.

5. **State.** The minimum length of the cable is 125 ft.   **TRY EXERCISE** 27

EXAMPLE   6   *Bridge design.*   A 50-ft diagonal brace on a bridge connects a support at the center of the bridge to a side support on the bridge. The horizontal distance that it spans is 10 ft longer than the height that it reaches on the side of the bridge. Find both distances.

SOLUTION

1. **Familiarize.** We first make a drawing. The diagonal brace and the missing distances form the hypotenuse and the legs of a right triangle. We let x = the length of the vertical leg. Then $x + 10$ = the length of the horizontal leg. The hypotenuse has length 50 ft.

2. **Translate.** Since the triangle is a right triangle, we can use the Pythagorean theorem:

$$a^2 + b^2 = c^2$$
$$x^2 + (x + 10)^2 = 50^2. \qquad \text{Substituting}$$

3. **Carry out.** We solve the equation as follows:

$x^2 + (x^2 + 20x + 100) = 2500$	Squaring
$2x^2 + 20x + 100 = 2500$	Combining like terms
$2x^2 + 20x - 2400 = 0$	Subtracting 2500 to get 0 on one side
$2(x^2 + 10x - 1200) = 0$	Factoring out a common factor
$2(x + 40)(x - 30) = 0$	Factoring. A calculator would be helpful here.
$x + 40 = 0 \quad or \quad x - 30 = 0$	Using the principle of zero products
$x = -40 \quad or \qquad x = 30.$	

4. **Check.** The integer -40 cannot be a length of a side because it is negative. If the length is 30 ft, $x + 10 = 40$, and $30^2 + 40^2 = 900 + 1600 = 2500$, which is 50^2. So the solution 30 checks.

5. **State.** The height that the brace reaches on the side of the bridge is 30 ft, and the distance that it reaches to the middle of the bridge is 40 ft.

TRY EXERCISE 31

Translating for Success

1. *Angle measures.* The measures of the angles of a triangle are three consecutive integers. Find the measures of the angles.

2. *Rectangle dimensions.* The area of a rectangle is 3604 ft². The length is 15 ft longer than the width. Find the dimensions of the rectangle.

3. *Sales tax.* Claire paid $3604 for a used pickup truck. This included 6% for sales tax. How much did the truck cost before tax?

4. *Wire cutting.* A 180-m wire is cut into three pieces. The third piece is 2 m longer than the first. The second is two-thirds as long as the first. How long is each piece?

5. *Perimeter.* The perimeter of a rectangle is 240 ft. The length is 2 ft greater than the width. Find the length and the width.

Translate each word problem to an equation and select a correct translation from equations A–O.

A. $2x \cdot x = 288$

B. $x(x + 60) = 7021$

C. $59 = x \cdot 60$

D. $x^2 + (x + 15)^2 = 3604$

E. $x^2 + (x + 70)^2 = 130^2$

F. $0.06x = 3604$

G. $2(x + 2) + 2x = 240$

H. $\frac{1}{2}x(x - 1) = 1770$

I. $x + \frac{2}{3}x + (x + 2) = 180$

J. $0.59x = 60$

K. $x + 0.06x = 3604$

L. $2x^2 + x = 288$

M. $x(x + 15) = 3604$

N. $x^2 + 60 = 7021$

O. $x + (x + 1) + (x + 2) = 180$

Answers on page A-24

An additional, animated version of this activity appears in MyMathLab. To use MyMathLab, you need a course ID and a student access code. Contact your instructor for more information.

6. *Cell-phone tower.* A guy wire on a cell-phone tower is 130 ft long and is attached to the top of the tower. The height of the tower is 70 ft longer than the distance from the point on the ground where the wire is attached to the bottom of the tower. Find the height of the tower.

7. *Sales meeting attendance.* PTQ Corporation holds a sales meeting in Tucson. Of the 60 employees, 59 of them attend the meeting. What percent attend the meeting?

8. *Dimensions of a pool.* A rectangular swimming pool is twice as long as it is wide. The area of the surface is 288 ft². Find the dimensions of the pool.

9. *Dimensions of a triangle.* The height of a triangle is 1 cm less than the length of the base. The area of the triangle is 1770 cm². Find the height and the length of the base.

10. *Width of a rectangle.* The length of a rectangle is 60 ft longer than the width. Find the width if the area of the rectangle is 7021 ft².

Solve. Use the five-step problem-solving approach.

1. A number is 6 less than its square. Find all such numbers.

2. A number is 30 less than its square. Find all such numbers.

3. One leg of a right triangle is 2 m longer than the other leg. The length of the hypotenuse is 10 m. Find the length of each side.

4. One leg of a right triangle is 7 cm shorter than the other leg. The length of the hypotenuse is 13 cm. Find the length of each side.

5. *Parking-space numbers.* The product of two consecutive parking spaces is 132. Find the parking-space numbers.

6. *Page numbers.* The product of the page numbers on two facing pages of a book is 420. Find the page numbers.

7. The product of two consecutive even integers is 168. Find the integers.

8. The product of two consecutive odd integers is 195. Find the integers.

9. *Construction.* The front porch on Trent's new home is five times as long as it is wide. If the area of the porch is 180 ft^2, find the dimensions.

5w
w

10. *Furnishings.* The work surface of Anita's desk is a rectangle that is twice as long as it is wide. If the area

w
2w

of the desktop is 18 ft^2, find the length and the width of the desk.

11. *Design.* The screen of the TI-84 Plus graphing calculator is nearly rectangular. The length of the rectangle is 2 cm more than the width. If the area of the rectangle is 24 cm^2, find the length and the width.

w + 2
w

12. *Area of a garden.* The length of a rectangular garden is 4 m greater than the width. The area of the garden is 96 m^2. Find the length and the width.

w
w + 4

13. *Dimensions of a triangle.* The height of a triangle is 3 in. less than the length of the base. If the area of the triangle is 54 in^2, find the height and the length of the base.

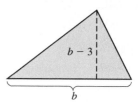

b − 3
b

14. *Dimensions of a triangle.* A triangle is 10 cm wider than it is tall. The area is 48 cm^2. Find the height and the base.

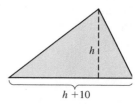

h
h + 10

15. *Dimensions of a sail.*   The height of the jib sail on a Lightning sailboat is 5 ft greater than the length of its "foot." If the area of the sail is 42 ft², find the length of the foot and the height of the sail.

16. *Road design.*   A triangular traffic island has a base half as long as its height. Find the base and the height if the island has an area of 64 m².

17. *Medicine.*   For many people suffering from constricted bronchial muscles, the drug Albuterol is prescribed. The number of micrograms A of Albuterol in a person's bloodstream t minutes after 200 micrograms have been inhaled can be approximated by

$$A = -50t^2 + 200t.$$

How long after an inhalation will there be about 150 micrograms of Albuterol in the bloodstream?
Source: Based on information in Chohan, Naina, Rita M. Doyle, and Patricia Nayle (eds.), *Nursing Handbook*, 21st ed. Springhouse, PA: Springhouse Corporation, 2001

18. *Medicine.*   For adults with certain heart conditions, the drug Primacor (milrinone lactate) is prescribed. The number of milligrams M of Primacor in the bloodstream of a 132-lb patient t hours after a 3-mg dose has been injected can be approximated by

$$M = -\frac{1}{2}t^2 + \frac{5}{2}t.$$

How long after an injection will there be about 2 mg in the bloodstream?
Source: Based on information in Chohan, Naina, Rita M. Doyle, and Patricia Nayle (eds.), *Nursing Handbook*, 21st ed. Springhouse, PA: Springhouse Corporation, 2001

19. *High-speed Internet.*   The number N, in millions, of broadband cable and DSL subscribers in the United States t years after 1998 can be approximated by

$$N = 0.3t^2 + 0.6t.$$

When will there be 36 million broadband cable and DSL subscribers?
Source: Based on information from Leichtman Research Group

20. *Wave height.*   The height of waves in a storm depends on the speed of the wind. Assuming the wind has no obstructions for a long distance, the maximum wave height H for a wind speed x can be approximated by

$$H = 0.006x^2 + 0.6x.$$

Here H is in feet and x is in knots (nautical miles per hour). For what wind speed would the maximum wave height be 6.6 ft?
Source: Based on information from cimss.ssec.wisc.edu

Games in a league's schedule.   *In a sports league of x teams in which all teams play each other twice, the total number N of games played is given by*

$$x^2 - x = N.$$

Use this formula for Exercises 21 and 22.

21. The Colchester Youth Soccer League plays a total of 240 games, with all teams playing each other twice. How many teams are in the league?

22. The teams in a women's softball league play each other twice, for a total of 132 games. How many teams are in the league?

Number of handshakes.   *The number of possible handshakes H within a group of n people is given by* $H = \frac{1}{2}(n^2 - n)$. *Use this formula for Exercises 23–26.*

23. At a meeting, there are 12 people. How many handshakes are possible?

24. At a party, there are 25 people. How many handshakes are possible?

25. *High-fives.* After winning the championship, all San Antonio Spurs teammates exchanged "high-fives." Altogether there were 66 high-fives. How many players were there?

26. *Toasting.* During a toast at a party, there were 105 "clicks" of glasses. How many people took part in the toast?

27. *Construction.* The diagonal braces in a lookout tower are 15 ft long and span a horizontal distance of 12 ft. How high does each brace reach vertically?

28. *Reach of a ladder.* Twyla has a 26-ft ladder leaning against her house. If the bottom of the ladder is 10 ft from the base of the house, how high does the ladder reach?

29. *Roadway design.* Elliott Street is 24 ft wide when it ends at Main Street in Brattleboro, Vermont. A 40-ft long diagonal crosswalk allows pedestrians to cross Main Street to or from either corner of Elliott Street (see the figure). Determine the width of Main Street.

30. *Aviation.* Engine failure forced Robbin to pilot her Cessna 150 to an emergency landing. To land, Robbin's plane glided 17,000 ft over a 15,000-ft stretch of deserted highway. From what altitude did the descent begin?

31. *Archaeology.* Archaeologists have discovered that the 18th-century garden of the Charles Carroll House in Annapolis, Maryland, was a right triangle. One leg of the triangle was formed by a 400-ft long sea wall. The hypotenuse of the triangle was 200 ft longer than the other leg. What were the dimensions of the garden?
Source: www.bsos.umd.edu

32. *Guy wire.* The guy wire on a TV antenna is 1 m longer than the height of the antenna. If the guy wire is anchored 3 m from the foot of the antenna, how tall is the antenna?

33. *Architecture.* An architect has allocated a rectangular space of 264 ft^2 for a square dining room and a 10-ft wide kitchen, as shown in the figure. Find the dimensions of each room.

34. *Design.*   A window panel for a sun porch consists of a 7-ft high rectangular window stacked above a square window. The windows have the same width. If the total area of the window panel is 18 ft², find the dimensions of each window.

7 ft

Height of a rocket.   *For Exercises 35–38, assume that a water rocket is launched upward with an initial velocity of 48 ft/sec. Its height h, in feet, after t seconds, is given by* $h = 48t - 16t^2$.

35. Determine the height of the rocket $\frac{1}{2}$ sec after it has been launched.

36. Determine the height of the rocket 2.5 sec after it has been launched.

37. When will the rocket be exactly 32 ft above the ground?

38. When will the rocket crash into the ground?

39. Do we now have the ability to solve *any* problem that translates to a quadratic equation? Why or why not?

40. Write a problem for a classmate to solve such that only one of two solutions of a quadratic equation can be used as an answer.

Skill Review

To prepare for Chapter 6, review addition, subtraction, multiplication, and division using fraction notation (Sections 1.3, 1.5, 1.6, and 1.7).

Simplify.

41. $-\dfrac{3}{5} \cdot \dfrac{4}{7}$ [1.7]

42. $-\dfrac{3}{5} \div \dfrac{4}{7}$ [1.7]

43. $-\dfrac{5}{6} - \dfrac{1}{6}$ [1.6]

44. $\dfrac{3}{4} + \left(-\dfrac{5}{2}\right)$ [1.5]

45. $-\dfrac{3}{8} \cdot \left(-\dfrac{10}{15}\right)$ [1.7]

46. $\dfrac{-\dfrac{8}{15}}{-\dfrac{2}{3}}$ [1.7]

47. $\dfrac{5}{24} + \dfrac{3}{28}$ [1.3]

48. $\dfrac{5}{6} - \left(-\dfrac{2}{9}\right)$ [1.6]

Synthesis

The converse of the Pythagorean theorem is also true. That is, if $a^2 + b^2 = c^2$, then the triangle is a right triangle (where a and b are the lengths of the legs and c is the length of the hypotenuse). Use this result to answer Exercises 49 and 50.

49. An archaeologist has measuring sticks of 3 ft, 4 ft, and 5 ft. Explain how she could draw a 7-ft by 9-ft rectangle on a piece of land being excavated.

50. Explain how measuring sticks of 5 cm, 12 cm, and 13 cm can be used to draw a right triangle that has two 45° angles.

51. *Sailing.*   The mainsail of a Lightning sailboat is a right triangle in which the hypotenuse is called the leech. If a 24-ft tall mainsail has a leech length of 26 ft and if Dacron® sailcloth costs $1.50 per square foot, find the cost of the fabric for a new mainsail.

26 ft

24 ft

52. *Roofing.*   A *square* of shingles covers 100 ft² of surface area. How many squares will be needed to re-shingle the house shown?

25 ft

16 ft

24 ft

32 ft

53. Solve for *x*.

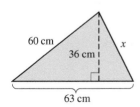

60 cm

36 cm

x

63 cm

54. *Pool sidewalk.* A cement walk of uniform width is built around a 20-ft by 40-ft rectangular pool. The total area of the pool and the walk is 1500 ft². Find the width of the walk.

55. *Folding sheet metal.* An open rectangular gutter is made by turning up the sides of a piece of metal 20 in. wide, as shown. The area of the cross-section of the gutter is 48 in². Find the possible depths of the gutter.

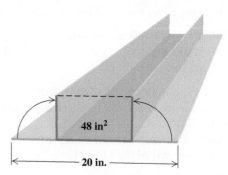

48 in²

20 in.

56. Find a polynomial for the shaded area in the figure below.

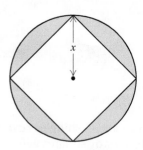

x

57. *Telephone service.* Use the information in the figure below to determine the height of the telephone pole.

5 ft

34 ft

x

$\frac{1}{2}x + 1$

58. *Dimensions of a closed box.* The total surface area of a closed box is 350 m². The box is 9 m high and has a square base and lid. Find the length of a side of the base.

Medicine. *For certain people with acid reflux, the drug Pepcid (famotidine) is used. The number of milligrams N of Pepcid in an adult's bloodstream t hours after a 20-mg tablet has been swallowed can be approximated by*

$$N = -0.009t(t - 12)^3.$$

Use a graphing calculator with the window $[-1, 13, -1, 25]$ *and the* TRACE *feature to answer Exercises 59–61.*

Source: Based on information in Chohan, Naina, Rita M. Doyle, and Patricia Nayle (eds.), *Nursing Handbook*, 21st ed. Springhouse, PA: Springhouse Corporation, 2001

59. Approximately how long after a tablet has been swallowed will there be 18 mg in the bloodstream?

60. Approximately how long after a tablet has been swallowed will there be 10 mg in the bloodstream?

61. Approximately how long after a tablet has been swallowed will the peak dosage in the bloodstream occur?

Study Summary

KEY TERMS AND CONCEPTS	EXAMPLES

SECTION 6.1: INTRODUCTION TO FACTORING

To **factor** a polynomial means to write it as a product. Always begin by factoring out the **largest common factor**.

Factor: $12x^4 - 30x^3$.
$$12x^4 - 30x^3 = 6x^3(2x - 5)$$

Some polynomials with four terms can be **factored by grouping**.

Factor: $3x^3 - x^2 - 6x + 2$.
$$3x^3 - x^2 - 6x + 2 = x^2(3x - 1) - 2(3x - 1)$$
$$= (3x - 1)(x^2 - 2)$$

SECTION 6.2: FACTORING TRINOMIALS OF THE TYPE $x^2 + bx + c$

Some trinomials of the type $x^2 + bx + c$ can be factored by reversing the steps of FOIL.

Factor: $x^2 - 11x + 18$.

Pairs of Factors of 18	Sums of Factors
$-1, -18$	-19
$-2, \ -9$	-11

18 is positive and -11 is negative, so both factors will be negative.

←The numbers we need are -2 and -9.

The factorization is $(x - 2)(x - 9)$.

SECTION 6.3: FACTORING TRINOMIALS OF THE TYPE $ax^2 + bx + c$

One method for factoring trinomials of the type $ax^2 + bx + c$ is a FOIL-based method.

Factor: $6x^2 - 5x - 6$.

The factors will be in the form $(3x + \ )(2x + \ )$ or $(6x + \ )(x + \ )$. We list all pairs of factors of -6, and check possible products by multiplying any possibilities that do not contain a common factor.

$$(3x - 2)(2x + 3) = 6x^2 + 5x - 6,$$
$$(3x + 2)(2x - 3) = 6x^2 - 5x - 6. \ \leftarrow\text{This is the correct product,}$$
$$\text{so we stop here.}$$

The factorization is $(3x + 2)(2x - 3)$.

Another method for factoring trinomials of the type $ax^2 + bx + c$ involves factoring by grouping.

Factor: $6x^2 - 5x - 6$.

Multiply the leading coefficient and the constant term: $6(-6) = -36$. Look for factors of -36 that add to -5.

Pairs of Factors of -36	Sums of Factors
$1, -36$	-35
$2, -18$	-16
$3, -12$	-9
$4, \ -9$	-5

-5 is negative, so the negative factor must have the greater absolute value.

←The numbers we want are 4 and -9.

Rewrite $-5x$ as $4x - 9x$ and factor by grouping:
$$6x^2 - 5x - 6 = 6x^2 + 4x - 9x - 6$$
$$= 2x(3x + 2) - 3(3x + 2)$$
$$= (3x + 2)(2x - 3).$$

SECTION 6.4: FACTORING PERFECT-SQUARE TRINOMIALS AND DIFFERENCES OF SQUARES

Factoring a perfect-square trinomial

$$A^2 + 2AB + B^2 = (A + B)^2;$$
$$A^2 - 2AB + B^2 = (A - B)^2$$

Factor: $y^2 + 100 - 20y$.

$$A^2 - 2AB + B^2 = (A - B)^2$$
$$y^2 + 100 - 20y = y^2 - 20y + 100 = (y - 10)^2$$

Factoring a difference of squares

$$A^2 - B^2 = (A + B)(A - B)$$

Factor: $9t^2 - 1$.

$$A^2 - B^2 = (A + B)(A - B)$$
$$9t^2 - 1 = (3t + 1)(3t - 1)$$

SECTION 6.5: FACTORING SUMS OR DIFFERENCES OF CUBES

Factoring a sum or a difference of cubes

$$A^3 + B^3 = (A + B)(A^2 - AB + B^2)$$
$$A^3 - B^3 = (A - B)(A^2 + AB + B^2)$$

$$x^3 + 1000 = (x + 10)(x^2 - 10x + 100)$$
$$z^6 - 8w^3 = (z^2 - 2w)(z^4 + 2wz^2 + 4w^2)$$

SECTION 6.6: FACTORING: A GENERAL STRATEGY

To factor a polynomial:

A. Factor out the largest common factor.

B. Look at the number of terms.

Two terms: If a difference of squares, use $A^2 - B^2 = (A + B)(A - B)$. If a sum of cubes, use $A^3 + B^3 = (A + B)(A^2 - AB + B^2)$. If a difference of cubes, use $A^3 - B^3 = (A - B)(A^2 + AB + B^2)$.

Three terms: If a trinomial square, use $A^2 + 2AB + B^2 = (A + B)^2$ or $A^2 - 2AB + B^2 = (A - B)^2$. Otherwise, try FOIL or grouping.

Four terms: Try factoring by grouping.

C. Factor completely.

D. Check by multiplying.

Factor: $5x^5 - 80x$.

$$5x^5 - 80x = 5x(x^4 - 16)$$ $5x$ is the largest common factor.

$$= 5x(x^2 + 4)(x^2 - 4)$$ $x^4 - 16$ is a difference of squares.

$$= 5x(x^2 + 4)(x + 2)(x - 2)$$ $x^2 - 4$ is also a difference of squares.

Check: $5x(x^2 + 4)(x + 2)(x - 2) = 5x(x^2 + 4)(x^2 - 4)$
$$= 5x(x^4 - 16) = 5x^5 - 80x.$$

Factor: $-x^2y^2 - 3xy + 10$.

$$-x^2y^2 - 3xy + 10 = -(x^2y^2 + 3xy - 10)$$ Factor out -1 to make the leading coefficient positive.

$$= -(xy + 5)(xy - 2)$$

Check: $-(xy + 5)(xy - 2) = -(x^2y^2 + 3xy - 10)$
$$= -x^2y^2 - 3xy + 10.$$

SECTION 6.7: SOLVING POLYNOMIAL EQUATIONS BY FACTORING

The Principle of Zero Products

An equation $AB = 0$ is true if and only if $A = 0$ or $B = 0$, or both.

Solve: $x^2 + 7x = 30$.

$$x^2 + 7x = 30$$
$$x^2 + 7x - 30 = 0$$ Getting 0 on one side
$$(x + 10)(x - 3) = 0$$ Factoring
$$x + 10 = 0 \quad or \quad x - 3 = 0$$ Using the principle of zero products

$$x = -10 \quad or \quad x = 3$$

The solutions are -10 and 3.

SECTION 6.8: SOLVING APPLICATIONS

The Pythagorean Theorem

In any right triangle, if a and b are the lengths of the legs and c is the length of the hypotenuse, then

$a^2 + b^2 = c^2$, or

$(\text{Leg})^2 + (\text{Other leg})^2 = (\text{Hypotenuse})^2$.

Aaron has a 25-ft ladder leaning against his house. The height that the ladder reaches on the house is 17 ft more than the distance that the bottom of the ladder is from the house. Find both distances.

$$x^2 + (x + 17)^2 = 25^2$$
$$x^2 + x^2 + 34x + 289 = 625 \qquad \text{Squaring}$$
$$2x^2 + 34x - 336 = 0$$
$$2(x + 24)(x - 7) = 0 \qquad \text{Factoring}$$
$$x + 24 = 0 \quad or \quad x - 7 = 0 \qquad \text{Using the principle of zero products}$$
$$x = -24 \quad or \qquad x = 7.$$

Since -24 cannot be a length, we check 7. When $x = 7$, $x + 17 = 24$, and $7^2 + 24^2 = 49 + 576 = 625 = 25^2$.

The ladder reaches 24 ft up the side of the house, and the bottom of the ladder is 7 ft from the house.

Review Exercises: Chapter 6

🦢 *Concept Reinforcement* *Classify each statement as either true or false.*

1. The largest common variable factor is the largest power of the variable in the polynomial. [6.1]

2. A prime polynomial has no common factor other than 1 or −1. [6.2]

3. Every perfect-square trinomial can be expressed as a binomial squared. [6.4]

4. Every binomial can be regarded as a difference of squares. [6.4]

5. Every quadratic equation has two different solutions. [6.7]

6. The principle of zero products can be applied whenever a product equals 0. [6.7]

7. In a right triangle, the hypotenuse is always longer than either leg. [6.8]

8. The Pythagorean theorem can be applied to any triangle that has an angle measuring at least 90°. [6.8]

Find three factorizations of each monomial. [6.1]

9. $20x^3$

10. $-18x^5$

Factor completely. If a polynomial is prime, state this.

11. $12x^4 - 18x^3$ [6.1]

12. $8a^2 - 12a$ [6.1]

13. $100t^2 - 1$ [6.4]

14. $x^2 + x - 12$ [6.2]

15. $x^2 + 14x + 49$ [6.4]

16. $12x^3 + 12x^2 + 3x$ [6.4]

17. $6x^3 + 9x^2 + 2x + 3$ [6.1]

18. $6a^2 + a - 5$ [6.3]

19. $25t^2 + 9 - 30t$ [6.4]

20. $48t^2 - 28t + 6$ [6.1]

21. $81a^4 - 1$ [6.4]

22. $9x^3 + 12x^2 - 45x$ [6.3]

23. $2x^3 - 250$ [6.5]

24. $x^4 + 4x^3 - 2x - 8$ [6.1]

25. $a^2b^4 - 64$ [6.4]

26. $-8x^6 + 32x^5 - 4x^4$ [6.1]

27. $75 + 12x^2 - 60x$ [6.4]

28. $y^2 + 9$ [6.4]

29. $-t^3 + t^2 + 42t$ [6.2]

30. $4x^2 - 25$ [6.4]

31. $n^2 - 60 - 4n$ [6.2]

32. $5z^2 - 30z + 10$ [6.1]

33. $4t^2 + 13t + 10$ [6.3]

34. $2t^2 - 7t - 4$ [6.3]

35. $7x^3 + 35x^2 + 28x$ [6.2]

36. $8y^3 + 27x^6$ [6.5]

37. $20x^2 - 20x + 5$ [6.4]

38. $-6x^3 + 150x$ [6.4]

39. $15 - 8x + x^2$ [6.2]

40. $3x + x^2 + 5$ [6.2]

41. $x^2y^2 + 6xy - 16$ [6.2]

42. $12a^2 + 84ab + 147b^2$ [6.4]

43. $m^2 + 5m + mt + 5t$ [6.1]

44. $32x^4 - 128y^4z^4$ [6.4]

45. $6m^2 + 2mn + n^2 + 3mn$ [6.1], [6.3]

46. $6r^2 + rs - 15s^2$ [6.3]

Solve. [6.7]

47. $(x - 9)(x + 11) = 0$

48. $x^2 + 2x - 35 = 0$

49. $16x^2 = 9$

50. $3x^2 + 2 = 5x$

51. $2x^2 - 7x = 30$

52. $(x + 1)(x - 2) = 4$

53. $9t - 15t^2 = 0$

54. $3x^2 + 3 = 6x$

55. The square of a number is 12 more than the number. Find all such numbers. [6.8]

56. The formula $x^2 - x = N$ can be used to determine the total number of games played, N, in a league of x teams in which all teams play each other twice. Serena referees for a soccer league in which all teams play each other twice and a total of 90 games is played. How many teams are in the league? [6.8]

57. Find the x-intercepts for the graph of $y = 2x^2 - 3x - 5$. [6.7]

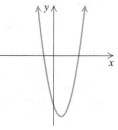

58. The front of a house is a triangle that is as wide as it is tall. Its area is 98 ft². Find the height and the base. [6.8]

59. Josh needs to add a diagonal brace to his LEGO® robot. The brace must span a height of 8 holes and a width of 6 holes. How long should the brace be? [6.8]

Synthesis

60. On a quiz, Celia writes the factorization of $4x^2 - 100$ as $(2x - 10)(2x + 10)$. If this were a 10-point question, how many points would you give Celia? Why? [6.4]

61. How do the equations solved in this chapter differ from those solved in previous chapters? [6.7]

Solve.

62. The pages of a book measure 15 cm by 20 cm. Margins of equal width surround the printing on each page and constitute one half of the area of the page. Find the width of the margins. [6.8]

15 cm

20 cm

When in the Course of human events, it becomes necessary for one people to dissolve the political bands which have connected them with another, and to assume among the powers of the earth, the separate and equal station to which the Laws of Nature and of

Nature's God entitle them, a decent respect to the opinions of mankind requires that they should declare the causes which impel them to the separation.
We hold these truths to be self-evident, that all men are created equal, that they are endowed by their Creator with certain unalienable

63. The cube of a number is the same as twice the square of the number. Find the number. [6.8]

64. The length of a rectangle is two times its width. When the length is increased by 20 cm and the width is decreased by 1 cm, the area is 160 cm². Find the original length and width. [6.8]

65. The length of each side of a square is increased by 5 cm to form a new square. The area of the new square is $2\frac{1}{4}$ times the area of the original square. Find the area of each square. [6.8]

Solve. [6.7]

66. $(x - 2)2x^2 + x(x - 2) - (x - 2)15 = 0$

Aha! **67.** $x^2 + 25 = 0$

Test: Chapter 6

CHAPTER
Test Prep
VIDEO CD

Step-by-step test solutions are found on the video CD in the front of this book.

1. Find three factorizations of $12x^4$.

Factor completely. If a polynomial is prime, state this.

2. $x^2 - 13x + 36$

3. $x^2 + 25 - 10x$

4. $6y^2 - 8y^3 + 4y^4$

5. $x^3 + x^2 + 2x + 2$

6. $t^7 - 3t^5$

7. $a^3 + 3a^2 - 4a$

8. $28x - 48 + 10x^2$

9. $4t^2 - 25$

10. $x^2 - x - 6$

11. $-6m^3 - 9m^2 - 3m$

12. $3r^3 - 3$

13. $45r^2 + 60r + 20$

14. $3x^4 - 48$

15. $49t^2 + 36 + 84t$

16. $x^4 + 2x^3 - 3x - 6$

17. $x^2 + 3x + 6$

18. $4x^2 - 4x - 15$

19. $6t^3 + 9t^2 - 15t$

20. $3m^2 - 9mn - 30n^2$

Solve.

21. $x^2 - 6x + 5 = 0$

22. $2x^2 - 7x = 15$

23. $4t - 10t^2 = 0$

24. $25t^2 = 1$

25. $x(x - 1) = 20$

26. Find the x-intercepts for the graph of $y = 3x^2 - 5x - 8$.

27. The length of a rectangle is 6 m more than the width. The area of the rectangle is 40 m². Find the length and the width.

28. The number of possible handshakes H within a group of n people is given by $H = \frac{1}{2}(n^2 - n)$. At a meeting, everyone shook hands once with everyone else. If there were 45 handshakes, how many people were at the meeting?

29. A mason wants to be sure she has a right corner in a building's foundation. She marks a point 3 ft from the corner along one wall and another point 4 ft from the corner along the other wall. If the corner is a right angle, what should the distance be between the two marked points?

Synthesis

30. *Dimensions of an open box.* A rectangular piece of cardboard is twice as long as it is wide. A 4-cm square is cut out of each corner, and the sides are turned up to make a box with an open top. The volume of the box is 616 cm³. Find the original dimensions of the cardboard.

31. Factor: $(a + 3)^2 - 2(a + 3) - 35$.

32. Solve: $20x(x + 2)(x - 1) = 5x^3 - 24x - 14x^2$.

Cumulative Review: Chapters 1-3, 5, 6

Simplify. Do not use negative exponents in the answer.

1. $\frac{3}{8} \div \frac{3}{4}$ [1.3]

2. $\frac{3}{8} \cdot \frac{3}{4}$ [1.3]

3. $\frac{3}{8} + \frac{3}{4}$ [1.3]

4. $-2 + (20 \div 4)^2 - 6 \cdot (-1)^3$ [1.8]

5. $(3x^2y^3)^{-2}$ [5.2]

6. $(t^2)^3 \cdot t^4$ [5.1]

7. $(3x^4 - 2x^2 + x - 7) + (5x^3 + 2x^2 - 3)$ [5.4]

8. $(a^2b - 2ab^2 + 3b^3) - (4a^2b - ab^2 + b^3)$ [5.7]

9. $\dfrac{3t^3s^{-1}}{12t^{-5}s}$ [5.2]

10. $\left(\dfrac{-2x^2y}{3z^4}\right)^3$ [5.1]

11. Evaluate $-x$ for $x = -8$. [1.6]

12. Evaluate $-(-x)$ for $x = -8$. [1.6]

13. Determine the leading term of the polynomial $4x^3 - 6x^2 - x^4 + 7$. [5.3]

14. Divide: $(8x^4 - 20x^3 + 2x^2 - 4x) \div (4x)$. [5.8]

Multiply.

15. $-4t^8(t^3 - 2t - 5)$ [5.5]

16. $(3x - 5)^2$ [5.6]

17. $(10x^5 + y)(10x^5 - y)$ [5.7]

18. $(x - 1)(x^2 - x - 1)$ [5.5]

Factor completely.

19. $c^2 - 1$ [6.4]

20. $5x + 5y + 10x^2 + 10xy$ [6.1]

21. $4r^2 - 4rt + t^2$ [6.4]

22. $6x^2 - 19x + 10$ [6.3]

23. $10y^2 + 40$ [6.1]

24. $x^2y - 3xy + 2y$ [6.2]

25. $12x^2 - 5xy - 2y^2$ [6.3]

26. $125a^3 + 64b^3$ [6.5]

Solve.

27. $\frac{1}{3} + 2x = \frac{1}{2}$ [2.2]

28. $3(t - 1) = 2 - (t + 1)$ [2.2]

29. $8y - 6(y - 2) = 3(2y + 7)$ [2.2]

30. $3x - 7 \geq 4 - 8x$ [2.6]

31. $(x - 1)(x + 3) = 0$ [6.7]

32. $x^2 + x = 12$ [6.7]

33. $3x^2 = 12$ [6.7]

34. $3x^2 = 12x$ [6.7]

35. Solve $a = bc + dc$ for c. [2.3]

36. Find the slope of the line containing the points $(6, 7)$ and $(-2, 7)$. [3.5]

37. Find the slope and the y-intercept of the line given by $2x + y = 5$. [3.6]

38. Write the slope–intercept equation for the line with slope 5 and y-intercept $\left(0, -\frac{1}{3}\right)$. [3.6]

39. Write the slope–intercept equation for the line with slope 5 that contains the point $\left(-\frac{1}{3}, 0\right)$. [3.7]

Graph.

40. $4(x + 1) = 8$ [3.3]

41. $x + y = 5$ [3.3]

42. $y = \frac{3}{2}x - 2$ [3.6]

43. $3x + 5y = 10$ [3.6]

44. Use a grid 10 squares wide and 10 squares high to plot $(5, 40)$, $(18, -60)$, and $(30, -22)$. Choose the scale carefully. [3.1]

Solve.

45. On average, men talk 97 min more per month on cell phones than do women. The sum of men's average minutes and women's average minutes is 647 min. What is the average number of minutes per month that men talk on cell phones? [2.5]
Source: *International Communications Research for Cingular Wireless*

46. The number of cell-phone subscribers increased from 680,000 in 1986 to 233,000,000 in 2006. What was the average rate of increase? [3.4]
Source: CTIA – The Wireless Association

47. In 2007, there were 1.2 billion Internet users worldwide. Of these, 5% spoke French. How many Internet users spoke French? [2.4]
Source: Internetworldstats.com

48. The number of people in the United States, in thousands, who are on a waiting list for an organ transplant can be approximated by the polynomial $2.38t + 77.38$, where t is the number of years since 2000. Estimate the number of people on a waiting list for an organ transplant in 2010. [5.3]
Source: Based on information from The Organ Procurement and Transplantation Network

49. A 13-ft ladder is placed against a building in such a way that the distance from the top of the ladder to the ground is 7 ft more than the distance from the bottom of the ladder to the building. Find both distances. [6.8]

50. A rectangular table in Arlo's House of Tunes is six times as long as it is wide. If the area of the table is 24 ft^2, find the length and the width of the table. [6.8]

51. Donna's quiz grades are 8, 3, 5, and 10. What scores on the fifth quiz will make her average quiz grade at least 7? [2.7]

52. The average amount of sodium in a serving of Chef Boyardee foods dropped from 1100 mg in 2003 to 900 mg in 2007. [3.7]
Source: *The Indianapolis Star*, 11/25/07

   a) Graph the data and determine an equation for the related line. Let s represent the average amount of sodium per serving and t the number of years after 2000.

   b) Use the equation of part (a) to estimate the average amount of sodium in a serving of Chef Boyardee foods in 2006.

Synthesis

53. Solve $x = \dfrac{abx}{2 - b}$ for b. [2.3]

54. Write an equation of the line parallel to the x-axis and passing through $(-6, -8)$. [3.3]

55. a) Multiply: $(3y + 2 + x)(3y + 2 - x)$. [5.6]
   b) Factor: $9y^2 + 12y + 4 - x^2$. [6.4]

56. Solve: $6x^3 + 4x^2 = 2x$. [6.7]

Rational Expressions and Equations

FRED JENKINS
TECHNICAL SERVICES MANAGER
Goose Creek, South Carolina

As a chemist involved in the quality control of all chemicals used and manufactured where I work, I use mathematics to calculate purities, density, refractive index, acidity, and other parameters that determine whether a material meets intended specifications. Even though many calculations are performed by instrument software, it is important for me as a chemist and manager to know how to verify results and troubleshoot with math when problems occur.

AN APPLICATION

As one alternative to gasoline-powered vehicles, flex fuel vehicles can use both regular gasoline and E85, a fuel containing 85% ethanol. Because using E85 results in a lower fuel economy, its price per gallon must be lower than the price of gasoline in order to make it an economical fuel option. A 2007 Chevrolet Tahoe gets 21 mpg on the highway using gasoline and only 15 mpg on the highway using E85. If the price of gasoline is $3.36 a gallon, what must the price of E85 be in order for the fuel cost per mile to be the same?

Source: www.caranddriver.com

This problem appears as Example 7 in Section 7.7.

R ational expressions are similar to fractions in arithmetic, in that both are ratios of two expressions. We now learn how to simplify, add, subtract, multiply, and divide rational expressions. These skills will then be used to solve the equations that arise from real-life problems like the one on the preceding page.

7.1 Rational Expressions

Simplifying Rational Expressions ▪ Factors That Are Opposites

Just as a rational number is any number that can be written as a quotient of two integers, a **rational expression** is any expression that can be written as a quotient of two polynomials. The following are examples of rational expressions:

$$\frac{7}{3}, \quad \frac{5}{x+6}, \quad \frac{t^2 - 5t + 6}{4t^2 - 7}.$$

Rational expressions are examples of *algebraic fractions*. They are also examples of *fraction expressions*.

Because rational expressions indicate division, we must be careful to avoid denominators that are 0. For example, in the expression

$$\frac{x+3}{x-7},$$

when x is replaced with 7, the denominator is 0, and the expression is undefined:

$$\frac{x+3}{x-7} = \frac{7+3}{7-7} = \frac{10}{0}. \leftarrow \text{ As explained in Chapter 1, division by 0 is undefined.}$$

When x is replaced with a number other than 7—say, 6—the expression *is* defined because the denominator is not 0:

$$\frac{x+3}{x-7} = \frac{6+3}{6-7} = \frac{9}{-1} = -9.$$

The expression is also defined when $x = -3$:

$$\frac{x+3}{x-7} = \frac{-3+3}{-3-7} = \frac{0}{-10} = 0. \qquad \text{0 divided by a nonzero number is 0.}$$

Any replacement for the variable that makes the *denominator* 0 will cause an expression to be undefined.

EXAMPLE **1**   Find all numbers for which the rational expression

$$\frac{x+4}{x^2 - 3x - 10}$$

is undefined.

SOLUTION   The value of the numerator has no bearing on whether or not a rational expression is defined. To determine which numbers make the rational expression undefined, we set the *denominator* equal to 0 and solve:

$$x^2 - 3x - 10 = 0 \qquad \text{We set the denominator equal to 0.}$$
$$(x - 5)(x + 2) = 0 \qquad \text{Factoring}$$
$$x - 5 = 0 \quad or \quad x + 2 = 0 \qquad \text{Using the principle of zero products}$$
$$x = 5 \quad or \qquad x = -2. \qquad \text{Solving each equation}$$

Check:

For $x = 5$:

$$\frac{x + 4}{x^2 - 3x - 10} = \frac{5 + 4}{5^2 - 3 \cdot 5 - 10} \qquad \text{There are no restrictions on the numerator.}$$

$$= \frac{9}{25 - 15 - 10} = \frac{9}{0}. \qquad \text{This expression is undefined, as expected.}$$

For $x = -2$:

$$\frac{x + 4}{x^2 - 3x - 10} = \frac{-2 + 4}{(-2)^2 - 3(-2) - 10}$$

$$= \frac{2}{4 + 6 - 10} = \frac{2}{0}. \qquad \text{This expression is undefined, as expected.}$$

Thus, $\dfrac{x + 4}{x^2 - 3x - 10}$ is undefined for $x = 5$ and $x = -2$.   **TRY EXERCISE** ▶ 7

TECHNOLOGY CONNECTION

To check Example 1 with a graphing calculator, let $y_1 = x^2 - 3x - 10$ and $y_2 = (x + 4)/(x^2 - 3x - 10)$ or $(x + 4)/y_1$ and use the TABLE feature. Since $x^2 - 3x - 10$ is 0 for $x = 5$, it is impossible to evaluate y_2 for $x = 5$.

TBLSTART = 0   ΔTBL = 1

X	Y₁	Y₂
0	−10	−.4
1	−12	−.4167
2	−12	−.5
3	−10	−.7
4	−6	−1.333
5	0	ERROR
6	8	1.25

X = 5

Simplifying Rational Expressions

A rational expression is said to be *simplified* when the numerator and the denominator have no factors (other than 1) in common. To simplify a rational expression, we first factor the numerator and the denominator. We then identify factors common to the numerator and the denominator, rewrite the expression as a product of two rational expressions (one of which is equal to 1), and then remove the factor equal to 1. The process is identical to that used in Section 1.3 to simplify $\frac{15}{40}$:

$$\frac{15}{40} = \frac{3 \cdot 5}{8 \cdot 5} \qquad \text{Factoring the numerator and the denominator. Note the common factor, 5.}$$

$$= \frac{3}{8} \cdot \frac{5}{5} \qquad \text{Rewriting as a product of two fractions}$$

$$= \frac{3}{8} \cdot 1 \qquad \frac{5}{5} = 1$$

$$= \frac{3}{8}. \qquad \text{Using the identity property of 1 to remove the factor 1}$$

Similar steps are followed when simplifying rational expressions: We factor and remove a factor equal to 1, using the fact that

$$\frac{ab}{cb} = \frac{a}{c} \cdot \frac{b}{b}.$$

EXAMPLE **2** Simplify: $\dfrac{8x^2}{24x}$.

SOLUTION

$$\dfrac{8x^2}{24x} = \dfrac{8 \cdot x \cdot x}{3 \cdot 8 \cdot x}$$ Factoring the numerator and the denominator. Note the common factor of $8 \cdot x$.

$$= \dfrac{x}{3} \cdot \dfrac{8x}{8x}$$ Rewriting as a product of two rational expressions

$$= \dfrac{x}{3} \cdot 1 \qquad \dfrac{8x}{8x} = 1$$

$$= \dfrac{x}{3}$$ Removing the factor 1   **TRY EXERCISE** 17

We say that $\dfrac{8x^2}{24x}$ *simplifies* to $\dfrac{x}{3}$.* In the work that follows, we assume that all denominators are nonzero.

EXAMPLE **3** Simplify: $\dfrac{5a + 15}{10}$.

SOLUTION

$$\dfrac{5a + 15}{10} = \dfrac{5(a + 3)}{5 \cdot 2}$$ Factoring the numerator and the denominator. Note the common factor of 5.

$$= \dfrac{5}{5} \cdot \dfrac{a + 3}{2}$$ Rewriting as a product of two rational expressions

$$= 1 \cdot \dfrac{a + 3}{2} \qquad \dfrac{5}{5} = 1$$

$$= \dfrac{a + 3}{2}$$ Removing the factor 1   **TRY EXERCISE** 19

The result in Example 3 can be partially checked using a replacement for *a*—say, $a = 2$.

Original expression: *Simplified expression:*

$$\dfrac{5a + 15}{10} = \dfrac{5 \cdot 2 + 15}{10} \qquad\qquad \dfrac{a + 3}{2} = \dfrac{2 + 3}{2}$$

$$= \dfrac{25}{10} = \dfrac{5}{2} \quad \text{The results} \qquad = \dfrac{5}{2} \qquad$$
are the same.

> To see why this check is not foolproof, see Exercise 65.

If we do not get the same result when evaluating both expressions, we know that a mistake has been made. For example, if $(5a + 15)/10$ is *incorrectly* simplified as $(a + 15)/2$ and we evaluate using $a = 2$, we have the following.

Original expression: *Incorrectly simplified expression:*

$$\dfrac{5a + 15}{10} = \dfrac{5 \cdot 2 + 15}{10} \qquad\qquad \dfrac{a + 15}{2} = \dfrac{2 + 15}{2}$$

$$= \dfrac{5}{2} \quad \text{The results are} \qquad = \dfrac{17}{2}$$
different.

This demonstrates that a mistake has been made.

---

*In more advanced courses, we would *not* say that $8x^2/(24x)$ simplifies to $x/3$, but would instead say that $8x^2/(24x)$ simplifies to $x/3$ *with the restriction that* $x \neq 0$.

Sometimes the common factor has two or more terms.

Simplify.

a) $\dfrac{6x - 12}{7x - 14}$ **b)** $\dfrac{18t^2 + 6t}{6t^2 + 15t}$ **c)** $\dfrac{x^2 + 3x + 2}{x^2 - 1}$

SOLUTION

a) $\dfrac{6x - 12}{7x - 14} = \dfrac{6(x - 2)}{7(x - 2)}$ Factoring the numerator and the denominator. Note the common factor of $x - 2$.

$= \dfrac{6}{7} \cdot \dfrac{x - 2}{x - 2}$ Rewriting as a product of two rational expressions

$= \dfrac{6}{7} \cdot 1$ $\dfrac{x - 2}{x - 2} = 1$

$= \dfrac{6}{7}$ Removing the factor 1

b) $\dfrac{18t^2 + 6t}{6t^2 + 15t} = \dfrac{3t \cdot 2(3t + 1)}{3t(2t + 5)}$ Factoring the numerator and the denominator. Note the common factor of $3t$.

$= \dfrac{3t}{3t} \cdot \dfrac{2(3t + 1)}{2t + 5}$ Rewriting as a product of two rational expressions

$= 1 \cdot \dfrac{2(3t + 1)}{2t + 5}$ $\dfrac{3t}{3t} = 1$

$= \dfrac{2(3t + 1)}{2t + 5}$ Removing the factor 1. The numerator and the denominator have no common factor so the simplification is complete.

c) $\dfrac{x^2 + 3x + 2}{x^2 - 1} = \dfrac{(x + 1)(x + 2)}{(x + 1)(x - 1)}$ Factoring; $x + 1$ is the common factor.

$= \dfrac{x + 1}{x + 1} \cdot \dfrac{x + 2}{x - 1}$ Rewriting as a product of two rational expressions

$= 1 \cdot \dfrac{x + 2}{x - 1}$ $\dfrac{x + 1}{x + 1} = 1$

$= \dfrac{x + 2}{x - 1}$ Removing the factor 1

TRY EXERCISE 23

Canceling is a shortcut that can be used—and easily *misused*—to simplify rational expressions. As stated in Section 1.3, canceling must be done with care and understanding. Essentially, canceling streamlines the process of removing a factor equal to 1. Example 4(c) could have been streamlined as follows:

$$\dfrac{x^2 + 3x + 2}{x^2 - 1} = \dfrac{\cancel{(x + 1)}(x + 2)}{\cancel{(x + 1)}(x - 1)}$$ When a factor equal to 1 is noted, it is "canceled": $\dfrac{x + 1}{x + 1} = 1$.

$$= \dfrac{x + 2}{x - 1}.$$ Simplifying

TECHNOLOGY CONNECTION

We can use the TABLE feature as a partial check that rational expressions have been simplified correctly. To check the simplification in Example 4(c),

$$\dfrac{x^2 + 3x + 2}{x^2 - 1} = \dfrac{x + 2}{x - 1},$$

we enter $y_1 = (x^2 + 3x + 2)/(x^2 - 1)$ and $y_2 = (x + 2)/(x - 1)$ and select the mode AUTO to look at a table of values of y_1 and y_2. The values should match for all allowable replacements.

X	Y1	Y2
-4	.4	.4
-3	.25	.25
-2	0	0
-1	ERROR	-.5
0	-2	-2
1	ERROR	ERROR
2	4	4
X = -4		

The ERROR messages indicate that -1 and 1 are not allowable replacements in y_1 and 1 is not an allowable replacement in y_2. For all other numbers, y_1 and y_2 are the same, so the simplification appears to be correct.

Use the TABLE feature to determine whether each of the following appears to be correct.

1. $\dfrac{8x^2}{24x} = \dfrac{x}{3}$

2. $\dfrac{5x + 15}{10} = \dfrac{x + 3}{2}$

3. $\dfrac{x + 3}{x} = 3$

4. $\dfrac{x^2 + 3x - 4}{x^2 - 16} = \dfrac{x - 1}{x + 4}$

CAUTION! Canceling is often used incorrectly. The following cancellations are *incorrect*:

$$\frac{\cancel{x+7}}{\cancel{x+3}}, \quad \frac{a^2-5}{5}, \quad \frac{6x^2+5x+1}{4x^2-3x}.$$

Wrong!   Wrong!   Wrong!

None of the above cancellations removes a factor equal to 1. Factors are parts of products. For example, in $x \cdot 7$, x and 7 are factors, but in $x + 7$, x and 7 are terms, *not* factors. Only factors can be canceled.

EXAMPLE 5   Simplify: $\dfrac{3x^2 - 2x - 1}{x^2 - 3x + 2}$.

SOLUTION   We factor the numerator and the denominator and look for common factors:

$$\frac{3x^2 - 2x - 1}{x^2 - 3x + 2} = \frac{(3x+1)(x-1)}{(x-2)(x-1)}$$

Try to visualize this as $\dfrac{3x+1}{x-2} \cdot \dfrac{x-1}{x-1}$.

$$= \frac{3x+1}{x-2}.$$

Removing a factor equal to 1: $\dfrac{x-1}{x-1} = 1$

TRY EXERCISE 31

Factors That Are Opposites

Consider

$$\frac{x-4}{8-2x}, \quad \text{or, equivalently,} \quad \frac{x-4}{2(4-x)}.$$

At first glance, the numerator and the denominator do not appear to have any common factors. But $x - 4$ and $4 - x$ are opposites, or additive inverses, of each other. Thus we can find a common factor by factoring out -1 in one expression.

EXAMPLE 6   Simplify $\dfrac{x-4}{8-2x}$ and check by evaluating.

SOLUTION   We have

$$\frac{x-4}{8-2x} = \frac{x-4}{2(4-x)}$$

Factoring

$$= \frac{x-4}{2(-1)(x-4)}$$

Note that $4 - x = -x + 4 = -1(x-4)$.

$$= \frac{x-4}{-2(x-4)}$$

Had we originally factored out -2, we could have gone directly to this step.

$$= \frac{1}{-2} \cdot \frac{x-4}{x-4}$$

Rewriting as a product. It is important to write the 1 in the numerator.

$$= -\frac{1}{2}.$$

Removing a factor equal to 1: $(x-4)/(x-4) = 1$

As a partial check, note that for any choice of x other than 4, the value of the rational expression is $-\frac{1}{2}$. For example, if $x = 5$, then

$$\frac{x - 4}{8 - 2x} = \frac{5 - 4}{8 - 2 \cdot 5}$$

$$= \frac{1}{-2} = -\frac{1}{2}.$$

TRY EXERCISE 47

7.1 EXERCISE SET

For Extra Help

🖐 *Concept Reinforcement* *In each of Exercises 1–6, match the rational expression with the list of numbers in the column on the right for which the rational expression is undefined.*

1. ___ $\dfrac{x - 5}{(x - 2)(x + 3)}$

2. ___ $\dfrac{3t}{(t + 1)(t - 4)}$

3. ___ $\dfrac{a + 7}{a^2 - a - 12}$

4. ___ $\dfrac{m - 3}{m^2 - 2m - 15}$

5. ___ $\dfrac{2t + 7}{(2t - 1)(3t + 4)}$

6. ___ $\dfrac{4x - 1}{(3x - 1)(3x - 2)}$

a) $-1, 4$

b) $-3, 5$

c) $-\dfrac{4}{3}, \dfrac{1}{2}$

d) $-3, 4$

e) $-3, 2$

f) $\dfrac{1}{3}, \dfrac{2}{3}$

List all numbers for which each rational expression is undefined.

7. $\dfrac{18}{-11x}$

8. $\dfrac{13}{-5t}$

9. $\dfrac{y - 3}{y + 5}$

10. $\dfrac{a + 6}{a - 10}$

11. $\dfrac{t - 5}{3t - 15}$

12. $\dfrac{x^2 - 4}{5x + 10}$

13. $\dfrac{x^2 - 25}{x^2 - 3x - 28}$

14. $\dfrac{p^2 - 9}{p^2 - 7p + 10}$

15. $\dfrac{t^2 + t - 20}{2t^2 + 11t - 6}$

16. $\dfrac{x^2 + 2x + 1}{3x^2 - x - 14}$

Simplify by removing a factor equal to 1. Show all steps.

17. $\dfrac{50a^2b}{40ab^3}$

18. $\dfrac{-24x^4y^3}{6x^7y}$

19. $\dfrac{6t + 12}{6t - 18}$

20. $\dfrac{5n - 30}{5n + 5}$

21. $\dfrac{21t - 7}{24t - 8}$

22. $\dfrac{10n + 25}{8n + 20}$

23. $\dfrac{a^2 - 9}{a^2 + 4a + 3}$

24. $\dfrac{a^2 + 5a + 6}{a^2 - 9}$

Simplify, if possible. Then check by evaluating, as in Example 6.

25. $\dfrac{-36x^8}{54x^5}$

26. $\dfrac{45a^4}{30a^6}$

27. $\dfrac{-2y + 6}{-8y}$

28. $\dfrac{-4m^2 + 4m}{-8m^2 + 12m}$

29. $\dfrac{t^2 - 16}{t^2 - t - 20}$

30. $\dfrac{a^2 - 4}{a^2 + 5a + 6}$

31. $\dfrac{3a^2 + 9a - 12}{6a^2 - 30a + 24}$

32. $\dfrac{2t^2 - 6t + 4}{4t^2 + 12t - 16}$

33. $\dfrac{x^2 - 8x + 16}{x^2 - 16}$

34. $\dfrac{x^2 - 25}{x^2 + 10x + 25}$

35. $\dfrac{n - 2}{n^3 - 8}$

36. $\dfrac{n^6 + 27}{n^2 + 3}$

37. $\dfrac{t^2 - 1}{t + 1}$

38. $\dfrac{a^2 - 1}{a - 1}$

39. $\dfrac{y^2 + 4}{y + 2}$

40. $\dfrac{m^2 + 9}{m + 3}$

41. $\dfrac{5x^2 + 20}{10x^2 + 40}$

42. $\dfrac{6x^2 + 54}{4x^2 + 36}$

43. $\dfrac{y^2 + 6y}{2y^2 + 13y + 6}$

44. $\dfrac{t^2 + 2t}{2t^2 + t - 6}$

45. $\dfrac{4x^2 - 12x + 9}{10x^2 - 11x - 6}$

46. $\dfrac{4x^2 - 4x + 1}{6x^2 + 5x - 4}$

47. $\dfrac{10 - x}{x - 10}$

48. $\dfrac{x - 8}{8 - x}$

49. $\dfrac{7t - 14}{2 - t}$

50. $\dfrac{3 - n}{5n - 15}$

51. $\dfrac{a - b}{4b - 4a}$

52. $\dfrac{2p - 2q}{q - p}$

53. $\dfrac{3x^2 - 3y^2}{2y^2 - 2x^2}$

54. $\dfrac{7a^2 - 7b^2}{3b^2 - 3a^2}$

Aha! **55.** $\dfrac{7s^2 - 28t^2}{28t^2 - 7s^2}$

56. $\dfrac{9m^2 - 4n^2}{4n^2 - 9m^2}$

57. Explain how simplifying is related to the identity property of 1.

58. If a rational expression is undefined for $x = 5$ and $x = -3$, what is the degree of the denominator? Why?

Skill Review

To prepare for Section 7.2, review multiplication and division using fraction notation (Section 1.7).

Simplify.

59. $-\dfrac{2}{15} \cdot \dfrac{10}{7}$ [1.7]

60. $\left(\dfrac{3}{4}\right)\left(\dfrac{-20}{9}\right)$ [1.7]

61. $\dfrac{5}{8} \div \left(-\dfrac{1}{6}\right)$ [1.7]

62. $\dfrac{7}{10} \div \left(-\dfrac{8}{15}\right)$ [1.7]

63. $\dfrac{7}{9} - \dfrac{2}{3} \cdot \dfrac{6}{7}$ [1.8]

64. $\dfrac{2}{3} - \left(\dfrac{3}{4}\right)^2$ [1.8]

Synthesis

65. Keith *incorrectly* simplifies

$$\dfrac{x^2 + x - 2}{x^2 + 3x + 2} \quad \text{as} \quad \dfrac{x - 1}{x + 2}.$$

He then checks his simplification by evaluating both expressions for $x = 1$. Use this situation to explain why evaluating is not a foolproof check.

66. How could you convince someone that $a - b$ and $b - a$ are opposites of each other?

Simplify.

67. $\dfrac{16y^4 - x^4}{(x^2 + 4y^2)(x - 2y)}$

68. $\dfrac{(x - 1)(x^4 - 1)(x^2 - 1)}{(x^2 + 1)(x - 1)^2(x^4 - 2x^2 + 1)}$

69. $\dfrac{x^5 - 2x^3 + 4x^2 - 8}{x^7 + 2x^4 - 4x^3 - 8}$

70. $\dfrac{10t^4 - 8t^3 + 15t - 12}{8 - 10t + 12t^2 - 15t^3}$

71. $\dfrac{(t^4 - 1)(t^2 - 9)(t - 9)^2}{(t^4 - 81)(t^2 + 1)(t + 1)^2}$

72. $\dfrac{(t + 2)^3(t^2 + 2t + 1)(t + 1)}{(t + 1)^3(t^2 + 4t + 4)(t + 2)}$

73. $\dfrac{(x^2 - y^2)(x^2 - 2xy + y^2)}{(x + y)^2(x^2 - 4xy - 5y^2)}$

74. $\dfrac{x^4 - y^4}{(y - x)^4}$

75. Select any number x, multiply by 2, add 5, multiply by 5, subtract 25, and divide by 10. What do you get? Explain how this procedure can be used for a number trick.

Multiplication ▪ Division

Multiplication and division of rational expressions are similar to multiplication and division with fractions. In this section, we again assume that all denominators are nonzero.

Multiplication

Recall that to multiply fractions, we multiply numerator times numerator and denominator times denominator. Rational expressions are multiplied in a similar way.

The Product of Two Rational Expressions

To multiply rational expressions, multiply numerators and multiply denominators:

$$\frac{A}{B} \cdot \frac{C}{D} = \frac{AC}{BD}.$$

Then factor and, if possible, simplify the result.

For example,

$$\frac{3}{5} \cdot \frac{8}{11} = \frac{3 \cdot 8}{5 \cdot 11} \quad \text{and} \quad \frac{x}{3} \cdot \frac{x+2}{y} = \frac{x(x+2)}{3y}.$$

Fraction bars are grouping symbols, so parentheses are needed when writing some products. Because we generally simplify, we often leave products involving variables in factored form. There is no need to multiply further.

EXAMPLE   1   Multiply and, if possible, simplify.

a) $\dfrac{5a^3}{4} \cdot \dfrac{2}{5a}$

b) $(x^2 - 3x - 10) \cdot \dfrac{x+4}{x^2 - 10x + 25}$

c) $\dfrac{10x + 20}{2x^2 - 3x + 1} \cdot \dfrac{x^2 - 1}{5x + 10}$

SOLUTION

a) $\dfrac{5a^3}{4} \cdot \dfrac{2}{5a} = \dfrac{5a^3(2)}{4(5a)}$ Forming the product of the numerators and the product of the denominators

$\qquad = \dfrac{5 \cdot a \cdot a \cdot a \cdot 2}{2 \cdot 2 \cdot 5 \cdot a}$ Factoring the numerator and the denominator

$\qquad = \dfrac{5 \cdot a \cdot a \cdot a \cdot 2}{2 \cdot 2 \cdot 5 \cdot a}$

$\qquad = \dfrac{a^2}{2}$ Removing a factor equal to 1: $\dfrac{2 \cdot 5 \cdot a}{2 \cdot 5 \cdot a} = 1$

b) $(x^2 - 3x - 10) \cdot \dfrac{x + 4}{x^2 - 10x + 25}$

$= \dfrac{x^2 - 3x - 10}{1} \cdot \dfrac{x + 4}{x^2 - 10x + 25}$ Writing $x^2 - 3x - 10$ as a rational expression

$= \dfrac{(x^2 - 3x - 10)(x + 4)}{1(x^2 - 10x + 25)}$ Multiplying the numerators and the denominators

$= \dfrac{(x - 5)(x + 2)(x + 4)}{(x - 5)(x - 5)}$ Factoring the numerator and the denominator

$= \dfrac{\cancel{(x - 5)}(x + 2)(x + 4)}{\cancel{(x - 5)}(x - 5)}$ Removing a factor equal to 1: $\dfrac{x - 5}{x - 5} = 1$

$= \dfrac{(x + 2)(x + 4)}{x - 5}$

c) $\dfrac{10x + 20}{2x^2 - 3x + 1} \cdot \dfrac{x^2 - 1}{5x + 10}$

$= \dfrac{(10x + 20)(x^2 - 1)}{(2x^2 - 3x + 1)(5x + 10)}$ Multiply.

$= \dfrac{5(2)(x + 2)(x + 1)(x - 1)}{(x - 1)(2x - 1)5(x + 2)}$ **Factor.** Try to go directly to this step.

$= \dfrac{\cancel{5}(2)\cancel{(x + 2)}(x + 1)\cancel{(x - 1)}}{\cancel{(x - 1)}(2x - 1)\cancel{5}\cancel{(x + 2)}}$ **Simplify.** $\dfrac{5(x + 2)(x - 1)}{5(x + 2)(x - 1)} = 1$

$= \dfrac{2(x + 1)}{2x - 1}$

> **TRY EXERCISE 19**

Because our results are often used in problems that require factored form, there is no need to multiply out the numerator or the denominator.

Division

As with fractions, reciprocals of rational expressions are found by interchanging the numerator and the denominator. For example,

the reciprocal of $\dfrac{2}{7}$ is $\dfrac{7}{2}$,   and   the reciprocal of $\dfrac{3x}{x + 5}$ is $\dfrac{x + 5}{3x}$.

The Quotient of Two Rational Expressions

To divide by a rational expression, multiply by its reciprocal:

$$\frac{A}{B} \div \frac{C}{D} = \frac{A}{B} \cdot \frac{D}{C} = \frac{AD}{BC}.$$

Then factor and, if possible, simplify.

For an explanation of why we divide this way, see Exercise 55 in Section 7.5.

EXAMPLE 2   Divide: **(a)** $\dfrac{x}{5} \div \dfrac{7}{y}$; **(b)** $(x + 2) \div \dfrac{x - 1}{x + 3}$.

SOLUTION

a) $\dfrac{x}{5} \div \dfrac{7}{y} = \dfrac{x}{5} \cdot \dfrac{y}{7}$ Multiplying by the reciprocal of the divisor

$\qquad\quad = \dfrac{xy}{35}$ Multiplying rational expressions

b) $(x + 2) \div \dfrac{x - 1}{x + 3} = \dfrac{x + 2}{1} \cdot \dfrac{x + 3}{x - 1}$ Multiplying by the reciprocal of the divisor. Writing $x + 2$ as $\dfrac{x + 2}{1}$ can be helpful.

$\qquad\qquad\qquad\quad = \dfrac{(x + 2)(x + 3)}{x - 1}$

TRY EXERCISE ▶ 41

As usual, we should simplify when possible. Often that requires us to factor one or more polynomials, hoping to discover a common factor that appears in both the numerator and the denominator.

EXAMPLE 3   Divide and, if possible, simplify: $\dfrac{x + 1}{x^2 - 1} \div \dfrac{x + 1}{x^2 - 2x + 1}$.

SOLUTION

$\dfrac{x + 1}{x^2 - 1} \div \dfrac{x + 1}{x^2 - 2x + 1} = \dfrac{x + 1}{x^2 - 1} \cdot \dfrac{x^2 - 2x + 1}{x + 1}$ Rewrite as multiplication.

$\qquad\qquad\qquad\qquad\qquad = \dfrac{(x + 1)(x - 1)(x - 1)}{(x + 1)(x - 1)(x + 1)}$ Multiply. Factor.

$\qquad\qquad\qquad\qquad\qquad = \dfrac{(x + 1)(x - 1)(x - 1)}{(x + 1)(x - 1)(x + 1)}$ Simplify.

$\qquad\qquad\qquad\qquad\qquad = \dfrac{x - 1}{x + 1}$ $\dfrac{(x + 1)(x - 1)}{(x + 1)(x - 1)} = 1$

TRY EXERCISE ▶ 47

EXAMPLE 4   Divide and, if possible, simplify.

a) $\dfrac{a^2 + 3a + 2}{a^2 + 4} \div (5a^2 + 10a)$ **b)** $\dfrac{x^2 - 2x - 3}{x^2 - 4} \div \dfrac{x + 1}{x + 5}$

SOLUTION

a) $\dfrac{a^2 + 3a + 2}{a^2 + 4} \div (5a^2 + 10a)$

$\qquad = \dfrac{a^2 + 3a + 2}{a^2 + 4} \cdot \dfrac{1}{5a^2 + 10a}$ Multiplying by the reciprocal of the divisor

$\qquad = \dfrac{(a + 2)(a + 1)}{(a^2 + 4)5a(a + 2)}$ Multiplying rational expressions and factoring

$\qquad = \dfrac{(a + 2)(a + 1)}{(a^2 + 4)5a(a + 2)}$

$\qquad = \dfrac{a + 1}{(a^2 + 4)5a}$ Removing a factor equal to 1: $\dfrac{a + 2}{a + 2} = 1$

TECHNOLOGY CONNECTION

In performing a partial check of Example 4(b), we must be careful placing parentheses. We enter the original expression as $y_1 = ((x^2 - 2x - 3)/(x^2 - 4))/((x + 1)/(x + 5))$ and the simplified expression as $y_2 = ((x - 3)(x + 5))/((x - 2)(x + 2))$. Comparing values of y_1 and y_2, we see that

(continued)

the simplification is probably correct.

X	Y₁	Y₂
-5	ERROR	0
-4	-.5833	-.5833
-3	-2.4	-2.4
-2	ERROR	ERROR
-1	ERROR	5.3333
0	3.75	3.75
1	4	4

X = -5

1. Check Example 4(a).
2. Why are there 3 ERROR messages shown for y_1 on the screen above, and only 1 for y_2?

b) $\dfrac{x^2 - 2x - 3}{x^2 - 4} \div \dfrac{x + 1}{x + 5}$

$= \dfrac{x^2 - 2x - 3}{x^2 - 4} \cdot \dfrac{x + 5}{x + 1}$ Multiplying by the reciprocal of the divisor

$= \dfrac{(x - 3)(x + 1)(x + 5)}{(x - 2)(x + 2)(x + 1)}$ Multiplying rational expressions and factoring

$= \dfrac{(x - 3)\cancel{(x + 1)}(x + 5)}{(x - 2)(x + 2)\cancel{(x + 1)}}$

$= \dfrac{(x - 3)(x + 5)}{(x - 2)(x + 2)}$ Removing a factor equal to 1: $\dfrac{x + 1}{x + 1} = 1$

TRY EXERCISE 51

7.2 EXERCISE SET

For Extra Help   MyMathLab   Math XL PRACTICE   WATCH   DOWNLOAD

Multiply. Leave each answer in factored form.

1. $\dfrac{3x}{8} \cdot \dfrac{x + 2}{5x - 1}$

2. $\dfrac{2x}{7} \cdot \dfrac{3x + 5}{x - 1}$

3. $\dfrac{a - 4}{a + 6} \cdot \dfrac{a + 2}{a + 6}$

4. $\dfrac{a + 3}{a + 6} \cdot \dfrac{a + 3}{a - 1}$

5. $\dfrac{2x + 3}{4} \cdot \dfrac{x + 1}{x - 5}$

6. $\dfrac{x + 2}{3x - 4} \cdot \dfrac{4}{5x + 6}$

7. $\dfrac{n - 4}{n^2 + 4} \cdot \dfrac{n + 4}{n^2 - 4}$

8. $\dfrac{t + 3}{t^2 - 2} \cdot \dfrac{t + 3}{t^2 - 4}$

9. $\dfrac{y + 6}{1 + y} \cdot \dfrac{y - 3}{y + 3}$

10. $\dfrac{m + 4}{m + 8} \cdot \dfrac{2 + m}{m + 5}$

Multiply and, if possible, simplify.

11. $\dfrac{8t^3}{5t} \cdot \dfrac{3}{4t}$

12. $\dfrac{18}{a^5} \cdot \dfrac{2a^2}{3a}$

13. $\dfrac{3c}{d^2} \cdot \dfrac{8d}{6c^3}$

14. $\dfrac{3x^2y}{2} \cdot \dfrac{4}{xy^3}$

15. $\dfrac{x^2 - 3x - 10}{(x - 2)^2} \cdot (x - 2)$

16. $t + 2 \cdot \dfrac{t^2 - 5t + 6}{(t + 2)^2}$

17. $\dfrac{n^2 - 6n + 5}{n + 6} \cdot \dfrac{n - 6}{n^2 + 36}$

18. $\dfrac{a + 2}{a - 2} \cdot \dfrac{a^2 + 4}{a^2 + 5a + 4}$

19. $\dfrac{a^2 - 9}{a^2} \cdot \dfrac{7a}{a^2 + a - 12}$

20. $\dfrac{x^2 + 10x - 11}{9x} \cdot \dfrac{x^3}{x + 11}$

21. $\dfrac{4v - 8}{5v} \cdot \dfrac{15v^2}{4v^2 - 16v + 16}$

22. $\dfrac{m - 2}{3m + 9} \cdot \dfrac{m^2 + 6m + 9}{2m^2 - 8}$

23. $\dfrac{t^2 + 2t - 3}{t^2 + 4t - 5} \cdot \dfrac{t^2 - 3t - 10}{t^2 + 5t + 6}$

24. $\dfrac{x^2 + 5x + 4}{x^2 - 6x + 8} \cdot \dfrac{x^2 + 5x - 14}{x^2 + 8x + 7}$

25. $\dfrac{12y + 12}{5y + 25} \cdot \dfrac{3y^2 - 75}{8y^2 - 8}$

26. $\dfrac{9t^2 - 900}{5t^2 - 20} \cdot \dfrac{5t + 10}{3t - 30}$

Aha! 27. $\dfrac{x^2 + 4x + 4}{(x - 1)^2} \cdot \dfrac{x^2 - 2x + 1}{(x + 2)^2}$

28. $\dfrac{x^2 + 7x + 12}{x^2 + 6x + 8} \cdot \dfrac{4 - x^2}{x^2 + x - 6}$

29. $\dfrac{t^2 - 4t + 4}{2t^2 - 7t + 6} \cdot \dfrac{2t^2 + 7t - 15}{t^2 - 10t + 25}$

30. $\dfrac{5y^2 - 4y - 1}{3y^2 + 5y - 12} \cdot \dfrac{y^2 + 6y + 9}{y^2 - 2y + 1}$

31. $(10x^2 - x - 2) \cdot \dfrac{4x^2 - 8x + 3}{10x^2 - 11x - 6}$

32. $\dfrac{2x^2 - 5x + 3}{6x^2 - 5x - 1} \cdot (6x^2 + 13x + 2)$

33. $\dfrac{c^3 + 8}{c^5 - 4c^3} \cdot \dfrac{c^6 - 4c^5 + 4c^4}{c^2 - 2c + 4}$

34. $\dfrac{t^3 - 27}{t^4 - 9t^2} \cdot \dfrac{t^5 - 6t^4 + 9t^3}{t^2 + 3t + 9}$

Find the reciprocal of each expression.

35. $\dfrac{2x}{9}$

36. $\dfrac{3 - x}{x^2 + 4}$

37. $a^4 + 3a$

38. $\dfrac{1}{a^2 - b^2}$

Divide and, if possible, simplify.

39. $\dfrac{5}{9} \div \dfrac{3}{4}$

40. $\dfrac{3}{8} \div \dfrac{4}{7}$

41. $\dfrac{x}{4} \div \dfrac{5}{x}$

42. $\dfrac{5}{x} \div \dfrac{x}{12}$

43. $\dfrac{a^5}{b^4} \div \dfrac{a^2}{b}$

44. $\dfrac{x^5}{y^2} \div \dfrac{x^2}{y}$

45. $\dfrac{t - 3}{6} \div \dfrac{t + 1}{8}$

46. $\dfrac{10}{a + 3} \div \dfrac{15}{a}$

47. $\dfrac{4y - 8}{y + 2} \div \dfrac{y - 2}{y^2 - 4}$

48. $\dfrac{x^2 - 1}{x} \div \dfrac{x + 1}{2x - 2}$

49. $\dfrac{a}{a - b} \div \dfrac{b}{b - a}$

50. $\dfrac{x - y}{6} \div \dfrac{y - x}{3}$

51. $(n^2 + 5n + 6) \div \dfrac{n^2 - 4}{n + 3}$

52. $(v^2 - 1) \div \dfrac{(v + 1)(v - 3)}{v^2 + 9}$

53. $\dfrac{-3 + 3x}{16} \div \dfrac{x - 1}{5}$

54. $\dfrac{-4 + 2x}{15} \div \dfrac{x - 2}{3}$

55. $\dfrac{x - 1}{x + 2} \div \dfrac{1 - x}{4 + x^2}$

56. $\dfrac{-12 + 4x}{12} \div \dfrac{6 - 2x}{6}$

57. $\dfrac{a + 2}{a - 1} \div \dfrac{3a + 6}{a - 5}$

58. $\dfrac{t - 3}{t + 2} \div \dfrac{4t - 12}{t + 1}$

59. $(2x - 1) \div \dfrac{2x^2 - 11x + 5}{4x^2 - 1}$

60. $(a + 7) \div \dfrac{3a^2 + 14a - 49}{a^2 + 8a + 7}$

61. $\dfrac{w^2 - 14w + 49}{2w^2 - 3w - 14} \div \dfrac{3w^2 - 20w - 7}{w^2 - 6w - 16}$

62. $\dfrac{2m^2 + 59m - 30}{m^2 - 10m + 25} \div \dfrac{2m^2 - 21m + 10}{m^2 + m - 30}$

63. $\dfrac{c^2 + 10c + 21}{c^2 - 2c - 15} \div (5c^2 + 32c - 21)$

64. $\dfrac{z^2 - 2z + 1}{z^2 - 1} \div (4z^2 - z - 3)$

65. $\dfrac{x - y}{x^2 + 2xy + y^2} \div \dfrac{x^2 - y^2}{x^2 - 5xy + 4y^2}$

66. $\dfrac{a^2 - b^2}{a^2 - 4ab + 4b^2} \div \dfrac{a^2 - 3ab + 2b^2}{a - 2b}$

67. $\dfrac{x^3 - 64}{x^3 + 64} \div \dfrac{x^2 - 16}{x^2 - 4x + 16}$

68. $\dfrac{8y^3 - 27}{64y^3 - 1} \div \dfrac{4y^2 - 9}{16y^2 + 4y + 1}$

69. $\dfrac{8a^3 + b^3}{2a^2 + 3ab + b^2} \div \dfrac{8a^2 - 4ab + 2b^2}{4a^2 + 4ab + b^2}$

70. $\dfrac{x^3 + 8y^3}{2x^2 + 5xy + 2y^2} \div \dfrac{x^3 - 2x^2y + 4xy^2}{8x^2 - 2y^2}$

71. Why is it important to insert parentheses when multiplying rational expressions such as

$$\dfrac{x + 2}{5x - 7} \cdot \dfrac{3x - 1}{x + 4}?$$

72. As a first step in dividing $\dfrac{x}{3}$ by $\dfrac{7}{x}$, Jan canceled the x's. Explain why this was incorrect, and show the correct division.

Skill Review

To prepare for Section 7.3, review addition and subtraction with fraction notation (Sections 1.3 and 1.6) and subtraction of polynomials (Section 5.4).

Simplify.

73. $\dfrac{3}{4} + \dfrac{5}{6}$ [1.3]

74. $\dfrac{7}{8} + \dfrac{5}{6}$ [1.3]

75. $\dfrac{2}{9} - \dfrac{1}{6}$ [1.3]

76. $\dfrac{3}{10} - \dfrac{7}{15}$ [1.6]

77. $2x^2 - x + 1 - (x^2 - x - 2)$ [5.4]

78. $3x^2 + x - 7 - (5x^2 + 5x - 8)$ [5.4]

Synthesis

79. Is the reciprocal of a product the product of the two reciprocals? Why or why not?

80. Explain why the quotient

$$\dfrac{x + 3}{x - 5} \div \dfrac{x - 7}{x + 1}$$

is undefined for $x = 5$, $x = -1$, and $x = 7$, but *is* defined for $x = -3$.

81. Find the reciprocal of $2\frac{1}{3}x$.

82. Find the reciprocal of $7.25x$.

Simplify.

83. $(x - 2a) \div \dfrac{a^2x^2 - 4a^4}{a^2x + 2a^3}$

84. $\dfrac{2a^2 - 5ab}{c - 3d} \div (4a^2 - 25b^2)$

85. $\dfrac{3x^2 - 2xy - y^2}{x^2 - y^2} \div (3x^2 + 4xy + y^2)^2$

86. $\dfrac{3a^2 - 5ab - 12b^2}{3ab + 4b^2} \div (3b^2 - ab)^2$

Aha! **87.** $\dfrac{a^2 - 3b}{a^2 + 2b} \cdot \dfrac{a^2 - 2b}{a^2 + 3b} \cdot \dfrac{a^2 + 2b}{a^2 - 3b}$

88. $\dfrac{y^2 - 4xy}{y - x} \div \dfrac{16x^2y^2 - y^4}{4x^2 - 3xy - y^2} \div \dfrac{4}{x^3y^3}$

89. $\dfrac{z^2 - 8z + 16}{z^2 + 8z + 16} \div \dfrac{(z - 4)^5}{(z + 4)^5} \div \dfrac{3z + 12}{z^2 - 16}$

90. $\dfrac{(t + 2)^3}{(t + 1)^3} \div \dfrac{t^2 + 4t + 4}{t^2 + 2t + 1} \cdot \dfrac{t + 1}{t + 2}$

91. $\dfrac{a^4 - 81b^4}{a^2c - 6abc + 9b^2c} \cdot \dfrac{a + 3b}{a^2 + 9b^2} \div \dfrac{a^2 + 6ab + 9b^2}{(a - 3b)^2}$

92. $\dfrac{3y^3 + 6y^2}{y^2 - y - 12} \div \dfrac{y^2 - y}{y^2 - 2y - 8} \cdot \dfrac{y^2 + 5y + 6}{y^2}$

93. Use a graphing calculator to check that

$$\dfrac{x - 1}{x^2 + 2x + 1} \div \dfrac{x^2 - 1}{x^2 - 5x + 4}$$

is equivalent to

$$\dfrac{x^2 - 5x + 4}{(x + 1)^3}.$$

CORNER

Currency Exchange

Focus: Least common multiples and proportions

Time: 20 minutes

Group size: 2

International travelers usually exchange currencies. Recently one New Zealand dollar was worth 76 U.S. cents. Use this exchange rate for the activity that follows.

ACTIVITY

1. Within each group of two students, one student should play the role of a U.S. citizen visiting New Zealand. The other student should play the role of a New Zealander visiting the United States. Use the exchange rate of one New Zealand dollar for 76 U.S. cents.

2. The "U.S." student should exchange $76 U.S. and $100 U.S. for New Zealand money. The "New Zealand" student should exchange $76 New Zealand and $100 New Zealand for U.S. money.

3. The exchanges in part (2) should indicate that coins smaller than a dollar are needed to exchange $76 New Zealand for U.S. funds, or

to exchange $100 U.S. for New Zealand money. What is the smallest amount of New Zealand dollars that can be exchanged for a whole-number amount of U.S. dollars? What is the smallest amount of U.S. dollars that can be exchanged for a whole-number amount of New Zealand dollars? (*Hint*: See part 2.)

4. Use the results from part (3) to find two other amounts of U.S. dollars that can be exchanged for a whole-number amount of New Zealand dollars. Answers may vary.

5. Find the smallest number *a* for which both conversions—from *a* New Zealand dollars to U.S. funds and from *a* U.S. dollars to New Zealand funds—use only whole numbers. (*Hint*: Use LCMs and the results of part 2 above.)

6. At one time in 2008, one Polish zloty was worth about 40 U.S. cents. Find the smallest number *a* for which both conversions—from *a* Polish zlotys to U.S. funds and from *a* U.S. dollars to Polish funds—use only whole numbers. (*Hint*: See part 5.)

Addition When Denominators Are the Same ▪ Subtraction When Denominators Are the Same ▪ Least Common Multiples and Denominators

Addition When Denominators Are the Same

Recall that to add fractions having the same denominator, like $\frac{2}{7}$ and $\frac{3}{7}$, we add the numerators and keep the common denominator: $\frac{2}{7} + \frac{3}{7} = \frac{5}{7}$. The same procedure is used when rational expressions share a common denominator.

> ### The Sum of Two Rational Expressions
>
> To add when the denominators are the same, add the numerators and keep the common denominator:
> $$\frac{A}{B} + \frac{C}{B} = \frac{A + C}{B}.$$

In this section, we again assume that all denominators are nonzero.

EXAMPLE   1

Add. Simplify the result, if possible.

a) $\dfrac{4}{a} + \dfrac{3 + a}{a}$ b) $\dfrac{3x}{x - 5} + \dfrac{2x + 1}{x - 5}$

c) $\dfrac{2x^2 + 3x - 7}{2x + 1} + \dfrac{x^2 + x - 8}{2x + 1}$ d) $\dfrac{x - 5}{x^2 - 9} + \dfrac{2}{x^2 - 9}$

SOLUTION

a) $\dfrac{4}{a} + \dfrac{3 + a}{a} = \dfrac{7 + a}{a}$ When the denominators are alike, add the numerators and keep the common denominator.

b) $\dfrac{3x}{x - 5} + \dfrac{2x + 1}{x - 5} = \dfrac{5x + 1}{x - 5}$ The denominators are alike, so we add the numerators.

c) $\dfrac{2x^2 + 3x - 7}{2x + 1} + \dfrac{x^2 + x - 8}{2x + 1} = \dfrac{(2x^2 + 3x - 7) + (x^2 + x - 8)}{2x + 1}$

$= \dfrac{3x^2 + 4x - 15}{2x + 1}$ Combining like terms

$= \dfrac{(3x - 5)(x + 3)}{2x + 1}$ Factoring. There are no common factors, so we cannot simplify further.

d) $\dfrac{x - 5}{x^2 - 9} + \dfrac{2}{x^2 - 9} = \dfrac{x - 3}{x^2 - 9}$ Combining like terms in the numerator: $x - 5 + 2 = x - 3$

$= \dfrac{x - 3}{(x - 3)(x + 3)}$ Factoring

$= \dfrac{1 \cdot (x - 3)}{(x - 3)(x + 3)}$ Removing a factor equal to 1: $\dfrac{x - 3}{x - 3} = 1$

$= \dfrac{1}{x + 3}$

TRY EXERCISE   7

STUDY SKILLS

Visualize the Steps

If you have completed all assignments and are studying for a quiz or test, don't feel that you need to redo every assigned problem. A more productive use of your time would be to work through one problem of each type. Then read through the other problems, visualizing the steps that lead to a solution. When you are unsure of how to solve a problem, work that problem in its entirety, seeking outside help as needed.

Subtraction When Denominators Are the Same

When two fractions have the same denominator, we subtract one numerator from the other and keep the common denominator: $\frac{5}{7} - \frac{2}{7} = \frac{3}{7}$. The same procedure is used with rational expressions.

The Difference of Two Rational Expressions

To subtract when the denominators are the same, subtract the second numerator from the first numerator and keep the common denominator:

$$\frac{A}{B} - \frac{C}{B} = \frac{A - C}{B}.$$

CAUTION! The fraction bar under a numerator is a grouping symbol, just like parentheses. Thus, when a numerator is subtracted, it is important to subtract *every* term in that numerator.

EXAMPLE   2   Subtract and, if possible, simplify: **(a)** $\dfrac{3x}{x + 2} - \dfrac{x - 5}{x + 2}$; **(b)** $\dfrac{x^2}{x - 4} - \dfrac{x + 12}{x - 4}$.

SOLUTION

a) $\dfrac{3x}{x + 2} - \dfrac{x - 5}{x + 2} = \dfrac{3x - (x - 5)}{x + 2}$ The parentheses are needed to make sure that we subtract both terms.

$= \dfrac{3x - x + 5}{x + 2}$ Removing the parentheses and changing signs (using the distributive law)

$= \dfrac{2x + 5}{x + 2}$ Combining like terms

b) $\dfrac{x^2}{x - 4} - \dfrac{x + 12}{x - 4} = \dfrac{x^2 - (x + 12)}{x - 4}$ Remember the parentheses!

$= \dfrac{x^2 - x - 12}{x - 4}$ Removing parentheses (using the distributive law)

$= \dfrac{(x - 4)(x + 3)}{x - 4}$ Factoring, in hopes of simplifying

$= \dfrac{(x - 4)(x + 3)}{x - 4}$ Removing a factor equal to 1: $\dfrac{x - 4}{x - 4} = 1$

$= x + 3$

TRY EXERCISE   21

Least Common Multiples and Denominators

Thus far, every pair of rational expressions that we have added or subtracted shared a common denominator. To add or subtract rational expressions that have different denominators, we must first find equivalent rational expressions that *do* have a common denominator.

In algebra, we find a common denominator much as we do in arithmetic. Recall that to add $\frac{1}{12}$ and $\frac{7}{30}$, we first identify the smallest number that contains both 12 and 30 as factors. Such a number, the **least common multiple (LCM)** of the denominators, is then used as the **least common denominator (LCD)**.

Let's find the LCM of 12 and 30 using a method that can also be used with polynomials. We begin by writing the prime factorizations of 12 and 30:

$$12 = 2 \cdot 2 \cdot 3;$$
$$30 = 2 \cdot 3 \cdot 5.$$

The LCM must include the factors of each number, so it must include each prime factor the greatest number of times that it appears in either of the factorizations. To find the LCM for 12 and 30, we select one factorization, say

$$2 \cdot 2 \cdot 3,$$

and note that because it lacks a factor of 5, it does not contain the entire factorization of 30. If we multiply $2 \cdot 2 \cdot 3$ by 5, every prime factor occurs just often enough to contain both 12 and 30 as factors.

$$\text{LCM} = 2 \cdot 2 \cdot 3 \cdot 5$$

12 is a factor of the LCM.

30 is a factor of the LCM.

Note that each prime factor—2, 3, and 5—is used the greatest number of times that it appears in either of the individual factorizations. The factor 2 occurs twice and the factors 3 and 5 once each.

To Find the Least Common Denominator (LCD)

1. Write the prime factorization of each denominator.
2. Select one of the factorizations and inspect it to see if it completely contains the other factorization.

   a) If it does, it represents the LCM of the denominators.
   b) If it does not, multiply that factorization by any factors of the other denominator that it lacks. The final product is the LCM of the denominators.

The LCD is the LCM of the denominators. It should contain each factor the greatest number of times that it occurs in any of the individual factorizations.

STUDENT NOTES

The terms *least common multiple* and *least common denominator* are similar enough that they may be confusing. We find the LCM of polynomials, and we find the LCD of rational expressions.

EXAMPLE 3 Find the LCD of $\dfrac{5}{36x^2}$ and $\dfrac{7}{24x}$.

SOLUTION

1. We begin by writing the prime factorizations of $36x^2$ and $24x$:

$$36x^2 = 2 \cdot 2 \cdot 3 \cdot 3 \cdot x \cdot x;$$
$$24x = 2 \cdot 2 \cdot 2 \cdot 3 \cdot x.$$

2. We select the factorization of $36x^2$. Except for a third factor of 2, this factorization contains the entire factorization of $24x$. Thus we multiply $36x^2$ by a third factor of 2.

$36x^2$ is a factor of the LCM.

$$\text{LCM} = 2 \cdot 2 \cdot 3 \cdot 3 \cdot x \cdot x \cdot 2$$

Note that each factor appears the greatest number of times that it occurs in either of the above factorizations.

$24x$ is a factor of the LCM.

Since $2^3 \cdot 3^2 \cdot x^2$, or $72x^2$, is the smallest multiple of both $36x^2$ and $24x$, the LCM of the denominators is $72x^2$. The LCD of the expressions is $72x^2$.

Let's add $\dfrac{1}{12}$ and $\dfrac{7}{30}$:

$$\frac{1}{12} + \frac{7}{30} = \frac{1}{2 \cdot 2 \cdot 3} + \frac{7}{2 \cdot 3 \cdot 5}. \qquad \text{The least common denominator (LCD) is } 2 \cdot 2 \cdot 3 \cdot 5.$$

We found above that the LCD is $2 \cdot 2 \cdot 3 \cdot 5$, or 60. To get the LCD, we see that the first denominator needs a factor of 5, and the second denominator needs another factor of 2. Therefore, we multiply $\frac{1}{12}$ by 1, using $\frac{5}{5}$, and we multiply $\frac{7}{30}$ by 1, using $\frac{2}{2}$. Since $a \cdot 1 = a$, for any number a, the values of the fractions are not changed.

$$\frac{1}{12} + \frac{7}{30} = \frac{1}{2 \cdot 2 \cdot 3} \cdot \frac{5}{5} + \frac{7}{2 \cdot 3 \cdot 5} \cdot \frac{2}{2} \qquad \frac{5}{5} = 1 \text{ and } \frac{2}{2} = 1$$

$$= \frac{5}{60} + \frac{14}{60} \qquad\qquad\qquad \text{Both denominators are now the LCD.}$$

$$= \frac{19}{60} \qquad\qquad\qquad\qquad \text{Adding the numerators and keeping the LCD}$$

Expressions like $\dfrac{5}{36x^2}$ and $\dfrac{7}{24x}$ are added in much the same manner. In Example 3, we found that the LCD is $2 \cdot 2 \cdot 2 \cdot 3 \cdot 3 \cdot x \cdot x$, or $72x^2$. To obtain equivalent expressions with this LCD, we multiply each expression by 1, using the missing factors of the LCD to write 1:

$$\frac{5}{36x^2} + \frac{7}{24x} = \frac{5}{2 \cdot 2 \cdot 3 \cdot 3 \cdot x \cdot x} + \frac{7}{2 \cdot 2 \cdot 2 \cdot 3 \cdot x}$$

$$= \frac{5}{2 \cdot 2 \cdot 3 \cdot 3 \cdot x \cdot x} \cdot \frac{2}{2} + \frac{7}{2 \cdot 2 \cdot 2 \cdot 3 \cdot x} \cdot \frac{3 \cdot x}{3 \cdot x}$$

The LCD requires another factor of 2.   The LCD requires additional factors of 3 and x.

$$= \frac{10}{72x^2} + \frac{21x}{72x^2} \qquad \text{Both denominators are now the LCD.}$$

$$= \frac{21x + 10}{72x^2}.$$

You now have the "big picture" of why LCMs are needed when adding rational expressions. For the remainder of this section, we will practice finding LCMs and rewriting rational expressions so that they have the LCD as the denominator. In Section 7.4, we will return to the addition and subtraction of rational expressions.

EXAMPLE   4   For each pair of polynomials, find the least common multiple.

a) $15a$ and $35b$

b) $21x^3y^6$ and $7x^5y^2$

c) $x^2 + 5x - 6$ and $x^2 - 1$

SOLUTION

a) We write the prime factorizations and then construct the LCM, starting with the factorization of $15a$.

$$15a = 3 \cdot 5 \cdot a$$
$$35b = 5 \cdot 7 \cdot b$$

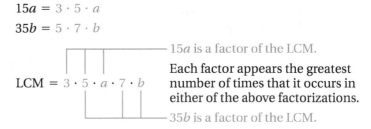

LCM $= 3 \cdot 5 \cdot a \cdot 7 \cdot b$

$15a$ is a factor of the LCM.

Each factor appears the greatest number of times that it occurs in either of the above factorizations.

$35b$ is a factor of the LCM.

The LCM is $3 \cdot 5 \cdot a \cdot 7 \cdot b$, or $105ab$.

b) $21x^3y^6 = 3 \cdot 7 \cdot x \cdot x \cdot x \cdot y \cdot y \cdot y \cdot y \cdot y \cdot y$ Try to visualize the factors of x and y mentally.

$$7x^5y^2 = 7 \cdot x \cdot x \cdot x \cdot x \cdot y \cdot y$$

LCM $= 3 \cdot 7 \cdot x \cdot x \cdot x \cdot y \cdot y \cdot y \cdot y \cdot y \cdot y \cdot x \cdot x$

We start with the prime factorization of $21x^3y^6$.

We multiply by the factors of $7x^5y^2$ that are lacking.

Note that we used the highest power of each factor in $21x^3y^6$ and $7x^5y^2$. The LCM is $21x^5y^6$.

c) $x^2 + 5x - 6 = (x - 1)(x + 6)$
       $x^2 - 1 = (x - 1)(x + 1)$

LCM $= (x - 1)(x + 6)(x + 1)$

We start with the factorization of $x^2 + 5x - 6$.

We multiply by the factor of $x^2 - 1$ that is missing.

The LCM is $(x - 1)(x + 6)(x + 1)$. There is no need to multiply this out.

> **TRY EXERCISE** 43

The procedure above can be used to find the LCM of three or more polynomials as well. We factor each polynomial and then construct the LCM using each factor the greatest number of times that it appears in any one factorization.

EXAMPLE 5   For each group of polynomials, find the LCM.

a) $12x$, $16y$, and $8xyz$

b) $x^2 + 4$, $x + 1$, and 5

SOLUTION

a) $12x = 2 \cdot 2 \cdot 3 \cdot x$

$16y = 2 \cdot 2 \cdot 2 \cdot 2 \cdot y$

$8xyz = 2 \cdot 2 \cdot 2 \cdot x \cdot y \cdot z$

We start with the factorization of $12x$.

$\text{LCM} = 2 \cdot 2 \cdot 3 \cdot x \cdot 2 \cdot 2 \cdot y \cdot z$

We multiply by the factors of $16y$ that are missing.

We multiply by the factor of $8xyz$ that is missing.

The LCM is $2^4 \cdot 3 \cdot xyz$, or $48xyz$.

b) Since $x^2 + 4, x + 1$, and 5 are not factorable, the LCM is their product: $5(x^2 + 4)(x + 1)$.

> **TRY EXERCISE** ▶ 51

To add or subtract rational expressions with different denominators, we first write equivalent expressions that have the LCD. To do this, we multiply each rational expression by a carefully constructed form of 1.

EXAMPLE   6   Find equivalent expressions that have the LCD:

$$\frac{x + 3}{x^2 + 5x - 6}, \quad \frac{x + 7}{x^2 - 1}.$$

SOLUTION   From Example 4(c), we know that the LCD is

$$(x + 6)(x - 1)(x + 1).$$

Since

$$x^2 + 5x - 6 = (x + 6)(x - 1),$$

the factor of the LCD that is missing from the first denominator is $x + 1$. We multiply by 1 using $(x + 1)/(x + 1)$:

$$\frac{x + 3}{x^2 + 5x - 6} = \frac{x + 3}{(x + 6)(x - 1)} \cdot \frac{x + 1}{x + 1}$$

$$= \frac{(x + 3)(x + 1)}{(x + 6)(x - 1)(x + 1)}.$$

Finding an equivalent expression that has the least common denominator

For the second expression, we have

$$x^2 - 1 = (x + 1)(x - 1).$$

The factor of the LCD that is missing is $x + 6$. We multiply by 1 using $(x + 6)/(x + 6)$:

$$\frac{x + 7}{x^2 - 1} = \frac{x + 7}{(x + 1)(x - 1)} \cdot \frac{x + 6}{x + 6}$$

$$= \frac{(x + 7)(x + 6)}{(x + 1)(x - 1)(x + 6)}.$$

Finding an equivalent expression that has the least common denominator

We leave the results in factored form. In Section 7.4, we will carry out the actual addition and subtraction of such rational expressions.

> **TRY EXERCISE** ▶ 61

7.3	EXERCISE SET

For Extra Help

🖐 *Concept Reinforcement*   *Use one or more words to complete each of the following sentences.*

1. To add two rational expressions when the denominators are the same, add _____ and keep the common _____.

2. When a numerator is being subtracted, use parentheses to make sure to subtract every _____ in that numerator.

3. The least common multiple of two denominators is usually referred to as the _____ and is abbreviated _____.

4. The least common denominator of two fractions must contain the prime _____ of both _____.

Perform the indicated operation. Simplify, if possible.

5. $\dfrac{3}{t} + \dfrac{5}{t}$

6. $\dfrac{8}{y^2} + \dfrac{2}{y^2}$

7. $\dfrac{x}{12} + \dfrac{2x+5}{12}$

8. $\dfrac{a}{7} + \dfrac{3a-4}{7}$

9. $\dfrac{4}{a+3} + \dfrac{5}{a+3}$

10. $\dfrac{5}{x+2} + \dfrac{8}{x+2}$

11. $\dfrac{11}{4x-7} - \dfrac{3}{4x-7}$

12. $\dfrac{9}{2x+3} - \dfrac{5}{2x+3}$

13. $\dfrac{3y+8}{2y} - \dfrac{y+1}{2y}$

14. $\dfrac{5+3t}{4t} - \dfrac{2t+1}{4t}$

15. $\dfrac{5x+7}{x+3} + \dfrac{x+11}{x+3}$

16. $\dfrac{3x+4}{x-1} + \dfrac{2x-9}{x-1}$

17. $\dfrac{5x+7}{x+3} - \dfrac{x+11}{x+3}$

18. $\dfrac{3x+4}{x-1} - \dfrac{2x-9}{x-1}$

19. $\dfrac{a^2}{a-4} + \dfrac{a-20}{a-4}$

20. $\dfrac{x^2}{x+5} + \dfrac{7x+10}{x+5}$

21. $\dfrac{y^2}{y+2} - \dfrac{5y+14}{y+2}$

22. $\dfrac{t^2}{t-3} - \dfrac{8t-15}{t-3}$

Aha! **23.** $\dfrac{t^2-5t}{t-1} + \dfrac{5t-t^2}{t-1}$

24. $\dfrac{y^2+6y}{y+2} + \dfrac{2y+12}{y+2}$

25. $\dfrac{x-6}{x^2+5x+6} + \dfrac{9}{x^2+5x+6}$

26. $\dfrac{x-5}{x^2-4x+3} + \dfrac{2}{x^2-4x+3}$

27. $\dfrac{t^2-5t}{t^2+6t+9} + \dfrac{4t-12}{t^2+6t+9}$

28. $\dfrac{y^2-7y}{y^2+8y+16} + \dfrac{6y-20}{y^2+8y+16}$

29. $\dfrac{2y^2+3y}{y^2-7y+12} - \dfrac{y^2+4y+6}{y^2-7y+12}$

30. $\dfrac{3a^2+7}{a^2-2a-8} - \dfrac{7+3a^2}{a^2-2a-8}$

31. $\dfrac{3-2x}{x^2-6x+8} + \dfrac{7-3x}{x^2-6x+8}$

32. $\dfrac{1-2t}{t^2-5t+4} + \dfrac{4-3t}{t^2-5t+4}$

33. $\dfrac{x-9}{x^2+3x-4} - \dfrac{2x-5}{x^2+3x-4}$

34. $\dfrac{5-3x}{x^2-2x+1} - \dfrac{x+1}{x^2-2x+1}$

Find the LCM.

35. 15, 36   **36.** 18, 30   **37.** 8, 9

38. 12, 15   **39.** 6, 12, 15   **40.** 8, 32, 50

Find the LCM.

41. $18t^2,\ 6t^5$ **42.** $8x^5,\ 24x^2$

43. $15a^4b^7,\ 10a^2b^8$ **44.** $6a^2b^7,\ 9a^5b^2$

45. $2(y-3),\ 6(y-3)$ **46.** $4(x-1),\ 8(x-1)$

47. $x^2-2x-15,\ x^2-9$ **48.** $t^2-4,\ t^2+7t+10$

49. $t^3+4t^2+4t,\ t^2-4t$ **50.** $y^3-y^2,\ y^4-y^2$

51. $6xz^2,\ 8x^2y,\ 15y^3z$ **52.** $12s^3t,\ 15sv^2,\ 6t^4v$

53. $a+1,\ (a-1)^2,\ a^2-1$

54. $x-2,\ (x+2)^2,\ x^2-4$

55. $2n^2+n-1,\ 2n^2+3n-2$

56. $m^2-2m-3,\ 2m^2+3m+1$

57. $6x^3-24x^2+18x,\ 4x^5-24x^4+20x^3$

58. $9x^3-9x^2-18x,\ 6x^5-24x^4+24x^3$

59. $2x^3-2,\ x^2-1$

60. $3a^3+24,\ a^2-4$

Find equivalent expressions that have the LCD.

61. $\dfrac{5}{6t^4}, \dfrac{s}{18t^2}$

62. $\dfrac{7}{10y^2}, \dfrac{x}{5y^6}$

63. $\dfrac{7}{3x^4y^2}, \dfrac{4}{9xy^3}$

64. $\dfrac{3}{2a^2b}, \dfrac{7}{8ab^2}$

65. $\dfrac{2x}{x^2-4}, \dfrac{4x}{x^2+5x+6}$

66. $\dfrac{5x}{x^2-9}, \dfrac{2x}{x^2+11x+24}$

67. Explain why the product of two numbers is not always their least common multiple.

68. If the LCM of two numbers is their product, what can you conclude about the two numbers?

Skill Review

To prepare for Section 7.4, review opposites (Sections 1.7 and 1.8).

Write each number in two equivalent forms. [1.7]

69. $-\dfrac{5}{8}$

70. $\dfrac{4}{-11}$

Write an equivalent expression without parentheses. [1.8]

71. $-(x-y)$

72. $-(3-a)$

Multiply and simplify. [1.8]

73. $-1(2x-7)$

74. $-1(a-b)$

Synthesis

75. If the LCM of two third-degree polynomials is a sixth-degree polynomial, what can be concluded about the two polynomials?

76. If the LCM of a binomial and a trinomial is the trinomial, what relationship exists between the two expressions?

Perform the indicated operations. Simplify, if possible.

77. $\dfrac{6x-1}{x-1} + \dfrac{3(2x+5)}{x-1} + \dfrac{3(2x-3)}{x-1}$

78. $\dfrac{2x+11}{x-3} \cdot \dfrac{3}{x+4} + \dfrac{-1}{4+x} \cdot \dfrac{6x+3}{x-3}$

79. $\dfrac{x^2}{3x^2-5x-2} - \dfrac{2x}{3x+1} \cdot \dfrac{1}{x-2}$

80. $\dfrac{x+y}{x^2-y^2} + \dfrac{x-y}{x^2-y^2} - \dfrac{2x}{x^2-y^2}$

African artistry. In Southeast Mozambique, the design of every woven handbag, or gipatsi *(plural,* sipatsi*) is created by repeating two or more geometric patterns.*

Each pattern encircles the bag, sharing the strands of fabric with any pattern above or below. The length, or period, of each pattern is the number of strands required to construct the pattern. For a gipatsi to be considered beautiful, each individual pattern must fit a whole number of times around the bag.
Source: Gerdes, Paulus, *Women, Art and Geometry in Southern Africa.* Asmara, Eritrea: Africa World Press, Inc., p. 5

81. A weaver is using two patterns to create a gipatsi. Pattern A is 10 strands long, and pattern B is 3 strands long. What is the smallest number of strands that can be used to complete the gipatsi?

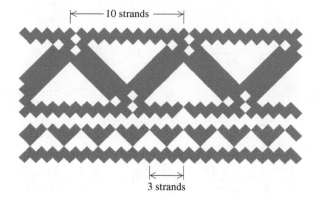

82. A weaver is using a four-strand pattern, a six-strand pattern, and an eight-strand pattern. What is the smallest number of strands that can be used to complete the gipatsi?

83. For technical reasons, the number of strands is generally a multiple of 4. Answer Exercise 79 with this additional requirement in mind.

Find the LCM.

84. 80, 96, 108

85. $4x^2-25,\ 6x^2-7x-20,\ (9x^2+24x+16)^2$

86. $9n^2 - 9$, $(5n^2 - 10n + 5)^2$, $15n - 15$

87. *Copiers.* The Brother® MFC240C copier can print 20 color pages per minute. The Lexmark X5470 copier can print 18 color pages per minute. If both machines begin printing at the same instant, how long will it be until they again begin printing a page at exactly the same time?

88. *Running.* Kim and Trey leave the starting point of a fitness loop at the same time. Kim jogs a lap in 6 min and Trey jogs one in 8 min. Assuming they continue to run at the same pace, when will they next meet at the starting place?

89. *Bus schedules.* Beginning at 5:00 A.M., a hotel shuttle bus leaves Salton Airport every 25 min, and the downtown shuttle bus leaves the airport every 35 min. What time will it be when both shuttles again leave at the same time?

90. *Appliances.* Smoke detectors last an average of 10 yr, water heaters an average of 12 yr, and refrigerators an average of 15 yr. If an apartment house is equipped with new smoke detectors, water heaters, and refrigerators in 2010, in what year will all three appliances need to be replaced at once?
Source: Demesne.info

91. Explain how evaluating can be used to perform a partial check on the result of Example 1(d):
$$\frac{x - 5}{x^2 - 9} + \frac{2}{x^2 - 9} = \frac{1}{x + 3}.$$

92. On p. 449, the second step in finding an LCD is to select one of the factorizations of the denominators. Does it matter which one is selected? Why or why not?

7.4   Addition and Subtraction with Unlike Denominators

Adding and Subtracting with LCDs ■ When Factors Are Opposites

Adding and Subtracting with LCDs

We now know how to rewrite two rational expressions in equivalent forms that use the LCD. Once rational expressions share a common denominator, they can be added or subtracted just as in Section 7.3.

> **To Add or Subtract Rational Expressions Having Different Denominators**
>
> 1. Find the LCD.
> 2. Multiply each rational expression by a form of 1 made up of the factors of the LCD missing from that expression's denominator.
> 3. Add or subtract the numerators, as indicated. Write the sum or the difference over the LCD.
> 4. Simplify, if possible.

EXAMPLE **1**   Add: $\dfrac{5x^2}{8} + \dfrac{7x}{12}$.

SOLUTION

1. First, we find the LCD:

$$\left.\begin{array}{l} 8 = 2 \cdot 2 \cdot 2 \\ 12 = 2 \cdot 2 \cdot 3 \end{array}\right\} \quad \text{LCD} = 2 \cdot 2 \cdot 2 \cdot 3, \text{ or } 24.$$

2. The denominator 8 must be multiplied by 3 in order to obtain the LCD. The denominator 12 must be multiplied by 2 in order to obtain the LCD. Thus we multiply the first expression by $\frac{3}{3}$ and the second expression by $\frac{2}{2}$ to get the LCD:

$$\begin{aligned} \frac{5x^2}{8} + \frac{7x}{12} &= \frac{5x^2}{2 \cdot 2 \cdot 2} + \frac{7x}{2 \cdot 2 \cdot 3} \\ &= \frac{5x^2}{2 \cdot 2 \cdot 2} \cdot \frac{3}{3} + \frac{7x}{2 \cdot 2 \cdot 3} \cdot \frac{2}{2} \quad \begin{array}{l}\text{Multiplying each}\\ \text{expression by a form of 1}\\ \text{to get the LCD}\end{array} \\ &= \frac{15x^2}{24} + \frac{14x}{24}. \end{aligned}$$

3. Next, we add the numerators:

$$\frac{15x^2}{24} + \frac{14x}{24} = \frac{15x^2 + 14x}{24}.$$

4. Since $15x^2 + 14x$ and 24 have no common factor,

$$\frac{15x^2 + 14x}{24}$$

cannot be simplified any further.   **TRY EXERCISE** ▶ 13

Subtraction is performed in much the same way.

EXAMPLE **2**   Subtract: $\dfrac{7}{8x} - \dfrac{5}{12x^2}$.

SOLUTION   We follow the four steps shown above. First, we find the LCD:

$$\left.\begin{array}{l} 8x = 2 \cdot 2 \cdot 2 \cdot x \\ 12x^2 = 2 \cdot 2 \cdot 3 \cdot x \cdot x \end{array}\right\} \quad \text{LCD} = 2 \cdot 2 \cdot 3 \cdot x \cdot x \cdot 2, \text{ or } 24x^2.$$

The denominator $8x$ must be multiplied by $3x$ in order to obtain the LCD. The denominator $12x^2$ must be multiplied by 2 in order to obtain the LCD. Thus we multiply by $\dfrac{3x}{3x}$ and $\dfrac{2}{2}$ to get the LCD. Then we subtract and, if possible, simplify.

$$\begin{aligned} \frac{7}{8x} - \frac{5}{12x^2} &= \frac{7}{8x} \cdot \frac{3x}{3x} - \frac{5}{12x^2} \cdot \frac{2}{2} \\ &= \frac{21x}{24x^2} - \frac{10}{24x^2} \\ &= \frac{21x - 10}{24x^2} \end{aligned}$$

> **CAUTION!** Do not simplify *these* rational expressions or you will lose the LCD.

This cannot be simplified, so we are done.   **TRY EXERCISE** ▶ 5

When denominators contain polynomials with two or more terms, the same steps are used.

EXAMPLE 3

Add: $\dfrac{2a}{a^2 - 1} + \dfrac{1}{a^2 + a}$.

SOLUTION   First, we find the LCD:

Find the LCD. $\left.\begin{array}{l} a^2 - 1 = (a - 1)(a + 1) \\ a^2 + a = a(a + 1). \end{array}\right\}$ $LCD = (a - 1)(a + 1)a$

We multiply by a form of 1 to get the LCD in each expression:

Write each expression with the LCD.

$\dfrac{2a}{a^2 - 1} + \dfrac{1}{a^2 + a} = \dfrac{2a}{(a - 1)(a + 1)} \cdot \dfrac{a}{a} + \dfrac{1}{a(a + 1)} \cdot \dfrac{a - 1}{a - 1}$ Multiplying by $\dfrac{a}{a}$ and $\dfrac{a - 1}{a - 1}$ to get the LCD

$= \dfrac{2a^2}{(a - 1)(a + 1)a} + \dfrac{a - 1}{a(a + 1)(a - 1)}$

Add numerators. $= \dfrac{2a^2 + a - 1}{a(a - 1)(a + 1)}$ Adding numerators

Simplify. $= \dfrac{(2a - 1)\cancel{(a + 1)}}{a(a - 1)\cancel{(a + 1)}}$ Simplifying by factoring and removing a factor equal to 1:

$= \dfrac{2a - 1}{a(a - 1)}.$ $\dfrac{a + 1}{a + 1} = 1$ ▶ TRY EXERCISE 33

EXAMPLE 4

Perform the indicated operations.

a) $\dfrac{x + 4}{x - 2} - \dfrac{x - 7}{x + 5}$

b) $\dfrac{t}{t^2 + 11t + 30} + \dfrac{-5}{t^2 + 9t + 20}$

c) $\dfrac{x}{x^2 + 5x + 6} - \dfrac{2}{x^2 + 3x + 2}$

STUDENT NOTES

As you can see, adding or subtracting rational expressions can involve many steps. Therefore, it is important to double-check each step of your work as you work through each problem. Waiting to inspect your work at the end of each problem is usually a less efficient use of your time.

SOLUTION

a) First, we find the LCD. It is just the product of the denominators:

$LCD = (x - 2)(x + 5).$

We multiply by a form of 1 to get the LCD in each expression. Then we subtract and try to simplify.

$\dfrac{x + 4}{x - 2} - \dfrac{x - 7}{x + 5} = \dfrac{x + 4}{x - 2} \cdot \dfrac{x + 5}{x + 5} - \dfrac{x - 7}{x + 5} \cdot \dfrac{x - 2}{x - 2}$

$= \dfrac{x^2 + 9x + 20}{(x - 2)(x + 5)} - \dfrac{x^2 - 9x + 14}{(x - 2)(x + 5)}$ Multiplying out numerators (but not denominators)

$= \dfrac{x^2 + 9x + 20 - (x^2 - 9x + 14)}{(x - 2)(x + 5)}$ When subtracting a numerator with more than one term, parentheses are important.

$= \dfrac{x^2 + 9x + 20 - x^2 + 9x - 14}{(x - 2)(x + 5)}$ Removing parentheses and subtracting every term

$= \dfrac{18x + 6}{(x - 2)(x + 5)}$

$= \dfrac{6(3x + 1)}{(x - 2)(x + 5)}$ We cannot simplify.

b) $\dfrac{t}{t^2 + 11t + 30} + \dfrac{-5}{t^2 + 9t + 20}$

$= \dfrac{t}{(t + 5)(t + 6)} + \dfrac{-5}{(t + 5)(t + 4)}$ Factoring the denominators in order to find the LCD. The LCD is $(t + 5)(t + 6)(t + 4)$.

$= \dfrac{t}{(t + 5)(t + 6)} \cdot \dfrac{t + 4}{t + 4} + \dfrac{-5}{(t + 5)(t + 4)} \cdot \dfrac{t + 6}{t + 6}$ Multiplying to get the LCD

$= \dfrac{t^2 + 4t}{(t + 5)(t + 6)(t + 4)} + \dfrac{-5t - 30}{(t + 5)(t + 6)(t + 4)}$ Multiplying in each numerator

$= \dfrac{t^2 + 4t - 5t - 30}{(t + 5)(t + 6)(t + 4)}$ Adding numerators

$= \dfrac{t^2 - t - 30}{(t + 5)(t + 6)(t + 4)}$ Combining like terms in the numerator

$= \dfrac{\cancel{(t + 5)}(t - 6)}{\cancel{(t + 5)}(t + 6)(t + 4)}$

$= \dfrac{t - 6}{(t + 6)(t + 4)}$ Always simplify the result, if possible, by removing a factor equal to 1; here $\dfrac{t + 5}{t + 5} = 1$.

c) $\dfrac{x}{x^2 + 5x + 6} - \dfrac{2}{x^2 + 3x + 2}$

Find the LCD. $= \dfrac{x}{(x + 2)(x + 3)} - \dfrac{2}{(x + 2)(x + 1)}$ Factoring denominators. The LCD is $(x + 2)(x + 3)(x + 1)$.

Write each expression with the LCD. $= \dfrac{x}{(x + 2)(x + 3)} \cdot \dfrac{x + 1}{x + 1} - \dfrac{2}{(x + 2)(x + 1)} \cdot \dfrac{x + 3}{x + 3}$

$= \dfrac{x^2 + x}{(x + 2)(x + 3)(x + 1)} - \dfrac{2x + 6}{(x + 2)(x + 3)(x + 1)}$

Subtract numerators. $= \dfrac{x^2 + x - (2x + 6)}{(x + 2)(x + 3)(x + 1)}$ Don't forget the parentheses!

$= \dfrac{x^2 + x - 2x - 6}{(x + 2)(x + 3)(x + 1)}$ Remember to subtract each term in $2x + 6$.

$= \dfrac{x^2 - x - 6}{(x + 2)(x + 3)(x + 1)}$ Combining like terms in the numerator

Simplify. $= \dfrac{\cancel{(x + 2)}(x - 3)}{\cancel{(x + 2)}(x + 3)(x + 1)}$

$= \dfrac{x - 3}{(x + 3)(x + 1)}$ Factoring and simplifying; $\dfrac{x + 2}{x + 2} = 1$

▶ TRY EXERCISE 45

When Factors Are Opposites

When one denominator is the opposite of the other, we can first multiply either expression by 1 using $-1/-1$.

EXAMPLE 5   Add: **(a)** $\dfrac{t}{2} + \dfrac{3}{-2}$; **(b)** $\dfrac{x}{x-5} + \dfrac{7}{5-x}$.

SOLUTION

a) $\dfrac{t}{2} + \dfrac{3}{-2} = \dfrac{t}{2} + \dfrac{3}{-2} \cdot \dfrac{-1}{-1}$ Multiplying by 1 using $\dfrac{-1}{-1}$

$\phantom{\dfrac{t}{2} + \dfrac{3}{-2}} = \dfrac{t}{2} + \dfrac{-3}{2}$ The denominators are now the same.

$\phantom{\dfrac{t}{2} + \dfrac{3}{-2}} = \dfrac{t + (-3)}{2}$

$\phantom{\dfrac{t}{2} + \dfrac{3}{-2}} = \dfrac{t - 3}{2}$

b) Recall that when an expression of the form $a - b$ is multiplied by -1, the subtraction is reversed: $-1(a - b) = -a + b = b + (-a) = b - a$. Since $x - 5$ and $5 - x$ are opposites, we can find a common denominator by multiplying one of the rational expressions by $-1/-1$. Because polynomials are usually written in descending order, we choose to reverse the subtraction in the second denominator:

$\dfrac{x}{x-5} + \dfrac{7}{5-x} = \dfrac{x}{x-5} + \dfrac{7}{5-x} \cdot \dfrac{-1}{-1}$ Multiplying by 1, where $1 = \dfrac{-1}{-1}$

$\phantom{\dfrac{x}{x-5} + \dfrac{7}{5-x}} = \dfrac{x}{x-5} + \dfrac{-7}{-5+x}$

$\phantom{\dfrac{x}{x-5} + \dfrac{7}{5-x}} = \dfrac{x}{x-5} + \dfrac{-7}{x-5}$ Note that $-5 + x = x + (-5) = x - 5$.

$\phantom{\dfrac{x}{x-5} + \dfrac{7}{5-x}} = \dfrac{x-7}{x-5}$.

TRY EXERCISE 53

Sometimes, after factoring to find the LCD, we find a factor in one denominator that is the opposite of a factor in the other denominator. When this happens, multiplication by $-1/-1$ can again be helpful.

EXAMPLE 6   Perform the indicated operations and simplify.

a) $\dfrac{x}{x^2 - 25} + \dfrac{3}{5-x}$ **b)** $\dfrac{x+9}{x^2-4} + \dfrac{6-x}{4-x^2} - \dfrac{1+x}{x^2-4}$

SOLUTION

a) $\dfrac{x}{x^2-25} + \dfrac{3}{5-x} = \dfrac{x}{(x-5)(x+5)} + \dfrac{3}{5-x}$ Factoring

$\phantom{\dfrac{x}{x^2-25} + \dfrac{3}{5-x}} = \dfrac{x}{(x-5)(x+5)} + \dfrac{3}{5-x} \cdot \dfrac{-1}{-1}$ Multiplication by $-1/-1$ changes $5 - x$ to $x - 5$.

$\phantom{\dfrac{x}{x^2-25} + \dfrac{3}{5-x}} = \dfrac{x}{(x-5)(x+5)} + \dfrac{-3}{x-5}$ $(5 - x)(-1) = x - 5$

$\phantom{\dfrac{x}{x^2-25} + \dfrac{3}{5-x}} = \dfrac{x}{(x-5)(x+5)} + \dfrac{-3}{(x-5)} \cdot \dfrac{x+5}{x+5}$ The LCD is $(x-5)(x+5)$.

$\phantom{\dfrac{x}{x^2-25} + \dfrac{3}{5-x}} = \dfrac{x}{(x-5)(x+5)} + \dfrac{-3x-15}{(x-5)(x+5)}$

$\phantom{\dfrac{x}{x^2-25} + \dfrac{3}{5-x}} = \dfrac{-2x-15}{(x-5)(x+5)}$

b) Since $4 - x^2$ is the opposite of $x^2 - 4$, multiplying the second rational expression by $-1/-1$ will lead to a common denominator:

$$\frac{x + 9}{x^2 - 4} + \frac{6 - x}{4 - x^2} - \frac{1 + x}{x^2 - 4} = \frac{x + 9}{x^2 - 4} + \frac{6 - x}{4 - x^2} \cdot \frac{-1}{-1} - \frac{1 + x}{x^2 - 4}$$

$$= \frac{x + 9}{x^2 - 4} + \frac{x - 6}{x^2 - 4} - \frac{1 + x}{x^2 - 4}$$

$$= \frac{x + 9 + x - 6 - 1 - x}{x^2 - 4} \quad \text{Adding and subtracting numerators}$$

$$= \frac{x + 2}{x^2 - 4}$$

$$= \frac{(x + 2) \cdot 1}{(x + 2)(x - 2)} \quad \text{Simplifying}$$

$$= \frac{1}{x - 2}.$$

TRY EXERCISE 59

7.4 EXERCISE SET

Concept Reinforcement   In Exercises 1–4, the four steps for adding rational expressions with different denominators are listed. Fill in the missing word or words for each step.

1. To add or subtract when the denominators are different, first find the _____.

2. Multiply each rational expression by a form of 1 made up of the factors of the LCD that are _____ from that expression's _____.

3. Add or subtract the _____, as indicated. Write the sum or the difference over the _____.

4. _____, if possible.

Perform the indicated operation. Simplify, if possible.

5. $\dfrac{3}{x^2} + \dfrac{5}{x}$

6. $\dfrac{6}{x} + \dfrac{7}{x^2}$

7. $\dfrac{1}{6r} - \dfrac{3}{8r}$

8. $\dfrac{4}{9t} - \dfrac{7}{6t}$

9. $\dfrac{3}{uv^2} + \dfrac{4}{u^3v}$

10. $\dfrac{8}{cd^2} + \dfrac{1}{c^2d}$

11. $\dfrac{-2}{3xy^2} - \dfrac{6}{x^2y^3}$

12. $\dfrac{8}{9t^3} - \dfrac{5}{6t^2}$

13. $\dfrac{x + 3}{8} + \dfrac{x - 2}{6}$

14. $\dfrac{x - 4}{9} + \dfrac{x + 5}{12}$

15. $\dfrac{x - 2}{6} - \dfrac{x + 1}{3}$

16. $\dfrac{a + 2}{2} - \dfrac{a - 4}{4}$

17. $\dfrac{a + 3}{15a} + \dfrac{2a - 1}{3a^2}$

18. $\dfrac{5a + 1}{2a^2} + \dfrac{a + 2}{6a}$

19. $\dfrac{4z - 9}{3z} - \dfrac{3z - 8}{4z}$

20. $\dfrac{x - 1}{4x} - \dfrac{2x + 3}{x}$

21. $\dfrac{3c + d}{cd^2} + \dfrac{c - d}{c^2d}$

22. $\dfrac{u + v}{u^2v} + \dfrac{2u + v}{uv^2}$

23. $\dfrac{4x + 2t}{3xt^2} - \dfrac{5x - 3t}{x^2t}$

24. $\dfrac{5x + 3y}{2x^2y} - \dfrac{3x + 4y}{xy^2}$

25. $\dfrac{3}{x - 2} + \dfrac{3}{x + 2}$

26. $\dfrac{5}{x - 1} + \dfrac{5}{x + 1}$

27. $\dfrac{t}{t + 3} - \dfrac{1}{t - 1}$

28. $\dfrac{y}{y - 3} + \dfrac{12}{y + 4}$

29. $\dfrac{3}{x + 1} + \dfrac{2}{3x}$

30. $\dfrac{2}{x + 5} + \dfrac{3}{4x}$

31. $\dfrac{3}{2t^2 - 2t} - \dfrac{5}{2t - 2}$

32. $\dfrac{8}{3t^2 - 15t} - \dfrac{3}{2t - 10}$

33. $\dfrac{3a}{a^2 - 9} + \dfrac{a}{a + 3}$

34. $\dfrac{5p}{p^2 - 16} + \dfrac{p}{p - 4}$

35. $\dfrac{6}{z + 4} - \dfrac{2}{3z + 12}$

36. $\dfrac{t}{t - 3} - \dfrac{5}{4t - 12}$

37. $\dfrac{5}{q - 1} + \dfrac{2}{(q - 1)^2}$

38. $\dfrac{3}{w + 2} + \dfrac{7}{(w + 2)^2}$

39. $\dfrac{t - 3}{t^3 - 1} - \dfrac{2}{1 - t^3}$

40. $\dfrac{1 - 6m}{1 - m^3} - \dfrac{5}{m^3 - 1}$

41. $\dfrac{3a}{4a - 20} + \dfrac{9a}{6a - 30}$

42. $\dfrac{4a}{5a - 10} + \dfrac{3a}{10a - 20}$

Aha! **43.** $\dfrac{x}{x - 5} + \dfrac{x}{5 - x}$

44. $\dfrac{x + 4}{x} + \dfrac{x}{x + 4}$

45. $\dfrac{6}{a^2 + a - 2} + \dfrac{4}{a^2 - 4a + 3}$

46. $\dfrac{x}{x^2 + 2x + 1} + \dfrac{1}{x^2 + 5x + 4}$

47. $\dfrac{x}{x^2 + 9x + 20} - \dfrac{4}{x^2 + 7x + 12}$

48. $\dfrac{x}{x^2 + 5x + 6} - \dfrac{2}{x^2 + 3x + 2}$

49. $\dfrac{3z}{z^2 - 4z + 4} + \dfrac{10}{z^2 + z - 6}$

50. $\dfrac{3}{x^2 - 9} + \dfrac{2}{x^2 - x - 6}$

Aha! **51.** $\dfrac{-7}{x^2 + 25x + 24} - \dfrac{0}{x^2 + 11x + 10}$

52. $\dfrac{x}{x^2 + 17x + 72} - \dfrac{1}{x^2 + 15x + 56}$

53. $\dfrac{5x}{4} - \dfrac{x - 2}{-4}$

54. $\dfrac{x}{6} - \dfrac{2x - 3}{-6}$

55. $\dfrac{y^2}{y - 3} + \dfrac{9}{3 - y}$

56. $\dfrac{t^2}{t - 2} + \dfrac{4}{2 - t}$

57. $\dfrac{c - 5}{c^2 - 64} - \dfrac{5 - c}{64 - c^2}$

58. $\dfrac{b - 4}{b^2 - 49} + \dfrac{b - 4}{49 - b^2}$

59. $\dfrac{4 - p}{25 - p^2} + \dfrac{p + 1}{p - 5}$

60. $\dfrac{y + 2}{y - 7} + \dfrac{3 - y}{49 - y^2}$

61. $\dfrac{x}{x - 4} - \dfrac{3}{16 - x^2}$

62. $\dfrac{x}{3 - x} - \dfrac{2}{x^2 - 9}$

63. $\dfrac{a}{a^2 - 1} + \dfrac{2a}{a - a^2}$

64. $\dfrac{3x + 2}{3x + 6} + \dfrac{x}{4 - x^2}$

65. $\dfrac{4x}{x^2 - y^2} - \dfrac{6}{y - x}$

66. $\dfrac{4 - a^2}{a^2 - 9} - \dfrac{a - 2}{3 - a}$

Perform the indicated operations. Simplify, if possible.

67. $\dfrac{x - 3}{2 - x} - \dfrac{x + 3}{x + 2} + \dfrac{x + 6}{4 - x^2}$

68. $\dfrac{t - 5}{1 - t} - \dfrac{t + 4}{t + 1} + \dfrac{t + 2}{t^2 - 1}$

69. $\dfrac{2x + 5}{x + 1} + \dfrac{x + 7}{x + 5} - \dfrac{5x + 17}{(x + 1)(x + 5)}$

70. $\dfrac{x + 5}{x + 3} + \dfrac{x + 7}{x + 2} - \dfrac{7x + 19}{(x + 3)(x + 2)}$

71. $\dfrac{1}{x + y} + \dfrac{1}{x - y} - \dfrac{2x}{x^2 - y^2}$

72. $\dfrac{2r}{r^2 - s^2} + \dfrac{1}{r + s} - \dfrac{1}{r - s}$

73. What is the advantage of using the *least* common denominator—rather than just *any* common denominator—when adding or subtracting rational expressions?

74. Describe a procedure that can be used to add any two rational expressions.

Skill Review

To prepare for Section 7.5, review division of fractions and rational expressions (Sections 1.3, 1.7, and 7.2).

Simplify.

75. $-\dfrac{3}{8} \div \dfrac{11}{4}$ [1.7]

76. $-\dfrac{7}{12} \div \left(-\dfrac{3}{4}\right)$ [1.7]

77. $\dfrac{\frac{3}{4}}{\frac{5}{6}}$ [1.3]

78. $\dfrac{\frac{8}{15}}{\frac{9}{10}}$ [1.3]

79. $\dfrac{2x + 6}{x - 1} \div \dfrac{3x + 9}{x - 1}$ [7.2]

80. $\dfrac{x^2 - 9}{x^2 - 4} \div \dfrac{x^2 + 6x + 9}{x^2 + 4x + 4}$ [7.2]

Synthesis

81. How could you convince someone that

$$\dfrac{1}{3 - x} \quad \text{and} \quad \dfrac{1}{x - 3}$$

are opposites of each other?

82. Are parentheses as important for adding rational expressions as they are for subtracting rational expressions? Why or why not?

Write expressions for the perimeter and the area of each rectangle.

83.

$\frac{3}{x+4}$

$\frac{2}{x-5}$

84.

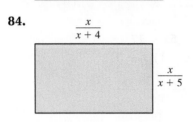

$\frac{x}{x+4}$

$\frac{x}{x+5}$

Perform the indicated operations.

85. $\dfrac{x^2}{3x^2 - 5x - 2} - \dfrac{2x}{3x + 1} \cdot \dfrac{1}{x - 2}$

86. $\dfrac{2x + 11}{x - 3} \cdot \dfrac{3}{x + 4} + \dfrac{2x + 1}{4 + x} \cdot \dfrac{3}{3 - x}$

Aha! **87.** $\left(\dfrac{x}{x + 7} - \dfrac{3}{x + 2} \right)\left(\dfrac{x}{x + 7} + \dfrac{3}{x + 2} \right)$

88. $\dfrac{1}{ay - 3a + 2xy - 6x} - \dfrac{xy + ay}{a^2 - 4x^2}\left(\dfrac{1}{y - 3} \right)^2$

89. $\left(\dfrac{a}{a - b} + \dfrac{b}{a + b} \right)\left(\dfrac{1}{3a + b} + \dfrac{2a + 6b}{9a^2 - b^2} \right)$

90. $\dfrac{2x^2 + 5x - 3}{2x^2 - 9x + 9} + \dfrac{x + 1}{3 - 2x} + \dfrac{4x^2 + 8x + 3}{x - 3} \cdot \dfrac{x + 3}{9 - 4x^2}$

91. Express

$$\frac{a - 3b}{a - b}$$

as a sum of two rational expressions with denominators that are opposites of each other. Answers may vary.

92. Use a graphing calculator to check the answer to Exercise 29.

93. Why does the word ERROR appear in the table displayed on p. 460?

CONNECTING | the CONCEPTS

The process of adding and subtracting rational expressions is significantly different from multiplying and dividing them. The first thing you should take note of when combining rational expressions is the operation sign.

Operation	Need Common Denominator?	Procedure	Tips and Cautions
Addition	Yes	Write with a common denominator. Add numerators. Keep denominator.	Do not simplify after writing with the LCD. Instead, simplify after adding the numerators.
Subtraction	Yes	Write with a common denominator. Subtract numerators. Keep denominator.	Use parentheses around the numerator being subtracted. Simplify after subtracting the numerators.
Multiplication	No	Multiply numerators. Multiply denominators.	Do not carry out the multiplications. Instead, factor and try to simplify.
Division	No	Multiply by the reciprocal of the divisor.	Begin by rewriting as a multiplication using the reciprocal of the divisor.

MIXED REVIEW

Tell what operation is being performed. Then perform the operation and, if possible, simplify.

1. $\dfrac{3}{5x} + \dfrac{2}{x^2}$

2. $\dfrac{3}{5x} \cdot \dfrac{2}{x^2}$

3. $\dfrac{3}{5x} \div \dfrac{2}{x^2}$

4. $\dfrac{3}{5x} - \dfrac{2}{x^2}$

5. $\dfrac{2x - 6}{5x + 10} \cdot \dfrac{x + 2}{6x - 12}$

6. $\dfrac{2}{x + 3} \cdot \dfrac{3}{x + 4}$

7. $\dfrac{2}{x - 5} \div \dfrac{6}{x - 5}$

8. $\dfrac{x}{x + 2} - \dfrac{1}{x - 1}$

9. $\dfrac{2}{x + 3} + \dfrac{3}{x + 4}$

10. $\dfrac{5}{2x - 1} + \dfrac{10x}{1 - 2x}$

11. $\dfrac{3}{x - 4} - \dfrac{2}{4 - x}$

12. $\dfrac{(x - 2)(2x + 3)}{(x + 1)(x - 5)} \div \dfrac{(x - 2)(x + 1)}{(x - 5)(x + 3)}$

13. $\dfrac{a}{6a - 9b} - \dfrac{b}{4a - 6b}$

14. $\dfrac{x^2 - 16}{x^2 - x} \cdot \dfrac{x^2}{x^2 - 5x + 4}$

15. $\dfrac{x + 1}{x^2 - 7x + 10} + \dfrac{3}{x^2 - x - 2}$

16. $\dfrac{3u^2 - 3}{4} \div \dfrac{4u + 4}{3}$

17. $\dfrac{t + 2}{10} + \dfrac{2t + 1}{15}$

18. $(t^2 + t - 20) \cdot \dfrac{t + 5}{t - 4}$

19. $\dfrac{a^2 - 2a + 1}{a^2 - 4} \div (a^2 - 3a + 2)$

20. $\dfrac{2x - 7}{x} - \dfrac{3x - 5}{2}$

7.5   Complex Rational Expressions

Using Division to Simplify ▪ Multiplying by the LCD

A **complex rational expression** is a rational expression that has one or more rational expressions within its numerator or denominator. Here are some examples:

$$\dfrac{1 + \dfrac{2}{x}}{3}, \qquad \dfrac{\dfrac{x + y}{7}}{\dfrac{2x}{x + 1}}, \qquad \dfrac{\dfrac{4}{3} + \dfrac{1}{5}}{\dfrac{2}{x} - \dfrac{x}{y}}.$$

These are rational expressions within the complex rational expression.

When we simplify a complex rational expression, we rewrite it so that it is no longer complex. We will consider two methods for simplifying complex rational expressions. Each method offers certain advantages.

Using Division to Simplify (Method 1)

Our first method for simplifying complex rational expressions involves rewriting the expression as a quotient of two rational expressions.

> **To Simplify a Complex Rational Expression by Dividing**
> 1. Add or subtract, as needed, to get a single rational expression in the numerator.
> 2. Add or subtract, as needed, to get a single rational expression in the denominator.
> 3. Divide the numerator by the denominator (invert and multiply).
> 4. If possible, simplify by removing a factor equal to 1.

The key here is to express a complex rational expression as one rational expression divided by another. We can then proceed as in Section 7.2.

EXAMPLE 1 Simplify: $\dfrac{\dfrac{x}{x-3}}{\dfrac{4}{5x-15}}$.

SOLUTION Here the numerator and the denominator are already single rational expressions. This allows us to start by dividing (step 3), as in Section 7.2:

$$\dfrac{\dfrac{x}{x-3}}{\dfrac{4}{5x-15}} = \dfrac{x}{x-3} \div \dfrac{4}{5x-15} \quad \text{Rewriting with a division symbol}$$

$$= \dfrac{x}{x-3} \cdot \dfrac{5x-15}{4} \quad \begin{array}{l}\text{Multiplying by the reciprocal of the}\\ \text{divisor (inverting and multiplying)}\end{array}$$

$$= \dfrac{x}{x-3} \cdot \dfrac{5(x-3)}{4} \quad \begin{array}{l}\text{Factoring and removing a factor}\\ \text{equal to 1: } \dfrac{x-3}{x-3} = 1\end{array}$$

$$= \dfrac{5x}{4}.$$

TRY EXERCISE 21

All four steps of the division method are used in Example 2(a).

EXAMPLE 2 Simplify.

a) $\dfrac{\dfrac{5}{2a}+\dfrac{1}{a}}{\dfrac{1}{4a}-\dfrac{5}{6}}$

b) $\dfrac{\dfrac{x^2}{y}-\dfrac{5}{x}}{xz}$

SOLUTION

a) $\dfrac{\dfrac{5}{2a}+\dfrac{1}{a}}{\dfrac{1}{4a}-\dfrac{5}{6}} = \dfrac{\dfrac{5}{2a}+\dfrac{1}{a}\cdot\dfrac{2}{2}}{\dfrac{1}{4a}\cdot\dfrac{3}{3}-\dfrac{5}{6}\cdot\dfrac{2a}{2a}}$

$\left.\rule{0pt}{18pt}\right\}$ ← Multiplying by 1 to get the LCD, $2a$, for the numerator of the complex rational expression

$\left.\rule{0pt}{18pt}\right\}$ ← Multiplying by 1 to get the LCD, $12a$, for the denominator of the complex rational expression

1. Add to get a single rational expression in the numerator.

2. Subtract to get a single rational expression in the denominator.

3. Divide the numerator by the denominator.

4. Simplify.

$$= \frac{\dfrac{5}{2a} + \dfrac{2}{2a}}{\dfrac{3}{12a} - \dfrac{10a}{12a}} = \frac{\dfrac{7}{2a}}{\dfrac{3 - 10a}{12a}}$$ ← Adding

↙ Subtracting

$$= \frac{7}{2a} \div \frac{3 - 10a}{12a}$$ Rewriting with a division symbol. This is often done mentally.

$$= \frac{7}{2a} \cdot \frac{12a}{3 - 10a}$$ Multiplying by the reciprocal of the divisor (inverting and multiplying)

$$= \frac{7}{\cancel{2a}} \cdot \frac{\cancel{2a} \cdot 6}{3 - 10a}$$ Removing a factor equal to 1: $\dfrac{2a}{2a} = 1$

$$= \frac{42}{3 - 10a}$$

b) $$\frac{\dfrac{x^2}{y} - \dfrac{5}{x}}{xz} = \frac{\dfrac{x^2}{y} \cdot \dfrac{x}{x} - \dfrac{5}{x} \cdot \dfrac{y}{y}}{xz}$$ ← Multiplying by 1 to get the LCD, xy, for the numerator of the complex rational expression

$$= \frac{\dfrac{x^3}{xy} - \dfrac{5y}{xy}}{xz}$$

$$= \frac{\dfrac{x^3 - 5y}{xy}}{xz}$$ ← Subtracting

← If you prefer, write xz as $\dfrac{xz}{1}$.

$$= \frac{x^3 - 5y}{xy} \div (xz)$$ Rewriting with a division symbol

$$= \frac{x^3 - 5y}{xy} \cdot \frac{1}{xz}$$ Multiplying by the reciprocal of the divisor (inverting and multiplying)

$$= \frac{x^3 - 5y}{x^2yz}$$

TRY EXERCISE 11

Multiplying by the LCD (Method 2)

A second method for simplifying complex rational expressions relies on multiplying by a carefully chosen expression that is equal to 1. This multiplication by 1 will result in an expression that is no longer complex.

> **To Simplify a Complex Rational Expression by Multiplying by the LCD**
>
> **1.** Find the LCD of *all* rational expressions within the complex rational expression.
> **2.** Multiply the complex rational expression by an expression equal to 1. Write 1 as the LCD over itself (LCD/LCD).
> **3.** Simplify. No fraction expressions should remain within the complex rational expression.
> **4.** Factor and, if possible, simplify.

EXAMPLE 3   Simplify: $\dfrac{\dfrac{1}{2} + \dfrac{3}{4}}{\dfrac{5}{6} - \dfrac{3}{8}}$.

Pay careful attention to the difference in the ways in which Method 1 and Method 2 use an LCD. In Method 1, separate LCDs are found in the numerator and in the denominator. In Method 2, *all* rational expressions are considered in order to find one LCD.

SOLUTION

1. The LCD of $\frac{1}{2}, \frac{3}{4}, \frac{5}{6},$ and $\frac{3}{8}$ is 24.

2. We multiply by an expression equal to 1:

$$\frac{\dfrac{1}{2}+\dfrac{3}{4}}{\dfrac{5}{6}-\dfrac{3}{8}}=\frac{\dfrac{1}{2}+\dfrac{3}{4}}{\dfrac{5}{6}-\dfrac{3}{8}}\cdot\frac{24}{24}. \qquad \text{Multiplying by an expression equal to 1,}$$
$$\text{using the LCD: } \frac{24}{24}=1$$

3. Using the distributive law, we perform the multiplication:

$$\frac{\dfrac{1}{2}+\dfrac{3}{4}}{\dfrac{5}{6}-\dfrac{3}{8}}\cdot\frac{24}{24}=\frac{\left(\dfrac{1}{2}+\dfrac{3}{4}\right)24}{\left(\dfrac{5}{6}-\dfrac{3}{8}\right)24}$$
← Multiplying the numerator by 24
Don't forget the parentheses!
← Multiplying the denominator by 24

$$=\frac{\dfrac{1}{2}(24)+\dfrac{3}{4}(24)}{\dfrac{5}{6}(24)-\dfrac{3}{8}(24)} \qquad \text{Using the distributive law}$$

$$=\frac{12+18}{20-9}, \quad \text{or} \quad \frac{30}{11}. \qquad \text{Simplifying}$$

4. The result, $\frac{30}{11}$, cannot be factored or simplified, so we are done.

> **TRY EXERCISE** ▷ 5

Multiplying like this effectively clears fractions in both the top and the bottom of the complex rational expression. Compare the steps in Example 4(a) with those in Example 2(a).

EXAMPLE 4   Simplify.

a) $\dfrac{\dfrac{5}{2a}+\dfrac{1}{a}}{\dfrac{1}{4a}-\dfrac{5}{6}}$

b) $\dfrac{1-\dfrac{1}{x}}{1-\dfrac{1}{x^2}}$

SOLUTION

1. Find the LCD.

a) The denominators within the complex expression are $2a$, a, $4a$, and 6, so the LCD is $12a$. We multiply by 1 using $(12a)/(12a)$:

2. Multiply by LCD/LCD.

$$\frac{\dfrac{5}{2a}+\dfrac{1}{a}}{\dfrac{1}{4a}-\dfrac{5}{6}}=\frac{\dfrac{5}{2a}+\dfrac{1}{a}}{\dfrac{1}{4a}-\dfrac{5}{6}}\cdot\frac{12a}{12a}=\frac{\dfrac{5}{2a}(12a)+\dfrac{1}{a}(12a)}{\dfrac{1}{4a}(12a)-\dfrac{5}{6}(12a)}. \qquad \begin{array}{l}\text{Using the}\\ \text{distributive law}\end{array}$$

When we multiply by $12a$, all fractions in the numerator and the denominator of the complex rational expression are cleared:

3., 4. Simplify.

$$\frac{\dfrac{5}{2a}(12a)+\dfrac{1}{a}(12a)}{\dfrac{1}{4a}(12a)-\dfrac{5}{6}(12a)}=\frac{30+12}{3-10a}=\frac{42}{3-10a}. \qquad \begin{array}{l}\text{All fractions have been}\\ \text{cleared.}\end{array}$$

Be careful to place parentheses properly when entering complex rational expressions into a graphing calculator. Remember to enclose the entire numerator of the complex rational expression in one set of parentheses and the entire denominator in another. For example, we enter the expression in Example 4(a) as

$$y_1 = (5/(2x) + 1/x) /(1/(4x) - 5/6).$$

1. Write Example 4(b) as you would to enter it into a graphing calculator.

2. When must the numerator of a rational expression be enclosed in parentheses? the denominator?

b) $\dfrac{1 - \dfrac{1}{x}}{1 - \dfrac{1}{x^2}} = \dfrac{1 - \dfrac{1}{x}}{1 - \dfrac{1}{x^2}} \cdot \dfrac{x^2}{x^2}$ The LCD is x^2 so we multiply by 1 using x^2/x^2.

$= \dfrac{1 \cdot x^2 - \dfrac{1}{x} \cdot x^2}{1 \cdot x^2 - \dfrac{1}{x^2} \cdot x^2}$ Using the distributive law

$= \dfrac{x^2 - x}{x^2 - 1}$ All fractions have been cleared within the complex rational expression.

$= \dfrac{x(x - 1)}{(x + 1)(x - 1)}$ Factoring and simplifying: $\dfrac{x - 1}{x - 1} = 1$

$= \dfrac{x}{x + 1}$

TRY EXERCISE 15

It is important to understand both of the methods studied in this section. Sometimes, as in Example 1, the complex rational expression is either given as—or easily written as—a quotient of two rational expressions. In these cases, Method 1 (using division) is probably the easier method to use. Other times, as in Example 4, it is not difficult to find the LCD of all denominators in the complex rational expression. When this occurs, it is usually easier to use Method 2 (multiplying by the LCD). The more practice you get using both methods, the better you will be at selecting the easier method for any given problem.

7.5 EXERCISE SET

Concept Reinforcement In each of Exercises 1–4, use the method listed to match the accompanying expression with the expression in the column on the right that arises when that method is used.

1. $\dfrac{\dfrac{5}{x^2} + \dfrac{1}{x}}{\dfrac{7}{2} - \dfrac{3}{4x}}$;

Multiplying by the LCD (Method 2)

2. $\dfrac{\dfrac{5}{x^2} + \dfrac{1}{x}}{\dfrac{7}{2} - \dfrac{3}{4x}}$;

Using division to simplify (Method 1)

3. $\dfrac{\dfrac{4}{5x} - \dfrac{1}{10}}{\dfrac{8}{x^2} + \dfrac{7}{2}}$;

Using division to simplify (Method 1)

4. $\dfrac{\dfrac{4}{5x} - \dfrac{1}{10}}{\dfrac{8}{x^2} + \dfrac{7}{2}}$;

Multiplying by the LCD (Method 2)

a) $\dfrac{\dfrac{5 + x}{x^2}}{\dfrac{14x - 3}{4x}}$

b) $\dfrac{\dfrac{8 - x}{10x}}{\dfrac{16 + 7x^2}{2x^2}}$

c) $\dfrac{\dfrac{4}{5x} \cdot 10x^2 - \dfrac{1}{10} \cdot 10x^2}{\dfrac{8}{x^2} \cdot 10x^2 + \dfrac{7}{2} \cdot 10x^2}$

d) $\dfrac{\dfrac{5}{x^2} \cdot 4x^2 + \dfrac{1}{x} \cdot 4x^2}{\dfrac{7}{2} \cdot 4x^2 - \dfrac{3}{4x} \cdot 4x^2}$

Simplify. Use either method or the method specified by your instructor.

5. $\dfrac{1 + \dfrac{1}{4}}{2 + \dfrac{3}{4}}$

6. $\dfrac{3 + \dfrac{1}{4}}{1 + \dfrac{1}{2}}$

7. $\dfrac{\dfrac{1}{2} + \dfrac{1}{3}}{\dfrac{1}{4} - \dfrac{1}{6}}$

8. $\dfrac{\dfrac{2}{5} - \dfrac{1}{10}}{\dfrac{7}{20} - \dfrac{4}{15}}$

9. $\dfrac{\dfrac{x}{4} + x}{\dfrac{4}{x} + x}$

10. $\dfrac{\dfrac{1}{c} + 2}{\dfrac{1}{c} - 5}$

11. $\dfrac{\dfrac{10}{t}}{\dfrac{2}{t^2} - \dfrac{5}{t}}$

12. $\dfrac{\dfrac{5}{x} - \dfrac{2}{x^2}}{\dfrac{2}{x^2}}$

13. $\dfrac{\dfrac{2a - 5}{3a}}{\dfrac{a - 7}{6a}}$

14. $\dfrac{\dfrac{a + 5}{a^2}}{\dfrac{a - 2}{3a}}$

15. $\dfrac{\dfrac{x}{6} - \dfrac{3}{x}}{\dfrac{1}{3} + \dfrac{1}{x}}$

16. $\dfrac{\dfrac{2}{x} + \dfrac{x}{4}}{\dfrac{3}{4} - \dfrac{2}{x}}$

17. $\dfrac{\dfrac{1}{s} - \dfrac{1}{5}}{\dfrac{s - 5}{s}}$

18. $\dfrac{\dfrac{1}{9} - \dfrac{1}{n}}{\dfrac{n + 9}{9}}$

19. $\dfrac{\dfrac{1}{t^2} + 1}{\dfrac{1}{t} - 1}$

20. $\dfrac{2 + \dfrac{1}{x}}{2 - \dfrac{1}{x^2}}$

21. $\dfrac{\dfrac{x^2}{x^2 - y^2}}{\dfrac{x}{x + y}}$

22. $\dfrac{\dfrac{a^2}{a - 2}}{\dfrac{3a}{a^2 - 4}}$

23. $\dfrac{\dfrac{7}{c^2} + \dfrac{4}{c}}{\dfrac{6}{c} - \dfrac{3}{c^3}}$

24. $\dfrac{\dfrac{4}{t^3} - \dfrac{1}{t^2}}{\dfrac{3}{t} + \dfrac{5}{t^2}}$

25. $\dfrac{\dfrac{2}{7a^4} - \dfrac{1}{14a}}{\dfrac{3}{5a^2} + \dfrac{2}{15a}}$

26. $\dfrac{\dfrac{5}{4x^3} - \dfrac{3}{8x}}{\dfrac{3}{2x} + \dfrac{3}{4x^3}}$ Aha!

27. $\dfrac{\dfrac{x}{5y^3} + \dfrac{3}{10y}}{\dfrac{3}{10y} + \dfrac{x}{5y^3}}$

28. $\dfrac{\dfrac{a}{6b^3} + \dfrac{4}{9b^2}}{\dfrac{5}{6b} - \dfrac{1}{9b^3}}$

29. $\dfrac{\dfrac{3}{ab^4} + \dfrac{4}{a^3b}}{\dfrac{5}{a^3b} - \dfrac{3}{ab}}$

30. $\dfrac{\dfrac{2}{x^2y} + \dfrac{3}{xy^2}}{\dfrac{3}{xy^2} + \dfrac{2}{x^2y}}$

31. $\dfrac{t - \dfrac{9}{t}}{t + \dfrac{4}{t}}$

32. $\dfrac{s + \dfrac{2}{s}}{s - \dfrac{3}{s}}$

33. $\dfrac{\dfrac{1}{a} + \dfrac{1}{b}}{\dfrac{1}{a^3} + \dfrac{1}{b^3}}$

34. $\dfrac{x - y}{\dfrac{1}{x^3} - \dfrac{1}{y^3}}$

35. $\dfrac{3 + \dfrac{4}{ab^3}}{\dfrac{3 + a}{a^2b}}$

36. $\dfrac{5 + \dfrac{3}{x^2y}}{\dfrac{3 + x}{x^3y}}$

37. $\dfrac{t + 5 + \dfrac{3}{t}}{t + 2 + \dfrac{1}{t}}$

38. $\dfrac{a + 3 + \dfrac{2}{a}}{a + 2 + \dfrac{5}{a}}$

39. $\dfrac{x - 2 - \dfrac{1}{x}}{x - 5 - \dfrac{4}{x}}$

40. $\dfrac{x - 3 - \dfrac{2}{x}}{x - 4 - \dfrac{3}{x}}$

41. Is it possible to simplify complex rational expressions without knowing how to divide rational expressions? Why or why not?

42. Why is the distributive law important when simplifying complex rational expressions?

Skill Review

To prepare for Section 6.6, review solving linear and quadratic equations (Sections 2.2 and 6.7).

Solve.

43. $3x - 5 + 2(4x - 1) = 12x - 3$ [2.2]

44. $(x - 1)7 - (x + 1)9 = 4(x + 2)$ [2.2]

45. $\dfrac{3}{4}x - \dfrac{5}{8} = \dfrac{3}{8}x + \dfrac{7}{4}$ [2.2]

46. $\dfrac{5}{9} - \dfrac{2x}{3} = \dfrac{5x}{6} + \dfrac{4}{3}$ [2.2]

47. $x^2 - 7x + 12 = 0$ [6.7]

48. $x^2 + 13x - 30 = 0$ [6.7]

Synthesis

49. Which of the two methods presented would you use to simplify Exercise 30? Why?

50. Which of the two methods presented would you use to simplify Exercise 22? Why?

In Exercises 51–54, find all x-values for which the given expression is undefined.

51. $\dfrac{\dfrac{x - 5}{x - 6}}{\dfrac{x - 7}{x - 8}}$

52. $\dfrac{\dfrac{x + 1}{x + 2}}{\dfrac{x + 3}{x + 4}}$

53. $\dfrac{\dfrac{2x + 3}{5x + 4}}{\dfrac{3}{7} - \dfrac{x^2}{21}}$

54. $\dfrac{\dfrac{3x - 5}{2x - 7}}{\dfrac{4x}{5} - \dfrac{8}{15}}$

55. Use multiplication by the LCD (Method 2) to show that

$$\dfrac{A}{B} \div \dfrac{C}{D} = \dfrac{A}{B} \cdot \dfrac{D}{C}.$$

(*Hint*: Begin by forming a complex rational expression.)

56. The formula

$$\frac{P\left(1 + \dfrac{i}{12}\right)^2}{\dfrac{\left(1 + \dfrac{i}{12}\right)^2 - 1}{\dfrac{i}{12}}},$$

where P is a loan amount and i is an interest rate, arises in certain business situations. Simplify this expression. (*Hint*: Expand the binomials.)

Simplify.

57. $\dfrac{\dfrac{x}{x+5} + \dfrac{3}{x+2}}{\dfrac{2}{x+2} - \dfrac{x}{x+5}}$

58. $\dfrac{\dfrac{5}{x+2} - \dfrac{3}{x-2}}{\dfrac{x}{x-1} + \dfrac{x}{x+1}}$

Aha! **59.** $\left[\dfrac{\dfrac{x-1}{x-1} - 1}{\dfrac{x+1}{x-1} + 1}\right]^5$

60. $1 + \dfrac{1}{1 + \dfrac{1}{1 + \dfrac{1}{x}}}$

61. $\dfrac{\dfrac{z}{1 - \dfrac{z}{2+2z}} - 2z}{\dfrac{2z}{5z-2} - 3}$

62. Find the simplified form for the reciprocal of

$$\frac{2}{x-1} - \frac{1}{3x-2}.$$

63. Under what circumstance(s) will there be no restrictions on the variable appearing in a complex rational expression?

64. Use a graphing calculator to check Example 2(a).

7.6   Solving Rational Equations

Solving a New Type of Equation   ▪   A Visual Interpretation

Our study of rational expressions allows us to solve a type of equation that we could not have solved prior to this chapter.

Solving a New Type of Equation

A **rational**, or **fraction**, **equation** is an equation containing one or more rational expressions, often with the variable in a denominator. Here are some examples:

$$\frac{2}{3} + \frac{5}{6} = \frac{x}{9}, \qquad t + \frac{7}{t} = -5, \qquad \frac{x^2}{x-1} = \frac{1}{x-1}.$$

> **To Solve a Rational Equation**
> 1. List any restrictions that exist. Numbers that make a denominator equal 0 can never be solutions.
> 2. Clear the equation of fractions by multiplying both sides by the LCM of the denominators.
> 3. Solve the resulting equation using the addition principle, the multiplication principle, and the principle of zero products, as needed.
> 4. Check the possible solution(s) in the original equation.

When clearing an equation of fractions, we use the terminology LCM instead of LCD because we are *not* adding or subtracting rational expressions.

EXAMPLE   **1**

Solve: $\dfrac{x}{6} - \dfrac{x}{8} = \dfrac{1}{12}$.

STUDY SKILLS ───────────

Does More Than One Solution Exist?

Keep in mind that many problems—in math and elsewhere—have more than one solution. When asked to solve an equation, we are expected to find any and all solutions of the equation.

SOLUTION   Because no variable appears in a denominator, no restrictions exist. The LCM of 6, 8, and 12 is 24, so we multiply both sides by 24:

$$24\left(\frac{x}{6} - \frac{x}{8}\right) = 24 \cdot \frac{1}{12}$$

Using the multiplication principle to multiply both sides by the LCM. Parentheses are important!

$$24 \cdot \frac{x}{6} - 24 \cdot \frac{x}{8} = 24 \cdot \frac{1}{12}$$

Using the distributive law

Be sure to multiply *each* term by the LCM.

$$\left.\begin{array}{c}\dfrac{24x}{6} - \dfrac{24x}{8} = \dfrac{24}{12}\\[2mm] 4x - 3x = 2\end{array}\right\}$$

Simplifying. Note that all fractions have been cleared. If fractions remain, we have either made a mistake or have not used the LCM of the denominators.

$$x = 2.$$

Check:

$$\begin{array}{c|c} \dfrac{x}{6} - \dfrac{x}{8} & = \dfrac{1}{12} \\[2mm] \dfrac{2}{6} - \dfrac{2}{8} & \dfrac{1}{12} \\[2mm] \dfrac{1}{3} - \dfrac{1}{4} & \\[2mm] \dfrac{4}{12} - \dfrac{3}{12} & \\[2mm] \dfrac{1}{12} \overset{?}{=} \dfrac{1}{12} & \text{TRUE} \end{array}$$

This checks, so the solution is 2.

▶ **TRY EXERCISE** ▶ 5

Recall that the multiplication principle states that $a = b$ is equivalent to $a \cdot c = b \cdot c$, *provided c is not zero.* Because rational equations often have variables in a denominator, clearing fractions will now require us to multiply both sides by a variable expression. Since a variable expression could represent 0, *multiplying both sides of an equation by a variable expression does not always produce an equivalent equation.* Thus checking each solution in the original equation is essential.

EXAMPLE   **2**

Solve.

a) $\dfrac{2}{3x} + \dfrac{1}{x} = 10$

b) $x + \dfrac{6}{x} = -5$

c) $1 + \dfrac{3x}{x + 2} = \dfrac{-6}{x + 2}$

d) $\dfrac{3}{x - 5} + \dfrac{1}{x + 5} = \dfrac{2}{x^2 - 25}$

e) $\dfrac{x^2}{x - 1} = \dfrac{1}{x - 1}$

SOLUTION

List restrictions.

a) If $x = 0$, both denominators are 0. We list this restriction:

$$x \neq 0.$$

We now clear the equation of fractions and solve:

$$\frac{2}{3x} + \frac{1}{x} = 10 \qquad \text{We cannot have } x = 0. \text{ The LCM is } 3x.$$

Clear fractions.

$$3x\left(\frac{2}{3x} + \frac{1}{x}\right) = 3x \cdot 10 \qquad \begin{array}{l}\text{Using the multiplication principle to} \\ \text{multiply both sides by the LCM.} \\ \textit{Don't forget the parentheses!}\end{array}$$

$$3x \cdot \frac{2}{3x} + 3x \cdot \frac{1}{x} = 3x \cdot 10 \qquad \text{Using the distributive law}$$

$$2 + 3 = 30x \qquad \begin{array}{l}\text{Removing factors equal to 1:} \\ (3x)/(3x) = 1 \text{ and } x/x = 1. \text{ This} \\ \text{clears all fractions.}\end{array}$$

Solve.

$$5 = 30x$$

$$\frac{5}{30} = x, \quad \text{so } x = \frac{1}{6}. \qquad \begin{array}{l}\text{Dividing both sides by 30, or} \\ \text{multiplying both sides by } 1/30\end{array}$$

Since $\frac{1}{6} \neq 0$, and 0 is the only restricted value, $\frac{1}{6}$ *should* check.

Check.

Check:

$$\frac{2}{3x} + \frac{1}{x} = 10$$

$$\begin{array}{c|c} \dfrac{2}{3 \cdot \frac{1}{6}} + \dfrac{1}{\frac{1}{6}} & 10 \\[2ex] \dfrac{2}{\frac{1}{2}} + \dfrac{1}{\frac{1}{6}} & \\[2ex] 2 \cdot \frac{2}{1} + 1 \cdot \frac{6}{1} & \\[1ex] 4 + 6 & \\[1ex] 10 \overset{?}{=} 10 & \text{TRUE} \end{array}$$

The solution is $\frac{1}{6}$.

b) Again, note that if $x = 0$, the expression $6/x$ is undefined. We list the restriction:

$$x \neq 0.$$

We now clear the equation of fractions and solve:

$$x + \frac{6}{x} = -5 \qquad \text{We cannot have } x = 0. \text{ The LCM is } x.$$

$$x\left(x + \frac{6}{x}\right) = x(-5) \qquad \begin{array}{l}\text{Multiplying both sides by the LCM.} \\ \textit{Don't forget the parentheses!}\end{array}$$

$$x \cdot x + x \cdot \frac{6}{x} = -5x \qquad \text{Using the distributive law}$$

$$x^2 + 6 = -5x \qquad \begin{array}{l}\text{Removing a factor equal to 1: } x/x = 1. \\ \text{We are left with a quadratic equation.}\end{array}$$

$$x^2 + 5x + 6 = 0 \qquad \begin{array}{l}\text{Using the addition principle to add } 5x \text{ to} \\ \text{both sides}\end{array}$$

$$(x + 3)(x + 2) = 0 \qquad \text{Factoring}$$

$$x + 3 = 0 \quad \textit{or} \quad x + 2 = 0 \qquad \text{Using the principle of zero products}$$

$$x = -3 \quad \textit{or} \qquad x = -2. \qquad \begin{array}{l}\text{The only restricted value is 0, so} \\ \text{both answers should check.}\end{array}$$

Check: For -3:   For -2:

$$x + \frac{6}{x} = -5$$

$$\begin{array}{c|c} -3 + \dfrac{6}{-3} & -5 \\ \hline -3 - 2 & \\ -5 \overset{?}{=} -5 & \text{TRUE} \end{array}$$

$$x + \frac{6}{x} = -5$$

$$\begin{array}{c|c} -2 + \dfrac{6}{-2} & -5 \\ \hline -2 - 3 & \\ -5 \overset{?}{=} -5 & \text{TRUE} \end{array}$$

Both of these check, so there are two solutions, -3 and -2.

c) The only denominator is $x + 2$. We set this equal to 0 and solve:

$$x + 2 = 0$$
$$x = -2.$$

If $x = -2$, the rational expressions are undefined. We list the restriction:

$$x \neq -2.$$

We clear fractions and solve:

$$1 + \frac{3x}{x + 2} = \frac{-6}{x + 2}$$

We cannot have $x = -2$. The LCM is $x + 2$.

$$(x + 2)\left(1 + \frac{3x}{x + 2}\right) = (x + 2)\frac{-6}{x + 2}$$

Multiplying both sides by the LCM. *Don't forget the parentheses!*

$$(x + 2) \cdot 1 + (x + 2)\frac{3x}{x+2} = (x+2)\frac{-6}{x+2}$$

Using the distributive law; removing a factor equal to 1: $(x + 2)/(x + 2) = 1$

$$x + 2 + 3x = -6$$
$$4x + 2 = -6$$
$$4x = -8$$
$$x = -2.$$

Above, we stated that $x \neq -2$.

Because of the above restriction, -2 must be rejected as a solution. The check below simply confirms this.

Check:

$$1 + \frac{3x}{x + 2} = \frac{-6}{x + 2}$$

$$\begin{array}{c|c} 1 + \dfrac{3(-2)}{-2 + 2} & \dfrac{-6}{-2 + 2} \\ \hline 1 + \dfrac{-6}{0} \overset{?}{=} \dfrac{-6}{0} & \text{FALSE} \end{array}$$

The equation has no solution.

d) The denominators are $x - 5$, $x + 5$, and $x^2 - 25$. Setting them equal to 0 and solving, we find that the rational expressions are undefined when $x = 5$ or $x = -5$. We list the restrictions:

$$x \neq 5, \quad x \neq -5.$$

We clear fractions and solve:

$$\frac{3}{x-5} + \frac{1}{x+5} = \frac{2}{x^2-25}$$

We cannot have $x = 5$ or $x = -5$. The LCM is $(x-5)(x+5)$.

$$(x-5)(x+5)\left(\frac{3}{x-5} + \frac{1}{x+5}\right) = (x-5)(x+5)\frac{2}{(x-5)(x+5)}$$

$$\frac{\cancel{(x-5)}(x+5)3}{\cancel{x-5}} + \frac{(x-5)\cancel{(x+5)}}{\cancel{x+5}} = \frac{2\cancel{(x-5)}\cancel{(x+5)}}{\cancel{(x-5)}\cancel{(x+5)}}$$

Using the distributive law

$$(x+5)3 + (x-5) = 2$$

Removing factors equal to 1: $(x-5)/(x-5) = 1$, $(x+5)/(x+5) = 1$, and $\dfrac{(x-5)(x+5)}{(x-5)(x+5)} = 1$

$$3x + 15 + x - 5 = 2$$

Using the distributive law

$$4x + 10 = 2$$

$$4x = -8$$

$$x = -2.$$

$-2 \neq 5$ and $-2 \neq -5$, so -2 *should* check.

The student can check to confirm that -2 is the solution.

e) If $x = 1$, the denominators are 0. We list the restriction:

$$x \neq 1.$$

We clear fractions and solve:

$$\frac{x^2}{x-1} = \frac{1}{x-1}$$

We cannot have $x = 1$.

$$\cancel{(x-1)} \cdot \frac{x^2}{\cancel{x-1}} = \cancel{(x-1)} \cdot \frac{1}{\cancel{x-1}}$$

Multiplying both sides by $x - 1$, the LCM

$$x^2 = 1$$

Removing a factor equal to 1: $(x-1)/(x-1) = 1$

$$x^2 - 1 = 0$$

Subtracting 1 from both sides

$$(x-1)(x+1) = 0$$

Factoring

$$x - 1 = 0 \quad or \quad x + 1 = 0$$

Using the principle of zero products

$$x = 1 \quad or \quad x = -1.$$

Above, we stated that $x \neq 1$.

Because of the above restriction, 1 must be rejected as a solution. The student should check in the original equation that -1 *does* check. The solution is -1.

TRY EXERCISES   21 and 29

A Visual Interpretation

ALGEBRAIC–GRAPHICAL CONNECTION

We can obtain a visual check of the solutions of a rational equation by graphing. For example, consider the equation

$$\frac{x}{4} + \frac{x}{2} = 6.$$

We can examine the solution by graphing the equations

$$y = \frac{x}{4} + \frac{x}{2} \quad \text{and} \quad y = 6$$

using the same set of axes, as shown below.

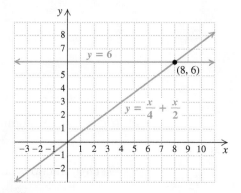

The *y*-values for each equation will be the same where the graphs intersect. The *x*-value of that point will yield that value, so it will be a solution of the equation. It appears from the graph that when $x = 8$, the value of $x/4 + x/2$ is 6. We can check by substitution:

$$\frac{x}{4} + \frac{x}{2} = \frac{8}{4} + \frac{8}{2} = 2 + 4 = 6.$$

Thus the solution is 8.

TECHNOLOGY CONNECTION

We can use a table to check possible solutions of rational equations. Consider the equation in Example 2(e),

$$\frac{x^2}{x - 1} = \frac{1}{x - 1},$$

and the possible solutions that were found, 1 and -1. To check these solutions, we enter $y_1 = x^2/(x - 1)$ and $y_2 = 1/(x - 1)$. After setting Indpnt to Ask and Depend to Auto in the TBLSET menu, we display the table and enter $x = 1$. The ERROR messages indicate that 1 is not a solution because it is not an allowable replacement for x in the equation. Next, we enter $x = -1$. Since y_1 and y_2 have the same value, we know that the equation is true when $x = -1$, and thus -1 is a solution.

X	Y₁	Y₂
1	ERROR	ERROR
−1	−.5	−.5
X =		

Use a graphing calculator to check the possible solutions of Example 1 and Example 2, parts (a)–(d).

For Extra Help

MyMathLab | Math XL PRACTICE | WATCH | DOWNLOAD

🖐 *Concept Reinforcement* *Classify each statement as either true or false.*

1. Every rational equation has at least one solution.

2. It is possible for a rational equation to have more than one solution.

3. When both sides of an equation are multiplied by a variable expression, the result is not always an equivalent equation.

4. All the equation-solving principles studied thus far may be needed when solving a rational equation.

Solve. If no solution exists, state this.

5. $\dfrac{3}{5} - \dfrac{2}{3} = \dfrac{x}{6}$

6. $\dfrac{5}{8} - \dfrac{3}{5} = \dfrac{x}{10}$

7. $\dfrac{1}{3} + \dfrac{5}{6} = \dfrac{1}{x}$

8. $\dfrac{3}{5} + \dfrac{1}{8} = \dfrac{1}{x}$

9. $\dfrac{1}{8} + \dfrac{1}{12} = \dfrac{1}{t}$

10. $\dfrac{1}{6} + \dfrac{1}{10} = \dfrac{1}{t}$

11. $y + \dfrac{4}{y} = -5$

12. $n + \dfrac{3}{n} = -4$

13. $\dfrac{x}{6} - \dfrac{6}{x} = 0$

14. $\dfrac{x}{7} - \dfrac{7}{x} = 0$

15. $\dfrac{2}{x} = \dfrac{5}{x} - \dfrac{1}{4}$

16. $\dfrac{3}{t} = \dfrac{4}{t} - \dfrac{1}{5}$

17. $\dfrac{5}{3t} + \dfrac{3}{t} = 1$

18. $\dfrac{3}{4x} + \dfrac{5}{x} = 1$

19. $\dfrac{n+2}{n-6} = \dfrac{1}{2}$

20. $\dfrac{a-4}{a+6} = \dfrac{1}{3}$

21. $x + \dfrac{12}{x} = -7$

22. $x + \dfrac{8}{x} = -9$

23. $\dfrac{3}{x-4} = \dfrac{5}{x+1}$

24. $\dfrac{1}{x+3} = \dfrac{4}{x-1}$

25. $\dfrac{a}{6} - \dfrac{a}{10} = \dfrac{1}{6}$

26. $\dfrac{t}{8} - \dfrac{t}{12} = \dfrac{1}{8}$

27. $\dfrac{x+1}{3} - 1 = \dfrac{x-1}{2}$

28. $\dfrac{x+2}{5} - 1 = \dfrac{x-2}{4}$

29. $\dfrac{y+3}{y-3} = \dfrac{6}{y-3}$

30. $\dfrac{3}{a+7} = \dfrac{a+10}{a+7}$

31. $\dfrac{3}{x+4} = \dfrac{5}{x}$

32. $\dfrac{2}{x+3} = \dfrac{7}{x}$

33. $\dfrac{n+1}{n+2} = \dfrac{n-3}{n+1}$

34. $\dfrac{n+2}{n-3} = \dfrac{n+1}{n-2}$

35. $\dfrac{5}{t-2} + \dfrac{3t}{t-2} = \dfrac{4}{t^2 - 4t + 4}$

36. $\dfrac{4}{t-3} + \dfrac{2t}{t-3} = \dfrac{12}{t^2 - 6t + 9}$

37. $\dfrac{x}{x+5} - \dfrac{5}{x-5} = \dfrac{14}{x^2 - 25}$

38. $\dfrac{5}{x+1} + \dfrac{2x}{x^2 - 1} = \dfrac{1}{x+1}$

39. $\dfrac{5}{t-3} - \dfrac{30}{t^2 - 9} = 1$

40. $\dfrac{1}{y+3} + \dfrac{1}{y-3} = \dfrac{1}{y^2 - 9}$

41. $\dfrac{7}{6-a} = \dfrac{a+1}{a-6}$

42. $\dfrac{t-12}{t-10} = \dfrac{1}{10-t}$

Aha! **43.** $\dfrac{-2}{x+2} = \dfrac{x}{x+2}$

44. $\dfrac{3}{2x-6} = \dfrac{x}{2x-6}$

45. $\dfrac{12}{x} = \dfrac{x}{3}$

46. $\dfrac{x}{2} = \dfrac{18}{x}$

📝 **47.** When solving rational equations, why do we multiply each side by the LCM of the denominators?

📝 **48.** Explain the difference between adding rational expressions and solving rational equations.

Skill Review

To prepare for Section 7.7, review solving applications and rates of change (Sections 2.5, 3.4, and 6.8).

49. The sum of two consecutive odd numbers is 276. Find the numbers. [2.5]

50. The length of a rectangular picture window is 3 yd greater than the width. The area of the rectangle is 10 yd². Find the perimeter. [6.8]

51. The height of a triangle is 3 cm longer than its base. If the area of the triangle is 54 cm², find the measurements of the base and the height. [6.8]

52. The product of two consecutive even integers is 48. Find the numbers. [6.8]

53. *Human physiology.* Between June 9 and June 24, Seth's beard grew 0.9 cm. Find the rate at which Seth's beard grows. [3.4]

54. *Gardening.* Between July 7 and July 12, Carla's string beans grew 1.4 in. Find the growth rate of the string beans. [3.4]

Synthesis

55. Describe a method that can be used to create rational equations that have no solution.

56. How can a graph be used to determine how many solutions an equation has?

Solve.

57. $1 + \dfrac{x - 1}{x - 3} = \dfrac{2}{x - 3} - x$

58. $\dfrac{4}{y - 2} + \dfrac{3}{y^2 - 4} = \dfrac{5}{y + 2} + \dfrac{2y}{y^2 - 4}$

59. $\dfrac{12 - 6x}{x^2 - 4} = \dfrac{3x}{x + 2} - \dfrac{3 - 2x}{2 - x}$

60. $\dfrac{x}{x^2 + 3x - 4} + \dfrac{x + 1}{x^2 + 6x + 8} = \dfrac{2x}{x^2 + x - 2}$

61. $7 - \dfrac{a - 2}{a + 3} = \dfrac{a^2 - 4}{a + 3} + 5$

62. $\dfrac{x^2}{x^2 - 4} = \dfrac{x}{x + 2} - \dfrac{2x}{2 - x}$

63. $\dfrac{1}{x - 1} + x - 5 = \dfrac{5x - 4}{x - 1} - 6$

64. $\dfrac{5 - 3a}{a^2 + 4a + 3} - \dfrac{2a + 2}{a + 3} = \dfrac{3 - a}{a + 1}$

65. $\dfrac{\dfrac{1}{x} + 1}{x} = \dfrac{\dfrac{1}{x}}{2}$

66. $\dfrac{\dfrac{1}{3}}{x} = \dfrac{1 - \dfrac{1}{x}}{x}$

67. Use a graphing calculator to check your answers to Exercises 13, 21, 31, and 57.

CONNECTING the CONCEPTS

An equation contains an equals sign; an expression does not. Be careful not to confuse simplifying an expression with solving an equation. When expressions are simplified, the result is an equivalent expression. When equations are solved, the result is a solution. Compare the following.

Simplify: $\dfrac{x - 1}{6x} + \dfrac{4}{9}$.

> The equals signs indicate that all the expressions are equivalent.

SOLUTION

$\dfrac{x - 1}{6x} + \dfrac{4}{9} = \dfrac{x - 1}{6x} \cdot \dfrac{3}{3} + \dfrac{4}{9} \cdot \dfrac{2x}{2x}$

$= \dfrac{3x - 3}{18x} + \dfrac{8x}{18x}$ Writing with the LCD, $18x$

$= \dfrac{11x - 3}{18x}$ The result is an expression equivalent to $\dfrac{x - 1}{6x} + \dfrac{4}{9}$.

Solve: $\dfrac{x - 1}{6x} = \dfrac{4}{9}$.

SOLUTION

$\dfrac{x - 1}{6x} = \dfrac{4}{9}$ Each line is an equivalent equation.

$18x \cdot \dfrac{x - 1}{6x} = 18x \cdot \dfrac{4}{9}$ Multiplying by the LCM, $18x$

$3 \cdot 6x \cdot \dfrac{x - 1}{6x} = 2 \cdot 9 \cdot x \cdot \dfrac{4}{9}$

$3(x - 1) = 2x \cdot 4$

$3x - 3 = 8x$

$-3 = 5x$

$-\dfrac{3}{5} = x$ The result is a solution; $-\dfrac{3}{5}$ is the solution of $\dfrac{x - 1}{6x} = \dfrac{4}{9}$.

MIXED REVIEW

Tell whether each of the following is an expression or an equation. Then simplify the expression or solve the equation.

1. Simplify: $\dfrac{4x^2 - 8x}{4x^2 + 4x}$.

2. Add and, if possible, simplify: $\dfrac{2}{5n} + \dfrac{3}{2n - 1}$.

3. Solve: $\dfrac{3}{y} - \dfrac{1}{4} = \dfrac{1}{y}$.

4. Simplify: $\dfrac{\dfrac{1}{z} + 1}{\dfrac{1}{z^2 - 1}}$.

5. Solve: $\dfrac{5}{x + 3} = \dfrac{3}{x + 2}$.

6. Multiply and, if possible, simplify:

$\dfrac{8t + 8}{2t^2 + t - 1} \cdot \dfrac{t^2 - 1}{t^2 - 2t + 1}$.

7. Subtract and, if possible, simplify:

$\dfrac{2a}{a + 1} - \dfrac{4a}{1 - a^2}$.

8. Solve: $\dfrac{15}{x} - \dfrac{15}{x + 2} = 2$.

9. Divide and, if possible, simplify:

$\dfrac{18x^2}{25} \div \dfrac{12x}{5}$.

10. Solve: $\dfrac{20}{x} = \dfrac{x}{5}$.

7.7   Applications Using Rational Equations and Proportions

Problems Involving Work ▪ Problems Involving Motion ▪ Problems Involving Proportions

In many areas of study, applications involving rates, proportions, or reciprocals translate to rational equations. By using the five steps for problem solving and the lessons of Section 7.6, we can now solve such problems.

Problems Involving Work

EXAMPLE 1

The roof of Finn and Paige's townhouse needs to be reshingled. Finn can do the job alone in 8 hr and Paige can do the job alone in 10 hr. How long will it take the two of them, working together, to reshingle the roof?

SOLUTION

1. **Familiarize.** This *work problem* is a type of problem we have not yet encountered. Work problems are often *incorrectly* translated to mathematical language in several ways.

   a) Add the times together: 8 hr + 10 hr = 18 hr. ← Incorrect

   This cannot be the correct approach since Finn and Paige working together should not take longer than either of them working alone.

   b) Average the times: (8 hr + 10 hr)/2 = 9 hr. ← Incorrect

   Again, this is longer than it would take Finn to do the job alone.

   c) Assume that each person does half the job. ← Incorrect

Finn would reshingle $\frac{1}{2}$ the roof in $\frac{1}{2}$(8 hr), or 4 hr, and Paige would reshingle $\frac{1}{2}$ the roof in $\frac{1}{2}$(10 hr), or 5 hr, so Finn would finish an hour before Paige. The problem assumes that the two are working together, so Finn will help Paige after completing his half. This tells us that the job will take between 4 and 5 hr.

Each incorrect approach started with the time it took each worker to do the job. The correct approach instead focuses on the *rate* of work, or the amount of the job that each person completes in 1 hr.

Since Finn takes 8 hr to reshingle the entire roof, in 1 hr he reshingles $\frac{1}{8}$ of the roof. Since Paige takes 10 hr to reshingle the entire roof, in 1 hr she reshingles $\frac{1}{10}$ of the roof. Thus Finn works at a rate of $\frac{1}{8}$ roof per hour, and Paige works at a rate of $\frac{1}{10}$ roof per hour.

Working together, Finn and Paige reshingle $\frac{1}{8} + \frac{1}{10}$ roof in 1 hr, so their rate, as a team, is $\frac{1}{8} + \frac{1}{10} = \frac{5}{40} + \frac{4}{40} = \frac{9}{40}$ roof per hour.

We are looking for the time required to reshingle 1 entire roof, not just a part of it. Setting up a table helps us organize the information.

Time	Fraction of the Roof Reshingled		
	By Finn	**By Paige**	**Together**
1 hr	$\frac{1}{8}$	$\frac{1}{10}$	$\frac{1}{8} + \frac{1}{10}$, or $\frac{9}{40}$
2 hr	$\frac{1}{8} \cdot 2$	$\frac{1}{10} \cdot 2$	$\left(\frac{1}{8} + \frac{1}{10}\right)2$, or $\frac{9}{40} \cdot 2$, or $\frac{9}{20}$
3 hr	$\frac{1}{8} \cdot 3$	$\frac{1}{10} \cdot 3$	$\left(\frac{1}{8} + \frac{1}{10}\right)3$, or $\frac{9}{40} \cdot 3$, or $\frac{27}{40}$
t hr	$\frac{1}{8} \cdot t$	$\frac{1}{10} \cdot t$	$\left(\frac{1}{8} + \frac{1}{10}\right)t$, or $\frac{9}{40} \cdot t$

2. Translate. From the table, we see that t must be some number for which

Fraction of roof done by Finn in t hr $\quad \frac{1}{8} \cdot t + \frac{1}{10} \cdot t = 1,\quad$ Fraction of roof done by Paige in t hr

or

$$\frac{t}{8} + \frac{t}{10} = 1.$$

3. Carry out. We solve the equation:

$$\frac{t}{8} + \frac{t}{10} = 1 \qquad \text{The LCD is 40.}$$

$$40\left(\frac{t}{8} + \frac{t}{10}\right) = 40 \cdot 1 \qquad \text{Multiplying to clear fractions}$$

$$\frac{40t}{8} + \frac{40t}{10} = 40$$

$$5t + 4t = 40 \qquad \text{Simplifying}$$

$$9t = 40$$

$$t = \frac{40}{9}, \text{ or } 4\frac{4}{9}.$$

4. **Check.** In $\frac{40}{9}$ hr, Finn reshingles $\frac{1}{8} \cdot \frac{40}{9}$, or $\frac{5}{9}$, of the roof and Paige reshingles $\frac{1}{10} \cdot \frac{40}{9}$, or $\frac{4}{9}$, of the roof. Together, they reshingle $\frac{5}{9} + \frac{4}{9}$, or 1 roof. The fact that our solution is between 4 and 5 hr (see step 1 above) is also a check.

5. **State.** It will take $4\frac{4}{9}$ hr for Finn and Paige, working together, to reshingle the roof.

> TRY EXERCISE 7

EXAMPLE 2

It takes Manuel 9 hr longer than Zoe to rebuild an engine. Working together, they can do the job in 20 hr. How long would it take each, working alone, to rebuild an engine?

SOLUTION

1. **Familiarize.** Unlike Example 1, this problem does not provide us with the times required by the individuals to do the job alone. Let's have $z =$ the number of hours it would take Zoe working alone and $z + 9 =$ the number of hours it would take Manuel working alone.

2. **Translate.** Using the same reasoning as in Example 1, we see that Zoe completes $\frac{1}{z}$ of the job in 1 hr and Manuel completes $\frac{1}{z+9}$ of the job in 1 hr. Thus, in 20 hr, Zoe completes $\frac{1}{z} \cdot 20$ of the job and Manuel completes $\frac{1}{z+9} \cdot 20$ of the job.

We know that, together, Zoe and Manuel can complete the entire job in 20 hr. This gives the following:

Fraction of job done by Zoe in 20 hr $\quad \dfrac{1}{z} \cdot 20 + \dfrac{1}{z+9} \cdot 20 = 1,\quad$ Fraction of job done by Manuel in 20 hr

or $\quad \dfrac{20}{z} + \dfrac{20}{z+9} = 1.$

3. **Carry out.** We solve the equation:

$$\frac{20}{z} + \frac{20}{z+9} = 1 \qquad \text{The LCD is } z(z+9).$$

$$z(z+9)\left(\frac{20}{z} + \frac{20}{z+9}\right) = z(z+9)1 \qquad \text{Multiplying to clear fractions}$$

$$(z+9)20 + z \cdot 20 = z(z+9) \qquad \text{Distributing and simplifying}$$

$$40z + 180 = z^2 + 9z$$

$$0 = z^2 - 31z - 180 \qquad \text{Getting 0 on one side}$$

$$0 = (z-36)(z+5) \qquad \text{Factoring}$$

$$z - 36 = 0 \quad or \quad z + 5 = 0 \qquad \text{Principle of zero products}$$

$$z = 36 \quad or \quad z = -5.$$

4. **Check.** Since negative time has no meaning in the problem, -5 is not a solution to the original problem. The number 36 checks since, if Zoe takes 36 hr alone and Manuel takes $36 + 9 = 45$ hr alone, in 20 hr they would have finished

$$\frac{20}{36} + \frac{20}{45} = \frac{5}{9} + \frac{4}{9} = 1 \text{ complete rebuild.}$$

5. **State.** It would take Zoe 36 hr to rebuild an engine alone, and Manuel 45 hr.

> TRY EXERCISE 13

The equations used in Examples 1 and 2 can be generalized as follows.

> ## The Work Principle
>
> If
>
> a = the time needed for A to complete the work alone,
>
> b = the time needed for B to complete the work alone, and
>
> t = the time needed for A and B to complete the work together,
>
> then
>
> $$\frac{t}{a} + \frac{t}{b} = 1.$$
>
> The following are equivalent equations that can also be used:
>
> $$\frac{1}{a} \cdot t + \frac{1}{b} \cdot t = 1 \quad \text{and} \quad \frac{1}{a} + \frac{1}{b} = \frac{1}{t}.$$

Problems Involving Motion

Problems dealing with distance, rate (or speed), and time are called **motion problems**. To translate them, we use either the basic motion formula, $d = rt$, or the formulas $r = d/t$ or $t = d/r$, which can be derived from $d = rt$.

EXAMPLE **3**

On her road bike, Olivia bikes 15 km/h faster than Jason does on his mountain bike. In the time it takes Olivia to travel 80 km, Jason travels 50 km. Find the speed of each bicyclist.

SOLUTION

STUDENT NOTES

You need remember only the motion formula $d = rt$. Then you can divide both sides by t to get $r = d/t$, or you can divide both sides by r to get $t = d/r$.

1. **Familiarize.** Let's guess that Jason is going 10 km/h. Then the following would be true.

   Olivia's speed would be $10 + 15$, or 25 km/h.

   Jason would cover 50 km in $50/10 = 5$ hr.

   Olivia would cover 80 km in $80/25 = 3.2$ hr.

Since the times are not the same, our guess is wrong, but we can make some observations.

   If r = the rate, in kilometers per hour, of Jason's bike, then the rate of Olivia's bike = $r + 15$.

   Jason's travel time is the same as Olivia's travel time.

We make a drawing and construct a table, listing the information we know.

r km/h
50 km

(r + 15) km/h
80 km

	Distance	Speed	Time
Jason's Mountain Bike	50	r	
Olivia's Road Bike	80	$r + 15$	

2. **Translate.** By looking at how we checked our guess, we see that we can fill in the **Time** column of the table using the formula *Time = Distance/Rate*, as follows.

	Distance	Speed	Time
Jason's Mountain Bike	50	r	$50/r$
Olivia's Road Bike	80	$r + 15$	$80/(r + 15)$

Since we know that the times are the same, we can write an equation:

$$\frac{50}{r} = \frac{80}{r + 15}.$$

3. **Carry out.** We solve the equation:

$$\frac{50}{r} = \frac{80}{r + 15} \qquad \text{The LCD is } r(r + 15).$$

$$r(r + 15)\frac{50}{r} = r(r + 15)\frac{80}{r + 15} \qquad \text{Multiplying to clear fractions}$$

$$50r + 750 = 80r \qquad \text{Simplifying}$$

$$750 = 30r$$

$$25 = r.$$

4. **Check.** If our answer checks, Jason's mountain bike is going 25 km/h and Olivia's road bike is going 25 + 15 = 40 km/h.

Traveling 80 km at 40 km/h, Olivia is riding for $\frac{80}{40} = 2$ hr. Traveling 50 km at 25 km/h, Jason is riding for $\frac{50}{25} = 2$ hr. Our answer checks since the two times are the same.

5. **State.** Olivia's speed is 40 km/h, and Jason's speed is 25 km/h.

> TRY EXERCISE ▶ 19

In the next example, although distance is the same in both directions, the key to the translation lies in an additional piece of given information.

EXAMPLE 4 A Hudson River tugboat goes 10 mph in still water. It travels 24 mi upstream and 24 mi back in a total time of 5 hr. What is the speed of the current?

Sources: Based on information from the Department of the Interior, U.S. Geological Survey, and *The Tugboat Captain*, Montgomery County Community College

SOLUTION

1. **Familiarize.** Let's guess that the speed of the current is 4 mph. Then the following would be true.

The tugboat would move 10 − 4 = 6 mph upstream.

The tugboat would move 10 + 4 = 14 mph downstream.

To travel 24 mi upstream would require $\frac{24}{6} = 4$ hr.

To travel 24 mi downstream would require $\frac{24}{14} = 1\frac{5}{7}$ hr.

Since the total time, $4 + 1\frac{5}{7} = 5\frac{5}{7}$ hr, is not the 5 hr mentioned in the problem, our guess is wrong, but we can make some observations.

If c = the current's rate, in miles per hour, we have the following.

The tugboat's speed upstream is $(10 - c)$ mph.

The tugboat's speed downstream is $(10 + c)$ mph.

The total travel time is 5 hr.

We make a sketch and construct a table, listing the information we know.

	Distance	Speed	Time
Upstream	24	$10 - c$	
Downstream	24	$10 + c$	

2. Translate. From examining our guess, we see that the time traveled can be represented using the formula *Time = Distance/Rate*.

	Distance	Speed	Time
Upstream	24	$10 - c$	$24/(10 - c)$
Downstream	24	$10 + c$	$24/(10 + c)$

Since the total time upstream and back is 5 hr, we use the last column of the table to form an equation:

$$\frac{24}{10 - c} + \frac{24}{10 + c} = 5.$$

3. Carry out. We solve the equation:

$$\frac{24}{10 - c} + \frac{24}{10 + c} = 5 \qquad \text{The LCD is } (10 - c)(10 + c).$$

$$(10 - c)(10 + c)\left[\frac{24}{10 - c} + \frac{24}{10 + c}\right] = (10 - c)(10 + c)5 \qquad \text{Multiplying to clear fractions}$$

$$24(10 + c) + 24(10 - c) = (100 - c^2)5$$

$$480 = 500 - 5c^2 \qquad \text{Simplifying}$$

$$5c^2 - 20 = 0$$

$$5(c^2 - 4) = 0$$

$$5(c - 2)(c + 2) = 0$$

$$c = 2 \quad or \quad c = -2.$$

4. Check. Since speed cannot be negative in this problem, −2 cannot be a solution. You should confirm that 2 checks in the original problem.

5. State. The speed of the current is 2 mph.

▶ TRY EXERCISE ▶ 21

Problems Involving Proportions

A **ratio** of two quantities is their quotient. For example, 37% is the ratio of 37 to 100, or $\frac{37}{100}$. A **proportion** is an equation stating that two ratios are equal.

> ### Proportion
>
> An equality of ratios,
>
> $$\frac{A}{B} = \frac{C}{D},$$
>
> is called a *proportion*. The numbers within a proportion are said to be *proportional* to each other.

Proportions arise in geometry when we are studying *similar triangles*. If two triangles are **similar**, then their corresponding angles have the same measure and their corresponding sides are proportional. To illustrate, if triangle *ABC* is similar to triangle *RST*, then angles *A* and *R* have the same measure, angles *B* and *S* have the same measure, angles *C* and *T* have the same measure, and

$$\frac{a}{r} = \frac{b}{s} = \frac{c}{t}.$$

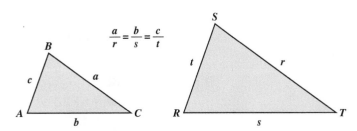

EXAMPLE 5   *Similar triangles.*   Triangles *ABC* and *XYZ* are similar. Solve for *z* if *x* = 10, *a* = 8, and *c* = 5.

SOLUTION   We make a drawing, write a proportion, and then solve. Note that side *a* is always opposite angle *A*, side *x* is always opposite angle *X*, and so on.

We have

$$\frac{z}{5} = \frac{10}{8} \qquad \text{The proportions } \frac{5}{z} = \frac{8}{10}, \ \frac{5}{8} = \frac{z}{10}, \text{ or }$$
$$\frac{8}{5} = \frac{10}{z} \text{ could also be used.}$$

$$40 \cdot \frac{z}{5} = 40 \cdot \frac{10}{8} \qquad \text{Multiplying both sides by the LCM, 40}$$

$$8z = 50 \qquad \text{Simplifying}$$

$$z = \frac{50}{8}, \text{ or } 6.25.$$

> TRY EXERCISE 33

EXAMPLE   6

Architecture. A *blueprint* is a scale drawing of a building representing an architect's plans. Ellia is adding 12 ft to the length of an apartment and needs to indicate the addition on an existing blueprint. If a 10-ft long bedroom is represented by $2\frac{1}{2}$ in. on the blueprint, how much longer should Ellia make the drawing in order to represent the addition?

SOLUTION   We let w represent the width, in inches, of the addition that Ellia is drawing. Because the drawing must be to scale, we have

Inches on drawing $\rightarrow$ $\dfrac{w}{12} = \dfrac{2.5}{10}.$ $\leftarrow$ Inches on drawing
Feet in real life $\rightarrow$ $\quad\quad\quad\quad$ $\leftarrow$ Feet in real life

To solve for w, we multiply both sides by the LCM of the denominators, 60:

$$60 \cdot \frac{w}{12} = 60 \cdot \frac{2.5}{10}$$

$$5w = 6 \cdot 2.5 \qquad \text{Simplifying}$$

$$w = \frac{15}{5}, \text{ or } 3.$$

Ellia should make the blueprint 3 in. longer.

TRY EXERCISE   37

Proportions can be used to solve a variety of applied problems.

EXAMPLE   7

Alternative fuels. As one alternative to gasoline-powered vehicles, flex fuel vehicles can use both regular gasoline and E85, a fuel containing 85% ethanol. The ethanol in E85 is derived from corn and other plants, a renewable resource, and burning E85 results in less pollution than gasoline. Because using E85 results in a lower fuel economy, its price per gallon must be lower than the price of gasoline in order to make it an economical fuel option. A 2007 Chevrolet Tahoe gets 21 mpg on the highway using gasoline and only 15 mpg on the highway using E85. If the price of gasoline is $3.36 a gallon, what must the price of E85 be in order for the fuel cost per mile to be the same?

Source: www.caranddriver.com

Alternative fuels

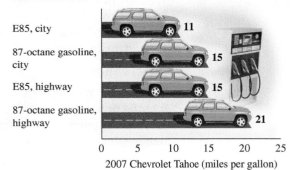

E85, city   11

87-octane gasoline, city   15

E85, highway   15

87-octane gasoline, highway   21

0   5   10   15   20   25

2007 Chevrolet Tahoe (miles per gallon)

Source: www.caranddriver.com

SOLUTION

1. **Familiarize.** We let x = the price per gallon of E85, and organize the given information:

   Gasoline miles per gallon: 21,

   E85 miles per gallon: 15,

   Gasoline price per gallon: $3.36,

   E85 price per gallon: x.

   We need to use the given information to find the fuel cost per mile. If we divide the number of dollars per gallon by the number of miles per gallon, we can find the number of dollars per mile:

   $$\frac{\text{dollars}}{\text{gal}} \div \frac{\text{mi}}{\text{gal}} = \frac{\text{dollars}}{\text{gal}} \cdot \frac{\text{gal}}{\text{mi}} = \frac{\text{dollars}}{\text{mi}}.$$

   Thus we form ratios of the form

   $$\frac{\text{dollars per gallon}}{\text{miles per gallon}}.$$

2. **Translate.** We form a proportion in which the ratio of price per gallon and number of miles per gallon is expressed in two ways:

   $$\begin{array}{c} \text{Gasoline price} \rightarrow \\ \text{Gasoline mpg} \rightarrow \end{array} \frac{\$3.36}{21} = \frac{x}{15}. \begin{array}{c} \leftarrow \text{E85 price} \\ \leftarrow \text{E85 mpg} \end{array}$$

3. **Carry out.** To solve for x, we multiply both sides of the equation by the LCM, 105:

   $$105 \cdot \frac{3.36}{21} = 105 \cdot \frac{x}{15}$$

   $$5 \cdot 21 \cdot \frac{3.36}{21} = 7 \cdot 15 \cdot \frac{x}{15} \qquad \text{Removing factors equal to 1: } 21/21 = 1 \text{ and } 15/15 = 1$$

   $$16.8 = 7x$$

   $$2.4 = x. \qquad \text{Dividing both sides by 7 and simplifying}$$

4. **Check.** If E85 costs $2.40 per gallon, the fuel cost per mile will be $2.40/15 = $0.16 per mile. The fuel cost per mile for gasoline is $3.36/21 = $0.16 per mile. The fuel costs are the same.

5. **State.** The price of E85 must be $2.40 per gallon.   **TRY EXERCISE** 45

EXAMPLE   **8**   *Wildlife population.*   To determine the number of brook trout in River Denys, Cape Breton, Nova Scotia, a team of volunteers and professionals caught and marked 1190 brook trout. Later, they captured 915 brook trout, of which 24 were marked. Estimate the number of brook trout in River Denys.

Source: www.gov.ns.ca

SOLUTION   We let T = the brook trout population in River Denys. If we assume that the percentage of marked trout in the second group of trout captured is the same as the percentage of marked trout in the entire river, we can form a proportion in which this percentage is expressed in two ways:

Trout originally marked $\rightarrow$ $\dfrac{1190}{T} = \dfrac{24}{915}$. $\leftarrow$ Marked trout in second group
Entire population $\rightarrow$ $\hspace{2.5em}$ $\leftarrow$ Total trout in second group

To solve for T, we multiply by the LCM, $915T$:

$$915T \cdot \frac{1190}{T} = 915T \cdot \frac{24}{915} \qquad \text{Multiplying both sides by } 915T$$

$$915 \cdot 1190 = 24T \qquad \text{Removing factors equal to 1:}$$
$$\hspace{6em} T/T = 1 \text{ and } 915/915 = 1$$

$$\frac{915 \cdot 1190}{24} = T \text{ or } T \approx 45{,}369. \qquad \text{Dividing both sides by 24}$$

There are about 45,369 brook trout in the river.   **TRY EXERCISE** ▸ 57

Translating for Success

1. **Search-engine ads.** In 2006, North American advertisers spent $9.4 billion in marketing through Internet search engines such as Google®. This was a 62% increase over the amount spent in 2005. How much was spent in 2005?
   Source: Search Engine Marketing Professional Organization

2. **Bicycling.** The speed of one bicyclist is 2 km/h faster than the speed of another bicyclist. The first bicyclist travels 60 km in the same amount of time that it takes the second to travel 50 km. Find the speed of each bicyclist.

3. **Filling time.** A swimming pool can be filled in 5 hr by hose A alone and in 6 hr by hose B alone. How long would it take to fill the tank if both hoses were working?

4. **Payroll.** In 2007, the total payroll for Kraftside Productions was $9.4 million. Of this amount, 62% was paid to employees working on an assembly line. How much money was paid to assembly-line workers?

Translate each word problem to an equation and select a correct translation from equations A–O.

A. $2x + 2(x + 1) = 613$

B. $x^2 + (x + 1)^2 = 613$

C. $\dfrac{60}{x + 2} = \dfrac{50}{x}$

D. $x = 62\% \cdot 9.4$

E. $\dfrac{197}{7} = \dfrac{x}{30}$

F. $x + (x + 1) = 613$

G. $\dfrac{7}{197} = \dfrac{x}{30}$

H. $x^2 + (x + 2)^2 = 612$

I. $x^2 + (x + 1)^2 = 612$

J. $\dfrac{50}{x + 2} = \dfrac{60}{x}$

K. $x + 62\% \cdot x = 9.4$

L. $\dfrac{5 + 6}{2} = t$

M. $x^2 + (x + 1)^2 = 452$

N. $\dfrac{1}{5} + \dfrac{1}{6} = \dfrac{1}{t}$

O. $x^2 + (x + 2)^2 = 452$

Answers on page A-27

An additional, animated version of this activity appears in MyMathLab. To use MyMathLab, you need a course ID and a student access code. Contact your instructor for more information.

---

5. **Cycling distance.** A bicyclist traveled 197 mi in 7 days. At this rate, how many miles could the cyclist travel in 30 days?

6. **Sides of a square.** If the sides of a square are increased by 2 ft, the area of the original square plus the area of the enlarged square is 452 ft². Find the length of a side of the original square.

7. **Consecutive integers.** The sum of two consecutive integers is 613. Find the integers.

8. **Sums of squares.** The sum of the squares of two consecutive odd integers is 612. Find the integers.

9. **Sums of squares.** The sum of the squares of two consecutive integers is 613. Find the integers.

10. **Rectangle dimensions.** The length of a rectangle is 1 ft longer than its width. Find the dimensions of the rectangle such that the perimeter of the rectangle is 613 ft.

7.7   EXERCISE SET

Concept Reinforcement   Find each rate.

1. If Sandy can decorate a cake in 2 hr, what is her rate?

2. If Eric can decorate a cake in 3 hr, what is his rate?

3. If Sandy can decorate a cake in 2 hr and Eric can decorate the same cake in 3 hr, what is their rate, working together?

4. If Lisa and Mark can mow a lawn together in 1 hr, what is their rate?

5. If Lisa can mow a lawn by herself in 3 hr, what is her rate?

6. If Lisa and Mark can mow a lawn together in 1 hr, and Lisa can mow the same lawn by herself in 3 hr, what is Mark's rate, working alone?

---

7. *Home restoration.*   Bryan can refinish the floor of an apartment in 8 hr. Caroline can refinish the floor in 6 hr. How long will it take them, working together, to refinish the floor?

8. *Custom embroidery.*   Chandra can embroider logos on a team's sweatshirts in 6 hr. Traci, a new employee, needs 9 hr to complete the same job. Working together, how long will it take them to do the job?

9. *Multifunction copiers.*   The Aficio SP C210SF can copy Mousa's dissertation in 7 min. The MX-3501N can copy the same document in 6 min. If the two machines work together, how long would they take to copy the dissertation?
Source: Manufacturers' marketing brochures

10. *Fax machines.*   The FAXPHONE L80 can fax a year-end report in 7 min while the HP 1050 Fax Series can fax the same report in 14 min. How long would it take the two machines, working together, to fax the report? (Assume that the recipient has at least two machines for incoming faxes.)
Source: Manufacturers' marketing brochures

11. *Pumping water.*   A $\frac{1}{2}$ HP Wayne stainless-steel sump pump can remove water from Carmen's flooded basement in 42 min. The $\frac{1}{2}$ HP Craftsman Professional sump pump can complete the same job in 35 min. How long would it take the two pumps together to pump out the basement?
Source: Based on data from manufacturers

12. *Hotel management.*   The Honeywell Enviracaire Silent Comfort air cleaner can clean the air in an 11-ft by 17-ft conference room in 10 min. The Blueair 201 Air Purifier can clean the air in a room of the same size in 12 min. How long would it take the two machines together to clean the air in such a room?
Source: Based on information from manufacturers' and retailers' websites

13. *Photocopiers.*   The HP Officejet H470 Mobile Printer takes twice the time required by the HP Officejet Pro K5400 color printer to photocopy brochures for the New Bretton Arts Council annual arts fair. If, working together, the two machines can complete the job in 45 min, how long would it take each machine, working alone, to copy the brochures?
Source: www.shoppinghp.com

14. *Forest fires.*   The Erickson Air-Crane helicopter can scoop water and douse a certain forest fire four times as fast as an S-58T helicopter. Working together, the two helicopters can douse the fire in 8 hr. How long would it take each helicopter, working alone, to douse the fire?
Sources: Based on information from www.emergency.com and www.arishelicopters.com

15. *Hotel management.*   The Austin Healthmate 400 can purify the air in a conference hall in 15 fewer minutes than it takes the Airgle 750 Air Purifier to do the same job. Together the two machines can purify the air in the conference hall in 10 min. How long would it take each machine, working alone, to purify the air in the room?
Source: Based on information from manufacturers' and retailers' websites

16. *Photo printing.*   It takes the Canon PIXMA iP6310D 15 min longer to print a set of photo proofs than it takes the HP Officejet H470b Mobile Printer. Together it would take them $\frac{180}{7}$, or $25\frac{5}{7}$ min to print the photos. How long would it take each machine, working alone, to print the photos?
Sources: www.shoppinghp.com; www.staples.com

17. *Sorting recyclables.*   Together, it takes Kim and Chris 2 hr 55 min to sort recyclables. Alone, Kim would require 2 hr more than Chris. How long would it take Chris to do the job alone? (*Hint*: Convert minutes to hours or hours to minutes.)

18. *Paving.*   Together, Steve and Bill require 4 hr 48 min to pave a driveway. Alone, Steve would require 4 hr more than Bill. How long would it take Bill to do the job alone? (*Hint*: Convert minutes to hours.)

19. *Train speeds.*   A B & M freight train is traveling 14 km/h slower than an AMTRAK passenger train. The B & M train travels 330 km in the same time that it takes the AMTRAK train to travel 400 km. Find their speeds. Complete the following table as part of the familiarization.

| Distance | = | Rate | · | Time |

	Distance (in km)	Speed (in km/h)	Time (in hours)
B & M	330		
AMTRAK	400	r	$\dfrac{400}{r}$

20. *Speed of travel.*   A loaded Roadway truck is moving 40 mph faster than a New York Railways freight train. In the time that it takes the train to travel 150 mi, the truck travels 350 mi. Find their speeds. Complete the following table as part of the familiarization.

| Distance | = | Rate | · | Time |

	Distance (in miles)	Speed (in miles per hour)	Time (in hours)
Truck	350	r	$\dfrac{350}{r}$
Train	150		

21. *Kayaking.*   The speed of the current in Catamount Creek is 3 mph. Sean can kayak 4 mi upstream in the same time it takes him to kayak 10 mi downstream. What is the speed of Sean's kayak in still water?

22. *Boating.*   The current in the Lazy River moves at a rate of 4 mph. Nicole's dinghy motors 6 mi upstream in the same time it takes to motor 12 mi downstream. What is the speed of the dinghy in still water?

23. *Moving sidewalks.*   The moving sidewalk at O'Hare Airport in Chicago moves 1.8 ft/sec. Walking on the moving sidewalk, Roslyn travels 105 ft forward in the time it takes to travel 51 ft in the opposite direction. How fast does Roslyn walk on a nonmoving sidewalk?

24. *Moving sidewalks.*   Newark Airport's moving sidewalk moves at a speed of 1.7 ft/sec. Walking on the moving sidewalk, Drew can travel 120 ft forward in the same time it takes to travel 52 ft in the opposite direction. What is Drew's walking speed on a nonmoving sidewalk?

Aha! **25.** *Tractor speed.*   Manley's tractor is just as fast as Caledonia's. It takes Manley 1 hr more than it takes Caledonia to drive to town. If Manley is 20 mi from town and Caledonia is 15 mi from town, how long does it take Caledonia to drive to town?

26. *Boat speed.*   Tory and Emilio's motorboats travel at the same speed. Tory pilots her boat 40 km before docking. Emilio continues for another 2 hr, traveling a total of 100 km before docking. How long did it take Tory to navigate the 40 km?

27. *Boating.*   LeBron's Mercruiser travels 15 km/h in still water. He motors 140 km downstream in the same time it takes to travel 35 km upstream. What is the speed of the river?

28. *Boating.* Annette's paddleboat travels 2 km/h in still water. The boat is paddled 4 km downstream in the same time it takes to go 1 km upstream. What is the speed of the river?

29. *Shipping.* A barge moves 7 km/h in still water. It travels 45 km upriver and 45 km downriver in a total time of 14 hr. What is the speed of the current?

30. *Aviation.* A Citation CV jet travels 460 mph in still air and flies 525 mi into the wind and 525 mi with the wind in a total of 2.3 hr. Find the wind speed.
Source: Blue Star Jets, Inc.

31. *Train travel.* A freight train covered 120 mi at a certain speed. Had the train been able to travel 10 mph faster, the trip would have been 2 hr shorter. How fast did the train go?

32. *Moped speed.* Cameron's moped travels 8 km/h faster than Ellia's. Cameron travels 69 km in the same time that Ellia travels 45 km. Find the speed of each person's moped.

Geometry. *For each pair of similar triangles, find the value of the indicated letter.*

33. *b*

34. *a*

35. *f*

36. *r*

Architecture. *Use the blueprint below to find the indicated length.*

37. *p*, in inches on blueprint

38. *s*, in inches on blueprint

39. *r*, in feet on actual building

40. *n*, in feet on actual building

Find the indicated length.

41. *l*

42. *h*

Graphing. *Find the indicated length.*

43. *r*

44. *s*

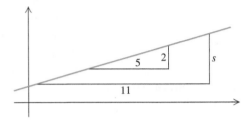

45. *Text messaging.* Brett sent or received 384 text messages in 8 days. At this rate, how many text messages would he send or receive in 30 days?

46. *Burning calories.* The average 140-lb adult burns about 380 calories bicycling 10 mi at a moderate rate. How far should the average 140-lb adult ride in order to burn 100 calories?
Source: *ACE Fitness Matters*, Volume 1, Number 4, 1997

47. *Illegal immigration.* Between 2001 and 2006, the Border Patrol caught 12,334 people trying to cross illegally from Canada to the United States along a 295-mi stretch of the border. If this rate were the same for the entire 5525-mi border between the two countries, how many would the Border Patrol catch in those same years along the entire border?
Source: *The Wall Street Journal*, July 10, 2007

Aha! **48.** *Photography.* Aziza snapped 234 photos over a period of 14 days. At this rate, how many would she take in 42 days?

49. *Mileage.* The Honda Civic Hybrid is a gasoline–electric car that travels approximately 180 mi on 4 gal of gas. Find the amount of gas required for an 810-mi trip.
Source: www.greenhybrid.com

50. *Baking.* In a potato bread recipe, the ratio of milk to flour is $\frac{3}{13}$. If 5 cups of milk are used, how many cups of flour are used?

51. *Wing aspect ratio.* The wing aspect ratio for a bird or an airplane is the ratio of the wing span to the wing width. Generally, higher aspect ratios are more efficient during low speed flying. Herons and storks, both waders, have comparable wing aspect ratios. A grey heron has a wing span of

180 cm and a wing width of 24 cm. A white stork has a wing span of 200 cm. What is the wing width of a stork?
Source: birds.ecoport.org

Aha! **52.** *Money.* The ratio of the weight of copper to the weight of zinc in a U.S. penny is $\frac{1}{39}$. If 50 kg of zinc is being turned into pennies, how much copper is needed?
Source: United States Mint

53. *Light bulbs.* A sample of 220 compact fluorescent light bulbs contained 8 defective bulbs. How many defective bulbs would you expect in a batch of 1430 bulbs?

54. *Flash drives.* A sample of 150 flash drives contained 7 defective drives. How many defective flash drives would you expect in a batch of 2700 flash drives?

55. *Veterinary science.* The amount of water needed by a small dog depends on its weight. A moderately active 8-lb Shih Tzu needs approximately 12 oz of water per day. How much water does a moderately active 5-lb Bolognese require each day?
Source: www.smalldogsparadise.com

56. *Miles driven.* Emmanuel is allowed to drive his leased car for 45,000 mi in 4 yr without penalty. In the first $1\frac{1}{2}$ yr, Emmanuel has driven 16,000 mi. At this rate will he exceed the mileage allowed for 4 yr?

57. *Environmental science.* To determine the number of humpback whales in a pod, a marine biologist, using tail markings, identifies 27 members of the pod. Several weeks later, 40 whales from the pod are randomly sighted. Of the 40 sighted, 12 are from the 27 originally identified. Estimate the number of whales in the pod.

58. *Fox population.* To determine the number of foxes in King County, a naturalist catches, tags, and then releases 25 foxes. Later, 36 foxes are caught; 4 of them have tags. Estimate the fox population of the county.

59. *Weight on the moon.*   The ratio of the weight of an object on the moon to the weight of that object on Earth is 0.16 to 1.

    a) How much would a 12-ton rocket weigh on the moon?

    b) How much would a 180-lb astronaut weigh on the moon?

60. *Weight on Mars.*   The ratio of the weight of an object on Mars to the weight of that object on Earth is 0.4 to 1.

    a) How much would a 12-ton rocket weigh on Mars?

    b) How much would a 120-lb astronaut weigh on Mars?

61. Is it correct to assume that two workers will complete a task twice as quickly as one person working alone? Why or why not?

62. If two triangles are exactly the same shape and size, are they similar? Why or why not?

Skill Review

To prepare for Chapter 7, review graphing linear equations (Section 3.2).

Graph. [3.2]

63. $y = 2x - 6$

64. $y = -2x + 6$

65. $3x + 2y = 12$

66. $x - 3y = 6$

67. $y = -\dfrac{3}{4}x + 2$

68. $y = \dfrac{2}{5}x - 4$

Synthesis

69. Two steamrollers are paving a parking lot. Working together, will the two steamrollers take less than half as long as the slower steamroller would working alone? Why or why not?

70. Two fuel lines are filling a freighter with oil. Will the faster fuel line take more or less than twice as long to fill the freighter by itself? Why?

71. *Filling a bog.*   The Norwich cranberry bog can be filled in 9 hr and drained in 11 hr. How long will it take to fill the bog if the drainage gate is left open?

72. *Filling a tub.*   Jillian's hot tub can be filled in 10 min and drained in 8 min. How long will it take to empty a full tub if the water is left on?

73. *Escalators.*   Together, a 100-cm wide escalator and a 60-cm wide escalator can empty a 1575-person auditorium in 14 min. The wider escalator moves twice as many people as the narrower one. How many people per hour does the 60-cm wide escalator move?
Source: *McGraw-Hill Encyclopedia of Science and Technology*

74. *Aviation.*   A Coast Guard plane has enough fuel to fly for 6 hr, and its speed in still air is 240 mph. The plane departs with a 40-mph tailwind and returns to the same airport flying into the same wind. How far can the plane travel under these conditions?

75. *Boating.*   Shoreline Travel operates a 3-hr paddleboat cruise on the Missouri River. If the speed of the boat in still water is 12 mph, how far upriver can the pilot travel against a 5-mph current before it is time to turn around?

76. *Travel by car.*   Angenita drives to work at 50 mph and arrives 1 min late. She drives to work at 60 mph and arrives 5 min early. How far does Angenita live from work?

77. *Grading.*   Alma can grade a batch of placement exams in 3 hr. Kevin can grade a batch in 4 hr. If they work together to grade a batch of exams, what percentage of the exams will have been graded by Alma?

78. According to the U.S. Census Bureau, Population Division, in July 2007, there was one birth every 7 sec, one death every 13 sec, and one new international migrant every 27 sec. How many seconds does it take for a net gain of one person?

79. *Photocopying.*   The printer in an admissions office can print a 500-page document in 50 min, while the printer in the business office can print the same document in 40 min. If the two printers work together to print the document, with the faster machine starting on page 1 and the slower machine working backwards from page 500, at what page will the two machines meet to complete the job?

80. *Distances.*   The shadow from a 40-ft cliff just reaches across a water-filled quarry at the same time that a 6-ft tall diver casts a 10-ft shadow. How wide is the quarry?

81. Given that

$$\frac{A}{B} = \frac{C}{D},$$

write three other proportions using *A, B, C,* and *D.*

Average speed is defined as total distance divided by total time.

82. Ferdaws drove 200 km. For the first 100 km of the trip, she drove at a speed of 40 km/h. For the second half of the trip, she traveled at a speed of 60 km/h. What was the average speed of the entire trip? (It was *not* 50 km/h.)

83. For the first 50 mi of a 100-mi trip, Garry drove 40 mph. What speed would he have to travel for the last half of the trip so that the average speed for the entire trip would be 45 mph?

84. If two triangles are similar, are their areas and perimeters proportional? Why or why not?

85. Are the equations

$$\frac{A + B}{B} = \frac{C + D}{D} \quad \text{and} \quad \frac{A}{B} = \frac{C}{D}$$

equivalent? Why or why not?

COLLABORATIVE CORNER

Sharing the Workload

Focus: Modeling, estimation, and work problems

Time: 15–20 minutes

Group size: 3

Materials: Paper, pencils, textbooks, and a watch

Many tasks can be done by two people working together. If both people work at the same rate, each does half the task, and the project is completed in half the time. However, when the work rates differ, the faster worker performs more than half of the task.

ACTIVITY

1. The project is to write down (but not answer) Review Exercises 27–36 from Chapter 7 (p. 497) on a sheet of paper. The problems should be spaced apart and written clearly so that they can be used for studying in the future. Two of the members in each group should write down the exercises, one working slowly and one working quickly. The third group member should record the time required for each to write down all 10 exercises.

2. Using the times from step (1), calculate how long it will take the two workers, working together, to complete the task.

3. Next, have the same workers as in step (1)— working at the same speeds as in step (1)— perform the task together. To do this, one person should begin writing with Exercise 27, while the other worker begins with Exercise 36 and lists the problems counting backward. The third member is again the timekeeper and should observe when the two workers have written all the exercises. To avoid collision, each of the two writers should use a separate sheet of paper.

4. Compare the actual experimental time from part (3) with the time predicted by the model in part (2). List reasons that might account for any discrepancy.

5. Let t_1, t_2, and t_3 represent the times required for the first worker, the second worker, and the two workers together, respectively, to complete a task. Then develop a model that can be used to find t_3 when t_1 and t_2 are known.

Time Required for Worker A, Working Alone	Time Required for Worker B, Working Alone	Estimated Time for the Two Workers, Working Together	Actual Time Required for the Two Workers, Working Together

Study Summary

KEY TERMS AND CONCEPTS	EXAMPLES

SECTION 7.1: RATIONAL EXPRESSIONS

A **rational expression** can be written as a quotient of two polynomials and is undefined when the denominator is 0. We simplify rational expressions by removing a factor equal to 1.

$$\frac{x^2 - 3x - 4}{x^2 - 1} = \frac{(x+1)(x-4)}{(x+1)(x-1)}$$

Factoring the numerator and the denominator

$$= \frac{x-4}{x-1}$$

$$\frac{x+1}{x+1} = 1$$

SECTION 7.2: MULTIPLICATION AND DIVISION

The Product of Two Rational Expressions

$$\frac{A}{B} \cdot \frac{C}{D} = \frac{AC}{BD}$$

$$\frac{5v+5}{v-2} \cdot \frac{2v^2 - 8v + 8}{v^2 - 1}$$

$$= \frac{5(v+1) \cdot 2(v-2)(v-2)}{(v-2)(v+1)(v-1)}$$

Multiplying numerators, multiplying denominators, and factoring

$$= \frac{10(v-2)}{v-1}$$

$$\frac{(v+1)(v-2)}{(v+1)(v-2)} = 1$$

The Quotient of Two Rational Expressions

$$\frac{A}{B} \div \frac{C}{D} = \frac{A}{B} \cdot \frac{D}{C} = \frac{AD}{BC}$$

$$(x^2 - 5x - 6) \div \frac{x^2 - 1}{x + 6}$$

$$= \frac{x^2 - 5x - 6}{1} \cdot \frac{x+6}{x^2 - 1}$$

Multiplying by the reciprocal of the divisor

$$= \frac{(x-6)(x+1)(x+6)}{(x+1)(x-1)}$$

Multiplying numerators, multiplying denominators, and factoring

$$= \frac{(x-6)(x+6)}{x-1}$$

$$\frac{x+1}{x+1} = 1$$

SECTION 7.3: ADDITION, SUBTRACTION, AND LEAST COMMON DENOMINATORS

The Sum of Two Rational Expressions

$$\frac{A}{B} + \frac{C}{B} = \frac{A+C}{B}$$

$$\frac{7x+8}{x+1} + \frac{4x+3}{x+1} = \frac{7x+8+4x+3}{x+1}$$

Adding numerators and keeping the denominator

$$= \frac{11x + 11}{x+1}$$

$$= \frac{11(x+1)}{x+1}$$

Factoring

$$= 11$$

$$\frac{x+1}{x+1} = 1$$

The Difference of Two Rational Expressions

$$\frac{A}{B} - \frac{C}{B} = \frac{A-C}{B}$$

$$\frac{7x+8}{x+1} - \frac{4x+3}{x+1} = \frac{7x+8-(4x+3)}{x+1}$$

Subtracting numerators and keeping the denominator. The parentheses are necessary.

$$= \frac{7x+8-4x-3}{x+1}$$

Removing parentheses

$$= \frac{3x+5}{x+1}$$

The **least common denominator (LCD)** of rational expressions is the **least common multiple (LCM)** of the denominators. To find the LCM, write the prime factorizations of the denominators. The LCM contains each factor the greatest number of times that it occurs in any of the individual factorizations.

Find the LCM of $m^2 - 5m + 6$ and $m^2 - 4m + 4$.

$$m^2 - 5m + 6 = (m - 2)(m - 3)$$
$$m^2 - 4m + 4 = (m - 2)(m - 2)$$

Factoring each expression

LCM $= (m - 2)(m - 2)(m - 3)$

The LCM contains 2 factors of $(m - 2)$ and 1 factor of $(m - 3)$.

SECTION 7.4: ADDITION AND SUBTRACTION WITH UNLIKE DENOMINATORS

To add or subtract rational expressions with different denominators, first rewrite the expressions as equivalent expressions with a common denominator.

$$\frac{2x}{x^2 - 16} + \frac{x}{x - 4}$$

$$= \frac{2x}{(x + 4)(x - 4)} + \frac{x}{x - 4}$$

Factoring denominators: The LCD is $(x + 4)(x - 4)$.

$$= \frac{2x}{(x + 4)(x - 4)} + \frac{x}{x - 4} \cdot \frac{x + 4}{x + 4}$$

Multiplying by 1 to get the LCD in the second expression

$$= \frac{2x}{(x + 4)(x - 4)} + \frac{x^2 + 4x}{(x + 4)(x - 4)}$$

$$= \frac{x^2 + 6x}{(x + 4)(x - 4)}$$

Adding numerators and keeping the denominator. This cannot be simplified.

SECTION 7.5: COMPLEX RATIONAL EXPRESSIONS

Complex rational expressions contain one or more rational expressions within the numerator and/or the denominator. They can be simplified either by using division or by multiplying by a form of 1 to clear the fractions.

Using division to simplify:

$$\frac{\dfrac{1}{6} - \dfrac{1}{x}}{\dfrac{6 - x}{6}} = \frac{\dfrac{1}{6} \cdot \dfrac{x}{x} - \dfrac{1}{x} \cdot \dfrac{6}{6}}{\dfrac{6 - x}{6}} = \frac{\dfrac{x - 6}{6x}}{\dfrac{6 - x}{6}}$$

Subtracting to get a single rational expression in the numerator

$$= \frac{x - 6}{6x} \div \frac{6 - x}{6} = \frac{x - 6}{6x} \cdot \frac{6}{6 - x}$$

Dividing the numerator by the denominator

$$= \frac{6(x - 6)}{6x(-1)(x - 6)} = \frac{1}{-x} = -\frac{1}{x}$$

Factoring and simplifying; $\dfrac{6(x - 6)}{6(x - 6)} = 1$

Multiplying by 1:

$$\frac{\dfrac{4}{x}}{\dfrac{3}{x} + \dfrac{2}{x^2}} = \frac{\dfrac{4}{x}}{\dfrac{3}{x} + \dfrac{2}{x^2}} \cdot \frac{x^2}{x^2}$$

$$= \frac{\dfrac{4}{x} \cdot \dfrac{x^2}{1}}{\left(\dfrac{3}{x} + \dfrac{2}{x^2}\right) \cdot \dfrac{x^2}{1}}$$

The LCD of all the denominators is x^2; multiplying by $\dfrac{x^2}{x^2}$

$$= \frac{\dfrac{4 \cdot x \cdot x}{x}}{\dfrac{3 \cdot x \cdot x}{x} + \dfrac{2 \cdot x^2}{x^2}} = \frac{4x}{3x + 2}$$

The fractions are cleared.

SECTION 7.6: SOLVING RATIONAL EQUATIONS

To Solve a Rational Equation

1. List any restrictions.
2. Clear the equation of fractions.
3. Solve the resulting equation.
4. Check the possible solution(s) in the original equation.

Solve: $\dfrac{2}{x+1} = \dfrac{1}{x-2}$.   The restrictions are $x \neq -1, x \neq 2$.

$$\frac{2}{x+1} = \frac{1}{x-2}$$

$$(x+1)(x-2) \cdot \frac{2}{x+1} = (x+1)(x-2) \cdot \frac{1}{x-2}$$

$$2(x-2) = x+1$$
$$2x - 4 = x + 1$$
$$x = 5$$

Check: Since $\dfrac{2}{5+1} = \dfrac{1}{5-2}$, the solution is 5.

SECTION 7.7: APPLICATIONS USING RATIONAL EQUATIONS AND PROPORTIONS

The Work Principle

If a = the time needed for A to complete the work alone,

  b = the time needed for B to complete the work alone,

  and

  t = the time needed for A and B to complete the work together, then:

$$\frac{t}{a} + \frac{t}{b} = 1; \quad \frac{1}{a} \cdot t + \frac{1}{b} \cdot t = 1;$$

$$\frac{1}{a} + \frac{1}{b} = \frac{1}{t}.$$

It takes Manuel 9 hr longer than Zoe to rebuild an engine. Working together, they can do the job in 20 hr. How long would it take each, working alone, to rebuild an engine?

We model the situation using the work principle, with $a = z$, $b = z + 9$, and $t = 20$:

$$\frac{20}{z} + \frac{20}{z+9} = 1 \qquad \text{Using the work principle}$$

$$z = 36. \qquad \text{Solving the equation}$$

It would take Zoe 36 hr to rebuild an engine alone, and Manuel 45 hr.

See Example 2 in Section 7.7 for a complete solution of this problem.

The Motion Formula

$$d = r \cdot t, \quad r = \frac{d}{t}, \quad \text{or} \quad t = \frac{d}{r}$$

On her road bike, Olivia bikes 15 km/h faster than Jason does on his mountain bike. In the time it takes Olivia to travel 80 km, Jason travels 50 km. Find the speed of each bicyclist.

Jason's speed: r km/h   Jason's time: $50/r$ hr

Olivia's speed: $(r + 15)$ km/h   Olivia's time: $80/(r + 15)$ hr

The times are equal:

$$\frac{50}{r} = \frac{80}{r+15}$$

$$r = 25 \qquad \text{Solving the equation}$$

Olivia's speed is 40 km/h, and Jason's speed is 25 km/h.

See Example 3 in Section 7.7 for a complete solution of this problem.

In geometry, proportions arise in the study of **similar triangles**.

Triangles DEF and UVW are similar. Solve for u.

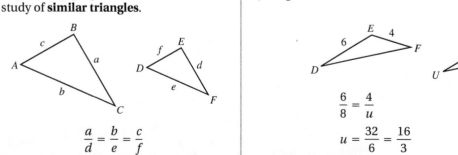

$$\frac{a}{d} = \frac{b}{e} = \frac{c}{f}$$

$$\frac{6}{8} = \frac{4}{u}$$

$$u = \frac{32}{6} = \frac{16}{3}$$

Review Exercises: Chapter 7

Concept Reinforcement   *Classify each statement as either true or false.*

1. Every rational expression can be simplified. [7.1]

2. The expression $(t - 3)/(t^2 - 4)$ is undefined for $t = 2$. [7.1]

3. The expression $(t - 3)/(t^2 - 4)$ is undefined for $t = 3$. [7.1]

4. To multiply rational expressions, a common denominator is never required. [7.2]

5. To divide rational expressions, a common denominator is never required. [7.2]

6. To add rational expressions, a common denominator is never required. [7.3]

7. To subtract rational expressions, a common denominator is never required. [7.3]

8. The number 0 can never be a solution of a rational equation. [7.6]

List all numbers for which each expression is undefined. [7.1]

9. $\dfrac{17}{-x^2}$

10. $\dfrac{9}{2a + 10}$

11. $\dfrac{x - 5}{x^2 - 36}$

12. $\dfrac{x^2 + 3x + 2}{x^2 + x - 30}$

13. $\dfrac{-6}{(t + 2)^2}$

Simplify. [7.1]

14. $\dfrac{3x^2 - 9x}{3x^2 + 15x}$

15. $\dfrac{14x^2 - x - 3}{2x^2 - 7x + 3}$

16. $\dfrac{6y^2 - 36y + 54}{4y^2 - 36}$

17. $\dfrac{5x^2 - 20y^2}{2y - x}$

Multiply or divide and, if possible, simplify. [7.2]

18. $\dfrac{a^2 - 36}{10a} \cdot \dfrac{2a}{a + 6}$

19. $\dfrac{6y - 12}{2y^2 + 3y - 2} \cdot \dfrac{y^2 - 4}{8y - 8}$

20. $\dfrac{16 - 8t}{3} \div \dfrac{t - 2}{12t}$

21. $\dfrac{4x^4}{x^2 - 1} \div \dfrac{2x^3}{x^2 - 2x + 1}$

22. $\dfrac{x^2 + 1}{x - 2} \cdot \dfrac{2x + 1}{x + 1}$

23. $(t^2 + 3t - 4) \div \dfrac{t^2 - 1}{t + 4}$

Find the LCM. [7.3]

24. $10a^3b^8,\ 12a^5b$

25. $x^2 - x,\ x^5 - x^3,\ x^4$

26. $y^2 - y - 2,\ y^2 - 4$

Add or subtract and, if possible, simplify.

27. $\dfrac{x + 6}{x + 3} + \dfrac{9 - 4x}{x + 3}$ [7.3]

28. $\dfrac{6x - 3}{x^2 - x - 12} - \dfrac{2x - 15}{x^2 - x - 12}$ [7.3]

29. $\dfrac{3x - 1}{2x} - \dfrac{x - 3}{x}$ [7.4]

30. $\dfrac{2a + 4b}{5ab^2} - \dfrac{5a - 3b}{a^2b}$ [7.4]

31. $\dfrac{y^2}{y - 2} + \dfrac{6y - 8}{2 - y}$ [7.4]

32. $\dfrac{t}{t + 1} + \dfrac{t}{1 - t^2}$ [7.4]

33. $\dfrac{d^2}{d - 2} + \dfrac{4}{2 - d}$ [7.4]

34. $\dfrac{1}{x^2 - 25} - \dfrac{x - 5}{x^2 - 4x - 5}$ [7.4]

35. $\dfrac{3x}{x + 2} - \dfrac{x}{x - 2} + \dfrac{8}{x^2 - 4}$ [7.4]

36. $\dfrac{3}{4t} + \dfrac{3}{3t + 2}$ [7.4]

Simplify. [7.5]

37. $\dfrac{\frac{1}{z} + 1}{\frac{1}{z^2} - 1}$

38. $\dfrac{\frac{5}{2x^2}}{\frac{3}{4x} + \frac{4}{x^3}}$

39. $\dfrac{\frac{c}{d} - \frac{d}{c}}{\frac{1}{c} + \frac{1}{d}}$

Solve. [7.6]

40. $\dfrac{3}{x} - \dfrac{1}{4} = \dfrac{1}{2}$

41. $\dfrac{3}{x + 4} = \dfrac{1}{x - 1}$

42. $x + \dfrac{6}{x} = -7$

Solve. [7.7]

43. Jackson can sand the oak floors and stairs in a two-story home in 12 hr. Charis can do the same job in 9 hr. How long would it take if they worked together? (Assume that two sanders are available.)

44. A research company uses employees' computers to process data while the employee is not using the computer. An Intel Core 2 Quad processor can process a data file in 15 sec less time than an Intel Core 2 Duo processor. Working together, the computers can process the file in 18 sec. How long does it take each computer to process the file?

45. The distance by highway between Richmond and Waterbury is 70 km, and the distance by rail is 60 km. A car and a train leave Richmond at the same time and arrive in Waterbury at the same time, the car having traveled 15 km/h faster than the train. Find the speed of the car and the speed of the train.

46. The Black River's current is 6 mph. A boat travels 50 mi downstream in the same time that it takes to travel 30 mi upstream. What is the speed of the boat in still water?

47. To estimate the harbor seal population in Bristol Bay, scientists radio-tagged 33 seals. Several days later, they collected a sample of 40 seals, and 24 of them were tagged. Estimate the seal population of the bay.

48. Triangles *ABC* and *XYZ* are similar. Find the value of *x*.

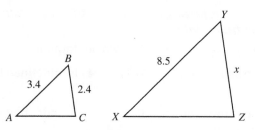

Synthesis

49. For what procedures in this chapter is the LCM of denominators used to clear fractions? [7.5], [7.6]

50. A student always uses the common denominator found by multiplying the denominators of the expressions being added. How could this approach be improved? [7.3]

Simplify.

51. $\dfrac{2a^2 + 5a - 3}{a^2} \cdot \dfrac{5a^3 + 30a^2}{2a^2 + 7a - 4} \div \dfrac{a^2 + 6a}{a^2 + 7a + 12}$ [7.2]

52. $\dfrac{12a}{(a - b)(b - c)} - \dfrac{2a}{(b - a)(c - b)}$ [7.4]

Aha! **53.** $\dfrac{5(x - y)}{(x - y)(x + 2y)} - \dfrac{5(x - 3y)}{(x + 2y)(x - 3y)}$ [7.3]

Test: Chapter 7

CHAPTER Test Prep VIDEO CD   *Step-by-step test solutions are found on the video CD in the front of this book.*

List all numbers for which each expression is undefined.

1. $\dfrac{2 - x}{5x}$

2. $\dfrac{5}{x + 8}$

3. $\dfrac{x - 7}{x^2 - 1}$

4. $\dfrac{x^2 + x - 30}{x^2 - 3x + 2}$

5. Simplify: $\dfrac{6x^2 + 17x + 7}{2x^2 + 7x + 3}$.

Multiply or divide and, if possible, simplify.

6. $\dfrac{t^2 - 9}{12t} \cdot \dfrac{8t^2}{t^2 - 4t + 3}$

7. $\dfrac{25y^2 - 1}{9y^2 - 6y} \div \dfrac{5y^2 + 9y - 2}{3y^2 + y - 2}$

8. $\dfrac{4a^2 + 1}{4a^2 - 1} \div \dfrac{4a^2}{4a^2 + 4a + 1}$

9. $(x^2 + 6x + 9) \cdot \dfrac{(x - 3)^2}{x^2 - 9}$

10. Find the LCM:
$$y^2 - 9, \ y^2 + 10y + 21, \ y^2 + 4y - 21.$$

Add or subtract, and, if possible, simplify.

11. $\dfrac{2 + x}{x^3} + \dfrac{7 - 4x}{x^3}$

12. $\dfrac{5 - t}{t^2 + 1} - \dfrac{t - 3}{t^2 + 1}$

13. $\dfrac{2x - 4}{x - 3} + \dfrac{x - 1}{3 - x}$

14. $\dfrac{2x - 4}{x - 3} - \dfrac{x - 1}{3 - x}$

15. $\dfrac{7}{t-2} + \dfrac{4}{t}$

16. $\dfrac{y}{y^2+6y+9} + \dfrac{1}{y^2+2y-3}$

17. $\dfrac{1}{x-1} + \dfrac{4}{x^2-1} - \dfrac{2}{x^2-2x+1}$

Simplify.

18. $\dfrac{9 - \dfrac{1}{y^2}}{3 - \dfrac{1}{y}}$

19. $\dfrac{\dfrac{x}{8} - \dfrac{8}{x}}{\dfrac{1}{8} + \dfrac{1}{x}}$

Solve.

20. $\dfrac{1}{t} + \dfrac{1}{3t} = \dfrac{1}{2}$

21. $\dfrac{15}{x} - \dfrac{15}{x-2} = -2$

22. Kopy Kwik has 2 copiers. One can copy a year-end report in 20 min. The other can copy the same document in 30 min. How long would it take both machines, working together, to copy the report?

23. The average 140-lb adult burns about 320 calories walking 4 mi at a moderate speed. How far should the average 140-lb adult walk in order to burn 100 calories?
Source: www.walking.about.com

24. Ryan drives 20 km/h faster than Alicia. In the same time that Alicia drives 225 km, Ryan drives 325 km. Find the speed of each car.

25. Pe'rez and Rema work together to mulch the flower beds around an office complex in $2\frac{6}{7}$ hr. Working alone, it would take Pe'rez 6 hr more than it would take Rema. How long would it take each of them to complete the landscaping working alone?

Synthesis

26. Simplify: $1 - \dfrac{1}{1 - \dfrac{1}{1 - \dfrac{1}{a}}}$.

27. The square of a number is the opposite of the number's reciprocal. Find the number.

Cumulative Review: Chapters 1–3, 5-7

1. Use the commutative law of multiplication to write an expression equivalent to $a + bc$. [1.2]

2. Evaluate $-x^2$ for $x = 5$. [1.8]

3. Evaluate $(-x)^2$ for $x = 5$. [1.8]

4. Simplify: $-3[2(x-3) - (x+5)]$. [1.8]

Solve.

5. $5(x-2) = 40$ [2.2]

6. $49 = x^2$ [6.7]

7. $-18n = 30$ [2.1]

8. $4x - 3 = 9x - 11$ [2.2]

9. $4(y-5) = -2(y-2)$ [2.2]

10. $x^2 + 11x + 10 = 0$ [6.7]

11. $\dfrac{4}{9}t + \dfrac{2}{3} = \dfrac{1}{3}t - \dfrac{2}{9}$ [2.2]

12. $\dfrac{4}{x} + x = 5$ [7.6]

13. $6 - y \geq 2y + 8$ [2.6]

14. $\dfrac{2}{x-3} = \dfrac{5}{3x+1}$ [7.6]

15. $2x^2 + 7x = 4$ [6.7]

16. $4(x+7) < 5(x-3)$ [2.6]

17. $\dfrac{t^2}{t+5} = \dfrac{25}{t+5}$ [7.6]

18. $(2x+7)(x-5) = 0$ [6.7]

19. $\dfrac{2}{x^2-9} + \dfrac{5}{x-3} = \dfrac{3}{x+3}$ [7.6]

Solve each formula. [2.3]

20. $3a - b + 9 = c$, for b

21. $\frac{3}{4}(x+2y) = z$, for y

Graph. [3.2], [3.3], [3.6]

22. $y = \frac{3}{4}x + 5$

23. $x = -3$

24. $4x + 5y = 20$

25. $y = 6$

26. Find the slope of the line containing the points $(1, 5)$ and $(2, 3)$. [3.5]

27. Find the slope and the y-intercept of the line given by $2x - 4y = 1$. [3.6]

28. Write the slope–intercept equation of the line with slope $-\frac{5}{8}$ and y-intercept $(0, -4)$. [3.6]

Simplify.

29. $\dfrac{x^{-5}}{x^{-3}}$ [5.2]

30. $y \cdot y^{-8}$ [5.2]

31. $-(2a^2b^7)^2$ [5.1]

32. Subtract: [5.4]

$$(-8y^2 - y + 2) - (y^3 - 6y^2 + y - 5).$$

Multiply.

33. $-5(3a - 2b + c)$ [1.2]

34. $(2x^2 - 1)(x^3 + x - 3)$ [5.5]

35. $(6x - 5y)^2$ [5.6]

36. $(3n + 2)(n - 5)$ [5.6]

37. $(2x^3 + 1)(2x^3 - 1)$ [5.6]

Factor.

38. $6x - 2x^2 - 24x^4$ [6.1]

39. $16x^2 - 81$ [6.4]

40. $10t^3 + 10$ [6.5]

41. $8x^2 + 10x + 3$ [6.3]

42. $6x^2 - 28x + 16$ [6.3]

43. $25t^2 + 40t + 16$ [6.4]

44. $x^2y^2 - xy - 20$ [6.2]

45. $x^4 + 2x^3 - 3x - 6$ [6.1]

Simplify.

46. $\dfrac{4t - 20}{t^2 - 16} \cdot \dfrac{t - 4}{t - 5}$ [7.2]

47. $\dfrac{x^2 - 1}{x^2 - x - 2} \div \dfrac{x - 1}{x - 2}$ [7.2]

48. $\dfrac{5ab}{a^2 - b^2} + \dfrac{a + b}{a - b}$ [7.4]

49. $\dfrac{x + 2}{4 - x} - \dfrac{x + 3}{x - 4}$ [7.4]

50. $\dfrac{1 + \dfrac{2}{x}}{1 - \dfrac{4}{x^2}}$ [7.5]

51. $\dfrac{3y + \dfrac{2}{y}}{y - \dfrac{3}{y^2}}$ [7.5]

Divide. [5.8]

52. $\dfrac{18x^4 - 15x^3 + 6x^2 + 12x + 3}{3x^2}$

53. $(15x^4 - 12x^3 + 6x^2 + 2x + 18) \div (x + 3)$

54. For each order, HanBooks.com charges a shipping fee of $5.50 plus $1.99 per book. The shipping cost for Dae's book order was $35.35. How many books did she order? [2.5]
Source: hanbooks.com

55. In 2006, the attendance at movie theaters was 1448.5 billion. This was 425% more than the number of admissions to theme parks. How many theme park admissions were there in 2006? [2.4]
Source: MPAA, PricewaterhouseCoopers

56. A pair of 1976 two-dollar bills with consecutive serial numbers is being sold in an auction. The sum of the serial numbers is 66,679,015. What are the serial numbers of the bills? [2.5]

57. Nikki is laying out two square flower gardens in a client's lawn. Each side of one garden is 2 ft longer than each side of the smaller garden. Together, the area of the gardens is 340 ft². Find the length of a side of the smaller garden. [6.8]

58. It takes Wes 25 min to file a week's worth of receipts. Corey, a new employee, takes 75 min to do the same job. How long would it take if they worked together? [7.7]

59. A game warden catches, tags, and then releases 18 antelope. A month later, a sample of 30 antelope is caught and released and 6 of them have tags. Use this information to estimate the size of the antelope population in that area. [7.7]

60. Rachel burned 450 calories in a workout. She burned twice as many in her aerobics session as she did doing calisthenics. How many calories did she burn doing calisthenics? [2.5]

Synthesis

61. Solve: $\frac{1}{3}|n| + 8 = 56$. [1.4], [2.2]

Aha! **62.** Multiply: $[4y^3 - (y^2 - 3)][4y^3 + (y^2 - 3)]$. [5.6]

63. Solve: $x(x^2 + 3x - 28) - 12(x^2 + 3x - 28) = 0$. [6.7]

64. Solve: $\dfrac{2}{x - 3} \cdot \dfrac{3}{x + 3} - \dfrac{4}{x^2 - 7x + 12} = 0$. [7.6]

Functions and Graphs

MELANIE CHAMBERS
MATH TEACHER/RECIPIENT OF
THE MILKEN FAMILY
FOUNDATION'S NATIONAL
EDUCATOR AWARD
Cedar Hill, Texas

Being proficient in math not only has multiplied my career options but also opens many doors for those students who choose to sharpen their math skills. As a math instructor, I use math to calculate students' performance on assessments, disaggregate data to differentiate instruction to better meet student learning needs, and demonstrate daily how real-world problem solving often entails mathematical analysis.

AN APPLICATION

According to the National Assessment of Educational Progress (NAEP), the percentage of fourth-graders who are proficient in math has grown from 21% in 1996 to 24% in 2000 and 39% in 2007.

Estimate the percentage of fourth-graders who showed proficiency in 2004 and predict the percentage who will demonstrate proficiency in 2011.

Source: nationsreportcard.gov

This problem appears as Example 6 in Section 8.1.

n this chapter we introduce the concept of a *function*. As we will see, many functions are described using linear, polynomial, and rational expressions. Functions can also often be visualized graphically, as well as added, subtracted, multiplied, and divided. Near the end of the chapter, we solve formulas using equation-solving techniques studied earlier, and we use function notation when describing *direct* and *inverse variation*.

8.1 Introduction to Functions

Correspondences and Functions and Equations ▪ Applications ▪ Functions and Graphs ▪ Function Notation

We now develop the idea of a *function*—one of the most important concepts in mathematics.

Correspondences and Functions

When forming ordered pairs to graph equations, we often say that the first coordinate of each ordered pair *corresponds* to the second coordinate. In much the same way, a function is a special kind of correspondence between two sets. For example,

To each person in a class	there corresponds	a date of birth.
To each bar code in a store	there corresponds	a price.
To each real number	there corresponds	the cube of that number.

In each example, the first set is called the **domain**. The second set is called the **range**. For any member of the domain, there is *exactly one* member of the range to which it corresponds. This kind of correspondence is called a **function**.

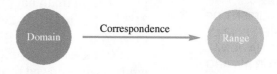

EXAMPLE 1

Determine whether each correspondence is a function.

a)

Domain   *Range*

4 ⟶ 2
1 ⟶ 2
−3 ⟶ 5

b) *Domain*   *Range*

Ford ⟶ Sebring
Chrysler ⟶ F150 Pickup
General Motors ⟶ Malibu
⟶ Cobalt

SOLUTION

a) The correspondence *is* a function because each member of the domain corresponds to *exactly one* member of the range.

b) The correspondence *is not* a function because a member of the domain (General Motors) corresponds to more than one member of the range.

TRY EXERCISE ▸ 9

> **Function**
>
> A *function* is a correspondence between a first set, called the *domain*, and a second set, called the *range*, such that each member of the domain corresponds to *exactly one* member of the range.

EXAMPLE 2   Determine whether each correspondence is a function.

Domain	*Correspondence*	*Range*
a) People in a doctor's waiting room	Each person's weight	A set of positive numbers
b) $\{-2, 0, 1, 2\}$	Each number's square	$\{0, 1, 4\}$
c) Authors of best-selling books	The titles of books written by each author	A set of book titles

SOLUTION

a) The correspondence *is* a function, because each person has *only one* weight.

b) The correspondence *is* a function, because every number has *only one* square.

c) The correspondence *is not* a function, because some authors have written *more than one* book.   17

Although the correspondence in Example 2(c) is not a function, it is a *relation*.

> **Relation**
>
> A *relation* is a correspondence between a first set, called the *domain*, and a second set, called the *range*, such that each member of the domain corresponds to *at least one* member of the range.

Functions and Graphs

The functions in Examples 1(a) and 2(b) can be expressed as sets of ordered pairs. Example 1(a) can be written $\{(-3, 5), (1, 2), (4, 2)\}$ and Example 2(b) can be written $\{(-2, 4), (0, 0), (1, 1), (2, 4)\}$. We can graph these functions as follows.

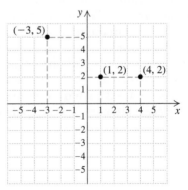

The function $\{(-3, 5), (1, 2), (4, 2)\}$
Domain is $\{-3, 1, 4\}$
Range is $\{5, 2\}$

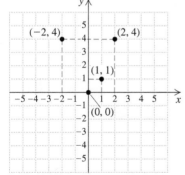

The function $\{(-2, 4), (0, 0), (1, 1), (2, 4)\}$
Domain is $\{-2, 0, 1, 2\}$
Range is $\{4, 0, 1\}$

We can find the domain and the range of a function directly from its graph. The domain is read from the horizontal axis and the range is read from the vertical axis. Note in the graphs above that if we move along the red dashed lines from the points to the horizontal axis, we find the members, or elements, of the domain. Similarly, if we move along the blue dashed lines from the points to the vertical axis, we find the elements of the range.

Functions are generally named using lowercase or uppercase letters. The function in the following example is named *f*.

EXAMPLE 3   For the function *f* represented below, determine each of the following.

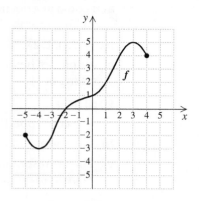

a) The member of the range that is paired with 2

b) The member of the domain that is paired with −3

SOLUTION

a) To determine what member of the range is paired with 2, first note that we are considering 2 in the domain. Thus we locate 2 on the horizontal axis. Next, we find the point directly above 2 on the graph of *f*. From that point, we can look to the vertical axis to find the corresponding *y*-coordinate, 4. Thus, 4 is the member of the range that is paired with 2.

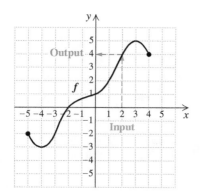

b) To determine what member of the domain is paired with −3, we note that we are considering −3 in the range. Thus we locate −3 on the vertical axis. From there we look at the graph of *f* to find any points for which −3 is the second coordinate. One such point exists, $(-4, -3)$. We observe that −4 is the only element of the domain paired with −3.

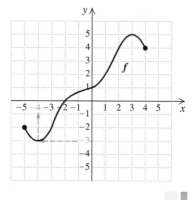

A closed dot on a graph, such as in Example 3, indicates that the point is part of the function. An open dot indicates that the point is *not* part of the function. (See Exercises 33 and 34 on p. 510.)

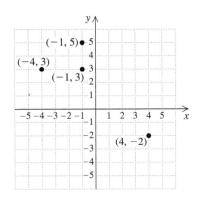

Recall that a function is a correspondence in which each member of the domain corresponds to *exactly* one member of the range. Thus the correspondence

$$\{(-1, 3), (4, -2), (-4, 3), (-1, 5)\}$$

is not a function because the member -1 of the domain corresponds to the members 3 and 5 of the range. Note on the graph at left that the point $(-1, 5)$ is directly above the point $(-1, 3)$.

Any time two points, such as $(-1, 3)$ and $(-1, 5)$, lie on the same vertical line, the graph containing those points cannot represent a function. This observation is the basis of the *vertical-line test*.

The Vertical-Line Test

If it is possible for a vertical line to cross a graph more than once, then the graph is not the graph of a function.

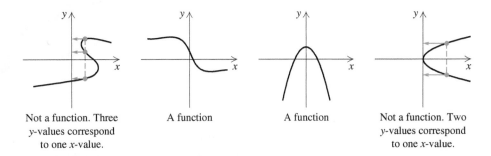

| Not a function. Three y-values correspond to one x-value. | A function | A function | Not a function. Two y-values correspond to one x-value. |

Function Notation and Equations

To understand function notation, it helps to imagine a "function machine." Think of putting a member of the domain (an *input*) into the machine. The machine is programmed to produce the appropriate member of the range (the *output*).

The function pictured has been named f. Here x represents an input, and $f(x)$ represents the corresponding output. In function notation, "$f(x)$" is read "f of x," or "f at x," or "the value of f at x." In Example 3(a), we showed that $f(2) = 4$, read "f of 2 equals 4."

CAUTION! $f(x)$ *does not* mean f times x.

Most functions are described by equations. For example, $f(x) = 2x + 3$ describes the function that takes an input x, multiplies it by 2, and then adds 3.

$$\underset{\text{Double}}{f(x) \quad = \quad \overset{\text{Input}}{2x} \quad \underset{\text{Add 3}}{+\ 3}}$$

To calculate the output $f(4)$, we take the input 4, double it, and add 3 to get 11. That is, we substitute 4 into the formula for $f(x)$:

$$f(4) = 2 \cdot 4 + 3$$
$$= 11.$$

Sometimes, in place of $f(x) = 2x + 3$, we write $y = 2x + 3$, where it is understood that the value of y, the *dependent variable*, depends on our choice of x, the *independent variable*. To understand why $f(x)$ notation is so useful, consider two equivalent statements:

a) If $f(x) = 2x + 3$, then $f(4) = 11$.

b) If $y = 2x + 3$, then the value of y is 11 when x is 4.

The notation used in part (a) is far more concise and emphasizes that x is the independent variable.

EXAMPLE **4**   Find each indicated function value.

a) $f(5)$, for $f(x) = 3x + 2$ **b)** $g(-2)$, for $g(r) = 5r^2 + 3r$
c) $h(4)$, for $h(x) = 11$ **d)** $F(a) + 1$, for $F(x) = 2x - 7$
e) $F(a + 1)$, for $F(x) = 2x - 7$

SOLUTION   Finding function values is much like evaluating an algebraic expression.

a) $f(5) = 3(5) + 2 = 17$

b) $g(-2) = 5(-2)^2 + 3(-2)$
      $= 5 \cdot 4 - 6 = 14$

c) For the function given by $h(x) = 11$, all inputs share the same output, 11. Therefore, $h(4) = 11$. The function h is an example of a *constant function*.

d) $F(a) + 1 = 2(a) - 7 + 1$ The input is a; $F(a) = 2a - 7$
      $= 2a - 6$

e) $F(a + 1) = 2(a + 1) - 7$ The input is $a + 1$.
      $= 2a + 2 - 7 = 2a - 5$

▶ TRY EXERCISE 41

STUDENT NOTES

In Example 4(e), it is important to note that the parentheses on the left are for function notation, whereas those on the right indicate multiplication.

Note that whether we write $f(x) = 3x + 2$, or $f(t) = 3t + 2$, or $f(\square) = 3\square + 2$, we still have $f(5) = 17$. The variable in the parentheses (the independent variable) is the variable used in the algebraic expression. The letter chosen for the independent variable is not as important as the algebraic manipulations to which it is subjected.

Applications

Function notation is often used in formulas. For example, to emphasize that the area A of a circle is a function of its radius r, instead of

$$A = \pi r^2,$$

we can write

$$A(r) = \pi r^2.$$

EXAMPLE 5 A typical adult dosage of an antihistamine is 24 mg. Young's rule for determining the dosage size $c(a)$ for a typical child of age a is

$$c(a) = \frac{24a}{a + 12}.^*$$

What should the dosage be for a typical 8-yr-old child?

SOLUTION We find $c(8)$:

$$c(8) = \frac{24(8)}{8 + 12} = \frac{192}{20} = 9.6.$$

The dosage for a typical 8-yr-old child is 9.6 mg.　　TRY EXERCISE 47

When a function is given as a graph, we can use the graph to estimate an unknown function value using known values.

EXAMPLE 6 *Elementary school math proficiency.* According to the National Assessment of Educational Progress (NAEP), the percentage of fourth-graders who are proficient in math has grown from 21% in 1996 to 24% in 2000 and 39% in 2007. Estimate the percentage of fourth-graders who showed proficiency in 2004 and predict the percentage who will demonstrate proficiency in 2011.

Source: nationsreportcard.gov

SOLUTION

1., 2. **Familiarize., Translate.** The given information enables us to plot and connect three points. We let the horizontal axis represent the year and the vertical axis the percentage of fourth-graders demonstrating mathematical proficiency. We label the function itself P.

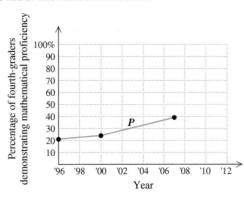

*Source: Olsen, June Looby, Leon J. Ablon, and Anthony Patrick Giangrasso, *Medical Dosage Calculations*, 6th ed.

3. Carry out.   To estimate the percentage of fourth-graders showing mathematical proficiency in 2004, we locate the point directly above the year 2004. We then estimate its second coordinate by moving horizontally from that point to the *y*-axis. Although our result is not exact, we see that $P(2004) \approx 33$.

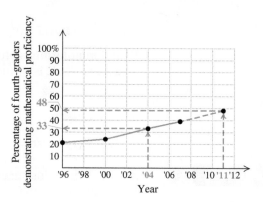

To predict the percentage of fourth-graders showing proficiency in 2011, we extend the graph and extrapolate. It appears that $P(2011) \approx 48$.

4. Check.   A precise check requires consulting an outside information source. Since 33% is between 24% and 39% and 48% is greater than 39%, our estimates seem plausible.

5. State.   In 2004, about 33% of all fourth-graders showed proficiency in math. By 2011, that figure is predicted to grow to 48%.

TRY EXERCISE ⟩ 59

8.1   EXERCISE SET

For Extra Help   MyMathLab   Math XL PRACTICE   WATCH   DOWNLOAD

🖎 *Concept Reinforcement   Complete each of the following sentences.*

1. A function is a special kind of _____ between two sets.

2. In any function, each member of the domain is paired with _____ one member of the range.

3. For any function, the set of all inputs, or first values, is called the _____.

4. For any function, the set of all outputs, or second values, is called the _____.

5. When a function is graphed, members of the domain are located on the _____ axis.

6. When a function is graphed, members of the range are located on the _____ axis.

7. The notation $f(3)$ is read _____.

8. The _____-line test can be used to determine whether or not a graph represents a function.

Determine whether each correspondence is a function.

9. a ⟶ 2
    b ↗
    d ⟶ 3
    g ⟶ 4
    h ↗

10. 2 ⟶ a
    ↘ b
    3 ⟶ d
    4 ⟶ g
    ↘ h

11.

Girl's age (in months)	Average daily weight gain (in grams)
2	21.8
9	11.7
16	8.5
23	7.0

Source: *American Family Physician*, December 1993, p. 1435

12.

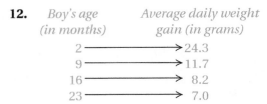

Boy's age (in months)	Average daily weight gain (in grams)
2	24.3
9	11.7
16	8.2
23	7.0

Source: *American Family Physician*, December 1993, p. 1435

13.

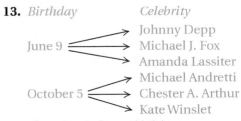

Birthday   *Celebrity*

June 9

October 5

Johnny Depp
Michael J. Fox
Amanda Lassiter
Michael Andretti
Chester A. Arthur
Kate Winslet

Source: www.leannesbirthdays.com

14.

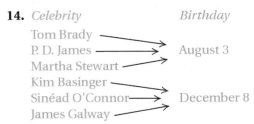

Celebrity   *Birthday*

Tom Brady
P. D. James
Martha Stewart
Kim Basinger
Sinéad O'Connor
James Galway

August 3

December 8

Source: www.leannesbirthdays.com

15.

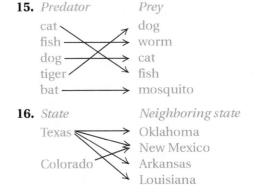

Predator   *Prey*

cat
fish
dog
tiger
bat

dog
worm
cat
fish
mosquito

16.

State   *Neighboring state*

Texas

Colorado

Oklahoma
New Mexico
Arkansas
Louisiana

Determine whether each of the following is a function. Identify any relations that are not functions.

Domain	**Correspondence**	*Range*
17. A pile of USB flash drives	The storage capacity of each flash drive	A set of storage capacities
18. The members of a rock band	An instrument the person can play	A set of instruments
19. The players on a team	The uniform number of each player	A set of numbers
20. A set of triangles	The area of each triangle	A set of numbers

*For each graph of a function, determine **(a)** f(1) and* **(b)** *any x-values for which f(x) = 2.*

21.

22.

23.

24.

25.

26.

27.

28.

29.

30.

31.

32.

33.

34.

Determine whether each of the following is the graph of a function.

35.

36.

37.

38.

39.

40.

Find the function values.

41. $g(x) = 2x + 5$

   a) $g(0)$ **b)** $g(-4)$ **c)** $g(-7)$
   d) $g(8)$ **e)** $g(a + 2)$ **f)** $g(a) + 2$

42. $h(x) = 5x - 1$

   a) $h(4)$ **b)** $h(8)$ **c)** $h(-3)$
   d) $h(-4)$ **e)** $h(a - 1)$ **f)** $h(a) + 3$

43. $f(n) = 5n^2 + 4n$

   a) $f(0)$ **b)** $f(-1)$ **c)** $f(3)$
   d) $f(t)$ **e)** $f(2a)$ **f)** $f(3) - 9$

44. $g(n) = 3n^2 - 2n$

   a) $g(0)$ **b)** $g(-1)$ **c)** $g(3)$
   d) $g(t)$ **e)** $g(2a)$ **f)** $g(3) - 4$

45. $f(x) = \dfrac{x - 3}{2x - 5}$

   a) $f(0)$ **b)** $f(4)$ **c)** $f(-1)$
   d) $f(3)$ **e)** $f(x + 2)$ **f)** $f(a + h)$

46. $r(x) = \dfrac{3x - 4}{2x + 5}$

   a) $r(0)$ **b)** $r(2)$ **c)** $r\left(\frac{4}{3}\right)$
   d) $r(-1)$ **e)** $r(x + 3)$ **f)** $r(a + h)$

The function A described by $A(s) = s^2 \dfrac{\sqrt{3}}{4}$ gives the area of an equilateral triangle with side s.

47. Find the area when a side measures 4 cm.

48. Find the area when a side measures 6 in.

The function V described by $V(r) = 4\pi r^2$ gives the surface area of a sphere with radius r.

49. Find the surface area when the radius is 3 in.

50. Find the surface area when the radius is 5 cm.

Archaeology. *The function H described by*

$$H(x) = 2.75x + 71.48$$

can be used to predict the height, in centimeters, of a woman whose humerus (the bone from the elbow to the shoulder) is x cm long. Predict the height of a woman whose humerus is the length given.

51. 34 cm   **52.** 31 cm

Chemistry.   *The function F described by*

$$F(C) = \frac{9}{5}C + 32$$

gives the Fahrenheit temperature corresponding to the Celsius temperature C.

53. Find the Fahrenheit temperature equivalent to −5° Celsius.

54. Find the Fahrenheit temperature equivalent to 10° Celsius.

Heart attacks and cholesterol.   *For Exercises 55 and 56, use the following graph, which shows the annual heart attack rate per 10,000 men as a function of blood cholesterol level.**

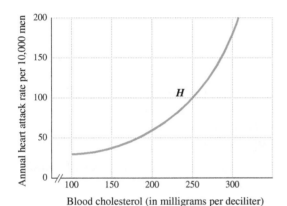

55. Approximate the annual heart attack rate for those men whose blood cholesterol level is 225 mg/dl. That is, find *H*(225).

56. Approximate the annual heart attack rate for those men whose blood cholesterol level is 275 mg/dl. That is, find *H*(275).

Films.   *For Exercises 57 and 58, use the following graph, which shows the number of movies released in the United States.*
Source: Nash Information Services

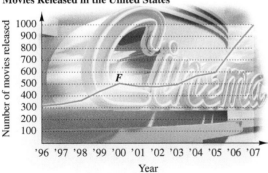

Movies Released in the United States

Year

---

*Copyright 1989, CSPI. Adapted from *Nutrition Action Health-letter* (1875 Connecticut Avenue, N.W., Suite 300, Washington, DC 20009-5728. $24 for 10 issues).

57. Approximate the number of movies released in 2000. That is, find *F*(2000).

58. Approximate the number of movies released in 2007. That is, find *F*(2007).

Energy-saving lightbulbs.   *An energy bill signed into law in 2007 requires the United States to phase out standard incandescent lightbulbs. A more efficient replacement is the compact fluorescent (CFL) bulb. The table below lists incandescent wattage and the CFL wattage required to create the same amount of light.*
Source: U.S. Department of Energy

Input, Incandescent wattage	Output, Wattage of CFL equivalent
25	5
60	15
100	25

59. Use the data in the figure above to draw a graph. Estimate the wattage of a CFL bulb that creates light equivalent to a 75-watt incandescent bulb. Then predict the wattage of a CFL bulb that creates light equivalent to a 120-watt incandescent bulb.

60. Use the graph from Exercise 59 to estimate the wattage of a CFL bulb that creates light equivalent to a 40-watt incandescent bulb. Then predict the wattage of a CFL bulb that creates light equivalent to a 150-watt incandescent bulb.

Blood alcohol level.   *The following table can be used to predict the number of drinks required for a person of a specified weight to be considered legally intoxicated (blood alcohol level of 0.08 or above). One 12-oz glass of beer, a 5-oz glass of wine, or a cocktail containing 1 oz of a distilled liquor all count as one drink. Assume that all drinks are consumed within one hour.*

12 oz   5 oz   1 oz

Input, Body Weight (in pounds)	Output, Number of Drinks
100	2.5
160	4
180	4.5
200	5

61. Use the data in the table above to draw a graph and to estimate the number of drinks that a 140-lb person would have to drink to be considered intoxicated. Then predict the number of drinks it would take for a 230-lb person to be considered intoxicated.

62. Use the graph from Exercise 61 to estimate the number of drinks that a 120-lb person would have to drink to be considered intoxicated. Then predict the number of drinks it would take for a 250-lb person to be considered intoxicated.

63. *Retailing.* Mountain View Gifts is experiencing constant growth. They recorded a total of $250,000 in sales in 2003 and $285,000 in 2008. Use a graph that displays the store's total sales as a function of time to estimate sales for 2004 and for 2011.

64. Use the graph in Exercise 63 to estimate sales for 2006 and for 2012.

Researchers at Yale University have suggested that the following graphs* may represent three different aspects of love.

Passion   Intimacy   Commitment

65. In what unit would you measure time if the horizontal length of each graph were ten units? Why?

66. Do you agree with the researchers that these graphs should be shaped as they are? Why or why not?

---

*From "A Triangular Theory of Love," by R. J. Sternberg, 1986, *Psychological Review*, **93**(2), 119–135. Copyright 1986 by the American Psychological Association, Inc. Reprinted by permission.

Skill Review

Review solving equations (Sections 2.2, 6.7, and 7.6).

Solve.

67. $2(x - 5) - 3 = 4 - (x - 1)$ [2.2]

68. $x^2 = 36$ [6.7]

69. $\dfrac{1}{x} = -2$ [7.6]

70. $\dfrac{1}{x} = x$ [7.6]

71. $(x - 2)(x + 3) = 6$ [6.7]

72. $\dfrac{1}{3}x + 2 = \dfrac{5}{4} + 3x$ [2.2]

73. $\dfrac{x + 1}{x} = 8$ [7.6]

74. $(x - 2)^2 = 36$ [6.7]

Synthesis

75. Jaylan is asked to write a function relating the number of fish in an aquarium to the amount of food needed for the fish. Which quantity should he choose as the independent variable? Why?

76. Explain in your own words why every function is a relation, but not every relation is a function.

For Exercises 77 and 78, let $f(x) = 3x^2 - 1$ and $g(x) = 2x + 5$.

77. Find $f(g(-4))$ and $g(f(-4))$.

78. Find $f(g(-1))$ and $g(f(-1))$.

79. If f represents the function in Exercise 15, find $f(f(f(f(\text{tiger}))))$.

Pregnancy. *For Exercises 80–83, use the following graph of a woman's "stress test." This graph shows the size of a pregnant woman's contractions as a function of time.*

Stress test

80. How large is the largest contraction that occurred during the test?

81. At what time during the test did the largest contraction occur?

82. On the basis of the information provided, how large a contraction would you expect 60 seconds after the end of the test? Why?

83. What is the frequency of the largest contraction?

84. Suppose that a function g is such that $g(-1) = -7$ and $g(3) = 8$. Find a formula for g if $g(x)$ is of the form $g(x) = mx + b$, where m and b are constants.

85. The *greatest integer function* $f(x) = [\![x]\!]$ is defined as follows: $[\![x]\!]$ is the greatest integer that is less than or equal to x. For example, if $x = 3.74$, then $[\![x]\!] = 3$; and if $x = -0.98$, then $[\![x]\!] = -1$. Graph the greatest integer function for $-5 \le x \le 5$. (The notation $f(x) = \text{INT}(x)$ is used in many graphing calculators and computer programs.)

86. *Energy expenditure.* On the basis of the information given below, what burns more energy: walking $4\frac{1}{2}$ mph for two hours or bicycling 14 mph for one hour?

Approximate Energy Expenditure by a 150-Pound Person in Various Activities

Activity	Calories per Hour
Walking, $2\frac{1}{2}$ mph	210
Bicycling, $5\frac{1}{2}$ mph	210
Walking, $3\frac{3}{4}$ mph	300
Bicycling, 13 mph	660

Source: Based on material prepared by Robert E. Johnson, M.D., Ph.D., and colleagues, University of Illinois.

8.2   Domain and Range

Determining the Domain and the Range ■ Restrictions on Domain ■ Functions Defined Piecewise

In Section 8.1, we saw that a function is a correspondence from a set called the *domain* to a set called the *range*. In this section, we look more closely at the concepts of domain and range.

Determining the Domain and the Range

When a function is given as a set of ordered pairs, the domain is the set of all first coordinates and the range is the set of all second coordinates.

EXAMPLE 1   Find the domain and the range for the function f given by

$$f = \{(2, 0), (-1, 5), (8, 0), (-3, 2)\}.$$

SOLUTION   The first coordinates are $2, -1, 8$, and -3. The second coordinates are $0, 5$, and 2. Thus we have

Domain of $f = \{2, -1, 8, -3\}$ and
Range of $f = \{0, 5, 2\}$.

TRY EXERCISE 7

We can also determine the domain and the range of a function from its graph.

EXAMPLE 2

Find the domain and the range of the function *f* below.

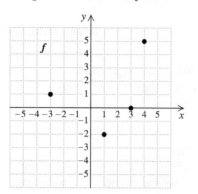

SOLUTION Here *f* can be written $\{(-3, 1), (1, -2), (3, 0), (4, 5)\}$. The domain is the set of all first coordinates, $\{-3, 1, 3, 4\}$, and the range is the set of all second coordinates, $\{1, -2, 0, 5\}$.

TRY EXERCISE 11

In Example 2, we could also have found the domain and the range directly, without first writing *f*, by observing the *x*- and *y*-values used in the graph.

EXAMPLE 3

Find the domain and the range of the function *f* shown here.

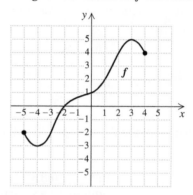

SOLUTION The domain of the function is the set of all *x*-values that are used in the points on the curve. Because there are no breaks in the graph of *f*, these extend continuously from −5 to 4 and can be viewed as the curve's shadow, or *projection*, on the *x*-axis. Thus the domain is $\{x \mid -5 \le x \le 4\}$, or $[-5, 4]$, shown below left.

The range of the function is the set of all *y*-values that are used in the points on the curve. These extend continuously from −3 to 5, and can be viewed as the curve's projection on the *y*-axis. Thus the range is $\{y \mid -3 \le y \le 5\}$, or $[-3, 5]$, shown below right.

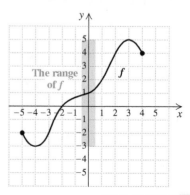

TRY EXERCISE 15

In Example 3, the *endpoints* $(-5, -2)$ and $(4, 4)$ emphasize that the function is not defined for values of x less than -5 or greater than 4.

The graphs of some functions have no endpoints. Thus a function may have a domain and/or a range that extends without bound toward positive infinity or negative infinity.

EXAMPLE 4   For the function g represented below, determine **(a)** the domain of g and **(b)** the range of g.

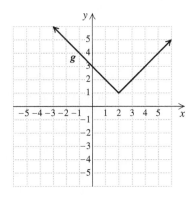

SOLUTION

a) The domain of g is the set of all x-values that are used in the points on the curve. The arrows on the ends of the graph indicate that it extends both left and right without end. Thus the shadow, or projection, of the graph on the x-axis is the entire x-axis. (See the graph on the left below.) The domain is $\{x \mid x \text{ is a real number}\}$, or $(-\infty, \infty)$.

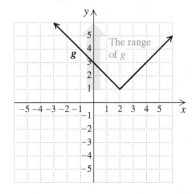

b) The range of g is the set of all y-values that are used in the points on the curve. The arrows on the ends of the graph indicate that it extends up without end. Thus the projection of the graph on the y-axis is the portion of the y-axis greater than or equal to 1. (See the graph on the right above.) The range is $\{y \mid y \geq 1\}$, or $[1, \infty)$.

TRY EXERCISE ▶ 25

The set of all real numbers is often abbreviated $\mathbb{R}$. Thus, in Example 4, we could write

Domain of $f = \mathbb{R}$.

EXAMPLE **5**   Find the domain and the range of the function f shown here.

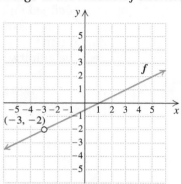

SOLUTION   The domain of f is the set of all x-values that are used in points on the curve. The open dot in the graph at $(-3, -2)$ indicates that there is no y-value that corresponds to $x = -3$; that is, the function is not defined for $x = -3$. Thus, -3 is not in the domain of the function, and

$$\text{Domain of } f = \{x \mid x \text{ is a real number } and \ x \neq -3\}.$$

There is no function value at $(-3, -2)$, so -2 is not in the range of the function. Thus we have

$$\text{Range of } f = \{y \mid y \text{ is a real number } and \ y \neq -2\}.$$ **TRY EXERCISE** 27

When a function is described by an equation, we assume that the domain is the set of all real numbers for which function values can be calculated. If an x-value is not in the domain of a function, the graph of the function will not include any point above or below that x-value.

EXAMPLE **6**   For each equation, determine the domain of f.

a) $f(x) = |x|$ **b)** $f(x) = \dfrac{7}{2x - 6}$ **c)** $f(t) = \dfrac{t + 1}{t^2 - 4}$

SOLUTION

a) We ask ourselves, "Is there any number x for which we cannot compute $|x|$?" Since we can find the absolute value of *any* number, the answer is no. Thus the domain of f is $\mathbb{R}$, the set of all real numbers.

b) Is there any number x for which $\dfrac{7}{2x - 6}$ cannot be computed? Since $\dfrac{7}{2x - 6}$ cannot be computed when $2x - 6$ is 0, the answer is yes. To determine what x-value causes the denominator to be 0, we solve an equation:

$2x - 6 = 0$	Setting the denominator equal to 0
$2x = 6$	Adding 6 to both sides
$x = 3.$	Dividing both sides by 2

Thus, 3 is *not* in the domain of f, whereas all other real numbers are. The domain of f is $\{x \mid x \text{ is a real number } and \ x \neq 3\}$.

c) The expression $\dfrac{t + 1}{t^2 - 4}$ is undefined when $t^2 - 4 = 0$:

$t^2 - 4 = 0$	Setting the denominator equal to 0
$(t + 2)(t - 2) = 0$	Factoring
$t + 2 = 0 \quad or \quad t - 2 = 0$	Using the principle of zero products
$t = -2 \quad or \quad t = 2.$	Solving; these are the values for which $(t + 1)/(t^2 - 4)$ is undefined.

Thus we have

Domain of $f = \{t \mid t$ is a real number $and\ t \neq -2\ and\ t \neq 2\}$.

Note that when the numerator, $t + 1$, is zero, the function value is 0 and *is* defined.

TRY EXERCISE 31

Restrictions on Domain

If a function is used as a model for an application, the problem situation may require restrictions on the domain; for example, length and time are generally nonnegative, and a person's age does not increase indefinitely.

EXAMPLE 7

Prize tee shirts. During intermission at sporting events, it has become common for team mascots to use a powerful slingshot to launch tightly rolled tee shirts into the stands. The height $h(t)$, in feet, of an airborne tee shirt t seconds after being launched can be approximated by

$$h(t) = -15t^2 + 70t + 25.$$

What is the domain of the function?

SOLUTION The expression $-15t^2 + 70t + 25$ can be evaluated for any number t, so any restrictions on the domain will come from the problem situation.

First, we note that t cannot be negative, since it represents time from launch, so we have $t \geq 0$. If we make a drawing, we also note that the function will not be defined for values of t that make the height negative.

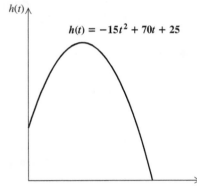

$h(t) = -15t^2 + 70t + 25$

Thus an upper limit for t will be the positive value of t for which $h(t) = 0$. Solving, we obtain

$$h(t) = 0$$
$$-15t^2 + 70t + 25 = 0 \qquad \text{Substituting}$$
$$\left.\begin{array}{r}-5(3t^2 - 14t - 5) = 0 \\ -5(3t + 1)(t - 5) = 0\end{array}\right\} \qquad \text{Factoring}$$
$$3t + 1 = 0 \quad or \quad t - 5 = 0 \qquad \text{Using the principle of zero products}$$
$$\left.\begin{array}{r}3t = -1 \quad or \quad t = 5 \\ t = -\dfrac{1}{3} \quad or \quad t = 5.\end{array}\right\} \qquad \text{Solving for } t$$

We already know that $-\frac{1}{3}$ is not in the domain of the function because of the restriction $t \geq 0$ above.

The tee shirt will hit the ground after 5 sec, so we have $t \leq 5$. Putting the two restrictions together, we have $t \geq 0\ and\ t \leq 5$, so the

Domain of $h = \{t \mid t$ is a real number $and\ 0 \leq t \leq 5\}$, or $[0, 5]$.

TRY EXERCISE 45

If the domain of a function is not specifically listed, it can be determined from a table, a graph, an equation, or an application.

Domain of a Function

The domain of a function $f(x)$ is the set of all inputs x.

- If the correspondence is listed in a table or as a set of ordered pairs, the domain is the set of all first coordinates.
- If the function is described by a graph, the domain is the set of all x-coordinates of the points on the graph.
- If the function is described by an equation, the domain is the set of all numbers for which the value can be calculated.
- If the function is used in an application, the domain is the set of all numbers that make sense in the problem.

Functions Defined Piecewise

Piecewise-defined functions are described by different equations for various parts of their domains. For example, the function $f(x) = |x|$ is described by

$$f(x) = \begin{cases} x, & \text{if } x \geq 0, \\ -x, & \text{if } x < 0. \end{cases}$$

To evaluate a piecewise-defined function for an input a, we first determine what part of the domain a belongs to. Then we use the formula corresponding to that part of the domain.

EXAMPLE 8   Find each function value for the function f given by

$$f(x) = |x| = \begin{cases} x, & \text{if } x \geq 0, \\ -x, & \text{if } x < 0. \end{cases}$$

a) $f(4)$ **b)** $f(-10)$

SOLUTION

a) Since $4 \geq 0$, we use the equation $f(x) = x$. Thus, $f(4) = 4$.

b) Since $-10 < 0$, we use the equation $f(x) = -x$. Thus, $f(-10) = -(-10) = 10$.

> TRY EXERCISE 53

EXAMPLE 9   Find each function value for the function g given by

$$g(x) = \begin{cases} x + 2, & \text{if } x \leq -2, \\ x^2, & \text{if } -2 < x \leq 5, \\ 3x, & \text{if } x > 5. \end{cases}$$

a) $g(-2)$ **b)** $g(3)$ **c)** $g(10)$

SOLUTION

a) Since $-2 \leq -2$, we use the first equation, $g(x) = x + 2$:

$$g(-2) = -2 + 2 = 0.$$

b) Since $-2 < 3 \leq 5$, we use the second equation, $g(x) = x^2$:

$$g(3) = 3^2 = 9.$$

c) Since $10 > 5$, we use the last equation, $g(x) = 3x$:

$$g(10) = 3 \cdot 10 = 30.$$

> TRY EXERCISE 55

8.2 EXERCISE SET

For Extra Help
MyMathLab
PRACTICE   WATCH   DOWNLOAD

Concept Reinforcement *For Exercises 1–6, use the function f given by*

$$f(x) = \begin{cases} x - 5, & \text{if } x < -6, \\ 2x^2, & \text{if } -6 \le x < -1, \\ |x|, & \text{if } -1 \le x < 10, \\ 3x + 1, & \text{if } x \ge 10. \end{cases}$$

Write the letter of the equation that should be used to find each function value. Letters may be used more than once or not at all.

1. ___ $f(0)$
2. ___ $f(15)$
3. ___ $f(10)$
4. ___ $f(-6)$
5. ___ $f(-1)$
6. ___ $f(-3)$

a) $f(x) = x - 5$
b) $f(x) = 2x^2$
c) $f(x) = |x|$
d) $f(x) = 3x + 1$

Find the domain and the range for each function given.

7. $f = \{(2, 8), (9, 3), (-2, 10), (-4, 4)\}$

8. $g = \{(1, 2), (2, 3), (3, 4), (4, 5)\}$

9. $g = \{(0, 0), (4, -2), (-5, 0), (-1, -2)\}$

10. $f = \{(3, 7), (2, 7), (1, 7), (0, 7)\}$

For each graph of a function f, determine the domain and the range of f.

11.

12.

13.

14.

15.

16.

17.

18.

19.

20.

21.

22.

23.

24.

25.

26.

27.

28.

29.

30.

Find the domain of f.

31. $f(x) = \dfrac{5}{x - 3}$

32. $f(x) = \dfrac{7}{6 - x}$

33. $f(x) = \dfrac{x}{2x - 1}$

34. $f(x) = \dfrac{2x}{4x + 3}$

35. $f(x) = 2x + 1$

36. $f(x) = x^2 + 3$

37. $f(x) = |5 - x|$

38. $f(x) = |3x - 4|$

39. $f(x) = \dfrac{5}{x^2 - 9}$

40. $f(x) = \dfrac{x}{x^2 - 2x + 1}$

41. $f(x) = x^2 - 9$

42. $f(x) = x^2 - 2x + 1$

43. $f(x) = \dfrac{2x - 7}{x^2 + 8x + 7}$

44. $f(x) = \dfrac{x + 5}{2x^2 - x - 3}$

45. *Records in the 400-m run.* The record R for the 400-m run t years after 1930 is given by

$$R(t) = 46.8 - 0.075t.$$

What is the domain of the function?

46. *Records in the 1500-m run.* The record R for the 1500-m run t years after 1930 is given by

$$R(t) = 3.85 - 0.0075t.$$

What is the domain of the function?

47. *Consumer demand.* The amount A of coffee that consumers are willing to buy at price p is given by

$$A(p) = -2.5p + 26.5.$$

What is the domain of the function?

48. *Seller's supply.* The amount A of coffee that suppliers are willing to supply at price p is given by

$$A(p) = 2p - 11.$$

What is the domain of the function?

49. *Pressure at sea depth.* The pressure P, in atmospheres, at a depth d feet beneath the surface of the ocean is given by

$$P(d) = 0.03d + 1.$$

What is the domain of the function?

50. *Perimeter.* The perimeter P of an equilateral triangle with sides of length s is given by

$$P(s) = 3s.$$

What is the domain of the function?

51. *Fireworks displays.* The height h, in feet, of a "weeping willow" fireworks display, t seconds after having been launched from an 80-ft high rooftop, is given by

$$h(t) = -16t^2 + 64t + 80.$$

What is the domain of the function?

52. *Safety flares.* The height h, in feet, of a safety flare, t seconds after having been launched from a height of 224 ft, is given by

$$h(t) = -16t^2 + 80t + 224.$$

What is the domain of the function?

Find the indicated function values for each function.

53. $f(x) = \begin{cases} x, & \text{if } x < 0, \\ 2x + 1, & \text{if } x \geq 0 \end{cases}$

a) $f(-5)$ **b)** $f(0)$ **c)** $f(10)$

54. $g(x) = \begin{cases} x - 5, & \text{if } x \leq 5, \\ 3x, & \text{if } x > 5 \end{cases}$

a) $g(0)$ **b)** $g(5)$ **c)** $g(6)$

55. $G(x) = \begin{cases} x - 5, & \text{if } x < -1, \\ x, & \text{if } -1 \leq x \leq 2, \\ x + 2, & \text{if } x > 2 \end{cases}$

a) $G(0)$ **b)** $G(2)$ **c)** $G(5)$

56. $F(x) = \begin{cases} 2x, & \text{if } x \leq 0, \\ x, & \text{if } 0 < x \leq 3, \\ -5x, & \text{if } x > 3 \end{cases}$

a) $F(-1)$ **b)** $F(3)$ **c)** $F(10)$

57. $f(x) = \begin{cases} x^2 - 10, & \text{if } x < -10, \\ x^2, & \text{if } -10 \le x \le 10, \\ x^2 + 10, & \text{if } x > 10 \end{cases}$

    a) $f(-10)$ **b)** $f(10)$ **c)** $f(11)$

58. $f(x) = \begin{cases} 2x^2 - 3, & \text{if } x < 2, \\ x^2, & \text{if } 2 \le x \le 4, \\ 5x - 7, & \text{if } x > 4 \end{cases}$

    a) $f(0)$ **b)** $f(3)$ **c)** $f(6)$

59. Explain why the domain of the function given by $f(x) = \dfrac{x + 3}{2}$ is $\mathbb{R}$, but the domain of the function given by $g(x) = \dfrac{2}{x + 3}$ is not $\mathbb{R}$.

60. Chloe asserts that for a function described by a set of ordered pairs, the range of the function will always have the same number of elements as there are ordered pairs. Is she correct? Why or why not?

Skill Review

To prepare for Section 8.3, review graphs of linear equations (Section 3.6).

Graph. [3.6]

61. $y = 2x - 3$ **62.** $y = x + 5$

Find the slope and the y-intercept of each line. [3.6]

63. $y = \dfrac{2}{3}x - 4$ **64.** $y = -\dfrac{1}{4}x + 6$

65. $y = \dfrac{4}{3}x$ **66.** $y = -5x$

Synthesis

67. Ramiro states that $f(x) = \dfrac{x^2}{x}$ and $g(x) = x$ represent the same function. Is he correct? Why or why not?

68. Explain why the domain of a function can be viewed as the projection of its graph on the x-axis.

Sketch the graph of a function for which the domain and range are as given. Graphs may vary.

69. Domain: $\mathbb{R}$; range: $\mathbb{R}$

70. Domain: $\{3, 1, 4\}$; range: $\{0, 5\}$

71. Domain: $\{x \mid 1 \le x \le 5\}$; range: $\{y \mid 0 \le y \le 2\}$

72. Domain: $\{x \mid x \text{ is a real number } and \ x \ne 1\}$; range: $\{y \mid y \text{ is a real number } and \ y \ne -2\}$

For each graph of a function f, determine the domain and the range of f.

73.

74.

75.

76.

Graph each function on a graphing calculator and estimate its domain and range from the graph.

77. $f(x) = |x - 3|$ **78.** $f(x) = |x| - 3$

79. $f(x) = \dfrac{3}{x - 2}$ **80.** $f(x) = \dfrac{-1}{x + 3}$

81. Use a graphing calculator to estimate the range of the function in Exercise 51.

82. Use a graphing calculator to estimate the range of the function in Exercise 52.

83.–88. *For Exercises 83–88, graph the functions given in each of Exercises 53–58, respectively.*

89. A graphing calculator will interpret an expression like $x \ge 1$ as true or false, depending on the value of x. If the expression is true, the graphing calculator assigns a value of 1 to the expression. If the expression is false, the graphing calculator assigns a value of 0. To graph a piecewise-defined function using a graphing calculator, multiply each part of the definition by its domain, using the TEST menu to enter the inequality symbol. Thus the function in Exercise 53 is entered as $y_1 = x(x < 0) + (2x + 1)(x \ge 0)$. Use a graphing calculator in DOT mode to check your answers to Exercises 83–88.

8.3   Graphs of Functions

Linear Functions   ■   Nonlinear Functions

A function can be classified both by the type of equation that is used and by the type of graph it represents. In this section, we will graph a variety of functions that are described by different equations.

Linear Functions

In Chapter 3, we graphed *linear equations*. Here we review such graphs and determine which types of linear graphs represent functions.

Any linear equation can be written in *standard form* $Ax + By = C$. If $B \neq 0$, the equation can also be written in *slope–intercept form*. The *point–slope form* is often used to write equations.

> **Equations of Lines**
>
> | | |
> |---|---|
> | Standard form: | $Ax + By = C$ |
> | Slope–intercept form: | $y = mx + b$ |
> | Point–slope form: | $y - y_1 = m(x - x_1)$ |

Two points determine a line. If we know that an equation is linear, we can graph the equation by plotting two points that are on the line and drawing the line that goes through those points.

When an equation is written in slope–intercept form $y = mx + b$, the slope of the line is m and the y-intercept is $(0, b)$. Knowing the y-intercept gives us one point on the line, and we can use the slope to determine another point.

EXAMPLE   1   Graph: $4y = -3x + 8$.

SOLUTION   To graph $4y = -3x + 8$, we first rewrite it in slope–intercept form:

$$4y = -3x + 8$$
$$y = \tfrac{1}{4}(-3x + 8) \qquad \text{Multiplying both sides by } \tfrac{1}{4}$$
$$y = -\tfrac{3}{4}x + 2. \qquad \text{Using the distributive law}$$

The slope is $-\tfrac{3}{4}$ and the y-intercept is $(0, 2)$. We plot $(0, 2)$ and think of the slope as either $\tfrac{-3}{4}$ or $\tfrac{3}{-4}$. Using the form $\tfrac{-3}{4}$, we start at $(0, 2)$ and move *down* 3 units (since the numerator is *negative*) and *to the right* 4 units (since the denominator is *positive*). We plot the new point, $(4, -1)$.

Alternatively, we can think of the slope as $\tfrac{3}{-4}$. Starting at $(0, 2)$, we move *up* 3 units (since the numerator is *positive*) and *to the left* 4 units (since the denominator is *negative*). This leads to another point on the graph, $(-4, 5)$. Using the points found, we draw and label the graph at left.   TRY EXERCISE   7

The graphs of equations of the form $y = b$ are horizontal lines with a slope of 0, and the graphs of equations of the form $x = a$ are vertical lines. The slope of a vertical line is undefined.

We can use the vertical-line test to determine which types of linear graphs represent functions. Consider the following graphs.

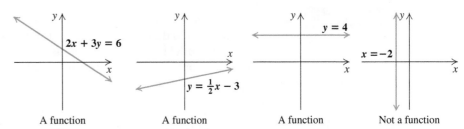

| A function | A function | A function | Not a function |

Any vertical line that passes through the graphs of $2x + 3y = 6$, $y = \frac{1}{2}x - 3$, and $y = 4$ will cross the graph only once. However, the vertical line through the point $(-2, 0)$ will cross the graph of $x = -2$ at *every* point. In general, *any* straight line that is not vertical is the graph of a function. A **linear function** is a function described by any linear equation whose graph is not vertical. A horizontal line represents a **constant function**.

> ## Linear Function
>
> A function described by an equation of the form $f(x) = mx + b$ is a *linear function*. Its graph is a straight line with slope m and y-intercept $(0, b)$.
>
> When $m = 0$, the function described by $f(x) = b$ is called a *constant function*. Its graph is a horizontal line through $(0, b)$.

EXAMPLE   2

Graph: $f(x) = 3x + 2$.

SOLUTION   The notations

$$f(x) = 3x + 2 \quad \text{and} \quad y = 3x + 2$$

are often used interchangeably. The function notation emphasizes that the second coordinate in each ordered pair is determined by the first coordinate of that pair.

We graph $f(x) = 3x + 2$ in the same way that we would graph $y = 3x + 2$. The vertical axis can be labeled y or $f(x)$. We could use a table of values or, since this is a linear function, use the slope and the y-intercept to graph the function.

Since $f(x) = 3x + 2$ is in the form $f(x) = mx + b$, we can tell from the equation that the slope is 3, or $\frac{3}{1}$, and the y-intercept is $(0, 2)$. We plot $(0, 2)$ and go *up* 3 units and *to the right* 1 unit to determine another point on the line, $(1, 5)$. After we have sketched the line, a third point can be calculated as a check.

TRY EXERCISE   19

EXAMPLE   3

Graph: $f(x) = -3$.

SOLUTION   This is a constant function. For every input x, the output is -3. The graph is a horizontal line.

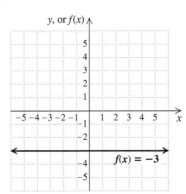

TRY EXERCISE   23

Linear functions are common in today's world.

EXAMPLE 4

Cell-phone costs. In 2008, an Apple iPhone cost $400. AT&T offered a plan including 450 daytime minutes a month for $60 per month. Formulate a mathematical model for the cost. Then use the model to estimate the number of months required for the total cost to reach $700.

Source: www.apple.com

SOLUTION

1. **Familiarize.** For this plan, a monthly fee is charged after an initial purchase has been made. After 1 month of service, the total cost will be $400 + $60 = $460. After 2 months, the total cost will be $400 + $60 · 2 = $520. We can write a general model if we let $C(t)$ represent the total cost, in dollars, for t months of service.

2. **Translate.** We reword and translate as follows:

where $t \geq 0$ (since there cannot be a negative number of months).

3. **Carry out.** To determine the time required for the total cost to reach $700, we substitute 700 for $C(t)$ and solve for t:

$$C(t) = 400 + 60t$$
$$700 = 400 + 60t \qquad \text{Substituting}$$
$$300 = 60t \qquad \text{Subtracting 400 from both sides}$$
$$5 = t. \qquad \text{Dividing both sides by 60}$$

4. **Check.** We evaluate:

$$C(5) = 60 \cdot 5 + 400 = 300 + 400 = 700.$$

5. **State.** It takes 5 months for the total cost to reach $700..   **TRY EXERCISE** 25

Since $f(x) = mx + b$ can be evaluated for any choice of x, the domain of all linear functions is $\mathbb{R}$, the set of all real numbers.

The second coordinate of every ordered pair in a constant function $f(x) = b$ is the number b. The range of a constant function thus consists of one number, b. For a nonconstant linear function, the graph extends indefinitely both up and down, so the range is the set of all real numbers, or $\mathbb{R}$.

Domain and Range of a Linear Function

The domain of any linear function $f(x) = mx + b$ is

$$\{x \mid x \text{ is a real number}\}, \text{ or } \mathbb{R}.$$

The range of any linear function $f(x) = mx + b$, $m \neq 0$, is

$$\{y \mid y \text{ is a real number}\}, \text{ or } \mathbb{R}.$$

The range of any constant function $f(x) = b$ is $\{b\}$.

EXAMPLE 5

Determine the domain and the range of each of the following functions.

a) f, where $f(x) = 2x - 10$ **b)** g, where $g(x) = 4$

SOLUTION

a) Since $f(x) = 2x - 10$ describes a linear function, but not a constant function,

Domain of $f = \mathbb{R}$ and

Range of $f = \mathbb{R}$.

b) The function described by $g(x) = 4$ is a constant function. Thus,

Domain of $g = \mathbb{R}$ and

Range of $g = \{4\}$.

TRY EXERCISE   41

The graphs of nonlinear functions can get quite complex. We will now define several types of nonlinear functions and discuss some of their characteristics. The detailed study of their graphs appears later in this text or in other courses.

Nonlinear Functions

A function for which the graph is not a straight line is a **nonlinear function**. Some important types of nonlinear functions are listed below.

Type of function	*Example*
Absolute-value function	$f(x) = \lvert x \rvert$
Polynomial function	$p(x) = x^3 - 4x^2 + 1$
Quadratic function	$q(x) = x^2 + 5x + 2$
Rational function	$r(x) = \dfrac{x + 1}{x - 2}$

Note that linear and quadratic functions are special kinds of polynomial functions.

EXAMPLE   6   State whether each equation describes a linear function, an absolute-value function, a general polynomial function, a quadratic function, or a rational function.

a) $f(x) = x^2 - 9$ b) $g(x) = \dfrac{3}{x}$

c) $h(x) = \dfrac{1}{4}x - 16$ d) $v(x) = 4x^4 - 13$

SOLUTION

a) Since f is described by a polynomial equation of degree 2, f is a *quadratic function.*

b) Since g is described by a rational equation, g is a *rational function.*

c) The function h is described by a linear equation, so h is a *linear function.* Note that although $\frac{1}{4}$ is a fraction, there are no variables in a denominator.

d) Since v is described by a polynomial equation, v is a *polynomial function.*

Since the graphs of nonlinear functions are not straight lines, we usually need to calculate more than two or three points to determine the shape of the graph.

EXAMPLE   7   Graph the function given by $f(x) = \lvert x \rvert$, and determine the domain and the range of f.

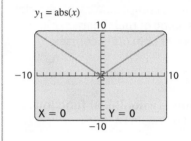
SOLUTION We calculate function values for several choices of x and list the results in a table.

$$f(0) = |0| = 0,$$
$$f(1) = |1| = 1,$$
$$f(2) = |2| = 2,$$
$$f(-1) = |-1| = 1,$$
$$f(-2) = |-2| = 2$$

x	$f(x) = |x|$	$(x, f(x))$
0	0	$(0, 0)$
1	1	$(1, 1)$
2	2	$(2, 2)$
-1	1	$(-1, 1)$
-2	2	$(-2, 2)$

When we plot these points, we observe a pattern. The value of the function is 0 when x is 0. Function values increase both as x increases from 0 and as x decreases from 0. The graph of f is V-shaped, with the "point" of the V at the origin.

Because we can find the absolute value of any real number, we have

Domain of $f = \mathbb{R}$, or $(-\infty, \infty)$.

Because the absolute value of a number is never negative, we have

Range of $f = \{y | y \geq 0\}$, or $[0, \infty)$.

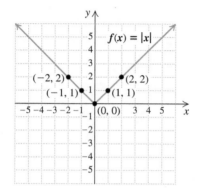

TRY EXERCISE 65

Graphs of *polynomial functions* generally become more complex as the degree of the polynomial increases. We will study in greater detail the graphs of *quadratic functions*, or functions of the form

$$q(x) = ax^2 + bx + c, a \neq 0.$$

Since a polynomial can be evaluated for any real number, the domain of a polynomial is the set of all real numbers.

A *rational function* contains a variable in a denominator; thus its domain may be restricted. Division by zero is undefined, so any values of the variable that make a denominator 0 are not in the domain of the function.

EXAMPLE 8   Determine the domain of f.

a) $f(x) = x^3 + 5x^2 - 4x + 1$ **b)** $f(x) = \dfrac{x^2 - 4}{x + 2}$

SOLUTION

a) $f(x) = x^3 + 5x^2 - 4x + 1$ describes a polynomial function. The domain of any polynomial function is $\mathbb{R}$, so the domain of f is $\mathbb{R}$.

b) $f(x) = \dfrac{x^2 - 4}{x + 2}$ describes a rational function. Note that $f(x)$ is undefined for $x + 2 = 0$, or, equivalently, for $x = -2$. Thus the domain of $f = \{x | x \text{ is a real number and } x \neq -2\}$.

TRY EXERCISE 43

Visualizing for Success

A

B

C

D

E

Match each equation or function with its graph.

1. $f(x) = x$

2. $f(x) = |x|$

3. $f(x) = x^2$

4. $f(x) = 3$

5. $x = 3$

6. $f(x) = x + 3$

7. $f(x) = x - 3$

8. $f(x) = 2x$

9. $f(x) = -2x$

10. $f(x) = \dfrac{1}{x}$

Answers on page A-30

An alternate, animated version of this activity appears in MyMathLab. To use MyMathLab, you need a course ID and a student access code. Contact your instructor for more information.

F

G

H

I

J

↬ *Concept Reinforcement* *Answer true or false.*

1. The vertical-line test states that a graph is not that of a function if it contains a vertical line.

2. The graph of a constant function is a horizontal line.

3. The domain of a constant function consists of a single element.

4. The domain of a linear function is the set of all real numbers.

5. Linear functions are typically written in slope–intercept form.

6. Rational functions may have some restrictions on their domains.

Graph.

7. $y = 2x - 1$ **8.** $y = \frac{1}{3}x + 2$

9. $y = -\frac{2}{3}x + 3$ **10.** $y = -4x - 2$

11. $3y = 6 - 4x$ **12.** $5y = 2x - 15$

13. $x - y = 4$ **14.** $x + y = 3$

15. $y = -2$ **16.** $y = 3$

17. $x = 4$ **18.** $x = -1$

19. $f(x) = x + 3$ **20.** $f(x) = 2 - x$

21. $f(x) = \frac{3}{4}x + 1$ **22.** $f(x) = 3x + 2$

23. $g(x) = 4$ **24.** $g(x) = -5$

25. *Truck rentals.* Titanium Trucks charges $30 for a one-day truck rental, plus $0.75 per mile. Formulate a linear function to model the cost $C(d)$ of a one-day rental driven d miles, and determine the number of miles driven if the total cost is $75.

26. *Taxis.* A taxi ride in New York City costs $2.50 plus $2.00 per mile.* Formulate a linear function to model the cost $C(d)$ of a d-mile taxi ride, and determine the length of a ride that cost $23.50.

27. *Hair growth.* Lauren had her hair cut to a length of 5 inches in order to donate the hair to Locks of Love. Her hair then grew at a rate of $\frac{1}{2}$ inch per month. Formulate a linear function to model the length $L(t)$

---

*Rates are higher between 4 P.M. and 8 P.M. (Source: Based on data from New York City Taxi and Limousine Commission, 2007)

of Lauren's hair t months after she had the haircut, and determine when her hair will be 15 inches long.

28. *Landscaping.* On Saturday, Shelby Lawncare cut the lawn at Great Harrington Community College to a height of 2 in. Since then, the grass has grown at a rate of $\frac{1}{8}$ in. per day. Formulate a linear function to model the length $L(t)$ of the lawn t days after having been cut, and determine when the grass will be $3\frac{1}{2}$ in. high.

29. *Organic cotton.* In 2006, 5960 acres in the U.S. were planted with organic cotton. This number is increasing by 849 acres each year. Formulate a linear function to model the number of acres of organic cotton $A(t)$ that is planted t years after 2006, and determine when 10,205 acres of organic cotton will be planted.
Source: Based on data from the Organic Trade Association

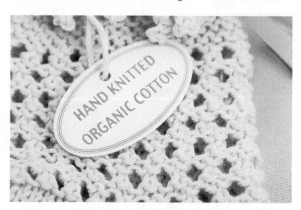

30. *Catering.* Chrissie's Catering charges a setup fee of $75 plus $25 a person for catering a party. Formulate a linear function to model the cost $C(x)$ for a party for x people, and determine the number of people at a party if the cost was $775.

In Exercises 31–40, assume that a constant rate of change exists for each model formed.

31. *Automobile production.* As demand has grown, worldwide production of small cars rose from 14.5 million in 2002 to 19 million in 2007. Let $a(t)$ represent the number of small cars produced t years after 2000.
Source: The Wall Street Journal, 10/22/07

a) Find a linear function that fits the data.

b) Use the function from part (a) to predict the number of small cars produced in 2013.

c) In what year will 25 million small cars be produced?

32. *Convention attendees.*   In recent years, Las Vegas has become a popular location for conventions. The number of convention attendees in Las Vegas rose from 4.6 million in 2002 to 6.1 million in 2006. Let $v(t)$ represent the number of convention attendees in Las Vegas t years after 2000.
Source: Las Vegas Convention and Visitors Authority

a) Find a linear function that fits the data.
b) Use the function from part (a) to predict the number of convention attendees in Las Vegas in 2011.
c) In what year will there be 8 million convention attendees in Las Vegas?

33. *Life expectancy of females in the United States.* In 1994, the life expectancy of females was 79.0 yr. In 2004, it was 80.4 yr. Let $E(t)$ represent life expectancy and t the number of years since 1990.
Source: *Statistical Abstract of the United States*, 2007

a) Find a linear function that fits the data.
Aha! **b)** Use the function of part (a) to predict the life expectancy of females in 2012.

34. *Life expectancy of males in the United States.*   In 1994, the life expectancy of males was 72.4 yr. In 2004, it was 75.2 yr. Let $E(t)$ represent life expectancy and t the number of years since 1990.
Source: *Statistical Abstract of the United States*, 2007

a) Find a linear function that fits the data.
b) Use the function of part (a) to predict the life expectancy of males in 2012.

35. *PAC contributions.*   In 2002, Political Action Committees (PACs) contributed $282 million to federal candidates. In 2006, the figure rose to $372.1 million. Let $A(t)$ represent the amount of PAC contributions, in millions, and t the number of years since 2000.
Source: Federal Election Commission

PAC contributions to federal candidates

2002 $282 million

2006 $372.1 million

a) Find a linear function that fits the data.
b) Use the function of part (a) to predict the amount of PAC contributions in 2010.

36. *Recycling.*   In 2000, Americans recycled 52.7 million tons of solid waste. In 2005, the figure grew to 58.4 million tons. Let $N(t)$ represent the number of tons recycled, in millions, and t the number of years since 2000.
Sources: U.S. EPA; Franklin Associates, Ltd.

a) Find a linear function that fits the data.
b) Use the function of part (a) to predict the amount recycled in 2012.

37. *Online banking.*   In 2000, about 16 million Americans conducted at least some of their banking online. By 2005, that number had risen to about 63 million. Let $N(t)$ represent the number of Americans using online banking, in millions, t years after 2000.

a) Find a linear function that fits the data.
Aha! **b)** Use the function of part (a) to predict the number of Americans who will use online banking in 2010.
c) In what year will 157 million Americans use online banking?

38. *Records in the 100-meter run.*   In 1999, the record for the 100-m run was 9.79 sec. In 2007, it was 9.77 sec. Let $R(t)$ represent the record in the 100-m run and t the number of years since 1999.
Sources: International Association of Athletics Federation; *Guinness World Records*

a) Find a linear function that fits the data.
b) Use the function of part (a) to predict the record in 2015 and in 2030.
c) When will the record be 9.6 sec?

39. *National Park land.* In 1994, the National Park system consisted of about 74.9 million acres. By 2005, the figure had grown to 79 million acres. Let $A(t)$ represent the amount of land in the National Park system, in millions of acres, t years after 1990.

Source: *Statistical Abstract of the United States*, 2007

a) Find a linear function that fits the data.
b) Use the function of part (a) to predict the amount of land in the National Park system in 2010.

40. *Pressure at sea depth.* The pressure 100 ft beneath the ocean's surface is approximately 4 atm (atmospheres), whereas at a depth of 200 ft, the pressure is about 7 atm.

a) Find a linear function that expresses pressure as a function of depth.
b) Use the function of part (a) to determine the pressure at a depth of 690 ft.

Classify each function as a linear function, an absolute-value function, a quadratic function, another polynomial function, or a rational function, and determine the domain of the function.

41. $f(x) = \dfrac{1}{3}x - 7$

42. $g(x) = \dfrac{x}{x + 1}$

43. $p(x) = x^2 + x + 1$

44. $t(x) = |x - 7|$

45. $f(t) = \dfrac{12}{3t + 4}$

46. $g(n) = 15 - 10n$

47. $f(x) = 0.02x^4 - 0.1x + 1.7$

48. $f(a) = 2|a + 3|$

49. $f(x) = \dfrac{x}{2x - 5}$

50. $g(x) = \dfrac{2x}{3x - 4}$

51. $f(n) = \dfrac{4n - 7}{n^2 + 3n + 2}$

52. $h(x) = \dfrac{x - 5}{2x^2 - 2}$

53. $f(n) = 200 - 0.1n$

54. $g(t) = \dfrac{t^2 - 3t + 7}{8}$

Given the graph of each function, determine the range of f.

55.

56.

57.

58.

59.

60.

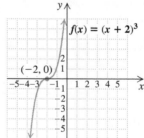

Graph each function and determine its domain and range.

61. $f(x) = x + 3$

62. $f(x) = 2x - 1$

63. $f(x) = -1$

64. $g(x) = 2$

65. $f(x) = |x| + 1$

66. $g(x) = |x - 3|$

67. $g(x) = x^2$

68. $f(x) = x^2 + 2$

69. Bob believes that the domain and range of all polynomial functions is $\mathbb{R}$. How could you convince him that he is mistaken?

70. Explain why the range of a constant function consists of only one number.

Skill Review

To prepare for Section 8.4, review polynomial operations (Sections 5.4 and 5.6).

Perform the indicated operations.

71. $(x^2 + 2x + 7) + (3x^2 - 8)$ [5.4]

72. $(3x^3 - x^2 + x) - (x^3 + 2x - 7)$ [5.4]

73. $(2x + 1)(x - 7)$ [5.6]

74. $(x - 3)(x + 4)$ [5.6]

75. $(x^3 + x^2 - 4x + 7) - (3x^2 - x + 2)$ [5.4]

76. $(2x^2 + x - 3) + (x^3 + 7)$ [5.4]

Synthesis

77. In 2004, Political Action Committees contributed $310.5 million to federal candidates. Does this information make your answer to Exercise 35(b) seem too low or too high? Why?

78. On the basis of your answers to Exercises 33 and 34, would you predict that at some point in the future the life expectancy of males will exceed that of females? Why or why not?

Given that $f(x) = mx + b$, classify each of the following as true or false.

79. $f(c + d) = f(c) + f(d)$

80. $f(cd) = f(c)f(d)$

81. $f(kx) = kf(x)$

82. $f(c - d) = f(c) - f(d)$

For Exercises 83–86, assume that a linear equation models each situation.

83. *Temperature conversion.* Water freezes at 32° Fahrenheit and at 0° Celsius. Water boils at 212°F and at 100°C. What Celsius temperature corresponds to a room temperature of 70°F?

84. *Depreciation of a computer.* After 6 mos of use, the value of Don's computer had dropped to $900. After 8 mos, the value had gone down to $750. How much did the computer cost originally?

85. *Cell-phone charges.* The total cost of Tam's cell phone was $410 after 5 mos of service and $690 after 9 mos. What costs had Tam already incurred when her service just began? Assume that Tam's monthly charge is constant.

86. *Operating expenses.* The total cost for operating Ming's Wings was $7500 after 4 mos and $9250 after 7 mos. Predict the total cost after 10 mos.

87. For a linear function g, $g(3) = -5$ and $g(7) = -1$.
   a) Find an equation for g.
   b) Find $g(-2)$.
   c) Find a such that $g(a) = 75$.

88. When several data points are available and they appear to be nearly collinear, a procedure known as *linear regression* can be used to find an equation for the line that most closely fits the data.

   a) Use a graphing calculator with a LINEAR REGRESSION option and the table that follows to find a linear function that predicts the wattage of a CFL (compact fluorescent) lightbulb as a function of the wattage of a standard incandescent bulb of equivalent brightness. Round coefficients to the nearest thousandth.

Energy Conservation

Incandescent Wattage	CFL Equivalent
25 W	5 W
50 W	9 W
60 W	15 W
100 W	25 W
120 W	28 W

Source: U.S. Department of Energy

   b) Use the function from part (a) to estimate the CFL wattage that is equivalent to a 75-watt incandescent bulb. Then compare your answer with the corresponding answer to Exercise 59 in Section 8.1. Which answer seems more reliable? Why?

CONNECTING the CONCEPTS

A function is a correspondence. This correspondence can be listed as a set of ordered pairs or described by an equation. The correspondence is between two sets, the domain and the range, and each member of the domain corresponds to exactly one member of the range.

For the function f: $\{(2, 3), (0, -4), (-8, 7)\}$:

The domain is $\{-8, 0, 2\}$.

The range is $\{-4, 3, 7\}$.

The input 2 corresponds to the output 3.

$f(2) = 3$

For the function given by $f(x) = x^2$:

The domain is $\mathbb{R}$.

The range is $[0, \infty)$.

The input -3 corresponds to the output 9.

$f(-3) = 9$

The independent variable is x.

MIXED REVIEW

Let $f = \{(3, 6), (4, 8), (-1, -2), (0, 0)\}$.

1. Find the domain of f.

2. Find the range of f.

3. Find $f(-1)$.

4. Graph f.

Let $g(x) = x - 1$ and $h(x) = \dfrac{2}{x}$.

5. Find the domain of g.

6. Find the domain of h.

7. Find $h(10)$.

8. Find $g(1) + h(1)$.

9. Find $(g \cdot h)(-2)$.

10. Find the domain of h/g.

11. Determine whether g is a linear function, a quadratic function, or a rational function.

12. Determine whether h is a linear function, a quadratic function, or a rational function.

13. Graph g and determine its range.

Use the following graph of F for Exercises 14–17.

14. Determine from the graph whether F is a function.

15. Find $F(2)$.

16. Find the domain of F.

17. Find the range of F.

Let $G(x) = \begin{cases} 1 - x, & \text{if } x < 1, \\ 10, & \text{if } x = 1, \\ x + 1, & \text{if } x > 1. \end{cases}$

18. Find $G(3)$.

19. Find $G(1)$.

20. Find $G(-12)$.

8.4   The Algebra of Functions

The Sum, Difference, Product, or Quotient of Two Functions   ■   Domains and Graphs

We now examine four ways in which functions can be combined.

The Sum, Difference, Product, or Quotient of Two Functions

Suppose that a is in the domain of two functions, f and g. The input a is paired with $f(a)$ by f and with $g(a)$ by g. The outputs can then be added to get $f(a) + g(a)$.

EXAMPLE   **1**   Let $f(x) = x + 4$ and $g(x) = x^2 + 1$. Find $f(2) + g(2)$.

SOLUTION   We visualize two function machines. Because 2 is in the domain of each function, we can compute $f(2)$ and $g(2)$.

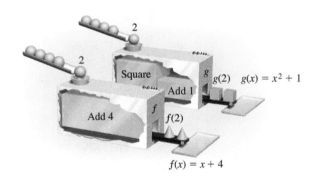

Since

$$f(2) = 2 + 4 = 6 \quad \text{and} \quad g(2) = 2^2 + 1 = 5,$$

we have

$$f(2) + g(2) = 6 + 5 = 11.$$

TRY EXERCISE   7

In Example 1, suppose that we were to write $f(x) + g(x)$ as $(x + 4) + (x^2 + 1)$, or $f(x) + g(x) = x^2 + x + 5$. This could then be regarded as a "new" function. The notation $(f + g)(x)$ is generally used to denote a function formed in this manner. Similar notations exist for subtraction, multiplication, and division of functions.

The Algebra of Functions

If f and g are functions and x is in the domain of both functions, then:

1. $(f + g)(x) = f(x) + g(x)$;
2. $(f - g)(x) = f(x) - g(x)$;
3. $(f \cdot g)(x) = f(x) \cdot g(x)$;
4. $(f/g)(x) = f(x)/g(x)$, provided $g(x) \neq 0$.

EXAMPLE 2 For $f(x) = x^2 - x$ and $g(x) = x + 2$, find the following.

a) $(f + g)(4)$
b) $(f - g)(x)$ and $(f - g)(-1)$
c) $(f/g)(x)$ and $(f/g)(-4)$
d) $(f \cdot g)(4)$

SOLUTION

a) Since $f(4) = 4^2 - 4 = 12$ and $g(4) = 4 + 2 = 6$, we have

$$(f + g)(4) = f(4) + g(4)$$
$$= 12 + 6 \qquad \text{Substituting}$$
$$= 18.$$

Alternatively, we could first find $(f + g)(x)$:

$$(f + g)(x) = f(x) + g(x)$$
$$= x^2 - x + x + 2$$
$$= x^2 + 2. \qquad \text{Combining like terms}$$

Thus,

$$(f + g)(4) = 4^2 + 2 = 18. \qquad \text{Our results match.}$$

b) We have

$$(f - g)(x) = f(x) - g(x)$$
$$= x^2 - x - (x + 2) \qquad \text{Substituting}$$
$$= x^2 - 2x - 2. \qquad \text{Removing parentheses and combining like terms}$$

Thus,

$$(f - g)(-1) = (-1)^2 - 2(-1) - 2 \qquad \text{Using } (f - g)(x) \text{ is faster than using } f(x) - g(x).$$
$$= 1. \qquad \text{Simplifying}$$

c) We have

$$(f/g)(x) = f(x)/g(x)$$
$$= \frac{x^2 - x}{x + 2}. \qquad \text{We assume that } x \neq -2.$$

Thus,

$$(f/g)(-4) = \frac{(-4)^2 - (-4)}{-4 + 2} \qquad \text{Substituting}$$
$$= \frac{20}{-2} = -10.$$

d) Using our work in part (a), we have

$$(f \cdot g)(4) = f(4) \cdot g(4)$$
$$= 12 \cdot 6$$
$$= 72.$$

Alternatively, we could first find $(f \cdot g)(x)$:

$$(f \cdot g)(x) = f(x) \cdot g(x)$$
$$= (x^2 - x)(x + 2)$$
$$= x^3 + x^2 - 2x. \quad \text{Multiplying and combining like terms.}$$

Then

$$(f \cdot g)(4) = 4^3 + 4^2 - 2 \cdot 4$$
$$= 64 + 16 - 8$$
$$= 72.$$

> **TRY EXERCISE** 17

Domains and Graphs

Although applications involving products and quotients of functions rarely appear in newspapers, situations involving sums or differences of functions often do appear in print. For example, the following graphs are similar to those published by the California Department of Education to promote breakfast programs in which students eat a balanced meal of fruit or juice, toast or cereal, and 2% or whole milk. The combination of carbohydrate, protein, and fat gives a sustained release of energy, delaying the onset of hunger for several hours.

When the three graphs are superimposed, and the calorie expenditures added, it becomes clear that a balanced meal results in a steady, sustained supply of energy.

For any point $(t, N(t))$, we have

$$N(t) = (C + P + F)(t) = C(t) + P(t) + F(t).$$

To find $(f + g)(a)$, $(f - g)(a)$, $(f \cdot g)(a)$, or $(f/g)(a)$, we must know that $f(a)$ and $g(a)$ exist. This means a must be in the domain of both f and g.

EXAMPLE **3** Let

$$f(x) = \frac{5}{x} \quad \text{and} \quad g(x) = \frac{2x - 6}{x + 1}.$$

Find the domain of $f + g$, the domain of $f - g$, and the domain of $f \cdot g$.

SOLUTION Note that because division by 0 is undefined, we have

Domain of $f = \{x \mid x \text{ is a real number } and \ x \neq 0\}$

and

Domain of $g = \{x \mid x \text{ is a real number } and \ x \neq -1\}$.

In order to find $f(a) + g(a)$, $f(a) - g(a)$, or $f(a) \cdot g(a)$, we must know that a is in *both* of the above domains. Thus,

Domain of $f + g =$ Domain of $f - g =$ Domain of $f \cdot g$
$$= \{x \mid x \text{ is a real number } and \ x \neq 0 \ and \ x \neq -1\}.$$

> **TRY EXERCISE** 43

Suppose that for $f(x) = x^2 - x$ and $g(x) = x + 2$, we want to find $(f/g)(-2)$. Finding $f(-2)$ and $g(-2)$ poses no problem:

$$f(-2) = 6 \quad \text{and} \quad g(-2) = 0;$$

but then

$$(f/g)(-2) = f(-2)/g(-2)$$
$$= 6/0. \quad \text{Division by 0 is undefined.}$$

Thus, although -2 is in the domain of both f and g, it is not in the domain of f/g.

We can also see this by writing $(f/g)(x)$:

$$(f/g)(x) = \frac{f(x)}{g(x)} = \frac{x^2 - x}{x + 2}.$$

Since $x + 2 = 0$ when $x = -2$, the domain of f/g must exclude -2.

Determining the Domain

The domain of $f + g$, $f - g$, or $f \cdot g$ is the set of all values common to the domains of f and g.

The domain of f/g is the set of all values common to the domains of f and g, excluding any values for which $g(x)$ is 0.

Domain of $f + g$, $f - g$, and $f \cdot g$

Domain of f/g

EXAMPLE 4   Given $f(x) = 1/x$ and $g(x) = 2x - 7$, find the domains of $f + g$, $f - g$, $f \cdot g$, and f/g.

SOLUTION   We first find the domain of f and the domain of g:

The domain of f is $\{x \mid x$ is a real number $and\ x \neq 0\}$.

The domain of g is $\mathbb{R}$.

The domains of $f + g$, $f - g$, and $f \cdot g$ are the set of all elements common to the domains of f and g. This consists of all real numbers except 0.

The domain of $f + g$ = the domain of $f - g$ = the domain of $f \cdot g$
$$= \{x \mid x \text{ is a real number } and\ x \neq 0\}.$$

Because we cannot divide by 0, the domain of f/g must also exclude any values of x for which $g(x)$ is 0. We determine those values by solving $g(x) = 0$:

$$g(x) = 0$$
$$2x - 7 = 0 \qquad \text{Replacing } g(x) \text{ with } 2x - 7$$
$$2x = 7$$
$$x = \tfrac{7}{2}.$$

The domain of f/g is the domain of the sum, difference, and product of f and g, found above, excluding $\tfrac{7}{2}$.

The domain of $f/g = \{x \mid x \text{ is a real number } and\ x \neq 0\ and\ x \neq \tfrac{7}{2}\}$.

TRY EXERCISE   55

STUDENT NOTES

The concern over a denominator being 0 arises throughout this course. Try to develop the habit of checking for any possible input values that would create a denominator of 0 whenever you work with functions.

TECHNOLOGY CONNECTION

A partial check of Example 4 can be performed by setting up a table so the TBLSTART is 0 and the increment of change (ΔTbl) is 0.7. (Other choices, like 0.1, will also work.) Next, we let $y_1 = 1/x$ and $y_2 = 2x - 7$. Using Y-VARS to write $y_3 = y_1 + y_2$ and $y_4 = y_1/y_2$, we can create the table of values shown here. Note that when x is 3.5, a value for y_3 can be found, but y_4 is undefined. If we "de-select" y_1 and y_2 as we enter them, the columns for y_3 and y_4 appear without scrolling through the table.

X	Y3	Y4
0	ERROR	ERROR
.7	-4.171	-.2551
1.4	-3.486	-.1701
2.1	-2.324	-.1701
2.8	-1.043	-.2551
3.5	.28571	ERROR
4.2	1.6381	.17007

X = 0

Use a similar approach to partially check Example 3.

Division by 0 is not the only condition that can force restrictions on the domain of a function. We will examine functions similar to that given by $f(x) = \sqrt{x}$, for which the concern is taking the square root of a negative number.

8.4   EXERCISE SET

> **Concept Reinforcement** *Make each of the following sentences true by selecting the correct word for each blank.*

1. If f and g are functions, then $(f + g)(x)$ is the _____ of the functions.
   sum/difference

2. One way to compute $(f - g)(2)$ is to _____ $g(2)$ from $f(2)$.
   erase/subtract

3. One way to compute $(f - g)(2)$ is to simplify $f(x) - g(x)$ and then _____ the result
   evaluate/substitute
   for $x = 2$.

4. The domain of $f + g$, $f - g$, and $f \cdot g$ is the set of all values common to the _____ of f and g.
   domains/ranges

5. The domain of f/g is the set of all values common to the domains of f and g, _____ any
   including/excluding
   values for which $g(x)$ is 0.

6. The height of $(f + g)(a)$ on a graph is the _____ of the heights of $f(a)$ and $g(a)$.
   product/sum

Let $f(x) = -2x + 3$ and $g(x) = x^2 - 5$. Find each of the following.

7. $f(3) + g(3)$ 8. $f(4) + g(4)$

9. $f(1) - g(1)$ 10. $f(2) - g(2)$

11. $f(-2) \cdot g(-2)$ 12. $f(-1) \cdot g(-1)$

13. $f(-4)/g(-4)$ 14. $f(3)/g(3)$

15. $g(1) - f(1)$ 16. $g(-3)/f(-3)$

17. $(f + g)(x)$ 18. $(g - f)(x)$

Let $F(x) = x^2 - 2$ and $G(x) = 5 - x$. Find each of the following.

19. $(F + G)(x)$ 20. $(F + G)(a)$

21. $(F - G)(3)$ 22. $(F - G)(2)$

23. $(F \cdot G)(a)$ 24. $(G \cdot F)(x)$

25. $(F/G)(x)$ 26. $(G - F)(x)$

27. $(G/F)(-2)$ 28. $(F/G)(-1)$

29. $(F + F)(1)$ 30. $(G \cdot G)(6)$

The following graph shows the number of births in the United States, in millions, from 1970–2004. Here $C(t)$ represents the number of Caesarean section births, $B(t)$ the number of non-Caesarean section births, and $N(t)$ the total number of births in year t.

Source: National Center for Health Statistics

31. Use estimates of $C(2004)$ and $B(2004)$ to estimate $N(2004)$.

32. Use estimates of $C(1985)$ and $B(1985)$ to estimate $N(1985)$.

In 2004, a study comparing high doses of the cholesterol-lowering drugs Lipitor and Pravachol indicated that patients taking Lipitor were significantly less likely to have heart attacks or require angioplasty or surgery.

In the graph below, $L(t)$ is the percentage of patients on Lipitor (80 mg) and $P(t)$ is the percentage of patients on Pravachol (40 mg) who suffered heart problems or death t years after beginning to take the medication.
Source: New York Times, March 9, 2004

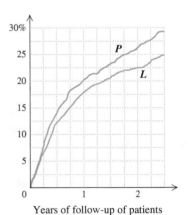

Years of follow-up of patients
Source: New England Journal of Medicine

33. Use estimates of $P(2)$ and $L(2)$ to estimate $(P - L)(2)$.

34. Use estimates of $P(1)$ and $L(1)$ to estimate $(P - L)(1)$.

Often function addition is represented by stacking the individual functions directly on top of each other. The graph below indicates how U.S. municipal solid waste has been managed. The braces indicate the values of the individual functions.

Talking trash

Year

Source: Environmental Protection Agency

35. Estimate $(p + r)('05)$. What does it represent?

36. Estimate $(p + r + b)('05)$. What does it represent?

37. Estimate $F('96)$. What does it represent?

38. Estimate $F('06)$. What does it represent?

39. Estimate $(F - p)('04)$. What does it represent?

40. Estimate $(F - l)('03)$. What does it represent?

For each pair of functions f and g, determine the domain of the sum, difference, and product of the two functions.

41. $f(x) = x^2$,
$g(x) = 7x - 4$

42. $f(x) = 5x - 1$,
$g(x) = 2x^2$

43. $f(x) = \dfrac{1}{x + 5}$,
$g(x) = 4x^3$

44. $f(x) = 3x^2$,
$g(x) = \dfrac{1}{x - 9}$

45. $f(x) = \dfrac{2}{x}$,
$g(x) = x^2 - 4$

46. $f(x) = x^3 + 1$,
$g(x) = \dfrac{5}{x}$

47. $f(x) = x + \dfrac{2}{x - 1}$,
$g(x) = 3x^3$

48. $f(x) = 9 - x^2$,
$g(x) = \dfrac{3}{x + 6} + 2x$

49. $f(x) = \dfrac{3}{2x + 9}$,

$g(x) = \dfrac{5}{1 - x}$

50. $f(x) = \dfrac{5}{3 - x}$,

$g(x) = \dfrac{1}{4x - 1}$

For each pair of functions f and g, determine the domain of f/g.

51. $f(x) = x^4$,
$g(x) = x - 3$

52. $f(x) = 2x^3$,
$g(x) = 5 - x$

53. $f(x) = 3x - 2$,
$g(x) = 2x + 8$

54. $f(x) = 5 + x$,
$g(x) = 6 - 2x$

55. $f(x) = \dfrac{3}{x - 4}$,
$g(x) = 5 - x$

56. $f(x) = \dfrac{1}{2 - x}$,
$g(x) = 7 + x$

57. $f(x) = \dfrac{2x}{x + 1}$,
$g(x) = 2x + 5$

58. $f(x) = \dfrac{7x}{x - 2}$,
$g(x) = 3x + 7$

For Exercises 59–66, consider the functions F and G as shown.

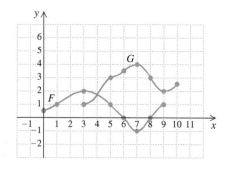

59. Determine $(F + G)(5)$ and $(F + G)(7)$.

60. Determine $(F \cdot G)(6)$ and $(F \cdot G)(9)$.

61. Determine $(G - F)(7)$ and $(G - F)(3)$.

62. Determine $(F/G)(3)$ and $(F/G)(7)$.

63. Find the domains of F, G, $F + G$, and F/G.

64. Find the domains of $F - G$, $F \cdot G$, and G/F.

65. Graph $F + G$.

66. Graph $G - F$.

In the following graph, S(t) represents the number of gallons of carbonated soft drinks consumed by the average American in year t, M(t) the number of gallons of milk, J(t) the number of gallons of fruit juice, and W(t) the number of gallons of bottled water.

Beverage consumption

Source: Economic Research Service, U. S. Department of Agriculture

67. Between what years did the average American drink more soft drinks than juice, bottled water, and milk combined? Explain how you determined this.

68. Examine the graphs before Exercises 31 and 32. Did the total number of births increase or decrease from 1970 to 2004? Did the percent of births by Caesarean section increase or decrease from 1970 to 2004? Explain how you determined your answers.

Skill Review

To prepare for Section 8.5, review solving a formula for a variable (Section 2.3).

Solve. [2.3]

69. $ac = b$, for c

70. $x - wz = y$, for w

71. $pq - rq = st$, for q

72. $ab = d - cb$, for b

73. $ab - cd = 3b + d$, for b

74. $ab - cd = 3b + d$, for d

Synthesis

75. Examine the graphs following Example 2 and explain how they might be modified to represent the absorption of 200 mg of Advil® taken four times a day.

76. If $f(x) = c$, where c is some positive constant, describe how the graphs of $y = g(x)$ and $y = (f + g)(x)$ will differ.

77. Find the domain of F/G, if

$$F(x) = \dfrac{1}{x - 4} \quad \text{and} \quad G(x) = \dfrac{x^2 - 4}{x - 3}.$$

78. Find the domain of f/g, if

$$f(x) = \dfrac{3x}{2x + 5} \quad \text{and} \quad g(x) = \dfrac{x^4 - 1}{3x + 9}.$$

79. Sketch the graph of two functions f and g such that the domain of f/g is
$$\{x\,|-2 \le x \le 3 \text{ and } x \ne 1\}.$$

80. Find the domains of $f + g$, $f - g$, $f \cdot g$, and f/g, if
$$f = \{(-2, 1), (-1, 2), (0, 3), (1, 4), (2, 5)\}$$
and
$$g = \{(-4, 4), (-3, 3), (-2, 4), (-1, 0), (0, 5), (1, 6)\}.$$

81. Find the domain of m/n, if
$$m(x) = 3x \quad \text{for } -1 < x < 5$$
and
$$n(x) = 2x - 3.$$

82. For f and g as defined in Exercise 80, find $(f + g)(-2)$, $(f \cdot g)(0)$, and $(f/g)(1)$.

83. Write equations for two functions f and g such that the domain of $f + g$ is
$$\{x\,|\,x \text{ is a real number } \text{and } x \ne -2 \text{ and } x \ne 5\}.$$

84. Let $y_1 = 2.5x + 1.5$, $y_2 = x - 3$, and $y_3 = y_1/y_2$. Depending on whether the CONNECTED or DOT mode is used, the graph of y_3 appears as follows. Use algebra to determine which graph more accurately represents y_3.

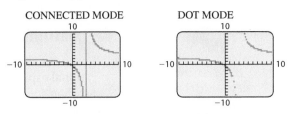

85. Using the window $[-5, 5, -1, 9]$, graph $y_1 = 5$, $y_2 = x + 2$, and $y_3 = \sqrt{x}$. Then predict what shape the graphs of $y_1 + y_2$, $y_1 + y_3$, and $y_2 + y_3$ will take. Use a graphing calculator to check each prediction.

86. Use the TABLE feature on a graphing calculator to check your answers to Exercises 45, 47, 55, and 57. (See the Technology Connection on p. 538.)

CORNER

COLLABORATIVE

Time On Your Hands

Focus: The algebra of functions

Time: 10–15 minutes

Group size: 2–3

The graph and the data at right chart the average retirement age $R(x)$ and life expectancy $E(x)$ of U.S. citizens in year x.

ACTIVITY

1. Working as a team, perform the appropriate calculations and then graph $E - R$.

2. What does $(E - R)(x)$ represent? In what fields of study or business might the function $E - R$ prove useful?

3. Should E and R really be calculated separately for men and women? Why or why not?

4. What advice would you give to someone considering early retirement?

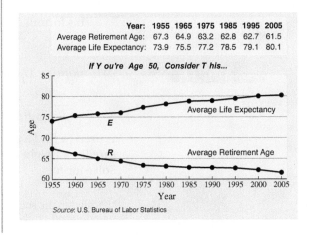

8.5   Formulas, Applications, and Variation

Formulas ▪ Direct Variation ▪ Inverse Variation ▪ Joint Variation and Combined Variation

Formulas

Formulas occur frequently as mathematical models. Many formulas contain rational expressions, and to solve such formulas for a specified letter, we proceed as when solving rational equations.

EXAMPLE 1

Electronics. The formula

$$\frac{1}{R} = \frac{1}{r_1} + \frac{1}{r_2}$$

is used by electricians to determine the resistance R of two resistors r_1 and r_2 connected in parallel.* Solve for r_1.

SOLUTION   We use the same approach as in Section 7.6:

$$Rr_1r_2 \cdot \frac{1}{R} = Rr_1r_2 \cdot \left(\frac{1}{r_1} + \frac{1}{r_2}\right)$$ Multiplying both sides by the LCD to clear fractions

$$Rr_1r_2 \cdot \frac{1}{R} = Rr_1r_2 \cdot \frac{1}{r_1} + Rr_1r_2 \cdot \frac{1}{r_2}$$ Multiplying to remove parentheses

$$r_1r_2 = Rr_2 + Rr_1.$$ Simplifying by removing factors equal to 1: $\frac{R}{R} = 1; \frac{r_1}{r_1} = 1; \frac{r_2}{r_2} = 1$

At this point it is tempting to multiply by $1/r_2$ to get r_1 alone on the left, *but* note that there is an r_1 on the right. We must get all the terms involving r_1 on the *same side* of the equation.

$$r_1r_2 - Rr_1 = Rr_2$$ Subtracting Rr_1 from both sides

$$r_1(r_2 - R) = Rr_2$$ Factoring out r_1 in order to combine like terms

$$r_1 = \frac{Rr_2}{r_2 - R}$$ Dividing both sides by $r_2 - R$ to get r_1 alone

This formula can be used to calculate r_1 whenever R and r_2 are known.

> **TRY EXERCISE** 17

EXAMPLE 2

Astronomy. The formula

$$\frac{V^2}{R^2} = \frac{2g}{R + h}$$

is used to find a satellite's *escape velocity V*, where R is a planet's radius, h is the satellite's height above the planet, and g is the planet's gravitational constant. Solve for h.

---

*Recall that the subscripts 1 and 2 merely indicate that r_1 and r_2 are different variables representing similar quantities.

SOLUTION   We first multiply by the LCD, $R^2(R + h)$, to clear fractions:

$$\frac{V^2}{R^2} = \frac{2g}{R + h}$$

$$R^2(R + h)\frac{V^2}{R^2} = R^2(R + h)\frac{2g}{R + h} \qquad \text{Multiplying to clear fractions}$$

$$\frac{R^2(R + h)V^2}{R^2} = \frac{R^2(R + h)2g}{R + h}$$

$$(R + h)V^2 = R^2 \cdot 2g. \qquad \text{Removing factors equal to 1:}$$
$$\frac{R^2}{R^2} = 1 \text{ and } \frac{R + h}{R + h} = 1$$

Remember: We are solving for h. Although we *could* distribute V^2, since h appears only within the factor $R + h$, it is easier to divide both sides by V^2:

$$\frac{(R + h)V^2}{V^2} = \frac{2R^2g}{V^2} \qquad \text{Dividing both sides by } V^2$$

$$R + h = \frac{2R^2g}{V^2} \qquad \text{Removing a factor equal to 1: } \frac{V^2}{V^2} = 1$$

$$h = \frac{2R^2g}{V^2} - R. \qquad \text{Subtracting } R \text{ from both sides}$$

The last equation can be used to determine the height of a satellite above a planet when the planet's radius and gravitational constant, along with the satellite's escape velocity, are known.

TRY EXERCISE 29

EXAMPLE 3   *Acoustics (the Doppler Effect).*   The formula

$$f = \frac{sg}{s + v}$$

is used to determine the frequency f of a sound that is moving at velocity v toward a listener who hears the sound as frequency g. Here s is the speed of sound in a particular medium. Solve for s.

STUDENT NOTES ———

The steps used to solve equations are precisely the same steps used to solve formulas. If you feel "rusty" in this regard, study the earlier section in which this type of equation first appeared. Then make sure that you can consistently solve those equations before returning to the work with formulas.

SOLUTION   We first clear fractions by multiplying by the LCD, $s + v$:

$$f \cdot (s + v) = \frac{sg}{s + v}(s + v)$$

$$fs + fv = sg. \qquad \text{The variable for which we are solving, } s,$$
$$\text{appears on both sides, forcing us to}$$
$$\text{distribute on the left side.}$$

Next, we must get all terms containing *s* on one side:

$$fv = sg - fs \qquad \text{Subtracting } fs \text{ from both sides}$$
$$fv = s(g - f) \qquad \text{Factoring out } s. \text{ This is like combining like terms.}$$
$$\frac{fv}{g - f} = s. \qquad \text{Dividing both sides by } g - f$$

Since *s* is isolated on one side, we have solved for *s*. This last equation can be used to determine the speed of sound whenever *f*, *v*, and *g* are known.

> **TRY EXERCISE** 19

> **To Solve a Rational Equation for a Specified Variable**
> 1. Multiply both sides by the LCD to clear fractions, if necessary.
> 2. Multiply to remove parentheses, if necessary.
> 3. Get all terms with the specified variable alone on one side.
> 4. Factor out the specified variable if it is in more than one term.
> 5. Multiply or divide on both sides to isolate the specified variable.

Variation

To extend our study of formulas and functions, we now examine three real-world situations: direct variation, inverse variation, and combined variation.

DIRECT VARIATION

A computer technician earns $22 per hour. In 1 hr, $22 is earned. In 2 hr, $44 is earned. In 3 hr, $66 is earned, and so on. This gives rise to a set of ordered pairs:

$$(1, 22), (2, 44), (3, 66), (4, 88), \quad \text{and so on.}$$

Note that the ratio of earnings *E* to time *t* is $\frac{22}{1}$ in every case.

If a situation is modeled by pairs for which the ratio is constant, we say there is **direct variation**. Here earnings *vary directly* as the time:

We have $\frac{E}{t} = 22$, so $E = 22t$ or, using function notation, $E(t) = 22t$.

> **Direct Variation**
> When a situation is modeled by a linear function of the form $f(x) = kx$, or $y = kx$, where *k* is a nonzero constant, we say that there is *direct variation*, that *y varies directly* as *x*, or that *y is proportional to x*. The number *k* is called the *variation constant*, or *constant of proportionality*.

Note that for $k > 0$, any equation of the form $y = kx$ indicates that as *x* increases, *y* increases as well.

EXAMPLE 4   Find the variation constant and an equation of variation if y varies directly as x, and $y = 32$ when $x = 2$.

SOLUTION   We know that $(2, 32)$ is a solution of $y = kx$. Therefore,

$$32 = k \cdot 2 \qquad \text{Substituting}$$

$$\frac{32}{2} = k, \quad \text{or} \quad k = 16. \qquad \text{Solving for } k$$

The variation constant is 16. The equation of variation is $y = 16x$. The notation $y(x) = 16x$ or $f(x) = 16x$ is also used.   TRY EXERCISE ▶ 43

EXAMPLE 5

Ocean waves.   The speed v of a train of ocean waves varies directly as the swell period t, or time between successive waves. Waves with a swell period of 12 sec are traveling 21 mph. How fast are waves traveling that have a swell period of 20 sec?

Source: www.rodntube.com

SOLUTION

1. **Familiarize.** Because of the phrase "v . . . varies directly as . . . t," we express the speed of the wave v, in miles per hour, as a function of the swell period t, in seconds. Thus, $v(t) = kt$, where k is the variation constant. Because we are using ratios, we can use the units "seconds" and "miles per hour" without converting sec to hr or hr to sec. Knowing that waves with a swell period of 12 sec are traveling 21 mph, we have $v(12) = 21$.

2. **Translate.** We find the variation constant using the data and then use it to write the equation of variation:

$$v(t) = kt$$
$$v(12) = k \cdot 12 \qquad \text{Replacing } t \text{ with } 12$$
$$21 = k \cdot 12 \qquad \text{Replacing } v(12) \text{ with } 21$$
$$\frac{21}{12} = k \qquad \text{Solving for } k$$
$$1.75 = k. \qquad \text{This is the variation constant.}$$

The equation of variation is $v(t) = 1.75t$. This is the translation.

3. **Carry out.** To find the speed of waves with a swell period of 20 sec, we compute $v(20)$:

$$v(t) = 1.75t$$
$$v(20) = 1.75(20) \qquad \text{Substituting 20 for } t$$
$$= 35.$$

4. **Check.** To check, we could reexamine all our calculations. Note that our answer seems reasonable since the ratios 21/12 and 35/20 are both 1.75.

5. **State.** Waves with a swell period of 20 sec are traveling 35 mph.

    TRY EXERCISE ▶ 55

INVERSE VARIATION

Suppose a bus travels 20 mi. At 20 mph, the trip takes 1 hr. At 40 mph, it takes $\frac{1}{2}$ hr. At 60 mph, it takes $\frac{1}{3}$ hr, and so on. This gives pairs of numbers, all having the same product:

$$(20, 1), \left(40, \tfrac{1}{2}\right), \left(60, \tfrac{1}{3}\right), \left(80, \tfrac{1}{4}\right), \quad \text{and so on.}$$

Note that the product of each pair is 20. When a situation is modeled by pairs for which the product is constant, we say that there is **inverse variation**. Since $r \cdot t = 20$, we have

$$t = \frac{20}{r} \quad \text{or, using function notation,} \quad t(r) = \frac{20}{r}.$$

Inverse Variation

When a situation is modeled by a rational function of the form $f(x) = k/x$, or $y = k/x$, where k is a nonzero constant, we say that there is *inverse variation*, that *y varies inversely as x*, or that *y is inversely proportional to x*. The number k is called the *variation constant*, or *constant of proportionality*.

Note that for $k > 0$, any equation of the form $y = k/x$ indicates that as x increases, y decreases.

EXAMPLE   6   Find the variation constant and an equation of variation if y varies inversely as x, and $y = 32$ when $x = 0.2$.

SOLUTION   We know that $(0.2, 32)$ is a solution of

$$y = \frac{k}{x}.$$

Therefore,

$$32 = \frac{k}{0.2} \qquad \text{Substituting}$$

$$(0.2)32 = k$$

$$6.4 = k. \qquad \text{Solving for } k$$

The variation constant is 6.4. The equation of variation is

$$y = \frac{6.4}{x}.$$

 TRY EXERCISE   49

There are many real-life quantities that vary inversely.

EXAMPLE   7   *Movie downloads.*   The time t that it takes to download a movie file varies inversely as the transfer speed s of the Internet connection. A typical full-length movie file will transfer in 48 min at a transfer speed of 256 KB/s (kilobytes per second). How long will it take to transfer the same movie file at a transfer speed of 32 KB/s?

Source: www.xsvidmovies.com

SOLUTION

1. **Familiarize.** Because of the phrase ". . . varies inversely as the transfer speed," we express the download time t, in minutes, as a function of the transfer speed s, in kilobytes per second. Thus, $t(s) = k/s$.

2. **Translate.** We use the given information to solve for k. We will then use that result to write the equation of variation.

$$t(s) = \frac{k}{s}$$

$$t(256) = \frac{k}{256} \qquad \text{Replacing } s \text{ with } 256$$

$$48 = \frac{k}{256} \qquad \text{Replacing } t(256) \text{ with } 48$$

$$12{,}288 = k.$$

The equation of variation is $t(s) = 12{,}288/s$. This is the translation.

3. **Carry out.** To find the download time at a transfer speed of 32 KB/s, we calculate $t(32)$:

$$t(32) = \frac{12{,}288}{32} = 384.$$

4. **Check.** Note that, as expected, as the transfer speed goes *down*, the download time goes *up*. Also, the products $48 \cdot 256$ and $32 \cdot 384$ are both 12,288.

5. **State.** At a transfer speed of 32 KB/s, it will take 384 min, or 6 hr 24 min, to download the movie file.

▶ **TRY EXERCISE** 57

JOINT VARIATION AND COMBINED VARIATION

When a variable varies directly with more than one other variable, we say that there is *joint variation*. For example, in the formula for the volume of a right circular cylinder, $V = \pi r^2 h$, we say that V varies *jointly* as h and the square of r.

> ### Joint Variation
> y varies *jointly* as x and z if, for some nonzero constant k, $y = kxz$.

EXAMPLE **8**   Find an equation of variation if y varies jointly as x and z, and $y = 30$ when $x = 2$ and $z = 3$.

SOLUTION   We have

$$y = kxz,$$

so

$$30 = k \cdot 2 \cdot 3$$

$$k = 5. \qquad \text{The variation constant is 5.}$$

The equation of variation is $y = 5xz$.

▶ **TRY EXERCISE** 73

Joint variation is one form of *combined variation*. In general, when a variable varies directly and/or inversely, at the same time, with more than one other variable, there is **combined variation**. Examples 8 and 9 are both examples of combined variation.

EXAMPLE 9 Find an equation of variation if y varies jointly as x and z and inversely as the square of w, and $y = 105$ when $x = 3$, $z = 20$, and $w = 2$.

SOLUTION   The equation of variation is of the form

$$y = k \cdot \frac{xz}{w^2},$$

so, substituting, we have

$$105 = k \cdot \frac{3 \cdot 20}{2^2}$$

$$105 = k \cdot 15$$

$$k = 7.$$

Thus,

$$y = 7 \cdot \frac{xz}{w^2}.$$

TRY EXERCISE 75

8.5   EXERCISE SET

Concept Reinforcement   Match each statement with the correct term that completes it from the list on the right.

1. To clear fractions, we can multiply both sides of an equation by the ____.

2. With direct variation, pairs of numbers have a constant ____.

3. With inverse variation, pairs of numbers have a constant ____.

4. If $y = k/x$, then y varies ____ as x.

5. If $y = kx$, then y varies ____ as x.

6. If $y = kxz$, then y varies ____ as x and z.

a) Directly

b) Inversely

c) Jointly

d) LCD

e) Product

f) Ratio

Determine whether each situation represents direct variation or inverse variation.

7. Two painters can scrape a house in 9 hr, whereas three painters can scrape the house in 6 hr.

8. Andres planted 5 bulbs in 20 min and 7 bulbs in 28 min.

9. Salma swam 2 laps in 7 min and 6 laps in 21 min.

10. It took 2 band members 80 min to set up for a show; with 4 members working, it took 40 min.

11. It took 3 hr for 4 volunteers to wrap the campus' collection of Toys for Tots, but only 1.5 hr with 8 volunteers working.

12. Ayana's air conditioner cooled off 1000 ft³ in 10 min and 3000 ft³ in 30 min.

Solve each formula for the specified variable.

13. $f = \dfrac{L}{d}$; d

14. $\dfrac{W_1}{W_2} = \dfrac{d_1}{d_2}$; W_1

15. $s = \dfrac{(v_1 + v_2)t}{2}$; v_1

16. $s = \dfrac{(v_1 + v_2)t}{2}$; t

17. $\dfrac{t}{a} + \dfrac{t}{b} = 1$; b

18. $\dfrac{1}{R} = \dfrac{1}{r_1} + \dfrac{1}{r_2}$; R

19. $R = \dfrac{gs}{g + s}$; g

20. $K = \dfrac{rt}{r - t}$; t

21. $I = \dfrac{nE}{R + nr}$; n

22. $I = \dfrac{nE}{R + nr}$; r

23. $\dfrac{1}{p} + \dfrac{1}{q} = \dfrac{1}{f}$; q

24. $\dfrac{1}{p} + \dfrac{1}{q} = \dfrac{1}{f}$; p

25. $S = \dfrac{H}{m(t_1 - t_2)}$; t_1

26. $S = \dfrac{H}{m(t_1 - t_2)}$; H

27. $\dfrac{E}{e} = \dfrac{R + r}{r}$; r

28. $\dfrac{E}{e} = \dfrac{R + r}{R}$; R

29. $S = \dfrac{a}{1 - r}$; r

30. $S = \dfrac{a - ar^n}{1 - r}$; a

Aha! **31.** $c = \dfrac{f}{(a + b)c}$; $a + b$

32. $d = \dfrac{g}{d(c + f)}$; $c + f$

33. *Interest.* The formula

$$P = \dfrac{A}{1 + r}$$

is used to determine what principal P should be invested for one year at $(100 \cdot r)$% simple interest in order to have A dollars after a year. Solve for r.

34. *Taxable interest.* The formula

$$I_t = \dfrac{I_f}{1 - T}$$

gives the *taxable interest rate* I_t equivalent to the *tax-free interest rate* I_f for a person in the $(100 \cdot T)$% tax bracket. Solve for T.

35. *Average speed.* The formula

$$v = \dfrac{d_2 - d_1}{t_2 - t_1}$$

gives an object's average speed v when that object has traveled d_1 miles in t_1 hours and d_2 miles in t_2 hours. Solve for t_1.

36. *Average acceleration.* The formula

$$a = \dfrac{v_2 - v_1}{t_2 - t_1}$$

gives a vehicle's *average acceleration* when its velocity changes from v_1 at time t_1 to v_2 at time t_2. Solve for t_2.

37. *Work rate.* The formula

$$\dfrac{1}{t} = \dfrac{1}{a} + \dfrac{1}{b}$$

gives the total time t required for two workers to complete a job, if the workers' individual times are a and b. Solve for t.

38. *Planetary orbits.* The formula

$$\dfrac{x^2}{a^2} + \dfrac{y^2}{b^2} = 1$$

can be used to plot a planet's elliptical orbit of width $2a$ and length $2b$. Solve for b^2.

39. *Semester average.* The formula

$$A = \dfrac{2Tt + Qq}{2T + Q}$$

gives a student's average A after T tests and Q quizzes, where each test counts as 2 quizzes, t is the test average, and q is the quiz average. Solve for Q.

40. *Astronomy.* The formula

$$L = \dfrac{dR}{D - d},$$

where D is the diameter of the sun, d is the diameter of the earth, R is the earth's distance from the sun, and L is some fixed distance, is used in calculating when lunar eclipses occur. Solve for D.

41. *Body-fat percentage.* The YMCA calculates men's body-fat percentage p using the formula

$$p = \dfrac{-98.42 + 4.15c - 0.082w}{w},$$

where c is the waist measurement, in inches, and w is the weight, in pounds. Solve for w.
Source: YMCA guide to Physical Fitness Assessment

42. *Preferred viewing distance.* Researchers model the distance D from which an observer prefers to watch television in "picture heights"—that is, multiples of the height of the viewing screen. The preferred viewing distance is given by

$$D = \frac{3.55H + 0.9}{H},$$

where D is in picture heights and H is in meters. Solve for H.

Source: www.tid.es, Telefonica Investigación y Desarrollo, S.A. Unipersonal

Find the variation constant and an equation of variation if y varies directly as x and the following conditions apply.

43. $y = 30$ when $x = 5$

44. $y = 80$ when $x = 16$

45. $y = 3.4$ when $x = 2$

46. $y = 2$ when $x = 5$

47. $y = 2$ when $x = \frac{1}{5}$

48. $y = 0.9$ when $x = 0.5$

Find the variation constant and an equation of variation in which y varies inversely as x, and the following conditions exist.

49. $y = 5$ when $x = 20$

50. $y = 40$ when $x = 8$

51. $y = 11$ when $x = 4$

52. $y = 9$ when $x = 10$

53. $y = 27$ when $x = \frac{1}{3}$

54. $y = 81$ when $x = \frac{1}{9}$

55. *Hooke's law.* Hooke's law states that the distance d that a spring is stretched by a hanging object varies directly as the mass m of the object. If the distance is 20 cm when the mass is 3 kg, what is the distance when the mass is 5 kg?

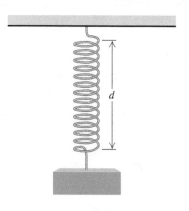

56. *Ohm's law.* The electric current I, in amperes, in a circuit varies directly as the voltage V. When 15 volts are applied, the current is 5 amperes. What is the current when 18 volts are applied?

57. *Work rate.* The time T required to do a job varies inversely as the number of people P working. It takes 5 hr for 7 volunteers to pick up rubbish from 1 mi of roadway. How long would it take 10 volunteers to complete the job?

58. *Pumping rate.* The time t required to empty a tank varies inversely as the rate r of pumping. If a Briggs and Stratton pump can empty a tank in 45 min at the rate of 600 kL/min, how long will it take the pump to empty the tank at 1000 kL/min?

59. *Water from melting snow.* The number of centimeters W of water produced from melting snow varies directly as the number of centimeters S of snow. Meteorologists know that under certain conditions, 150 cm of snow will melt to 16.8 cm of water. The average annual snowfall in Alta, Utah, is 500 in. Assuming the above conditions, how much water will replace the 500 in. of snow?

60. *Gardening.* The number of calories burned by a gardener is directly proportional to the time spent gardening. It takes 30 min to burn 180 calories. How long would it take to burn 240 calories when gardening?

Source: www.healthstatus.com

Aha! **61.** *Mass of water in a human.* The number of kilograms W of water in a human body varies directly as the mass of the body. A 96-kg person contains 64 kg of water. How many kilograms of water are in a 48-kg person?

62. *Weight on Mars.* The weight M of an object on Mars varies directly as its weight E on Earth. A person who weighs 95 lb on Earth weighs 38 lb on Mars. How much would a 100-lb person weigh on Mars?

63. *String length and frequency.*   The frequency of a string is inversely proportional to its length. A violin string that is 33 cm long vibrates with a frequency of 260 Hz. What is the frequency when the string is shortened to 30 cm?

64. *Wavelength and frequency.*   The wavelength W of a radio wave varies inversely as its frequency F. A wave with a frequency of 1200 kilohertz has a length of 300 meters. What is the length of a wave with a frequency of 800 kilohertz?

65. *Ultraviolet index.*   At an ultraviolet, or UV, rating of 4, those people who are less sensitive to the sun will burn in 75 min. Given that the number of minutes it takes to burn, t, varies inversely with the UV rating, u, how long will it take less sensitive people to burn when the UV rating is 14?
Source: *The Electronic Textbook of Dermatology* at www.telemedicine.org

66. *Current and resistance.*   The current I in an electrical conductor varies inversely as the resistance R of the conductor. If the current is $\frac{1}{2}$ ampere when the resistance is 240 ohms, what is the current when the resistance is 540 ohms?

67. *Air pollution.*   The average U.S. household of 2.6 people released 0.94 ton of carbon monoxide into the environment in a recent year. How many tons were released nationally? Use 305,000,000 as the U.S. population.
Sources: Based on data from the U.S. Environmental Protection Agency and the U.S. Census Bureau

68. *Relative aperture.*   The relative aperture, or f-stop, of a 23.5-mm lens is directly proportional to the focal length F of the lens. If a lens with a 150-mm focal length has an f-stop of 6.3, find the f-stop of a 23.5-mm lens with a focal length of 80 mm.

Find an equation of variation in which:

69. y varies directly as the square of x, and $y = 50$ when $x = 10$.

70. y varies directly as the square of x, and $y = 0.15$ when $x = 0.1$.

71. y varies inversely as the square of x, and $y = 50$ when $x = 10$.

72. y varies inversely as the square of x, and $y = 0.15$ when $x = 0.1$.

73. y varies jointly as x and z, and $y = 105$ when $x = 14$ and $z = 5$.

74. y varies jointly as x and z, and $y = \frac{3}{2}$ when $x = 2$ and $z = 10$.

75. y varies jointly as w and the square of x and inversely as z, and $y = 49$ when $w = 3$, $x = 7$, and $z = 12$.

76. y varies directly as x and inversely as w and the square of z, and $y = 4.5$ when $x = 15$, $w = 5$, and $z = 2$.

77. *Stopping distance of a car.*   The stopping distance d of a car after the brakes have been applied varies directly as the square of the speed r. Once the brakes are applied, a car traveling 60 mph can stop in 138 ft. What stopping distance corresponds to a speed of 40 mph?
Source: Based on data from Edmunds.com

78. *Reverberation time.*   A sound's reverberation time T is the time it takes for the sound level to decrease by 60 dB (decibels) after the sound has been turned off. Reverberation time varies directly as the volume V of a room and inversely as the sound absorption A of the room. A given sound has a reverberation time of 1.5 sec in a room with a volume of 90 m^3 and a sound absorption of 9.6. What is the reverberation time of the same sound in a room with a volume of 84 m^3 and a sound absorption of 10.5?
Source: www.isover.co.uk

79. *Volume of a gas.* The volume V of a given mass of a gas varies directly as the temperature T and inversely as the pressure P. If $V = 231$ cm^3 when $T = 300°$K (Kelvin) and $P = 20$ lb/cm^2, what is the volume when $T = 320°$K and $P = 16$ lb/cm^2?

80. *Intensity of a signal.* The intensity I of a television signal varies inversely as the square of the distance d from the transmitter. If the intensity is 25 W/m^2 at a distance of 2 km, what is the intensity 6.25 km from the transmitter?

81. *Atmospheric drag.* Wind resistance, or atmospheric drag, tends to slow down moving objects. Atmospheric drag W varies jointly as an object's surface area A and velocity v. If a car traveling at a speed of 40 mph with a surface area of 37.8 ft^2 experiences a drag of 222 N (Newtons), how fast must a car with 51 ft^2 of surface area travel in order to experience a drag force of 430 N?

82. *Drag force.* The drag force F on a boat varies jointly as the wetted surface area A and the square of the velocity of the boat. If a boat traveling 6.5 mph experiences a drag force of 86 N when the wetted surface area is 41.2 ft^2, find the wetted surface area of a boat traveling 8.2 mph with a drag force of 94 N.

83. If y varies directly as x, does doubling x cause y to be doubled as well? Why or why not?

84. Which exercise did you find easier to work: Exercise 15 or Exercise 19? Why?

Skill Review

To prepare for Chapter 8, review solving an equation for y and translating phrases to algebraic expressions (Sections 1.1 and 2.3).

Solve. [2.3]

85. $x - 6y = 3$, for y

86. $3x - 8y = 5$, for y

87. $5x + 2y = -3$, for y

88. $x + 8y = 4$, for y

Translate each of the following. Do not solve. [1.1]

89. Five more than twice a number is 49.

90. Three less than half of some number is 57.

91. The sum of two consecutive integers is 145.

92. The difference between a number and its opposite is 20.

Synthesis

93. Suppose that the number of customer complaints is inversely proportional to the number of employees hired. Will a firm reduce the number of complaints more by expanding from 5 to 10 employees, or from 20 to 25? Explain. Consider using a graph to help justify your answer.

94. Why do you think subscripts are used in Exercises 15 and 25 but not in Exercises 27 and 28?

95. *Escape velocity.* A satellite's escape velocity is 6.5 mi/sec, the radius of the earth is 3960 mi, and the earth's gravitational constant is 32.2 ft/sec^2. How far is the satellite from the surface of the earth? (See Example 2.)

96. The *harmonic mean* of two numbers a and b is a number M such that the reciprocal of M is the average of the reciprocals of a and b. Find a formula for the harmonic mean.

97. *Health-care.* Young's rule for determining the size of a particular child's medicine dosage c is

$$c = \frac{a}{a + 12} \cdot d,$$

where a is the child's age and d is the typical adult dosage. If a child's age is doubled, the dosage increases. Find the ratio of the larger dosage to the smaller dosage. By what percent does the dosage increase?

Source: Olsen, June Looby, Leon J. Ablon, and Anthony Patrick Giangrasso, *Medical Dosage Calculations*, 6th ed.

98. Solve for x:

$$x^2\left(1 - \frac{2pq}{x}\right) = \frac{2p^2q^3 - pq^2x}{-q}.$$

99. *Average acceleration.* The formula

$$a = \frac{\dfrac{d_4 - d_3}{t_4 - t_3} - \dfrac{d_2 - d_1}{t_2 - t_1}}{t_4 - t_2}$$

can be used to approximate average acceleration, where the d's are distances and the t's are the corresponding times. Solve for t_1.

100. If y varies inversely as the cube of x and x is multiplied by 0.5, what is the effect on y?

101. *Intensity of light.* The intensity I of light from a bulb varies directly as the wattage of the bulb and inversely as the square of the distance d from the bulb. If the wattage of a light source and its distance from reading matter are both doubled, how does the intensity change?

102. Describe in words the variation represented by $W = \dfrac{k m_1 M_1}{d^2}$. Assume k is a constant.

103. *Tension of a musical string.* The tension T on a string in a musical instrument varies jointly as the string's mass per unit length m, the square of its length l, and the square of its fundamental frequency f. A 2-m long string of mass 5 gm/m with a fundamental frequency of 80 has a tension of 100 N (Newtons). How long should the same string be if its tension is going to be changed to 72 N?

104. *Volume and cost.* A peanut butter jar in the shape of a right circular cylinder is 4 in. high and 3 in. in diameter and sells for $1.20. If we assume that cost is proportional to volume, how much should a jar 6 in. high and 6 in. in diameter cost?

105. *Golf distance finder.* A device used in golf to estimate the distance d to a hole measures the size s that the 7-ft pin *appears* to be in a viewfinder. The viewfinder uses the principle, diagrammed here, that s gets bigger when d gets smaller. If $s = 0.56$ in. when $d = 50$ yd, find an equation of variation that expresses d as a function of s. What is d when $s = 0.40$ in.?

HOW IT WORKS:

Just sight the flagstick through the viewfinder...
fit flag between top dashed line and the solid line below...
...read the distance, 50 – 220 yards.

50 70 90 110 130 150 170 190 210
RANGE YARDS

Nothing to focus.
•
Gives you exact distance that your ball
lies from the flagstick.
•
Choose proper club on every approach shot.
•
Figure new pin placement instantly.
•
Train your naked eye for formal and tournament play.
•
Eliminate the need to remember every stake,
tree, and bush on the course.

Study Summary

KEY TERMS AND CONCEPTS	EXAMPLES

SECTION 8.1: INTRODUCTION TO FUNCTIONS

A **function** is a correspondence between a first set, called the **domain**, and a second set, called the **range**, such that each member of the domain corresponds to *exactly one* member of the range.

The correspondence $f: \left\{ \left(-1, \frac{1}{2}\right), (0, 1), (1, 2), (2, 4), (3, 8) \right\}$ is a function.

The domain of $f = \{-1, 0, 1, 2, 3\}$.

The range of $f = \left\{ \frac{1}{2}, 1, 2, 4, 8 \right\}$.

$f(-1) = \frac{1}{2}$

The input -1 corresponds to the output $\frac{1}{2}$.

The Vertical-Line Test

If it is possible for a vertical line to cross a graph more than once, then the graph is not the graph of a function.

 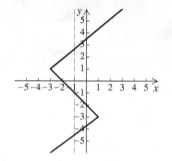

This *is* the graph of a function.   This *is not* the graph of a function.

SECTION 8.2: DOMAIN AND RANGE

The domain of a function is the set of all x-coordinates of the points on the graph.

The range of a function is the set of all y-coordinates of the points on the graph.

Consider the function given by $f(x) = |x| - 3$.

    The domain of the function is $\mathbb{R}$.

    The range of the function is $\{y \mid y \geq -3\}$, or $[-3, \infty)$.

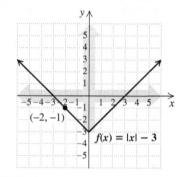

Unless otherwise stated, the domain of a function is the set of all numbers for which function values can be calculated.

Consider the function given by $f(x) = \dfrac{x + 2}{x - 7}$.

Function values cannot be calculated when the denominator is 0. Since $x - 7 = 0$ when $x = 7$, the domain of f is

$$\{x \mid x \text{ is a real number } and \ x \neq 7\}.$$

SECTION 8.3: GRAPHS OF FUNCTIONS

Linear Function

$$f(x) = mx + b$$

Constant Function

$$f(x) = b$$

Graph: $f(x) = \frac{1}{2}x - 3$.

We plot the y-intercept, $(0, -3)$. From there, we count off a slope of $\frac{1}{2}$: We go up 1 unit and to the right 2 units to the point $(2, -2)$. We then draw the graph.

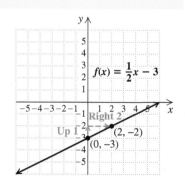

Graphs of nonlinear functions are not straight lines.

x	$f(x) = x^2 - 3$	$(x, f(x))$
0	-3	$(0, -3)$
-1	-2	$(-1, -2)$
1	-2	$(1, -2)$
-2	1	$(-2, 1)$
2	1	$(2, 1)$

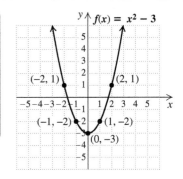

f is a quadratic function.

Domain of $f = \mathbb{R}$, or $(-\infty, \infty)$.

Range of $f = \{y | y \geq -3\}$, or $[-3, \infty)$.

SECTION 8.4: THE ALGEBRA OF FUNCTIONS

For $f(x) = x^2 + 3x$ and $g(x) = x - 5$:

$(f + g)(x) = f(x) + g(x)$

$$(f + g)(x) = f(x) + g(x)$$
$$= x^2 + 3x + x - 5 = x^2 + 4x - 5;$$

$(f - g)(x) = f(x) - g(x)$

$$(f - g)(x) = f(x) - g(x)$$
$$= x^2 + 3x - (x - 5) = x^2 + 2x + 5;$$

$(f \cdot g)(x) = f(x) \cdot g(x)$

$$(f \cdot g)(x) = f(x) \cdot g(x)$$
$$= (x^2 + 3x)(x - 5) = x^3 - 2x^2 - 15x;$$

$(f/g)(x) = f(x)/g(x)$, provided $g(x) \neq 0$

$$(f/g)(x) = f(x)/g(x), \text{ provided } g(x) \neq 0$$
$$= \frac{x^2 + 3x}{x - 5}, \text{ provided } x \neq 5. \quad g(5) = 0$$

SECTION 8.5: FORMULAS, APPLICATIONS, AND VARIATION

Direct Variation

$$y = kx$$

If y varies directly as x and $y = 45$ when $x = 0.15$, find the equation of variation.

$$y = kx$$
$$45 = k(0.15)$$
$$300 = k$$

The equation of variation is $y = 300x$.

Inverse Variation

$$y = \frac{k}{x}$$

If y varies inversely as x and $y = 45$ when $x = 0.15$, find the equation of variation.

$$y = \frac{k}{x}$$
$$45 = \frac{k}{0.15}$$
$$6.75 = k$$

The equation of variation is $y = \dfrac{6.75}{x}$.

Joint Variation	*If y varies jointly as x and z and y = 40 when x = 5 and z = 4, find the equation of variation.*
$y = kxz$	$$y = kxz$$ $$40 = k \cdot 5 \cdot 4$$ $$2 = k$$ The equation of variation is $y = 2xz$.

Review Exercises: Chapter 8

↪ *Concept Reinforcement*   *Classify each of the following as either true or false.*

1. Every function is a relation. [8.1]

2. When we are discussing functions, the notation $f(3)$ does not mean $f \cdot 3$. [8.1]

3. If a graph includes both $(9, 5)$ and $(7, 5)$, it cannot represent a function. [8.1]

4. The domain and the range of a function can be the same set of numbers. [8.2]

5. The horizontal-line test is a quick way to determine whether a graph represents a function. [8.1]

6. In a piecewise-defined function, the function values are determined using more than one rule. [8.2]

7. $(f + g)(x) = f(x) + g(x)$ is not an example of the distributive law when f and g are functions. [8.4]

8. In order for $(f/g)(a)$ to exist, we must have $g(a) \neq 0$. [8.4]

9. If x varies inversely as y, then there exists some constant k for which $x = k/y$. [8.5]

10. If 2 people can decorate for a party in 5 hr, and 10 people can decorate for the same party in 4 hr, the situation represents inverse variation. [8.5]

11. For the following graph of f, determine **(a)** $f(2)$; **(b)** the domain of f; **(c)** any x-values for which $f(x) = 2$; and **(d)** the range of f. [8.1], [8.2]

12. Find $g(-3)$ for $g(x) = \dfrac{x}{x + 1}$. [8.1]

13. Find $f(2a)$ for $f(x) = x^2 + 2x - 3$. [8.1]

14. The function $A(t) = 0.233t + 5.87$ can be used to estimate the median age of cars in the United States t years after 1990. (In this context, a median age of 3 yr means that half the cars are more than 3 yr old and half are less.) Predict the median age of cars in 2010; that is, find $A(20)$. [8.1]
    Source: The Polk Co.

15. The following table shows the U.S. minimum hourly wage. Use the data in the table to draw a graph and to estimate the U.S. minimum hourly wage in 2012. [8.1]

Input, Year	Output, U.S. Minimum Hourly Wage
1997	$5.15
2007	5.85
2008	6.55
2009	7.25

For each of the graphs in Exercises 16–19, **(a)** *determine whether the graph represents a function and* **(b)** *if so, determine the domain and the range of the function.* [8.1], [8.2]

16.

17.

18.

19.

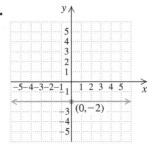

Find the domain of each function.

20. $f(x) = 3x^2 - 7$ [8.2]

21. $g(x) = \dfrac{x^2}{x - 1}$ [8.2]

22. $f(t) = \dfrac{1}{t^2 + 5t + 4}$ [8.2]

23. If a service agreement is cancelled, the amount that Vale Appliances will refund on the agreement is given by the function

$$r(t) = 900 - 15t,$$

where t is the number of weeks since the date of purchase. What is the domain of the function? [8.2]

24. For the function given by

$$f(x) = \begin{cases} 2 - x, & \text{if } x \leq -2, \\ x^2, & \text{if } -2 < x \leq 5, \\ x + 10, & \text{if } x > 5, \end{cases}$$

find **(a)** $f(-3)$; **(b)** $f(-2)$; **(c)** $f(4)$; and **(d)** $f(25)$. [8.2]

25. It costs $90 plus $30 a month to join the Family Fitness Center. Formulate a linear function to model the cost $C(t)$ for t months of membership, and determine the time required for the cost to reach $300. [8.3]

26. *Records in the 200-meter run.* In 1983, the record for the 200-m run was 19.75 sec. In 2007, it was 19.32 sec. Let $R(t)$ represent the record in the 200-m run and t the number of years since 1980. [8.3]

Source: International Association of Athletics Federation

a) Find a linear function that fits the data.

b) Use the function of part (a) to predict the record in 2013 and in 2020.

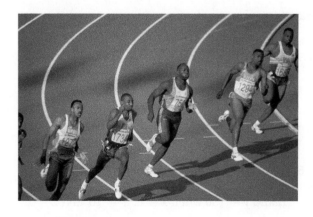

Classify each function as a linear function, an absolute-value function, a quadratic function, another polynomial function, or a rational function. [8.3]

27. $f(x) = |3x - 7|$

28. $g(x) = 4x^5 - 8x^3 + 7$

29. $p(x) = x^2 + x - 10$

30. $h(n) = 4n - 17$

31. $s(t) = \dfrac{t + 1}{t + 2}$

Graph each function and determine its domain and range. [8.3]

32. $f(x) = 3$

33. $f(x) = 2x + 1$

34. $g(x) = |x + 1|$

Let $g(x) = 3x - 6$ and $h(x) = x^2 + 1$. Find the following.

35. $(g \cdot h)(4)$ [8.4]

36. $(g - h)(-2)$ [8.4]

37. $(g/h)(-1)$ [8.4]

38. The domains of $g + h$ and $g \cdot h$ [8.4]

39. The domain of h/g [8.4]

Solve. [8.5]

40. $I = \dfrac{2V}{R + 2r}$, for r

41. $S = \dfrac{H}{m(t_1 - t_2)}$, for m

42. $\dfrac{1}{ac} = \dfrac{2}{ab} - \dfrac{3}{bc}$, for c

43. $T = \dfrac{A}{v(t_2 - t_1)}$, for t_1

44. Find an equation of variation in which y varies directly as x, and $y = 30$ when $x = 4$. [8.5]

45. Find an equation of variation in which y varies inversely as x, and $y = 3$ when $x = \frac{1}{4}$. [8.5]

46. Find an equation of variation in which y varies jointly as x and the square of w and inversely as z, and $y = 150$ when $x = 6$, $w = 10$, and $z = 2$. [8.5]

Solve. [8.5]

47. For those people with highly sensitive skin, an ultra-violet, or UV, rating of 6 will cause sunburn after 10 min. Given that the number of minutes it takes to burn t varies inversely as the UV rating u, how long will it take a highly sensitive person to burn on a day with a UV rating of 4?
Source: *The Electronic Textbook of Dermatology* found at www.telemedicine.org

48. The amount of waste generated by a family varies directly as the number of people in the family. The average U.S. family has 3.2 people and generates 14.4 lb of waste daily. How many pounds of waste would be generated daily by a family of 5?
Sources: Based on data from the U.S. Census Bureau and the U.S. Statistical Abstract 2007

49. *Electrical safety.* The amount of time t needed for an electrical shock to stop a 150-lb person's heart varies inversely as the square of the current flowing through the body. It is known that a 0.089-amp current is deadly to a 150-lb person after 3.4 sec. How long would it take a 0.096-amp current to be deadly?
Source: Safety Consulting Services

Synthesis

50. If two functions have the same domain and range, are the functions identical? Why or why not? [8.2]

51. Jenna believes that 0 is never in the domain of a rational function. Is she correct? Why or why not? [8.2]

52. Treasure Tea charges $7.99 for each package of loose tea. Shipping charges are $2.95 per package plus $20 per order for overnight delivery. Find a linear function for determining the cost of one order of x packages of tea, including shipping and overnight delivery. [8.3]

53. Determine the domain and the range of the function graphed below. [8.2]

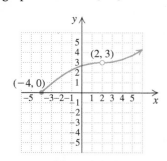

Test: Chapter 8

1. For the following graph of f, determine (a) $f(-2)$; (b) the domain of f; (c) any x-value for which $f(x) = \frac{1}{2}$; and (d) the range of f.

2. There were 41.9 million international visitors to the United States in 2002 and 51.0 million visitors in 2006. Draw a graph and estimate the number of international visitors in 2005.

   Sources: U.S. Department of Commerce, ITA, Office of Travel and Tourism Industries; Global Insight, Inc.

For each of the following graphs, (a) determine whether the graph represents a function and (b) if so, determine the domain and the range of the function.

3.

4.

5.

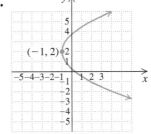

6. The distance d, in miles, that Kerry is from Chicago is given by the function $d(t) = 240 - 60t$, where t is the number of hours since he left Indianapolis. What is the domain of the function?

7. For the function given by

$$f(x) = \begin{cases} x^2, & \text{if } x < 0, \\ 3x - 5, & \text{if } 0 \le x \le 2, \\ x + 7, & \text{if } x > 2, \end{cases}$$

   find (a) $f(0)$; (b) $f(3)$.

8. Porter paid \$180 for his phone. His monthly service fee is \$55. Formulate a linear function to model the cost $C(t)$ for t months of service, and determine the amount of time required for the total cost to reach \$840.

9. If you rent a truck for one day and drive it 250 mi, the cost is \$100. If you rent it for one day and drive it 300 mi, the cost is \$115. Let $C(m)$ represent the cost, in dollars, of driving m miles.

   a) Find a linear function that fits the data.
   b) Use the function to determine how much it will cost to rent the truck for one day and drive it 500 mi.

Classify each function as a linear function, a quadratic function, another polynomial function, an absolute-value function, or a rational function. Then find the domain of each function.

10. $f(x) = \dfrac{1}{4}x + 7$

11. $g(x) = \dfrac{3}{x^2 - 16}$

12. $p(x) = 4x^2 + 7$

Graph each function and determine its domain and range.

13. $f(x) = \dfrac{1}{3}x - 2$

14. $g(x) = x^2 - 1$

15. $h(x) = -\dfrac{1}{2}$

Find the following, given that $g(x) = \dfrac{1}{x}$ and $h(x) = 2x + 1$.

16. $g(-1)$

17. $h(5a)$

18. $(g + h)(x)$

19. The domain of g

20. The domain of $g + h$

21. The domain of g/h

22. Solve $R = \dfrac{gs}{g + s}$ for s.

23. Find an equation of variation in which y varies directly as x, and $y = 10$ when $x = 20$.

24. The number of workers n needed to clean a stadium after a game varies inversely as the amount of time t allowed for the cleanup. If it takes 25 workers to clean the stadium when there are 6 hr allowed for the job, how many workers are needed if the stadium must be cleaned in 5 hr?

25. The surface area of a balloon varies directly as the square of its radius. The area is 325 in² when the radius is 5 in. What is the area when the radius is 7 in.?

Synthesis

26. The function $f(t) = 5 + 15t$ can be used to determine a bicycle racer's location, in miles from the starting line, measured t hours after passing the 5-mi mark.

    a) How far from the start will the racer be 1 hr and 40 min after passing the 5-mi mark?

    b) Assuming a constant rate, how fast is the racer traveling?

27. Given that $f(x) = 5x^2 + 1$ and $g(x) = 4x - 3$, find an expression for $h(x)$ so that the domain of $f/g/h$ is

$$\left\{ x \mid x \text{ is a real number } and \ x \neq \tfrac{3}{4} \ and \ x \neq \tfrac{2}{7} \right\}.$$

Answers may vary.

Cumulative Review: Chapters 1–3, 5-8

1. Evaluate

$$\frac{2x - y^2}{x + y}$$

for $x = 3$ and $y = -4$. [1.8]

2. Convert to scientific notation: 391,000,000. [5.2]

3. Determine the slope and the y-intercept for the line given by $7x - 4y = 12$. [3.6]

4. Find an equation for the line that passes through the points $(-1, 7)$ and $(4, -3)$. [3.7]

5. If

$$f(x) = \frac{x - 3}{x^2 - 11x + 30},$$

find **(a)** $f(3)$ and **(b)** the domain of f. [8.1], [8.2]

Graph on a plane.

6. $5x = y$ [3.2]

7. $8y + 2x = 16$ [3.3]

8. $f(x) = -4$ [8.2]

9. $y = \tfrac{1}{3}x - 2$ [3.6]

Perform the indicated operations and simplify.

10. $(8x^3 y^2)(-3xy^2)$ [5.1]

11. $(5x^2 - 2x + 1)(3x^2 + x - 2)$ [5.5]

12. $(3x^2 + y)^2$ [5.6]

13. $(2x^2 - 9)(2x^2 + 9)$ [5.6]

14. $(-5m^3 n^2 - 3mn^3) + (-4m^2 n^2 + 4m^3 n^2) - (2mn^3 - 3m^2 n^2)$ [5.4]

15. $\dfrac{y^2 - 36}{2y + 8} \cdot \dfrac{y + 4}{y + 6}$ [7.2]

16. $\dfrac{x^4 - 1}{x^2 - x - 2} \div \dfrac{x^2 + 1}{x - 2}$ [7.2]

17. $\dfrac{5ab}{a^2 - b^2} + \dfrac{a + b}{a - b}$ [7.4]

18. $\dfrac{2}{m + 1} + \dfrac{3}{m - 5} - \dfrac{m^2 - 1}{m^2 - 4m - 5}$ [7.4]

19. $y - \dfrac{2}{3y}$ [7.4]

20. Simplify: $\dfrac{\dfrac{1}{x} - \dfrac{1}{y}}{x + y}$. [7.5]

Factor.

21. $4x^3 + 400x$ [6.1]

22. $x^2 + 8x - 84$ [6.2]

23. $16y^2 - 25$ [6.4]

24. $64x^3 + 8$ [6.5]

25. $t^2 - 16t + 64$ [6.4]

26. $x^6 - x^2$ [6.4]

27. $\frac{1}{8}b^3 - c^3$ [6.5]

28. $3t^2 + 17t - 28$ [6.3]

29. $x^5 - x^3y + x^2y - y^2$ [6.1]

Solve.

30. $8x = 1 + 16x^2$ [6.7]

31. $288 = 2y^2$ [6.7]

32. $\frac{1}{3}x - \frac{1}{5} \geq \frac{1}{5}x - \frac{1}{3}$ [2.6]

33. $5(x - 2) - (x - 3) = 7x - 2(5 - x)$ [2.2]

34. $\dfrac{6}{x - 5} = \dfrac{2}{2x}$ [7.6]

35. $\dfrac{3x}{x - 2} - \dfrac{6}{x + 2} = \dfrac{24}{x^2 - 4}$ [7.6]

36. $P = \dfrac{4a}{a + b}$, for a [8.5]

37. Find the slope of the line containing $(2, 5)$ and $(1, 10)$. [3.5]

38. Find the slope of the line given by $f(x) = 8x + 3$. [8.3]

39. Find the slope of the line given by $y + 6 = -4$. [3.5]

40. Find an equation of the line containing $(5, -2)$ and perpendicular to the line given by $x - y = 5$. [3.7]

Find the following, given that $f(x) = x + 5$ and $g(x) = x^2 - 1$.

41. $g(-10)$ [8.1]   **42.** $(g/f)(x)$ [8.4]

43. Find the domain of f if $f(x) = \dfrac{x}{x + 6}$. [8.2]

44. Determine the domain and the range of the function f represented below. [8.2]

45. *Broadway revenue.* Gross revenue from Broadway shows has grown from $20 million in 1986–1987 to $939 million in 2006–2007. Let $r(t)$ represent gross revenue, in millions of dollars, from Broadway shows t seasons after the 1986–1987 season. [8.3]
Source: The League of American Theatres and Producers

a) Find a linear function that fits the data.

b) Use the function from part (a) to predict the gross revenue from Broadway shows in 2009–2010.

c) In what season will the gross revenue from Broadway shows reach $1.4 billion?

46. *Broadway performances.* In January 2006, *The Phantom of the Opera* became the longest-running Broadway show with 7486 performances. By January 2008, the show had played 8302 times. Calculate the rate at which the number of performances was rising. [3.4]

47. *Quilting.* A rectangular quilted wall hanging is 4 in. longer than it is wide. The area of the quilt is 320 in². Find the perimeter of the quilt. [6.8]

48. *Hotel management.* The IQAir HealthPro Plus air purifier can clean the air in a 20-ft by 25-ft meeting room in 5 fewer minutes than it takes the Austin Healthmate HM400 to do the same job. Together the two machines can purify the air in the room in 6 min. How long would it take each machine, working alone, to purify the air in the room? [7.7]
Source: Manufacturers' and retailers' websites

49. *Driving delays.* According to the National Surface Transportation Policy and Revenue Study Commission, the best-case scenario for driving delays due to road work in 2055 will be 250% of the delays in 2005. If the commission predicts 30 billion hr of driving delays in 2055, how many hours of driving delays were there in 2005? [2.5]

50. *Driving time.*   The time t that it takes for Johann to drive to work varies inversely as his speed. On a day when Johann averages 45 mph, it takes him 20 min to drive to work. How long will it take him to drive to work when he averages only 40 mph? [8.5]

51. *Disaster relief.*   Six months after Hurricane Katrina struck the Gulf Coast in 2005, $2.18 billion of relief money had been distributed to disaster victims. This was $\frac{2}{3}$ of the amount raised by charity for disaster relief. How much money was still to be distributed? [2.5]
Source: www.washingtonpost.com

Synthesis

52. Multiply: $(x - 4)^3$. [5.5]

53. Find all roots for $f(x) = x^4 - 34x^2 + 225$. [6.6], [8.3]

Solve.

54. $\dfrac{18}{x - 9} + \dfrac{10}{x + 5} = \dfrac{28x}{x^2 - 4x - 45}$ [7.6]

55. $16x^3 = x$ [6.7]

56. *Photo books.*   An Everyday Photo Book costs $12 for the first 20 pages plus $0.75 for each additional page. Formulate a piecewise-defined function to model the cost $C(x)$ for a book with x pages. [8.2]
Source: snapfish.com

Elementary Algebra Review

9

This chapter is a review of the first six chapters of this text. Each section corresponds to a chapter of the text. For further explanation of the topics in this chapter, refer to the section or pages referenced in the margin.

9.1   Introduction to Algebraic Expressions

- The Real Numbers

- Operations on Real Numbers

- Algebraic Expressions

Sets of real numbers

THE REAL NUMBERS

Sets of Numbers

Natural numbers:	$\{1, 2, 3, \ldots\}$
Whole numbers:	$\{0, 1, 2, 3, \ldots\}$
Integers:	$\{\ldots, -3, -2, -1, 0, 1, 2, 3, \ldots\}$
Rational numbers:	$\left\{\dfrac{a}{b} \,\middle|\, a \text{ and } b \text{ are integers and } b \neq 0\right\}$

Terminating decimals

Repeating decimals

Irrational numbers

Real numbers

Rational numbers can always be written as **terminating** decimals or **repeating** decimals. **Irrational numbers,** like $\sqrt{2}$ or π, can be thought of as nonterminating, nonrepeating decimals. The set of **real numbers** consists of all rational numbers and irrational numbers, taken together.

Taken from *Elementary and Intermediate Algebra: Graphs and Models*, Fourth Edition by Marvin L. Bittinger, David J. Ellenbogen, and Barbara L. Johnson.

Real numbers can be represented by points on the number line. For any two numbers, the one to the left is less than the one to the right.

Equation

Inequality

Sentences like $\frac{1}{4} = 0.25$, containing an equals sign, are called **equations.** An **inequality** is a sentence containing $>$ (is greater than), $<$ (is less than), $\geq$ (is greater than or equal to), or $\leq$ (is less than or equal to). Equations and inequalities can be true or false.

EXAMPLE 1 Write true or false for each equation or inequality.

a) $-2\frac{1}{3} = -\frac{7}{3}$ **b)** $1 = -1$ **c)** $-5 < -2$

d) $-3 \geq 2$ **e)** $1.1 \leq 1.1$

SOLUTION

a) $-2\frac{1}{3} = -\frac{7}{3}$ is *true* because $-2\frac{1}{3}$ and $-\frac{7}{3}$ represent the same number.

b) $1 = -1$ is a *false* equation.

c) $-5 < -2$ is *true* because -5 is to the left of -2 on the number line.

d) $-3 \geq 2$ is *false* because neither $-3 > 2$ nor $-3 = 2$ is true.

e) $1.1 \leq 1.1$ is *true* because $1.1 = 1.1$ is true.

Try Exercise 1.

Absolute value

The distance of a number from 0 is called the **absolute value** of the number. The notation $|-4|$ represents the absolute value of -4. The absolute value of a number is never negative.

EXAMPLE 2 Find the absolute value: **(a)** $|-4|$; **(b)** $\left|\frac{11}{3}\right|$; **(c)** $|0|$.

SOLUTION

a) $|-4| = 4$ since -4 is 4 units from 0.

b) $\left|\frac{11}{3}\right| = \frac{11}{3}$ since $\frac{11}{3}$ is $\frac{11}{3}$ units from 0.

c) $|0| = 0$ since 0 is 0 units from itself.

Try Exercise 7.

OPERATIONS ON REAL NUMBERS

Addition

Rules for Addition of Real Numbers

1. *Positive numbers*: Add as usual. The answer is positive.
2. *Negative numbers*: Add absolute values and make the answer negative.
3. *A positive number and a negative number*: Subtract absolute values. Then:

   a) If the positive number has the greater absolute value, the answer is positive.
   b) If the negative number has the greater absolute value, the answer is negative.
   c) If the numbers have the same absolute value, the answer is 0.

4. *One number is zero*: The sum is the other number.

Opposite

Every real number has an **opposite.** The opposite of -6 is 6, the opposite of 3.7 is -3.7, and the opposite of 0 is itself. When opposites are added, the result is 0. Finding the opposite of a number is often called "changing its sign."

Subtraction of real numbers is defined in terms of addition and opposites.

Subtraction

> **Subtraction of Real Numbers** To subtract, add the opposite of the number being subtracted.

The rules for multiplication and division can be stated together.

Multiplication and division

> **Rules for Multiplication and Division** To multiply or divide two real numbers:
> 1. Using the absolute values, multiply or divide, as indicated.
> 2. If the signs are the same, the answer is positive.
> 3. If the signs are different, the answer is negative.

EXAMPLE 3 Perform the indicated operations: **(a)** $-13 + (-9)$; **(b)** $-\frac{4}{5} + \frac{1}{10}$; **(c)** $-6 - (-7.3)$; **(d)** $3(-1.5)$; **(e)** $\left(-\frac{4}{9}\right) \div \left(-\frac{2}{5}\right)$.

SOLUTION

a) $-13 + (-9) = -22$

Two negatives. *Think*: Add the absolute values, 13 and 9, to get 22. Make the answer *negative*, -22.

b) $-\frac{4}{5} + \frac{1}{10} = -\frac{8}{10} + \frac{1}{10} = -\frac{7}{10}$

A negative and a positive. *Think*: The difference of absolute values is $\frac{8}{10} - \frac{1}{10}$, or $\frac{7}{10}$. The negative number has the larger absolute value, so the answer is *negative*, $-\frac{7}{10}$.

c) $-6 - (-7.3) = -6 + 7.3 = 1.3$

Change the subtraction to addition and add the opposite.

d) $3(-1.5) = -4.5$

Think: $3(1.5) = 4.5$. The signs are different, so the answer is negative.

e) $\left(-\frac{4}{9}\right) \div \left(-\frac{2}{5}\right) = \left(-\frac{4}{9}\right) \cdot \left(-\frac{5}{2}\right)$
$= \frac{20}{18} = \frac{10}{9} \cdot \frac{2}{2} = \frac{10}{9}$

Multiplying by the reciprocal. The answer is positive.

Try Exercises 11 and 25.

Addition, subtraction, and multiplication are defined for all real numbers, but we cannot divide by 0. For example, $\frac{0}{3} = 0 \div 3 = 0$, but $\frac{3}{0} = 3 \div 0$ is *undefined*.

A product like $2 \cdot 2 \cdot 2 \cdot 2$, in which the factors are the same, is called a **power.**

Exponential notation

Powers are often written using **exponential notation:**

$$2 \cdot 2 \cdot 2 \cdot 2 = 2^4. \longleftarrow \text{There are 4 factors; 4 is the } exponent.$$
$$\text{2 is the } base.$$

A number raised to the exponent of 1 is the number itself; for example, $3^1 = 3$.

An expression containing a series of operations is not necessarily evaluated from left to right. Instead, we perform the operations according to the following rules.

> ### Rules for Order of Operations
> 1. Calculate within the innermost grouping symbols, ( ), [ ], { }, | |, and above or below fraction bars.
> 2. Simplify all exponential expressions.
> 3. Perform all multiplication and division, working from left to right.
> 4. Perform all addition and subtraction, working from left to right.

EXAMPLE 4 Simplify: $3 - [(4 \times 5) + 12 \div 2^3 \times 6] + 5$.

SOLUTION

$3 - [(4 \times 5) + 12 \div 2^3 \times 6] + 5$

$= 3 - [20 + 12 \div 2^3 \times 6] + 5$ Doing the calculations in the innermost parentheses first

$= 3 - [20 + 12 \div 8 \times 6] + 5$ Working inside the brackets; evaluating 2^3

$= 3 - [20 + 1.5 \times 6] + 5$ $12 \div 8$ is the first multiplication or division working from left to right.

$= 3 - [20 + 9] + 5$ Multiplying

$= 3 - 29 + 5$ Completing the calculations within the brackets

$= -26 + 5$ Adding and subtracting from left to right

$= -21$

Try Exercise 45.

ALGEBRAIC EXPRESSIONS

Algebraic expression

Constant

Variable

Substitute

Evaluate

In an **algebraic expression** like $2xt^3$, the number 2 is a **constant** and x and t are **variables**. Algebraic expressions containing variables can be **evaluated** by **substituting** a number for each variable in the expression and following the rules for order of operations.

EXAMPLE 5 The perimeter P of a rectangle of length l and width w is given by the formula $P = 2l + 2w$. Find the perimeter when l is 16 in. and w is 7.5 in.

SOLUTION We evaluate, substituting 16 in. for l and 7.5 in. for w and carrying out the operations:

$P = 2l + 2w$

Substitute. $= 2 \cdot 16 + 2 \cdot 7.5$

Carry out the operations. $= 32 + 15$

$= 47$ in.

Try Exercise 55.

Expressions that represent the same number are said to be **equivalent.** The laws that follow provide methods for writing equivalent expressions.

Laws and Properties of Real Numbers

Commutative laws:	$a + b = b + a; ab = ba$
Associative laws:	$a + (b + c) = (a + b) + c;$
	$a(bc) = (ab)c$
Distributive law:	$a(b + c) = ab + ac$
Identity property of 1:	$1 \cdot a = a \cdot 1 = a$
Identity property of 0:	$a + 0 = 0 + a = a$
Law of opposites:	$a + (-a) = 0$
Multiplicative property of 0:	$0 \cdot a = a \cdot 0 = 0$
Property of -1:	$-1 \cdot a = -a$
Opposite of a sum:	$-(a + b) = -a + (-b)$
$\dfrac{-a}{b} = \dfrac{a}{-b} = -\dfrac{a}{b},$	$\dfrac{-a}{-b} = \dfrac{a}{b}$

Factor

The distributive law can be used to multiply and to **factor** expressions. We factor an expression when we write an equivalent expression that is a product.

EXAMPLE 6   Write an equivalent expression as indicated.

a) Multiply: $-2(5x - 3)$.   **b)** Factor: $5x + 10y + 5$.

SOLUTION

a)
$$-2(5x - 3) = -2(5x + (-3))$$ Adding the opposite
$$= -2 \cdot 5x + (-2) \cdot (-3)$$ Using the distributive law
$$= (-2 \cdot 5)x + 6$$ Using the associative law for multiplication
$$= -10x + 6$$

b)
$$5x + 10y + 5 = 5 \cdot x + 5 \cdot 2y + 5 \cdot 1$$ The common factor is 5.
$$= 5(x + 2y + 1)$$ Using the distributive law

Factoring can be checked by multiplying:

$$5(x + 2y + 1) = 5 \cdot x + 5 \cdot 2y + 5 \cdot 1 = 5x + 10y + 5.$$

Try Exercises 61 and 69.

Terms

The **terms** of an algebraic expression are separated by plus signs. When two terms have variable factors that are exactly the same, the terms are called **like, or similar, terms.** The distributive law enables us to **combine,** or **collect, like terms.**

Combine like terms

EXAMPLE 7   Combine like terms: $-5m + 3n - 4n + 10m$.

SOLUTION

$$-5m + 3n - 4n + 10m$$

$$= -5m + 3n + (-4n) + 10m \qquad \text{Rewriting as addition}$$

$$= -5m + 10m + 3n + (-4n) \qquad \text{Using the commutative law of addition}$$

$$= (-5 + 10)m + (3 + (-4))n \qquad \text{Using the distributive law}$$

$$= 5m + (-n)$$

$$= 5m - n \qquad\qquad\qquad\qquad \text{Rewriting as subtraction}$$

Try Exercise 77.

We can also use the distributive law to help simplify algebraic expressions containing parentheses.

EXAMPLE 8   Simplify: **(a)** $4x - (y - 2x)$; **(b)** $3(t + 2) - 6(t - 1)$.

SOLUTION

a) $4x - (y - 2x) = 4x - y + 2x \qquad$ Removing parentheses and changing the sign of every term

$$= 6x - y \qquad\qquad \text{Combining like terms}$$

b) $3(t + 2) - 6(t - 1) = 3t + 6 - 6t + 6 \qquad$ Multiplying each term of $t + 2$ by 3 and each term of $t - 1$ by -6

$$= -3t + 12 \qquad\qquad \text{Combining like terms}$$

Try Exercise 83.

Value

Solution

If the expressions on each side of an equation have the same **value** for a given number, then that number is a **solution** of the equation.

EXAMPLE 9   Determine whether each number is a solution of $x - 2 = -5$.

a) 3   **b)** -3

SOLUTION

a) We have

$$x - 2 = -5 \qquad \text{Writing the equation}$$

$$\overline{3 - 2 \mid -5} \qquad \text{Substituting 3 for } x$$

$$1 \overset{?}{=} -5 \qquad 1 = -5 \text{ is FALSE}$$

Since $3 - 2 = -5$ is false, 3 is not a solution of $x - 2 = -5$.

b) We have

$$x - 2 = -5$$

$$\overline{-3 - 2 \mid -5}$$

$$\qquad\quad \overset{?}{} $$

$$-5 = -5 \qquad \text{TRUE}$$

Since $-3 - 2 = -5$ is true, -3 is a solution of $x - 2 = -5$.

Try Exercise 89.

Translating to algebraic expressions

Translating to equations

Certain word phrases can be translated to algebraic expressions. These in turn can often be used to translate problems to equations.

EXAMPLE 10 Energy Use. Translate this problem to an equation. Do not solve.

On average, a home spa costs about $192 per year to operate. This is 16 times as much as the average annual operating cost of a home computer. How much does it cost to operate a home computer for a year?
Source: U.S. Department of Energy

SOLUTION We let c represent the annual cost of operating a home computer. We then reword the problem to make the translation more direct.

$$
\begin{array}{ccccccc}
 & & & \text{home computer} & & \\
\textit{Rewording:} & 16 & \text{times} & \overbrace{\qquad\text{cost}\qquad} & \text{is} & 192 \\
 & \downarrow & \downarrow & \downarrow & \downarrow & \downarrow \\
\textit{Translating:} & 16 & \cdot & c & = & 192
\end{array}
$$

Try Exercise 95.

9.1 Exercise Set

FOR EXTRA HELP *MyMathLab*

Classify each equation or inequality as true or false.

1. $2.3 = 2.31$

2. $-3 \geq -3$

3. $-10 < -1$

4. $0 \leq -1$

5. $0 > -5$

6. $\frac{1}{10} = 0.1$

Find each absolute value.

7. $|4|$

8. $\left|\frac{11}{4}\right|$

9. $|-1.3|$

10. $|-105|$

Simplify.

11. $(-13) + (-12)$

12. $3 - (-2)$

13. $-\frac{1}{3} - \frac{2}{5}$

14. $\frac{3}{8} \div \frac{3}{5}$

15. $4.2 - 10.7$

16. $(-1.3)(2.8)$

17. $-15 + 0$

18. $\left(-\frac{1}{2}\right) + \frac{1}{8}$

19. $0 \div (-10)$

20. $0 - 32$

21. $\left(-\frac{3}{10}\right) + \left(-\frac{1}{5}\right)$

22. $\left(-\frac{4}{7}\right)\left(\frac{7}{4}\right)$

23. $-3.8 + 9.6$

24. $-0.01 + 1$

25. $(-12) \div 4$

26. $(-87)(0)$

27. $32 - (-7)$

28. $-100 + 35$

29. $(-10)(-17.5)$

30. $-10 - 2.68$

31. $(-68) + 36$

32. $175 \div (-25)$

33. $2 + (-3) + 7 + 10$

34. $-5 + (-15) + 13 + (-1)$

35. $3 \cdot (-2) \cdot (-1) \cdot (-1)$

36. $(-6) \cdot (-5) \cdot (-4) \cdot (-3) \cdot (-2) \cdot (-1)$

37. $(-1)^4 + 2^3$

38. $(-1)^5 + 2^4$

39. $2 \cdot 6 - 3 \cdot 5$

40. $12 \div 4 + 15 \div 3$

41. $3 - (2 \cdot 4 + 11)$

42. $3 - 11 + 2 \cdot 4$

43. $4 \cdot 5^2$

44. $7 \cdot 2^3$

45. $25 - 8 \cdot 3 + 1$

46. $12 - 16 \cdot 5 + 4$

47. $2 - (3^3 + 16 \div (-2)^3)$

48. $-7 - (8 + 10 \cdot 2^2)$

49. $|6(-3)| + |(-2)(-9)|$

50. $3 - |2 - 7 + 4|$

51. $\dfrac{7000 + (-10)^3}{10^2 \cdot (2 + 4)}$

52. $\dfrac{3 - 2 \cdot 6 - 5}{2(3 + 7)^2}$

53. $2 + 8 \div 2 \cdot 2$

54. $2 + 8 \div (2 \cdot 2)$

Evaluate.

55. $y - x$, for $x = 10$ and $y = 3$

56. $n - 2m$, for $m = 6$ and $n = 11$

57. $-3 - x^2 + 12x$, for $x = 5$

58. $14 + (y - 5)^2 - 12 \div y$, for $y = -2$

59. The area of a parallelogram with base b and height h is bh. Find the area of the parallelogram when the height is 3.5 cm and the base is 8 cm.

60. The area of a triangle with base b and height h is $\frac{1}{2}bh$. Find the area of the triangle when the height is 2 in. and the base is 6.2 in.

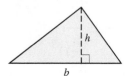

Multiply.

61. $4(2x + 7)$

62. $3(5y + 1)$

63. $-2(15 - 3x)$

64. $-7(3x - 5)$

65. $2(4a + 6b - 3c)$

66. $5(8p + q - 5r)$

67. $-3(2x - y + z)$

68. $-10(-6 - y - z)$

Factor.

69. $8x + 6y$

70. $7p + 14q$

71. $3 + 3w$

72. $4x + 4y$

73. $10x + 50y + 100$

74. $81p + 27q + 9$

Combine like terms.

75. $3p - 2p$

76. $4x + 3x$

77. $4m + 10 - 5m + 12$

78. $3a - 4b - 5b - 6a$

79. $-6x + 7 + 9x$

80. $16r + (-7r) + 3s$

Remove parentheses and simplify.

81. $2p - (7 - 4p)$

82. $4r - (3r + 5)$

83. $6x + 5y - 7(x - y)$

84. $14m - 6(2n - 3m) + n$

85. $6[2a + 4(a - 2b)]$

86. $2[2a + 1 - (3a - 6)]$

87. $3 - 2[5(x - 10y) - (3 + 2y)]$

88. $7 - 4[2(3 - 2x) - 5(4x - 3)]$

Determine whether the given number is a solution of the given equation.

89. 4; $3x - 2 = 10$

90. 12; $100 = 4x + 50$

91. -3; $4 - x = 1$

92. -1; $2 = 5 + 3x$

93. 4.6; $\dfrac{x}{2} = 2.3$

94. 144; $\dfrac{x}{9} = 16$

Translate each problem to an equation. Do not solve.

95. Three times what number is 348?

96. What number added to 256 is 113?

97. *Fast-Food Calories.* A McDonald's Big Mac® contains 500 calories. This is 69 more calories than a Taco Bell Beef Burrito® provides. How many calories are in a Taco Bell Beef Burrito?

98. *Coca-Cola® Consumption.* The average U.S. citizen consumes 296 servings of Coca-Cola each year. This is 7.4 times the international average. What is the international average per capita consumption of Coke?

99. *Vegetable Production.* It takes 42 gal of water to produce 1 lb of broccoli. This is twice the amount of water used to produce 1 lb of lettuce. How many gallons of water does it take to produce 1 lb of lettuce?

100. *Sports Costs.* The average annual cost for badminton is $12. This is $458 less than the average annual cost for scuba diving. What is the average annual cost for scuba diving?

9.2 Equations, Inequalities, and Problem Solving

- Solving Equations and Formulas
- Solving Inequalities
- Problem Solving

Equivalent equations

The addition principle

The multiplication principle

SOLVING EQUATIONS AND FORMULAS

Any replacement for the variable in an equation that makes the equation true is called a *solution* of the equation. To **solve** an equation means to find all of its solutions.

We use the following principles to write **equivalent equations,** or equations with the same solutions.

> ### The Addition and Multiplication Principles for Equations
>
> **The Addition Principle**
> For any real numbers a, b, and c,
>
> $$a = b \text{ is equivalent to } a + c = b + c.$$
>
> **The Multiplication Principle**
> For any real numbers a, b, and c, with $c \neq 0$,
>
> $$a = b \text{ is equivalent to } a \cdot c = b \cdot c.$$

To solve $x + a = b$ for x, we add $-a$ to (or subtract a from) both sides. To solve $ax = b$ for x, we multiply both sides by $\frac{1}{a}$ (or divide both sides by a).

To solve an equation like $-3x - 10 = 14$, we first isolate the variable term, $-3x$, using the addition principle. Then we use the multiplication principle to get the variable by itself.

EXAMPLE 1   Solve: $-3x - 10 = 14$.

SOLUTION

$$-3x - 10 = 14$$

Isolate the x-term.

$$-3x - 10 + 10 = 14 + 10 \qquad \text{Using the addition principle:}$$
$$\text{Adding 10 to both sides}$$

$$-3x = 24 \qquad \text{Simplifying}$$

$$\frac{-3x}{-3} = \frac{24}{-3} \qquad \text{Dividing both sides by } -3$$

Isolate x.

$$x = -8 \qquad \text{Simplifying}$$

Check:

$$\begin{array}{c|c} -3x - 10 = 14 \\ \hline -3(-8) - 10 & 14 \\ 24 - 10 & \\ & 14 \overset{?}{=} 14 \quad \text{TRUE} \end{array}$$

Always check in the original equation.

The solution is -8.

Try Exercise 13.

Clearing fractions

Equations are generally easier to solve when they do not contain fractions. The easiest way to clear an equation of fractions is to multiply *every term on both sides* of the equation by the least common denominator.

EXAMPLE 2 Solve: $\frac{5}{2} - \frac{1}{6}t = \frac{2}{3}$.

SOLUTION The number 6 is the least common denominator, so we multiply both sides by 6.

$$6\left(\frac{5}{2} - \frac{1}{6}t\right) = 6 \cdot \frac{2}{3}$$ Multiplying both sides by 6

$$6 \cdot \frac{5}{2} - 6 \cdot \frac{1}{6}t = 6 \cdot \frac{2}{3}$$ Using the distributive law. Be sure to multiply every term by 6.

$$15 - t = 4$$ The fractions are cleared.

$$15 - t - 15 = 4 - 15$$ Subtracting 15 from both sides

$$-t = -11$$

$$(-1)(-t) = (-1)(-11)$$ Multiplying both sides by -1 to change the sign

$$t = 11$$

Check:

$$\frac{5}{2} - \frac{1}{6}t = \frac{2}{3}$$

$$\begin{array}{c|c} \frac{5}{2} - \frac{1}{6}(11) & \frac{2}{3} \\ \frac{5}{2} - \frac{11}{6} & \\ \frac{15}{6} - \frac{11}{6} & \\ \frac{2}{3} \overset{?}{=} \frac{2}{3} & \text{TRUE} \end{array}$$

The solution is 11.

▌ Try Exercise 21.

To solve equations that contain parentheses, we can use the distributive law to first remove the parentheses. If like terms appear in an equation, we combine them and then solve.

EXAMPLE 3 Solve: $1 - 3(4 - x) = 2(x + 5) - 3x$.

SOLUTION

$$1 - 3(4 - x) = 2(x + 5) - 3x$$

$$1 - 12 + 3x = 2x + 10 - 3x$$ Using the distributive law

$$-11 + 3x = -x + 10$$ Combining like terms; $1 - 12 = -11$ and $2x - 3x = -x$

$$-11 + 3x + x = 10$$ Adding x to both sides to get all x-terms on one side

$$-11 + 4x = 10$$ Combining like terms

$$4x = 10 + 11$$ Adding 11 to both sides to isolate the x-term

$$4x = 21$$ Simplifying

$$x = \frac{21}{4}$$ Dividing both sides by 4

Check:

$$\frac{1 - 3(4 - x) = 2(x + 5) - 3x}{1 - 3\left(4 - \frac{21}{4}\right) \quad \bigg| \quad 2\left(\frac{21}{4} + 5\right) - 3\left(\frac{21}{4}\right)}$$

$$1 - 3\left(-\frac{5}{4}\right) \quad \bigg| \quad 2\left(\frac{41}{4}\right) - \frac{63}{4}$$

$$1 + \frac{15}{4} \quad \bigg| \quad \frac{82}{4} - \frac{63}{4}$$

$$\frac{19}{4} \stackrel{?}{=} \frac{19}{4} \qquad \text{TRUE}$$

```
1-3(4-21/4)
                         4.75
2(21/4+5)-3*21/4
                         4.75
```

We can also check using a calculator, as shown at left. The solution is $\frac{21}{4}$.

Try Exercise 29.

Conditional equation

Identity

Contradiction

Formulas

The equations in Examples 1–3 are **conditional**—that is, they are true for some values of x and false for other values of x. An **identity** is an equation like $x + 1 = x + 1$ that is true for all values of x. A **contradiction** is an equation like $x + 1 = x + 2$ that is never true.

A **formula** is an equation using two or more letters that represents a relationship between two or more quantities. A formula can be solved for a specified letter using the principles for solving equations.

EXAMPLE 4 The formula

$$A = \frac{a + b + c + d}{4}$$

gives the average A of four test scores a, b, c, and d. Solve for d.

SOLUTION We have

$$A = \frac{a + b + c + d}{4} \qquad \text{We want the letter } d \text{ alone.}$$

$$4A = a + b + c + d \qquad \text{Multiplying by 4 to clear the fraction}$$

$$4A - a - b - c = d. \qquad \begin{array}{l}\text{Subtracting } a + b + c \text{ from}\\ \text{(or adding } -a - b - c \text{ to)}\\ \text{both sides. The letter } d \text{ is now}\\ \text{isolated.}\end{array}$$

We can also write this as $d = 4A - a - b - c$. This formula can be used to determine the test score needed to obtain a specified average if three tests have already been taken.

Try Exercise 39.

SOLVING INEQUALITIES

Solutions of inequalities

Graphs of inequalities

A **solution of an inequality** is a replacement of the variable that makes the inequality true. The solutions of an inequality in one variable can be **graphed,** or represented by a drawing, on the number line. All points that are solutions are shaded. A parenthesis indicates an endpoint that is not a solution and a bracket indicates an endpoint that is a solution.

For example, the graph of the inequality $m \leq 2$ is shown below. The solutions of $m \leq 2$ are shown on the number line by shading points to the left of 2 as well as the point at 2. The bracket at 2 indicates that 2 is a part of the graph (that is, it is a solution of $m \leq 2$).

Also shown below is the graph of $-1 \leq x < 4$. In order to be a solution of this inequality, a number must be a solution of both $-1 \leq x$ and $x < 4$. The solutions are shaded on the number line, with a parenthesis indicating that 4 is not a solution and a bracket indicating that -1 is a solution.

Set-builder notation

Since it is impossible to list all the solutions of most inequalities, we use **set-builder notation** or **interval notation** to write such sets.

Using set-builder notation, we write the solution set of $m \leq 2$ as

$$\{m \mid m \leq 2\}.$$

This is read "the set of all m such that m is less than or equal to 2."

Interval notation uses parentheses, ( ), and brackets, [ ], to describe a set of real numbers.

Interval notation

Interval Notation	Set-builder Notation	Graph
(a, b) open interval	$\{x \mid a < x < b\}$	
$[a, b]$ closed interval	$\{x \mid a \leq x \leq b\}$	
$(a, b]$ half-open interval	$\{x \mid a < x \leq b\}$	
$[a, b)$ half-open interval	$\{x \mid a \leq x < b\}$	
(a, ∞)	$\{x \mid x > a\}$	
$[a, \infty)$	$\{x \mid x \geq a\}$	
$(-\infty, a)$	$\{x \mid x < a\}$	
$(-\infty, a]$	$\{x \mid x \leq a\}$	

Equivalent inequalities

Thus, for example, the solution set of $m \leq 2$, in interval notation, is $(-\infty, 2]$.

To solve inequalities, we use principles that enable us to write **equivalent inequalities**—inequalities having the same solution set. The addition principle is similar to the addition principle for equations; the multiplication principle contains an important difference.

The addition principle for inequalities

The multiplication principle for inequalities

The Addition and Multiplication Principles for Inequalities

The Addition Principle

For any real numbers a, b, and c,

$$a < b \text{ is equivalent to } a + c < b + c, \text{ and}$$
$$a > b \text{ is equivalent to } a + c > b + c.$$

The Multiplication Principle

For any real numbers a and b, and for any *positive* number c,

$$a < b \text{ is equivalent to } ac < bc, \text{ and}$$
$$a > b \text{ is equivalent to } ac > bc.$$

For any real numbers a and b, and for any *negative* number c,

$$a < b \text{ is equivalent to } ac > bc, \text{ and}$$
$$a > b \text{ is equivalent to } ac < bc.$$

Similar statements hold for $\leq$ and $\geq$.

Note that when we multiply both sides of an inequality by a negative number, we must reverse the direction of the inequality symbol in order to have an equivalent inequality.

EXAMPLE 5 Solve $-2x \geq 5$ and then graph the solution.

SOLUTION We have

$$-2x \geq 5$$
$$\frac{-2x}{-2} \leq \frac{5}{-2} \qquad \text{Multiplying by } -\frac{1}{2} \text{ or dividing by } -2$$
$$\text{The symbol must be reversed!}$$

$$x \leq -\frac{5}{2}.$$

Any number less than or equal to $-\frac{5}{2}$ is a solution. The graph is as follows.

The solution set is $\left\{ x \mid x \leq -\frac{5}{2} \right\}$, or $\left(-\infty, -\frac{5}{2} \right]$.

Try Exercise 51.

We can use the addition and multiplication principles together to solve inequalities. We can also combine like terms, remove parentheses, and clear fractions and decimals.

EXAMPLE 6 Solve: $2 - 3(x + 5) > 4 - 6(x - 1)$.

SOLUTION We have

$$2 - 3(x + 5) > 4 - 6(x - 1)$$

$2 - 3x - 15 > 4 - 6x + 6$	Using the distributive law to remove parentheses
$-3x - 13 > -6x + 10$	Simplifying
$-3x + 6x > 10 + 13$	Adding $6x$ and 13, to get all x-terms on one side and the remaining terms on the other side
$3x > 23$	Combining like terms
$x > \frac{23}{3}.$	Multiplying by $\frac{1}{3}$. The inequality symbol stays the same because $\frac{1}{3}$ is positive.

The solution set is $\left\{ x \mid x > \frac{23}{3} \right\}$, or $\left(\frac{23}{3}, \infty \right)$.

▌ Try Exercise 57.

PROBLEM SOLVING

Problem solving

One of the most important uses of algebra is as a tool for problem solving. The following five steps can be used to help solve problems of many types.

Five Steps for Problem Solving in Algebra

1. *Familiarize* yourself with the problem.
2. *Translate* to mathematical language. (This often means write an equation.)
3. *Carry out* some mathematical manipulation. (This often means *solve* an equation.)
4. *Check* your possible answer in the original problem.
5. *State* the answer clearly.

EXAMPLE 7 Kitchen Cabinets. Cherry kitchen cabinets cost 10% more than oak cabinets. Shelby Custom Cabinets designs a kitchen using $7480 worth of cherry cabinets. How much would the same kitchen cost using oak cabinets?

SOLUTION

Familiarize step

Percent

1. **Familiarize.** Be sure to allow sufficient time for the *Familiarize* step; it is often the most important step of the five. Listed below are several helpful strategies.

   • List known (and unknown) information.
   • Define a variable to represent the unknown.
   • Make a drawing or a table.
   • Make a guess and check it.
   • Look up further information.

   For this problem, let's make a guess and check it.

   Guess: The oak cabinets cost $6500.

   Check: The cherry cabinets cost 10% more, or an additional $650. The total cost of the cherry cabinets would be $6500 + $650 = $7150.

Our guess does *not* check, since $7150 \neq 7480$, but we see that the price of the cherry cabinets is the price of the oak cabinets plus 10% of the price of the oak cabinets.

We let c = the cost of the oak cabinets.

2. **Translate.** What we learned in the *Familiarize* step leads to the translation of the problem to an equation.

Rewording:	Cost of oak cabinets	plus	10% of cost of oak cabinets	is	cost of cherry cabinets.
Translating:	c	$+$	$0.10c$	$=$	7480

3. **Carry out.** We solve the equation:

$$c + 0.10c = 7480$$
$$1c + 0.10c = 7480 \qquad \text{Writing } c \text{ as 1c before combining terms}$$
$$1.10c = 7480 \qquad \text{Combining like terms}$$
$$c = \frac{7480}{1.10} \qquad \text{Dividing by 1.10}$$
$$c = 6800.$$

4. **Check.** We check in the wording of the stated problem.

Additional cost of cherry cabinets $= 0.10(\$6800) = \$680.$
Total cost of cherry cabinets $= \$6800 + \$680 + \$7480.$

Our answer checks.

5. **State.** The oak cabinets would cost \$6800.

Try Exercise 67.

Sometimes the translation of a problem is an inequality.

EXAMPLE 8   Phone Bills.   Elyse pays 10¢ per text message. The monthly charge for her wireless service is \$39.50. How many text messages can she send or receive in a month and not exceed her phone budget of \$50?

SOLUTION

1. **Familiarize.** Suppose that Elyse sends or receives 200 text messages one month. Then her bill would be the monthly fee plus the texting charges, or $\$39.50 + \$0.10(200) = \$59.50$. This amount exceeds \$50, so we know that the number of text messages must be fewer than 200. We let t = the number of text messages sent or received in a month.

Solving applications with inequalities

2. **Translate.** The *Familiarize* step helps us reword and translate.

Rewording:	The monthly charge	plus	the texting charge	cannot exceed	\$50.
Translating:	39.50	$+$	$0.10t$	$\leq$	50

3. **Carry out.** We solve the inequality:

$$39.50 + 0.10t \leq 50$$
$$0.10t \leq 10.50 \qquad \text{Subtracting 39.50 from both sides}$$
$$t \leq 105. \qquad \text{Dividing by 0.10. The inequality symbol stays the same.}$$

4. **Check.** As a partial check, we determine the bill for 105 texts:

$$\$39.50 + \$0.10(105) = \$50.$$

Since this does not exceed the $50 budget, and fewer texts will cost even less, our answer checks. We also note that 105 is less than 200, as noted in the *Familiarize* step.

5. **State.** Elyse will not exceed her budget if she sends or receives no more than 105 text messages.

Try Exercise 77.

9.2 Exercise Set

Solve.

1. $-6 + x = 10$

2. $y + 7 = -3$

3. $t + \frac{1}{3} = \frac{1}{4}$

4. $-\frac{2}{3} + p = \frac{1}{6}$

5. $-1.9 = x - 1.1$

6. $x + 4.6 = 1.7$

7. $-x = \frac{5}{3}$

8. $-y = -\frac{2}{5}$

9. $-\frac{2}{7}x = -12$

10. $-\frac{1}{4}x = 3$

11. $\frac{-t}{5} = 1$

12. $\frac{2}{3} = -\frac{z}{8}$

13. $3x + 7 = 13$

14. $4x + 3 = -1$

15. $3y - 10 = 15$

16. $12 = 5y - 18$

17. $4x + 7 = 3 - 5x$

18. $2x = 5 + 7x$

19. $2x - 7 = 5x + 1 - x$

20. $a + 7 - 2a = 14 + 7a - 10$

21. $\frac{2}{5} + \frac{1}{3}t = 5$

22. $-\frac{5}{6} + t = \frac{1}{2}$

23. $x + 0.45 = 2.6x$

24. $1.8x + 0.16 = 4.2 - 0.05x$

25. $8(3 - m) + 7 = 47$

26. $2(5 - m) = 5(6 + m)$

27. $4 - (6 + x) = 13$

28. $18 = 9 - (3 - x)$

29. $2 + 3(4 + c) = 1 - 5(6 - c)$

30. $b + (b + 5) - 2(b - 5) = 18 + b$

31. $0.1(a - 0.2) = 1.2 + 2.4a$

32. $\frac{2}{3}\left(\frac{1}{2} - x\right) + \frac{5}{6} = \frac{3}{2}\left(\frac{2}{3}x + 1\right)$

33. $A = lw$, for l

34. $A = lw$, for w

35. $p = 30q$, for q

36. $d = 20t$, for t

37. $I = \dfrac{P}{V}$, for P

38. $b = \dfrac{A}{h}$, for A

39. $q = \dfrac{p + r}{2}$, for p

40. $q = \dfrac{p - r}{2}$, for r

41. $A = \pi r^2 + \pi r^2 h$, for π

42. $ax + by = c$, for a

Determine whether each number is a solution of the given inequality.

43. $x \le -5$

   a) 5   b) -5

   c) 0   d) -10

44. $y > 0$

   a) -1 b) 1

   c) 0   d) 100

Solve and graph. Write each answer in set-builder notation and in interval notation.

45. $x + 3 \le 15$

46. $y + 7 < -10$

47. $m - 17 > -5$

48. $x + 9 \ge -8$

49. $2x \ge -3$

50. $-\frac{1}{2}n \le 4$

51. $-5t > 15$

52. $3x > 10$

Solve. Write each answer in set-builder notation and in interval notation.

53. $2y - 7 > 13$

54. $2 - 6y \leq 18$

55. $6 - 5a \leq a$

56. $4b + 7 > 2 - b$

57. $2(3 + 5x) \geq 7(10 - x)$

58. $2(x + 5) < 8 - 3x$

59. $\frac{2}{3}(6 - x) < \frac{1}{4}(x + 3)$

60. $\frac{2}{3}t + \frac{8}{9} \geq \frac{4}{6} - \frac{1}{4}t$

61. $0.7(2 + x) \geq 1.1x + 5.75$

62. $0.4x + 5.7 \leq 2.6 - 3(1.2x - 7)$

Solve. Use the five-step problem-solving process.

63. Three less than the sum of 2 and some number is 6. What is the number?

64. Five times some number is 10 less than the number. What is the number?

65. The sum of two consecutive even integers is 34. Find the numbers.

66. The sum of three consecutive integers is 195. Find the numbers.

67. *Reading.* Leisa is reading a 500-page book. She has twice as many pages to read as she has already finished. How many pages has she already read?

68. *Mowing.* It takes Caleb 50 min to mow his lawn. It will take him three times as many minutes to finish as he has already spent mowing. How long has he already spent mowing?

69. *Perimeter of a Rectangle.* The perimeter of a rectangle is 28 cm. The width is 5 cm less than the length. Find the width and the length.

l − 5

l

70. *Triangles.* The second angle of a triangle is one-third as large as the first. The third angle is 5° more than the first. Find the measure of the second angle.

71. *Water Usage.* Rural Water Company charges a monthly service fee of $9.70 plus a volume charge of $2.60 for every hundred cubic feet of water used. How much water was used if the monthly bill is $33.10?

72. *Phone Bills.* Brandon pays $4.95 per month for a long-distance phone service that offers a flat rate of 7¢ per minute. One month his total long-distance phone

bill was $10.69. How many minutes of long-distance phone calls were made that month?

73. *Sale Price.* A can of tomatoes is on sale at 20% off for 64¢. What is the normal selling price of the tomatoes?

74. *Plywood.* The price of a piece of plywood rose 5% to $42. What was the original price of the plywood?

75. *Practice.* Dierdre's basketball coach requires each team member to average at least 15 min per day shooting baskets. One week Dierdre spent 10 min, 20 min, 5 min, 0 min, 25 min, and 15 min shooting baskets. How long must she practice shooting baskets on the seventh day if she is to meet the requirement?

76. *Perimeter of a Garden.* The perimeter of Garry's rectangular garden cannot exceed the 100 ft of fencing that he purchased. He wants the length to be twice the width. What widths of the garden will meet these conditions?

77. *Meeting Costs.* The Winds charges a $75 cleaning fee plus $45 per hour for the use of its meeting room. Complete Consultants has budgeted $200 to rent a room for a seminar. For how many hours can they rent the meeting room at The Winds?

78. *Meeting Costs.* Spring Haven charges a $15 setup fee, a $30 cleanup fee, and $50 per hour for the use of its meeting room. For what lengths of time will Spring Haven's room be less expensive than the room at The Winds? (See Exercise 77.)

Try Exercise Answers: Section 9.2

13. 2 **21.** $\frac{69}{5}$ **29.** $\frac{43}{2}$ **39.** $p = 2q - r$

51. $\{t \mid t < -3\}$, or $(-\infty, -3)$

57. $\{x \mid x \geq \frac{64}{17}\}$, or $[\frac{64}{17}, \infty)$ **67.** $166\frac{2}{3}$ pages

77. For $2\frac{7}{9}$ hr or less

9.3 Introduction to Graphing and Functions

- Points and Ordered Pairs
- Graphs and Slope
- Linear Equations
- Functions

Coordinates

Quadrants

Solutions of equations

POINTS AND ORDERED PAIRS

To graph pairs of numbers such as $(2, -5)$ on a plane, we use two perpendicular number lines called **axes.** The axes cross at a point called the **origin.** Arrows on the axes show the positive directions.

The order of the **coordinates,** or numbers in a pair, is important. The **first coordinate** indicates horizontal position and the **second coordinate** indicates vertical position. Such pairs of numbers are called **ordered pairs.** Thus the ordered pairs $(1, -2)$ and $(-2, 1)$ correspond to different points, as shown in the figure below.

The axes divide the plane into four regions, or **quadrants,** as indicated by Roman numerals in the figure below. Points on the axes are not considered to be in any quadrant. The horizontal axis is often labeled the x-axis, and the vertical axis the y-axis.

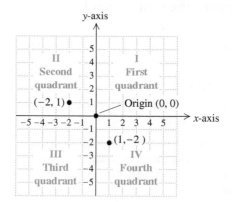

GRAPHS AND SLOPE

When an equation contains two variables, solutions must be ordered pairs. Unless stated otherwise, the first number in each pair replaces the variable that occurs first alphabetically.

EXAMPLE 1 Determine whether $(1, 4)$ is a solution of $y - x = 3$.

SOLUTION We substitute 1 for x and 4 for y since x occurs first alphabetically:

$$\frac{y - x = 3}{4 - 1 \mid 3}$$
$$3 \stackrel{?}{=} 3 \quad \text{TRUE}$$

Since $3 = 3$ is true, the pair $(1, 4)$ *is* a solution.

Try Exercise 9.

A curve or a line that represents all the solutions of an equation is called its **graph.**

EXAMPLE 2 Graph: $y = -2x + 1$.

SOLUTION We select a value for x, calculate the corresponding value of y, and form an ordered pair.

If $x = 0$, then $y = -2 \cdot 0 + 1 = 1$, and $(0, 1)$ is a solution. Repeating this step, we find other ordered pairs and list the results in a table. We then plot the points corresponding to the pairs. They appear to form a straight line, so we draw a line through the points.

$y = -2x + 1$

x	y	(x, y)
0	1	$(0, 1)$
-1	3	$(-1, 3)$
3	-5	$(3, -5)$
1	-1	$(1, -1)$

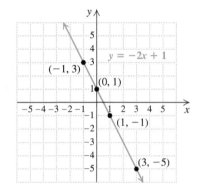

$y = -2x + 1$

To graph using a graphing calculator, we let $y_1 = -2x + 1$, as shown at left.

$y = -2x + 1$

▌ Try Exercise 13.

Slope

The graph in Example 2 is a straight line. An equation whose graph is a straight line is a **linear equation.** The *rate of change* of y with respect to x is called the **slope** of a graph. A linear graph has a constant slope that can be found using any two points on a line.

Slope The *slope* of the line containing points (x_1, y_1) and (x_2, y_2) is given by

$$m = \frac{\text{change in } y}{\text{change in } x} = \frac{\text{rise}}{\text{run}} = \frac{y_2 - y_1}{x_2 - x_1}.$$

EXAMPLE 3 Find the slope of the line containing the points $(-2, 1)$ and $(3, -4)$.

SOLUTION From $(-2, 1)$ to $(3, -4)$, the change in y, or the rise, is $-4 - 1$, or -5. The change in x, or the run, is $3 - (-2)$, or 5. Thus,

$$\text{Slope} = \frac{\text{change in } y}{\text{change in } x} = \frac{\text{rise}}{\text{run}} = \frac{-4 - 1}{3 - (-2)} = \frac{-5}{5} = -1.$$

▌ Try Exercise 23.

The slope of a line indicates the direction and the steepness of its slant. The larger the absolute value of the slope, the steeper the line. The direction of the slant is indicated by the sign of the slope, as shown in the figures below.

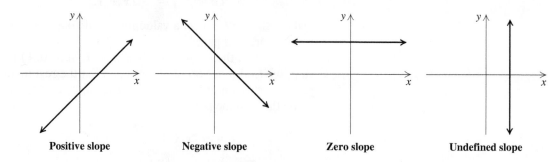

Positive slope   Negative slope   Zero slope   Undefined slope

x-intercept

The **x-intercept** of a line, if it exists, is the point at which the graph crosses the x-axis. To find an x-intercept, we replace y with 0 and calculate x.

y-intercept

The **y-intercept** of a line, if it exists, is the point at which the graph crosses the y-axis. To find a y-intercept, we replace x with 0 and calculate y.

LINEAR EQUATIONS

Any equation that can be written in the **standard form** $Ax + By = C$ is linear. Linear equations can also be written in other forms.

Forms of Linear Equations

Standard form:	$Ax + By = C$
Slope–intercept form:	$y = mx + b$
Point–slope form:	$y - y_1 = m(x - x_1)$

The slope and the y-intercept of a line can be read from the slope–intercept form of the line's equation.

Slope and y-intercept   For the graph of any equation $y = mx + b$,

- the slope is m, and
- the y-intercept is $(0, b)$.

EXAMPLE 4   Find the slope and the y-intercept of the line given by the equation $4x - 3y = 9$.

SOLUTION   We write the equation in slope–intercept form $y = mx + b$:

$$4x - 3y = 9 \qquad \text{We must solve for } y.$$
$$-3y = -4x + 9 \qquad \text{Adding } -4x \text{ to both sides}$$
$$y = \tfrac{4}{3}x - 3. \qquad \text{Dividing both sides by } -3$$

The slope is $\tfrac{4}{3}$ and the y-intercept is $(0, -3)$.

Try Exercise 29.

If we know that the graph of an equation is a straight line, we can plot two points on the line and draw the line through those points. The intercepts are often convenient points to use.

EXAMPLE 5   Graph $2x - 5y = 10$ using intercepts.

SOLUTION   To find the x-intercept, we let $y = 0$ and solve for x:

$$2x - 5 \cdot 0 = 10 \qquad \text{Replacing } y \text{ with } 0$$
$$2x = 10$$
$$x = 5.$$

To find the y-intercept, we let $x = 0$ and solve for y:

$$2 \cdot 0 - 5y = 10 \qquad \text{Replacing } x \text{ with } 0$$
$$-5y = 10$$
$$y = -2.$$

Thus the x-intercept is $(5, 0)$ and the y-intercept is $(0, -2)$. The graph is a line, since $2x - 5y = 10$ is in the form $Ax + By = C$. It passes through these two points.

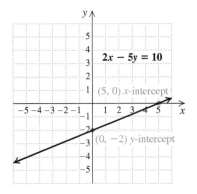

Try Exercise 33.

Alternatively, if we know a point on the line and its slope, we can plot the point and "count off" its slope to locate another point on the line.

EXAMPLE 6   Graph: $y = -\dfrac{1}{2}x + 3$.

SOLUTION   The equation is in slope–intercept form, so we can read the slope and the y-intercept directly from the equation.

Slope: $-\dfrac{1}{2}$

y-intercept: $(0, 3)$

We plot the y-intercept and use the slope to find another point.

Another way to write the slope is $\dfrac{-1}{2}$. This means that for a run of 2 units, there is a negative rise, or a fall, of 1 unit. Starting at $(0, 3)$, we move 2 units in the positive horizontal direction and then 1 unit down, to locate the point $(2, 2)$. Then we draw the graph. A third point can be calculated and plotted as a check.

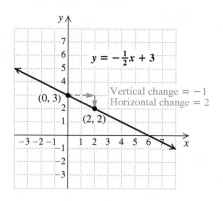

Try Exercise 39.

Horizontal lines and vertical lines intersect only one axis.

Horizontal line

Vertical line

Horizontal Lines and Vertical Lines

Horizontal Line	**Vertical Line**
$y = b$	$x = a$
y-intercept $(0, b)$	x-intercept $(a, 0)$
Slope is 0	Undefined slope
Example: $y = -3$	Example: $x = 2$

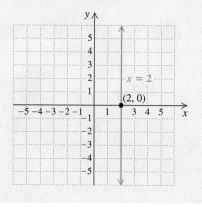

If we know the slope of a line and the coordinates of a point on the line, we can find an equation of the line, using either the slope–intercept equation $y = mx + b$, or the point–slope equation $y - y_1 = m(x - x_1)$.

EXAMPLE 7 Find the slope–intercept equation of a line given the following:

a) The slope is 2, and the y-intercept is $(0, -5)$.

b) The graph contains the points $(-2, 1)$ and $(3, -4)$.

SOLUTION

a) Since the slope and the y-intercept are given, we use the slope–intercept equation:

$y = mx + b$

$y = 2x - 5.$ Substituting 2 for m and -5 for b

b) To use the point–slope equation, we need a point on the line and its slope. The slope can be found from the points given:

Find the slope.

$$m = \frac{1 - (-4)}{-2 - 3} = \frac{5}{-5} = -1.$$

Either point can be used for (x_1, y_1). Using $(-2, 1)$, we have

Find a point–slope equation for the line.

$$y - y_1 = m(x - x_1)$$
$$y - 1 = -1(x - (-2)) \qquad \text{Substituting } -2 \text{ for } x_1,$$
$$ \qquad 1 \text{ for } y_1, \text{ and } -1 \text{ for } m$$
$$y - 1 = -(x + 2)$$
$$y - 1 = -x - 2$$

Find the slope–intercept equation for the line.

$$y = -x - 1. \qquad \text{This is in slope–intercept form.}$$

Try Exercise 47.

We can tell from the slopes of two lines whether they are parallel (never intersect) or perpendicular (intersect at right angles).

Parallel lines

Perpendicular lines

Parallel Lines and Perpendicular Lines

Two lines are parallel if they have the same slope.
Two lines are perpendicular if the product of the slopes is -1.

EXAMPLE 8 Tell whether the graphs of each pair of lines are parallel, perpendicular, or neither.

a) $2x - y = 7,$
$\quad y = 2x + 3$

b) $4x - y = 8,$
$\quad x + 4y = 8$

SOLUTION

a) The slope of $y = 2x + 3$ is 2. To find the slope of $2x - y = 7$, we solve for y:

$$2x - y = 7$$
$$-y = -2x + 7$$
$$y = 2x - 7. \qquad \text{The slope of } 2x - y = 7 \text{ is 2.}$$

Since the slopes are equal, the lines are parallel.

b) We solve both equations for y in order to determine the slopes of the lines:

$$4x - y = 8$$
$$-y = -4x + 8$$
$$y = 4x - 8. \qquad \text{The slope of } 4x - y = 8 \text{ is 4.}$$

For the second line, we have

$$x + 4y = 8$$
$$4y = -x + 8$$
$$y = -\tfrac{1}{4}x + 2. \qquad \text{The slope of } x + 4y = 8 \text{ is } -\tfrac{1}{4}.$$

We multiply the slopes 4 and $-\tfrac{1}{4}$. Since $4 \cdot \left(-\tfrac{1}{4}\right) = -1$, the lines are perpendicular.

Try Exercise 51.

FUNCTIONS

A correspondence from one set to another is a pairing of one element of the first set with one element of a second set. Such a match can be written as an ordered pair. One type of correspondence used extensively in mathematics is called a **function.**

Function

Domain

Range

> **Function**   A *function* is a correspondence between a first set, called the *domain*, and a second set, called the *range*, such that each member of the domain corresponds to *exactly one* member of the range.

Function notation

Output

Input

A function is often labeled with a letter, such as f or g. The notation $f(x)$—read "f of x," "f at x," or "the value of f at x"—represents the **output** that corresponds to the **input** x. For example, if a function f contains the ordered pair $(0, -5)$, we can write

$$f(0) = -5.$$

Many functions are described by equations. To find a function value, we substitute a given number or expression for the variable in the equation.

EXAMPLE 9   For $f(x) = 2x^2 - x + 4$, find $f(-1)$.

SOLUTION   We have

$$f(-1) = 2(-1)^2 - (-1) + 4$$
$$= 2(1) + 1 + 4$$
$$= 7.$$

Try Exercise 55.

When the domain and the range of a function are sets of numbers, we can graph the function. If a graph contains two or more points with the same first coordinate, that graph cannot represent a function.

Vertical-line test

> **The Vertical-Line Test**   A graph represents a function if it is not possible to draw a vertical line that intersects the graph more than once.

A function   Not a function.
                               Two y-values correspond
                               to one x-value.

If a domain of a function is not specified, we assume that the domain is the set of all real numbers for which the function value can be computed.

EXAMPLE 10   Determine the domain of each of the following functions.

a) $f(x) = 2x^2 + x - 10$ **b)** $g(x) = \dfrac{1}{x + 2}$

c) $h(x) = \sqrt{7 - x}$

SOLUTION   We look for any restrictions on the domain—that is, any numbers for which the function value cannot be computed.

a) We can compute $2x^2 + x - 10$ for any number that replaces x. Therefore, the domain of f is $(-\infty, \infty)$, or $\{x \mid x \text{ is a real number}\}$, or $\mathbb{R}$. We can confirm this by examining a graph of $f(x) = 2x^2 + x - 10$, as shown at left.

b) The expression $1/(x + 2)$ cannot be computed when the denominator, $x + 2$, is 0. We set $x + 2$ equal to 0 and solve:

$$x + 2 = 0$$
$$x = -2.$$

Thus, -2 is *not* in the domain of g, but all other real numbers are. The domain of g is $\{x \mid x \text{ is a real number } and \ x \neq -2\}$.

c) Since the square root of a negative number is not a real number, only inputs for which $7 - x$ is nonnegative are in the domain of the function. We solve an inequality:

$$7 - x \geq 0$$
$$7 \geq x.$$

We see that all numbers less than or equal to 7 will be in the domain. The domain of h is $(-\infty, 7]$, or $\{x \mid x \leq 7\}$. The graph of $h(x) = \sqrt{7 - x}$, as shown at left, confirms this result.

Try Exercise 63.

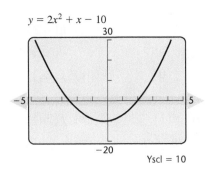

$y = 2x^2 + x - 10$

The domain is the set of all possible x-values.

$y = \sqrt{7 - x}$

9.3   **Exercise Set**

1. Plot these points.
$(2, -3), (5, 1), (0, 2), (-1, 0),$
$(0, 0), (-2, -5), (-1, 1), (1, -1)$

2. Plot these points.
$(0, -4), (-4, 0), (5, -2), (2, 5),$
$(3, 3), (-3, -1), (-1, 4), (0, 1)$

In which quadrant is each point located?

3. $(2, 1)$ **4.** $(-2, 5)$

5. $(3, -2.6)$ **6.** $(-1.7, -5.9)$

7. First coordinates are positive in quadrants
_____ and _____.

8. Second coordinates are negative in quadrants
_____ and _____.

Determine whether each equation has the given ordered pair as a solution.

9. $y = 2x - 5;\ (1, 3)$

10. $4x + 3y = 8;\ (-1, 4)$

11. $a - 5b = -3;\ (2, 1)$

12. $c = d + 1;\ (1, 2)$

Graph by hand.

13. $y = \frac{1}{3}x + 3$ **14.** $y = -x - 2$

15. $y = -4x$ **16.** $y = \frac{3}{4}x + 1$

Graph using a graphing calculator.

17. $y = x^2 - 7$

18. $y = 2x^2 - x + 3$

19. $y = |x + 3|$

20. $y = \sqrt{3 - x}$

21. $y = \sqrt{x^2 + 1}$

22. $y = |x^2 - x - 1|$

Find the slope of the line containing each given pair of points.

23. $(3, 6)$ and $(2, 5)$

24. $(-1, 7)$ and $(-3, 4)$

25. $(0, 3)$ and $(1, -2)$

26. $(-3, 8)$ and $(2, -7)$

27. $\left(-2, -\frac{1}{2}\right)$ and $\left(5, -\frac{1}{2}\right)$

28. $(6.8, 7.5)$ and $(6.8, -3.2)$

Find the slope and the y-intercept of each equation.

29. $y = 2x - 5$

30. $y = 4 - x$

31. $2x + 7y = 1$

32. $x - 2y = 3$

Find the intercepts. Then graph.

33. $2x - y = 4$

34. $2x + 5y = 10$

35. $y = x + 5$

36. $y = -x + 7$

37. $3 - y = 2x$

38. $2y + 1 = x$

Determine the coordinates of the y-intercept of each equation. Then graph the equation.

39. $y = 2x - 5$

40. $y = -\frac{5}{4}x - 3$

41. $2y + 4x = 6$

42. $3y + x = 4$

Find the slope of each line, and graph.

43. $y = 4$

44. $x = -5$

45. $x = 3$

46. $y = -1$

Find the slope–intercept equation of a line given the conditions.

47. The slope is $\frac{1}{3}$ and the y-intercept is $(0, 1)$.

48. The slope is -1 and the y-intercept is $(0, -5)$.

49. The graph contains the points $(0, 3)$ and $(-1, 4)$.

50. The graph contains the points $(5, 1)$ and $(8, 0)$.

Determine whether each pair of lines is parallel, perpendicular, or neither.

51. $x + y = 5,$
$x - y = 1$

52. $2x + y = 3,$
$y = 4 - 2x$

53. $2x + 3y = 1,$
$2x - 3y = 5$

54. $y = \frac{1}{3}x - 7,$
$y + 3x = 1$

Find the function values.

55. $g(x) = \frac{1}{3}x + 7$

  a) $g(-3)$ **b)** $g(4)$ **c)** $g(a + 3)$

56. $h(x) = \dfrac{1}{x + 2}$

  a) $h(0)$ **b)** $h(2)$ **c)** $h(-2)$

57. $f(x) = 5x^2 + 2x + 3$

  a) $f(-1)$ **b)** $f(0)$ **c)** $f(2a)$

58. $f(t) = 6 - t^2$

  a) $f(-1)$ **b)** $f(1)$ **c)** $f(3a)$

Determine whether each of the following is the graph of a function.

59.

60.

61.

62.

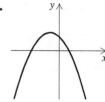

Determine the domain of each function.

63. $f(x) = \dfrac{x}{x - 3}$

64. $g(x) = \sqrt{x}$

65. $g(x) = 2x + 3$

66. $f(x) = |x + 3|$

67. $f(x) = \sqrt{\frac{1}{2}x + 3}$

68. $g(x) = \dfrac{1}{2x + 1}$

Try Exercise Answers: Section 9.3

9. No   **13.**   **23.** 1   **29.** Slope: 2;
y-intercept: $(0, -5)$

33.   **39.**   **47.** $y = \frac{1}{3}x + 1$

51. Perpendicular   **55.** (a) 6; (b) $8\frac{1}{3}$; (c) $\frac{1}{3}a + 8$
63. $\{x \mid x \text{ is a real number } and \ x \neq 3\}$

9.4   Systems of Equations in Two Variables

- Solving Systems Graphically
- Solving Systems Algebraically
- Applications
- Solving Equations by Graphing

A **system of equations** is a set of two or more equations that are to be solved simultaneously. An ordered pair is a solution of a system of equations in two variables if it makes *all* of the equations in the system true. We can solve systems of equations in two variables graphically or algebraically.

SOLVING SYSTEMS GRAPHICALLY

The solution of a system of equations is given by the point of intersection of the graphs of the equations.

> **EXAMPLE 1**   Solve by graphing:
>
> $$2x + y = 1,$$
> $$x + y = -2.$$
>
> **SOLUTION**

BY HAND

We graph each equation. The point of intersection has coordinates that make *both* equations true. Apparently, $(3, -5)$ is the solution. Because solving by graphing is not always accurate, we must check. As shown below, $(3, -5)$ is indeed the solution.

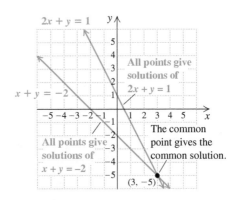

Check:

$$\begin{array}{c|c} 2x + y = 1 \\ \hline 2 \cdot 3 + (-5) & 1 \\ 1 \overset{?}{=} 1 & \text{TRUE} \end{array}$$

$$\begin{array}{c|c} x + y = -2 \\ \hline 3 + (-5) & -2 \\ -2 \overset{?}{=} -2 & \text{TRUE} \end{array}$$

WITH A GRAPHING CALCULATOR

We first solve each equation for y:

$$2x + y = 1, \qquad x + y = -2$$
$$y = 1 - 2x; \qquad y = -2 - x.$$

Then we enter and graph both equations using the same viewing window.

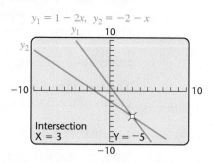

The point of intersection is $(3, -5)$. This ordered pair makes both equations true, so it is the solution of the system.

Try Exercise 1.

The graphs of two linear equations can intersect at one point, can be parallel with no points of intersection, or can have the same graph. Thus systems of two linear equations can have one solution, no solution, or an infinite number of solutions.

Consistent (p. 233)

Graphs intersect at one point.
The system is *consistent* and has one solution. Since neither equation is a multiple of the other, they are *independent*. The solution is $(1, 2)$.

Graphs are parallel.
The system is *inconsistent* because there is no solution. Since the equations are not equivalent, they are *independent*. The solution set is $\varnothing$.

Equations have the same graph.
The system is *consistent* and has an infinite number of solutions. The equations are *dependent* since they are equivalent. The solution set is $\{(x, y) | 3y - 2x = 6\}$.

Independent (p. 233)

SOLVING SYSTEMS ALGEBRAICALLY

Solving by substitution (Section 4.2)

Algebraic (nongraphical) methods for solving systems yield exact answers. The **substitution method** relies on having a variable isolated.

EXAMPLE 2 Solve the system

$$x + y = 4, \quad (1) \qquad \text{We have numbered the equations for easy reference.}$$
$$x - y = 1. \quad (2)$$

SOLUTION   First, we select an equation and solve for one variable. Here we choose to solve for x in equation (2):

Solve for x in terms of y.

$$x - y = 1 \qquad (2)$$
$$x = y + 1. \qquad (3) \qquad \text{Adding } y \text{ to both sides}$$

Equation (3) says that x and $y + 1$ name the same number. Thus we can substitute $y + 1$ for x in equation (1):

Substitute, using parentheses.

$$x + y = 4 \qquad \text{Equation (1)}$$
$$(y + 1) + y = 4. \qquad \text{Substituting } y + 1 \text{ for } x$$

We solve this last equation, using methods learned earlier:

$$(y + 1) + y = 4$$
$$2y + 1 = 4 \qquad \text{Removing parentheses and combining like terms}$$
$$2y = 3 \qquad \text{Subtracting 1 from both sides}$$

Solve for y.

$$y = \tfrac{3}{2}. \qquad \text{Dividing by 2}$$

We now return to the original pair of equations and substitute $\tfrac{3}{2}$ for y in either equation so that we can solve for x. For this problem, calculations are slightly easier if we use equation (3):

$$x = y + 1 \qquad \text{Equation (3)}$$
$$= \tfrac{3}{2} + 1 \qquad \text{Substituting } \tfrac{3}{2} \text{ for } y$$

Solve for x.

$$= \tfrac{3}{2} + \tfrac{2}{2} = \tfrac{5}{2}.$$

We obtain the ordered pair $\left(\tfrac{5}{2}, \tfrac{3}{2}\right)$. A check ensures that it is a solution.

Check.

$$\textit{Check:} \quad \begin{array}{c|c} x + y = 4 \\ \hline \frac{5}{2} + \frac{3}{2} & 4 \\ \frac{8}{2} & \\ 4 \overset{?}{=} 4 & \text{TRUE} \end{array} \qquad \begin{array}{c|c} x - y = 1 \\ \hline \frac{5}{2} - \frac{3}{2} & 1 \\ \frac{2}{2} & \\ 1 \overset{?}{=} 1 & \text{TRUE} \end{array}$$

Since $\left(\tfrac{5}{2}, \tfrac{3}{2}\right)$ checks, it is the solution.

> **Try Exercise 13.**

Solving by elimination (Section 4.3)

A second algebraic method, the **elimination method,** makes use of the addition principle: If $a = b$, then $a + c = b + c$. To use the elimination method, we multiply, if necessary, so that the coefficients of one variable are opposites. Then we add the equations, eliminating that variable.

EXAMPLE 3   Solve the system

$$2x + 3y = 17, \qquad (1)$$
$$5x + 7y = 29. \qquad (2)$$

SOLUTION   We multiply so that the x-terms are eliminated.

$$2x + 3y = 17, \xrightarrow[\text{sides by 5}]{\text{Multiplying both}} 10x + 15y = 85$$

$$5x + 7y = 29 \xrightarrow[\text{sides by} -2]{\text{Multiplying both}} \underline{-10x - 14y = -58}$$

$$0 + y = 27 \qquad \text{Adding}$$
$$y = 27$$

The coefficients of x, 10 and -10, are opposites.

Next, we substitute to find x:

$$2x + 3 \cdot 27 = 17 \qquad \text{Substituting 27 for } y \text{ in equation (1)}$$
$$2x + 81 = 17$$
$$\left.\begin{aligned} 2x &= -64 \\ x &= -32. \end{aligned}\right\} \quad \text{Solving for } x$$

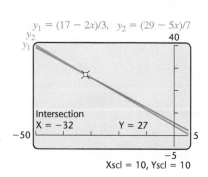

$y_1 = (17 - 2x)/3, \quad y_2 = (29 - 5x)/7$

Intersection
X = −32   Y = 27

Xscl = 10, Yscl = 10

Check:

$2x + 3y = 17$	
$2(-32) + 3(27)$	17
$-64 + 81$	
	$17 \overset{?}{=} 17$ TRUE

$5x + 7y = 29$	
$5(-32) + 7(27)$	29
$-160 + 189$	
	$29 \overset{?}{=} 29$ TRUE

We can also check using a graphing calculator, as shown in the figure at left. We obtain $(-32, 27)$, or $x = -32, y = 27$, as the solution.

Try Exercise 25.

When solving algebraically, we can tell whether a system has no solutions or an infinite number of solutions.

Rules for Special Cases When solving a system of two linear equations in two variables:

1. If an identity is obtained, such as $0 = 0$, then the system has an infinite number of solutions. The equations are dependent and, since a solution exists, the system is consistent.
2. If a contradiction is obtained, such as $0 = 7$, then the system has no solution. The system is inconsistent.

APPLICATIONS

Many problems that can be translated using two variables can be solved using systems of equations.

EXAMPLE 4 Blending Coffees. The Java Joint wants to mix organic Mexican Chiapas beans that sell for \$8.25 per pound with organic Dark Ethiopian Yirgacheffe beans that sell for \$9.50 per pound in order to form a 50-lb batch of Morning Blend that sells for \$9.00 per pound. How many pounds of each type of bean should go into the blend?

SOLUTION

Mixture problems (p. 261)

1. **Familiarize.** This problem is an example of a **mixture problem.** We can find two relationships in the problem:

   The *weight* of the separate beans must equal the weight of the mixture.

   The *value* of the separate beans must equal the value of the mixture.

   We let $c =$ the number of pounds of organic Mexican coffee used and $y =$ the number of pounds of organic Ethiopian coffee used.

2. **Translate.** Since a 50-lb batch is being made, we must have

$$c + y = 50.$$ This is the *weight* relationship.

To find a second equation, we consider the total value of the 50-lb batch. That value must be the same as the value of the Mexican beans and the value of the Ethiopian beans that go into the blend.

Rewording:	The value of the Mexican beans	plus	the value of the Ethiopian beans	is	the value of the Morning Blend.
Translating:	$c \cdot 8.25$	$+$	$y \cdot 9.50$	$=$	$50 \cdot 9.00$

This information can be presented in a table.

	Mexican	**Ethiopian**	**Morning Blend**	
Number of Pounds	c	y	50	$\rightarrow c + y = 50$
Price per Pound	$8.25	$9.50	$9.00	
Value of Beans	$8.25c$	$9.50y$	$50 \cdot 9$, or 450	$\rightarrow 8.25c + 9.50y = 450$

We have translated to a system of equations:

$$c + y = 50, \qquad (1)$$
$$8.25c + 9.50y = 450. \qquad (2)$$

3. **Carry out.** When equation (1) is solved for c, we have $c = 50 - y$. We then substitute $50 - y$ for c in equation (2):

$8.25(50 - y) + 9.50y = 450$	Solving by substitution
$412.50 - 8.25y + 9.50y = 450$	Using the distributive law
$1.25y = 37.50$	Combining like terms; subtracting 412.50 from both sides
$y = 30.$	Dividing both sides by 1.25

If $y = 30$, we see from equation (1) that $c = 20$.

4. **Check.** If 20 lb of Mexican beans and 30 lb of Ethiopian beans are mixed, a 50-lb blend will result. The value of 20 lb of Mexican beans is $20(\$8.25)$, or $165. The value of 30 lb of Ethiopian beans is $30(\$9.50)$, or $285, so the value of the blend is $165 + $285 = $450. A 50-lb blend priced at $9.00 per pound is also worth $450, so our answer checks.

5. **State.** The Morning Blend should be made by combining 20 lb of Mexican Chiapas beans with 30 lb of Dark Ethiopian Yirgacheffe beans.

Try Exercise 47.

When a problem deals with distance, speed (rate), and time, we use the following.

Distance, Rate, and Time Equations If r represents rate, t represents time, and d represents distance, then

$$d = rt, \qquad r = \frac{d}{t}, \quad \text{and} \quad t = \frac{d}{r}.$$

EXAMPLE 5 Marine Travel. A Coast-Guard patrol boat travels 4 hr on a trip downstream with a 6-mph current. The return trip against the same current takes 5 hr. Find the speed of the boat in still water.

Upstream, $r - 6$
6-mph current, 5 hours,
d miles

Downstream, $r + 6$
6-mph current, 4 hours,
d miles

1. **Familiarize.** We first make a drawing and note that the distances are the same. We let $d =$ the distance, in miles, and $r =$ the speed of the boat in still water, in miles per hour. Then, when the boat is traveling downstream, its speed is $r + 6$ (the current helps the boat along). When it is traveling upstream, its speed is $r - 6$ (the current holds the boat back). We can organize the information in a table, using the formula $d = rt$.

$$d \quad = \quad r \quad \cdot \quad t$$

	Distance	Rate	Time	
Downstream	d	$r + 6$	4	$\rightarrow d = (r + 6)4$
Upstream	d	$r - 6$	5	$\rightarrow d = (r - 6)5$

2. **Translate.** From each row of the table, we get an equation, $d = rt$:

$$d = 4r + 24, \qquad (1)$$
$$d = 5r - 30. \qquad (2)$$

3. **Carry out.** We solve the system by the substitution method:

$$4r + 24 = 5r - 30 \qquad \text{Substituting } 4r + 24 \text{ for } d \text{ in equation (2)}$$
$$\left. \begin{array}{r} 24 = r - 30 \\ 54 = r. \end{array} \right\} \quad \text{Solving for } r$$

4. **Check.** If $r = 54$, then $r + 6 = 60$; and $60 \cdot 4 = 240$, the distance traveled downstream. If $r = 54$, then $r - 6 = 48$; and $48 \cdot 5 = 240$, the distance traveled upstream. The speed of the boat in still water, 54 mph, checks.

5. **State.** The speed of the boat in still water is 54 mph.

Try Exercise 51.

SOLVING EQUATIONS BY GRAPHING

Solving equations graphically
(Section 4.5)

When two graphs intersect, that point of intersection represents a solution of *both* equations. We can use this fact to solve equations graphically.

EXAMPLE 6   Solve by graphing: $\frac{1}{2}x - 3 = 2(x + 7)$.

SOLUTION   We graph two equations, each corresponding to one side of the equation we wish to solve. For this equation, we graph $y_1 = \frac{1}{2}x - 3$ and $y_2 = 2(x + 7)$ using the same viewing window. We may need to adjust the dimensions of the viewing window in order to see the point of intersection.

Using INTERSECT, we see that the point of intersection is approximately $(-11.33333, -8.666667)$. The x-coordinate of the point of intersection is the solution of the original equation. Returning to the home screen, we can convert x to fraction notation if we wish. The solution is $-\frac{34}{3}$, or approximately -11.33333.

Try Exercise 59.

Intersect method (p. 270)

Zero method (p. 273)

Zero of a function (p. 273)

We solved the equation in Example 6 using the **Intersect method.** To use the **Zero method,** we find the **zeros of a function,** or inputs that make an output zero.

EXAMPLE 7   Find any zeros of the function given by $f(x) = 3 - 2x$.

SOLUTION   A zero is an input x such that $f(x) = 0$:

$$f(x) = 0 \qquad \text{The output } f(x) \text{ must be 0.}$$
$$3 - 2x = 0 \qquad \text{Substituting}$$
$$\left.\begin{array}{l} 3 = 2x \\ \frac{3}{2} = x. \end{array}\right\} \quad \text{Solving for } x$$

Since $f\left(\frac{3}{2}\right) = 3 - 2 \cdot \frac{3}{2} = 0, \frac{3}{2}$ is the zero of f.

Try Exercise 55.

EXAMPLE 8   Solve by graphing: $3x + 1 = 5x - 7$.

SOLUTION   We use the Zero method, first getting 0 on one side of the equation:

$$3x + 1 = 5x - 7$$
$$-2x + 1 = -7 \qquad \text{Subtracting } 5x \text{ from both sides}$$
$$-2x + 8 = 0. \qquad \text{Adding 7 to both sides}$$

We let $f(x) = -2x + 8$, and find the zero of the function by locating the x-intercept of its graph.

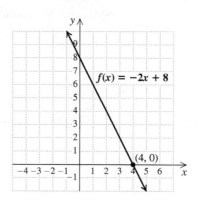

Since $f(4) = 0$, the zero of the function is 4. We check 4 in the original equation.

$$\text{Check:} \quad \begin{array}{c|c} 3x + 1 = 5x - 7 \\ \hline 3 \cdot 4 + 1 & 5 \cdot 4 - 7 \\ 12 + 1 & 20 - 7 \\ 13 \overset{?}{=} 13 \end{array} \quad \text{TRUE}$$

The solution is 4.

Try Exercise 61.

9.4 Exercise Set

FOR EXTRA HELP

MyMathLab Math XL
PRACTICE   WATCH DOWNLOAD READ REVIEW

Solve each system using the indicated method. Be sure to check your solution. If a system has an infinite number of solutions, use set-builder notation to write the solution set, as illustrated in the third graph after Example 1. If a system has no solution, state this.

9. $x = 6,$
$\quad y = -1$

10. $x = -2,$
$\quad y = 5$

11. $y = \frac{1}{5}x + 4,$
$\quad 2y = \frac{2}{5}x + 8$

12. $y = \frac{1}{3}x + 2,$
$\quad y = \frac{1}{3}x - 7$

Solve each system graphically.

1. $x + y = 7,$
$\quad x - y = 1$

2. $x - y = 1,$
$\quad x + y = 3$

Solve each system using the substitution method.

13. $y = 5 - 4x,$
$\quad 2x + y = 1$

14. $2y + x = 9,$
$\quad x = 3y - 3$

3. $y = -2x + 5,$
$\quad x + y = 4$

4. $y = 2x - 5,$
$\quad x + y = 4$

15. $3x + 5y = 3,$
$\quad x = 8 - 4y$

16. $9x + 2y = 3,$
$\quad 3x - 6 = y$

5. $y = x - 3,$
$\quad y = -2x + 3$

6. $y = -3x + 2,$
$\quad y = x - 2$

17. $3s - 4t = 14,$
$\quad t = 8 - 5s$

18. $m - 2n = 16,$
$\quad n = 1 - 4m$

7. $4x - 20 = 5y,$
$\quad 8x - 10y = 12$

8. $6x + 12 = 2y,$
$\quad 6 - y = -3x$

19. $4x - 2y = 6,$
$\quad 2x - 3 = y$

20. $t = 4 - 2s,$
$\quad t + 2s = 6$

21. $x - 4y = 3,$
$5x + 3y = 4$

22. $2a + 2b = 5,$
$3a - b = 7$

23. $2x - 3 = y,$
$y - 2x = 1$

24. $a - 2b = 3,$
$3a = 6b + 9$

Solve each system using the elimination method.

25. $x + 3y = 7,$
$-x + 4y = 7$

26. $2x + y = 6,$
$x - y = 3$

27. $2x - y = -3,$
$x + y = 9$

28. $x - 2y = 6,$
$-x + 3y = -4$

29. $3x + y = -1,$
$2x - 3y = -8$

30. $x + 3y = 2,$
$2x - y = 11$

31. $4x + 3y = 6,$
$2x - 2y = 1$

32. $3x + 2y = 3,$
$9x - 8y = -2$

33. $5r - 3s = 24,$
$3r + 5s = 28$

34. $5x - 7y = -16,$
$2x + 8y = 26$

35. $6s + 9t = 12,$
$4s + 6t = 5$

36. $10a + 6b = 8,$
$5a + 3b = 2$

37. $12x - 6y = -15,$
$-4x + 2y = 5$

38. $8s + 12t = 16,$
$6s + 9t = 12$

Solve using a system of equations.

39. The sum of two numbers is 89. One number is 3 more than the other. Find the numbers.

40. Find two numbers for which the sum is 108 and the difference is 50.

41. *Supplementary Angles.*   Supplementary angles are angles for which the sum of their measures is 180°. Two angles are supplementary. One angle is 33° more than twice the other. Find the measure of each angle.

42. *Complementary Angles.*   Complementary angles are angles for which the sum of their measures is 90°. Two angles are complementary. Their difference is 12°. Find the measure of each angle.

43. *Basketball Scoring.*   In winning the Western Conference finals, the San Antonio Spurs once scored 76 of their points on a combination of 36 two- and three-pointers. How many shots of each type did they make?
Source: National Basketball Association.

44. *Zoo Admissions.*   From April through November, the Bronx Zoo charges $15 per adult and $11 per child for a Total Experience admission. One May day, a total of $8428 was collected from 604 adults and children. How many adult admissions were there?

45. *Dance Lessons.*   Jean charges $20 for a private tap lesson and $12 for a group class. One Wednesday, Jean earned $216 from 14 students. How many students of each type did Jean teach?

46. *Used Books.*   A Book in Hand sells used paperback books for $1.99 and used hardbacks for $4.99. Holly recently purchased a total of 14 books for a total of $42.86 (before tax). How many paperbacks and how many hardbacks did she buy?

47. *Mixed Nuts.*   A grocer wishes to mix peanuts worth $3.20 per pound with Brazil nuts worth $6.40 per pound to make 480 lb of a mixture worth $5.50 per pound. How much of each nut should be used?

48. *Mixed Nuts.*   The Nuthouse has 10 kg of mixed cashews and pecans worth $8.40 per kilogram. Cashews alone sell for $8.00 per kilogram, and pecans sell for $9.00 per kilogram. How many kilograms of each nut are in the mixture?

49. *Production.*   Streakfree window cleaner is 12% alcohol and Sunstream window cleaner is 30% alcohol. How much of each cleaner should be used to make 90 oz of a cleaner that is 20% alcohol? Complete the following table as part of the *Translate* step.

Type of Solution	Streakfree	Sunstream	Mixture
Amount of Solution	x	y	
Percent Alcohol	12%		20%
Amount of Alcohol in Solution		$0.3y$	

50. *Chemistry.*   E-Chem Testing has a solution that is 80% base and another that is 30% base. A technician needs 200 L of a solution that is 62% base. The 200 L will be prepared by mixing the two solutions on hand. How much of each should be used?

51. *Car Travel.*   Two cars leave Denver traveling in opposite directions. One car travels at a speed of 75 km/h and the other at 88 km/h. In how many hours will they be 489 km apart?

52. *Canoeing.*   Darren paddled for 4 hr with a 6-km/h current to reach a campsite. The return trip against the same current took 16 hr. Find the speed of Darren's canoe in still water.

53. *Air Travel.*   Rod is a pilot for Crossland Airways. He computes his flight time against a headwind for a trip of 2900 mi at 5 hr. The flight would take 4 hr and 50 min if the headwind were half as great. Find the headwind and the plane's air speed.

54. *Motorcycle Travel.* Sally and Rocky travel on motorcycles toward each other from Chicago and Indianapolis, which are about 350 km apart. They started at the same time, and Sally is riding 20 km/h faster than Rocky. In how many hours will they meet?

Find the zero of each function.

55. $f(x) = 7 - x$

56. $f(x) = \frac{1}{2}x + 2$

57. $f(x) = 2x + 9$

58. $f(x) = 3 - 4x$

Solve by graphing.

59. $2x - 5 = 3x + 1$

60. $x - 7 = 2x + 5$

61. $3x = x + 6$

62. $4x - 7 = x + 2$

63. $5x + 1 = 11x - 3$

64. $2x - 5 = 8x$

Try Exercise Answers: Section 9.4
1. $(4, 3)$ **13.** $(2, -3)$ **25.** $(1, 2)$ **47.** Peanuts: 135 lb;
Brazil nuts: 345 lb **51.** 3 hr **55.** 7 **59.** -6 **61.** 3

9.5 Polynomials

- Exponents
- Polynomials
- Addition and Subtraction of Polynomials
- Multiplication of Polynomials
- Division of Polynomials

EXPONENTS

We know that x^4 means $x \cdot x \cdot x \cdot x$ and that x^1 means x. Exponential notation is also defined for zero and negative exponents.

Zero and Negative Exponents For any real number a, $a \neq 0$,

$$a^0 = 1 \quad \text{and} \quad a^{-n} = \frac{1}{a^n}.$$

The exponent zero

EXAMPLE 1 Simplify: **(a)** $(36)^0$; **(b)** $(-2x)^0$.

SOLUTION

a) $(36)^0 = 1$ since any number (other than 0 itself) raised to the 0 power is 1.

b) $(-2x)^0 = 1$ for any $x \neq 0$.

Try Exercise 1.

EXAMPLE 2 Write an equivalent expression using positive exponents.

a) x^{-2}

b) $\dfrac{1}{x^{-2}}$

c) $7y^{-1}$

SOLUTION

Negative exponents

a) $x^{-2} = \dfrac{1}{x^2}$ x^{-2} is the reciprocal of x^2.

b) $\dfrac{1}{x^{-2}} = x^{-(-2)} = x^2$ The reciprocal of x^{-2} is $x^{-(-2)}$, or x^2.

c) $7y^{-1} = 7\left(\dfrac{1}{y^1}\right) = \dfrac{7}{y}$ y^{-1} is the reciprocal of y^1.

Try Exercise 5.

The following properties hold for any integers m and n and any real numbers a and b, provided no denominators are 0 and 0^0 is not considered.

Properties of Exponents

The Product Rule: $a^m \cdot a^n = a^{m+n}$

The Quotient Rule: $\dfrac{a^m}{a^n} = a^{m-n}$

The Power Rule: $(a^m)^n = a^{mn}$

Raising a product to a power: $(ab)^n = a^n b^n$

Raising a quotient to a power: $\left(\dfrac{a}{b}\right)^n = \dfrac{a^n}{b^n}$

These properties are often used to simplify exponential expressions.

EXAMPLE 3 Simplify.

a) $(x^2 y^{-1})(xy^{-3})$ b) $\dfrac{(3p)^3}{(3p)^{-2}}$ c) $\left(\dfrac{ab^2}{3c^3}\right)^{-4}$

SOLUTION

The product rule

a) $(x^2 y^{-1})(xy^{-3}) = x^2 y^{-1} x y^{-3}$ Using an associative law

$\qquad\qquad\qquad\;\; = x^2 x^1 y^{-1} y^{-3}$ Using a commutative law; $x = x^1$

$\qquad\qquad\qquad\;\; = x^{2+1} y^{-1+(-3)}$ Using the product rule: Adding exponents

$\qquad\qquad\qquad\;\; = x^3 y^{-4}$, or $\dfrac{x^3}{y^4}$

The quotient rule

b) $\dfrac{(3p)^3}{(3p)^{-2}} = (3p)^{3-(-2)}$ Using the quotient rule: Subtracting exponents

$\qquad\qquad\; = (3p)^5$

The power rule

$\qquad\qquad\; = 3^5 p^5$ Raising each factor to the fifth power

$\qquad\qquad\; = 243 p^5$

Raising a quotient to a power

Raising a product to a power

c) $\left(\dfrac{ab^2}{3c^3}\right)^{-4} = \dfrac{(ab^2)^{-4}}{(3c^3)^{-4}}$ Raising the numerator and the denominator to the -4 power

$\qquad\qquad\quad = \dfrac{a^{-4}(b^2)^{-4}}{3^{-4}(c^3)^{-4}}$ Raising each factor to the -4 power

$\qquad\qquad\quad = \dfrac{a^{-4} b^{-8}}{3^{-4} c^{-12}}$ Multiplying exponents

$\qquad\qquad\quad = \dfrac{3^4 c^{12}}{a^4 b^8}$, or $\dfrac{81 c^{12}}{a^4 b^8}$ Rewriting without negative exponents

Try Exercise 25.

POLYNOMIALS

Polynomials

Algebraic expressions like

$$2x^3 + 3x - 5, \qquad 4x, \qquad -7, \quad \text{and} \quad 2a^3 b^2 + ab^3$$

Terms

are all examples of **polynomials.** All variables in a polynomial are raised to whole-number powers, and there are no variables in a denominator. The **terms** of a

Degree of a term

Leading term

Degree of a polynomial

Coefficient

Leading coefficient

polynomial are separated by addition signs. The **degree of a term** is the number of variable factors in that term. The **leading term** of a polynomial is the term of highest degree. The **degree of a polynomial** is the degree of the leading term. A polynomial is written in *descending order* when the leading term appears first, followed by the term of next highest degree, and so on.

The number -2 in the term $-2y^3$ is called the **coefficient** of that term. The coefficient of the leading term is the **leading coefficient** of the polynomial. To illustrate this terminology, consider the polynomial

$$4y^2 - 8y^5 + y^3 - 6y + 7.$$

The *terms* are $4y^2$, $-8y^5$, y^3, $-6y$, and 7.

The *coefficients* are 4, -8, 1, -6, and 7.

The *degree of each term* is 2, 5, 3, 1, and 0.

The *leading term* is $-8y^5$ and the *leading coefficient* is -8.

The *degree of the polynomial* is 5.

Polynomials are classified by the number of terms and by degree.

A **monomial** has one term.   *Example*: $-2x^3y$

A **binomial** has two terms.   *Example*: $1.4x^2 - 10$

A **trinomial** has three terms.   *Example*: $x^2 - 3x - 6$

A **constant** polynomial has degree 0.   *Example*: 7

A **linear** polynomial has degree 1.   *Example*: $3x + 5$

A **quadratic** polynomial has degree 2.   *Example*: $5x^2 - x$

A **cubic** polynomial has degree 3.   *Example*: $x^3 + 2x^2 - \frac{1}{3}$

A **quartic** polynomial has degree 4.   *Example*: $-6x^4 - 2x^2 + 19$

Like, or *similar*, *terms* are either constant terms or terms containing the same variable(s) raised to the same power(s). Polynomials containing like terms can be simplified by *combining* those terms.

EXAMPLE 4   Combine like terms: $4x^2y + 2xy - x^2y + xy^2$.

SOLUTION   The like terms are $4x^2y$ and $-x^2y$. Thus we have

$$4x^2y + 2xy - x^2y + xy^2 = 4x^2y - x^2y + 2xy + xy^2$$
$$= 3x^2y + 2xy + xy^2.$$

Try Exercise 39.

A polynomial can be evaluated by replacing the variable or variables with a number or numbers. We use parentheses when substituting negative numbers.

EXAMPLE 5   Evaluate $-a^2 + 2ab + 5b^2$ for $a = -1$ and $b = 3$.

SOLUTION   We replace a with -1 and b with 3 and calculate the value using the rules for order of operations:

$$-a^2 + 2ab + 5b^2 = -(-1)^2 + 2 \cdot (-1) \cdot 3 + 5 \cdot 3^2$$
$$= -1 - 6 + 45 = 38.$$

Try Exercise 43.

Polynomial function

A function described by a polynomial is called a **polynomial function.**

EXAMPLE 6 Find $P(-2)$ for the polynomial function given by $P(x) = -x^3 + 3x - 7$.

SOLUTION   We substitute -2 for x and carry out the operations using the rules for order of operations:

$$P(-2) = -(-2)^3 + 3(-2) - 7$$
$$= -(-8) + (-6) - 7 \qquad \text{We cube the input before}$$
$$\qquad\qquad\qquad\qquad\qquad \text{taking the opposite.}$$
$$= 8 - 6 - 7$$
$$= -5.$$

Try Exercise 49.

ADDITION AND SUBTRACTION OF POLYNOMIALS

Addition of polynomials

To add two polynomials, we write a plus sign between them and combine like terms.

EXAMPLE 7   Add: $(4x^3 + 3x^2 + 2x - 7) + (-5x^2 + x - 10)$.

SOLUTION

$$(4x^3 + 3x^2 + 2x - 7) + (-5x^2 + x - 10)$$
$$= 4x^3 + (3 - 5)x^2 + (2 + 1)x + (-7 - 10)$$
$$= 4x^3 - 2x^2 + 3x - 17$$

Try Exercise 53.

Opposite of a polynomial

To find the **opposite of a polynomial,** we replace each term with its opposite. This process is also called *changing the sign* of each term. For example, the opposite of

$$3y^4 - 7y^2 - \tfrac{1}{3}y + 17$$

is

$$-(3y^4 - 7y^2 - \tfrac{1}{3}y + 17) = -3y^4 + 7y^2 + \tfrac{1}{3}y - 17.$$

Subtraction of polynomials

To subtract polynomials, we add the opposite of the polynomial being subtracted.

EXAMPLE 8   Subtract: $(3a^4 - 2a + 7) - (-a^3 + 5a - 1)$.

SOLUTION

$$(3a^4 - 2a + 7) - (-a^3 + 5a - 1)$$
$$= 3a^4 - 2a + 7 + a^3 - 5a + 1 \qquad \text{Adding the opposite}$$
$$= 3a^4 + a^3 - 7a + 8 \qquad\qquad\quad \text{Combining like terms}$$

Try Exercise 55.

MULTIPLICATION OF POLYNOMIALS

Multiplication of polynomials

To multiply two monomials, we multiply coefficients and then multiply variables using the product rule for exponents. To multiply a monomial and a polynomial, we multiply each term of the polynomial by the monomial, using the distributive property.

EXAMPLE 9   Multiply: $4x^3(3x^4 - 2x^3 + 7x - 5)$.

SOLUTION

$$\text{\textit{Think:}}\quad \underbrace{4x^3 \cdot 3x^4} - \underbrace{4x^3 \cdot 2x^3} + \underbrace{4x^3 \cdot 7x} - \underbrace{4x^3 \cdot 5}$$

$$4x^3(3x^4 - 2x^3 + 7x - 5) = 12x^7 - 8x^6 + 28x^4 - 20x^3$$

Try Exercise 59.

To multiply any two polynomials P and Q, we select one of the polynomials—say, P. We then multiply each term of P by every term of Q and combine like terms.

EXAMPLE 10   Multiply: $(2a^3 + 3a - 1)(a^2 - 4a)$.

SOLUTION   It is often helpful to use columns for a long multiplication. We multiply each term at the top by every term at the bottom, write like terms in columns, and add the results.

$$
\begin{array}{r}
2a^3 \quad + 3a - 1 \\
a^2 - 4a \\
\hline
-8a^4 \qquad - 12a^2 + 4a \\
2a^5 \quad + 3a^3 \quad - a^2 \\
\hline
2a^5 - 8a^4 + 3a^3 - 13a^2 + 4a
\end{array}
$$

Multiplying the top row by $-4a$

Multiplying the top row by a^2

Combining like terms. Be sure that like terms are lined up in columns.

Try Exercise 63.

By observing the pattern of the products formed when multiplying two binomials, we can develop a more efficient method to find their product.

The FOIL Method   To multiply two binomials, $A + B$ and $C + D$, multiply the First terms AC, the Outer terms AD, the Inner terms BC, and then the Last terms BD. Then combine like terms, if possible.

$$(A + B)(C + D) = AC + AD + BC + BD$$

1. Multiply First terms: AC.
2. Multiply Outer terms: AD.
3. Multiply Inner terms: BC.
4. Multiply Last terms: BD.
$$\downarrow$$
FOIL

EXAMPLE 11   Multiply: $(3x + 4)(x - 2)$.

FOIL

SOLUTION

$$
\begin{array}{c}
\quad \text{F} \qquad \text{L} \\
(3x + 4)(x - 2) = 3x^2 - 6x + 4x - 8 \\
\qquad \text{I} \\
\quad \text{O}
\end{array}
$$

$$\qquad\qquad\qquad \overset{\text{F} \quad \text{O} \quad \text{I} \quad \text{L}}{= 3x^2 - 6x + 4x - 8}$$

$$= 3x^2 - 2x - 8 \qquad \text{Combining like terms}$$

Try Exercise 61.

Special products occur so often that specific formulas or methods for computing them have been developed.

Multiplying sums and differences of two terms

Squaring binomials

Special Products   The product of a sum and a difference of the same two terms:

$$(A + B)(A - B) = \underline{A^2 - B^2}$$

This is called a *difference of squares*.

The square of a binomial:

$$(A + B)^2 = A^2 + 2AB + B^2$$
$$(A - B)^2 = A^2 - 2AB + B^2$$

EXAMPLE 12   Multiply: **(a)** $(x + 3y)(x - 3y)$; **(b)** $(x^3 + 2)^2$.

SOLUTION

$$(A + B)\ (A - B)\ =\ A^2\ -\ B^2$$

a) $(x + 3y)(x - 3y) = x^2 - (3y)^2$ $A = x$ and $B = 3y$
$$= x^2 - 9y^2$$

$$(A + B)^2\ =\ A^2\ +\ 2 \cdot A \cdot B + B^2$$

b) $(x^3 + 2)^2 = (x^3)^2 + 2 \cdot x^3 \cdot 2 + 2^2$ $A = x^3$ and $B = 2$
$$= x^6 + 4x^3 + 4$$

Try Exercise 65.

DIVISION OF POLYNOMIALS

Division of polynomials

Polynomial division is similar to division in arithmetic. To divide a polynomial by a monomial, we divide each term by the monomial.

EXAMPLE 13   Divide: $(3x^5 + 8x^3 - 12x) \div (4x)$.

SOLUTION   This division can be written

$$\frac{3x^5 + 8x^3 - 12x}{4x} = \frac{3x^5}{4x} + \frac{8x^3}{4x} - \frac{12x}{4x}$$ Dividing each term by $4x$

$$= \frac{3}{4}x^{5-1} + \frac{8}{4}x^{3-1} - \frac{12}{4}x^{1-1}$$ Dividing coefficients and subtracting exponents

$$= \frac{3}{4}x^4 + 2x^2 - 3.$$

To check, we multiply the quotient by $4x$:

$$\left(\tfrac{3}{4}x^4 + 2x^2 - 3\right)4x = 3x^5 + 8x^3 - 12x.$$ The answer checks.

Try Exercise 75.

To use long division, we write polynomials in descending order, including terms with 0 coefficients for missing terms. As shown below in Example 14, the procedure ends when the degree of the remainder is less than the degree of the divisor.

EXAMPLE 14 Divide: $(4x^3 - 7x + 1) \div (2x + 1)$.

SOLUTION The polynomials are already written in descending order, but there is no x^2-term in the dividend. We fill in $0x^2$ for that term.

$$
\begin{array}{r}
2x^2 \phantom{{}+ 0x^2 - 7x + 1} \\
2x + 1 \overline{)\,4x^3 + 0x^2 - 7x + 1} \\
4x^3 + 2x^2 \phantom{{}- 7x + 1} \\
\hline
-2x^2 \phantom{{}- 7x + 1}
\end{array}
$$

Divide the first term of the dividend, $4x^3$, by the first term in the divisor, $2x$: $4x^3/(2x) = 2x^2$.

Multiply $2x^2$ by the divisor, $2x + 1$.

Subtract: $(4x^3 + 0x^2) - (4x^3 + 2x^2) = -2x^2$.

Then we bring down the next term of the dividend, $-7x$.

$$
\begin{array}{r}
2x^2 - x \phantom{{}- 7x + 1} \\
2x + 1 \overline{)\,4x^3 + 0x^2 - 7x + 1} \\
4x^3 + 2x^2 \phantom{{}- 7x + 1} \\
\hline
-2x^2 - 7x \phantom{{}+ 1} \\
-2x^2 - x \phantom{{}+ 1} \\
\hline
-6x \phantom{{}+ 1}
\end{array}
$$

Divide the first term of $-2x^2 - 7x$ by the first term in the divisor: $-2x^2/(2x) = -x$.

The $-7x$ has been "brought down."

Multiply $-x$ by the divisor, $2x + 1$.

Subtract: $(-2x^2 - 7x) - (-2x^2 - x) = -6x$.

Since the degree of the remainder, $-6x$, is *not* less than the degree of the divisor, we must continue dividing.

$$
\begin{array}{r}
2x^2 - x - 3 \\
2x + 1 \overline{)\,4x^3 + 0x^2 - 7x + 1} \\
4x^3 + 2x^2 \phantom{{}- 7x + 1} \\
\hline
-2x^2 - 7x \phantom{{}+ 1} \\
-2x^2 - x \phantom{{}+ 1} \\
\hline
-6x + 1 \\
-6x - 3 \\
\hline
4
\end{array}
$$

Divide the first term of $-6x + 1$ by the first term in the divisor: $-6x/(2x) = -3$.

The 1 has been "brought down."

Multiply -3 by $2x + 1$.

Subtract.

The answer is $2x^2 - x - 3$ with R 4, or

$$\text{Quotient} \longrightarrow 2x^2 - x - 3 + \underset{\longleftarrow \text{ Divisor}}{\frac{4}{2x + 1}} \overset{\longleftarrow \text{ Remainder}}{.}$$

Check: We multiply by the divisor and add the remainder:

$$(2x + 1)(2x^2 - x - 3) + 4 = 4x^3 - 7x - 3 + 4$$
$$= 4x^3 - 7x + 1.$$

Try Exercise 77.

Simplify.

1. a^0, for $a = -25$

2. y^0, for $y = 6.97$

3. $4^0 - 4^1$

4. $8^1 - 8^0$

Write an equivalent expression using positive exponents. Then, if possible, simplify.

5. 8^{-2}

6. $(-2)^{-3}$

7. $10x^{-5}$

8. $-16y^{-3}$

9. $(ab)^{-2}$

10. ab^{-2}

11. $\dfrac{1}{y^{-10}}$

12. $\dfrac{1}{x^{-t}}$

Write an equivalent expression using negative exponents.

13. $\dfrac{1}{y^4}$

14. $\dfrac{1}{a^2 b^3}$

15. $\dfrac{1}{x^t}$

16. $\dfrac{1}{n}$

Simplify. Write answers with positive exponents.

17. $x^5 \cdot x^8$

18. $a^4 \cdot a^{-2}$

19. $\dfrac{a}{a^{-5}}$

20. $\dfrac{p^{-3}}{p^{-8}}$

21. $\dfrac{(4x)^{10}}{(4x)^2}$

22. $\dfrac{a^2 b^9}{a^9 b^2}$

23. $(7^8)^5$

24. $(x^3)^{-7}$

25. $(x^{-2}y^{-3})^{-4}$

26. $(-2a^2)^3$

27. $\left(\dfrac{y^2}{4}\right)^3$

28. $\left(\dfrac{ab^2}{c^3}\right)^4$

29. $\left(\dfrac{2p^3}{3q^4}\right)^{-2}$

30. $\left(\dfrac{2}{x}\right)^{-5}$

Identify the terms of each polynomial.

31. $8x^3 - 6x^2 + x - 7$

32. $-a^2 b + 4a^2 - 8b + 17$

Determine the coefficient and the degree of each term in each polynomial. Then find the degree of each polynomial.

33. $18x^3 + 36x^9 - 7x + 3$ **34.** $-8y^7 + y + 19$

35. $-x^2 y + 4y^3 - 2xy$ **36.** $8 - x^2 y^4 + y^7$

Determine the leading term and the leading coefficient of each polynomial.

37. $-p^2 + 4 + 8p^4 - 7p$

38. $13 + 20t - 30t^2 - t^3$

Combine like terms. Write each answer in descending order.

39. $3x^3 - x^2 + x^4 + x^2$

40. $5t - 8t^2 + 4t^2$

41. $3 - 2t^2 + 8t - 3t - 5t^2 + 7$

42. $8x^5 - \frac{1}{3} + \frac{4}{5}x + 1 - \frac{1}{2}x$

Evaluate each polynomial for the given replacements of the variables.

43. $3x^2 - 7x + 10$, for $x = -2$

44. $-y + 3y^2 + 2y^3$, for $y = 3$

45. $a^2 b^3 + 2b^2 - 6a$, for $a = 2$ and $b = -1$

46. $2pq^3 - 5q^2 + 8p$, for $p = -4$ and $q = -2$

The distance s, in feet, traveled by a body falling freely from rest in t seconds is approximated by

$$s = 16t^2.$$

47. A pebble is dropped into a well and takes 3 sec to hit the water. How far down is the surface of the water?

48. An acorn falls from the top of an oak tree and takes 2 sec to hit the ground. How high is the tree?

Find each function value.

49. $f(3)$, if $f(x) = x^2 - x + 5$

50. $g(7)$, if $g(x) = 3x^2 + 2x$

51. $p(-1)$, if $p(x) = -x^3 - x^2 + 4x$

52. $F(-2)$, if $F(x) = 12 - x + 3x^2$

Add or subtract, as indicated.

53. $(3x^3 + 2x^2 + 8x) + (x^3 - 5x^2 + 7)$

54. $(-6x^4 + 3x^2 - 16) + (4x^2 + 4x - 7)$

55. $(8y^2 - 2y - 3) - (9y^2 - 7y - 1)$

56. $(4t^2 + 6t - 7) - (t + 5)$

57. $(-x^2 y + 2y^2 + y) - (3y^2 + 2x^2 y - 7y)$

58. $(ab + x^2 y^2) + (2ab - x^2 y^2)$

Multiply.

59. $4x^2(3x^3 - 7x + 7)$

60. $a^2b(a^3 + b^2 - ab - 2b)$

61. $(2a + y)(4a + b)$

62. $(x + 7y)(y - 3x)$

63. $(x + 7)(x^2 - 3x + 1)$

64. $(2x - 3)(x^2 - x - 1)$

65. $(x + 7)(x - 7)$

66. $(2x + 1)^2$

67. $(x + y)^2$

68. $(xy + 1)(xy - 1)$

69. $(2x^2 + 7)(3x^2 - 2)$

70. $(x^2 + 2)^2$

71. $(a - 3b)^2$

72. $(1.1x^2 + 5)(0.1x^2 - 2)$

73. $(6a - 5y)(7a + 3y)$

74. $(3p^2 - q^3)^2$

Divide and check.

75. $(3t^5 + 9t^3 - 6t^2 + 15t) \div (-3t)$

76. $(4x^5 + 10x^4 - 16x^2) \div (4x^2)$

77. $(15x^2 - 16x - 15) \div (3x - 5)$

78. $(x^3 - 2x^2 - 14x + 1) \div (x - 5)$

79. $(2x^3 - x^2 + 1) \div (x + 1)$

80. $(2x^3 + 3x^2 - 50) \div (2x - 5)$

81. $(5x^3 + 3x^2 - 5x) \div (x^2 - 1)$

82. $(2x^3 + 3x^2 + 6x + 10) \div (x^2 + 3)$

Try Exercise Answers: Section 9.5

1. 1   **5.** $\dfrac{1}{8^2} = \dfrac{1}{64}$ **25.** x^8y^{12} **39.** $x^4 + 3x^3$ **43.** 36
49. 11   **53.** $4x^3 - 3x^2 + 8x + 7$ **55.** $-y^2 + 5y - 2$
59. $12x^5 - 28x^3 + 28x^2$ **61.** $8a^2 + 2ab + 4ay + by$
63. $x^3 + 4x^2 - 20x + 7$ **65.** $x^2 - 49$
75. $-t^4 - 3t^2 + 2t - 5$ **77.** $5x + 3$

9.6 Polynomial Factorizations and Equations

- Common Factors and Factoring by Grouping

- Factoring Trinomials

- Factoring Special Forms

- Solving Polynomial Equations

Common factor

COMMON FACTORS AND FACTORING BY GROUPING

To *factor* a polynomial is to find an equivalent expression that is a product. For example, three *factorizations* of $50x^6$ are $5 \cdot 10x^6$, $5x^3 \cdot 10x^3$, and $2x \cdot 25x^5$.

If all the terms in a polynomial share a common factor, that factor can be "factored out" of the polynomial. Whenever you are factoring a polynomial with two or more terms, try to first find the largest common factor of the terms, if one exists.

EXAMPLE 1   Factor: $3x^6 + 15x^4 - 9x^3$.

SOLUTION   The largest factor common to 3, 15, and -9 is 3. The largest power of x common to x^6, x^4, and x^3 is x^3. Thus the largest common factor of the terms of the polynomial is $3x^3$. We factor as follows:

$$3x^6 + 15x^4 - 9x^3 = 3x^3 \cdot x^3 + 3x^3 \cdot 5x - 3x^3 \cdot 3 \qquad \text{Factoring each term}$$

$$= 3x^3(x^3 + 5x - 3). \qquad \text{Factoring out } 3x^3$$

Factorizations can always be checked by multiplying:

$$3x^3(x^3 + 5x - 3) = 3x^6 + 15x^4 - 9x^3.$$

Try Exercise 1.

A polynomial with two or more terms can be a common factor.

EXAMPLE 2 Factor: $3x^2(x - 2) + 5(x - 2)$.

SOLUTION The binomial $x - 2$ is a factor of both $3x^2(x - 2)$ and $5(x - 2)$. Thus we have

$$3x^2(x - 2) + 5(x - 2) = (x - 2)(3x^2 + 5).$$ Factoring out the common factor, $x - 2$

Try Exercise 5.

If a polynomial with four terms can be split into two groups of terms, and both groups share a common binomial factor, the polynomial can be factored. This method is known as **factoring by grouping.**

Factoring by grouping

EXAMPLE 3 Factor by grouping: $2x^3 + 6x^2 - x - 3$.

SOLUTION First, we consider the polynomial as two groups of terms, $2x^3 + 6x^2$ and $-x - 3$. Then we factor each group separately:

$$2x^3 + 6x^2 - x - 3 = 2x^2(x + 3) - 1(x + 3)$$ Factoring out $2x^2$ and -1 to give the common binomial factor, $x + 3$

$$= (x + 3)(2x^2 - 1).$$

The check is left to the student.

Try Exercise 23.

Prime polynomial

Not every polynomial with four terms is factorable by grouping. A polynomial that is not factorable is said to be **prime.**

FACTORING TRINOMIALS

Factoring trinomials of the type $x^2 + bx + c$

Many trinomials that have no common factor can be written as the product of two binomials. We look first at trinomials of the form $x^2 + bx + c$, for which the leading coefficient is 1.

Factoring trinomials involves a trial-and-error process. In order for the product of two binomials to be $x^2 + bx + c$, the binomials must look like

$$(x + p)(x + q),$$

where p and q are constants that must be determined. We look for two numbers p and q whose product is c and whose sum is b.

EXAMPLE 4 Factor.

a) $x^2 + 10x + 16$

b) $x^2 - 8x + 15$

c) $x^2 - 2x - 24$

d) $3t^2 - 33st + 84s^2$

SOLUTION

Constant term positive

a) The factorization is of the form

$$(x + \quad)(x + \quad).$$

To find the constant terms, we need a pair of factors whose product is 16 and whose sum is 10. Since 16 is positive, its factors will have the same sign as 10— that is, we need consider only positive factors of 16.

We list the possible factorizations in a table and calculate the sum of each pair of factors.

Pairs of Factors of 16	Sums of Factors
1, 16	17
2, 8	10 ←
4, 4	8

The numbers we seek are 2 and 8.

The factorization of $x^2 + 10x + 16$ is $(x + 2)(x + 8)$. To check, we multiply.

Check: $(x + 2)(x + 8) = x^2 + 8x + 2x + 16 = x^2 + 10x + 16$.

b) For $x^2 - 8x + 15$, c is positive and b is negative. Therefore, the factors of 15 will be negative. Again, we list the possible factorizations in a table.

Pairs of Factors of 15	Sums of Factors
−1, −15	−16
−3, −5	−8 ←

The numbers we need are −3 and −5.

The factorization is $(x - 3)(x - 5)$. The check is left to the student.

Constant term negative

c) For $x^2 - 2x - 24$, c is negative, so one factor of −24 will be negative and one will be positive. Since b is also negative, the negative factor must have the larger absolute value.

Pairs of Factors of −24	Sums of Factors
1, −24	−23
2, −12	−10
3, −8	−5
4, −6	−2 ←

The numbers we need are 4 and −6.

The factorization is $(x + 4)(x - 6)$.

Check: $(x + 4)(x - 6) = x^2 - 6x + 4x - 24 = x^2 - 2x - 24$.

d) Always look first for a common factor. There is a common factor, 3, which we factor out first:

$$3t^2 - 33st + 84s^2 = 3(t^2 - 11st + 28s^2).$$

Now we consider $t^2 - 11st + 28s^2$. Think of $28s^2$ as the "constant" term c and $-11s$ as the "coefficient" b of the middle term. We try to express $28s^2$ as the product of two factors whose sum is $-11s$. These factors are $-4s$ and $-7s$. Thus the factorization of $t^2 - 11st + 28s^2$ is

$$(t - 4s)(t - 7s).$$ This is not the entire factorization of $3t^2 - 33st + 84s^2$.

We now include the common factor, 3, and write

$$3t^2 - 33st + 84s^2 = 3(t - 4s)(t - 7s).$$ This is the factorization.

Check: $3(t - 4s)(t - 7s) = 3(t^2 - 11st + 28s^2)$
$$= 3t^2 - 33st + 84s^2.$$

Try Exercise 11.

When the leading coefficient of a trinomial is not 1, the number of trials needed to find a factorization can increase dramatically. We will consider two methods for factoring trinomials of the type $ax^2 + bx + c$: factoring by reversing FOIL and the *ac*-method.

Factoring trinomials of the type $ax^2 + bx + c$

To Factor $ax^2 + bx + c$ Using FOIL

1. Make certain that all common factors have been removed. If any remain, factor out the largest common factor.
2. Find two First terms whose product is ax^2:

$$(\boxed{}x + \quad)(\boxed{}x + \quad) = ax^2 + bx + c.$$
$$\underline{\qquad\qquad} \text{FOIL}$$

3. Find two Last terms whose product is c:

$$(\quad x + \boxed{})(\quad x + \boxed{}) = ax^2 + bx + c.$$
$$\underline{\qquad\qquad} \text{FOIL}$$

4. Check by multiplying to see if the sum of the Outer and Inner products is bx. If necessary, repeat steps (2) and (3) until the correct combination is found.

$$(\boxed{}x + \boxed{})(\boxed{}x + \boxed{}) = ax^2 + bx + c.$$
$$\underset{O}{\underline{\qquad\qquad}} \quad \text{FOIL}$$

If no correct combination exists, state that the polynomial is prime.

EXAMPLE 5   Factor: $20x^3 - 22x^2 - 12x$.

SOLUTION

1. First, we factor out the largest common factor, $2x$:

$$20x^3 - 22x^2 - 12x = 2x(10x^2 - 11x - 6).$$

2. Next, in order to factor the trinomial $10x^2 - 11x - 6$, we search for two terms whose product is $10x^2$. The possibilities are

$$(x + \quad)(10x + \quad) \quad \text{or} \quad (2x + \quad)(5x + \quad).$$

3. There are four pairs of factors of -6. Since the first terms of the binomials are different, the order of the factors is important. So there are eight possibilities for the last terms:

$$
\begin{array}{ccc}
1, -6 & & -6, \ 1 \\
-1, \ \ 6 & \text{and} & 6, -1 \\
2, -3 & & -3, \ \ 2 \\
-2, \ \ 3 & & 3, -2.
\end{array}
$$

4. Since each of the eight possibilities from step (3) could be used in either of the two possibilities from step (2), there are $2 \cdot 8$, or 16, possible factorizations. We check the possibilities systematically until we find one that gives the correct factorization. Let's first try factors with $(2x +)(5x +)$.

Pair of Factors	Corresponding Trial	Product
$1, -6$	$(2x + 1)(5x - 6)$	$10x^2 - 7x - 6$ ← Wrong middle term
$-1, 6$	$(2x - 1)(5x + 6)$	$10x^2 + 7x - 6$ ← Wrong middle term. Changing the signs in the binomials changed the sign of the middle term in the product.
$2, -3$	$(2x + 2)(5x - 3)$	$10x^2 + 4x - 6$ ← Wrong middle term. We need not consider $(2x - 2)(5x + 3)$.
$-6, 1$	$(2x - 6)(5x + 1)$	$10x^2 - 28x - 6$ ← Wrong middle term. We need not consider $(2x + 6)(5x - 1)$.
$-3, 2$	$(2x - 3)(5x + 2)$	$10x^2 - 11x - 6$ ← Correct middle term

We can stop when we find a correct factorization. Including the common factor $2x$, we now have

$$20x^3 - 22x^2 - 12x = 2x(2x - 3)(5x + 2).$$

This can be checked by multiplying.

Try Exercise 27.

With practice, some of the trials can be skipped or performed mentally.

The second method of factoring trinomials of the type $ax^2 + bx + c$ involves factoring by grouping.

Student Note

Both the third and the fourth trial factorizations in Example 5 contain a binomial with a common factor: $2x + 2 = 2(x + 1)$ and $2x - 6 = 2(x - 3)$. If all common factors are factored out as a first step, you can immediately eliminate any trial factorization containing a binomial with a common factor.

The *ac*-method

To Factor $ax^2 + bx + c$ Using the *ac*-Method

1. Factor out the largest common factor, if one exists.
2. Multiply the leading coefficient a and the constant c.
3. Find a pair of factors of ac whose sum is b.
4. Rewrite the middle term, bx, as a sum or a difference using the factors found in step (3).
5. Factor by grouping.
6. Include any common factor from step (1) and check by multiplying.

EXAMPLE 6 Factor: $7x^2 + 31x + 12$.

SOLUTION

1. There is no common factor (other than 1 or -1).
2. We multiply the leading coefficient, 7, and the constant, 12:

$$7 \cdot 12 = 84.$$

3. We look for a pair of factors of 84 whose sum is 31. Since both 84 and 31 are positive, we need consider only positive factors.

Pairs of Factors of 84	Sums of Factors
1, 84	85
2, 42	44
3, 28	31 ←——— 3 + 28 = 31

4. Next, we rewrite $31x$ using the factors 3 and 28:

$$31x = 3x + 28x.$$

5. We now factor by grouping:

$$7x^2 + 31x + 12 = 7x^2 + 3x + 28x + 12 \qquad \text{Substituting } 3x + 28x \text{ for } 31x$$

$$= x(7x + 3) + 4(7x + 3)$$

$$= (7x + 3)(x + 4). \qquad \text{Factoring out the common factor, } 7x + 3$$

6. *Check:* $(7x + 3)(x + 4) = 7x^2 + 31x + 12.$

Try Exercise 15.

FACTORING SPECIAL FORMS

We can factor certain types of polynomials directly, without using trial and error.

Factoring Formulas

Perfect-square trinomial:	$A^2 + 2AB + B^2 = (A + B)^2,$
	$A^2 - 2AB + B^2 = (A - B)^2$
Difference of squares:	$A^2 - B^2 = (A + B)(A - B)$
Sum of cubes:	$A^3 + B^3 = (A + B)(A^2 - AB + B^2)$
Difference of cubes:	$A^3 - B^3 = (A - B)(A^2 + AB + B^2)$

Before using the factoring formulas, it is important to check carefully that the expression being factored is indeed in one of the forms listed. Note that there is no factoring formula for the sum of two squares.

EXAMPLE 7 Factor.

a) $2x^2 - 2$ **b)** $x^2y^2 + 20xy + 100$
c) $p^3 - 64$ **d)** $3y^2 + 27$

SOLUTION

a) We first factor out a common factor, 2:

$$2x^2 - 2 = 2(x^2 - 1).$$

Recognizing and factoring differences of squares

Looking at $x^2 - 1$, we see that it is a difference of squares, with $A = x$ and $B = 1$. The factorization is thus

$$2x^2 - 2 = 2(x^2 - 1) = 2(x + 1)(x - 1).$$
$$\underset{A^2 - B^2}{\uparrow\ \uparrow}\qquad \underset{(A + B)\,(A - B)}{\uparrow\ \uparrow\ \uparrow\ \uparrow}$$

Recognizing and factoring perfect-square trinomials

b) First, we check for a common factor; there is none. The polynomial is a perfect-square trinomial, since x^2y^2 and 100 are squares; there is no minus sign before either square; and $20xy$ is $2 \cdot xy \cdot 10$, where xy and 10 are square roots of x^2y^2 and 100, respectively. The factorization is thus

$$x^2y^2 + 20xy + 100 = (xy)^2 + 2 \cdot xy \cdot 10 + 10^2 = (xy + 10)^2.$$
$$\underset{A^2\ \ +\ 2 \cdot A \cdot B\ +\ B^2\ =\ (A\ +\ B)^2}{\uparrow\qquad\uparrow\ \uparrow\ \uparrow\qquad\uparrow\qquad\uparrow\qquad\uparrow}$$

Factoring sums or differences of cubes

c) This is a difference of cubes, with $A = p$ and $B = 4$:

$$p^3 - 64 = (p)^3 - (4)^3$$
$$= (p - 4)(p^2 + 4p + 16).$$

d) We factor out the common factor, 3:

$$3y^2 + 27 = 3(y^2 + 9).$$

Since $y^2 + 9$ is a sum of squares, no further factorization is possible.

Try Exercise 29.

A polynomial is said to be *factored completely* when no factor can be factored further.

EXAMPLE 8 Factor completely: $x^4 - 1$.

SOLUTION

$$x^4 - 1 = (x^2 + 1)(x^2 - 1)$$ Factoring a difference of squares

$$= (x^2 + 1)(x + 1)(x - 1)$$ The factor $x^2 - 1$ is itself a difference of squares.

Try Exercise 13.

SOLVING POLYNOMIAL EQUATIONS

Polynomial equation

Intersect method

Zero method

Whenever two polynomials are set equal to each other, we have a **polynomial equation.** We can solve polynomial equations graphically using the Intersect method or the Zero method.

> **EXAMPLE 9**   Solve: $3x^3 = 5x^2 + 2x$.

INTERSECT METHOD	ZERO METHOD

INTERSECT METHOD

We graph $y_1 = 3x^3$ and $y_2 = 5x^2 + 2x$ and look for any points of intersection. The x-coordinates of those points will be the solutions of the equation.

From the first graph, we see that one point of intersection is $(2, 24)$. In the second graph, we enlarge the section of the graph near the origin and see that $(-0.33333, -0.11111)$ and $(0, 0)$ are also points of intersection.

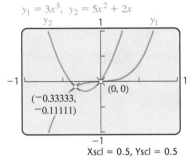

The solutions of the equation are -0.33333, 0, and 2.

ZERO METHOD

We rewrite the equation as $3x^3 - 5x^2 - 2x = 0$. We graph $f(x) = 3x^3 - 5x^2 - 2x$ and find the zeros of the function. Those zeros will be the solutions of the equation.

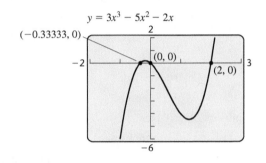

We see that $f(x) = 0$ when $x = -0.33333$, 0, or 2. Thus the solutions of the equation are -0.33333, 0, and 2.

Try Exercise 37.

Note in Example 9 that one of the solutions found is an approximation. If we can factor the polynomial that describes the function, we can find exact solutions using the following principle.

> **The Principle of Zero Products** An equation $ab = 0$ is true if and only if $a = 0$ or $b = 0$, or both. (A product is 0 if and only if at least one factor is 0.)

If we can write an equation as a product that equals 0, we can try to use the principle of zero products to solve the equation.

EXAMPLE 10 Solve.

a) $x^2 - 11x = 12$ **b)** $5x^2 + 10x + 5 = 0$
c) $9x^2 = 1$

SOLUTION

a) We must have 0 on one side of the equation before using the principle of zero products:

Get 0 on one side.
Factor.
Use the principle of zero products.
Solve.

$$x^2 - 11x = 12$$
$$x^2 - 11x - 12 = 0 \qquad \text{Subtracting 12 from both sides}$$
$$(x - 12)(x + 1) = 0 \qquad \text{Factoring}$$
$$x - 12 = 0 \quad or \quad x + 1 = 0 \qquad \text{Using the principle of zero products}$$
$$x = 12 \quad or \qquad x = -1.$$

The solutions are 12 and -1. The check is left to the student.

b) We have

$$5x^2 + 10x + 5 = 0$$
$$5(x^2 + 2x + 1) = 0 \qquad \text{Factoring out a common factor}$$
$$5(x + 1)(x + 1) = 0 \qquad \text{Factoring completely}$$
$$x + 1 = 0 \quad or \quad x + 1 = 0 \qquad \text{Using the principle of zero products}$$
$$x = -1 \quad or \qquad x = -1.$$

There is only one solution, -1. The check is left to the student.

c) We have

$$9x^2 = 1$$
$$9x^2 - 1 = 0 \qquad \text{Subtracting 1 from both sides to get 0 on one side}$$
$$(3x + 1)(3x - 1) = 0 \qquad \text{Factoring a difference of squares}$$
$$3x + 1 = 0 \quad or \quad 3x - 1 = 0 \qquad \text{Using the principle of zero products}$$
$$3x = -1 \quad or \qquad 3x = 1$$
$$x = -\tfrac{1}{3} \quad or \qquad x = \tfrac{1}{3}.$$

The solutions are $\tfrac{1}{3}$ and $-\tfrac{1}{3}$. The check is left to the student.

Try Exercise 35.

Quadratic equations can be used to solve problems. One important result that uses squared quantities is the Pythagorean theorem. It relates the lengths of the sides of a **right triangle**—that is, a triangle with a 90° angle. The side opposite the 90° angle is called the **hypotenuse,** and the other sides are called the **legs.**

The Pythagorean Theorem   The sum of the squares of the legs of a right triangle is equal to the square of the hypotenuse:

$$a^2 + b^2 = c^2.$$

This indicates 90°.

EXAMPLE 11   Hiking.   Cheri hiked 500 ft up a steep incline. Her global positioning unit indicated that her horizontal position had changed by 100 ft more than her vertical position had changed. What was the change in altitude?

SOLUTION

1. **Familiarize.** We make a drawing and let $x =$ the change in altitude, in feet. We know then that the horizontal change is $x + 100$, since Cheri's horizontal position has changed by 100 ft more than her vertical position. The hypotenuse has length 500 ft.

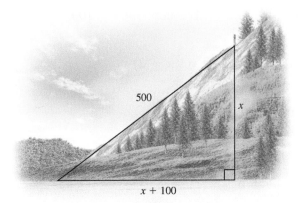

500

x

x + 100

2. **Translate.** Applying the Pythagorean theorem gives us

$$a^2 + b^2 = c^2$$
$$x^2 + (x + 100)^2 = 500^2.$$

3. **Carry out.** We solve the equation:

$$x^2 + (x + 100)^2 = 500^2$$
$$x^2 + x^2 + 200x + 10{,}000 = 250{,}000 \qquad \text{Squaring } x + 100;$$
$$\text{squaring 500}$$
$$2x^2 + 200x + 10{,}000 = 250{,}000 \qquad \text{Combining like terms}$$
$$2x^2 + 200x - 240{,}000 = 0 \qquad \text{Getting 0 on one side}$$
$$2(x^2 + 100x - 120{,}000) = 0 \qquad \text{Factoring out a}$$
$$\text{common factor}$$
$$2(x + 400)(x - 300) = 0 \qquad \text{Factoring a trinomial}$$
$$x + 400 = 0 \qquad or \quad x - 300 = 0 \qquad \text{Using the principle}$$
$$\text{of zero products}$$
$$x = -400 \quad or \qquad\qquad x = 300.$$

4. **Check.** We know that the change in altitude is positive, so -400 cannot be a solution. When $x = 300$, the horizontal change is 400. Since $300^2 + 400^2 = 500^2$, the solution checks.

5. **State.** Cheri's change in altitude was 300 ft.

Try Exercise 49.

9.6 Exercise Set

Factor completely. If a polynomial is prime, state this.

1. $18t^5 - 12t^4 + 6t^3$ **2.** $x^2y^4 - 2xy^5 + 3x^3y^6$

3. $y^2 - 6y + 9$ **4.** $4z^2 - 25$

5. $2p^3(p + 2) + (p + 2)$ **6.** $6y^2 + y - 1$

7. $x^2 + 100$ **8.** $y^3 - 1$

9. $8t^3 + 27$ **10.** $a^2b^2 + 24ab + 144$

11. $m^2 + 13m + 42$ **12.** $2x^3 - 6x^2 + x - 3$

13. $x^4 - 81$ **14.** $x^2 + x + 1$

15. $8x^2 + 22x + 15$ **16.** $4x^2 - 40x + 100$

17. $x^3 + 2x^2 - x - 2$

18. $(x + 2y)(x - 1) + (x + 2y)(x - 2)$

19. $0.001t^6 - 0.008$

20. $x^2 - 20 - x$

21. $-\frac{1}{16} + x^4$

22. $5x^8 - 5z^{16}$

23. $mn - 2m + 3n - 6$

24. $t^6 - p^6$

25. $5mn + m^2 - 150n^2$

26. $\frac{1}{27} + x^3$

27. $24x^2y - 6y - 10xy$ **28.** $-3y^2 - 12y - 12$

29. $y^2 - 121$ **30.** $t^3 - 2t^2 - 5t + 10$

Solve.

31. $(x - 2)(x + 7) = 0$ **32.** $(3x - 5)(7 - 4x) = 0$

33. $8x(11 - x) = 0$

34. $(x - 3)(x + 1)(2x - 9) = 0$

35. $x^2 = 100$ **36.** $8x^2 = 2x$

37. $4x^2 - 18x = 70$ **38.** $x^2 + 2x + 1 = 0$

39. $2x^3 - 10x^2 = 0$ **40.** $100x^2 = 81$

41. $(a + 1)(a - 5) = 7$ **42.** $d(d - 3) = 40$

43. $x^2 + 6x - 55 = 0$ **44.** $x^2 + 7x - 60 = 0$

45. $\frac{1}{2}x^2 + 5x + \frac{25}{2} = 0$ **46.** $3 + 10x^2 = 11x$

47. *Design.* The base of a triangular fountain is 2 ft longer than its height. The area of the fountain

base is 24 ft^2. What are the dimensions of the fountain?

48. *Page Numbers.* The product of the page numbers on two facing pages of a book is 156. Find the page numbers.

49. *Right Triangles.* The hypotenuse of a right triangle is 17 ft. One leg is 1 ft shorter than twice the length of the other leg. Find the length of the legs.

50. *Swing Sets.* The length of a slide on a swing set is 10 ft. The distance from the base of the ladder to the base of the slide is 2 ft more than the height of the ladder. Find the height of the ladder.

Try Exercise Answers: Section 9.6
1. $6t^3(3t^2 - 2t + 1)$ **5.** $(p + 2)(2p^3 + 1)$
11. $(m + 6)(m + 7)$ **13.** $(x^2 + 9)(x + 3)(x - 3)$
15. $(2x + 3)(4x + 5)$ **23.** $(n - 2)(m + 3)$
27. $2y(3x + 1)(4x - 3)$ **29.** $(y + 11)(y - 11)$
35. $-10, 10$ **37.** $-\frac{5}{2}, 7$ **49.** 8 ft, 15 ft

10

Inequalities

What Do You Do to Unwind?

As the graph indicates, on average, people are spending less time listening to music and more time playing video games. In Example 3 of Section 10.1, we predict when time spent playing video games will be greater than time spent listening to music.

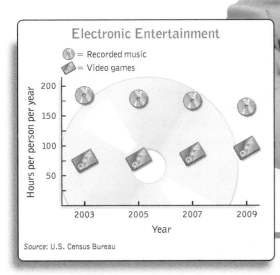

Electronic Entertainment

= Recorded music
= Video games

Hours per person per year

Source: U.S. Census Bureau

Inequalities are mathematical sentences containing symbols such as < (is less than). In this chapter, we use the principles for solving inequalities to solve various kinds of inequalities. We also combine our knowledge of inequalities and systems of equations to solve systems of inequalities.

10.1 Graphical Solutions and Compound Inequalities

- Solving Inequalities Graphically

- Intersections of Sets and Conjunctions of Sentences

- Unions of Sets and Disjunctions of Sentences

- Interval Notation and Domains

Recall that an **inequality** is any sentence containing $<, >, \leq, \geq,$ or $\neq$—for example,

$$-2 < a, \quad x > 4, \quad x + 3 \leq 6, \quad 7y \geq 10y - 4, \quad \text{and} \quad 5x \neq 10.$$

Any replacement for the variable that makes an inequality true is called a **solution.** The set of all solutions is called the **solution set.** When all solutions of an inequality are found, we say that we have **solved** the inequality.

We solved inequalities algebraically using the addition and multiplication principles for inequalities. These principles are similar to those used to solve equations with one important difference: The direction of the inequality symbol must be reversed when multiplying or dividing by a negative number.

We now look at a graphical method for solving inequalities.

SOLVING INEQUALITIES GRAPHICALLY

Consider the graphs of the functions $f(x) = 2x + 4$ and $g(x) = -x + 1$.

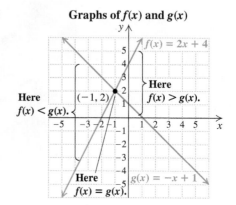

Graphs of $f(x)$ and $g(x)$

We can see the following from the graph:

- The graphs intersect at $(-1, 2)$. This means that $f(x) = g(x)$ when $x = -1$.
- The graph of f lies above the graph of g when $x > -1$. This is illustrated on the graph for $x = 1$. This means that $f(x) > g(x)$ when $x > -1$.
- The graph of f lies below the graph of g when $x < -1$. This is illustrated on the graph for $x = -4$. This means that $f(x) < g(x)$ when $x < -1$.

In summary, for $f(x) = 2x + 4$ and $g(x) = -x + 1$, we have the following.

Equation/Inequality	Solution Set	Graph of Solution Set
$f(x) = g(x)$	$\{-1\}$	
$f(x) < g(x)$	$(-\infty, -1)$	
$f(x) > g(x)$	$(-1, \infty)$	

EXAMPLE 1   Solve graphically: $-3x + 1 \geq x - 7$.

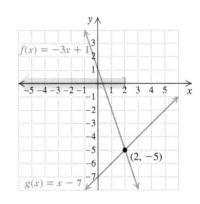

SOLUTION   We let $f(x) = -3x + 1$ and $g(x) = x - 7$, and graph both functions. The solution set will consist of the interval for which the graph of f lies on or above the graph of g.

We can confirm that $f(x) = g(x)$ when $x = 2$. The graph of f lies *on* the graph of g when $x = 2$. It lies *above* the graph of g when $x < 2$. Thus the solution of $-3x + 1 \geq x - 7$ is

$$\{x \mid x \leq 2\}, \quad \text{or} \quad (-\infty, 2].$$

This set is indicated by the purple shading on the x-axis.

Try Exercise 17.

EXAMPLE 2   Solve graphically: $16 - 7x \geq 10x - 4$.

SOLUTION   We let $y_1 = 16 - 7x$ and $y_2 = 10x - 4$, and graph y_1 and y_2 in the window $[-5, 5, -5, 15]$.

From the graph, we see that $y_1 = y_2$ at the point of intersection, or when $x \approx 1.1765$. To the left of the point of intersection, $y_1 > y_2$, as shown in the graph on the left below.

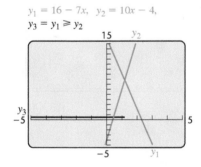

On many graphing calculators, the interval that is the solution set can be indicated by using the VARS and TEST keys. We enter and graph $y_3 = y_1 \geq y_2$. (The "$\geq$" symbol can be found in the TEST menu.) Where this is true, the value of y_3 will be 1, and where it is false, the value will be 0. The solution set is thus displayed as an interval, shown by a horizontal line 1 unit above the x-axis in the graph on the right above. The endpoint of the interval corresponds to the intersection of the graphs of the equations.

The solution set contains all x-values to the left of the point of intersection as well as the x-coordinate of the point of intersection. Thus the solution set is approximately $(-\infty, 1.1765]$, or converted to fraction notation, $\left(-\infty, \frac{20}{17}\right]$.

Try Exercise 25.

EXAMPLE 3 *Media Usage.* The table below lists the number of hours spent, on average, per person per year listening to recorded music and playing video games. Use linear regression to find two linear functions that can be used to estimate the number of hours $m(x)$ spent listening to music and the number of hours $v(x)$ spent playing video games x years after 2000. Then predict those years in which, on average, a person will spend more time playing video games than listening to music.

Year	Recorded Music (in hours per person per year)	Video Games (in hours per person per year)
2003	184	75
2005	179	78
2007	175	86
2009	165	96

Source: U.S. Census Bureau

SOLUTION We enter the number of years after 2000 as L1, the number of hours listening to music as L2, and the number of hours spent playing video games as L3. Graphing the data, we see that both sets appear to be linear, as shown at left.

We use linear regression to fit two lines to the data. In the figure on the left below, Y1 is the linear regression line relating L1 and L2, and Y2 is the line relating L1 and L3. Thus we have

$$m(x) = -3.05x + 194.05,$$
$$v(x) = 3.55x + 62.45.$$

We graph both lines in a viewing window that shows the point of intersection, approximately (19.9, 133.2), as shown in the figure on the right above. From the graph, we can see that when x is greater than 19.9, the number of hours spent playing video games will be greater than the number of hours spent listening to music. Since x is the number of years since 2000, we state that beginning in 2020, on average, a person will spend more time playing video games than listening to music.

Try Exercise 29.

Two inequalities joined by the word "and" or the word "or" are called **compound inequalities.** Thus, "$x < 3$ *or* $x > 4$" and "$x < 9$ *and* $x > -5$" are two examples of compound inequalities. Before discussing how to solve compound inequalities, we must first study ways in which sets can be combined.

INTERSECTIONS OF SETS AND CONJUNCTIONS OF SENTENCES

The **intersection** of two sets A and B is the set of all elements that are common to both A and B. We denote the intersection of sets A and B as

$$A \cap B.$$

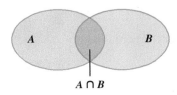

$A \cap B$

The intersection of two sets is represented by the purple region shown in the figure at left. For example, if $A = \{$all students who are taking a math class$\}$ and $B = \{$all students who are taking a history class$\}$, then $A \cap B = \{$all students who are taking a math class *and* a history class$\}$.

EXAMPLE 4   Find the intersection: $\{1, 2, 3, 4, 5\} \cap \{-2, -1, 0, 1, 2, 3\}$.

SOLUTION   The numbers 1, 2, and 3 are common to both sets, so the intersection is $\{1, 2, 3\}$.

Try Exercise 35.

When two or more sentences are joined by the word *and* to make a compound sentence, the new sentence is called a **conjunction** of the sentences. The following is a conjunction of inequalities:

$$-2 < x \quad and \quad x < 1.$$

The word *and* means that *both* sentences must be true if the conjunction is to be true.

A number is a solution of a conjunction if it is a solution of *both* of the separate parts. For example, -1 is a solution because it is a solution of $-2 < x$ as well as $x < 1$; that is, -1 is *both* greater than -2 *and* less than 1.

The solution set of a conjunction is the intersection of the solution sets of the individual sentences.

EXAMPLE 5   Graph and write interval notation for the conjunction

$$-2 < x \quad and \quad x < 1.$$

SOLUTION   We first graph $-2 < x$, then $x < 1$, and finally the conjunction $-2 < x$ *and* $x < 1$.

$\{x | -2 < x\}$ (-2, ∞)

$\{x | x < 1\}$ (-∞, 1)

$\{x | -2 < x\} \cap \{x | x < 1\}$
$= \{x | -2 < x \text{ and } x < 1\}$ (-2, 1)

Because there are numbers that are both greater than -2 and less than 1, the solution set of the conjunction $-2 < x$ *and* $x < 1$ is the interval $(-2, 1)$. In set-builder notation, this is written $\{x | -2 < x < 1\}$, the set of all numbers that are *simultaneously* greater than -2 *and* less than 1.

Try Exercise 55.

For $a < b$,

$$a < x \quad and \quad x < b \quad \text{can be abbreviated} \quad a < x < b;$$

and, equivalently,

$$b > x \quad and \quad x > a \quad \text{can be abbreviated} \quad b > x > a.$$

Mathematical Use of the Word "and"   The word "and" corresponds to "intersection" and to the symbol "$\cap$". Any solution of a conjunction must make each part of the conjunction true.

EXAMPLE 6 Solve and graph: $-1 \leq 2x + 5 < 13$.

SOLUTION This inequality is an abbreviation for the conjunction

$$-1 \leq 2x + 5 \quad and \quad 2x + 5 < 13.$$

We solve both algebraically and graphically.

ALGEBRAIC APPROACH	GRAPHICAL APPROACH

ALGEBRAIC APPROACH

The word *and* corresponds to set *intersection*. To solve the conjunction, we solve each of the two inequalities separately and then find the intersection of the solution sets:

$$-1 \leq 2x + 5 \quad and \quad 2x + 5 < 13$$
$$-6 \leq 2x \quad\quad and \quad\quad 2x < 8 \qquad \text{Subtracting 5 from both sides of each inequality}$$
$$-3 \leq x \quad\quad and \quad\quad x < 4. \qquad \text{Dividing both sides of each inequality by 2}$$

These steps are sometimes combined as follows:

$$-1 \leq 2x + 5 < 13$$
$$-1 - 5 \leq 2x + 5 - 5 < 13 - 5 \qquad \text{Subtracting 5 from all three regions}$$
$$-6 \leq 2x < 8$$
$$-3 \leq x < 4. \qquad \text{Dividing by 2 in all three regions}$$

The solution set is $\{x | -3 \leq x < 4\}$, or, in interval notation, $[-3, 4)$. The graph is the intersection of the two separate solution sets.

$\{x | -3 \leq x\}$, or $[-3, \infty)$

$\{x | x < 4\}$, or $(-\infty, 4)$

$\{x | -3 \leq x\} \cap \{x | x < 4\}$
$= \{x | -3 \leq x < 4\}$, or
$[-3, 4)$

GRAPHICAL APPROACH

We graph the equations $y_1 = -1$, $y_2 = 2x + 5$, and $y_3 = 13$, and determine those x-values for which $y_1 \leq y_2$ and $y_2 < y_3$.

From the graph, we see that $y_1 < y_2$ for x-values greater than -3, as indicated by the purple and blue shading on the x-axis. (The shading does not appear on the calculator, but is added here to illustrate the intervals.) We also see that $y_2 < y_3$ for x-values less than 4, as shown by the purple and red shading on the x-axis. The solution set, indicated by the purple shading, is the intersection of these sets, as well as the number -3. It includes all x-values for which the line $y_2 = 2x + 5$ is both on or above the line $y_1 = -1$ *and* below the line $y_3 = 13$. This can be written $\{x | -3 \leq x < 4\}$, or $[-3, 4)$.

Try Exercise 69.

CAUTION! The abbreviated form of a conjunction, like $-3 \leq x < 4$, can be written only if both inequality symbols point in the same direction.

EXAMPLE 7 Solve and graph: $2x - 5 \geq -3$ *and* $5x + 2 \geq 17$.

SOLUTION We first solve each inequality separately, retaining the word *and*:

$$2x - 5 \geq -3 \quad and \quad 5x + 2 \geq 17$$
$$2x \geq 2 \quad\quad and \quad\quad 5x \geq 15$$
$$x \geq 1 \quad\quad and \quad\quad x \geq 3.$$

$y_1 = 2x - 5, \ y_2 = 5x + 2,$
$y_3 = -3, \ y_4 = 17$

Next, we find the intersection of the two separate solution sets.

$\{x \mid x \geq 1\}$

$\{x \mid x \geq 3\}$

$\{x \mid x \geq 1\} \cap \{x \mid x \geq 3\}$
$= \{x \mid x \geq 3\}$

The numbers common to both sets are those greater than or equal to 3. Thus the solution set is $\{x \mid x \geq 3\}$, or, in interval notation, $[3, \infty)$. You should check that any number in $[3, \infty)$ satisfies the conjunction whereas numbers outside $[3, \infty)$ do not. The graph at left serves as another check.

Try Exercise 91.

Sometimes there is no way to solve both parts of a conjunction at once.

When $A \cap B = \varnothing$,
A and B are said to
be *disjoint*.

$A \cap B = \varnothing$

EXAMPLE 8   Solve and graph: $2x - 3 > 1 \ and \ 3x - 1 < 2$.

SOLUTION   We solve each inequality separately:

$$2x - 3 > 1 \quad and \quad 3x - 1 < 2$$
$$2x > 4 \quad and \quad 3x < 3$$
$$x > 2 \quad and \quad x < 1.$$

The solution set is the intersection of the individual inequalities.

$y_1 = 2x - 3, \ y_2 = 3x - 1,$
$y_3 = 1, \ y_4 = 2$

$\{x \mid x > 2\}$ $(2, \infty)$

$\{x \mid x < 1\}$ $(-\infty, 1)$

$\{x \mid x > 2\} \cap \{x \mid x < 1\}$ $\varnothing$
$= \{x \mid x > 2 \ and \ x < 1\} = \varnothing$

Since no number is both greater than 2 and less than 1, the solution set is the empty set, $\varnothing$. The graph at left confirms that the solution set is empty.

Try Exercise 93.

UNIONS OF SETS AND DISJUNCTIONS OF SENTENCES

The **union** of two sets A and B is the collection of elements belonging to A and/or B. We denote the union of A and B by

$$A \cup B.$$

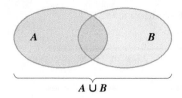

$A \cup B$

The union of two sets is often pictured as shown at left. For example, if $A = \{$all students who are taking a math class$\}$ and $B = \{$all students who are taking a history class$\}$, then $A \cup B = \{$all students who are taking a math class *or* a history class$\}$. Note that this set includes students who are taking a math class *and* a history class.

EXAMPLE 9 Find the union: $\{2, 3, 4\} \cup \{3, 5, 7\}$.

SOLUTION The numbers in either or both sets are 2, 3, 4, 5, and 7, so the union is $\{2, 3, 4, 5, 7\}$.

Try Exercise 37.

Student Notes

Remember that the union or the intersection of two sets is itself a set and should be written with set braces.

When two or more sentences are joined by the word *or* to make a compound sentence, the new sentence is called a **disjunction** of the sentences. Here is an example:

$x < -3$ *or* $x > 3$.

A number is a solution of a disjunction if it is a solution of at least one of the separate parts. For example, -5 is a solution of the disjunction since -5 is a solution of $x < -3$.

> *The solution set of a disjunction is the union of the solution sets of the individual sentences.*

EXAMPLE 10 Graph and write interval notation for the disjunction

$x < -3$ *or* $x > 3$.

SOLUTION We first graph $x < -3$, then $x > 3$, and finally the disjunction $x < -3 \text{ or } x > 3$.

$\{x \mid x < -3\}$

$(-\infty, -3)$

$\{x \mid x > 3\}$

$(3, \infty)$

$\{x \mid x < -3\} \cup \{x \mid x > 3\}$
$= \{x \mid x < -3 \text{ or } x > 3\}$

$(-\infty, -3) \cup (3, \infty)$

The solution set of $x < -3 \text{ or } x > 3$ is $\{x \mid x < -3 \text{ or } x > 3\}$, or, in interval notation, $(-\infty, -3) \cup (3, \infty)$. There is no simpler way to write the solution.

Try Exercise 51.

Mathematical Use of the Word "or" The word "or" corresponds to "union" and to the symbol "$\cup$". For a number to be a solution of a disjunction, it must be in *at least one* of the solution sets of the individual sentences.

EXAMPLE 11 Solve and graph: $7 + 2x < -1 \text{ or } 13 - 5x \le 3$.

SOLUTION We solve each inequality separately, retaining the word *or*:

$$7 + 2x < -1 \quad or \quad 13 - 5x \le 3$$
$$2x < -8 \quad or \quad -5x \le -10$$

Dividing by a negative number and reversing the symbol

$$x < -4 \quad or \quad x \ge 2.$$

To find the solution set of the disjunction, we consider the individual graphs. We graph $x < -4$ and then $x \geq 2$. Then we take the union of the graphs.

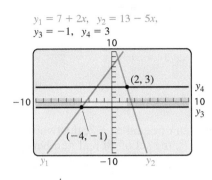

$y_1 = 7 + 2x, \quad y_2 = 13 - 5x,$
$y_3 = -1, \quad y_4 = 3$

$\{x \mid x < -4\}$ $(-\infty, -4)$

$\{x \mid x \geq 2\}$ $[2, \infty)$

$\{x \mid x < -4\} \cup \{x \mid x \geq 2\}$
$= \{x \mid x < -4 \text{ or } x \geq 2\}$ $(-\infty, -4) \cup [2, \infty)$

The solution set is $\{x \mid x < -4 \text{ or } x \geq 2\}$, or $(-\infty, -4) \cup [2, \infty)$. This is confirmed by the graph at left.

Try Exercise 73.

CAUTION!   A compound inequality like

$$x < -4 \quad or \quad x \geq 2,$$

as in Example 11, *cannot* be expressed as $2 \leq x < -4$ because to do so would be to say that x is *simultaneously* less than -4 and greater than or equal to 2. No number is both less than -4 *and* greater than 2, but many are less than -4 *or* greater than 2.

EXAMPLE 12   Solve: $-2x - 5 < -2 \text{ or } x - 3 < -10$.

SOLUTION   We solve the individual inequalities separately, retaining the word *or*:

$$-2x - 5 < -2 \quad or \quad x - 3 < -10$$

Dividing by a negative number and reversing the symbol ——→
$$-2x < 3 \quad or \quad x < -7$$
———— Keep the word "or."
$$x > -\tfrac{3}{2} \quad or \quad x < -7.$$

The solution set is $\left\{x \mid x < -7 \text{ or } x > -\tfrac{3}{2}\right\}$, or $(-\infty, -7) \cup \left(-\tfrac{3}{2}, \infty\right)$.

Try Exercise 89.

EXAMPLE 13   Solve: $3x - 11 < 4 \text{ or } 4x + 9 \geq 1$.

SOLUTION   We solve the individual inequalities separately, retaining the word *or*:

$$3x - 11 < 4 \quad or \quad 4x + 9 \geq 1$$
$$3x < 15 \quad or \quad 4x \geq -8$$
$$x < 5 \quad or \quad x \geq -2.$$
———— Keep the word "or."

To find the solution set, we first look at the individual graphs.

$\{x \mid x < 5\}$ $(-\infty, 5)$

$\{x \mid x \geq -2\}$ $[-2, \infty)$

$\begin{aligned}\{x \mid x < 5\} \cup \{x \mid x \geq -2\} \\ = \{x \mid x < 5 \ or \ x \geq -2\}\end{aligned}$ $(-\infty, \infty) = \mathbb{R}$

Since *all* numbers are less than 5 or greater than or equal to -2, the two sets fill the entire number line. Thus the solution set is $\mathbb{R}$, the set of all real numbers.

Try Exercise 75.

INTERVAL NOTATION AND DOMAINS

We saw that if $g(x) = \dfrac{5x - 2}{3x - 7}$, then the domain of a real number *and* $x \neq \frac{7}{3}\}$. We can now represent such a set using interval notation:

$$\left\{x \mid x \text{ is a real number } and \ x \neq \tfrac{7}{3}\right\} = \left(-\infty, \tfrac{7}{3}\right) \cup \left(\tfrac{7}{3}, \infty\right).$$

EXAMPLE 14 Use interval notation to write the domain of f given that $f(x) = \sqrt{x + 2}$.

SOLUTION The expression $\sqrt{x + 2}$ is not a real number when $x + 2$ is negative. Thus the domain of f is the set of all x-values for which $x + 2 \geq 0$:

$\begin{aligned} x + 2 &\geq 0 && \textit{x + 2 cannot be negative.} \\ x &\geq -2. && \textit{Adding } -2 \textit{ to both sides} \end{aligned}$

$[-2, \infty)$

$y = \sqrt{x + 2}$

We have the domain of $f = \{x \mid x \geq -2\} = [-2, \infty)$.

We can partially check that $[-2, \infty)$ is the domain of f either by using a table of values or by viewing the graph of $f(x)$, as shown at left. By tracing the curve, we can confirm that no y-value is given for x-values less than -2.

Try Exercise 103.

Interactive Discovery

Consider the functions $f(x) = \sqrt{3 - x}$ and $g(x) = \sqrt{x + 1}$. Enter these in a graphing calculator as $y_1 = \sqrt{(3 - x)}$ and $y_2 = \sqrt{(x + 1)}$.

1. Determine algebraically the domain of f and the domain of g. Then graph y_1 and y_2, and trace each curve to verify the domains.

2. Graph $y_1 + y_2$, $y_1 - y_2$, and $y_1 \cdot y_2$. Use the graphs to determine the domains of $f + g$, $f - g$, and $f \cdot g$.

3. How can the domains of the sum, the difference, and the product of f and g be found algebraically?

Domain of the Sum, Difference, or Product of Functions

The domain of the sum, the difference, or the product of the functions f and g is the intersection of the domains of f and g.

EXAMPLE 15 Find the domain of $f + g$ given that $f(x) = \sqrt{2x - 5}$ and $g(x) = \sqrt{x + 1}$.

SOLUTION We first find the domain of f and the domain of g. The domain of f is the set of all x-values for which $2x - 5 \geq 0$, or $\left\{x \mid x \geq \frac{5}{2}\right\}$, or $\left[\frac{5}{2}, \infty\right)$. Similarly, the domain of g is $\{x \mid x \geq -1\}$, or $[-1, \infty)$. The intersection of the domains is $\left\{x \mid x \geq \frac{5}{2}\right\}$, or $\left[\frac{5}{2}, \infty\right)$. We can confirm this at least approximately by tracing the graph of $f + g$.

$$y = \sqrt{2x - 5} + \sqrt{x + 1}$$

Thus the

$$\text{Domain of } f + g = \left\{x \mid x \geq \frac{5}{2}\right\}, \text{ or } \left[\frac{5}{2}, \infty\right).$$

Try Exercise 109.

10.1 Exercise Set

Concept Reinforcement In each of Exercises 1–10, match the set with the most appropriate choice from the column on the right.

1. _____ $\{x \mid x < -2 \text{ or } x > 2\}$

2. _____ $\{x \mid x < -2 \text{ and } x > 2\}$

3. _____ $\{x \mid x > -2\} \cap \{x \mid x < 2\}$

4. _____ $\{x \mid x \leq -2\} \cup \{x \mid x \geq 2\}$

5. _____ $\{x \mid x \leq -2\} \cup \{x \mid x \leq 2\}$

6. _____ $\{x \mid x \leq -2\} \cap \{x \mid x \leq 2\}$

7. _____ $\{x \mid x \geq -2\} \cap \{x \mid x \geq 2\}$

8. _____ $\{x \mid x \geq -2\} \cup \{x \mid x \geq 2\}$

9. _____ $\{x \mid x \leq 2\} \text{ and } \{x \mid x \geq -2\}$

10. _____ $\{x \mid x \leq 2\} \text{ or } \{x \mid x \geq -2\}$

a)

b)

c)

d)

e)

f)

g)

h)

i) $\mathbb{R}$

j) $\varnothing$

Solve each inequality using the given graph.

11. $f(x) \geq g(x)$

12. $f(x) < g(x)$

13. $y_1 < y_2$

14. $y_1 \geq y_2$

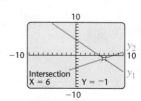

15. The graphs of $f(x) = 2x + 1$, $g(x) = -\frac{1}{2}x + 3$, and $h(x) = x - 1$ are as shown below. Solve each inequality, referring only to the figure.

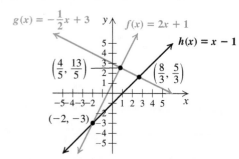

a) $2x + 1 \leq x - 1$
b) $x - 1 > -\frac{1}{2}x + 3$
c) $-\frac{1}{2}x + 3 < 2x + 1$

16. The graphs of $y_1 = -\frac{1}{2}x + 5$, $y_2 = x - 1$, and $y_3 = 2x - 3$ are as shown below. Solve each inequality, referring only to the figure.

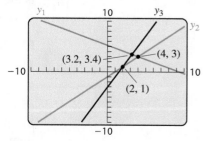

a) $-\frac{1}{2}x + 5 > x - 1$
b) $x - 1 \leq 2x - 3$
c) $2x - 3 \geq -\frac{1}{2}x + 5$

Solve graphically.

17. $x - 3 < 4$

18. $x + 4 \geq 6$

19. $2x - 3 \geq 1$

20. $3x + 1 < 1$

21. $x + 3 > 2x - 5$

22. $3x - 5 \leq 3 - x$

23. $\frac{1}{2}x - 2 \leq 1 - x$

24. $x + 5 > \frac{1}{3}x - 1$

25. $4x + 7 \leq 3 - 5x$

26. $5x + 6 < 8x - 11$

Use a graph to estimate the solution in each of the following. Be sure to use graph paper and a straightedge if graphing by hand.

27. *Show Business.* A band receives $750 plus 15% of receipts over $750 for playing a club date. If a club charges a $6 cover charge, how many people must attend in order for the band to receive at least $1200?

28. *Temperature Conversion.* The function
$$C(F) = \frac{5}{9}(F - 32)$$
can be used to find the Celsius temperature $C(F)$ that corresponds to $F°$ Fahrenheit.

a) Gold is solid at Celsius temperatures less than 1063°C. Find the Fahrenheit temperatures for which gold is solid.
b) Silver is solid at Celsius temperatures less than 960.8°C. Find the Fahrenheit temperatures for which silver is solid.

29. *Amusement Park Attendance.*   The table below lists the estimated annual ridership at amusement parks for various years. Use linear regression to find a linear function that can be used to predict the ridership $r(x)$, in billions, where x is the number of years after 2000. Then predict those years in which there will be fewer than 1.5 billion riders.

Year	Ridership (in billions of people)
2003	1.95
2004	1.81
2005	1.82
2006	1.76
2007	1.78
2008	1.70

Source: Heiden & McGonegal

30. *Smoking.*   The table below lists the percent of teenagers in the United States who smoked cigarettes during various years. Use linear regression to find a linear function that can be used to predict the percent $p(x)$ of teenagers who smoked, where x is the number of years after 2000. Then predict those years in which the *Healthy People 2010* goal of no more than 16% teenage smokers will be met.

Year	Percent of Teenagers Who Smoked
2000	31.4%
2001	29.5
2002	26.7
2003	24.4
2004	25
2005	23.2
2007	20

Source: Centers for Disease Control and Prevention

31. *Advertising.*   The table below lists advertising revenue for newspapers and the Internet for various years. Use linear regression to find two linear functions that can be used to estimate advertising revenue $n(x)$, in billions of dollars, for newspapers and $t(x)$ for the Internet, where x is the number of years after 2006. Then predict the years for which advertising revenue for the Internet will exceed that for newspapers.

Year	Advertising Revenue, Newspapers (in billions)	Advertising Revenue, Internet (in billions)
2007	$50	$15
2008	45	20
2009	35	24
2010	32	26

Source: Based on information from ZenithOptimedia Advertising Forecast

32. *Income.*   The table below lists the median adjusted household income for unmarried and married men for various years. Use linear regression to find two linear functions that can be used to estimate the median household earnings $u(x)$ for unmarried men and $m(x)$ for married men, where x is the number of years after 1970. Then estimate the years for which the household earnings for married men exceeds that for unmarried men.

Year	Median Adjusted Household Income, Unmarried Men	Median Adjusted Household Income, Married Men
1970	$58,000	$42,000
1980	63,000	56,000
1990	64,000	62,000
2000	65,000	70,000
2007	66,000	74,000

Source: Based on data from Pew Research Center

33. *100-Meter Freestyle.* The table below lists the world record for the women's 100-meter freestyle long-course swim for various years. Use linear regression to find a linear function that can be used to predict the world record x years after 1990. Then predict those years in which the world record will be less than 50 sec.

Year	Time (in seconds)	Athlete
1992	54.48	Jenny Thompson (United States)
1994	54.01	Jingyi Le (China)
2000	53.77	Inge de Bruijn (Netherlands)
2004	53.52	Jodie Henry (Australia)
2006	53.30	Britta Steffen (Germany)
2008	52.88	Lisbeth Trickett (Australia)

Source: www.iaaf.org

34. *Mile Run.* The table below lists the world record for the mile run for various years. Use linear regression to find a linear function that can be used to predict the world record for the mile run x years after 1954. Then predict those years in which the world record will be less than 3.5 min.

Year	Time for Mile (in minutes)	Athlete
1954	3.99	Sir Roger Bannister (Great Britain)
1962	3.9017	Peter Snell (New Zealand)
1975	3.8233	John Walker (New Zealand)
1981	3.7888	Sebastian Coe (Great Britain)
1993	3.7398	Noureddine Morceli (Algeria)
1999	3.7188	Hican El Guerrouj (Morocco)

Source: www.iaaf.org

Find each indicated intersection or union.

35. $\{5, 9, 11\} \cap \{9, 11, 18\}$

36. $\{2, 4, 8\} \cup \{8, 9, 10\}$

37. $\{0, 5, 10, 15\} \cup \{5, 15, 20\}$

38. $\{2, 5, 9, 13\} \cap \{5, 8, 10\}$

39. $\{a, b, c, d, e, f\} \cap \{b, d, f\}$

40. $\{a, b, c\} \cup \{a, c\}$

41. $\{r, s, t\} \cup \{r, u, t, s, v\}$

42. $\{m, n, o, p\} \cap \{m, o, p\}$

43. $\{3, 6, 9, 12\} \cap \{5, 10, 15\}$

44. $\{1, 5, 9\} \cup \{4, 6, 8\}$

45. $\{3, 5, 7\} \cup \varnothing$

46. $\{3, 5, 7\} \cap \varnothing$

Graph and write interval notation for each compound inequality.

47. $3 < x < 7$

48. $0 \leq y \leq 4$

49. $-6 \leq y \leq 0$

50. $-9 \leq x < -5$

51. $x < -1 \text{ or } x > 4$

52. $x < -5 \text{ or } x > 1$

53. $x \leq -2 \text{ or } x > 1$

54. $x \leq -5 \text{ or } x > 2$

55. $x > -2 \text{ and } x < 4$

56. $x > -7 \text{ and } x < -2$

57. $-4 \leq -x < 2$

58. $3 > -x \geq -1$

59. $5 > a \text{ or } a > 7$

60. $t \geq 2 \text{ or } -3 > t$

61. $x \geq 5 \text{ or } -x \geq 4$

62. $-x < 3 \text{ or } x < -6$

63. $7 > y \text{ and } y \geq -3$

64. $6 > -x \geq 0$

65. $x < 7 \text{ and } x \geq 3$

66. $x \geq -3 \text{ and } x < 3$

Aha! **67.** $t < 2 \text{ or } t < 5$

68. $t > 4 \text{ or } t > -1$

Solve and graph each solution set.

69. $-2 < t + 1 < 8$

70. $-3 < t + 1 \leq 5$

71. $4 < x + 4 \text{ and } x - 1 < 3$

72. $-1 < x + 2 \text{ and } x - 4 < 3$

73. $-7 \leq 2a - 3 \text{ or } 3a + 1 > 7$

74. $-4 \leq 3n + 5 \text{ or } 2n - 3 \leq 7$

Aha! **75.** $x + 7 \leq -2 \text{ or } x + 7 \geq -3$

76. $x + 5 < -3 \text{ or } x + 5 \geq 4$

77. $-7 \leq 4x + 5 \leq 13$

78. $-4 \leq 2x + 3 \leq 15$

79. $5 > \dfrac{x - 3}{4} > 1$

80. $3 \geq \dfrac{x - 1}{2} \geq -4$

81. $-2 \leq \dfrac{x + 2}{-5} \leq 6$

82. $-10 \leq \dfrac{x + 6}{-3} \leq -8$

83. $2 \leq f(x) \leq 8$, where $f(x) = 3x - 1$

84. $7 \geq g(x) \geq -2$, where $g(x) = 3x - 5$

85. $-21 \leq f(x) < 0$, where $f(x) = -2x - 7$

86. $4 > g(t) \geq 2$, where $g(t) = -3t - 8$

87. $f(t) < 3$ *or* $f(t) > 8$, where $f(t) = 5t + 3$

88. $g(x) \leq -2$ *or* $g(x) \geq 10$, where $g(x) = 3x - 5$

89. $6 > 2a - 1$ *or* $-4 \leq -3a + 2$

90. $3a - 7 > -10$ *or* $5a + 2 \leq 22$

91. $a + 3 < -2$ *and* $3a - 4 < 8$

92. $1 - a < -2$ *and* $2a + 1 > 9$

93. $3x + 2 < 2$ *and* $3 - x < 1$

94. $2x - 1 > 5$ *and* $2 - 3x > 11$

95. $2t - 7 \leq 5$ *or* $5 - 2t > 3$

96. $5 - 3a \leq 8$ *or* $2a + 1 > 7$

97. Use the accompanying graph of $f(x) = 2x - 5$ to solve $-7 < 2x - 5 < 7$.

98. Use the accompanying graph of $g(x) = 4 - x$ to solve $4 - x < -2$ *or* $4 - x > 7$.

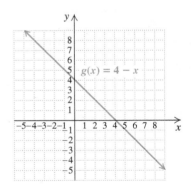

For $f(x)$ as given, use interval notation to write the domain of f.

99. $f(x) = \dfrac{9}{x + 8}$

100. $f(x) = \dfrac{2}{x + 3}$

101. $f(x) = \dfrac{-8}{x}$

102. $f(x) = \dfrac{x + 3}{2x - 8}$

103. $f(x) = \sqrt{x - 6}$

104. $f(x) = \sqrt{x - 2}$

105. $f(x) = \sqrt{2x + 7}$

106. $f(x) = \sqrt{8 - 5x}$

107. $f(x) = \sqrt{8 - 2x}$

108. $f(x) = \sqrt{10 - 2x}$

Use interval notation to write each domain.

109. The domain of $f + g$, if $f(x) = \sqrt{x - 5}$ and $g(x) = \sqrt{\frac{1}{2}x + 1}$

110. The domain of $f - g$, if $f(x) = \sqrt{x + 3}$ and $g(x) = \sqrt{2x - 1}$

111. The domain of $f \cdot g$, if $f(x) = \sqrt{3 - x}$ and $g(x) = \sqrt{3x - 2}$

112. The domain of $f + g$, if $f(x) = \sqrt{3 - 4x}$ and $g(x) = \sqrt{x + 2}$

TW 113. Why can the conjunction $2 < x$ *and* $x < 5$ be rewritten as $2 < x < 5$, but the disjunction $2 < x$ *or* $x < 5$ cannot be rewritten as $2 < x < 5$?

TW 114. Can the solution set of a disjunction be empty? Why or why not?

SKILL REVIEW

To prepare for Section 10.2, review graphing and solving equations by graphing.

Graph.

115. $g(x) = 2x$

116. $f(x) = 4$

117. $g(x) = -3$

118. $f(x) = |x|$

Solve by graphing.

119. $x + 4 = 3$

120. $x - 1 = -5$

SYNTHESIS

TW 121. What can you conclude about a, b, c, and d, if $[a, b] \cup [c, d] = [a, d]$? Why?

TW 122. What can you conclude about a, b, c, and d, if $[a, b] \cap [c, d] = [a, b]$? Why?

123. *Counseling.* The function given by $s(t) = 500t + 16{,}500$ can be used to estimate the number of student visits to Cornell University's counseling center t years after 2000. For what years is the number of student visits between 18,000 and 21,000?
Source: Based on data from Cornell University

124. *Pressure at Sea Depth.* The function given by $P(d) = 1 + (d/33)$ gives the pressure, in atmospheres (atm), at a depth of d feet in the sea. For what depths d is the pressure at least 1 atm and at most 7 atm?

125. *Converting Dress Sizes.* The function given by $f(x) = 2(x + 10)$ can be used to convert dress sizes x in the United States to dress sizes $f(x)$ in Italy. For what dress sizes in the United States will dress sizes in Italy be between 32 and 46?

126. *Solid-Waste Generation.* The function given by $w(t) = 0.0125t + 4.525$ can be used to estimate the number of pounds of solid waste, $w(t)$, produced daily, on average, by each person in the United States, t years after 2000. For what years will waste production range from 4.6 lb to 4.8 lb per person per day?

127. *Body-Fat Percentage.* The function given by $F(d) = (4.95/d - 4.50) \times 100$ can be used to estimate the body fat percentage $F(d)$ of a person with an average body density d, in kilograms per liter. A woman's body fat percentage is considered acceptable if $25 \le F(d) \le 31$. What body densities are considered acceptable for a woman?

128. *Minimizing Tolls.* A \$6.00 toll is charged to cross the bridge from mainland Florida to Sanibel Island. A six-month reduced-fare pass, costing \$50.00, reduces the toll to \$2.00. A six-month unlimited-trip pass costs \$300 and allows free crossings. How many crossings in six months does it take for the reduced-fare pass to be the more economical choice?
Source: www.leewayinfo.com

Solve and graph.

129. $4m - 8 > 6m + 5 \text{ or } 5m - 8 < -2$

130. $4a - 2 \le a + 1 \le 3a + 4$

131. $3x < 4 - 5x < 5 + 3x$

132. $x - 10 < 5x + 6 \le x + 10$

Determine whether each sentence is true or false for all real numbers a, b, and c.

133. If $-b < -a$, then $a < b$.

134. If $a \le c$ and $c \le b$, then $b > a$.

135. If $a < c$ and $b < c$, then $a < b$.

136. If $-a < c$ and $-c > b$, then $a > b$.

For $f(x)$ as given, use interval notation to write the domain of f.

137. $f(x) = \dfrac{\sqrt{3 - 4x}}{x + 7}$

138. $f(x) = \dfrac{\sqrt{5 + 2x}}{x - 1}$

139. On many graphing calculators, the TEST key provides access to inequality symbols, while the LOGIC option of that same key accesses the conjunction *and* and the disjunction *or*. Thus, if $y_1 = x > -2$ and $y_2 = x < 4$, Exercise 55 can be checked by forming the expression $y_3 = y_1$ *and* y_2. The interval(s) in the solution set appears as a horizontal line 1 unit above the x-axis. (Be careful to "deselect" y_1 and y_2 so that only y_3 is drawn.) Use the TEST key to check Exercises 59, 63, 65, and 67.

Try Exercise Answers: Section 10.1

17. $\{x \mid x < 7\}$, or $(-\infty, 7)$ **25.** $\left\{x \mid x \le -\frac{4}{9}\right\}$, or $\left(-\infty, -\frac{4}{9}\right]$

29. $r(x) = -0.04x + 2.0233$; years after 2013   **35.** $\{9, 11\}$

37. $\{0, 5, 10, 15, 20\}$ **51.** ◄——► $(-\infty, -1) \cup (4, \infty)$

55. ◄——► $(-2, 4)$

69. $\{t \mid -3 < t < 7\}$, or $(-3, 7)$ ◄——►

73. $\{a \mid a \le -2 \text{ or } a > 2\}$, or $(-\infty, -2] \cup (2, \infty)$
◄——►   **75.** $\mathbb{R}$, or $(-\infty, \infty)$ ◄——►

89. $\left\{a \mid a < \frac{7}{2}\right\}$, or $\left(-\infty, \frac{7}{2}\right)$ ◄——►

91. $\{a \mid a < -5\}$, or $(-\infty, -5)$ ◄——►   **93.** $\varnothing$

103. $[6, \infty)$ **109.** $[5, \infty)$

10.2 Absolute-Value Equations and Inequalities

- Equations with
  Absolute Value

- Inequalities with
  Absolute Value

EQUATIONS WITH ABSOLUTE VALUE

Recall the definition of absolute value.

Absolute Value   The absolute value of x, denoted $|x|$, is defined as

$$|x| = \begin{cases} x, & \text{if } x \geq 0, \\ -x, & \text{if } x < 0. \end{cases}$$

(When x is nonnegative, the absolute value of x is x. When x is negative, the absolute value of x is the opposite of x.)

To better understand this definition, suppose x is -5. Then $|x| = |-5| = 5$, and 5 is the opposite of -5. When x represents a negative number, the absolute value of x is the opposite of x, which is positive.

Since distance is always nonnegative, we can think of a number's absolute value as its distance from zero on the number line.

EXAMPLE 1   Find the solution set.

a) $|x| = 4$ **b)** $|x| = 0$ **c)** $|x| = -7$

SOLUTION

a) We interpret $|x| = 4$ to mean that the number x is 4 units from zero on the number line. There are two such numbers, 4 and -4. Thus the solution set is $\{-4, 4\}$.

$|x| = 4$

b) We interpret $|x| = 0$ to mean that x is 0 units from zero on the number line. The only number that satisfies this is 0 itself. Thus the solution set is $\{0\}$.

c) Since distance is always nonnegative, it doesn't make sense to talk about a number that is -7 units from zero. *Remember*: The absolute value of a number is never negative. Thus, $|x| = -7$ has no solution; the solution set is $\varnothing$.

 Try Exercise 21.

$y_1 = |x|, y_2 = 4, y_3 = 0, y_4 = -7$

The graph at left illustrates that, in Example 1, there are two solutions of $|x| = 4$, one solution of $|x| = 0$, and no solutions of $|x| = -7$.

Other equations involving absolute value can be solved graphically.

EXAMPLE 2 Solve: $|x - 3| = 5$.

SOLUTION We let $y_1 = \text{abs}(x - 3)$ and $y_2 = 5$. The solution set of the equation consists of the x-coordinates of any points of intersection of the graphs of y_1 and y_2. We see that the graphs intersect at two points. We use INTERSECT twice to find the coordinates of the points of intersection. Each time, we enter a GUESS that is close to the point we are looking for.

The graphs intersect at $(-2, 5)$ and $(8, 5)$. Thus the solutions are -2 and 8. To check, we substitute each in the original equation.

Check: For -2:

$$\begin{array}{c|c} |x - 3| = 5 \\ \hline |-2 - 3| & 5 \\ |-5| & \\ & 5 \stackrel{?}{=} 5 \quad \text{TRUE} \end{array}$$

For 8:

$$\begin{array}{c|c} |x - 3| = 5 \\ \hline |8 - 3| & 5 \\ |5| & \\ & 5 \stackrel{?}{=} 5 \quad \text{TRUE} \end{array}$$

The solution set is $\{-2, 8\}$.

■ Try Exercise 31.

We can solve equations involving absolute value algebraically using the following principle.

The Absolute-Value Principle for Equations

For any positive number p and any algebraic expression X:

a) The solutions of $|X| = p$ are those numbers that satisfy

$$X = -p \quad or \quad X = p.$$

b) The equation $|X| = 0$ is equivalent to the equation $X = 0$.

c) The equation $|X| = -p$ has no solution.

EXAMPLE 3   Find the solution set: **(a)** $|2x + 5| = 13$; **(b)** $|4 - 7x| = -8$.

a)

ALGEBRAIC APPROACH	GRAPHICAL APPROACH

ALGEBRAIC APPROACH

We use the absolute-value principle:

$$|X| = p$$
$$|2x + 5| = 13 \quad \text{Substituting}$$
$$2x + 5 = -13 \quad \text{or} \quad 2x + 5 = 13$$
$$2x = -18 \quad \text{or} \quad 2x = 8$$
$$x = -9 \quad \text{or} \quad x = 4.$$

The solutions are -9 and 4.

Check:

For -9:

$$\begin{array}{c|c} |2x + 5| = 13 & \\ \hline |2(-9) + 5| & 13 \\ |-18 + 5| & \\ |-13| & \\ & 13 \stackrel{?}{=} 13 \quad \text{TRUE} \end{array}$$

For 4:

$$\begin{array}{c|c} |2x + 5| = 13 & \\ \hline |2 \cdot 4 + 5| & 13 \\ |8 + 5| & \\ |13| & \\ & 13 \stackrel{?}{=} 13 \quad \text{TRUE} \end{array}$$

The number $2x + 5$ is 13 units from zero if x is replaced with -9 or 4. The solution set is $\{-9, 4\}$.

GRAPHICAL APPROACH

We graph $y_1 = \text{abs}(2x + 5)$ and $y_2 = 13$ and use INTERSECT to find any points of intersection. The graphs intersect at $(-9, 13)$ and $(4, 13)$. The x-coordinates, -9 and 4, are the solutions.

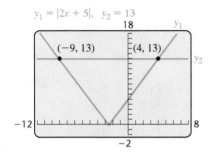

$y_1 = |2x + 5|, \quad y_2 = 13$

The algebraic solution serves as a check. The solution set is $\{-9, 4\}$.

b)

ALGEBRAIC APPROACH	GRAPHICAL APPROACH

ALGEBRAIC APPROACH

The absolute-value principle reminds us that absolute value is always nonnegative. Thus the equation $|4 - 7x| = -8$ has no solution. The solution set is $\varnothing$.

GRAPHICAL APPROACH

We graph $y_1 = \text{abs}(4 - 7x)$ and $y_2 = -8$. There are no points of intersection, so the solution set is $\varnothing$.

$y_1 = |4 - 7x|, \quad y_2 = -8$

Try Exercise 27.

To use the absolute-value principle, we must be sure that the absolute-value expression is alone on one side of the equation.

EXAMPLE 4 Given that $f(x) = 2|x + 3| + 1$, find all x for which $f(x) = 15$.

ALGEBRAIC APPROACH	GRAPHICAL APPROACH

ALGEBRAIC APPROACH

Since we are looking for $f(x) = 15$, we substitute:

$$f(x) = 15$$
$$2|x + 3| + 1 = 15 \quad \text{Replacing } f(x) \text{ with } 2|x + 3| + 1$$
$$2|x + 3| = 14 \quad \text{Subtracting 1 from both sides}$$
$$|x + 3| = 7 \quad \text{Dividing both sides by 2}$$
$$x + 3 = -7 \quad or \quad x + 3 = 7 \quad \begin{array}{l}\text{Using the absolute-value} \\ \text{principle for equations}\end{array}$$
$$x = -10 \quad or \quad x = 4.$$

Check: $\quad f(-10) = 2|-10 + 3| + 1 = 2|-7| + 1$
$$= 2 \cdot 7 + 1 = 15;$$

$\quad f(4) = 2|4 + 3| + 1 = 2|7| + 1$
$$= 2 \cdot 7 + 1 = 15$$

The solution set is $\{-10, 4\}$.

GRAPHICAL APPROACH

We graph $y_1 = 2\,\text{abs}(x + 3) + 1$ and $y_2 = 15$ and determine the coordinates of any points of intersection.

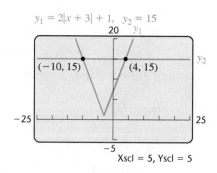

$y_1 = 2|x + 3| + 1, \quad y_2 = 15$

The solutions are the x-coordinates of the points of intersection, -10 and 4. The solution set is $\{-10, 4\}$.

Try Exercise 49.

EXAMPLE 5 Solve: $|x - 2| = 3$.

SOLUTION Because this equation is of the form $|a - b| = c$, it can be solved two ways.

Method 1. We interpret $|x - 2| = 3$ as stating that the number $x - 2$ is 3 units from zero. Using the absolute-value principle, we replace X with $x - 2$ and p with 3:

$$|X| = p$$
$$|x - 2| = 3$$
$$x - 2 = -3 \quad or \quad x - 2 = 3 \quad \text{Using the absolute-value principle}$$
$$x = -1 \quad or \quad x = 5.$$

> **CAUTION!** There are two solutions of $|x - 2| = 3$. Simply solving $x - 2 = 3$ will yield only one of those solutions.

Method 2. This approach is helpful in calculus. The expressions $|a - b|$ and $|b - a|$ can be used to represent the *distance between a and b* on the number line. For example, the distance between 7 and 8 is given by $|8 - 7|$ or $|7 - 8|$. From this viewpoint, the equation $|x - 2| = 3$ states that the distance between x and 2 is 3 units. We draw a number line and locate all numbers that are 3 units from 2.

The solutions of $|x - 2| = 3$ are -1 and 5.

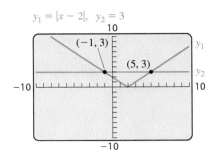

$y_1 = |x - 2|,\ y_2 = 3$

Check: The check consists of noting that both methods give the same solutions. The graphical solution shown at left serves as another check. The solution set is $\{-1, 5\}$.

Try Exercise 33.

Sometimes an equation has two absolute-value expressions. Consider $|a| = |b|$. This means that a and b are the same distance from zero.

If a and b are the same distance from zero, then either they are the same number or they are opposites.

For any algebraic expressions X and Y:

If $|X| = |Y|$,   then $X = Y$ or $X = -Y$.

EXAMPLE 6   Solve: $|2x - 3| = |x + 5|$.

ALGEBRAIC APPROACH

The given equation tells us that $2x - 3$ and $x + 5$ are the same distance from zero. This means that they are either the same number or opposites.

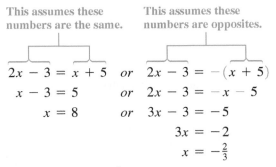

This assumes these numbers are the same.   This assumes these numbers are opposites.

$$2x - 3 = x + 5 \quad or \quad 2x - 3 = -(x + 5)$$
$$x - 3 = 5 \quad or \quad 2x - 3 = -x - 5$$
$$x = 8 \quad or \quad 3x - 3 = -5$$
$$3x = -2$$
$$x = -\tfrac{2}{3}$$

The solutions are 8 and $-\tfrac{2}{3}$. The solution set is $\left\{-\tfrac{2}{3}, 8\right\}$.

GRAPHICAL APPROACH

We graph $y_1 = \text{abs}(2x - 3)$ and $y_2 = \text{abs}(x + 5)$ and look for any points of intersection. The x-coordinates of the points of intersection are -0.6666667 and 8.

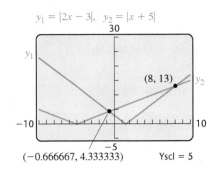

$y_1 = |2x - 3|,\ y_2 = |x + 5|$

$(8, 13)$

$(-0.666667, 4.333333)$ Yscl = 5

The solution set is $\{-0.6666667, 8\}$. Converted to fraction notation, the solution set is $\left\{-\tfrac{2}{3}, 8\right\}$.

Try Exercise 53.

INEQUALITIES WITH ABSOLUTE VALUE

Our methods for solving equations with absolute value can be adapted for solving inequalities.

EXAMPLE 7   Solve $|x| < 4$. Then graph.

SOLUTION   The solutions of $|x| < 4$ are all numbers whose *distance from zero is less than* 4. By substituting or by looking at the number line, we can see that numbers like $-3, -2, -1, -\tfrac{1}{2}, -\tfrac{1}{4}, 0, \tfrac{1}{4}, \tfrac{1}{2}, 1, 2$, and 3 are all solutions. In fact, the solutions are all the numbers between -4 and 4. The solution set is $\{x \mid -4 < x < 4\}$. In interval notation, the solution set is $(-4, 4)$. The graph is as follows:

$$|x| < 4$$

Try Exercise 63.

EXAMPLE 8 Solve $|x| \geq 4$. Then graph.

SOLUTION The solutions of $|x| \geq 4$ are all numbers that are at least 4 units from zero—in other words, those numbers x for which $x \leq -4 \ or \ 4 \leq x$. The solution set is $\{x \,|\, x \leq -4 \ or \ x \geq 4\}$. In interval notation, the solution set is $(-\infty, -4] \cup [4, \infty)$. We can check mentally with numbers like $-4.1, -5, 4.1$, and 5. The graph is as follows:

$|x| \geq 4$

Try Exercise 65.

Examples 1, 7, and 8 illustrate three types of problems in which absolute-value symbols appear. The following is a general principle for solving such problems.

Principles for Solving Absolute-Value Problems For any positive number p and any expression X:

a) The solutions of $|X| = p$ are those numbers that satisfy $X = -p \ or \ X = p.$

b) The solutions of $|X| < p$ are those numbers that satisfy $-p < X < p.$

c) The solutions of $|X| > p$ are those numbers that satisfy $X < -p \ or \ p < X.$

Student Notes

Simply ignoring the absolute-value symbol and solving the resulting equation or inequality will not lead to the correct solution.

$|X| = p$ corresponds to two equations.

$|X| < p$ corresponds to a conjunction.

$|X| > p$ corresponds to a disjunction.

The above principles are true for any positive number p.

If p is negative, any value of X will satisfy the inequality $|X| > p$ because absolute value is never negative. Thus, $|2x - 7| > -3$ is true for any real number x, and the solution set is $\mathbb{R}$.

If p is not positive, the inequality $|X| < p$ has no solution. Thus, $|2x - 7| < -3$ has no solution, and the solution set is $\varnothing$.

EXAMPLE 9   Solve: $|3x - 2| < 4$.

ALGEBRAIC APPROACH

The number $3x - 2$ must be less than 4 units from zero. We can visualize this on the number line:

The symbol in the inequality is $<$, so part (b) of the principles listed above applies.

$$|X| < p$$
$$|3x - 2| < 4 \qquad \text{Replacing } X \text{ with } 3x - 2 \text{ and } p \text{ with } 4$$
$$-4 < 3x - 2 < 4$$
$$-2 < \quad 3x \quad < 6 \qquad \text{Adding 2}$$
$$-\tfrac{2}{3} < \quad x \quad < 2 \qquad \text{Multiplying by } \tfrac{1}{3}$$

The solution set is $\left\{x \mid -\tfrac{2}{3} < x < 2\right\}$, or, in interval notation, $\left(-\tfrac{2}{3}, 2\right)$. The graph is as follows:

$$|3x - 2| < 4$$

When x is between $-\tfrac{2}{3}$ and 2, $3x - 2$ is between -4 and 4.

GRAPHICAL APPROACH

We graph $y_1 = \text{abs}(3x - 2)$ and $y_2 = 4$.

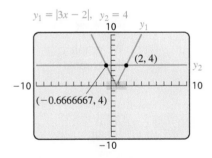

We see that y_1 is less than y_2 between the points $(-0.6666667, 4)$ and $(2, 4)$. The solution set of the inequality is thus the interval $(-0.6666667, 2)$, as indicated by the shading on the x-axis. Converted to fraction notation, the solution set is $\left(-\tfrac{2}{3}, 2\right)$.

Try Exercise 69.

EXAMPLE 10 Given that $f(x) = |4x + 2|$, find all x for which $f(x) \geq 6$.

ALGEBRAIC APPROACH

We have

$$f(x) \geq 6,$$

or $|4x + 2| \geq 6.$ Substituting

The number $4x + 2$ must be 6 or more units from zero. We can visualize this on the number line:

The symbol in the inequality is $\geq$, so we use part (c) of the principles listed above.

$$|X| \geq p$$
$$|4x + 2| \geq 6 \qquad \text{Replacing } X \text{ with } 4x + 2 \text{ and } p \text{ with } 6$$
$$4x + 2 \leq -6 \quad or \quad 6 \leq 4x + 2$$
$$4x \leq -8 \quad or \quad 4 \leq 4x \qquad \text{Adding } -2$$
$$x \leq -2 \quad or \quad 1 \leq x \qquad \text{Multiplying by } \tfrac{1}{4}$$

The solution set is $\{x \mid x \leq -2 \text{ or } x \geq 1\}$, or, in interval notation, $(-\infty, -2] \cup [1, \infty)$. The graph is as follows:

When $x \leq -2$ or when $x \geq 1$, $f(x) \geq 6$.

GRAPHICAL APPROACH

We graph $y_1 = \text{abs}(4x + 2)$ and $y_2 = 6$ and determine the points of intersection of the graphs.

The solution set consists of all x-values for which the graph of $y_1 = |4x + 2|$ is *on or above* the graph of $y_2 = 6$. The graph of y_1 lies *on* the graph of y_2 when $x = -2$ or $x = 1$. The graph of y_1 is *above* the graph of y_2 when $x < -2$ or $x > 1$. Thus the solution set is $(-\infty, -2] \cup [1, \infty)$, as indicated by the shading on the x-axis.

Try Exercise 93.

Connecting the Concepts

We can visualize Examples 1(a), 7, and 8 by graphing $f(x) = |x|$ and $g(x) = 4$.

Solve: $|x| = 4$.   The symbol is =.

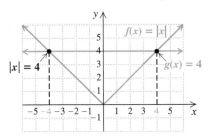

$|x| = 4$ when $x = -4$ or $x = 4$.

The solution set of $|x| = 4$ is $\{-4, 4\}$.

Solve: $|x| < 4$.   The symbol is <.

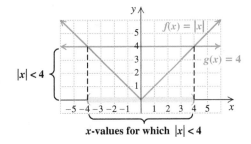

x-values for which $|x| < 4$

$|x| < 4$ when $-4 < x < 4$.

The solution set of $|x| < 4$ is $(-4, 4)$.

Solve: $|x| \geq 4$.   The symbol is ≥.

x-values for which $|x| \geq 4$

$|x| \geq 4$ when $x \leq -4$ or $x \geq 4$.

The solution set of $|x| \geq 4$ is $(-\infty, -4] \cup [4, \infty)$.

10.2   Exercise Set

FOR EXTRA HELP   *MyMathLab*   Math XL
PRACTICE   WATCH   DOWNLOAD   READ   REVIEW

↪ *Concept Reinforcement   Classify each of the following statements as either true or false.*

1. $|x|$ is never negative.

2. $|x|$ is always positive.

3. If x is negative, then $|x| = -x$.

4. The distance between a and b can be expressed as $|a - b|$.

5. The number a is $|a|$ units from 0.

6. There are two solutions of $|3x - 8| = 17$.

7. There is no solution of $|4x + 9| > -5$.

8. All real numbers are solutions of $|2x - 7| < -3$.

Match each equation or inequality with an equivalent statement from the column on the right. Letters may be used more than once or not at all.

9. $|x - 3| = 5$

10. $|x - 3| < 5$

11. $|x - 3| > 5$

12. $|x - 3| < -5$

13. $|x - 3| = -5$

14. $|x - 3| > -5$

a) The solution set is $\varnothing$.

b) The solution set is $\mathbb{R}$.

c) $x - 3 > 5$

d) $x - 3 < -5 \text{ or } x - 3 > 5$

e) $x - 3 = 5$

f) $x - 3 < 5$

g) $x - 3 = -5 \text{ or } x - 3 = 5$

h) $-5 < x - 3 < 5$

Use the following graph to solve Exercises 15–20.

$y_1 = |x + 2|, \quad y_2 = 3$

15. $|x + 2| = 3$

16. $|x + 2| \leq 3$

17. $|x + 2| < 3$

18. $|x + 2| > 3$

19. $|x + 2| \geq 3$

20. $|x + 2| = -1$

Solve.

21. $|x| = 7$

22. $|x| = 9$

Aha! **23.** $|x| = -6$

24. $|x| = -3$

25. $|p| = 0$

26. $|y| = 7.3$

27. $|2x - 3| = 4$

28. $|5x + 2| = 7$

29. $|3x - 5| = -8$

30. $|7x - 2| = -9$

31. $|x - 2| = 6$

32. $|x - 3| = 8$

33. $|x - 5| = 3$

34. $|x - 6| = 1$

35. $|t| + 1.1 = 6.6$

36. $|m| + 3 = 3$

37. $|5x| - 3 = 37$

38. $|2y| - 5 = 13$

39. $7|q| - 2 = 9$

40. $7|z| + 2 = 16$

41. $\left|\dfrac{2x - 1}{3}\right| = 4$

42. $\left|\dfrac{4 - 5x}{6}\right| = 3$

43. $|5 - m| + 9 = 16$

44. $|t - 7| + 1 = 4$

45. $5 - 2|3x - 4| = -5$

46. $3|2x - 5| - 7 = -1$

47. Let $f(x) = |2x + 6|$. Find all x for which $f(x) = 8$.

48. Let $f(x) = |2x + 4|$. Find all x for which $f(x) = 10$.

49. Let $f(x) = |x| - 3$. Find all x for which $f(x) = 5.7$.

50. Let $f(x) = |x| + 7$. Find all x for which $f(x) = 18$.

51. Let $f(x) = \left|\dfrac{3x - 2}{5}\right|$. Find all x for which $f(x) = 2$.

52. Let $f(x) = \left|\dfrac{1 - 2x}{3}\right|$. Find all x for which $f(x) = 1$.

Solve.

53. $|x + 4| = |2x - 7|$

54. $|3x + 2| = |x - 6|$

55. $|x + 4| = |x - 3|$

56. $|x - 9| = |x + 6|$

57. $|3a - 1| = |2a + 4|$

58. $|5t + 7| = |4t + 3|$

Aha! **59.** $|n - 3| = |3 - n|$

60. $|y - 2| = |2 - y|$

61. $|7 - 4a| = |4a + 5|$

62. $|6 - 5t| = |5t + 8|$

Solve and graph.

63. $|a| \leq 9$

64. $|x| < 2$

65. $|t| > 0$

66. $|t| \geq 1$

67. $|x - 1| < 4$

68. $|x - 1| < 3$

69. $|x + 2| \leq 6$

70. $|x + 4| \leq 1$

71. $|x - 3| + 2 > 7$

72. $|x - 4| + 5 > 2$

Aha! **73.** $|2y - 9| > -5$

74. $|3y - 4| > 8$

75. $|3a - 4| + 2 \geq 8$

76. $|2a - 5| + 1 \geq 9$

77. $|y - 3| < 12$

78. $|p - 2| < 3$

79. $9 - |x + 4| \leq 5$

80. $12 - |x - 5| \leq 9$

81. $6 + |3 - 2x| > 10$

82. $7 + |4a - 5| \leq 26$

Aha! **83.** $|5 - 4x| < -6$

84. $|7 - 2y| < -6$

85. $\left|\dfrac{2 - 5x}{4}\right| \geq \dfrac{2}{3}$

86. $\left|\dfrac{1 + 3x}{5}\right| > \dfrac{7}{8}$

87. $|m + 3| + 8 \leq 14$

88. $|t - 7| + 3 \geq 4$

89. $25 - 2|a + 3| > 19$

90. $30 - 4|a + 2| > 12$

91. Let $f(x) = |2x - 3|$. Find all x for which $f(x) \leq 4$.

92. Let $f(x) = |5x + 2|$. Find all x for which $f(x) \leq 3$.

93. Let $f(x) = 5 + |3x - 4|$. Find all x for which $f(x) \geq 16$.

94. Let $f(x) = |2 - 9x|$. Find all x for which $f(x) \geq 25$.

95. Let $f(x) = 7 + |2x - 1|$. Find all x for which $f(x) < 16$.

96. Let $f(x) = 5 + |3x + 2|$. Find all x for which $f(x) < 19$.

TW **97.** Explain in your own words why -7 is not a solution of $|x| < 5$.

TW **98.** Explain in your own words why $[6, \infty)$ is only part of the solution of $|x| \geq 6$.

SKILL REVIEW

To prepare for Section 10.3, review graphing equations and solving systems of equations.

Graph.

99. $3x - y = 6$

100. $y = \frac{1}{2}x - 1$

101. $x = -2$

102. $y = 4$

Solve using substitution or elimination.

103. $x - 3y = 8,$
$2x + 3y = 4$

104. $x - 2y = 3,$
$x = y + 4$

105. $y = 1 - 5x,$
$2x - y = 4$

106. $3x - 2y = 4,$
$5x - 3y = 5$

SYNTHESIS

TW **107.** Explain why the inequality $|x + 5| \geq 2$ can be interpreted as "the number x is at least 2 units from -5."

TW **108.** Isabel is using the following graph to solve $|x - 3| < 4$. How can you tell that a mistake has been made?

109. From the definition of absolute value, $|x| = x$ only when $x \geq 0$. Solve $|3t - 5| = 3t - 5$ using this same reasoning.

Solve.

110. $|3x - 5| = x$

111. $|x + 2| > x$

112. $2 \leq |x - 1| \leq 5$

113. $|5t - 3| = 2t + 4$

114. $t - 2 \leq |t - 3|$

Find an equivalent inequality with absolute value.

115. $-3 < x < 3$

116. $x \leq -6 \text{ or } 6 \leq x$

117. $x < -8 \text{ or } 2 < x$

118. $-5 < x < 1$

119. x is less than 2 units from 7.

120. x is less than 1 unit from 5.

Write an absolute-value inequality for which the interval shown is the solution.

121.
<---+---+---+---+---+---+---[=+=+=+=+=+=+=+=]--->
   -7 -6 -5 -4 -3 -2 -1 0 1 2 3 4 5 6 7

122.
<---+-[=+=+=+=+=+=+=+=+=+=+=+=+=+=]-+-+--->
   -5 -4 -3 -2 -1 0 1 2 3 4 5 6 7 8 9

123.
<---[=+=+=+=+=+=+=]--+---+---+---+---+---+--->
   -7 -6 -5 -4 -3 -2 -1 0 1 2 3 4 5 6 7

124.
<---+-+-[=+=+=+=+=+=+=+=+=+=]-+-+--->
    0 1 2 3 4 5 6 7 8 9 10 11 12 13 14

125. *Bungee Jumping.* A bungee jumper is bouncing up and down so that her distance d above a river satisfies the inequality $|d - 60 \text{ ft}| \leq 10 \text{ ft}$ (see the figure below). If the bridge from which she jumped is 150 ft above the river, how far is the bungee jumper from the bridge at any given time?

126. *Water Level.*   Depending on how dry or wet the weather has been, water in a well will rise and fall. The distance d that a well's water level is below the ground satisfies the inequality $|d - 15| \leq 2.5$ (see the figure below).

a) Solve for d.

b) How tall a column of water is in the well at any given time?

15 ft

d

d

300 ft

Mid-Chapter Review

The first step in solving the types of equations and inequalities that we have considered so far in this chapter is to determine the correct approach to finding the solution.

Type of Equation or Inequality	Approach
Conjunction of inequalities *Example:* $-3 < x - 5 < 6$	Find the intersection of the separate solution sets.
Disjunction of inequalities *Example:* $x + 8 < 2 \, or \, x - 4 > 9$	Find the union of the separate solution sets.
Absolute-value equation *Example:* $|x - 4| = 10$	Translate to two equations: If $|X| = p$, then $X = -p \, or \, X = p$.
Absolute-value inequality including < *Example:* $|x + 2| < 5$	Translate to a conjunction: If $|X| < p$, then $-p < X < p$.
Absolute-value inequality including > *Example:* $|x - 1| > 9$	Translate to a disjunction: If $|X| > p$, then $X < -p \, or \, p < X$.

GUIDED SOLUTIONS

1. Solve: $-3 < x - 5 < 6$. [10.1]

Solution

$\boxed{} < x < \boxed{}$ Adding 5

The solution is $\left(\boxed{}, \boxed{} \right)$.

2. Solve: $|x - 1| > 9$. [10.2]

Solution

$x - 1 < \boxed{}$ or $\boxed{} < x - 1$

$x < \boxed{}$ or $\boxed{} < x$ Adding 1

The solution is $\left(-\infty, \boxed{} \right) \cup \left(\boxed{}, \infty \right)$.

MIXED REVIEW

Solve.

1. $|x| = 15$ [10.2]

2. $|t| < 10$ [10.2]

3. $|p| > 15$ [10.2]

4. $|2x + 1| = 7$ [10.2]

5. $-3 < x - 5 < 6$ [10.1]

6. $5|t| < 20$ [10.2]

7. $x + 8 < 2$ *or* $x - 4 > 9$ [10.1]

8. $|x + 2| \leq 5$ [10.2]

9. $2 + |3x| = 10$ [10.2]

10. $|x - 3| \leq 10$ [10.2]

11. $-12 < 2n + 6$ *and* $3n - 1 \leq 7$ [10.1]

12. $|t| < 0$ [10.2]

13. $|2x + 5| + 1 \geq 13$ [10.2]

14. $5x + 1 < 1$ *and* $7 - x < 2$ [10.1]

15. $|m + 6| - 8 < 10$ [10.2]

16. $\left| \dfrac{x + 2}{5} \right| = 8$ [10.2]

17. $4 - |7 - t| \leq 1$ [10.2]

18. $|8x - 11| + 6 < 2$ [10.2]

19. $8 - 5|a + 6| > 3$ [10.2]

20. $|5x + 7| + 9 \geq 4$ [10.2]

10.3   Inequalities in Two Variables

- Graphs of Linear Inequalities

- Systems of Linear Inequalities

We have graphed inequalities in one variable on the number line. Now we graph inequalities in two variables on a plane.

GRAPHS OF LINEAR INEQUALITIES

When the equals sign in a linear equation is replaced with an inequality sign, a **linear inequality** is formed. Solutions of linear inequalities are ordered pairs.

EXAMPLE 1   Determine whether $(-3, 2)$ and $(6, -7)$ are solutions of the inequality $5x - 4y > 13$.

SOLUTION Below, on the left, we replace x with -3 and y with 2. On the right, we replace x with 6 and y with -7.

$$5x - 4y > 13$$
$$\frac{5(-3) - 4 \cdot 2 \ \big| \ 13}{-15 - 8 \ \big|}$$
$$-23 \overset{?}{>} 13 \quad \text{FALSE}$$

Since $-23 > 13$ is false, $(-3, 2)$ *is not* a solution.

$$5x - 4y > 13$$
$$\frac{5(6) - 4(-7) \ \big| \ 13}{30 + 28 \ \big|}$$
$$58 \overset{?}{>} 13 \quad \text{TRUE}$$

Since $58 > 13$ is true, $(6, -7)$ *is* a solution.

Try Exercise 7.

The graph of a linear equation is a straight line. The graph of a linear inequality is a **half-plane,** with a **boundary** that is a straight line. To find the equation of the boundary, we replace the inequality sign with an equals sign.

EXAMPLE 2 Graph: $y \leq x$.

SOLUTION We first graph the equation of the boundary, $y = x$. Every solution of $y = x$ is an ordered pair, like $(3, 3)$, in which both coordinates are the same. The graph of $y = x$ is shown on the left below. Since the inequality symbol is $\leq$, the line is drawn solid and is part of the graph of $y \leq x$.

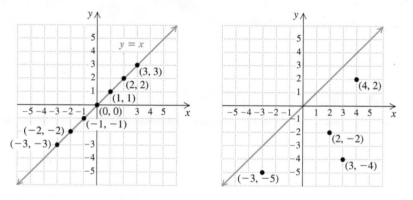

Note that in the graph on the right above each ordered pair on the half-plane below $y = x$ contains a y-coordinate that is less than the x-coordinate. All these pairs represent solutions of $y \leq x$. We check one pair, $(4, 2)$, as follows:

$$y \leq x$$
$$\overline{\quad\quad}$$
$$2 \overset{?}{\leq} 4 \quad \text{TRUE}$$

It turns out that *any* point on the same side of $y = x$ as $(4, 2)$ is also a solution. Thus, if one point in a half-plane is a solution, then *all* points in that half-plane are solutions. We finish drawing the solution set by shading the half-plane below $y = x$. The complete solution set consists of the shaded half-plane as well as the boundary line itself.

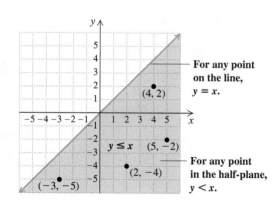

Try Exercise 11.

From Example 2, we see that for any inequality of the form $y \leq f(x)$ or $y < f(x)$, we shade *below* the graph of $y = f(x)$.

EXAMPLE 3   Graph: $8x + 3y > 24$.

SOLUTION   First, we sketch the graph of $8x + 3y = 24$. Since the inequality sign is $>$, points on this line do not represent solutions of the inequality, so the line is drawn dashed. Points representing solutions of $8x + 3y > 24$ are in either the half-plane above the line or the half-plane below the line. To determine which, we select a point that is not on the line and check whether it is a solution of $8x + 3y > 24$. Let's use $(-3, 4)$ as this *test point*:

$$\begin{array}{c|c} \multicolumn{2}{c}{8x + 3y > 24} \\ \hline 8(-3) + 3 \cdot 4 & 24 \\ -24 + 12 & \\ -12 \overset{?}{>} 24 & \text{FALSE} \end{array}$$

Since $-12 > 24$ is *false*, $(-3, 4)$ is not a solution. Thus no point in the half-plane containing $(-3, 4)$ is a solution. The points in the other half-plane *are* solutions, so we shade that half-plane and obtain the graph shown below.

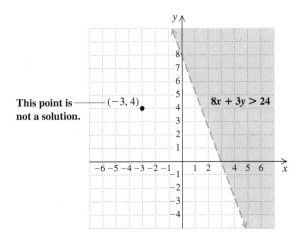

This point is not a solution. $(-3, 4)$

$8x + 3y > 24$

Try Exercise 19.

Steps for Graphing Linear Inequalities

1. Replace the inequality sign with an equals sign and graph this line as the boundary. If the inequality symbol is $<$ or $>$, draw the line dashed. If the symbol is $\leq$ or $\geq$, draw the line solid.

2. The graph of the inequality consists of a half-plane on one side of the line and, if the line is solid, the line as well.

   a) If the inequality is of the form $y < mx + b$ or $y \leq mx + b$, shade *below* the line.
      If the inequality is of the form $y > mx + b$ or $y \geq mx + b$, shade *above* the line.

   b) If y is not isolated, either solve for y and proceed as in part (a) or select a test point not on the line. If the test point *is* a solution of the inequality, shade the half-plane containing the point. If it is not a solution, shade the other half-plane.

Linear Inequalities

On most graphing calculators, an inequality like $y < \frac{6}{5}x + 3.49$ can be drawn by entering $(6/5)x + 3.49$ as y_1, moving the cursor to the Graph-Style icon just to the left of y_1, pressing **ENTER** until ◣ appears, and then pressing **GRAPH**.

Many calculators have an INEQUALZ program that is accessed using the **APPS** key. Running this program allows us to write inequalities at the **Y=** screen by pressing **ALPHA** and then one of the five keys just below the screen, as shown on the left below. With this program, the boundary line will appear dashed when $<$ or $>$ is selected.

$y_1 < (6/5)x + 3.49$, or
◣ $y_1 = (6/5)x + 3.49$

When you are finished with the INEQUALZ application, select it again from the **APPS** menu and quit the program.

Your Turn

1. Enter $y_1 = 3x - 5$.

2. Move the cursor to the GraphStyle icon to the left of Y1. Press **ENTER** until ◣ appears, and then press **ZOOM** **6**. You should see the graph of $y < 3x - 5$.

3. If your calculator has an **APPS** key, press the key and scroll through the options. If INEQUALZ appears, highlight INEQUALZ and press **ENTER**. From the **Y=** screen, change $=$ to $<$ for Y1 and graph the inequality. Then select INEQUALZ again and quit the program.

EXAMPLE 4 Graph: $6x - 2y < 12$.

SOLUTION We graph both by hand and using a graphing calculator.

BY HAND	USING A GRAPHING CALCULATOR

BY HAND

We could graph $6x - 2y = 12$ and use a test point, as in Example 3. Instead, let's solve $6x - 2y < 12$ for y:

$$6x - 2y < 12$$
$$-2y < -6x + 12 \qquad \text{Adding } -6x \text{ to both sides}$$
$$y > 3x - 6. \qquad \text{Dividing both sides by } -2$$
$$\text{and reversing the } <$$
$$\text{symbol}$$

The graph consists of the half-plane above the dashed boundary line $y = 3x - 6$.

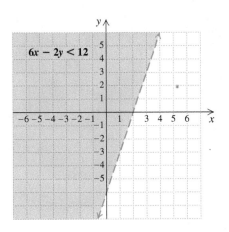

USING A GRAPHING CALCULATOR

We solve the inequality for y:

$$6x - 2y < 12$$
$$-2y < -6x + 12$$
$$y > 3x - 6. \qquad \text{Reversing the } < \text{ symbol}$$

We enter the boundary equation, $y = 3x - 6$, and use the INEQUALZ application to graph.

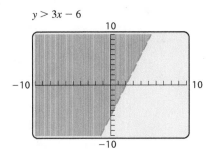

Many calculators do not draw a dashed line, so the graph of $y > 3x - 6$ appears to be the same as the graph of $y \geq 3x - 6$.

Quit the INEQUALZ application when you are finished.

Try Exercise 21.

Although a graphing calculator can be a very useful tool, some equations and inequalities are actually quicker to graph by hand. It is important to be able to quickly sketch basic linear equations and inequalities by hand. Also, when we are using a calculator to graph equations, knowing the basic shape of the graph can serve as a check that the equation was entered correctly.

EXAMPLE 5 Graph $x > -3$ on a plane.

SOLUTION There is only one variable in this inequality. If we graph the inequality on the number line, its graph is as follows:

However, we can also write this inequality as $x + 0y > -3$ and graph it on a plane. We can use the same technique as in the examples above. First, we graph the boundary $x = -3$ on a plane. Then we test some point, say, $(2, 5)$:

$$\frac{x + 0y > -3}{2 + 0 \cdot 5 \; | \; -3}$$
$$\overset{?}{}$$
$$2 > -3 \quad \text{TRUE}$$

Since (2, 5) is a solution, all points in the half-plane containing (2, 5) are solutions. We shade that half-plane. Another approach is to simply note that the solutions of $x > -3$ are all pairs with first coordinates greater than -3.

Although many graphing calculators can graph this inequality from the DRAW menu, it is simpler to graph it by hand.

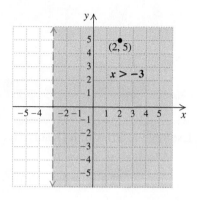

Try Exercise 25.

EXAMPLE 6   Graph $y \leq 4$ on a plane.

SOLUTION   The inequality is of the form $y \leq mx + b$ (with $m = 0$), so we shade below the solid horizontal line representing $y = 4$.

This inequality can also be graphed by drawing $y = 4$ and testing a point above or below the line. The half-plane below $y = 4$ should be shaded.

Try Exercise 27.

SYSTEMS OF LINEAR INEQUALITIES

To graph a system of equations, we graph the individual equations and then find the intersection of the graphs. We do the same thing for a system of inequalities: We graph each inequality and find the intersection of the graphs.

EXAMPLE 7   Graph the system

$$x + y \leq 4,$$
$$x - y < 4.$$

SOLUTION   To graph $x + y \leq 4$, we graph $x + y = 4$ using a solid line. Since the test point $(0, 0)$ *is* a solution and $(0, 0)$ is below the line, we shade the half-plane below the graph red. The arrows near the ends of the line are another way of indicating the half-plane containing solutions.

Next, we graph $x - y < 4$. We graph $x - y = 4$ using a dashed line and consider $(0, 0)$ as a test point. Again, $(0, 0)$ is a solution, so we shade that side of the line blue. The solution set of the system is the region that is shaded purple (both red and blue) and part of the line $x + y = 4$.

Graph the first inequality.

Graph the second inequality.

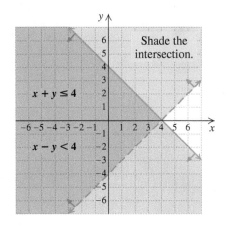

Shade the intersection.

❚ Try Exercise 39.

Student Notes

If you don't use differently colored pencils or pens to shade different regions, consider using a pencil to make slashes that tilt in different directions in each region, similar to the way shading is done on a graphing calculator. You may also find it useful to attach arrows to the lines, as in the examples shown.

EXAMPLE 8   Graph: $-2 < x \le 3$.

SOLUTION   This is a system of inequalities:

$$-2 < x,$$
$$x \le 3.$$

We graph the equation $-2 = x$, and see that the graph of the first inequality is the half-plane to the right of the boundary $-2 = x$. It is shaded red.

We graph the second inequality, starting with the line $x = 3$, and find that its graph is the line and also the half-plane to its left. It is shaded blue.

The solution set of the system is the region that is the intersection of the individual graphs. Since it is shaded both blue and red, it appears to be purple. All points in this region have x-coordinates that are greater than -2 but do not exceed 3.

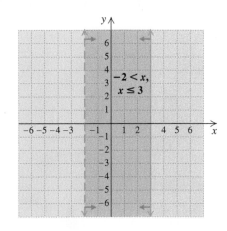

❚ Try Exercise 29.

A system of inequalities may have a graph that consists of a polygon and its interior. The corners of such a graph are called *vertices* (singular, *vertex*).

Systems of Linear Inequalities

Systems of inequalities can be graphed by solving for y and then graphing each inequality. The graph of the system will be the intersection of the shaded regions. To graph systems directly using the INEQUALZ application, enter the separate inequalities, press (GRAPH), and then press (ALPHA) and Shades ((F1) or (F2)). At the SHADES menu, select Ineq Intersection to see the final graph. To find the vertices, or points of intersection, select PoI-Trace from the graph menu.

Your Turn

1. Graph the system

$$y \geq -3,$$
$$y \leq 5.$$

Enter $y_1 = -3$ and $y_2 = 5$, and then indicate the half-plane above y_1 and the half-plane below y_2. Use INEQUALZ if it is available. Press (ZOOM) (6) when you are ready to graph.   The graph consists of the lines $y = -3$ and $y = 5$ and the area between them.

EXAMPLE 9   Graph the system of inequalities. Find the coordinates of any vertices formed.

$$6x - 2y \leq 12, \quad (1)$$
$$y - 3 \leq 0, \quad (2)$$
$$x + y \geq 0. \quad (3)$$

SOLUTION   We graph both by hand and using a graphing calculator.

BY HAND

We graph the boundaries

$$6x - 2y = 12,$$
$$y - 3 = 0,$$
and $\quad x + y = 0$

using solid lines. The regions for each inequality are indicated by the arrows near the ends of the lines. We note where the regions overlap and shade the region of solutions purple.

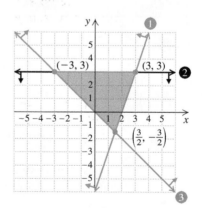

To find the vertices, we solve three different systems of two equations. The system of boundary equations from inequalities (1) and (2) is

$$6x - 2y = 12,$$
$$y - 3 = 0.$$

You can use graphing, substitution, or elimination to solve these systems.

Solving, we obtain the vertex $(3, 3)$.

The system of boundary equations from inequalities (1) and (3) is

$$6x - 2y = 12,$$
$$x + y = 0.$$

Solving, we obtain the vertex $\left(\frac{3}{2}, -\frac{3}{2}\right)$.

The system of boundary equations from inequalities (2) and (3) is

$$y - 3 = 0,$$
$$x + y = 0.$$

Solving, we obtain the vertex $(-3, 3)$.

USING A GRAPHING CALCULATOR

First, we solve each inequality for y and obtain the equivalent system of inequalities

$$y_1 \geq (12 - 6x)/(-2),$$
$$y_2 \leq 3,$$
$$y_3 \geq -x.$$

We run the INEQUALZ application, enter each inequality, and press (GRAPH). We then press ALPHA and (F1) or (F2) to choose Shades. Selecting the Ineq Intersection option results in the graph shown on the left below.

The vertices are the points of intersection of the graphs of the boundary equations y_1 and y_2, y_1 and y_3, and y_2 and y_3. We can find them by choosing PoI-Trace. Pressing the arrow keys moves the cursor to different vertices. The vertices are $(3, 3)$, $(-3, 3)$, and $(1.5, -1.5)$.

Try Exercise 53.

Graphs of systems of inequalities and the coordinates of vertices are used to solve a variety of problems using a branch of mathematics called *linear programming*.

Connecting the Concepts

We have now solved a variety of equations, inequalities, systems of equations, and systems of inequalities. Below is a list of the different types of problems we have solved, illustrations of each type, and descriptions of the solution. Note that a solution set may be empty.

Type	Example	Solution	Graph
Linear equation in one variable	$2x - 8 = 3(x + 5)$	A number	
Linear inequality in one variable	$-3x + 5 > 2$	A set of numbers; an interval	
Linear equation in two variables	$2x + y = 7$	A set of ordered pairs; a line	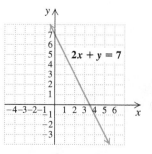
Linear inequality in two variables	$x + y \geq 4$	A set of ordered pairs; a half-plane	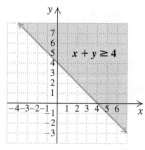
System of equations in two variables	$x + y = 3,$ $5x - y = -27$	An ordered pair or a set of ordered pairs	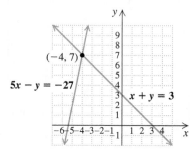
System of inequalities in two variables	$6x - 2y \leq 12,$ $y - 3 \leq 0,$ $x + y \geq 0$	A set of ordered pairs; a region of a plane	

A

F

Visualizing for Success

B

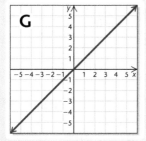

G

Match each equation, inequality, or system of equations or inequalities to its graph.

1. $x - y = 3,$
$2x + y = 1$

2. $3x - y \leq 5$

3. $x > -3$

4. $y = \dfrac{1}{3}x - 4$

5. $y > \dfrac{1}{3}x - 4,$
$y \leq x$

6. $x = y$

7. $y = 2x - 1,$
$y = 2x - 3$

8. $2x - 5y = 10$

9. $x + y \leq 3,$
$2y \leq x + 1$

10. $y = \dfrac{3}{2}$

Answers on page A-36

An additional, animated version of this activity appears in MyMathLab. To use MyMathLab, you need a course ID and a student access code. Contact your instructor for more information.

C

H

D

I

E

J

10.3 Exercise Set

Concept Reinforcement In each of Exercises 1–6, match the phrase with the most appropriate choice from the column on the right.

1. ____ A solution of a linear inequality

2. ____ The graph of a linear inequality

3. ____ The graph of a system of linear inequalities

4. ____ Often a convenient test point

5. ____ The name for the corners of a graph of a system of linear inequalities

6. ____ A dashed line

a) $(0, 0)$

b) Vertices

c) A half-plane

d) The intersection of two or more half-planes

e) An ordered pair that satisfies the inequality

f) Indicates the line is not part of the solution

Determine whether each ordered pair is a solution of the given inequality.

7. $(-4, 2)$; $2x + 3y < -1$

8. $(3, -6)$; $4x + 2y \le -2$

9. $(8, 14)$; $2y - 3x \ge 9$ 10. $(5, 8)$; $3y - 5x \le 0$

Graph on a plane.

11. $y \ge \frac{1}{2}x$ 12. $y \le 3x$

13. $y > x - 3$ 14. $y < x + 3$

15. $y \le x + 5$ 16. $y > x - 2$

17. $x - y \le 4$ 18. $x + y < 4$

19. $2x + 3y > 6$ 20. $3x + 4y \le 12$

21. $2y - x \le 4$ 22. $2y - 3x > 6$

23. $2x - 2y \ge 8 + 2y$ 24. $3x - 2 \le 5x + y$

25. $x > -2$ 26. $x \ge 3$

27. $y \le 6$ 28. $y < -1$

29. $-2 < y < 7$ 30. $-4 < y < -1$

31. $-4 \le x \le 2$ 32. $-3 \le y \le 4$

33. $0 \le y \le 3$ 34. $0 \le x \le 6$

Graph using a graphing calculator.

35. $y > x + 3.5$ 36. $7y \le 2x + 5$

37. $8x - 2y < 11$ 38. $11x + 13y + 4 \ge 0$

Graph each system.

39. $y > x$,   40. $y < x$,
    $y < -x + 3$ $y > -x + 1$

41. $y \le x$,   42. $y \ge x$,
    $y \le 2x - 5$ $y \le -x + 4$

43. $y \le -3$,   44. $y \ge -3$,
    $x \ge -1$ $x \ge 1$

45. $x > -4$,   46. $x < 3$,
    $y < -2x + 3$ $y > -3x + 2$

47. $y \le 5$,   48. $y \ge -2$,
    $y \ge -x + 4$ $y \ge x + 3$

49. $x + y \le 6$,   50. $x + y < 1$,
    $x - y \le 4$ $x - y < 2$

51. $y + 3x > 0$,   52. $y - 2x \ge 1$,
    $y + 3x < 2$ $y - 2x \le 3$

Graph each system of inequalities. Find the coordinates of any vertices formed.

53. $y \le 2x - 3$,   54. $2y - x \le 2$,
    $y \ge -2x + 1$, $y - 3x \ge -4$,
    $x \le 5$ $y \ge -1$

55. $x + 2y \le 12$,   56. $x - y \le 2$,
    $2x + y \le 12$, $x + 2y \ge 8$,
    $x \ge 0$, $y \le 4$
    $y \ge 0$

57. $8x + 5y \le 40$,   58. $4y - 3x \ge -12$,
    $x + 2y \le 8$, $4y + 3x \ge -36$,
    $x \ge 0$, $y \le 0$,
    $y \ge 0$ $x \le 0$

59. $y - x \ge 2$,   60. $3x + 4y \ge 12$,
    $y - x \le 4$, $5x + 6y \le 30$,
    $2 \le x \le 5$ $1 \le x \le 3$

^{TW} 61. Explain in your own words why a boundary line is drawn dashed for the symbols $<$ and $>$ and why it is drawn solid for the symbols $\le$ and $\ge$.

^{TW} 62. When graphing linear inequalities, Ron makes a habit of always shading above the line when the symbol $\ge$ is used. Is this wise? Why or why not?

SKILL REVIEW

To prepare for Section 10.4, review solving polynomial equations and rational equations.

Solve.

63. $x^2 - 1 = 0$

64. $5x^2 = 2x + 3$

65. $10x^3 - 30x^2 + 20x = 0$

66. $x^4 - x^3 - 6x^2 = 0$

Solve.

67. $\dfrac{x - 3}{x + 4} = 5$

68. $\dfrac{x}{x - 1} = 1$

69. $\dfrac{x}{(x - 3)(x + 7)} = 0$

70. $\dfrac{(x + 6)(x - 9)}{x + 5} = 0$

SYNTHESIS

TW **71.** Explain how a system of linear inequalities could have a solution set containing exactly one ordered pair.

TW **72.** In Example 7, is the point $(4, 0)$ part of the solution set? Why or why not?

Graph.

73. $x + y > 8$,
$\quad x + y \leq -2$

74. $\quad x + y \geq 1$,
$\quad -x + y \geq 2$,
$\quad\quad\quad x \geq -2$,
$\quad\quad\quad y \geq 2$,
$\quad\quad\quad y \leq 4$,
$\quad\quad\quad x \leq 2$

75. $\quad\quad x - 2y \leq 0$,
$\quad -2x + y \leq 2$,
$\quad\quad\quad\quad x \leq 2$,
$\quad\quad\quad\quad y \leq 2$,
$\quad\quad x + y \leq 4$

76. Write four systems of four inequalities that describe a 2-unit by 2-unit square that has $(0, 0)$ as one of the vertices.

77. *Luggage Size.* Unless an additional fee is paid, most major airlines will not check any luggage for which the sum of the item's length, width, and height exceeds 62 in. The U.S. Postal Service will ship a package only if the sum of the package's length and girth (distance around its midsection) does not exceed 130 in. Video Promotions is ordering several 30-in. long cases that will be both mailed and checked as luggage. Using w and h for width and height (in inches), respectively, write and graph an inequality that represents all acceptable combinations of width and height.
Sources: U.S. Postal Service; www.case2go.com

30 in.
h
w
Girth

78. *Hockey Wins and Losses.* The Skating Stars figure that they need at least 60 points for the season in order to make the playoffs. A win is worth 2 points and a tie is worth 1 point. Graph a system of inequalities that describes the situation. (*Hint*: Let $w =$ the number of wins and $t =$ the number of ties.)

79. *Waterfalls.* In order for a waterfall to be classified as a classical waterfall, its height must be no more than twice its crest width, and its crest width cannot exceed one-and-a-half times its height. The tallest waterfall in the world is about 3200 ft high. Let h represent a waterfall's height, in feet, and w the crest width, in feet. Write and graph a system of inequalities that represents all possible combinations of heights and crest widths of classical waterfalls.

80. *Widths of a Basketball Floor.* Sizes of basketball floors vary due to building sizes and other constraints such as cost. The length L is to be at most 94 ft and the width W is to be at most 50 ft. Graph a system of inequalities that describes the possible dimensions of a basketball floor.

81. *Graduate-School Admissions.* Students entering the Master of Science program in Computer Science and Engineering at University of Texas Arlington must meet minimum score requirements on the Graduate Records Examination (GRE). The GRE Quantitative score must be at least 700 and the GRE Verbal score must be at least 400. The sum of the GRE Quantitative and Verbal scores must be at least 1150. Both scores have a maximum of 800. Using q for the quantitative score and v for the verbal score, write and graph a system of inequalities that represents all combinations that meet the requirements for entrance into the program.
Source: University of Texas Arlington

82. *Elevators.* Many elevators have a capacity of 1 metric ton (1000 kg). Suppose that c children, each weighing 35 kg, and a adults, each 75 kg, are on an elevator. Graph a system of inequalities that indicates when the elevator is overloaded.

Write a system of inequalities for each region shown.

83.

84.

85.

86.

Try Exercise Answers: Section 10.3

7. Yes **11.** **19.**

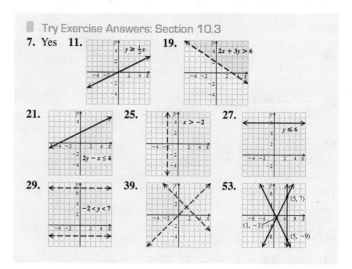

21. **25.** **27.**

29. **39.** **53.**

Collaborative Corner

How Old Is Old Enough?

Focus: Linear inequalities
Time: 15–25 minutes
Group Size: 2

It is not unusual for the ages of a bride and groom to differ significantly. Yet is it possible for the difference in age to be too great? In answer to this question, the following rule of thumb has emerged: *The younger spouse's age should be at least seven more than half the age of the older spouse.*
Source: http://home.earthlink.net/~mybrainhurts/2002_06_01_archive.html

ACTIVITY

1. Let b = the age of the bride, in years, and g = the age of the groom, in years. One group member

should write an equation for calculating the bride's minimum age if the groom's age is known. The other group member should write an equation for finding the groom's minimum age if the bride's age is known. The equations should look similar.

2. Convert each equation into an inequality by selecting the appropriate symbol from $<$, $>$, $\leq$, and $\geq$. Be sure to reflect the rule of thumb stated above.

3. Graph both inequalities from step (2) as a system of linear inequalities. What does the solution set represent?

4. If your group feels that a minimum or maximum age for marriage should exist, adjust your graph accordingly.

5. Compare your finished graph with those of other groups.

Polynomial Inequalities and Rational Inequalities

- Quadratic and Other Polynomial Inequalities

- Rational Inequalities

QUADRATIC AND OTHER POLYNOMIAL INEQUALITIES

Inequalities like the following are called *polynomial inequalities*:

$$x^3 - 5x > x^2 + 7, \qquad 4x - 3 < 9, \qquad 5x^2 - 3x + 2 \geq 0.$$

Second-degree polynomial inequalities in one variable are called *quadratic inequalities*. To solve polynomial inequalities, we often focus attention on where the outputs of a polynomial function are positive and where they are negative.

EXAMPLE 1   Solve: $x^2 + 3x - 10 > 0$.

SOLUTION   Consider the "related" function $f(x) = x^2 + 3x - 10$ and its graph. We are looking for those x-values for which $f(x) > 0$. Graphically, function values are positive when the graph is above the x-axis.

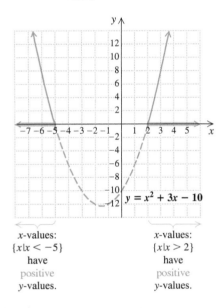

$$y = x^2 + 3x - 10$$

x-values: $\{x \mid x < -5\}$ have positive y-values.

x-values: $\{x \mid x > 2\}$ have positive y-values.

Values of y will be positive to the left and right of the x-intercepts, as shown. To find the intercepts, we set the polynomial equal to 0 and solve:

$$x^2 + 3x - 10 = 0$$
$$(x + 5)(x - 2) = 0$$
$$x + 5 = 0 \quad or \quad x - 2 = 0$$
$$x = -5 \quad or \quad x = 2. \qquad \text{The } x\text{-intercepts are } (-5, 0) \text{ and } (2, 0).$$

Thus the solution set of the inequality is

$$\{x \mid x < -5 \, or \, x > 2\}, \quad or \quad (-\infty, -5) \cup (2, \infty).$$

Try Exercise 7.

Any inequality with 0 on one side can be solved by considering a graph of the related function and finding intercepts as in Example 1.

EXAMPLE 2 Solve: $5x^2 - 2x \leq 7$.

SOLUTION We first find standard form with 0 on one side:

$$5x^2 - 2x - 7 \leq 0. \qquad \text{This is equivalent to the original inequality.}$$

If $f(x) = 5x^2 - 2x - 7$, then $5x^2 - 2x - 7 \leq 0$ when $f(x)$ is 0 or negative. As shown in the graphs below, values of $f(x)$ are negative for x-values between the x-intercepts. We find the x-intercepts by solving $f(x) = 0$:

$$5x^2 - 2x - 7 = 0$$
$$(5x - 7)(x + 1) = 0$$
$$5x - 7 = 0 \quad or \quad x + 1 = 0$$
$$5x = 7 \quad or \qquad x = -1$$
$$x = \frac{7}{5} \quad or \qquad x = -1. \qquad \text{The } x\text{-intercepts are } \left(\frac{7}{5}, 0\right) \text{ and } (-1, 0).$$

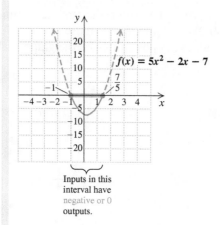

Inputs in this interval have negative or 0 outputs.

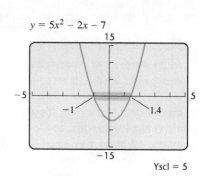

We can also find the x-intercepts using a graphing calculator. At the x-intercepts, the value of $f(x)$ is 0. Thus the solution set of the inequality is

$$\left\{x \mid -1 \leq x \leq \frac{7}{5}\right\}, \quad \text{or} \quad \left[-1, \frac{7}{5}\right], \quad \text{or} \quad [-1, 1.4].$$

Try Exercise 21.

In Example 2, it was not essential to draw the graph. The important information came from finding the x-intercepts and the sign of $f(x)$ on each side of those intercepts. We now solve a third-degree polynomial inequality, without graphing, by locating the x-intercepts, or *zeros*, of f and then using *test points* to determine the sign of $f(x)$ over each interval of the x-axis.

EXAMPLE 3 For $f(x) = 5x^3 + 10x^2 - 15x$, find all x-values for which $f(x) > 0$.

SOLUTION We first solve the related equation:

$$f(x) = 0$$
$$5x^3 + 10x^2 - 15x = 0 \qquad \text{Substituting}$$
$$5x(x^2 + 2x - 3) = 0$$
$$5x(x + 3)(x - 1) = 0 \qquad \text{Factoring completely}$$
$$5x = 0 \quad or \quad x + 3 = 0 \quad or \quad x - 1 = 0$$
$$x = 0 \quad or \qquad x = -3 \quad or \qquad x = 1.$$

The zeros of f are -3, 0, and 1. These zeros divide the number line, or x-axis, into four intervals: A, B, C, and D.

Next, selecting one convenient test value from each interval, we determine the sign of $f(x)$ for that interval. Within each interval, the sign of $f(x)$ cannot change. If it did, there would need to be another zero in that interval.

We choose -4 for a test value from interval A, -1 from interval B, 0.5 from interval C, and 2 from interval D. We enter $y_1 = 5x^3 + 10x^2 - 15x$ and use a table to evaluate the polynomial for each test value.

We are interested only in the signs of each function value. From the table at left, we see that $f(-4)$ and $f(0.5)$ are negative and that $f(-1)$ and $f(2)$ are positive. We indicate on the number line the sign of $f(x)$ in each interval.

Recall that we are looking for all x for which $5x^3 + 10x^2 - 15x > 0$. The calculations above indicate that $f(x)$ is positive for any number in intervals B and D. The solution set of the original inequality is

$$(-3, 0) \cup (1, \infty), \quad \text{or} \quad \{x \mid -3 < x < 0 \text{ or } x > 1\}.$$

Try Exercise 35.

The method of Example 3 works because polynomial function values can change signs only when the graph of the function crosses the x-axis. The graph of $f(x) = 5x^3 + 10x^2 - 15x$ illustrates the solution of Example 3. We can see from the graph at left that the function values are positive in the intervals $(-3, 0)$ and $(1, \infty)$.

One alternative to using a calculator's TABLE feature is to graph the function and determine the appropriate intervals visually.

An efficient algebraic approach involves using a factored form of the polynomial and focusing on only the *sign* of $f(x)$. By looking at how many positive or negative factors are multiplied, we are able to determine the sign of the polynomial function.

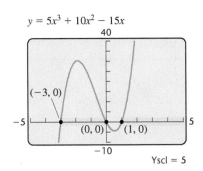

$y = 5x^3 + 10x^2 - 15x$

Yscl = 5

EXAMPLE 4   For $f(x) = 4x^4 - 4x^2$, find all x-values for which $f(x) < 0$.

SOLUTION   We first solve the related equation:

Solve $f(x) = 0$.

$$f(x) = 0$$
$$4x^4 - 4x^2 = 0$$
$$4x^2(x^2 - 1) = 0$$
$$4x^2(x + 1)(x - 1) = 0$$
$$4x^2 = 0 \quad or \quad x + 1 = 0 \quad or \quad x - 1 = 0$$
$$x = 0 \quad or \qquad x = -1 \quad or \qquad x = 1.$$

Divide the number line into intervals.

The function f has zeros at -1, 0, and 1, so we divide the number line into four intervals:

The product $4x^2(x + 1)(x - 1)$ is positive or negative, depending on the signs of $4x^2$, $x + 1$, and $x - 1$. This can be determined by making a chart.

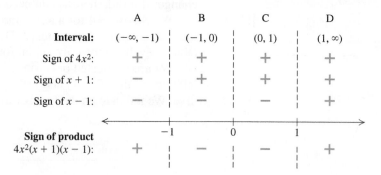

	A	B	C	D
Interval:	$(-\infty, -1)$	$(-1, 0)$	$(0, 1)$	$(1, \infty)$
Sign of $4x^2$:	$+$	$+$	$+$	$+$
Sign of $x + 1$:	$-$	$+$	$+$	$+$
Sign of $x - 1$:	$-$	$-$	$-$	$+$

Determine the sign of the function over each interval.

Sign of product $4x^2(x + 1)(x - 1)$:	$+$	$-$	$-$	$+$

A product is negative when it has an odd number of negative factors. Since the $<$ sign is used, the endpoints -1, 0, and 1 are not solutions. From the chart, we see that the solution set is

Select the interval(s) for which the inequality is satisfied.

$$\{x \,|\, -1 < x < 0 \; or \; 0 < x < 1\}, \quad or \quad (-1, 0) \cup (0, 1).$$

The graph of the function confirms the solution.

$y = 4x^4 - 4x^2$

Try Exercise 31.

In Example 4, if the inequality symbol were $\leq$, the endpoints of the intervals would be included in the solution set. The solution of $4x^4 - 4x^2 \leq 0$ is $[-1, 0] \cup [0, 1]$, or simply $[-1, 1]$.

To Solve a Polynomial Inequality

1. Add or subtract to get 0 on one side and solve the related polynomial equation $p(x) = 0$.
2. Use the numbers found in step (1) to divide the number line into intervals.
3. Using a test value from each interval or the graph of the related function, determine the sign of $p(x)$ over each interval.
4. Select the interval(s) for which the inequality is satisfied and write set-builder notation or interval notation for the solution set. Include the endpoints of the intervals when $\leq$ or $\geq$ is used.

RATIONAL INEQUALITIES

Inequalities involving rational expressions are called **rational inequalities.** Like polynomial inequalities, rational inequalities can be solved using test values. Unlike polynomials, however, rational expressions often have values for which the expression is undefined. These values must be used when dividing the number line into intervals.

EXAMPLE 5   Solve: $\dfrac{x - 3}{x + 4} \geq 2$.

SOLUTION   We write the related equation by changing the $\geq$ symbol to $=$:

$$\frac{x - 3}{x + 4} = 2. \qquad \text{Note that } x \neq -4.$$

We show both algebraic and graphical approaches.

ALGEBRAIC APPROACH	GRAPHICAL APPROACH

ALGEBRAIC APPROACH

We first solve the related equation:

$$(x + 4) \cdot \frac{x - 3}{x + 4} = (x + 4) \cdot 2 \qquad \begin{array}{l}\text{Multiplying both sides}\\ \text{by the LCD, } x + 4\end{array}$$

$$x - 3 = 2x + 8$$

$$-11 = x. \qquad \text{Solving for } x$$

In the case of rational inequalities, we must always find any values that make the denominator 0. As noted at the beginning of the example, $x \neq -4$.

   Now we use -11 and -4 to divide the number line into intervals:

We test a number in each interval to see where the original inequality is satisfied:

$$\frac{x - 3}{x + 4} \geq 2.$$

If we enter $y_1 = (x - 3)/(x + 4)$ and $y_2 = 2$, the inequality is satisfied when $y_1 \geq y_2$.

X	Y1	Y2
-15	1.6364	2
-8	2.75	2
1	-.4	2
X =		

$y_1 < y_2$; -15 *is not* a solution.
$y_1 > y_2$; -8 *is* a solution.
$y_1 < y_2$; 1 *is not* a solution.

The solution set includes interval B. The endpoint -11 is included because the inequality symbol is $\geq$ and -11 is a solution of the related equation. The number -4 is *not* included because $(x - 3)/(x + 4)$ is undefined for $x = -4$. Thus the solution set of the original inequality is

$$[-11, -4), \quad \text{or} \quad \{x \mid -11 \leq x < -4\}.$$

GRAPHICAL APPROACH

We graph $y_1 = (x - 3)/(x + 4)$ and $y_2 = 2$ using DOT mode. The inequality is true for those values of x for which the graph of y_1 is above or intersects the graph of y_2, or where $y_1 \geq y_2$.

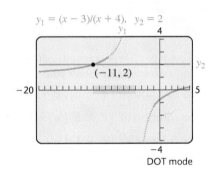

DOT mode

We see that

$$y_1 = y_2 \quad \text{when } x = -11$$

and

$$y_1 > y_2 \quad \text{when } -11 < x < -4.$$

Thus the solution set is $[-11, -4)$.

To Solve a Rational Inequality

1. Find any replacements for which the rational expression is undefined.
2. Change the inequality symbol to an equals sign and solve the related equation.
3. Use the numbers found in steps (1) and (2) to divide the number line into intervals.
4. Substitute a test value from each interval into the inequality. If the number is a solution, then the interval to which it belongs is part of the solution set. If solving graphically, examine the graph to determine the intervals that satisfy the inequality.
5. Select the interval(s) and any endpoints for which the inequality is satisfied and write set-builder notation or interval notation for the solution set. If the inequality symbol is $\leq$ or $\geq$, then the solutions from step (2) are also included in the solution set. Those numbers found in step (1) should be excluded from the solution set, even if they are solutions from step (2).

10.4 Exercise Set

FOR EXTRA HELP

↪ *Concept Reinforcement* *Classify each of the following statements as either true or false.*

1. The solution of $(x - 3)(x + 2) \leq 0$ is $[-2, 3]$.

2. The solution of $(x + 5)(x - 4) \geq 0$ is $[-5, 4]$.

3. The solution of $(x - 1)(x - 6) > 0$ is $\{x \mid x < 1 \ or \ x > 6\}$.

4. The solution of $(x + 4)(x + 2) < 0$ is $(-4, -2)$.

5. To solve $\dfrac{x + 2}{x - 3} < 0$ using intervals, we divide the number line into the intervals $(-\infty, -2)$ and $(-2, \infty)$.

6. To solve $\dfrac{x - 5}{x + 4} \geq 0$ using intervals, we divide the number line into the intervals $(-\infty, -4), (-4, 5)$, and $(5, \infty)$.

Determine the solution set of each inequality from the given graph.

7. $p(x) \leq 0$

8. $p(x) < 0$

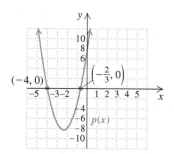

9. $x^4 + 12x > 3x^3 + 4x^2$

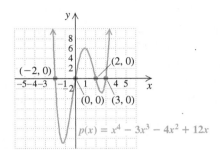

10. $x^4 + x^3 \geq 6x^2$

11. $\dfrac{x-1}{x+2} < 3$

12. $\dfrac{2x-1}{x-5} \geq 1$

Solve.

13. $(x+4)(x-3) < 0$

14. $(x+5)(x+2) > 0$

15. $(x+7)(x-2) \geq 0$

16. $(x-1)(x+4) \leq 0$

17. $x^2 - x - 2 > 0$

18. $x^2 + x - 2 < 0$

Aha! **19.** $x^2 + 4x + 4 < 0$

20. $x^2 + 6x + 9 < 0$

21. $x^2 - 4x < 12$

22. $x^2 + 6x > -8$

23. $3x(x+2)(x-2) < 0$

24. $5x(x+1)(x-1) > 0$

25. $(x-1)(x+2)(x-4) \geq 0$

26. $(x+3)(x+2)(x-1) < 0$

27. $4.32x^2 - 3.54x - 5.34 \leq 0$

28. $7.34x^2 - 16.55x - 3.89 \geq 0$

29. $x^3 - 2x^2 - 5x + 6 < 0$

30. $\frac{1}{3}x^3 - x + \frac{2}{3} > 0$

31. For $f(x) = 7 - x^2$, find all x-values for which $f(x) \geq 3$.

32. For $f(x) = 14 - x^2$, find all x-values for which $f(x) > 5$.

33. For $g(x) = (x-2)(x-3)(x+1)$, find all x-values for which $g(x) > 0$.

34. For $g(x) = (x+3)(x-2)(x+1)$, find all x-values for which $g(x) < 0$.

35. For $F(x) = x^3 - 7x^2 + 10x$, find all x-values for which $F(x) \leq 0$.

36. For $G(x) = x^3 - 8x^2 + 12x$, find all x-values for which $G(x) \geq 0$.

Solve.

37. $\dfrac{1}{x+5} < 0$

38. $\dfrac{1}{x+4} > 0$

39. $\dfrac{x+1}{x-3} \geq 0$

40. $\dfrac{x-2}{x+4} \leq 0$

41. $\dfrac{x+1}{x+6} \geq 1$

42. $\dfrac{x-1}{x-2} \leq 1$

43. $\dfrac{(x-2)(x+1)}{x-5} \leq 0$

44. $\dfrac{(x+4)(x-1)}{x+3} \geq 0$

45. $\dfrac{x}{x+3} \geq 0$

46. $\dfrac{x-2}{x} \leq 0$

47. $\dfrac{x-5}{x} < 1$

48. $\dfrac{x}{x-1} > 2$

49. $\dfrac{x-1}{(x-3)(x+4)} \leq 0$

50. $\dfrac{x+2}{(x-2)(x+7)} \geq 0$

51. For $f(x) = \dfrac{5 - 2x}{4x + 3}$, find all x-values for which

$f(x) \geq 0$.

52. For $g(x) = \dfrac{2 + 3x}{2x - 4}$, find all x-values for which

$g(x) \geq 0$.

53. For $G(x) = \dfrac{1}{x - 2}$, find all x-values for which

$G(x) \leq 1$.

54. For $F(x) = \dfrac{1}{x - 3}$, find all x-values for which

$F(x) \leq 2$.

TW **55.** Explain how any quadratic inequality can be solved by examining a parabola.

TW **56.** Describe a method for creating a quadratic inequality for which there is no solution.

SKILL REVIEW

To prepare for Chapter 11, review solving systems of equations using elimination.

Solve.

57. $3x - 2y = 7$,
$\quad x + 2y = 1$

58. $x + 3y = 5$,
$\quad x - 5y = 7$

59. $3x - 5y = 1$,
$\quad 2x + 3y = 7$

60. $10x - 2y = 4$,
$\quad 3x + 5y = 2$

61. $y - 5x = 2$,
$\quad 3x + y = -1$

62. $4x - 1 = 3y$,
$\quad 2y - 4 = 5x$

SYNTHESIS

TW **63.** Step (5) on p. 664 states that even when the inequality symbol is $\leq$ or $\geq$, the solutions from step (2) are not always part of the solution set. Why?

TW **64.** Describe a method that could be used to create quadratic inequalities that have $(-\infty, a] \cup [b, \infty)$ as the solution set.

Find each solution set.

65. $x^4 + x^2 < 0$

66. $x^4 + 2x^2 \geq 0$

67. $x^4 + 3x^2 \leq 0$

68. $\left| \dfrac{x + 2}{x - 1} \right| \leq 3$

69. *Total Profit.* Derex, Inc., determines that its total-profit function is given by

$$P(x) = -3x^2 + 630x - 6000.$$

a) Find all values of x for which Derex makes a profit.

b) Find all values of x for which Derex loses money.

70. *Height of a Thrown Object.* The function

$$S(t) = -16t^2 + 32t + 1920$$

gives the height S, in feet, of an object thrown from a cliff that is 1920 ft high. Here t is the time, in seconds, that the object is in the air.

a) For what times does the height exceed 1920 ft?

b) For what times is the height less than 640 ft?

71. *Number of Handshakes.* There are n people in a room. The number N of possible handshakes by the people is given by the function

$$N(n) = \dfrac{n(n - 1)}{2}.$$

For what number of people n is $66 \leq N \leq 300$?

72. *Number of Diagonals.* A polygon with n sides has D diagonals, where D is given by the function

$$D(n) = \dfrac{n(n - 3)}{2}.$$

Find the number of sides n if $27 \leq D \leq 230$.

Use a graphing calculator to graph each function and find solutions of $f(x) = 0$. Then solve the inequalities $f(x) < 0$ and $f(x) > 0$.

73. $f(x) = x + \dfrac{1}{x}$

74. $f(x) = x - \sqrt{x}, \; x \geq 0$

75. $f(x) = \dfrac{x^3 - x^2 - 2x}{x^2 + x - 6}$

76. $f(x) = x^4 - 4x^3 - x^2 + 16x - 12$

Find the domain of each function

77. $f(x) = \sqrt{x^2 - 4x - 45}$

78. $f(x) = \sqrt{9 - x^2}$

79. $f(x) = \sqrt{x^2 + 8x}$

80. $f(x) = \sqrt{x^2 + 2x + 1}$

■ Try Exercise Answers: Section 10.4

7. $\left[-4, \frac{3}{2} \right]$, or $\left\{ x \mid -4 \leq x \leq \frac{3}{2} \right\}$
21. $(-2, 6)$, or $\{ x \mid -2 < x < 6 \}$
31. $[-2, 2]$, or $\{ x \mid -2 \leq x \leq 2 \}$
35. $(-\infty, 0] \cup [2, 5]$, or $\{ x \mid x \leq 0 \; or \; 2 \leq x \leq 5 \}$
41. $(-\infty, -6)$, or $\{ x \mid x < -6 \}$

Study Summary

SECTION 10.1: GRAPHICAL SOLUTIONS AND COMPOUND INEQUALITIES

KEY TERMS AND CONCEPTS	EXAMPLES	PRACTICE EXERCISES
Inequalities can be solved graphically by determining the x-values for which one graph lies above or below another.	From the graph above, we can read the solution sets of the following inequalities.	**1.** Solve graphically: $2x - 1 < x$.

	Inequality	Solution Set
	$f(x) < g(x)$	$\{x \mid x > 2\}$, or $(2, \infty)$
	$f(x) \leq g(x)$	$\{x \mid x \geq 2\}$, or $[2, \infty)$
	$f(x) > g(x)$	$\{x \mid x < 2\}$, or $(-\infty, 2)$
	$f(x) \geq g(x)$	$\{x \mid x \leq 2\}$, or $(-\infty, 2]$

| A **conjunction** consists of two or more sentences joined by the word *and*. The solution set of the conjunction is the **intersection** of the solution sets of the individual sentences. | $$-4 \leq x - 1 \leq 5$$ $$-4 \leq x - 1 \quad and \quad x - 1 \leq 5$$ $$-3 \leq x \qquad and \qquad x \leq 6$$ The solution set is $\{x \mid -3 \leq x \leq 6\}$, or $[-3, 6]$.

 $\{x \mid -3 \leq x\}$
 $\{x \mid x \leq 6\}$
 $\{x \mid -3 \leq x \leq 6\}$ | **2.** Solve: $-5 < 4x + 3 \leq 0$. |

| A **disjunction** consists of two or more sentences joined by the word *or*. The solution set of the disjunction is the **union** of the solution sets of the individual sentences. | $$2x + 9 < 1 \quad or \quad 5x - 2 \geq 3$$ $$2x < -8 \quad or \quad 5x \geq 5$$ $$x < -4 \quad or \quad x \geq 1$$ The solution set is $\{x \mid x < -4 \text{ or } x \geq 1\}$, or $(-\infty, -4) \cup [1, \infty)$.

 $\{x \mid x < -4\}$
 $\{x \mid x \geq 1\}$
 $\{x \mid x < -4 \text{ or } x \geq 1\}$ | **3.** Solve: $x - 3 \leq 10 \quad or$ $25 - x < 3$. |

SECTION 10.2; ABSOLUTE-VALUE EQUATIONS AND INEQUALITIES

For any positive number p and any algebraic expression X:

a) The solutions of $|X| = p$ are those numbers that satisfy

$$X = -p \quad or \quad X = p.$$

b) The solutions of $|X| < p$ are those numbers that satisfy

$$-p < X < p.$$

c) The solutions of $|X| > p$ are those numbers that satisfy

$$X < -p \quad or \quad p < X.$$

If $|X| = 0$, then $X = 0$. If p is negative, then $|X| = p$ and $|X| < p$ have no solution, and any value of X will satisfy $|X| > p$.

$$|x + 3| = 4$$
$$x + 3 = 4 \quad or \quad x + 3 = -4 \qquad \text{Using part (a)}$$
$$x = 1 \quad or \qquad x = -7$$

The solution set is $\{-7, 1\}$.

$$|x + 3| < 4$$
$$-4 < x + 3 < 4 \qquad \text{Using part (b)}$$
$$-7 < x < 1$$

The solution set is $\{x \mid -7 < x < 1\}$, or $(-7, 1)$.

$$|x + 3| \geq 4$$
$$x + 3 \leq -4 \quad or \quad 4 \leq x + 3 \qquad \text{Using part (c)}$$
$$x \leq -7 \quad or \quad 1 \leq x$$

The solution set is $\{x \mid x \leq -7 \text{ or } x \geq 1\}$, or $(-\infty, -7] \cup [1, \infty)$.

Solve.

4. $|4x - 7| = 11$

5. $|x - 12| \leq 1$

6. $|2x + 3| > 7$

SECTION 10.3: INEQUALITIES IN TWO VARIABLES

To graph a linear inequality:

1. Graph the **boundary line.** Draw a dashed line if the inequality symbol is $<$ or $>$, and draw a solid line if the inequality symbol is $\leq$ or $\geq$.

2. Determine which side of the boundary line contains the solution set, and shade that **half-plane.**

Graph: $x + y < -1$.

1. Graph $x + y = -1$ using a dashed line.

2. Choose a test point not on the line: $(0, 0)$.

$$\frac{x + y < -1}{0 + 0 \;\vert\; -1}$$
$$0 \overset{?}{<} -1 \quad \text{FALSE}$$

Since $0 < -1$ is false, shade the half-plane that does *not* contain $(0, 0)$.

7. Graph: $2x - y < 5$.

SECTION 10.4: POLYNOMIAL INEQUALITIES AND RATIONAL INEQUALITIES

The x-intercepts, or **zeros,** of a function are used to divide the x-axis into intervals when solving a **polynomial inequality.** (See p. 662.)

Solve: $x^2 - 2x - 15 > 0$.
$$x^2 - 2x - 15 = 0 \qquad \text{Solving the related equation}$$
$$(x - 5)(x + 3) = 0$$
$$x = 5 \quad or \quad x = -3 \qquad \begin{array}{l}-3 \text{ and } 5 \text{ divide the}\\ \text{number line into}\\ \text{three intervals.}\end{array}$$

The solutions of a rational equation and any replacements that make a denominator zero are both used to divide the x-axis into intervals when solving a **rational inequality.** (See p. 664.)

For $f(x) = x^2 - 2x - 15 = (x - 5)(x + 3)$:

$f(x)$ is positive for $x < -3$;

$f(x)$ is negative for $-3 < x < 5$;

$f(x)$ is positive for $x > 5$.

Thus, $x^2 - 2x - 15 > 0$ for $(-\infty, -3) \cup (5, \infty)$, or $\{x \mid x < -3 \text{ or } x > 5\}$.

8. Solve:

$$x^2 - 11x - 12 < 0.$$

Review Exercises 10

Concept Reinforcement *Classify each of the following statements as either true or false.*

1. The solution of $|3x - 5| \leq 8$ is a closed interval. [10.2]

2. The inequality $2 < 5x + 1 < 9$ is equivalent to $2 < 5x + 1$ *or* $5x + 1 < 9$. [10.1]

3. The solution set of a disjunction is the union of two solution sets. [10.1]

4. In mathematics, the word "or" means "one or the other or both." [10.1]

5. The domain of the sum of two functions is the union of the domains of the individual functions. [10.1]

6. The equation $|x| = p$ has no solution when p is negative. [10.2]

7. $|f(x)| > 3$ is equivalent to $f(x) < -3$ *or* $f(x) > 3$. [10.2]

8. A test point is used to determine whether the line in a linear inequality is drawn solid or dashed. [10.3]

9. The graph of a system of linear inequalities is always a half-plane. [10.3]

10. To solve a polynomial inequality, we often must solve a polynomial equation. [10.4]

Solve graphically. [10.1]

11. $4 - 3x > 1$

12. $x - 3 < 3x + 5$

13. $x + 1 \geq \frac{1}{2}x - 2$

14. Let $f(x) = 3x + 2$ and $g(x) = 10 - x$. Find all values of x for which $f(x) \leq g(x)$. [10.1]

15. Find the intersection:
$$\{1, 2, 5, 6, 9\} \cap \{1, 3, 5, 9\}. \quad [10.1]$$

16. Find the union:
$$\{1, 2, 5, 6, 9\} \cup \{1, 3, 5, 9\}. \quad [10.1]$$

Graph and write interval notation. [10.1]

17. $x \leq 2$ *and* $x > -3$

18. $x \leq 3$ *or* $x > -5$

Solve and graph each solution set. [10.1]

19. $-4 < x + 8 \leq 5$

20. $-15 < -4x - 5 < 0$

21. $3x < -9$ *or* $-5x < -5$

22. $2x + 5 < -17$ *or* $-4x + 10 \leq 34$

23. $2x + 7 \leq -5$ *or* $x + 7 \geq 15$

24. $f(x) < -5$ *or* $f(x) > 5$, where $f(x) = 3 - 5x$

For $f(x)$ as given, use interval notation to write the domain of f. [10.1]

25. $f(x) = \dfrac{2x}{x - 8}$

26. $f(x) = \sqrt{x + 5}$

27. $f(x) = \sqrt{8 - 3x}$

Solve. [10.2]

28. $|x| = 5$

29. $|t| \geq 21$

30. $|x - 3| = 7$

31. $|4a + 3| < 11$

32. $|3x - 4| - 6 \geq 9$

33. $|2x + 5| = |x - 9|$

34. $|5n + 6| = -8$

35. $\left| \dfrac{x + 4}{6} \right| \leq 2$

36. $2|x - 5| - 7 > 3$

37. Let $f(x) = |3x - 5|$. Find all x for which $f(x) < 0$. [10.2]

38. Graph $x - 2y \geq 6$ on a plane. [10.3]

Graph each system of inequalities. Find the coordinates of any vertices formed. [10.3]

39. $x + 3y > -1$,
    $x + 3y < 4$

40. $x - 3y \leq 3$,
    $x + 3y \geq 9$,
    $y \leq 6$

Solve. [10.4]

41. $x^3 - 3x > 2x^2$

42. $\dfrac{x - 5}{x + 3} \leq 0$

SYNTHESIS

TW 43. Explain in your own words why $|X| = p$ has two solutions when p is positive and no solution when p is negative. [10.2]

TW 44. Explain why the graph of the solution of a system of linear inequalities is the intersection, not the union, of the individual graphs. [10.3]

45. Solve: $|2x + 5| \leq |x + 3|$. [10.2]

46. The Twinrocker Paper Company makes paper by hand. Each sheet is between 18 thousandths and 25 thousandths of an inch thick. Write the thickness t of a sheet of handmade paper as an inequality with absolute value. [10.2]

Chapter Test **10**

Solve graphically.

1. $3 - x < 2$

2. $2x - 3 \geq x + 1$

3. Find the intersection:

$$\{1, 3, 5, 7, 9\} \cap \{3, 5, 11, 13\}.$$

4. Find the union:

$$\{1, 3, 5, 7, 9\} \cup \{3, 5, 11, 13\}.$$

Write the domain of f using interval notation.

5. $f(x) = \sqrt{6 - 3x}$

6. $f(x) = \dfrac{x}{x - 7}$

Solve and graph each solution set.

7. $-2 < x - 3 < 5$

8. $-11 \leq -5t - 2 < 0$

9. $3x - 2 < 7 \text{ or } x - 2 > 4$

10. $-3x > 12 \text{ or } 4x > -10$

11. $|x| = 13$

12. $|a| > 7$

13. $|3x - 1| < 7$

14. $|-5t - 3| \geq 10$

15. $|2 - 5x| = -12$

16. $g(x) < -3 \text{ or } g(x) > 3$, where $g(x) = 4 - 2x$

17. Let $f(x) = |x + 10|$ and $g(x) = |x - 12|$. Find all values of x for which $f(x) = g(x)$.

18. Graph $y \leq 2x + 1$ on a plane.

Graph each system of inequalities. Find the coordinates of any vertices formed.

19. $x + y \geq 3,$
$x - y \geq 5$

20. $2y - x \geq -7,$
$2y + 3x \leq 15,$
$y \leq 0,$
$x \leq 0$

Solve.

21. $x^2 + 5x \leq 6$

22. $x - \dfrac{1}{x} > 0$

SYNTHESIS

Solve. Write the solution set using interval notation.

23. $|2x - 5| \leq 7 \text{ and } |x - 2| \geq 2$

24. $7x < 8 - 3x < 6 + 7x$

25. Write an absolute-value inequality for which the interval shown is the solution.

More on Systems

Is Silver Rarer Than Gold?

Some analysts think that silver is rarer than gold because silver has so many industrial applications. Products as diverse as toasters, toys, bandages, and clothing often contain silver, and, for most of these uses, silver is consumed and not recoverable. The graph below shows how industrial demand for silver has grown. In Exercise 46 in Section 11.5, we estimate when this demand will equal the above-ground stock of silver.

Industrial Silver

Source: World Silver Survey 2009

In this chapter, we extend the study of systems of equations that we began in Chapter 4. We solve systems of equations in three variables, solve systems using matrices and determinants, and look at some applications from economics.

11.1 Systems of Equations in Three Variables

- Identifying Solutions

- Solving Systems in Three Variables

- Dependency, Inconsistency, and Geometric Considerations

As we saw in Chapter 4, some problems translate directly to a system of two equations. Others call for a translation to three or more equations. In this section, we discuss how to solve systems of three linear equations. Later, we will use such systems in problem-solving situations.

IDENTIFYING SOLUTIONS

A **linear equation in three variables** is an equation equivalent to one in the form $Ax + By + Cz = D$, where A, B, C, and D are real numbers. We refer to the form $Ax + By + Cz = D$ as *standard form* for a linear equation in three variables.

A solution of a system of three equations in three variables is an ordered triple (x, y, z) that makes *all three* equations true. The numbers in an ordered triple correspond to the variables in alphabetical order unless otherwise indicated.

EXAMPLE 1 Determine whether $\left(\frac{3}{2}, -4, 3\right)$ is a solution of the system

$$4x - 2y - 3z = 5,$$
$$-8x - y + z = -5,$$
$$2x + y + 2z = 5.$$

SOLUTION We substitute $\left(\frac{3}{2}, -4, 3\right)$ into the three equations, using alphabetical order.

BY HAND	USING A GRAPHING CALCULATOR

BY HAND

We have the following:

$$4x - 2y - 3z = 5$$

$$\begin{array}{c|c} 4 \cdot \frac{3}{2} - 2(-4) - 3 \cdot 3 & 5 \\ 6 + 8 - 9 & \\ & 5 \stackrel{?}{=} 5 \quad \text{TRUE} \end{array}$$

$$-8x - y + z = -5$$

$$\begin{array}{c|c} -8 \cdot \frac{3}{2} - (-4) + 3 & -5 \\ -12 + 4 + 3 & \\ & -5 \stackrel{?}{=} -5 \quad \text{TRUE} \end{array}$$

$$2x + y + 2z = 5$$

$$\begin{array}{c|c} 2 \cdot \frac{3}{2} + (-4) + 2 \cdot 3 & 5 \\ 3 - 4 + 6 & \\ & 5 \stackrel{?}{=} 5 \quad \text{TRUE} \end{array}$$

The triple makes all three equations true, so it is a solution.

USING A GRAPHING CALCULATOR

We store $\frac{3}{2}$ as X, -4 as Y, and 3 as Z, using the **ALPHA** key to enter Y and Z.

```
3/2→X
                      1.5
-4→Y
                       -4
3→Z
                        3
```

Now we enter the expression on the left side of each equation and press **ENTER**. If the value is the same as the right side of the equation, the ordered triple makes the equation true.

```
4X−2Y−3Z
                        5
-8X−Y+Z
                       -5
2X+Y+2Z
                        5
```

The triple makes all three equations true, so it is a solution.

Try Exercise 7.

SOLVING SYSTEMS IN THREE VARIABLES

In Chapter 4, we solved systems of two equations using graphing, substitution, and elimination. The graph of a linear equation in three variables is a plane. Because a three-dimensional coordinate system is required, solving systems in three variables graphically is difficult. The substitution method *can* be used but is practical only when one or more of the equations has only two variables. Fortunately, the elimination method works well for a system of three equations in three variables.

EXAMPLE 2   Solve the following system of equations:

$$\begin{array}{rl} x + y + z = 4, & (1) \\ x - 2y - z = 1, & (2) \\ 2x - y - 2z = -1. & (3) \end{array}$$

SOLUTION   We select *any* two of the three equations and work to get an equation in two variables. Let's add equations (1) and (2):

$$\begin{array}{rll} x + y + z = 4 & (1) \\ x - 2y - z = 1 & (2) \\ \hline 2x - y \quad\quad = 5. & (4) & \text{Adding to eliminate } z \end{array}$$

Next, we select a different pair of equations and eliminate the *same variable* that we did above. Let's use equations (1) and (3) to again eliminate z. Be careful here! A common error is to eliminate a different variable in this step.

$$x + y + z = 4, \qquad \xrightarrow[\text{equation (1) by 2}]{\text{Multiplying both sides of}} \qquad \begin{aligned} 2x + 2y + 2z &= 8 \\ 2x - y - 2z &= -1 \\ \hline 4x + y &= 7 \qquad (5) \end{aligned}$$

$$2x - y - 2z = -1$$

Now we solve the resulting system of equations (4) and (5). That solution will give us two of the numbers in the solution of the original system.

$$\begin{aligned} 2x - y &= 5 \qquad (4) \\ 4x + y &= 7 \qquad (5) \\ \hline 6x &= 12 \qquad \text{Adding} \\ x &= 2 \end{aligned}$$

Note that we now have two equations in two variables. Had we not eliminated the *same* variable in both of the above steps, this would not be the case.

We can use either equation (4) or (5) to find y. We choose equation (5):

$$\begin{aligned} 4x + y &= 7 \qquad (5) \\ 4 \cdot 2 + y &= 7 \qquad \text{Substituting 2 for } x \text{ in equation (5)} \\ 8 + y &= 7 \\ y &= -1. \end{aligned}$$

We now have $x = 2$ and $y = -1$. To find the value for z, we use any of the original three equations and substitute to find the third number, z. Let's use equation (1) and substitute our two numbers in it:

$$\begin{aligned} x + y + z &= 4 \qquad (1) \\ 2 + (-1) + z &= 4 \qquad \text{Substituting 2 for } x \text{ and } -1 \text{ for } y \\ 1 + z &= 4 \\ z &= 3. \end{aligned}$$

We have obtained the triple $(2, -1, 3)$. It should check in *all three* equations:

$$\begin{array}{c|c} x + y + z = 4 \\ \hline 2 + (-1) + 3 \,\vert\, 4 \\ 4 \overset{?}{=} 4 \quad \text{TRUE} \end{array} \qquad \begin{array}{c|c} x - 2y - z = 1 \\ \hline 2 - 2(-1) - 3 \,\vert\, 1 \\ 1 \overset{?}{=} 1 \quad \text{TRUE} \end{array} \qquad \begin{array}{c|c} 2x - y - 2z = -1 \\ \hline 2 \cdot 2 - (-1) - 2 \cdot 3 \,\vert\, -1 \\ -1 \overset{?}{=} -1 \quad \text{TRUE} \end{array}$$

The solution is $(2, -1, 3)$.

Try Exercise 9.

Student Notes

Solving Systems of Three Linear Equations

To use the elimination method to solve systems of three linear equations:

1. Write all equations in the standard form $Ax + By + Cz = D$.
2. Clear any decimals or fractions.
3. Choose a variable to eliminate. Then select two of the three equations and work to get one equation in which the selected variable is eliminated.
4. Next, use a different pair of equations and eliminate the same variable that you did in step (3).
5. Solve the system of equations that resulted from steps (3) and (4).
6. Substitute the solution from step (5) into one of the original three equations and solve for the third variable. Then check.

EXAMPLE 3 Solve the system

$$4x - 2y - 3z = 5, \quad (1)$$
$$-8x - y + z = -5, \quad (2)$$
$$2x + y + 2z = 5. \quad (3)$$

SOLUTION

Write in standard form.

1., 2. The equations are already in standard form with no fractions or decimals.

Eliminate a variable. (We choose y.)

3. Next, select a variable to eliminate. We decide on y because the y-terms are opposites of each other in equations (2) and (3). We add:

$$-8x - y + z = -5 \quad (2)$$
$$\underline{2x + y + 2z = 5} \quad (3)$$
$$-6x \quad + 3z = 0. \quad (4) \qquad \text{Adding}$$

Eliminate the same variable using a different pair of equations.

4. We use another pair of equations to create a second equation in x and z. That is, we eliminate the same variable, y, as in step (3). We use equations (1) and (3):

$$4x - 2y - 3z = 5, \qquad \qquad \qquad 4x - 2y - 3z = 5$$
$$2x + y + 2z = 5 \quad \xrightarrow[\text{of equation (3) by 2}]{\text{Multiplying both sides}} \quad \underline{4x + 2y + 4z = 10}$$
$$8x \quad + z = 15. \quad (5)$$

Solve the system of two equations in two variables.

5. Now we solve the resulting system of equations (4) and (5). That allows us to find two parts of the ordered triple.

$$-6x + 3z = 0, \qquad \qquad \qquad -6x + 3z = 0$$
$$8x + z = 15 \quad \xrightarrow[\text{of equation (5) by } -3]{\text{Multiplying both sides}} \quad \underline{-24x - 3z = -45}$$
$$-30x \quad = -45$$
$$x = \frac{-45}{-30} = \frac{3}{2}$$

We use equation (5) to find z:

$$8x + z = 15 \qquad (5)$$
$$8 \cdot \tfrac{3}{2} + z = 15 \qquad \text{Substituting } \tfrac{3}{2} \text{ for } x$$
$$12 + z = 15$$
$$z = 3.$$

Solve for the remaining variable.

6. Finally, we use any of the original equations and substitute to find the third number, y. We choose equation (3):

$$2x + y + 2z = 5 \qquad (3)$$
$$2 \cdot \tfrac{3}{2} + y + 2 \cdot 3 = 5 \qquad \text{Substituting } \tfrac{3}{2} \text{ for } x \text{ and } 3 \text{ for } z$$
$$3 + y + 6 = 5$$
$$y + 9 = 5$$
$$y = -4.$$

Check.

The solution is $\left(\tfrac{3}{2}, -4, 3\right)$. The check was performed as Example 1.

Try Exercise 23.

Sometimes, certain variables are missing at the outset.

EXAMPLE 4 Solve the system

$$
\begin{aligned}
x + y + z &= 180, &&(1)\\
x \quad\quad - z &= -70, &&(2)\\
2y - z &= 0. &&(3)
\end{aligned}
$$

SOLUTION

1., 2. The equations appear in standard form with no fractions or decimals.

3., 4. Note that there is no y in equation (2). Thus, at the outset, we already have y eliminated from one equation. We need another equation with y eliminated, so we work with equations (1) and (3):

$$
\begin{aligned}
x + y + z &= 180, \\
2y - z &= 0
\end{aligned}
\quad
\xrightarrow[\text{of equation (1) by } -2]{\text{Multiplying both sides}}
\quad
\begin{aligned}
-2x - 2y - 2z &= -360 \\
2y - z &= 0 \\
\hline
-2x \quad - 3z &= -360. \quad (4)
\end{aligned}
$$

5., 6. Now we solve the resulting system of equations (2) and (4):

$$
\begin{aligned}
x - z &= -70, \\
-2x - 3z &= -360
\end{aligned}
\quad
\xrightarrow[\text{of equation (2) by } 2]{\text{Multiplying both sides}}
\quad
\begin{aligned}
2x - 2z &= -140 \\
-2x - 3z &= -360 \\
\hline
-5z &= -500 \\
z &= 100.
\end{aligned}
$$

Continuing as in Examples 2 and 3, we get the solution $(30, 50, 100)$. The check is left to the student.

Try Exercise 29.

DEPENDENCY, INCONSISTENCY, AND GEOMETRIC CONSIDERATIONS

Each equation in Examples 2, 3, and 4 has a graph that is a plane in three dimensions. The solutions are points common to the planes of each system. Since three planes can have an infinite number of points in common or no points at all in common, we need to generalize the concept of *consistency*.

Planes intersect at one point. System is *consistent* and has one solution.

Planes intersect along a common line. System is *consistent* and has an infinite number of solutions.

Three parallel planes. System is *inconsistent;* it has no solution.

Planes intersect two at a time, with no point common to all three. System is *inconsistent;* it has no solution.

Consistency

A system of equations that has at least one solution is said to be **consistent.**

A system of equations that has no solution is said to be **inconsistent.**

EXAMPLE 5 Solve:

$$y + 3z = 4, \quad (1)$$
$$-x - y + 2z = 0, \quad (2)$$
$$x + 2y + z = 1. \quad (3)$$

SOLUTION   The variable x is missing in equation (1). By adding equations (2) and (3), we can find a second equation in which x is missing:

$$-x - y + 2z = 0 \quad (2)$$
$$\underline{x + 2y + z = 1} \quad (3)$$
$$y + 3z = 1. \quad (4) \qquad \text{Adding}$$

Equations (1) and (4) form a system in y and z. We solve as before:

$$\begin{array}{ll} y + 3z = 4, \\ y + 3z = 1 \end{array} \quad \xrightarrow[\text{of equation (1) by } -1]{\text{Multiplying both sides}} \quad \begin{array}{l} -y - 3z = -4 \\ \underline{y + 3z = 1} \end{array}$$

This is a contradiction. $\longrightarrow 0 = -3.$ Adding

Since we end up with a *false* equation, or contradiction, we know that the system has no solution. It is *inconsistent*.

 Try Exercise 15.

The notion of *dependency* from Section 4.1 can also be extended.

EXAMPLE 6 Solve:

$$2x + y + z = 3, \quad (1)$$
$$x - 2y - z = 1, \quad (2)$$
$$3x + 4y + 3z = 5. \quad (3)$$

SOLUTION   Our plan is to first use equations (1) and (2) to eliminate z. Then we will select another pair of equations and again eliminate z:

$$\begin{array}{l} 2x + y + z = 3 \\ \underline{x - 2y - z = 1} \\ 3x - y = 4. \quad (4) \end{array}$$

Next, we use equations (2) and (3) to eliminate z again:

$$\begin{array}{ll} x - 2y - z = 1, \\ 3x + 4y + 3z = 5 \end{array} \quad \xrightarrow[\text{of equation (2) by } 3]{\text{Multiplying both sides}} \quad \begin{array}{l} 3x - 6y - 3z = 3 \\ \underline{3x + 4y + 3z = 5} \\ 6x - 2y = 8. \quad (5) \end{array}$$

We now try to solve the resulting system of equations (4) and (5):

$$\begin{array}{ll} 3x - y = 4, \\ 6x - 2y = 8 \end{array} \quad \xrightarrow[\text{of equation (4) by } -2]{\text{Multiplying both sides}} \quad \begin{array}{l} -6x + 2y = -8 \\ \underline{6x - 2y = 8} \\ 0 = 0. \quad (6) \end{array}$$

Equation (6), which is an identity, indicates that equations (1), (2), and (3) are *dependent*. This means that the original system of three equations is equivalent to a system of two equations. Note here that two times equation (1), minus equation (2), is equation (3). Thus removing equation (3) from the system does not affect the solution of the system.* In writing an answer to this problem, we simply state that "the equations are dependent."

Try Exercise 21.

Recall that when dependent equations appeared in Section 4.1, the solution sets were always infinite in size and were written in set-builder notation. There, all systems of dependent equations were *consistent*. This is not always the case for systems of three or more equations. The following figures illustrate some possibilities geometrically.

The planes intersect along a common line. The equations are dependent and the system is consistent. There is an infinite number of solutions.

The planes coincide. The equations are dependent and the system is consistent. There is an infinite number of solutions.

Two planes coincide. The third plane is parallel. The equations are dependent and the system is inconsistent. There is no solution.

11.1 Exercise Set

↪ *Concept Reinforcement*   *Classify each of the following statements as either true or false.*

1. $3x + 5y + 4z = 7$ is a linear equation in three variables.

2. It is not difficult to solve a system of three equations in three unknowns by graphing.

3. Every system of three equations in three unknowns has at least one solution.

4. If, when we are solving a system of three equations, a false equation results from adding a multiple of one equation to another, the system is inconsistent.

5. If, when we are solving a system of three equations, an identity results from adding a multiple of one equation to another, the equations are dependent.

6. Whenever a system of three equations contains dependent equations, there is an infinite number of solutions.

7. Determine whether $(2, -1, -2)$ is a solution of the system
$$\begin{aligned} x + y - 2z &= 5, \\ 2x - y - z &= 7, \\ -x - 2y - 3z &= 6. \end{aligned}$$

8. Determine whether $(-1, -3, 2)$ is a solution of the system
$$\begin{aligned} x - y + z &= 4, \\ x - 2y - z &= 3, \\ 3x + 2y - z &= 1. \end{aligned}$$

Solve each system. If a system's equations are dependent or if there is no solution, state this.

9. $\begin{aligned} x - y - z &= 0, \\ 2x - 3y + 2z &= 7, \\ -x + 2y + z &= 1 \end{aligned}$

10. $\begin{aligned} x + y - z &= 0, \\ 2x - y + z &= 3, \\ -x + 5y - 3z &= 2 \end{aligned}$

---

*A set of equations is dependent if at least one equation can be expressed as a sum of multiples of other equations in that set.

11. $x - y - z = 1,$
$2x + y + 2z = 4,$
$x + y + 3z = 5$

12. $x + y - 3z = 4,$
$2x + 3y + z = 6,$
$2x - y + z = -14$

13. $3x + 4y - 3z = 4,$
$5x - y + 2z = 3,$
$x + 2y - z = -2$

14. $2x - 3y + z = 5,$
$x + 3y + 8z = 22,$
$3x - y + 2z = 12$

15. $x + y + z = 0,$
$2x + 3y + 2z = -3,$
$-x - 2y - z = 1$

16. $3a - 2b + 7c = 13,$
$a + 8b - 6c = -47,$
$7a - 9b - 9c = -3$

17. $2x - 3y - z = -9,$
$2x + 5y + z = 1,$
$x - y + z = 3$

18. $4x + y + z = 17,$
$x - 3y + 2z = -8,$
$5x - 2y + 3z = 5$

Aha! **19.** $a + b + c = 5,$
$2a + 3b - c = 2,$
$2a + 3b - 2c = 4$

20. $u - v + 6w = 8,$
$3u - v + 6w = 14,$
$-u - 2v - 3w = 7$

21. $-2x + 8y + 2z = 4,$
$x + 6y + 3z = 4,$
$3x - 2y + z = 0$

22. $x - y + z = 4,$
$5x + 2y - 3z = 2,$
$4x + 3y - 4z = -2$

23. $2u - 4v - w = 8,$
$3u + 2v + w = 6,$
$5u - 2v + 3w = 2$

24. $4a + b + c = 3,$
$2a - b + c = 6,$
$2a + 2b - c = -9$

25. $r + \frac{3}{2}s + 6t = 2,$
$2r - 3s + 3t = 0.5,$
$r + s + t = 1$

26. $5x + 3y + \frac{1}{2}z = \frac{7}{2},$
$0.5x - 0.9y - 0.2z = 0.3,$
$3x - 2.4y + 0.4z = -1$

27. $4a + 9b = 8,$
$8a + 6c = -1,$
$6b + 6c = -1$

28. $3u + 2w = 11,$
$v - 7w = 4,$
$u - 6v = 1$

29. $x + y + z = 57,$
$-2x + y = 3,$
$x - z = 6$

30. $x + y + z = 105,$
$10y - z = 11,$
$2x - 3y = 7$

31. $a - 3c = 6,$
$b + 2c = 2,$
$7a - 3b - 5c = 14$

32. $2a - 3b = 2,$
$7a + 4c = \frac{3}{4},$
$2c - 3b = 1$

Aha! **33.** $x + y + z = 83,$
$y = 2x + 3,$
$z = 40 + x$

34. $l + m = 7,$
$3m + 2n = 9,$
$4l + n = 5$

35. $x + z = 0,$
$x + y + 2z = 3,$
$y + z = 2$

36. $x + y = 0,$
$x + z = 1,$
$2x + y + z = 2$

37. $x + y + z = 1,$
$-x + 2y + z = 2,$
$2x - y = -1$

38. $y + z = 1,$
$x + y + z = 1,$
$x + 2y + 2z = 2$

TW **39.** Rondel always begins solving systems of three equations in three variables by using the first two equations to eliminate x. Is this a good approach? Why or why not?

TW **40.** Describe a method for writing an inconsistent system of three equations in three variables.

SKILL REVIEW

To prepare for Section 11.2, review translating sentences to equations.

Translate each sentence to an equation.

41. One number is half another.

42. The difference of two numbers is twice the first number.

43. The sum of three consecutive numbers is 100.

44. The sum of three numbers is 100.

45. The product of two numbers is five times a third number.

46. The product of two numbers is twice their sum.

SYNTHESIS

TW **47.** Is it possible for a system of three linear equations to have exactly two ordered triples in its solution set? Why or why not?

TW **48.** Kadi and Ahmed both correctly solve the system

$$x + 2y - z = 1,$$
$$-x - 2y + z = 3,$$
$$2x + 4y - 2z = 2.$$

Kadi states "the equations are dependent" while Ahmed states "there is no solution." How did each person reach the conclusion?

Solve.

49. $\dfrac{x+2}{3} - \dfrac{y+4}{2} + \dfrac{z+1}{6} = 0,$

$\dfrac{x-4}{3} + \dfrac{y+1}{4} + \dfrac{z-2}{2} = -1,$

$\dfrac{x+1}{2} + \dfrac{y}{2} + \dfrac{z-1}{4} = \dfrac{3}{4}$

50. $w + x + y + z = 2,$
$w + 2x + 2y + 4z = 1,$
$w - x + y + z = 6,$
$w - 3x - y + z = 2$

51. $w + x - y + z = 0,$
$w - 2x - 2y - z = -5,$
$w - 3x - y + z = 4,$
$2w - x - y + 3z = 7$

For Exercises 52 and 53, let u represent $1/x$, v represent $1/y$, and w represent $1/z$. Solve for u, v, and w, and then solve for x, y, and z.

52. $\dfrac{2}{x} - \dfrac{1}{y} - \dfrac{3}{z} = -1,$

$\dfrac{2}{x} - \dfrac{1}{y} + \dfrac{1}{z} = -9,$

$\dfrac{1}{x} + \dfrac{2}{y} - \dfrac{4}{z} = 17$

53. $\dfrac{2}{x} + \dfrac{2}{y} - \dfrac{3}{z} = 3,$

$\dfrac{1}{x} - \dfrac{2}{y} - \dfrac{3}{z} = 9,$

$\dfrac{7}{x} - \dfrac{2}{y} + \dfrac{9}{z} = -39$

Determine k so that each system is dependent.

54. $x - 3y + 2z = 1,$
$2x + y - z = 3,$
$9x - 6y + 3z = k$

55. $5x - 6y + kz = -5,$
$x + 3y - 2z = 2,$
$2x - y + 4z = -1$

In each case, three solutions of an equation in x, y, and z are given. Find the equation.

56. $Ax + By + Cz = 12;$
$\left(1, \frac{3}{4}, 3\right), \left(\frac{4}{3}, 1, 2\right),$ and $(2, 1, 1)$

57. $z = b - mx - ny;$
$(1, 1, 2), (3, 2, -6),$ and $\left(\frac{3}{2}, 1, 1\right)$

58. Write an inconsistent system of equations that contains dependent equations.

> **Try Exercise Answers: Section 11.1**
> **7.** Yes **9.** $(3, 1, 2)$ **15.** No solution **21.** The equations are dependent. **23.** $\left(3, \frac{1}{2}, -4\right)$ **29.** $(15, 33, 9)$

Collaborative Corner

Finding the Preferred Approach

Focus: Systems of three linear equations
Time: 10–15 minutes
Group Size: 3

Consider the six steps outlined on p. 674 along with the following system:

$$2x + 4y = 3 - 5z,$$
$$0.3x = 0.2y + 0.7z + 1.4,$$
$$0.04x + 0.03y = 0.07 + 0.04z.$$

ACTIVITY

1. Working independently, each group member should solve the system above. One person

should begin by eliminating x, one should first eliminate y, and one should first eliminate z. Write neatly so that others can follow your steps.

2. Once all group members have solved the system, compare your answers. If the answers do not check, exchange notebooks and check each other's work. If a mistake is detected, allow the person who made the mistake to make the repair.

3. Decide as a group which of the three approaches above (if any) ranks as easiest and which (if any) ranks as most difficult. Then compare your rankings with the other groups in the class.

11.2 Solving Applications: Systems of Three Equations

- Applications of Three Equations in Three Unknowns

Solving systems of three or more equations is important in many applications. Such systems arise in the natural and social sciences, business, and engineering. To begin, let's look at a purely numerical application.

EXAMPLE 1 The sum of three numbers is 4. The first number minus twice the second, minus the third is 1. Twice the first number minus the second, minus twice the third is -1. Find the numbers.

Student Notes

It is quite likely that you are expected to remember that the sum of the measures of the angles in any triangle is 180°. You may want to ask your instructor which other formulas from geometry and elsewhere you are expected to know.

SOLUTION

1. **Familiarize.** There are three statements involving the same three numbers. Let's label these numbers x, y, and z.

2. **Translate.** We can translate directly as follows.

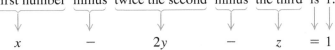

The sum of the three numbers is 4.

$$x + y + z = 4$$

The first number minus twice the second minus the third is 1.

$$x - 2y - z = 1$$

Twice the first number minus the second minus twice the third is −1.

$$2x - y - 2z = -1$$

We now have a system of three equations:

$$x + y + z = 4,$$
$$x - 2y - z = 1,$$
$$2x - y - 2z = -1.$$

3. **Carry out.** We need to solve the system of equations. Note that we found the solution, $(2, -1, 3)$, in Example 2 of Section 11.1.

4. **Check.** The first statement of the problem says that the sum of the three numbers is 4. That checks, because $2 + (-1) + 3 = 4$. The second statement says that the first number minus twice the second, minus the third is 1: $2 - 2(-1) - 3 = 1$. That checks. The check of the third statement is left to the student.

5. **State.** The three numbers are 2, −1, and 3.

Try Exercise 1.

EXAMPLE 2 Architecture. In a triangular cross section of a roof, the largest angle is 70° greater than the smallest angle. The largest angle is twice as large as the remaining angle. Find the measure of each angle.

SOLUTION

1. **Familiarize.** The first thing we do is make a drawing, or a sketch.

Since we don't know the size of any angle, we use x, y, and z to represent the three measures, from smallest to largest. Recall that the measures of the angles in any triangle add up to 180°.

2. Translate. This geometric fact about triangles gives us one equation:

$$x + y + z = 180.$$

Two of the statements can be translated almost directly.

The largest angle is 70° greater than the smallest angle.

$$z \qquad = \qquad x + 70$$

The largest angle is twice as large as the remaining angle.

$$z \qquad = \qquad 2y$$

We now have a system of three equations:

$$
\begin{aligned}
x + y + z &= 180, \\
x + 70 &= z, \\
2y &= z;
\end{aligned}
\quad \text{or} \quad
\begin{aligned}
x + y + z &= 180, \\
x \qquad - z &= -70, \\
2y - z &= 0,
\end{aligned}
\quad
\begin{array}{l}
\text{Rewriting in} \\
\text{standard form}
\end{array}
$$

3. Carry out. The system was solved in Example 4 of Section 11.1. The solution is (30, 50, 100).

4. Check. The sum of the numbers is 180, so that checks. The measure of the largest angle, 100°, is 70° greater than the measure of the smallest angle, 30°, so that checks. The measure of the largest angle is also twice the measure of the remaining angle, 50°. Thus we have a check.

5. State. The angles in the triangle measure 30°, 50° and 100°.

Try Exercise 5.

EXAMPLE 3 Downloads.   Kaya frequently downloads music, TV shows, and iPod games. In January, she downloaded 5 songs, 10 TV shows, and 3 games for a total of \$40. In February, she spent a total of \$135 for 25 songs, 25 TV shows, and 12 games. In March, she spent a total of \$56 for 15 songs, 8 TV shows, and 5 games. Assuming each song is the same price, each TV show is the same price, and each iPod game is the same price, how much does each cost?
Source: Based on information from www.iTunes.com

SOLUTION

1. Familiarize. We let $s =$ the cost, in dollars, per song, $t =$ the cost, in dollars, per TV show, and $g =$ the cost, in dollars, per game. Then in January, Kaya spent $5 \cdot s$ for songs, $10 \cdot t$ for TV shows, and $3 \cdot g$ for iPod games. The sum of these amounts was \$40. Each month's downloads will translate to an equation.

2. Translate. We can organize the information in a table.

	Cost of Songs	Cost of TV Shows	Cost of iPod Games	Total Cost	
January	$5s$	$10t$	$3g$	40	$\longrightarrow 5s + 10t + 3g = 40$
February	$25s$	$25t$	$12g$	135	$\longrightarrow 25s + 25t + 12g = 135$
March	$15s$	$8t$	$5g$	56	$\longrightarrow 15s + 8t + 5g = 56$

We now have a system of three equations:

$$5s + 10t + 3g = 40, \qquad (1)$$
$$25s + 25t + 12g = 135, \qquad (2)$$
$$15s + 8t + 5g = 56. \qquad (3)$$

3. Carry out. We begin by using equations (1) and (2) to eliminate s.

$$
\begin{aligned}
5s + 10t + 3g &= 40, \\
25s + 25t + 12g &= 135
\end{aligned}
\quad
\xrightarrow[\text{of equation (1) by } -5]{\text{Multiplying both sides}}
\quad
\begin{aligned}
-25s - 50t - 15g &= -200 \\
25s + 25t + 12g &= \quad 135 \\
\hline
-25t - 3g &= -65 \qquad (4)
\end{aligned}
$$

We then use equations (1) and (3) to again eliminate s.

$$
\begin{aligned}
5s + 10t + 3g &= 40, \\
15s + 8t + 5g &= 56
\end{aligned}
\quad
\xrightarrow[\text{of equation (1) by } -3]{\text{Multiplying both sides}}
\quad
\begin{aligned}
-15s - 30t - 9g &= -120 \\
15s + 8t + 5g &= \quad 56 \\
\hline
-22t - 4g &= -64 \qquad (5)
\end{aligned}
$$

Now we solve the resulting system of equations (4) and (5).

$$
\begin{aligned}
-25t - 3g &= -65 \quad \xrightarrow[\text{of equation (4) by } -4]{\text{Multiplying both sides}} \quad & 100t + 12g &= \quad 260 \\
-22t - 4g &= -64 \quad \xrightarrow[\text{of equation (5) by } 3]{\text{Multiplying both sides}} \quad & -66t - 12g &= -192 \\
& & \hline
& & 34t &= \quad 68 \\
& & t &= 2
\end{aligned}
$$

To find g, we use equation (4):

$$
\begin{aligned}
-25t - 3g &= -65 \\
-25 \cdot 2 - 3g &= -65 \qquad \text{Substituting 2 for } t \\
-50 - 3g &= -65 \\
-3g &= -15 \\
g &= 5.
\end{aligned}
$$

Finally, we use equation (1) to find s:

$$
\begin{aligned}
5s + 10t + 3g &= 40 \\
5s + 10 \cdot 2 + 3 \cdot 5 &= 40 \qquad \text{Substituting 2 for } t \text{ and 5 for } g \\
5s + 20 + 15 &= 40 \\
5s + 35 &= 40 \\
5s &= 5 \\
s &= 1.
\end{aligned}
$$

4. Check. If a song costs \$1, a TV show costs \$2, and an iPod game costs \$5, then the total cost for each month's downloads is as follows:

January: $5 \cdot \$1 + 10 \cdot \$2 + 3 \cdot \$5 = \$5 + \$20 + \$15 = \$40;$

February: $25 \cdot \$1 + 25 \cdot \$2 + 12 \cdot \$5 = \$25 + \$50 + \$60 = \$135;$

March: $15 \cdot \$1 + 8 \cdot \$2 + 5 \cdot \$5 = \$15 + \$16 + \$25 = \$56.$

This checks with the information given in the problem.

5. State. A song costs \$1, a TV show costs \$2, and an iPod game costs \$5.

Try Exercise 9.

Solve.

1. The sum of three numbers is 57. The second is 3 more than the first. The third is 6 more than the first. Find the numbers.

2. The sum of three numbers is 5. The first number minus the second plus the third is 1. The first minus the third is 3 more than the second. Find the numbers.

3. The sum of three numbers is 26. Twice the first minus the second is 2 less than the third. The third is the second minus three times the first. Find the numbers.

4. The sum of three numbers is 105. The third is 11 less than ten times the second. Twice the first is 7 more than three times the second. Find the numbers.

5. *Geometry.* In triangle *ABC*, the measure of angle *B* is three times that of angle *A*. The measure of angle *C* is 20° more than that of angle *A*. Find the angle measures.

6. *Geometry.* In triangle *ABC*, the measure of angle *B* is twice the measure of angle *A*. The measure of angle *C* is 80° more than that of angle *A*. Find the angle measures.

7. *Scholastic Aptitude Test.* Many high-school students take the Scholastic Aptitude Test (SAT). Beginning in March 2005, students taking the SAT received three scores: a critical reading score, a mathematics score, and a writing score. The average total score of 2009 high-school seniors who took the SAT was 1509. The average mathematics score exceeded the reading score by 14 points and the average writing score was 8 points less than the reading score. What was the average score for each category?
Source: College Entrance Examination Board

8. *Advertising.* In 2008, U.S. companies spent a total of $118.2 billion on newspaper, television, and magazine ads. The total amount spent on television ads was $10.8 billion more than the amount spent on newspaper and magazine ads together. The amount spent on magazine ads was $3.5 billion more than the amount spent on newspaper ads. How much was spent on each form of advertising?
Source: TNS Media Intelligence

9. *Nutrition.* Most nutritionists now agree that a healthy adult diet should include 25–35 g of fiber each day. A breakfast of 2 bran muffins, 1 banana, and a 1-cup serving of Wheaties® contains 9 g of fiber; a breakfast of 1 bran muffin, 2 bananas, and a 1-cup serving of Wheaties® contains 10.5 g of fiber; and a breakfast of 2 bran muffins and a 1-cup serving of Wheaties® contains 6 g of fiber. How much fiber is in each of these foods?
Sources: usda.gov; InteliHealth.com

10. *Nutrition.* Refer to Exercise 9. A breakfast consisting of 2 pancakes and a 1-cup serving of strawberries contains 4.5 g of fiber, whereas a breakfast of 2 pancakes and a 1-cup serving of Cheerios® contains 4 g of fiber. When a meal consists of 1 pancake, a 1-cup serving of Cheerios®, and a 1-cup serving of strawberries, it contains 7 g of fiber. How much fiber is in each of these foods?
Source: InteliHealth.com

Aha! 11. *Automobile Pricing.* The basic model of a 2010 Honda Civic Hybrid with a car cover cost $24,030. When equipped with satellite radio and a car cover, the vehicle's price rose to $24,340. The price of the basic model with satellite radio was $24,110. Find the basic price, the price of satellite radio, and the price of a car cover.

12. *Telemarketing.* Sven, Laurie, and Isaiah can process 740 telephone orders per day. Sven and Laurie together can process 470 orders, while Laurie and Isaiah together can process 520 orders per day. How many orders can each person process alone?

13. *Coffee Prices.* Reba works at a Starbucks® coffee shop where a 12-oz cup of coffee costs $1.65, a 16-oz cup costs $1.85, and a 20-oz cup costs $1.95. During one busy period, Reba served 55 cups of coffee, emptying six 144-oz "brewers" while collecting a total of $99.65. How many cups of each size did Reba fill?

14. *Restaurant Management.* Chick-fil-A® recently sold small lemonades for $1.29, medium lemonades for $1.49, and large lemonades for $1.85. During a lunch-time rush, Chris sold 40 lemonades for a total of $59.40. The number of small drinks and large drinks, combined, was 10 fewer than the number of medium drinks. How many drinks of each size were sold?

15. *Small-Business Loans.* Chelsea took out three loans for a total of $120,000 to start an organic orchard. Her bank loan was at an interest rate of 8%, the small-business loan was at an interest rate of 5%, and the mortgage on her house was at an interest rate of 4%. The total simple interest due on the loans in one year was $5750. The annual simple interest on the mortgage was $1600 more than the interest on the bank loan. How much did she borrow from each source?

16. *Investments.* A business class divided an imaginary investment of $80,000 among three mutual funds. The first fund grew by 10%, the second by 6%, and the third by 15%. Total earnings were $8850. The earnings from the first fund were $750 more than the earnings from the third. How much was invested in each fund?

17. *Gold Alloys.* Gold used to make jewelry is often a blend of gold, silver, and copper. The relative amounts of the metals determine the color of the alloy. Red gold is 75% gold, 5% silver, and 20% copper. Yellow gold is 75% gold, 12.5% silver, and 12.5% copper. White gold is 37.5% gold and 62.5% silver. If 100 g of red gold costs $2265.40, 100 g of yellow gold costs $2287.75, and 100 g of white gold costs $1312.50, how much do gold, silver, and copper cost?
Source: World Gold Council

18. *Blending Teas.* Verity has recently created three custom tea blends. A 5-oz package of Southern Sandalwood sells for $13.15 and contains 2 oz of Keemun tea, 2 oz of Assam tea, and 1 oz of a berry blend. A 4-oz package of Golden Sunshine sells for $12.50 and contains 3 oz of Assam tea and 1 oz of the berry blend. A 6-oz package of Mountain Morning sells for $12.50 and contains 2 oz of the berry blend, 3 oz of Keemun tea, and 1 oz of Assam tea. What is the price per ounce of Keemun tea, Assam tea, and the berry blend?

19. *Nutrition.* A dietician in a hospital prepares meals under the guidance of a physician. Suppose that for a particular patient a physician prescribes a meal to have 800 calories, 55 g of protein, and 220 mg of vitamin C. The dietician prepares a meal of roast beef, baked potatoes, and broccoli according to the data in the table below.

Serving Size	Calories	Protein (in grams)	Vitamin C (in milligrams)
Roast Beef, 3 oz	300	20	0
Baked Potato, 1	100	5	20
Broccoli, 156 g	50	5	100

How many servings of each food are needed in order to satisfy the doctor's orders?

20. *Nutrition.* Repeat Exercise 19 but replace the broccoli with asparagus, for which a 180-g serving contains 50 calories, 5 g of protein, and 44 mg of vitamin C. Which meal would you prefer eating?

21. *Concert Tickets.* Students in a Listening Responses class bought 40 tickets for a piano concert. The number of tickets purchased for seats either in the first mezzanine or on the main floor was the same as the number purchased for seats in the second mezzanine. First mezzanine seats cost $52, main floor seats cost $38, and second mezzanine seats cost $28. The total cost of the tickets was $1432. How many of each type of ticket were purchased?

22. *World Population Growth.* The world population is projected to be 9.4 billion in 2050. At that time, there is expected to be approximately 3.5 billion more people in Asia than in Africa. The population for the rest of the world will be approximately 0.3 billion less than two-fifths the population of Asia. Find the projected populations of Asia, Africa, and the rest of the world in 2050.
Source: U.S. Census Bureau

23. *Basketball Scoring.* The New York Knicks recently scored a total of 92 points on a combination of 2-point field goals, 3-point field goals, and 1-point foul shots. Altogether, the Knicks made 50 baskets and 19 more 2-pointers than foul shots. How many shots of each kind were made?

24. *History.* Find the year in which the first U.S. transcontinental railroad was completed. The following are some facts about the number. The sum of the digits in the year is 24. The ones digit is 1 more than the hundreds digit. Both the tens and the ones digits are multiples of 3.

ᵀᵂ 25. Problems like Exercises 13 and 14 could be classified as total-value problems. How do these problems differ from the total-value problems of Section 4.4?

ᵀᵂ 26. Write a problem for a classmate to solve. Design the problem so that it translates to a system of three equations in three variables.

SKILL REVIEW

To prepare for Section 11.3, review simplifying expressions.
Simplify.

27. $-2(2x - 3y)$

28. $-(x - 6y)$

29. $-6(x - 2y) + (6x - 5y)$

30. $3(2a + 4b) + (5a - 12b)$

31. $-(2a - b - 6c)$

32. $-10(5a + 3b - c)$

33. $-2(3x - y + z) + 3(-2x + y - 2z)$

34. $(8x - 10y + 7z) + 5(3x + 2y - 4z)$

SYNTHESIS

ᵀᵂ 35. Consider Exercise 23. Suppose there were no foul shots made. Would there still be a solution? Why or why not?

ᵀᵂ 36. Consider Exercise 13. Suppose Reba collected $50. Could the problem still be solved? Why or why not?

37. *Health Insurance.* In 2010, United Health One insurance for a 45-year-old and his or her spouse cost $135 per month. That rate increased to $154 per month if a child were included and $173 per month if two children were included. The rate dropped to $102 per month for just the applicant and one child. Find the separate costs for insuring the applicant, the spouse, the first child, and the second child.
Source: United Health One Insurance Company® through www.ehealth.com

38. Find a three-digit positive integer such that the sum of all three digits is 14, the tens digit is 2 more than the ones digit, and if the digits are reversed, the number is unchanged.

39. *Ages.* Tammy's age is the sum of the ages of Carmen and Dennis. Carmen's age is 2 more than the sum of the ages of Dennis and Mark. Dennis's age is four times Mark's age. The sum of all four ages is 42. How old is Tammy?

40. *Ticket Revenue.* A magic show's audience of 100 people consists of adults, students, and children. The ticket prices are $10 for adults, $3 for students, and 50¢ for children. The total amount of money taken in is $100. How many adults, students, and children are in attendance? Does there seem to be some information missing? Do some more careful reasoning.

41. *Sharing Raffle Tickets.* Hal gives Tom as many raffle tickets as Tom first had and Gary as many as Gary first had. In like manner, Tom then gives Hal and Gary as many tickets as each then has. Similarly, Gary gives Hal and Tom as many tickets as each then has. If each finally has 40 tickets, with how many tickets does Tom begin?

42. Find the sum of the angle measures at the tips of the star in this figure.

11.3   Elimination Using Matrices

- Matrices and Systems

- Row-Equivalent
  Operations

In solving systems of equations, we perform computations with the constants. If we keep all like terms in the same column, we can simplify writing a system by omitting the variables. For example, the system

$$3x + 4y = 5, \\ x - 2y = 1 \quad \text{simplifies to} \quad \begin{matrix} 3 & 4 & 5 \\ 1 & -2 & 1 \end{matrix}$$

if we do not write the variables, the operation of addition, and the equals signs. Note that the coefficients of the x-terms are written first, the coefficients of the y-terms are written next, and the constant terms are written last. Equations must be written in standard form $Ax + By = C$ before they are written without variables.

MATRICES AND SYSTEMS

In the example above, we have written a rectangular array of numbers. Such an array is called a **matrix** (plural, **matrices**). We ordinarily write brackets around matrices. The following are matrices:

$$\begin{bmatrix} -3 & 1 \\ 0 & 5 \end{bmatrix}, \quad \begin{bmatrix} 2 & 0 & -1 & 3 \\ -5 & 2 & 7 & -1 \\ 4 & 5 & 3 & 0 \end{bmatrix}, \quad \begin{bmatrix} 2 & 3 \\ 7 & 15 \\ -2 & 23 \\ 4 & 1 \end{bmatrix}.$$

The individual numbers are called *elements* or *entries.*

The **rows** of a matrix are horizontal, and the **columns** are vertical.

$$A = \begin{bmatrix} 5 & -2 & -2 \\ 1 & 0 & 1 \\ 4 & -3 & 2 \end{bmatrix} \begin{matrix} \leftarrow \text{row 1} \\ \leftarrow \text{row 2} \\ \leftarrow \text{row 3} \end{matrix}$$

column 1 column 2 column 3

Let's see how matrices can be used to solve a system.

EXAMPLE 1   Solve the system

$$5x - 4y = -1, \\ -2x + 3y = 2.$$

SOLUTION   We write a matrix using only coefficients and constants, listing x-coefficients in the first column and y-coefficients in the second. A dashed line separates the coefficients from the constants:

$$\begin{bmatrix} 5 & -4 & \vdots & -1 \\ -2 & 3 & \vdots & 2 \end{bmatrix}.$$

Refer to the notes in the margin for further information.

Our goal is to transform

$$\begin{bmatrix} 5 & -4 & \vdots & -1 \\ -2 & 3 & \vdots & 2 \end{bmatrix} \quad \text{into the form} \quad \begin{bmatrix} a & b & \vdots & c \\ 0 & d & \vdots & e \end{bmatrix}.$$

We can then reinsert the variables x and y, form equations, and complete the solution.

As an aid for understanding, we list the corresponding system in the margin.

$$5x - 4y = -1, \\ -2x + 3y = 2$$

Our calculations are similar to those that we would do if we wrote the entire equations. The first step is to multiply and/or interchange the rows so that each number in the first column below the first number is a multiple of that number. Here that means multiplying Row 2 by 5. This corresponds to multiplying both sides of the second equation by 5.

$$5x - 4y = -1,$$
$$-10x + 15y = 10$$

$$\begin{bmatrix} 5 & -4 & | & -1 \\ -10 & 15 & | & 10 \end{bmatrix}$$

New Row 2 = 5(Row 2 from the step above)
$$= 5(-2 \quad 3 \ | \ 2) = (-10 \quad 15 \ | \ 10)$$

Next, we multiply the first row by 2, add this to Row 2, and write that result as the "new" Row 2. This corresponds to multiplying the first equation by 2 and adding the result to the second equation in order to eliminate a variable. Write out these computations as necessary.

$$5x - 4y = -1,$$
$$7y = 8$$

$$\begin{bmatrix} 5 & -4 & | & -1 \\ 0 & 7 & | & 8 \end{bmatrix}$$

2(Row 1) $= 2(5 \quad -4 \ | \ -1) = (10 \quad -8 \ | \ -2)$
New Row 2 $= (10 \quad -8 \ | \ -2) + (-10 \quad 15 \ | \ 10)$
$= (0 \quad 7 \ | \ 8)$

If we now reinsert the variables, we have

$$5x - 4y = -1, \quad (1) \qquad \text{From Row 1}$$
$$7y = 8. \quad (2) \qquad \text{From Row 2}$$

Solving equation (2) for y gives us

$$7y = 8 \quad (2)$$
$$y = \tfrac{8}{7}.$$

Next, we substitute $\tfrac{8}{7}$ for y in equation (1):

$$5x - 4y = -1 \quad (1)$$
$$5x - 4 \cdot \tfrac{8}{7} = -1 \qquad \text{Substituting } \tfrac{8}{7} \text{ for } y \text{ in equation (1)}$$
$$x = \tfrac{5}{7}. \qquad \text{Solving for } x$$

The solution is $\left(\tfrac{5}{7}, \tfrac{8}{7}\right)$. The check is left to the student.

∎ Try Exercise 7.

All the systems of equations shown in the margin by Example 1 are **equivalent systems of equations;** that is, they all have the same solution.

EXAMPLE 2 Solve the system

$$2x - y + 4z = -3,$$
$$x \qquad - 4z = 5,$$
$$6x - y + 2z = 10.$$

SOLUTION We first write a matrix, using only the constants. Where there are missing terms, we must write 0's:

$$2x - y + 4z = -3,$$
$$x \qquad - 4z = 5,$$
$$6x - y + 2z = 10$$

$$\begin{bmatrix} 2 & -1 & 4 & | & -3 \\ 1 & 0 & -4 & | & 5 \\ 6 & -1 & 2 & | & 10 \end{bmatrix}.$$

Note that the x-coefficients are in column 1, the y-coefficients in column 2, the z-coefficients in column 3, and the constant terms in the last column.

Our goal is to transform the matrix to one of the form

$$ax + by + cz = d,$$
$$ey + fz = g,$$
$$hz = i$$

$$\begin{bmatrix} a & b & c & | & d \\ 0 & e & f & | & g \\ 0 & 0 & h & | & i \end{bmatrix}.$$

This matrix is in a form called *row-echelon form.*

A matrix of this form can be rewritten as a system of equations that is equivalent to the original system, and from which a solution can be easily found.

The first step is to multiply and/or interchange the rows so that each number in the first column is a multiple of the first number in the first row. In this case, we do so by interchanging Rows 1 and 2:

$$\begin{aligned} x \quad\;\; - 4z &= 5, \\ 2x - y + 4z &= -3, \\ 6x - y + 2z &= 10 \end{aligned}$$

$$\left[\begin{array}{ccc|c} 1 & 0 & -4 & 5 \\ 2 & -1 & 4 & -3 \\ 6 & -1 & 2 & 10 \end{array}\right].$$

This corresponds to interchanging the first two equations.

Next, we multiply the first row by -2, add it to the second row, and replace Row 2 with the result:

$$\begin{aligned} x \quad\;\; - 4z &= 5, \\ -y + 12z &= -13, \\ 6x - y + 2z &= 10 \end{aligned}$$

$$\left[\begin{array}{ccc|c} 1 & 0 & -4 & 5 \\ 0 & -1 & 12 & -13 \\ 6 & -1 & 2 & 10 \end{array}\right].$$

$-2(1 \;\; 0 \;\; -4 \mid 5) = (-2 \;\; 0 \;\; 8 \mid -10)$ and $(-2 \;\; 0 \;\; 8 \mid -10) + (2 \;\; -1 \;\; 4 \mid -3) = (0 \;\; -1 \;\; 12 \mid -13)$

Now we multiply the first row by -6, add it to the third row, and replace Row 3 with the result:

$$\begin{aligned} x \quad\;\; - 4z &= 5, \\ -y + 12z &= -13, \\ -y + 26z &= -20 \end{aligned}$$

$$\left[\begin{array}{ccc|c} 1 & 0 & -4 & 5 \\ 0 & -1 & 12 & -13 \\ 0 & -1 & 26 & -20 \end{array}\right].$$

$-6(1 \;\; 0 \;\; -4 \mid 5) = (-6 \;\; 0 \;\; 24 \mid -30)$ and $(-6 \;\; 0 \;\; 24 \mid -30) + (6 \;\; -1 \;\; 2 \mid 10) = (0 \;\; -1 \;\; 26 \mid -20)$

Next, we multiply Row 2 by -1, add it to the third row, and replace Row 3 with the result:

$$\begin{aligned} x \quad\;\; - 4z &= 5, \\ -y + 12z &= -13, \\ 14z &= -7 \end{aligned}$$

$$\left[\begin{array}{ccc|c} 1 & 0 & -4 & 5 \\ 0 & -1 & 12 & -13 \\ 0 & 0 & 14 & -7 \end{array}\right].$$

$-1(0 \;\; -1 \;\; 12 \mid -13) = (0 \;\; 1 \;\; -12 \mid 13)$ and $(0 \;\; 1 \;\; -12 \mid 13) + (0 \;\; -1 \;\; 26 \mid -20) = (0 \;\; 0 \;\; 14 \mid -7)$

Reinserting the variables gives us

$$\begin{aligned} x \quad\;\; - 4z &= 5, \\ -y + 12z &= -13, \\ 14z &= -7. \end{aligned}$$

We now solve this last equation for z and get $z = -\frac{1}{2}$. Next, we substitute $-\frac{1}{2}$ for z in the preceding equation and solve for y: $-y + 12\left(-\frac{1}{2}\right) = -13$, so $y = 7$. Since there is no y-term in the first equation of this last system, we need only substitute $-\frac{1}{2}$ for z to solve for x: $x - 4\left(-\frac{1}{2}\right) = 5$, so $x = 3$. The solution is $\left(3, 7, -\frac{1}{2}\right)$. The check is left to the student.

Try Exercise 13.

The operations used in the preceding example correspond to those used to produce equivalent systems of equations. We call the matrices **row-equivalent** and the operations that produce them **row-equivalent operations.**

ROW-EQUIVALENT OPERATIONS

Student Notes

Note that row-equivalent matrices are not *equal*. It is the solutions of the corresponding equations that are the same.

Row-Equivalent Operations

Each of the following row-equivalent operations produces a row-equivalent matrix:

a) Interchanging any two rows.
b) Multiplying all elements of a row by a nonzero constant.
c) Replacing a row with the sum of that row and a multiple of another row.

The best overall method for solving systems of equations is by row-equivalent matrices; even computers are programmed to use them. Matrices are part of a branch of mathematics known as linear algebra. They are also studied in many courses in finite mathematics.

We can continue to use row-equivalent operations to write a row-equivalent matrix in **reduced row-echelon form,** from which the solution of the system can often be read directly.

Reduced Row-Echelon Form

A matrix is in reduced row-echelon form if:

1. All rows consisting entirely of zeros are at the bottom of the matrix.
2. The first nonzero number in any nonzero row is 1, called a leading 1.
3. The leading 1 in any row is farther to the left than the leading 1 in any lower row.
4. Each column that contains a leading 1 has zeros everywhere else.

EXAMPLE 3 Solve the system

$$5x - 4y = -1,$$
$$-2x + 3y = 2$$

by writing a reduced row-echelon matrix.

SOLUTION We began this solution in Example 1, and used row-equivalent operations to write the row-equivalent matrix:

$$5x - 4y = -1,$$
$$7y = 8$$

$$\begin{bmatrix} 5 & -4 & | & -1 \\ 0 & 7 & | & 8 \end{bmatrix}.$$

Before we can write reduced row-echelon form, the first nonzero number in any nonzero row must be 1. We multiply Row 1 by $\frac{1}{5}$ and Row 2 by $\frac{1}{7}$:

$$x - \frac{4}{5}y = -\frac{1}{5},$$
$$y = \frac{8}{7}$$

$$\begin{bmatrix} 1 & -\frac{4}{5} & | & -\frac{1}{5} \\ 0 & 1 & | & \frac{8}{7} \end{bmatrix}.$$

New Row 1 = $\frac{1}{5}$(Row 1 from above)
New Row 2 = $\frac{1}{7}$(Row 2 from above)

There are no zero rows, there is a leading 1 in each row, and the leading 1 in Row 1 is farther to the left than the leading 1 in Row 2. Thus conditions (1)−(3) for reduced row-echelon form have been met.

To satisfy condition (4), we must obtain a 0 in Row 1, Column 2, above the leading 1 in Row 2. We multiply Row 2 by $\frac{4}{5}$ and add it to Row 1:

$$x = \frac{5}{7},$$
$$y = \frac{8}{7}$$

$$\begin{bmatrix} 1 & 0 & | & \frac{5}{7} \\ 0 & 1 & | & \frac{8}{7} \end{bmatrix}.$$

$$\frac{4}{5}\left(0 \quad 1 \; | \; \frac{8}{7}\right) = \left(0 \quad \frac{4}{5} \; | \; \frac{32}{35}\right) \text{ and}$$
$$\left(0 \quad \frac{4}{5} \; | \; \frac{32}{35}\right) + \left(1 \quad -\frac{4}{5} \; | \; -\frac{1}{5}\right) = \left(1 \quad 0 \; | \; \frac{5}{7}\right)$$

New Row 1 = $\frac{4}{5}$(Row 2) + Row 1

This matrix is in reduced row-echelon form. If we reinsert the variables, we have

$$x = \frac{5}{7},$$
$$y = \frac{8}{7}.$$

The solution, $\left(\frac{5}{7}, \frac{8}{7}\right)$, can be read directly from the last column of the matrix.

 Try Exercise 11.

Finding reduced row-echelon form often involves extensive calculations with fractions or decimals. Thus it is common to use a computer or a graphing calculator to store and manipulate matrices.

Matrix Operations

On many graphing calculators, matrix operations are accessed by pressing ⟨MATRIX⟩, often the 2nd feature associated with ⟨x⁻¹⟩. The MATRIX menu has three submenus: NAMES, MATH, and EDIT.

The EDIT menu allows matrices to be entered. For example, to enter

$$A = \begin{bmatrix} 1 & 2 & 5 \\ -3 & 0 & 4 \end{bmatrix},$$

choose option [A] from the MATRIX EDIT menu. Enter the **dimensions,** or number of rows and columns, of the matrix first, listing the number of rows before the number of columns. Thus the dimensions of A are 2×3, read "2 by 3." Then enter each element of A by pressing the number and ⟨ENTER⟩. The notation $2, 3 = 4$ indicates that the 3rd entry of the 2nd row is 4. Matrices are generally entered row by row rather than column by column.

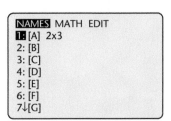

After entering the matrix, exit the matrix editor by pressing ⟨2ND⟩ ⟨QUIT⟩. To access a matrix once it has been entered, use the MATRIX NAMES submenu as shown above on the right. The brackets around A indicate that it is a matrix.

The submenu MATRIX MATH lists operations that can be performed on matrices.

Your Turn

1. Enter the matrix corresponding to the system in Example 1.

   a) Press ⟨MATRIX⟩ ⟨▷⟩ ⟨▷⟩ ⟨ENTER⟩ to choose matrix A from the EDIT menu.

   b) Press ⟨2⟩ ⟨ENTER⟩ ⟨3⟩ ⟨ENTER⟩ to enter the dimensions of the matrix.

   c) Type each of the numbers in Row 1, pressing ⟨ENTER⟩ after each number. Then do the same for Row 2. Press ⟨QUIT⟩.

2. Now find the reduced row-echelon form of the matrix.

   a) Press ⟨MATRIX⟩ ⟨▷⟩ to move to the MATRIX MATH menu. Scroll down the menu to the RREF(option and press ⟨ENTER⟩.

   b) Press ⟨MATRIX⟩ ⟨ENTER⟩ ⟨)⟩ to choose matrix A and close parentheses.

   c) Press ⟨MATH⟩ ⟨1⟩ ⟨ENTER⟩ to convert entries to fraction notation. You should see the same matrix that appears near the end of Example 3.

EXAMPLE 4   Solve the following system using a graphing calculator:

$$2x + 5y - 8z = 7,$$
$$3x + 4y - 3z = 8,$$
$$5y - 2x = 9.$$

SOLUTION   Before writing a matrix to represent this system, we rewrite the third equation in the form $ax + by + cz = d$:

$$2x + 5y - 8z = 7,$$
$$3x + 4y - 3z = 8,$$
$$-2x + 5y + 0z = 9.$$

The following matrix represents this system:

$$\begin{bmatrix} 2 & 5 & -8 & 7 \\ 3 & 4 & -3 & 8 \\ -2 & 5 & 0 & 9 \end{bmatrix}.$$

[A]

[[2 5 -8 7]
[3 4 -3 8]
[-2 5 0 9]]

We enter the matrix as A using the MATRIX EDIT menu, noting that its dimensions are 3×4. Once we have entered each element of the matrix, we return to the home screen to perform operations. The contents of matrix A can be displayed on the screen, using the MATRIX NAMES menu.

Each of the row-equivalent operations can be performed using the MATRIX MATH menu, or we can go directly to the reduced row-echelon form. To find this form, from the home screen, we choose the RREF option from the MATRIX MATH menu and then choose [A] from the MATRIX NAMES menu. We press **MATH** **1** **ENTER** to write the entries in the reduced row-echelon form using fraction notation.

rref ([A])▶Frac
 [[1 0 0 1/2]
 [0 1 0 2]
 [0 0 1 1/2]]

$$\begin{bmatrix} 1 & 0 & 0 & \frac{1}{2} \\ 0 & 1 & 0 & 2 \\ 0 & 0 & 1 & \frac{1}{2} \end{bmatrix}.$$

The reduced row-echelon form shown above is equivalent to the system of equations

$$x = \tfrac{1}{2},$$
$$y = 2,$$
$$z = \tfrac{1}{2}.$$

The solution of the system is thus $\left(\frac{1}{2}, 2, \frac{1}{2}\right)$, which can be read directly from the last column of the reduced row-echelon matrix.

Try Exercise 17.

Recall that some systems of equations are inconsistent, and some sets of equations are dependent. When these cases occur, the reduced row-echelon form of the corresponding matrix will have a row or a column of zeros. For example, the matrix

$$\begin{bmatrix} 1 & 0 & 4 \\ 0 & 0 & 0 \end{bmatrix}$$

is in reduced row-echelon form. The second row translates to the equation $0 = 0$, and indicates that the equations in the system are dependent. The second row of the matrix

$$\begin{bmatrix} 1 & 0 & 4 \\ 0 & 0 & 6 \end{bmatrix}$$

translates to the equation $0 = 6$. This system is inconsistent.

11.3 Exercise Set

Concept Reinforcement *Complete each of the following statements.*

1. A(n) _____ is a rectangular array of numbers.

2. The rows of a matrix are _____ and the _____ are vertical.

3. Each number in a matrix is called a(n) _____ or element.

4. The plural of the word matrix is _____.

5. As part of solving a system using matrices, we can interchange any two _____.

6. In the final step of solving a system of equations, the leftmost column has zeros in all rows except the _____ one.

Solve using matrices.

7. $x + 2y = 11,$
   $3x - y = 5$

8. $x + 3y = 16,$
   $6x + y = 11$

9. $x + 4y = 8,$
   $3x + 5y = 3$

10. $x + 4y = 5,$
    $-3x + 2y = 13$

11. $6x - 2y = 4,$
    $7x + y = 13$

12. $3x + 4y = 7,$
    $-5x + 2y = 10$

13. $3x + 2y + 2z = 3,$
    $x + 2y - z = 5,$
    $2x - 4y + z = 0$

14. $4x - y - 3z = 19,$
    $8x + y - z = 11,$
    $2x + y + 2z = -7$

15. $a - 2b - 3c = 3,$
    $2a - b - 2c = 4,$
    $4a + 5b + 6c = 4$

16. $x + 2y - 3z = 9,$
    $2x - y + 2z = -8,$
    $3x - y - 4z = 3$

17. $3u + 2w = 11,$
    $v - 7w = 4,$
    $u - 6v = 1$

18. $4a + 9b = 8,$
    $8a + 6c = -1,$
    $6b + 6c = -1$

19. $2x + 2y - 2z - 2w = -10,$
    $w + y + z + x = -5,$
    $x - y + 4z + 3w = -2,$
    $w - 2y + 2z + 3x = -6$

20. $-w - 3y + z + 2x = -8,$
    $x + y - z - w = -4,$
    $w + y + z + x = 22,$
    $x - y - z - w = -14$

Solve using matrices.

21. *Coin Value.* A collection of 42 coins consists of dimes and nickels. The total value is $3.00. How many dimes and how many nickels are there?

22. *Coin Value.* A collection of 43 coins consists of dimes and quarters. The total value is $7.60. How many dimes and how many quarters are there?

23. *Snack Mix.* Bree sells a dried-fruit mixture for $5.80 per pound and Hawaiian macadamia nuts for $14.75 per pound. She wants to blend the two to get a 15-lb mixture that she will sell for $9.38 per pound. How much of each should she use?

24. *Mixing Paint.* Higher quality paint typically contains more solids. Grant has available paint that contains 45% solids and paint that contains 25% solids. How much of each should he use to create 20 gal of paint that contains 39% solids?

25. *Investments.* Elena receives $212 per year in simple interest from three investments totaling $2500. Part is invested at 7%, part at 8%, and part at 9%. There is $1100 more invested at 9% than at 8%. Find the amount invested at each rate.

26. *Investments.* Alejandro receives $306 per year in simple interest from three investments totaling $3200. Part is invested at 8%, part at 9%, and part at 10%. There is $1900 more invested at 10% than at 9%. Find the amount invested at each rate.

TW 27. Explain how you can recognize dependent equations when solving with matrices.

TW 28. Explain how you can recognize an inconsistent system when solving with matrices.

SKILL REVIEW

To prepare for Section 11.4, review order of operations.
Simplify.

29. $5(-3) - (-7)4$

30. $8(-5) - (-2)9$

31. $-2(5 \cdot 3 - 4 \cdot 6) - 3(2 \cdot 7 - 15) + 4(3 \cdot 8 - 5 \cdot 4)$

32. $6(2 \cdot 7 - 3(-4)) - 4(3(-8) - 10) + 5(4 \cdot 3 - (-2)7)$

SYNTHESIS

TW **33.** If the systems corresponding to the matrices

$$\begin{bmatrix} a_1 & b_1 & c_1 \\ d_1 & e_1 & f_1 \end{bmatrix} \text{ and } \begin{bmatrix} a_2 & b_2 & c_2 \\ d_2 & e_2 & f_2 \end{bmatrix}$$

share the same solution, does it follow that the corresponding entries are all equal to each other ($a_1 = a_2, b_1 = b_2$, etc.)? Why or why not?

TW **34.** Explain how the row-equivalent operations make use of the addition, multiplication, and distributive properties.

35. The sum of the digits in a four-digit number is 10. Twice the sum of the thousands digit and the tens digit is 1 less than the sum of the other two digits. The tens digit is twice the thousands digit. The ones digit equals the sum of the thousands digit and the hundreds digit. Find the four-digit number.

36. Solve for x and y:

$$ax + by = c,$$
$$dx + ey = f.$$

Try Exercise Answers: Section 11.3

7. $(3, 4)$ **11.** $\left(\frac{3}{2}, \frac{5}{2}\right)$ **13.** $\left(2, \frac{1}{2}, -2\right)$ **17.** $\left(4, \frac{1}{2}, -\frac{1}{2}\right)$

Mid-Chapter Review

We solve systems of three or more equations using elimination. This process leads to the use of matrices and, eventually, computers for solving systems.

GUIDED SOLUTIONS

1. Solve:

$$x - y + z = 4, \quad (1)$$
$$x + y - 2z = 3, \quad (2)$$
$$2x - y - z = 9. \quad (3) \ [11.1]$$

Solution

$$x - y + z = 4$$
$$\underline{x + y - 2z = 3}$$
$$\boxed{} = \boxed{} \qquad \text{Adding equations (1) and (2) to eliminate } y$$

$$x + y - 2z = 3$$
$$\underline{2x - y - z = 9}$$
$$\boxed{} = \boxed{} \qquad \text{Adding equations (2) and (3) to again eliminate } y$$

$$\left.\begin{array}{l} 2x - z = 7 \\ 3x - 3z = 12 \end{array}\right\} \quad \text{Solving the resulting system of two equations in } x \text{ and } z$$

$$x = \boxed{}, z = \boxed{}$$

$$x + y - 2z = 3$$
$$\boxed{} + y - 2\boxed{} = 3$$
$$y = \boxed{} \qquad \text{Solving for } y$$

The solution is $\left(\boxed{}, \boxed{}, \boxed{}\right)$.

2. Solve using matrices:

$$2x + 3y = 6,$$
$$4x - 5y = 1. \ [11.3]$$

Solution

$$2x + 3y = 6 \qquad \text{Rewriting with the variables}$$
$$- 11y = \boxed{}$$

$$y = \boxed{} \qquad \text{Solving for } y$$

$$2x + 3\boxed{} = 6$$

$$x = \boxed{} \qquad \text{Solving for } x$$

The solution is $\left(\boxed{}, \boxed{}\right)$.

MIXED REVIEW

Solve.

1. $x + 2y + z = 4,$
   $2x - y - z = 1,$
   $x - 2y + z = 8$

2. $x + 2y - z = 3,$
   $x - y + z = -7,$
   $2x + 3y - z = 2$

3. $5a - 2b - c = 0,$
   $3a + 4b + c = 8,$
   $9a - 6b - 2c = -1$

4. $2u + v - w = 3,$
   $u + 5v + 2w = 2,$
   $2u - v - w = 4$

5. $y + 3z = 2,$
   $x - 2z = 4,$
   $2x - y = 0$

6. $2x - z = 1,$
   $x - 2y + 3z = 2,$
   $x + 2y - 4z = -2$

Solve using matrices.

7. $2x + 4y = -1,$
   $x + 3y = 2$

8. $4x - y = 5,$
   $2x + 3y = -1$

9. $2x + y + 2z = 5,$
   $x + 2y + 4z = 6,$
   $2x + 3y + 5z = 8$

10. $-2a + 8b + c = -2,$
    $4a - 2b - 6c = 1,$
    $2a - b - c = 2$

Solve.

11. The sum of three numbers is 15. The first number minus twice the second is twice the third. The first minus the second plus the third is 19. Find the numbers.

12. In triangle ABC, the measure of angle B is twice that of angle A. The measure of angle C is 40° more than that of angle B. Find the angle measures.

13. The Golden Eagles sell a brownie for 75¢, a bag of chips for $1.00, and a hot dog for $2.00 at their concession stand. At the last game, they sold a total of 125 items and took in $163.75. The number of hot dogs sold was 25 less than the total number of brownies and bags of chips. How many of each did they sell?

14. Christie owes $10,300 on three credit cards. On one card the monthly interest rate is 2%, on the second it is 1%, and on the third it is 1.5%. The total interest due one month was $151. She owes $3300 more on the 2% card and the 1.5% card, combined, than she does on the 1% card. How much does she owe on each card?

11.4 Determinants and Cramer's Rule

- Determinants of
  2 × 2 Matrices

- Cramer's Rule:
  2 × 2 Systems

- Cramer's Rule:
  3 × 3 Systems

DETERMINANTS OF 2 × 2 MATRICES

When a matrix has m rows and n columns, it is called an "m by n" matrix. Thus its *dimensions* are denoted by $m \times n$. If a matrix has the same number of rows and columns, it is called a **square matrix**. Associated with every square matrix is a number called its **determinant**, defined as follows for 2 × 2 matrices.

2 × 2 Determinants

The determinant of a two-by-two matrix $\begin{bmatrix} a & c \\ b & d \end{bmatrix}$ is denoted $\begin{vmatrix} a & c \\ b & d \end{vmatrix}$ and is defined as follows:

$$\begin{vmatrix} a & c \\ b & d \end{vmatrix} = ad - bc.$$

STUDY TIP

Catch the Emphasis

Pay attention to phrases from instructors such as "Write this down" and "You will need to know this." Most instructors will place special emphasis on the material they feel is important, and this is the material most likely to appear on a test.

EXAMPLE 1 Evaluate: $\begin{vmatrix} 2 & -5 \\ 6 & 7 \end{vmatrix}$.

SOLUTION We multiply and subtract as follows:

 $\begin{vmatrix} 2 & -5 \\ 6 & 7 \end{vmatrix} = 2 \cdot 7 - 6 \cdot (-5) = 14 + 30 = 44.$

Try Exercise 7.

CRAMER'S RULE: 2 × 2 SYSTEMS

One of the many uses for determinants is in solving systems of linear equations in which the number of variables is the same as the number of equations and the constants are not all 0. Let's consider a system of two equations:

$$a_1x + b_1y = c_1,$$
$$a_2x + b_2y = c_2.$$

If we use the elimination method, a series of steps can show that

$$x = \frac{c_1b_2 - c_2b_1}{a_1b_2 - a_2b_1} \quad \text{and} \quad y = \frac{a_1c_2 - a_2c_1}{a_1b_2 - a_2b_1}.$$

These fractions can be rewritten using determinants.

Cramer's Rule: 2 × 2 Systems

The solution of the system

$$a_1x + b_1y = c_1,$$
$$a_2x + b_2y = c_2,$$

if it is unique, is given by

$$x = \frac{\begin{vmatrix} c_1 & b_1 \\ c_2 & b_2 \end{vmatrix}}{\begin{vmatrix} a_1 & b_1 \\ a_2 & b_2 \end{vmatrix}}, \qquad y = \frac{\begin{vmatrix} a_1 & c_1 \\ a_2 & c_2 \end{vmatrix}}{\begin{vmatrix} a_1 & b_1 \\ a_2 & b_2 \end{vmatrix}}.$$

These formulas apply only if the denominator is not 0. If the denominator *is* 0, then one of two things happens:

1. If the denominator is 0 and the numerators are also 0, then the equations in the system are dependent.
2. If the denominator is 0 and at least one numerator is not 0, then the system is inconsistent.

To use Cramer's rule, we find the determinants and compute x and y as shown above. Note that the denominators are identical and the coefficients of x and y appear in the same position as in the original equations. In the numerator of x, the constants c_1 and c_2 replace a_1 and a_2. In the numerator of y, the constants c_1 and c_2 replace b_1 and b_2.

EXAMPLE 2   Solve using Cramer's rule:

$$2x + 5y = 7,$$
$$5x - 2y = -3.$$

SOLUTION   We have

$$x = \frac{\begin{vmatrix} 7 & 5 \\ -3 & -2 \end{vmatrix}}{\begin{vmatrix} 2 & 5 \\ 5 & -2 \end{vmatrix}}$$

← The constants $\begin{matrix} 7 \\ -3 \end{matrix}$ form the first column.

← The columns are the coefficients of the variables.

$$= \frac{7(-2) - (-3)5}{2(-2) - 5 \cdot 5} = -\frac{1}{29}$$

and

$$y = \frac{\begin{vmatrix} 2 & 7 \\ 5 & -3 \end{vmatrix}}{\begin{vmatrix} 2 & 5 \\ 5 & -2 \end{vmatrix}}$$

← The constants $\begin{matrix} 7 \\ -3 \end{matrix}$ form the second column.

← The denominator is the same as in the expression for x.

$$= \frac{2(-3) - 5 \cdot 7}{-29} = \frac{41}{29}.$$

The solution is $\left(-\frac{1}{29}, \frac{41}{29}\right)$. The check is left to the student.

■ Try Exercise 15.

CRAMER'S RULE: 3 × 3 SYSTEMS

Cramer's rule can be extended for systems of three linear equations. However, before doing so, we must define what a 3 × 3 determinant is.

3 × 3 Determinants   The determinant of a three-by-three matrix is defined as follows:

Subtract.   Add.

$$\begin{vmatrix} a_1 & b_1 & c_1 \\ a_2 & b_2 & c_2 \\ a_3 & b_3 & c_3 \end{vmatrix} = a_1 \begin{vmatrix} b_2 & c_2 \\ b_3 & c_3 \end{vmatrix} - a_2 \begin{vmatrix} b_1 & c_1 \\ b_3 & c_3 \end{vmatrix} + a_3 \begin{vmatrix} b_1 & c_1 \\ b_2 & c_2 \end{vmatrix}.$$

Student Notes

Cramer's rule and the evaluation of determinants rely on patterns. Recognizing and remembering the patterns will help you understand and use the definitions.

Note that the a's come from the first column. Note too that the 2 × 2 determinants above can be obtained by crossing out the row and the column in which the a occurs.

For a_1:   For a_2:   For a_3:

$$\begin{vmatrix} a_1 & b_1 & c_1 \\ a_2 & b_2 & c_2 \\ a_3 & b_3 & c_3 \end{vmatrix}$$

$$\begin{vmatrix} a_1 & b_1 & c_1 \\ a_2 & b_2 & c_2 \\ a_3 & b_3 & c_3 \end{vmatrix}$$

$$\begin{vmatrix} a_1 & b_1 & c_1 \\ a_2 & b_2 & c_2 \\ a_3 & b_3 & c_3 \end{vmatrix}$$

EXAMPLE 3   Evaluate:

$$\begin{vmatrix} -1 & 0 & 1 \\ -5 & 1 & -1 \\ 4 & 8 & 1 \end{vmatrix}.$$

SOLUTION   We have

Subtract.   Add.

$$\begin{vmatrix} -1 & 0 & 1 \\ -5 & 1 & -1 \\ 4 & 8 & 1 \end{vmatrix} = -1\begin{vmatrix} 1 & -1 \\ 8 & 1 \end{vmatrix} - (-5)\begin{vmatrix} 0 & 1 \\ 8 & 1 \end{vmatrix} + 4\begin{vmatrix} 0 & 1 \\ 1 & -1 \end{vmatrix}$$

$$= -1(1 + 8) + 5(0 - 8) + 4(0 - 1) \qquad \text{Evaluating the three determinants}$$

$$= -9 - 40 - 4 = -53.$$

Try Exercise 11.

Cramer's Rule: 3 × 3 Systems   The solution of the system

$$a_1x + b_1y + c_1z = d_1,$$
$$a_2x + b_2y + c_2z = d_2,$$
$$a_3x + b_3y + c_3z = d_3$$

can be found using the following determinants:

$$D = \begin{vmatrix} a_1 & b_1 & c_1 \\ a_2 & b_2 & c_2 \\ a_3 & b_3 & c_3 \end{vmatrix}, \qquad D_x = \begin{vmatrix} d_1 & b_1 & c_1 \\ d_2 & b_2 & c_2 \\ d_3 & b_3 & c_3 \end{vmatrix},$$

$$D_y = \begin{vmatrix} a_1 & d_1 & c_1 \\ a_2 & d_2 & c_2 \\ a_3 & d_3 & c_3 \end{vmatrix}, \qquad D_z = \begin{vmatrix} a_1 & b_1 & d_1 \\ a_2 & b_2 & d_2 \\ a_3 & b_3 & d_3 \end{vmatrix}.$$

D contains only coefficients.
In D_x, the d's replace the a's.
In D_y, the d's replace the b's.
In D_z, the d's replace the c's.

If a unique solution exists, it is given by

$$x = \frac{D_x}{D}, \qquad y = \frac{D_y}{D}, \qquad z = \frac{D_z}{D}.$$

EXAMPLE 4   Solve using Cramer's rule:

$$x - 3y + 7z = 13,$$
$$x + y + z = 1,$$
$$x - 2y + 3z = 4.$$

SOLUTION   We compute D, D_x, D_y, and D_z:

$$D = \begin{vmatrix} 1 & -3 & 7 \\ 1 & 1 & 1 \\ 1 & -2 & 3 \end{vmatrix} = -10; \qquad D_x = \begin{vmatrix} 13 & -3 & 7 \\ 1 & 1 & 1 \\ 4 & -2 & 3 \end{vmatrix} = 20;$$

$$D_y = \begin{vmatrix} 1 & 13 & 7 \\ 1 & 1 & 1 \\ 1 & 4 & 3 \end{vmatrix} = -6; \qquad D_z = \begin{vmatrix} 1 & -3 & 13 \\ 1 & 1 & 1 \\ 1 & -2 & 4 \end{vmatrix} = -24.$$

Then

$$x = \frac{D_x}{D} = \frac{20}{-10} = -2;$$

$$y = \frac{D_y}{D} = \frac{-6}{-10} = \frac{3}{5};$$

$$z = \frac{D_z}{D} = \frac{-24}{-10} = \frac{12}{5}.$$

The solution is $\left(-2, \frac{3}{5}, \frac{12}{5}\right)$. The check is left to the student.

 Try Exercise 19.

In Example 4, we need not have evaluated D_z. Once x and y were found, we could have substituted them into one of the equations to find z.

To use Cramer's rule, we divide by D, provided $D \neq 0$. If $D = 0$ and at least one of the other determinants is not 0, then the system is inconsistent. If *all* the determinants are 0, then the equations in the system are dependent.

—— Determinants

Determinants can be evaluated using the DET(option of the MATRIX MATH menu. After entering the matrix, we go to the home screen and select the determinant operation. Then we enter the name of the matrix using the MATRIX NAMES menu. The graphing calculator will return the value of the determinant of the matrix. For example, if

$$\mathbf{A} = \begin{bmatrix} 1 & 6 & -1 \\ -3 & -5 & 3 \\ 0 & 4 & 2 \end{bmatrix},$$

we have

```
det([A])
              26
```
.

Your Turn

1. Enter the matrix $\begin{bmatrix} 1 & -3 \\ 4 & -2 \end{bmatrix}$ as matrix A.

2. From the home screen, press MATRIX ▷ 1   MATRIX 1) ENTER .
    $\det([A]) = 10$

11.4 Exercise Set

↪ *Concept Reinforcement Classify each of the following statements as either true or false.*

1. A square matrix has the same number of rows and columns.

2. A 3×4 matrix has 3 rows and 4 columns.

3. A determinant is a number.

4. Cramer's rule exists only for 2×2 systems.

5. Whenever Cramer's rule yields a denominator that is 0, the system has no solution.

6. Whenever Cramer's rule yields a numerator that is 0, the equations are dependent.

Evaluate.

7. $\begin{vmatrix} 5 & 1 \\ 2 & 4 \end{vmatrix}$

8. $\begin{vmatrix} 3 & 2 \\ 2 & -3 \end{vmatrix}$

9. $\begin{vmatrix} 10 & 8 \\ -5 & -9 \end{vmatrix}$

10. $\begin{vmatrix} 3 & 2 \\ -7 & 5 \end{vmatrix}$

11. $\begin{vmatrix} 1 & 4 & 0 \\ 0 & -1 & 2 \\ 3 & -2 & 1 \end{vmatrix}$

12. $\begin{vmatrix} 2 & 4 & -2 \\ 1 & 0 & 2 \\ 0 & 1 & 3 \end{vmatrix}$

13. $\begin{vmatrix} -4 & -2 & 3 \\ -3 & 1 & 2 \\ 3 & 4 & -2 \end{vmatrix}$

14. $\begin{vmatrix} 2 & -1 & 1 \\ 1 & 2 & -1 \\ 3 & 4 & -3 \end{vmatrix}$

Solve using Cramer's rule.

15. $5x + 8y = 1,$
    $3x + 7y = 5$

16. $3x - 4y = 6,$
    $5x + 9y = 10$

17. $5x - 4y = -3,$
    $7x + 2y = 6$

18. $-2x + 4y = 3,$
    $3x - 7y = 1$

19. $3x - y + 2z = 1,$
    $x - y + 2z = 3,$
    $-2x + 3y + z = 1$

20. $3x + 2y - z = 4,$
    $3x - 2y + z = 5,$
    $4x - 5y - z = -1$

21. $2x - 3y + 5z = 27,$
    $x + 2y - z = -4,$
    $5x - y + 4z = 27$

22. $x - y + 2z = -3,$
    $x + 2y + 3z = 4,$
    $2x + y + z = -3$

23. $r - 2s + 3t = 6,$
    $2r - s - t = -3,$
    $r + s + t = 6$

24. $a - 3c = 6,$
    $b + 2c = 2,$
    $7a - 3b - 5c = 14$

TW **25.** Describe at least one of the patterns in Cramer's rule.

TW **26.** Which version of Cramer's rule do you find more useful: the version for 2×2 systems or the version for 3×3 systems? Why?

SKILL REVIEW

To prepare for Section 11.5, review functions.
Find each of the following, given $f(x) = 80x + 2500$ and $g(x) = 150x$.

27. $f(90)$

28. $(g - f)(x)$

29. $(g - f)(10)$

30. $(g - f)(100)$

31. All values of x for which $f(x) = g(x)$

32. All values of x for which $(g - f)(x) = 0$

SYNTHESIS

TW **33.** Cramer's rule states that if $a_1x + b_1y = c_1$ and $a_2x + b_2y = c_2$ are dependent, then
$$\begin{vmatrix} a_1 & b_1 \\ a_2 & b_2 \end{vmatrix} = 0.$$
Explain why this will always happen.

TW **34.** Under what conditions can a 3×3 system of linear equations be consistent but unable to be solved using Cramer's rule?

Solve.

35. $\begin{vmatrix} y & -2 \\ 4 & 3 \end{vmatrix} = 44$

36. $\begin{vmatrix} 2 & x & -1 \\ -1 & 3 & 2 \\ -2 & 1 & 1 \end{vmatrix} = -12$

37. $\begin{vmatrix} m+1 & -2 \\ m-2 & 1 \end{vmatrix} = 27$

38. Show that an equation of the line through (x_1, y_1) and (x_2, y_2) can be written
$$\begin{vmatrix} x & y & 1 \\ x_1 & y_1 & 1 \\ x_2 & y_2 & 1 \end{vmatrix} = 0.$$

▨ Try Exercise Answers: Section 11.4

7. 18   **11.** 27   **15.** $(-3, 2)$ **19.** $\left(-1, -\frac{6}{7}, \frac{11}{7}\right)$

11.5   Business and Economics Applications

- Break-Even Analysis

- Supply and Demand

CAUTION!   Do not confuse "cost" with "price." When we discuss the *cost* of an item, we are referring to what it costs to produce the item. The *price* of an item is what a consumer pays to purchase the item and is used when calculating revenue.

BREAK-EVEN ANALYSIS

The money that a business spends to manufacture a product is its *cost*. The **total cost** of production can be thought of as a function C, where $C(x)$ is the cost of producing x units. When the company sells the product, it takes in money. This is *revenue* and can be thought of as a function R, where $R(x)$ is the **total revenue** from the sale of x units. **Total profit** is the money taken in less the money spent, or total revenue minus total cost. Total profit from the production and sale of x units is a function P given by

$$\textbf{Profit} = \textbf{Revenue} - \textbf{Cost} \quad \text{or} \quad P(x) = R(x) - C(x).$$

If $R(x)$ is greater than $C(x)$, there is a gain and $P(x)$ is positive. If $C(x)$ is greater than $R(x)$, there is a loss and $P(x)$ is negative. When $R(x) = C(x)$, the company breaks even.

There are two kinds of costs. First, there are costs like rent, insurance, machinery, and so on. These costs, which must be paid regardless of how many items are produced, are called *fixed costs*. Second, costs for labor, materials, marketing, and so on are called *variable costs*, because they vary according to the amount being produced. The sum of the fixed cost and the variable cost gives the **total cost.**

EXAMPLE 1   Manufacturing Chairs.   Renewable Designs is planning to make a new chair. Fixed costs will be $90,000, and it will cost $150 to produce each chair (variable costs). Each chair sells for $400.

a) Find the total cost $C(x)$ of producing x chairs.

b) Find the total revenue $R(x)$ from the sale of x chairs.

c) Find the total profit $P(x)$ from the production and sale of x chairs.

d) What profit will the company realize from the production and sale of 300 chairs? of 800 chairs?

e) Graph the total-cost, total-revenue, and total-profit functions using the same set of axes. Determine the break-even point.

SOLUTION

a) Total cost, in dollars, is given by

$$C(x) = \text{(Fixed costs) plus (Variable costs)},$$

or $\quad C(x) = \quad 90{,}000 \quad + \quad 150x$

where x is the number of chairs produced.

b) Total revenue, in dollars, is given by

$$R(x) = 400x. \quad \text{\$400 times the number of chairs sold.}$$
We assume that every chair produced is sold.

c) Total profit, in dollars, is given by

$$P(x) = R(x) - C(x) \quad \text{Profit is revenue minus cost.}$$
$$= 400x - (90{,}000 + 150x)$$
$$= 250x - 90{,}000.$$

d) Profits will be

$$P(300) = 250 \cdot 300 - 90{,}000 = -\$15{,}000$$

when 300 chairs are produced and sold, and

$$P(800) = 250 \cdot 800 - 90{,}000 = \$110{,}000$$

when 800 chairs are produced and sold. These values can also be found using a graphing calculator, as shown in the figure at left. Thus the company loses money if only 300 chairs are sold, but makes money if 800 are sold.

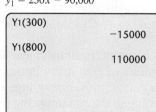

$y_1 = 250x - 90{,}000$

Y₁(300)	
	−15000
Y₁(800)	
	110000

e) The graphs of each of the three functions are shown below:

$$C(x) = 90{,}000 + 150x, \quad \text{This represents the cost function.}$$
$$R(x) = 400x, \quad \text{This represents the revenue function.}$$
$$P(x) = 250x - 90{,}000. \quad \text{This represents the profit function.}$$

$C(x)$, $R(x)$, and $P(x)$ are all in dollars.

The revenue function has a graph that goes through the origin and has a slope of 400. The cost function has an intercept on the \$-axis of 90,000 and has a slope of 150. The profit function has an intercept on the \$-axis of $-90{,}000$ and has a slope of 250. It is shown by the red and black dashed line. The red portion of the dashed line shows a "negative" profit, which is a loss. (That is what is known as "being in the red.") The black portion of the dashed line shows a "positive" profit, or gain. (That is what is known as "being in the black.")

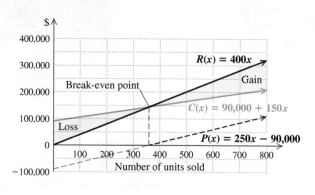

Gains occur where revenue exceeds cost. Losses occur where the revenue is less than cost. The **break-even point** occurs where the graphs of R and C cross. Thus to find the break-even point, we solve a system:

$$R(x) = 400x,$$
$$C(x) = 90,000 + 150x.$$

Since both revenue and cost are in *dollars* and they are equal at the break-even point, the system can be rewritten as

$$d = 400x, \qquad (1)$$
$$d = 90,000 + 150x \qquad (2)$$

and solved using substitution:

$$400x = 90,000 + 150x \qquad \text{Substituting } 400x \text{ for } d \text{ in equation (2)}$$
$$250x = 90,000$$
$$x = 360.$$

The figure at left shows the solution found using a graphing calculator.

The firm will break even if it produces and sells 360 chairs and takes in a total of $R(360) = \$400(360) = \$144,000$ in revenue. Note that the x-coordinate of the break-even point can also be found by solving $P(x) = 0$. The break-even point is (360 chairs, $144,000).

$y_1 = 400x, \quad y_2 = 90,000 + 150x$

Xscl = 100, Yscl = 50,000

📘 Try Exercise 9.

Student Notes

If you plan to study business or economics, expect to see these topics arise in other courses.

SUPPLY AND DEMAND

As the price of coffee varies, so too does the amount sold. The table and graph below show that *consumers will demand less as the price goes up*.

Demand function, D

Price, p, per Kilogram	Quantity, $D(p)$ (in millions of kilograms)
$ 8.00	25
9.00	20
10.00	15
11.00	10
12.00	5

As the price of coffee varies, the amount made available varies as well. The table and graph below show that *sellers will supply more as the price goes up*.

Supply function, S

Price, p, per Kilogram	Quantity, $S(p)$ (in millions of kilograms)
$ 9.00	5
9.50	10
10.00	15
10.50	20
11.00	25

Considering demand and supply together, we see that as price increases, demand decreases. As price increases, supply increases. The point of intersection is called the **equilibrium point.** At that price, the amount that the seller will supply is the same amount that the consumer will buy. The situation is similar to that of a buyer and a seller negotiating the price of an item. The equilibrium point is the price and the quantity that they finally agree on.

Any ordered pair of coordinates from the graph is (price, quantity), because the horizontal axis is the price axis and the vertical axis is the quantity axis. If D is a demand function and S is a supply function, then the equilibrium point is where demand equals supply:

$$D(p) = S(p).$$

EXAMPLE 2   Find the equilibrium point for the demand and supply functions given:

$$D(p) = 1000 - 60p, \quad (1)$$
$$S(p) = 200 + 4p. \quad (2)$$

SOLUTION   Since both demand and supply are *quantities* and they are equal at the equilibrium point, we rewrite the system as

$$q = 1000 - 60p, \quad (1)$$
$$q = 200 + 4p. \quad (2)$$

We substitute $200 + 4p$ for q in equation (1) and solve:

$$200 + 4p = 1000 - 60p \qquad \text{Substituting } 200 + 4p \text{ for } q \text{ in equation (1)}$$
$$200 + 64p = 1000 \qquad \text{Adding } 60p \text{ to both sides}$$
$$64p = 800 \qquad \text{Adding } -200 \text{ to both sides}$$
$$p = \tfrac{800}{64} = 12.5.$$

Thus the equilibrium price is $12.50 per unit.

To find the equilibrium quantity, we substitute $12.50 into either $D(p)$ or $S(p)$. We use $S(p)$:

$$S(12.5) = 200 + 4(12.5) = 200 + 50 = 250.$$

Thus the equilibrium quantity is 250 units, and the equilibrium point is ($12.50, 250). The graph at left confirms the solution.

$y_1 = 1000 - 60x, \quad y_2 = 200 + 4x$

Xscl = 2, Yscl = 50

Try Exercise 19.

A

F

Visualizing for Success

Match each equation, inequality, or set of equations or inequalities with its graph.

1. $y = -2$

2. $y = x^3$

3. $y = x^2$

4. $y = \dfrac{1}{x}$

5. $y = x + 1$

6. $y = |x + 1|$

7. $y \leq x + 1$

8. $y > 2x - 3$

9. $y = x + 1,$
   $y = 2x - 3$

10. $y \leq x + 1,$
    $y > 2x - 3$

Answers on page A-40

An additional, animated version of this activity appears in MyMathLab. To use MyMathLab, you need a course ID and a student access code. Contact your instructor for more information.

B

G

C

H

D

I

E

J

11.5 Exercise Set

↪ *Concept Reinforcement*   *In each of Exercises 1–8, match the word or phrase with the most appropriate choice from the column on the right.*

1. ____ Total cost

2. ____ Total revenue

3. ____ Total profit

4. ____ Fixed costs

5. ____ Variable costs

6. ____ Break-even point

7. ____ Equilibrium point

8. ____ Price

a) The amount of money that a company takes in

b) The sum of fixed costs and variable costs

c) The point at which total revenue equals total cost

d) What consumers pay per item

e) The difference between total revenue and total cost

f) What companies spend whether or not a product is produced

g) The point at which supply equals demand

h) The costs that vary according to the number of items produced

For each of the following pairs of total-cost and total-revenue functions, find (a) *the total-profit function and* (b) *the break-even point.*

9. $C(x) = 45x + 300,000;$
   $R(x) = 65x$

10. $C(x) = 25x + 270,000;$
    $R(x) = 70x$

11. $C(x) = 15x + 3100;$
    $R(x) = 40x$

12. $C(x) = 30x + 49,500;$
    $R(x) = 85x$

13. $C(x) = 40x + 22,500;$
    $R(x) = 85x$

14. $C(x) = 20x + 10,000;$
    $R(x) = 100x$

15. $C(x) = 24x + 50,000;$
    $R(x) = 40x$

16. $C(x) = 40x + 8010;$
    $R(x) = 58x$

Aha! 17. $C(x) = 75x + 100,000;$
    $R(x) = 125x$

18. $C(x) = 20x + 120,000;$
    $R(x) = 50x$

Find the equilibrium point for each of the following pairs of demand and supply functions.

19. $D(p) = 1000 - 10p,$
    $S(p) = 230 + p$

20. $D(p) = 2000 - 60p,$
    $S(p) = 460 + 94p$

21. $D(p) = 760 - 13p,$
    $S(p) = 430 + 2p$

22. $D(p) = 800 - 43p,$
    $S(p) = 210 + 16p$

23. $D(p) = 7500 - 25p,$
    $S(p) = 6000 + 5p$

24. $D(p) = 8800 - 30p,$
    $S(p) = 7000 + 15p$

25. $D(p) = 1600 - 53p,$
    $S(p) = 320 + 75p$

26. $D(p) = 5500 - 40p,$
    $S(p) = 1000 + 85p$

Solve.

27. *Manufacturing MP3 Players.* SoundGen, Inc., is planning to manufacture a new type of MP3 player/cell phone. The fixed costs for production are $45,000. The variable costs for producing each unit are estimated to be $40. The revenue from each unit is to be $130. Find the following.

a) The total cost $C(x)$ of producing x MP3/cell phones

b) The total revenue $R(x)$ from the sale of x MP3/cell phones

c) The total profit $P(x)$ from the production and sale of x MP3/cell phones

d) The profit or loss from the production and sale of 3000 MP3/cell phones; of 400 MP3/cell phones

e) The break-even point

28. *Computer Manufacturing.* Current Electronics is planning to introduce a new laptop computer. The fixed costs for production are $125,300. The variable costs for producing each computer are $450. The revenue from each computer is $800. Find the following.

a) The total cost $C(x)$ of producing x computers
b) The total revenue $R(x)$ from the sale of x computers
c) The total profit $P(x)$ from the production and sale of x computers
d) The profit or loss from the production and sale of 100 computers; of 400 computers
e) The break-even point

29. *Pet Safety.* Christine designed and is now producing a pet car seat. The fixed costs for setting up production are $10,000. The variable costs for producing each seat are $30. The revenue from each seat is to be $80. Find the following.

a) The total cost $C(x)$ of producing x seats
b) The total revenue $R(x)$ from the sale of x seats
c) The total profit $P(x)$ from the production and sale of x seats
d) The profit or loss from the production and sale of 2000 seats; of 50 seats
e) The break-even point

30. *Manufacturing Caps.* Martina's Custom Printing is planning to add painter's caps to its product line. For the first year, the fixed costs for setting up production are $16,404. The variable costs for producing a dozen caps are $6.00. The revenue on each dozen caps will be $18.00. Find the following.

a) The total cost $C(x)$ of producing x dozen caps
b) The total revenue $R(x)$ from the sale of x dozen caps
c) The total profit $P(x)$ from the production and sale of x dozen caps
d) The profit or loss from the production and sale of 3000 dozen caps; of 1000 dozen caps
e) The break-even point

31. *Dog Food Production.* Puppy Love, Inc., will soon begin producing a new line of puppy food. The marketing department predicts that the demand function will be $D(p) = -14.97p + 987.35$ and the supply function will be $S(p) = 98.55p - 5.13$.

a) To the nearest cent, what price per unit should be charged in order to have equilibrium between supply and demand?
b) The production of the puppy food involves $87,985 in fixed costs and $5.15 per unit in variable costs. If the price per unit is the value you found in part (a), how many units must be sold in order to break even?

32. *Computer Production.* Brushstroke Computers is planning a new line of computers, each of which will sell for $970. The fixed costs in setting up production are $1,235,580 and the variable costs for each computer are $697.

a) What is the break-even point? (Round to the nearest whole number.)
b) The marketing department at Brushstroke is not sure that $970 is the best price. Their demand function for the new computers is given by $D(p) = -304.5p + 374,580$ and their supply function is given by $S(p) = 788.7p - 576,504$. What price p would result in equilibrium between supply and demand?
c) If the computers are sold for the equilibrium price found in part (b), what is the break-even point?

33. In Example 1, the slope of the line representing Revenue is the sum of the slopes of the other two lines. This is not a coincidence. Explain why.

34. Variable costs and fixed costs are often compared to the slope and the y-intercept, respectively, of an equation for a line. Explain why you feel this analogy is or is not valid.

SKILL REVIEW

Review function notation and domains of functions (Sections 10.1, and 10.2).

35. If $f(x) = 4x - 7$, find $f(a) + h$.

36. If $f(x) = 4x - 7$, find $f(a + h)$.

Find the domain of f.

37. $f(x) = \dfrac{x - 5}{2x + 1}$
[10.2]

38. $f(x) = \dfrac{3x}{x^2 + 1}$
[10.2]

39. $f(x) = \sqrt{2x + 8}$
[10.1]

40. $f(x) = \dfrac{3x}{x^2 - 1}$
[10.2]

SYNTHESIS

TW **41.** Les claims that since his fixed costs are $3000, he need sell only 10 custom birdbaths at $300 each in order to break even. Does this sound plausible? Why or why not?

TW **42.** In this section, we examined supply and demand functions for coffee. Does it seem realistic to you for the graph of D to have a constant slope? Why or why not?

43. *Yo-yo Production.* Bing Boing Hobbies is willing to produce 100 yo-yo's at $2.00 each and 500 yo-yo's at $8.00 each. Research indicates that the public will buy 500 yo-yo's at $1.00 each and 100 yo-yo's at $9.00 each. Find the equilibrium point.

44. *Loudspeaker Production.* Sonority Speakers, Inc., has fixed costs of $15,400 and variable costs of $100 for each pair of speakers produced. If the speakers sell for $250 per pair, how many pairs of speakers must be produced (and sold) in order to have enough profit to cover the fixed costs of two additional facilities? Assume that all fixed costs are identical.

45. *Peanut Butter.* The table below lists the data for supply and demand of an 18-oz jar of peanut butter at various prices.

Price	Supply (in millions)	Demand (in millions)
$1.59	23.4	22.5
1.29	19.2	24.8
1.69	26.8	22.2
1.19	18.4	29.7
1.99	30.7	19.3

a) Use linear regression to find the supply function $S(p)$ for suppliers of peanut butter at price p.
b) Use linear regression to find the demand function $D(p)$ for consumers of peanut butter at price p.
c) Find the equilibrium point.

46. *Silver.* Because silver is a good conductor of electricity and heat, and is both antimicrobial and antibacterial, it is used in many industrial applications. For instance, silver is used in batteries, toasters, cell phones, flat-screen televisions, ink, and bandages for wounds, in clothing to minimize odor, and in wood to resist mold. Because of such a wide variety of applications, industrial demand for silver is growing, as shown in the table below.

Year	Amount of Silver Used in Industrial Applications (in millions of ounces)
2001	335.2
2002	339.1
2003	349.7
2004	367.1
2005	405.1
2006	424.5
2007	453.5
2008	447.2

Source: World Silver Survey 2009

a) Find a linear function that can be used to estimate the industrial demand $S(t)$, in millions of ounces, for silver t years after 2000.
b) In 2010, there were about one billion ounces of silver in above-ground supply. In what year will industrial demand of silver be one billion ounces?

Try Exercise Answers: Section 11.5
9. **(a)** $P(x) = 20x - 300,000$; **(b)** (15,000 units, $975,000)
19. ($70, 300)

Study Summary

KEY TERMS AND CONCEPTS	EXAMPLES	PRACTICE EXERCISES

SECTION 11.1: SYSTEMS OF EQUATIONS IN THREE VARIABLES

Systems of three equations in three variables are usually easiest to solve using elimination.	Solve: $x + y - z = 3,$ (1) $-x + y + 2z = -5,$ (2) $2x - y - 3z = 9.$ (3) *Eliminate x using two equations:* *Eliminate x again using two different equations:* $x + y - z = 3$ (1) $-2x - 2y + 2z = -6$ (1) $-x + y + 2z = -5$ (2) $2x - y - 3z = 9$ (3) $\overline{\quad 2y + z = -2\quad}$ $\overline{\quad -3y - z = 3\quad}$ *Solve the system of two* *Substitute and solve* *equations for y and z:* *for x:* $2y + z = -2$ $x + y - z = 3$ $\underline{-3y - z = 3}$ $x + (-1) - 0 = 3$ $-y = 1$ $x = 4.$ $y = -1$ $2(-1) + z = -2$ $z = 0.$ The solution is $(4, -1, 0)$.	**1.** Solve: $x - 2y - z = 8,$ $2x + 2y - z = 8,$ $x - 8y + z = 1.$

SECTION 11.2: SOLVING APPLICATIONS: SYSTEMS OF THREE EQUATIONS

Many problems with three unknowns can be solved after translating to a system of three equations.	In a triangular cross section of a roof, the largest angle is 70° greater than the smallest angle, and the largest angle is twice as large as the remaining angle. Find the measure of each angle. The angles in the triangle measure 30°, 50°, and 100°. (See Example 2 on pp. 681–682 for a complete solution.)	**2.** The sum of three numbers is 9. The third number is half the sum of the first and second numbers. The second number is 2 less than the sum of the first and third numbers. Find the numbers.

SECTION 11.3: ELIMINATION USING MATRICES

A **matrix** (plural, **matrices**) is a rectangular array of numbers. The individual numbers are called **entries** or **elements**. By using **row-equivalent** operations, we can solve systems of equations using matrices.	Solve: $x + 4y = 1,$ $2x - y = 3.$ Write as a matrix in row-echelon form: $\begin{bmatrix} 1 & 4 & \vdots & 1 \\ 2 & -1 & \vdots & 3 \end{bmatrix} \longrightarrow \begin{bmatrix} 1 & 4 & \vdots & 1 \\ 0 & -9 & \vdots & 1 \end{bmatrix}.$ Rewrite as equations and solve: $-9y = 1 \longrightarrow x + 4\left(-\frac{1}{9}\right) = 1$ $y = -\frac{1}{9} \qquad\qquad x = \frac{13}{9}.$ The solution is $\left(\frac{13}{9}, -\frac{1}{9}\right)$.	**3.** Solve using matrices: $3x - 2y = 10,$ $x + y = 5.$

SECTION 11.4: DETERMINANTS AND CRAMER'S RULE

A **determinant** is a number associated with a square matrix.

Determinant of a 2 × 2 Matrix

$$\begin{vmatrix} a & c \\ b & d \end{vmatrix} = ad - bc$$

Determinant of a 3 × 3 Matrix

$$\begin{vmatrix} a_1 & b_1 & c_1 \\ a_2 & b_2 & c_2 \\ a_3 & b_3 & c_3 \end{vmatrix} =$$

$$a_1 \begin{vmatrix} b_2 & c_2 \\ b_3 & c_3 \end{vmatrix}$$

$$- a_2 \begin{vmatrix} b_1 & c_1 \\ b_3 & c_3 \end{vmatrix}$$

$$+ a_3 \begin{vmatrix} b_1 & c_1 \\ b_2 & c_2 \end{vmatrix}$$

$$\begin{vmatrix} 2 & 3 \\ -1 & 5 \end{vmatrix} = 2 \cdot 5 - (-1)(3) = 13$$

$$\begin{vmatrix} 2 & 3 & 2 \\ 0 & 1 & 0 \\ -1 & 5 & -4 \end{vmatrix}$$

$$= 2 \begin{vmatrix} 1 & 0 \\ 5 & -4 \end{vmatrix} - 0 \begin{vmatrix} 3 & 2 \\ 5 & -4 \end{vmatrix} + (-1) \begin{vmatrix} 3 & 2 \\ 1 & 0 \end{vmatrix}$$

$$= 2(-4 - 0) - 0 - 1(0 - 2)$$

$$= -8 + 2 = -6$$

Evaluate.

4. $\begin{vmatrix} 3 & -5 \\ 2 & 6 \end{vmatrix}$

5. $\begin{vmatrix} 1 & 2 & -1 \\ 2 & 0 & 3 \\ 0 & 1 & 5 \end{vmatrix}$

We can use matrices and **Cramer's rule** to solve systems of equations.

Cramer's rule for 2 × 2 matrices is given on p. 696.

Cramer's rule for 3 × 3 matrices is given on p. 698.

Solve:

$$x - 3y = 7,$$
$$2x + 5y = 4.$$

$$x = \frac{\begin{vmatrix} 7 & -3 \\ 4 & 5 \end{vmatrix}}{\begin{vmatrix} 1 & -3 \\ 2 & 5 \end{vmatrix}}; \qquad y = \frac{\begin{vmatrix} 1 & 7 \\ 2 & 4 \end{vmatrix}}{\begin{vmatrix} 1 & -3 \\ 2 & 5 \end{vmatrix}}$$

$$x = \frac{47}{11} \qquad\qquad y = \frac{-10}{11}$$

The solution is $\left(\frac{47}{11}, -\frac{10}{11}\right)$.

6. Solve using Cramer's rule:

$$3x - 5y = 12,$$
$$2x + 6y = 1.$$

SECTION 11.5: BUSINESS AND ECONOMICS APPLICATIONS

The **break-even point** occurs where the **revenue** equals the **cost**, or where **profit** is 0.

Find **(a)** the total-profit function and **(b)** the break-even point for the total-cost and total-revenue functions

$$C(x) = 38x + 4320 \quad \text{and} \quad R(x) = 62x.$$

a) Profit = Revenue − Cost
$$P(x) = R(x) - C(x)$$
$$P(x) = 62x - (38x + 4320)$$
$$P(x) = 24x - 4320$$

b) $\quad\quad C(x) = R(x)$ At the break-even point, revenue = cost.

$$38x + 4320 = 62x$$
$$\quad\quad\quad 180 = x \quad\quad \text{Solving for } x$$
$$\quad\quad R(180) = 11{,}160 \quad \text{Finding the revenue (or cost) at the break-even point}$$

The break-even point is (180, $11,160).

7. Find **(a)** the total-profit function and **(b)** the break-even point for the total-cost and total-profit functions

$$C(x) = 15x + 9000,$$
$$R(x) = 90x.$$

An **equilibrium point** occurs where the **supply** equals the **demand**.

Find the equilibrium point for the demand and supply functions

$$S(p) = 60 + 7p \quad \text{and} \quad D(p) = 90 - 13p.$$

$$S(p) = D(p) \qquad \text{At the equilibrium point, supply = demand.}$$

$$60 + 7p = 90 - 13p$$

$$20p = 30$$

$$p = 1.5 \qquad \text{Solving for } p$$

$$S(1.5) = 70.5 \qquad \text{Finding the supply (or demand) at the equilibrium point}$$

The equilibrium point is ($1.50, 70.5).

8. Find the equilibrium point for the supply and demand functions

$$S(p) = 60 + 9p,$$
$$D(p) = 195 - 6p.$$

Review Exercises

⮑ *Concept Reinforcement* *Complete each of the following sentences.*

1. Systems of three equations in three variables are usually solved using the _____ method. [11.1]

2. If a system has at least one solution, it is said to be _____. [11.1]

3. The sum of the measures of the angles in any triangle is _____. [11.2]

4. When a matrix is in reduced row-echelon form, the first nonzero number in any nonzero row is _____. [11.3]

5. When a matrix has the same number of rows and columns, it is said to be _____. [11.4]

6. Cramer's rule is a formula in which the numerator and the denominator of each fraction is a(n) _____. [11.4]

7. Total revenue minus total cost is _____. [11.5]

8. _____ costs must be paid whether a product is produced or not. [11.5]

9. At the _____, the amount that the seller will supply is the same as the amount that the consumer will buy. [11.5]

10. At the break-even point, the value of the profit function is _____. [11.5]

Solve. If a system's equations are dependent or if there is no solution, state this. [11.1]

11. $x + 4y + 3z = 2,$
$2x + y + z = 10,$
$-x + y + 2z = 8$

12. $4x + 2y - 6z = 34,$
$2x + y + 3z = 3,$
$6x + 3y - 3z = 37$

13. $2x - 5y - 2z = -4,$
$7x + 2y - 5z = -6,$
$-2x + 3y + 2z = 4$

14. $2x - 3y + z = 1,$
$x - y + 2z = 5,$
$3x - 4y + 3z = -2$

15. $3x + y = 2,$
$x + 3y + z = 0,$
$x + z = 2$

Solve.

16. In triangle *ABC*, the measure of angle *A* is four times the measure of angle *C*, and the measure of angle *B* is 45° more than the measure of angle *C*. What are the measures of the angles of the triangle? [11.2]

17. The sum of the average number of times a man, a woman, and a one-year-old child cry each month is 56.7. A woman cries 3.9 more times than a man. The average number of times a one-year-old cries per month is 43.3 more than the average number of times combined that a man and a woman cry. What is the average number of times per month that each cries? [11.2]

Solve using matrices. Show your work. [11.3]

18. $3x + 4y = -13,$
$5x + 6y = 8$

19. $3x - y + z = -1,$
$2x + 3y + z = 4,$
$5x + 4y + 2z = 5$

Evaluate. [11.4]

20. $\begin{vmatrix} -2 & -5 \\ 3 & 10 \end{vmatrix}$

21. $\begin{vmatrix} 2 & 3 & 0 \\ 1 & 4 & -2 \\ 2 & -1 & 5 \end{vmatrix}$

Solve using Cramer's rule. Show your work. [11.4]

22. $2x + 3y = 6,$
$x - 4y = 14$

23. $2x + y + z = -2,$
$2x - y + 3z = 6,$
$3x - 5y + 4z = 7$

24. Find **(a)** the total-profit function and **(b)** the break-even point for the total-cost and total-revenue functions

$$C(x) = 30x + 15{,}800,$$
$$R(x) = 50x. \quad [11.5]$$

25. Find the equilibrium point for the demand and supply functions

$$S(p) = 60 + 7p,$$
$$D(p) = 120 - 13p. \quad [11.5]$$

26. Danae is beginning to produce organic honey. For the first year, the fixed costs for setting up production are $54,000. The variable costs for producing each pint of honey are $4.75. The revenue from each pint of honey is $9.25. Find the following. [11.5]

a) The total cost $C(x)$ of producing x pints of honey

b) The total revenue $R(x)$ from the sale of x pints of honey

c) The total profit $P(x)$ from the production and sale of x pints of honey

d) The profit or loss from the production and sale of 5000 pints of honey; of 15,000 pints of honey

e) The break-even point

SYNTHESIS

TW **27.** How would you go about solving a problem that involves four variables? [11.2]

TW **28.** Explain how a system of equations can be both dependent and inconsistent. [11.1]

29. Danae is leaving a job that pays $36,000 per year to make honey (see Exercise 26). How many pints of honey must she produce and sell in order to make as much money as she earned at her previous job? [11.5]

30. The graph of $f(x) = ax^2 + bx + c$ contains the points $(-2, 3)$, $(1, 1)$, and $(0, 3)$. Find a, b, and c and give a formula for the function. [11.2]

Chapter Test **11**

Solve. If a system's equations are dependent or if there is no solution, state this.

1. $-3x + y - 2z = 8,$
$-x + 2y - z = 5,$
$2x + y + z = -3$

2. $6x + 2y - 4z = 15,$
$-3x - 4y + 2z = -6,$
$4x - 6y + 3z = 8$

3. $2x + 2y = 0,$
$4x + 4z = 4,$
$2x + y + z = 2$

4. $3x + 3z = 0,$
$2x + 2y = 2,$
$3y + 3z = 3$

Solve using matrices. Show your work.

5. $4x + y = 12,$
$3x + 2y = 2$

6. $x + 3y - 3z = 12,$
$3x - y + 4z = 0,$
$-x + 2y - z = 1$

Evaluate.

7. $\begin{vmatrix} 4 & -2 \\ 3 & -5 \end{vmatrix}$

8. $\begin{vmatrix} 3 & 4 & 2 \\ -2 & -5 & 4 \\ 0 & 5 & -3 \end{vmatrix}$

9. Solve using Cramer's rule:
$3x + 4y = -1,$
$5x - 2y = 4.$

10. In triangle ABC, the measure of angle B is 5° less than three times that of angle A. The measure of angle C is 5° more than three times that of angle B. Find the angle measures.

11. An electrician, a carpenter, and a plumber are hired to work on a house. The electrician earns $30 per hour, the carpenter $28.50 per hour, and the plumber $34 per hour. The first day on the job, they worked a total of 21.5 hr and earned a total of $673.00. If the plumber worked 2 more hours than the carpenter did, how many hours did each work?

12. Find the equilibrium point for the demand and supply functions
$$D(p) = 79 - 8p \quad \text{and} \quad S(p) = 37 + 6p,$$
where p is the price, in dollars, $D(p)$ is the number of units demanded, and $S(p)$ is the number of units supplied.

13. Kick Back, Inc., is producing a new hammock. For the first year, the fixed costs for setting up production are $44,000. The variable costs for producing each hammock are $25. The revenue from each hammock is $80. Find the following.
   a) The total cost $C(x)$ of producing x hammocks
   b) The total revenue $R(x)$ from the sale of x hammocks
   c) The total profit $P(x)$ from the production and sale of x hammocks
   d) The profit or loss from the production and sale of 300 hammocks; of 900 hammocks
   e) The break-even point

SYNTHESIS

14. Solve:
$$2w - x + 5y - z = 1,$$
$$w + x - 2y + z = 2,$$
$$w + 3x - y + z = 0,$$
$$3w + x + y - z = 0.$$

15. At a county fair, an adult's ticket sold for $5.50, a senior citizen's ticket for $4.00, and a child's ticket for $1.50. On opening day, the number of adults' and senior citizens' tickets sold was 30 more than the number of children's tickets sold. The number of adults' tickets sold was 6 more than four times the number of senior citizens' tickets sold. Total receipts from the ticket sales were $11,219.50. How many of each type of ticket were sold?

Cumulative Review: Chapters 4, 11

Simplify. Do not leave negative exponents in your answers.

1. $3 + 24 \div 2^2 \cdot 3 - (6 - 7)$

2. $3c - [8 - 2(1 - c)]$

3. -10^{-2}

4. $(3xy^{-4})(-2x^3y)$

5. $\left(\dfrac{18a^2b^{-1}}{12a^{-1}b}\right)^2$

6. $\dfrac{2x - 10}{x^3 - 125}$

Perform the indicated operations.

7. $(x - 5)(x + 5)$

8. $(3n - 2)(5n + 7)$

9. $\dfrac{1}{x + 5} - \dfrac{1}{x - 5}$

10. $\dfrac{x^2 - 3x}{2x^2 - x - 3} \div \dfrac{x^3}{x^2 - 2x - 3}$

11. $y + \dfrac{2}{3y}$

Factor.

12. $4x^3 + 18x^2$

13. $x^2 + 8x - 84$

14. $16y^2 - 81$

15. $64x^3 + 8$

16. $t^2 - 16t + 64$

17. $x^6 - x^2$

18. $0.027b^3 - 0.008c^3$

19. $20x^2 + 7x - 3$

Solve.

20. $3(x - 2) = 14 - x$

21. $x - 2 < 6 \text{ or } 2x + 1 > 5$ [10.1]

22. $x^2 - 2x - 3 = 5$

23. $\dfrac{3}{x + 1} = \dfrac{x}{4}$

24. $y = \frac{1}{2}x - 7,$
 $2x - 4y = 3$ [4.2]

25. $x + 3y = 8,$
 $2x - 3y = 7$ [4.3]

26. $-3x + 4y + z = -5,$
 $x - 3y - z = 6,$
 $2x + 3y + 5z = -8$ [11.1]

27. $|2x - 1| = 8$ [10.2]

28. $9(x - 3) - 4x < 2 - (3 - x)$

29. $|4t| > 12$ [10.2]

30. $|3x - 2| \le 8$ [10.2]

In Exercises 31–34, match each equation with one of the following graphs.

a)   b)

c)   d)

31. $y = -2x + 7$

32. $y = |x - 4|$ [10.2]

33. $y = x^2 + x + 1$

34. $y = \dfrac{x - 1}{x + 3}$

Graph on a plane.

35. $y = \frac{2}{3}x - 4$

36. $x = -3$

37. $3x - y = 3$

38. $x + y \ge -2$ [10.3]

39. $f(x) = -x + 1$

40. $x - 2y > 4,$
 $x + 2y \ge -2$ [10.3]

41. Find the slope and the y-intercept of the line given by $4x - 9y = 18$.

42. Write a slope–intercept equation for the line with slope -7 and containing the point $(-3, -4)$.

43. Find an equation of the line with y-intercept $(0, 4)$ and perpendicular to the line given by $3x + 2y = 1$.

44. For the graph of f shown, determine the domain and the range of f.

45. Determine the domain of the function given by
$$f(x) = \frac{3}{2x + 5}.\ [4.1]$$

46. Find $g(-2)$ if $g(x) = 3x^2 - 5x$.

47. Find $(f - g)(x)$ if $f(x) = x^2 + 3x$ and $g(x) = 9 - 3x$.

48. Graph the solution set of $-3 \le f(x) \le 2$, where $f(x) = 1 - x$. [10.1]

49. Find the domain of h/g if $h(x) = \dfrac{1}{x}$ and $g(x) = 3x - 1$.

50. Solve for t: $at - dt = c$.

Find the solutions of each equation, inequality, or system from the given graph.

51. $10 - 5x = 3x + 2$ [4.5] 1

52. $f(x) \le g(x)$ [10.1]

53. $y = x - 5,$
$y = 1 - 2x$ [4.2]

54. $x - 5 = 1 - 2x$ [4.5]

55. $x^2 - 2x + 1 = 0$

56. The Baqueira, a resort in Spain, uses 549 snow cannons to make snow for its 4344 acres of ski runs. How many snow cannons should a resort containing 1448 acres of runs use in order to make a comparable amount of snow?
Source: www.bluebookski.com

57. *Water Usage.* In dry climates, it takes about 11,600 gal of water to produce a pound of beef and a pound of wheat. The pound of beef requires 7000 more gallons of water than the pound of wheat. How much water does it take to produce each? [4.4]
Source: *The Wall Street Journal*, 1/28/08

58. *Fundraising.* Michelle is planning a fundraising dinner for Happy Hollow Children's Camp. The banquet facility charges a rental fee of $1500, but will waive the rental fee if more than $6000 is spent for catering. Michelle knows that 150 people will attend the dinner.

 a) How much should each dinner cost in order for the rental fee to be waived?

 b) For what costs per person will the total cost (including the rental fee) exceed $6000?

59. *Perimeter of a Rectangle.* The perimeter of a rectangle is 32 cm. If five times the width equals three times the length, what are the dimensions of the rectangle? [4.4]

60. *Utility Bills.* One month Lori and Tony spent $920 for electricity, rent, and cell phone. The electric bill was $\frac{1}{4}$ the amount of the rent, and the phone bill was $40 less than the electric bill. How much was the rent? [11.2]

61. *Fast-Food Sales.* In 2006, 18- to 34-year-olds ate fast food an average of 19 times per month. By 2009, this figure had dropped to 14 times per month.

Source: Based on data from Sandelman & Associates

a) Let $f(t)$ = the average number of times per month that 18- to 34-year-olds ate fast food, where t is the number of years after 2006. Find a linear function that fits the data.

b) Use the function from part (a) to predict the average number of visits in 2012.

c) In what year will 18- to 34-year-olds eat fast food an average of 4 times per month?

62. *Theft.* The table below lists the number of truckloads of cargo stolen in the United States for various years.

Year	Number of Truckloads Stolen
2007	672
2008	767
2009	859

Source: FreightWatch International

a) Use linear regression to find a function $c(t)$ that can be used to estimate the number of truckloads stolen t years after 2007.

b) Use the function of part (a) to estimate the number of truckloads of cargo stolen in 2011.

SYNTHESIS

63. Use interval notation to write the domain of the function given by

$$f(x) = \frac{\sqrt{x + 4}}{x}. \quad [10.1]$$

64. Simplify: $\dfrac{2^{a-1} \cdot 2^{4a}}{2^{3(-2a+5)}}$.

65. Find all roots for $f(x) = x^4 - 34x^2 + 225$.

Solve.

66. $4 \le |3 - x| \le 6$ [10.1], [10.2]

67. $\dfrac{18}{x - 9} + \dfrac{10}{x + 5} = \dfrac{28x}{x^2 - 4x - 45}$

Exponents and Radical Functions

How Much Does Health Insurance Cost?

The graph below shows the average total cost to both employer and employee for family health insurance from 2001 through 2009. In Example 14 of Section 12.1, we use these data to estimate the average total cost for 2010.

COST OF HEALTH INSURANCE

Average total cost of health insurance for family (in thousands)

$14
12
10
8
6
4
2
0

'01 '02 '03 '04 '05 '06 '07 '08 '09

Year

I n this chapter, we learn about square roots, cube roots, fourth roots, and so on. These roots can be written using radical notation and appear in both radical expressions and radical equations. Exponents that are fractions are also studied and are used to ease some of our work with radicals. The chapter closes with an introduction to the complex-number system.

Radical Expressions, Functions, and Models

- Square Roots and Square-Root Functions

- Expressions of the Form $\sqrt{a^2}$

- Cube Roots

- Odd and Even nth Roots

- Radical Functions and Models

In this section, we consider roots, such as square roots and cube roots, and the *radical* expressions involving such roots.

SQUARE ROOTS AND SQUARE-ROOT FUNCTIONS

When a number is multiplied by itself, we say that the number is squared. If we can find a number that was squared in order to produce some value a, we call that number a *square root* of a.

> **Square Root**   The number c is a *square root* of a if $c^2 = a$.

For example,

9 has -3 and 3 as square roots because $(-3)^2 = 9$ and $3^2 = 9$.

25 has -5 and 5 as square roots because $(-5)^2 = 25$ and $5^2 = 25$.

-4 does not have a real-number square root because there is no real number c such that $c^2 = -4$.

Every positive number has two square roots, and 0 has only itself as a square root. Negative numbers do not have real-number square roots, although later in this chapter we introduce the *complex-number system* in which such square roots do exist.

EXAMPLE 1   Find the two square roots of 64.

SOLUTION   The square roots of 64 are 8 and -8, because $8^2 = 64$ and $(-8)^2 = 64$.

Try Exercise 9.

Whenever we refer to *the* square root of a number, we mean the nonnegative square root of that number. This is often referred to as the *principal square root* of the number.

Student Notes

It is important to remember the difference between *the* square root of 9 and *a* square root of 9. *A* square root of 9 means either 3 or -3, but *the* square root of 9, or $\sqrt{9}$, means the principal square root of 9, or 3.

> **Principal Square Root**   The *principal square root* of a nonnegative number is its nonnegative square root. The symbol $\sqrt{}$ is called a *radical sign* and is used to indicate the principal square root of the number over which it appears.

EXAMPLE 2 Simplify each of the following.

a) $\sqrt{25}$

b) $\sqrt{\dfrac{25}{64}}$

c) $-\sqrt{64}$

d) $\sqrt{0.0049}$

SOLUTION

a) $\sqrt{25} = 5$ $\sqrt{}$ indicates the principal square root. Note that $\sqrt{25} \neq -5$.

b) $\sqrt{\dfrac{25}{64}} = \dfrac{5}{8}$ Since $\left(\dfrac{5}{8}\right)^2 = \dfrac{25}{64}$

c) $-\sqrt{64} = -8$ Since $\sqrt{64} = 8, -\sqrt{64} = -8.$

d) $\sqrt{0.0049} = 0.07$ $(0.07)(0.07) = 0.0049.$ Note too that
$$\sqrt{0.0049} = \sqrt{\dfrac{49}{10{,}000}} = \dfrac{7}{100} = 0.07.$$

 Try Exercise 17.

In addition to being read as "the principal square root of a," $\sqrt{a}$ is also read as "the square root of a," or simply "root a" or "radical a." Any expression in which a radical sign appears is called a *radical expression*. The following are radical expressions:

$$\sqrt{5}, \qquad \sqrt{a}, \qquad -\sqrt{3x}, \qquad \sqrt{\dfrac{y^2 + 7}{y}}, \qquad \sqrt{x} + 8.$$

The expression under the radical sign is called the **radicand.** In the expressions above, the radicands are 5, a, $3x$, $(y^2 + 7)/y$, and x, respectively.

To calculate $\sqrt{5}$ on most graphing calculators, we press $\boxed{\sqrt{}}$ $\boxed{5}$ $\boxed{)}$ $\boxed{\text{ENTER}}$ if a left parenthesis is automatically supplied. On some calculators, $\boxed{\sqrt{}}$ is pressed after 5 has been entered. A calculator will display an approximation like

    2.23606798

for $\sqrt{5}$. The exact value of $\sqrt{5}$ is not given by any repeating or terminating decimal. In general, for any whole number a that is not a perfect square, $\sqrt{a}$ *is* a nonterminating, nonrepeating decimal, or an *irrational number*.

The square-root function, given by

$$f(x) = \sqrt{x},$$

has $[0, \infty)$ as its domain and $[0, \infty)$ as its range. We can draw its graph by selecting convenient values for x and calculating the corresponding outputs. Once these ordered pairs have been graphed, a smooth curve can be drawn.

\multicolumn{3}{c}{$f(x) = \sqrt{x}$}
x	$\sqrt{x}$	$(x, f(x))$
0	0	$(0, 0)$
1	1	$(1, 1)$
4	2	$(4, 2)$
9	3	$(9, 3)$

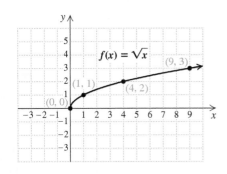

EXAMPLE 3 For each function, find the indicated function value.

a) $f(x) = \sqrt{3x - 2}$; $f(1)$

b) $g(z) = -\sqrt{6z + 4}$; $g(3)$

SOLUTION

a) $f(1) = \sqrt{3 \cdot 1 - 2}$ Substituting

       $= \sqrt{1} = 1$ Simplifying

b) $g(3) = -\sqrt{6 \cdot 3 + 4}$ Substituting

       $= -\sqrt{22}$ Simplifying. This answer is exact.

       ≈ -4.69041576 Using a calculator to approximate $\sqrt{22}$

Try Exercise 33.

EXPRESSIONS OF THE FORM $\sqrt{a^2}$

As the next example shows, $\sqrt{a^2}$ does not always simplify to a.

EXAMPLE 4 Evaluate $\sqrt{a^2}$ for the following values: (a) 5; (b) 0; (c) -5.

SOLUTION

a) $\underbrace{\sqrt{5^2} = \sqrt{25} = 5}$ Same

b) $\underbrace{\sqrt{0^2} = \sqrt{0} = 0}$ Same

c) $\underbrace{\sqrt{(-5)^2} = \sqrt{25} = 5}$ Opposites   Note that $\sqrt{(-5)^2} \neq -5$.

You may have noticed that evaluating $\sqrt{a^2}$ is just like evaluating $|a|$.

Interactive Discovery

Use graphs or tables to determine which of the following are identities. Be sure to enclose the entire radicand in parentheses, if your calculator requires them.

1. $\sqrt{x^2} = x$ 2. $\sqrt{x^2} = -x$

3. $\sqrt{x^2} = |x|$ 4. $\sqrt{(x + 3)^2} = x + 3$

5. $\sqrt{(x + 3)^2} = |x + 3|$ 6. $\sqrt{x^8} = x^4$

In general, we cannot say that $\sqrt{x^2} = x$. However, we can simplify $\sqrt{x^2}$ using absolute value.

Simplifying $\sqrt{a^2}$ For any real number a,

$$\sqrt{a^2} = |a|.$$

(The principal square root of a^2 is the absolute value of a.)

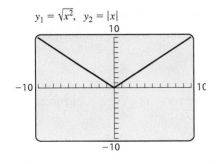

$y_1 = \sqrt{x^2}, \ y_2 = |x|$

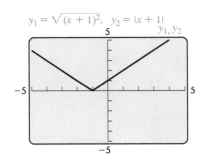

$y_1 = \sqrt{(x+1)^2}, \ y_2 = |x+1|$

Student Notes

Some absolute-value notation can be simplified.

- $|ab| = |a| \cdot |b|$, so an expression like $|3x|$ can be written

  $$|3x| = |3| \cdot |x| = 3|x|.$$

- Even powers of real numbers are always positive, so

  $$|x^2| = x^2,$$
  $$|x^4| = x^4,$$
  $$|x^6| = x^6, \quad \text{and so on.}$$

If we graph $f(x) = \sqrt{x^2}$ and $g(x) = |x|$, we find that the graphs of the functions coincide, as illustrated at left.

When a radicand is the square of a variable expression, like $(x + 1)^2$ or $36t^2$, absolute-value signs are needed when simplifying. We use absolute-value signs unless we know that the expression being squared is nonnegative. This ensures that our result is never negative.

EXAMPLE 5 Simplify each expression. Assume that the variable can represent any real number.

a) $\sqrt{36t^2}$
b) $\sqrt{(x+1)^2}$
c) $\sqrt{x^2 - 8x + 16}$
d) $\sqrt{a^8}$
e) $\sqrt{t^6}$

SOLUTION

a) $\sqrt{36t^2} = \sqrt{(6t)^2} = |6t|,$ or $6|t|$ Since t might be negative, absolute-value notation is necessary.

b) $\sqrt{(x+1)^2} = |x+1|$ Since $x + 1$ might be negative (for example, if $x = -3$), absolute-value notation is necessary.

The graph at left confirms the identity.

c) $\sqrt{x^2 - 8x + 16} = \sqrt{(x-4)^2} = |x-4|$ Since $x - 4$ might be negative, absolute-value notation is necessary.

d) Note that $(a^4)^2 = a^8$ and that a^4 is never negative. Thus,

$$\sqrt{a^8} = |a^4| = a^4. \quad \text{Absolute-value notation is unnecessary here.}$$

e) Note that $(t^3)^2 = t^6$. Thus,

$$\sqrt{t^6} = |t^3|. \quad \text{Since } t^3 \text{ can be negative, absolute-value notation is necessary.}$$

Try Exercise 39.

If we assume that the expression being squared is nonnegative, then absolute-value notation is not necessary.

EXAMPLE 6 Simplify each expression. Assume that no radicands were formed by squaring negative quantities.

a) $\sqrt{y^2}$
b) $\sqrt{a^{10}}$
c) $\sqrt{9x^2 - 6x + 1}$

SOLUTION

a) $\sqrt{y^2} = y$ We are assuming that y is nonnegative, so no absolute-value notation is necessary. When y is negative, $\sqrt{y^2} \neq y$.

b) $\sqrt{a^{10}} = a^5$ Assuming that a^5 is nonnegative. Note that $(a^5)^2 = a^{10}$.

c) $\sqrt{9x^2 - 6x + 1} = \sqrt{(3x-1)^2} = 3x - 1$ Assuming that $3x - 1$ is nonnegative

Try Exercise 69.

CUBE ROOTS

We often need to know what number cubed produces a certain value. When such a number is found, we say that we have found a *cube root*. For example,

2 is the cube root of 8 because $2^3 = 2 \cdot 2 \cdot 2 = 8$;

-4 is the cube root of -64 because $(-4)^3 = (-4)(-4)(-4) = -64$.

Cube Root The number c is the *cube root* of a if $c^3 = a$. In symbols, we write $\sqrt[3]{a}$ to denote the cube root of a.

Each real number has only one real-number cube root. The cube-root function, given by

$$f(x) = \sqrt[3]{x},$$

has $\mathbb{R}$ as its domain and $\mathbb{R}$ as its range. We can draw its graph by selecting convenient values for x and calculating the corresponding outputs. Once these ordered pairs have been graphed, a smooth curve can be drawn. Note that the cube root of a positive number is positive, the cube root of a negative number is negative, and the cube root of 0 is 0.

$$f(x) = \sqrt[3]{x}$$

x	$\sqrt[3]{x}$	$(x, f(x))$
0	0	$(0, 0)$
1	1	$(1, 1)$
8	2	$(8, 2)$
-1	-1	$(-1, -1)$
-8	-2	$(-8, -2)$

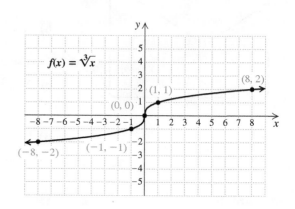

The following graphs illustrate that

$$\sqrt{x^2} = |x| \quad \text{and} \quad \sqrt[3]{x^3} = x.$$

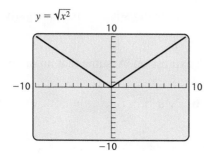

$y = \sqrt{x^2}$

The graphs of $y = \sqrt{x^2}$ and $y = |x|$ are the same. Note that $y = \sqrt{x^2}$ is never negative.

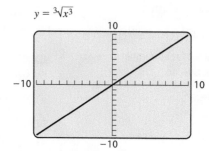

$y = \sqrt[3]{x^3}$

The graphs of $y = \sqrt[3]{x^3}$ and $y = x$ are the same. Note that $y = \sqrt[3]{x^3}$ can be negative.

EXAMPLE 7 For each function, find the indicated function value.

a) $f(y) = \sqrt[3]{y};\ f(125)$

b) $g(x) = \sqrt[3]{x} - 3;\ g(-24)$

SOLUTION

a) $f(125) = \sqrt[3]{125} = 5$ Since $5 \cdot 5 \cdot 5 = 125$

b) $g(-24) = \sqrt[3]{-24} - 3$
$$= \sqrt[3]{-27}$$
$$= -3 \quad \text{Since } (-3)(-3)(-3) = -27$$

Try Exercise 89.

EXAMPLE 8   Simplify: $\sqrt[3]{-8y^3}$.

SOLUTION

$$\sqrt[3]{-8y^3} = -2y \qquad \text{Since } (-2y)(-2y)(-2y) = -8y^3$$

Try Exercise 83.

ODD AND EVEN nTH ROOTS

The 4th root of a number a is the number c for which $c^4 = a$. There are also 5th roots, 6th roots, and so on. We write $\sqrt[n]{a}$ for the principal nth root. The number n is called the **index** (plural, **indices**). When the index is 2, we do not write it.

When the index is odd, we are taking an *odd root*.

> Every number has exactly one real root when n is odd. Odd roots of positive numbers are positive and odd roots of negative numbers are negative. Absolute-value signs are not used when finding odd roots.

EXAMPLE 9   Simplify each expression.

a) $\sqrt[5]{32}$

b) $\sqrt[5]{-32}$

c) $-\sqrt[5]{32}$

d) $-\sqrt[5]{-32}$

e) $\sqrt[7]{x^7}$

f) $\sqrt[9]{(t-1)^9}$

SOLUTION

a) $\sqrt[5]{32} = 2$ Since $2^5 = 32$

b) $\sqrt[5]{-32} = -2$ Since $(-2)^5 = -32$

c) $-\sqrt[5]{32} = -2$ Taking the opposite of $\sqrt[5]{32}$

d) $-\sqrt[5]{-32} = -(-2) = 2$ Taking the opposite of $\sqrt[5]{-32}$

e) $\sqrt[7]{x^7} = x$ No absolute-value signs are needed.

f) $\sqrt[9]{(t-1)^9} = t - 1$

Try Exercise 57.

When the index n is even, we are taking an *even root*.

> Every positive real number has two real nth roots when n is even—one positive and one negative. Negative numbers do not have real nth roots when n is even.
> When n is even, the notation $\sqrt[n]{a}$ indicates the nonnegative nth root. Thus, when finding nth roots, absolute-value signs are often necessary.

Compare the following.

Odd Root	Even Root
$\sqrt[3]{8} = 2$	$\sqrt[4]{16} = 2$
$\sqrt[3]{-8} = -2$	$\sqrt[4]{-16}$ is not a real number.
$\sqrt[3]{x^3} = x$	$\sqrt[4]{x^4} = |x|$

EXAMPLE 10 Simplify each expression, if possible. Assume that variables can represent any real number.

a) $\sqrt[4]{16}$ b) $-\sqrt[4]{16}$ c) $\sqrt[4]{-16}$

d) $\sqrt[4]{81x^4}$ e) $\sqrt[6]{(y + 7)^6}$

SOLUTION

a) $\sqrt[4]{16} = 2$ Since $2^4 = 16$

b) $-\sqrt[4]{16} = -2$ Taking the opposite of $\sqrt[4]{16}$

c) $\sqrt[4]{-16}$ cannot be simplified. $\sqrt[4]{-16}$ is not a real number.

d) $\sqrt[4]{81x^4} = |3x|$, or $3|x|$ Using absolute-value notation since x could represent a negative number

e) $\sqrt[6]{(y + 7)^6} = |y + 7|$ Using absolute-value notation since $y + 7$ is negative for $y < -7$

Try Exercise 63.

We summarize as follows.

Simplifying nth roots

n	a	$\sqrt[n]{a}$	$\sqrt[n]{a^n}$
Even	Positive	Positive	$|a|$
	Negative	Not a real number	
Odd	Positive	Positive	a
	Negative	Negative	

RADICAL FUNCTIONS AND MODELS

A **radical function** is a function that can be described by a radical expression. When the index of the expression is odd, the domain is the set of all real numbers. When the index is even, the radicand must be nonnegative. This often means that some numbers are not in the domain of a radical function.

EXAMPLE 11 Determine the domain of the function given by

$$g(x) = \sqrt[6]{7 - 3x}.$$

SOLUTION Since the index is even, the radicand, $7 - 3x$, must be nonnegative. We solve the inequality:

Set the radicand greater than or equal to 0.

$7 - 3x \geq 0$ We cannot find the 6th root of a negative number.

$-3x \geq -7$

Solve.

$x \leq \frac{7}{3}$.   Multiplying both sides by $-\frac{1}{3}$ and reversing the inequality

Thus the domain of g is $\left\{x \mid x \leq \frac{7}{3}\right\}$, or $\left(-\infty, \frac{7}{3}\right]$.

Try Exercise 93.

Radical Expressions and Functions

When entering radical expressions on a graphing calculator, care must be taken to place parentheses properly. For example, we enter

$$f(x) = \frac{-2 + \sqrt{1 - 6x}}{5}$$

on the Y = screen as ((-) 2 + 2ND √ 1 - 6 X,T,θ,n)) ÷ 5 . The outer parentheses enclose the numerator of the expression. The first right parenthesis) indicates the end of the radicand; the left parenthesis of the radicand is supplied by the calculator when √ is pressed.

Cube roots can be entered using the $\sqrt[3]{}$ (option in the MATH MATH menu, as shown at left. For an index other than 2 or 3, first enter the index, then choose the $\sqrt[x]{}$ option from the MATH MATH menu, and then enter the radicand. The $\sqrt[x]{}$ option may not supply the left parenthesis.

If we can determine the domain of the function algebraically, we can use that information to choose an appropriate viewing window. For example, compare the following graphs of the function $f(x) = 2\sqrt{15 - x}$. Note that the domain of f is $\{x \mid x \le 15\}$, or $(-\infty, 15]$.

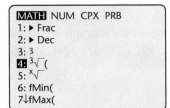

MATH NUM CPX PRB
1: ▶ Frac
2: ▶ Dec
3: 3
4: ³√(
5: ˣ√
6: fMin(
7↓fMax(

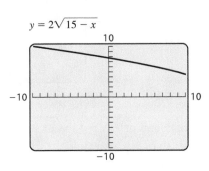

$y = 2\sqrt{15 - x}$

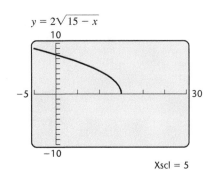

$y = 2\sqrt{15 - x}$

Xscl = 5

The graph on the left looks almost like a straight line. The viewing window on the right includes the endpoint, 15, on the x-axis. Knowing the domain of the function helps us choose Xmin and Xmax.

Your Turn

1. Enter $f(x) = \sqrt{x + 2} - 3$. Check your work by finding $f(7)$ and $f(-1)$ using a TABLE set to ASK. $f(7) = 0, f(-1) = -2$

2. Determine the domain of $g(x) = \sqrt{x + 30}$. Which of the following windows would best show the graph?   (b)
   a) $[-10, 50, -10, 10]$
   b) $[-50, 10, -10, 10]$
   Check by graphing.

Student Notes

Some calculators display radical expressions as they would be written by hand, without the need for additional parentheses. On such a calculator, the expression

$$\sqrt{x + 2} - 3$$

is entered by pressing √ X,T,θ,n + 2) - 3 .

Plot1 Plot2 Plot3
\Y1◼ √X+2 - 3
\Y2=
\Y3=
\Y4=
\Y5=
\Y6=

EXAMPLE 12 Find the domain of the function given by each of the following equations. Check by graphing the function. Then, from the graph, estimate the range of the function.

a) $t(x) = \sqrt{2x - 5} - 3$

b) $f(x) = \sqrt{x^2 + 1}$

SOLUTION

a) The function $t(x) = \sqrt{2x - 5} - 3$ is defined when $2x - 5 \geq 0$:

$2x - 5 \geq 0$	The radicand must be nonnegative.
$2x \geq 5$	Adding 5
$x \geq \frac{5}{2}.$	Dividing by 2

> Set the radicand greater than or equal to 0.

> Solve.

> The solution gives the domain.

The domain is $\left\{x \mid x \geq \frac{5}{2}\right\}$, or $\left[\frac{5}{2}, \infty\right)$, as indicated on the graph by the shading on the x-axis. The range appears to be $[-3, \infty)$, as indicated by the shading on the y-axis.

$y = \sqrt{2x - 5} - 3$

b) The radicand in $f(x) = \sqrt{x^2 + 1}$ is $x^2 + 1$. We must have

$x^2 + 1 \geq 0$	The radicand must be nonnegative.
$x^2 \geq -1.$	

Since x^2 is nonnegative for all real numbers x, the inequality is true for all real numbers. The domain is $(-\infty, \infty)$. The range appears to be $[1, \infty)$.

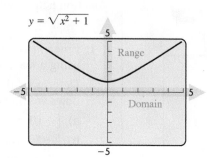

$y = \sqrt{x^2 + 1}$

⬤ Try Exercise 105.

Some situations can be modeled using radical functions. The graphs of radical functions can have many different shapes. However, radical functions given by equations of the form

$$r(x) = \sqrt{ax + b}$$

will have the general shape of the graph of $f(x) = \sqrt{x}$.

We can determine whether a radical function might fit a set of data by plotting the points.

EXAMPLE 13 Health Insurance. The average total cost of a family health insurance policy through an employer has risen every year from 2001 through 2009, as shown in the table below. Graph the data and determine whether a radical function can be used to model average total cost of family health insurance.

Year	Years Since 2000	Average Total Cost of Family Health Insurance (in thousands)
2001	1	$ 7.061
2002	2	8.003
2003	3	9.068
2004	4	9.950
2005	5	10.880
2006	6	11.480
2007	7	12.106
2008	8	12.680
2009	9	13.375

Source: Kaiser Family Foundation; Health Research & Educational Trust

SOLUTION To make the graph easier to read, we use the number of years since 2000 instead of the actual year, as shown in the second column of the table. We graph the data, entering the years since 2000 as L_1 and the costs as L_2. The data appear to follow the pattern of the graph of a radical function. Thus we determine that a radical function could be used to model family health insurance cost.

L_1	L_2	L_3	1
1	7.061	-----	
2	8.003		
3	9.068		
4	9.950		
5	10.880		
6	11.480		
7	12.106		

$L_1(1) = 1$

Try Exercise 115.

$y_1 = (0.3 + \sqrt{0.282 + 0.32x})/0.16$

The function in Example 14 is a good model of the data in Example 13.

EXAMPLE 14 Health Insurance. The average total cost of family health insurance, through an employer, can be modeled by the radical function

$$(0.3 + \sqrt{0.282 + 0.32x})/0.16,$$

where x is the number of years since 2000. Estimate the average total cost of family health insurance in 2010.

SOLUTION We enter the equation and use a table with Indpnt set to Ask. For 2010, $x = 10$, and the health insurance cost is estimated to be $13,538.

X	Y$_1$	Y$_2$
10	13.538	

Try Exercise 121.

A

Visualizing for Success

F

B

Match each function with its graph.

1. $f(x) = 2x - 5$

2. $f(x) = x^2 - 1$

3. $f(x) = \sqrt{x - 2}$

4. $f(x) = x - 2$

5. $f(x) = -\frac{1}{3}x$

6. $f(x) = x^3$

7. $f(x) = 4 - x$

8. $f(x) = |2x - 5|$

9. $f(x) = -2$

10. $f(x) = -\frac{1}{3}x + 4$

G

C

H

D

I

Answers on page A-41

An additional, animated version of this activity appears in MyMathLab. To use MyMathLab, you need a course ID and a student access code. Contact your instructor for more information.

E

J

12.1 Exercise Set

↪ *Concept Reinforcement* *Select the appropriate word to complete each of the following.*

1. Every positive number has _____ square root(s).
   one/two

2. The principal square root is never _____ .
   negative/positive

3. For any _____ number a, we have
   negative/positive
   $\sqrt{a^2} = a$.

4. For any _____ number a, we have
   negative/positive
   $\sqrt{a^2} = -a$.

5. If a is a whole number that is not a perfect square, then $\sqrt{a}$ is a(n) _____ number.
   irrational/rational

6. The domain of the function f given by $f(x) = \sqrt[3]{x}$ is the set of all _____ numbers.
   whole/real/positive

7. If $\sqrt[4]{x}$ is a real number, then x must be _____ .
   negative/positive/nonnegative

8. If $\sqrt[3]{x}$ is negative, then x must be _____ .
   negative/positive

For each number, find all of its square roots.

9. 49   10. 81

11. 144   12. 9

13. 400   14. 2500

15. 900   16. 225

Simplify.

17. $\sqrt{49}$ 18. $\sqrt{144}$

19. $-\sqrt{16}$ 20. $-\sqrt{100}$

21. $\sqrt{\dfrac{36}{49}}$ 22. $\sqrt{\dfrac{4}{9}}$

23. $-\sqrt{\dfrac{16}{81}}$ 24. $-\sqrt{\dfrac{81}{144}}$

25. $\sqrt{0.04}$ 26. $\sqrt{0.36}$

27. $\sqrt{0.0081}$ 28. $\sqrt{0.0016}$

Identify the radicand and the index for each expression.

29. $5\sqrt{p^2 + 4}$ 30. $-7\sqrt{y^2 - 8}$

31. $xy\sqrt[5]{\dfrac{x}{y+4}}$ 32. $\dfrac{a}{b}\sqrt[6]{a^2 + 1}$

For each function, find the specified function value, if it exists. If it does not exist, state this.

33. $f(t) = \sqrt{5t - 10}$; $f(3), f(2), f(1), f(-1)$

34. $g(x) = \sqrt{x^2 - 25}$; $g(-6), g(3), g(6), g(13)$

35. $t(x) = -\sqrt{2x^2 - 1}$; $t(5), t(0), t(-1), t\left(-\dfrac{1}{2}\right)$

36. $p(z) = \sqrt{2z - 20}$; $p(4), p(10), p(12), p(0)$

37. $f(t) = \sqrt{t^2 + 1}$; $f(0), f(-1), f(-10)$

38. $g(x) = -\sqrt{(x + 1)^2}$; $g(-3), g(4), g(-5)$

Simplify. Remember to use absolute-value notation when necessary. If a root cannot be simplified, state this.

39. $\sqrt{64x^2}$ 40. $\sqrt{25t^2}$

41. $\sqrt{(-4b)^2}$ 42. $\sqrt{(-7c)^2}$

43. $\sqrt{(8 - t)^2}$ 44. $\sqrt{(a + 3)^2}$

45. $\sqrt{y^2 + 16y + 64}$ 46. $\sqrt{x^2 - 4x + 4}$

47. $\sqrt{4x^2 + 28x + 49}$ 48. $\sqrt{9x^2 - 30x + 25}$

49. $-\sqrt[4]{256}$ 50. $-\sqrt[4]{625}$

51. $\sqrt[5]{-1}$ 52. $-\sqrt[3]{-1000}$

53. $-\sqrt[5]{-\dfrac{32}{243}}$ 54. $\sqrt[5]{-\dfrac{1}{32}}$

55. $\sqrt[6]{x^6}$ 56. $\sqrt[8]{y^8}$

57. $\sqrt[9]{t^9}$ 58. $\sqrt[5]{a^5}$

59. $\sqrt[4]{(6a)^4}$ 60. $\sqrt[4]{(8y)^4}$

61. $\sqrt[10]{(-6)^{10}}$ 62. $\sqrt[12]{(-10)^{12}}$

63. $\sqrt[414]{(a + b)^{414}}$ 64. $\sqrt[1976]{(2a + b)^{1976}}$

65. $\sqrt{a^{22}}$ 66. $\sqrt{x^{10}}$

67. $\sqrt{-25}$ 68. $\sqrt{-16}$

Simplify. Assume that no radicands were formed by raising negative quantities to even powers.

69. $\sqrt{16x^2}$ 70. $\sqrt{25t^2}$

71. $-\sqrt{(3t)^2}$ 72. $-\sqrt{(7c)^2}$

73. $\sqrt{(a+1)^2}$

74. $\sqrt{(5+b)^2}$

75. $\sqrt{9t^2 - 12t + 4}$

76. $\sqrt{25t^2 - 20t + 4}$

77. $\sqrt[3]{27a^3}$

78. $-\sqrt[3]{64y^3}$

79. $\sqrt[4]{16x^4}$

80. $\sqrt[4]{81x^4}$

81. $\sqrt[5]{(x-1)^5}$

82. $-\sqrt[7]{(1-x)^7}$

83. $-\sqrt[3]{-125y^3}$

84. $-\sqrt[3]{-64x^3}$

85. $\sqrt{t^{18}}$

86. $\sqrt{a^{14}}$

87. $\sqrt{(x-2)^8}$

88. $\sqrt{(x+3)^{10}}$

For each function, find the specified function value, if it exists. If it does not exist, state this.

89. $f(x) = \sqrt[3]{x+1}$; $f(7), f(26), f(-9), f(-65)$

90. $g(x) = -\sqrt[3]{2x-1}$; $g(0), g(-62), g(-13), g(63)$

91. $g(t) = \sqrt[4]{t-3}$; $g(19), g(-13), g(1), g(84)$

92. $f(t) = \sqrt[4]{t+1}$; $f(0), f(15), f(-82), f(80)$

Determine the domain of each function described.

93. $f(x) = \sqrt{x-6}$

94. $g(x) = \sqrt{x+8}$

95. $g(t) = \sqrt[4]{t+8}$

96. $f(x) = \sqrt[4]{x-9}$

97. $g(x) = \sqrt[4]{2x-10}$

98. $g(t) = \sqrt[3]{2t-6}$

99. $f(t) = \sqrt[5]{8-3t}$

100. $f(t) = \sqrt[6]{4-3t}$

101. $h(z) = -\sqrt[6]{5z+2}$

102. $d(x) = -\sqrt[4]{7x-5}$

Aha! **103.** $f(t) = 7 + \sqrt[8]{t^8}$

104. $g(t) = 9 + \sqrt[6]{t^6}$

Determine algebraically the domain of each function described. Then use a graphing calculator to confirm your answer and to estimate the range.

105. $f(x) = \sqrt{5-x}$

106. $g(x) = \sqrt{2x+1}$

107. $f(x) = 1 - \sqrt{x+1}$

108. $g(x) = 2 + \sqrt{3x-5}$

109. $g(x) = 3 + \sqrt{x^2+4}$

110. $f(x) = 5 - \sqrt{3x^2+1}$

In Exercises 111–114, match each function with one of the following graphs without using a calculator.

a)

b)

c)

d)

111. $f(x) = \sqrt{x-4}$

112. $g(x) = \sqrt{x+4}$

113. $h(x) = \sqrt{x^2+4}$

114. $f(x) = -\sqrt{x-4}$

In Exercises 115–120, determine whether a radical function would be a good model of the given situation.

115. *Sports Salaries.* The table below lists the average salary of a major-league baseball player, based on the number of years in his contract.

Length of Contract (in years)	Average Salary (in millions)
1	$ 2.1
2	3.6
3	7.0
4	9.6
5	10.5
6	12.5
7	13.8
8	14.3
9	14.6

Source: "Long-term contracts" by Dave Studeman, 12/06/07, on www.hardballtimes.com

116. *Firefighting.* The number of gallons per minute discharged from a fire hose depends on the diameter of the hose and the nozzle pressure. The table below lists the amount of water flow for a 2-in. diameter solid bore nozzle at various nozzle pressures.

Nozzle Pressure (in pounds per square inch, psi)	Water Flow (in gallons per minute, GPM)
40	752
60	921
80	1063
100	1188
120	1302
150	1455
200	1681

Source: www.firetactics.com

117. *Koi Growth.* Koi, a popular fish for backyard pools, grow from $\frac{1}{40}$ cm when newly hatched to an average length of 80 cm. The table below lists the length of a koi at various ages.

Age (in months)	Length (in centimeters)
1	2.9
2	5.0
4	9.1
13	24.9
16	29.3
30	45.8
36	51.1
48	59.3
60	65.2
72	69.4

Source: www.coloradokoi.com

118. *Farm Size.* The table below lists the average size of United States' farms for various years from 1960 to 2007.

Year	Average Size of Farm (in acres)
1960	303
1980	426
1997	431
2002	441
2007	418

Source: U.S. Department of Agriculture

119. *Cancer Research.* The table below lists the amount of federal funds allotted to the National Cancer Institute for cancer research in the United States from 2005 to 2010.

Year	Funds (in billions)
2005	$4.83
2006	4.79
2007	4.70
2008	4.93
2009	4.97
2010*	5.15

*Requested
Source: National Cancer Institute

120. *Cable Television.* The table below lists the percent of households with basic cable television service for various years.

Year	Percent of Households Served by Basic Cable Television
1985	46.2
1990	59.0
1995	65.7
2000	67.9
2005	66.8
2007	58.0

Source: Nielsen Media Research

121. *Firefighting.* The water flow, in number of gallons per minute (GPM), for a 2-in. diameter solid bore nozzle is given by
$$f(x) = 118.8\sqrt{x},$$
where x is the nozzle pressure, in pounds per square inch (psi). (See Exercise 116.) Use the function to estimate the water flow when the nozzle pressure is 50 psi and when it is 175 psi.

122. *Koi Growth.* The length, in centimeters, of a koi of age x months can be estimated using the function
$$f(x) = 0.27 + \sqrt{71.94x - 164.41}.$$
(See Exercise 117.) Use the function to estimate the length of a koi at 8 months and at 20 months.

TW **123.** Explain how to write the negative square root of a number using radical notation.

TW **124.** Does the square root of a number's absolute value always exist? Why or why not?

SKILL REVIEW

To prepare for Section 12.2, review exponents.
Simplify. Do not use negative exponents in your answer.

125. $(a^2b)(a^4b)$

126. $(3xy^8)(5x^2y)$

127. $(5x^2y^{-3})^3$

128. $(2a^{-1}b^2c)^{-3}$

129. $\left(\dfrac{10x^{-1}y^5}{5x^2y^{-1}}\right)^{-1}$

130. $\left(\dfrac{8x^3y^{-2}}{2xz^4}\right)^{-2}$

SYNTHESIS

TW **131.** If the domain of $f = [1, \infty)$ and the range of $f = [2, \infty)$, find a possible expression for $f(x)$ and explain how such an expression is formulated.

TW **132.** Natasha obtains the following graph of
$$f(x) = \sqrt{x^2 - 4x - 12}$$
and concludes that the domain of f is $(-\infty, -2]$. Is she correct? If not, what mistake is she making?

$y = \sqrt{x^2 - 4x - 12}$

TW **133.** Could the following situation possibly be modeled using a radical function? Why or why not? "For each year, the yield increases. The amount of increase is smaller each year."

TW **134.** Could the following situation possibly be modeled using a radical function? Why or why not? "For each year, the costs increase. The amount of increase is the same each year."

135. *Spaces in a Parking Lot.* A parking lot has attendants to park the cars. The number N of stalls needed for waiting cars before attendants can get to them is given by the formula $N = 2.5\sqrt{A}$, where A is the number of arrivals in peak hours. Find the number of spaces needed for the given number of arrivals in peak hours: **(a)** 25; **(b)** 36; **(c)** 49; **(d)** 64.

Determine the domain of each function described. Then draw the graph of each function.

136. $g(x) = \sqrt{x} + 5$

137. $f(x) = \sqrt{x + 5}$

138. $f(x) = \sqrt{x} - 2$

139. $g(x) = \sqrt{x - 2}$

140. Find the domain of f if
$$f(x) = \dfrac{\sqrt{x + 3}}{\sqrt[4]{2 - x}}.$$

141. Find the domain of g if
$$g(x) = \dfrac{\sqrt[4]{5 - x}}{\sqrt[6]{x + 4}}.$$

142. Find the domain of F if $F(x) = \dfrac{x}{\sqrt{x^2 - 5x - 6}}$.

143. Examine the graph of the data in Exercise 119. What type of function could be used to model the data?

TW **144.** In Exercise 120, a radical function could be used to model the data through 2000. What might have caused the number of basic cable subscribers to change its pattern of growth?

12.2 Rational Numbers as Exponents

- Rational Exponents
- Negative Rational Exponents
- Laws of Exponents
- Simplifying Radical Expressions

We have already considered natural-number exponents and integer exponents. We now expand the study of exponents further to include all rational numbers. This will give meaning to expressions like $a^{1/3}$, $7^{-1/2}$, and $(3x)^{4/5}$. Such notation will help us simplify certain radical expressions.

RATIONAL EXPONENTS

When defining rational exponents, we want the rules for exponents to hold for rational exponents just as they do for integer exponents. In particular, we still want to add exponents when multiplying.

If $a^{1/2} \cdot a^{1/2} = a^{1/2+1/2} = a^1$,   then $a^{1/2}$ should mean $\sqrt{a}$.

If $a^{1/3} \cdot a^{1/3} \cdot a^{1/3} = a^{1/3+1/3+1/3} = a^1$, then $a^{1/3}$ should mean $= \sqrt[3]{a}$.

$$a^{1/n} = \sqrt[n]{a} \qquad a^{1/n} \text{ means } \sqrt[n]{a}.$$
When a is nonnegative, n can be any natural number greater than 1. When a is negative, n can be any odd natural number greater than 1.

Thus, $a^{1/5} = \sqrt[5]{a}$ and $a^{1/10} = \sqrt[10]{a}$. Note that the denominator of the exponent becomes the index and the base becomes the radicand.

EXAMPLE 1   Write an equivalent expression using radical notation and, if possible, simplify.

a) $x^{1/2}$

b) $(-8)^{1/3}$

c) $(abc)^{1/5}$

d) $(25x^{16})^{1/2}$

SOLUTION

a) $x^{1/2} = \sqrt{x}$

b) $(-8)^{1/3} = \sqrt[3]{-8} = -2$

c) $(abc)^{1/5} = \sqrt[5]{abc}$

The denominator of the exponent becomes the index. The base becomes the radicand. Recall that for square roots, the index 2 is understood without being written.

d) $(25x^{16})^{1/2} = \sqrt{25x^{16}} = 5x^8$

 Try Exercise 9.

EXAMPLE 2   Write an equivalent expression using exponential notation.

a) $\sqrt[5]{7ab}$

b) $\sqrt[7]{\dfrac{x^3 y}{4}}$

c) $\sqrt{5x}$

SOLUTION   Parentheses are required to indicate the base.

a) $\sqrt[5]{7ab} = (7ab)^{1/5}$

b) $\sqrt[7]{\dfrac{x^3 y}{4}} = \left(\dfrac{x^3 y}{4}\right)^{1/7}$

The index becomes the denominator of the exponent. The radicand becomes the base.

c) $\sqrt{5x} = (5x)^{1/2}$ The index 2 is understood without being written. We assume $x \geq 0$.

Try Exercise 39.

STUDY TIP

It Looks Familiar

Sometimes a topic seems familiar and students are tempted to assume that they already know the material. Try to avoid this tendency. Often new extensions or applications are included when a topic reappears.

> **CAUTION!**   When we are converting from radical notation to exponential notation, parentheses are necessary to indicate the base.
>
> $$\sqrt{5x} = (5x)^{1/2}$$

Rational Exponents

We can enter a radical expression using rational exponents.

To use rational exponents, enter the radicand enclosed in parentheses, then press ⌃, and then enter the rational exponent, also enclosed in parentheses. If the rational exponent is written as a single decimal number, the parentheses around the exponent are unnecessary. If decimal notation for a rational exponent must be rounded, fraction notation should be used.

Your Turn

1. Use a calculator to find $256^{1/8}$.   2

2. Use rational exponents to find $\sqrt[4]{0.00390625}$.   0.25

EXAMPLE 3   Graph: $f(x) = \sqrt[4]{2x - 7}$.

SOLUTION   We can enter the equation in radical notation using $\sqrt[x]{}$. Alternatively, we can rewrite the radical expression using a rational exponent:

$$f(x) = (2x - 7)^{1/4}, \quad \text{or} \quad f(x) = (2x - 7)^{0.25}.$$

Then we let $y = (2x - 7)^{\wedge}(1/4)$ or $y = (2x - 7)^{\wedge}.25$. The screen on the left below shows all three forms of the equation; they are equivalent.

Knowing the domain of the function can help us determine an appropriate viewing window. Since the index is even, the domain is the set of all x for which the radicand is nonnegative, or $\left[\frac{7}{2}, \infty\right)$. We choose a viewing window of $[1, 10, -1, 5]$. This will show the axes and the first quadrant. The graph is shown on the right below.

Try Exercise 65.

How shall we define $a^{2/3}$? If the property for multiplying exponents is to hold, we must have $a^{2/3} = (a^{1/3})^2$ and $a^{2/3} = (a^2)^{1/3}$. This would suggest that $a^{2/3} = \left(\sqrt[3]{a}\right)^2$ and $a^{2/3} = \sqrt[3]{a^2}$. We make our definition accordingly.

Positive Rational Exponents   For any natural numbers m and n $(n \neq 1)$ and any real number a for which $\sqrt[n]{a}$ exists,

$$a^{m/n} \quad \text{means} \quad \left(\sqrt[n]{a}\right)^m, \quad \text{or} \quad \sqrt[n]{a^m}.$$

Student Notes

It is important to remember both meanings of $a^{m/n}$. When the root of the base a is known, $\left(\sqrt[n]{a}\right)^m$ is generally easier to work with. When it is not known, $\sqrt[n]{a^m}$ is often more convenient.

EXAMPLE 4   Write an equivalent expression using radical notation and simplify.

a) $27^{2/3}$

b) $25^{3/2}$

SOLUTION

a) $27^{2/3}$ means $\left(\sqrt[3]{27}\right)^2$ or, equivalently, $\sqrt[3]{27^2}$. Let's see which is easier to simplify:

$$\left(\sqrt[3]{27}\right)^2 = 3^2 \qquad\qquad \sqrt[3]{27^2} = \sqrt[3]{729}$$
$$= 9; \qquad\qquad\qquad\qquad = 9.$$

The simplification on the left is probably easier for most people.

b) $25^{3/2}$ means $\left(\sqrt[2]{25}\right)^3$ or, equivalently, $\sqrt[2]{25^3}$ (the index 2 is normally omitted). Since $\sqrt{25}$ is more commonly known than $\sqrt{25^3}$, we use that form:

$$25^{3/2} = \left(\sqrt{25}\right)^3 = 5^3 = 125.$$

Try Exercise 23.

EXAMPLE 5   Write an equivalent expression using exponential notation.

a) $\sqrt[3]{9^4}$

b) $\left(\sqrt[4]{7xy}\right)^5$

SOLUTION

$$\left.\begin{array}{l} \textbf{a)}\ \sqrt[3]{9^4} = 9^{4/3} \\[2mm] \textbf{b)}\ \left(\sqrt[4]{7xy}\right)^5 = (7xy)^{5/4} \end{array}\right\}$$

The index becomes the denominator of the fraction that is the exponent.

Try Exercise 43.

Rational roots of numbers can be approximated on a calculator.

EXAMPLE 6   Approximate $\sqrt[5]{(-23)^3}$. Round to the nearest thousandth.

SOLUTION   We first rewrite the expression using a rational exponent:

$$\sqrt[5]{(-23)^3} = (-23)^{3/5}.$$

Using a calculator, we have

$$(-23)^\wedge(3/5) \approx -6.562.$$

Try Exercise 71.

NEGATIVE RATIONAL EXPONENTS

Recall that $x^{-2} = \dfrac{1}{x^2}$. Negative rational exponents behave similarly.

Negative Rational Exponents   For any rational number m/n and any nonzero real number a for which $a^{m/n}$ exists,

$$a^{-m/n} \quad\text{means}\quad \frac{1}{a^{m/n}}.$$

CAUTION!   A negative exponent does not indicate that the expression in which it appears is negative.

EXAMPLE 7 Write an equivalent expression with positive exponents and, if possible, simplify.

a) $9^{-1/2}$
b) $(5xy)^{-4/5}$
c) $64^{-2/3}$

d) $4x^{-2/3}y^{1/5}$
e) $\left(\dfrac{3r}{7s}\right)^{-5/2}$

SOLUTION

a) $9^{-1/2} = \dfrac{1}{9^{1/2}}$ $9^{-1/2}$ is the reciprocal of $9^{1/2}$.

Since $9^{1/2} = \sqrt{9} = 3$, the answer simplifies to $\dfrac{1}{3}$.

b) $(5xy)^{-4/5} = \dfrac{1}{(5xy)^{4/5}}$ $(5xy)^{-4/5}$ is the reciprocal of $(5xy)^{4/5}$.

c) $64^{-2/3} = \dfrac{1}{64^{2/3}}$ $64^{-2/3}$ is the reciprocal of $64^{2/3}$.

Since $64^{2/3} = \left(\sqrt[3]{64}\right)^2 = 4^2 = 16$, the answer simplifies to $\dfrac{1}{16}$.

d) $4x^{-2/3}y^{1/5} = 4 \cdot \dfrac{1}{x^{2/3}} \cdot y^{1/5} = \dfrac{4y^{1/5}}{x^{2/3}}$

e) We found that $(a/b)^{-n} = (b/a)^n$. This property holds for *any* negative exponent:

$$\left(\frac{3r}{7s}\right)^{-5/2} = \left(\frac{7s}{3r}\right)^{5/2}.$$ Writing the reciprocal of the base and changing the sign of the exponent

Try Exercise 49.

LAWS OF EXPONENTS

The same laws hold for rational exponents as for integer exponents.

Laws of Exponents   For any real numbers a and b and any rational exponents m and n for which a^m, a^n, and b^m are defined:

1. $a^m \cdot a^n = a^{m+n}$ When multiplying, add exponents if the bases are the same.

2. $\dfrac{a^m}{a^n} = a^{m-n}$ When dividing, subtract exponents if the bases are the same. (Assume $a \neq 0$.)

3. $(a^m)^n = a^{m \cdot n}$ To raise a power to a power, multiply the exponents.

4. $(ab)^m = a^m b^m$ To raise a product to a power, raise each factor to the power and multiply.

EXAMPLE 8 Use the laws of exponents to simplify.

a) $3^{1/5} \cdot 3^{3/5}$
b) $\dfrac{a^{1/4}}{a^{1/2}}$

c) $(7.2^{2/3})^{3/4}$
d) $(a^{-1/3}b^{2/5})^{1/2}$

SOLUTION

a) $3^{1/5} \cdot 3^{3/5} = 3^{1/5+3/5} = 3^{4/5}$ Adding exponents

b) $\dfrac{a^{1/4}}{a^{1/2}} = a^{1/4-1/2} = a^{1/4-2/4}$ Subtracting exponents after finding a common denominator

$$= a^{-1/4}, \text{ or } \dfrac{1}{a^{1/4}}$$ $a^{-1/4}$ is the reciprocal of $a^{1/4}$.

c) $(7.2^{2/3})^{3/4} = 7.2^{(2/3)(3/4)} = 7.2^{6/12}$ Multiplying exponents

$$= 7.2^{1/2}$$ Using arithmetic to simplify the exponent

d) $(a^{-1/3}b^{2/5})^{1/2} = a^{(-1/3)(1/2)} \cdot b^{(2/5)(1/2)}$ Raising a product to a power and multiplying exponents

$$= a^{-1/6}b^{1/5}, \text{ or } \dfrac{b^{1/5}}{a^{1/6}}$$

Try Exercise 77.

SIMPLIFYING RADICAL EXPRESSIONS

Many radical expressions can be simplified using rational exponents.

To Simplify Radical Expressions

1. Convert radical expressions to exponential expressions.
2. Use arithmetic and the laws of exponents to simplify.
3. Convert back to radical notation as needed.

EXAMPLE 9   Use rational exponents to simplify. Do not use exponents that are fractions in the final answer.

a) $\sqrt[6]{(5x)^3}$ **b)** $\sqrt[5]{t^{20}}$

c) $\left(\sqrt[3]{ab^2c}\right)^{12}$ **d)** $\sqrt{\sqrt[3]{x}}$

$y_1 = \sqrt[6]{(5x)^3}, \quad y_2 = \sqrt{5x}$

X	Y1	Y2
0	0	0
1	2.2361	2.2361
2	3.1623	3.1623
3	3.873	3.873
4	4.4721	4.4721
5	5	5
6	5.4772	5.4772

X = 0

SOLUTION

a) $\sqrt[6]{(5x)^3} = (5x)^{3/6}$ Converting to exponential notation

$$= (5x)^{1/2}$$ Simplifying the exponent

$$= \sqrt{5x}$$ Returning to radical notation

To check on a graphing calculator, we let $y_1 = \sqrt[6]{(5x)^3}$ and $y_2 = \sqrt{5x}$ and compare values in a table. If we scroll through the table (see the figure at left), we see that $y_1 = y_2$, so our simplification is probably correct.

b) $\sqrt[5]{t^{20}} = t^{20/5}$ Converting to exponential notation

$$= t^4$$ Simplifying the exponent

c) $\left(\sqrt[3]{ab^2c}\right)^{12} = (ab^2c)^{12/3}$ Converting to exponential notation

$$= (ab^2c)^4$$ Simplifying the exponent

$$= a^4b^8c^4$$ Using the laws of exponents

$y_1 = \sqrt{\sqrt[3]{x}}, \quad y_2 = \sqrt[6]{x}$

X	Y₁	Y₂
3	1.2009	1.2009
4	1.2599	1.2599

X = 3

d) $\sqrt{\sqrt[3]{x}} = \sqrt{x^{1/3}}$ Converting the radicand to exponential notation

$= (x^{1/3})^{1/2}$

$= x^{1/6}$ Using the laws of exponents

$= \sqrt[6]{x}$ Returning to radical notation

We can check by graphing $y_1 = \sqrt{\sqrt[3]{x}}$ and $y_2 = \sqrt[6]{x}$. The graphs coincide, as we also see by scrolling through the table of values shown at left.

■ Try Exercise 91.

12.2 Exercise Set

FOR EXTRA HELP   MyMathLab   Math XL PRACTICE WATCH DOWNLOAD READ REVIEW

↪ *Concept Reinforcement* In each of Exercises 1–8, match the expression with the equivalent expression from the column on the right.

1. ____ $x^{2/5}$ a) $x^{3/5}$

2. ____ $x^{5/2}$ b) $\left(\sqrt[5]{x}\right)^4$

3. ____ $x^{-5/2}$ c) $\sqrt{x^5}$

4. ____ $x^{-2/5}$ d) $x^{1/2}$

5. ____ $x^{1/5} \cdot x^{2/5}$ e) $\dfrac{1}{\left(\sqrt{x}\right)^5}$

6. ____ $(x^{1/5})^{5/2}$

7. ____ $\sqrt[5]{x^4}$ f) $\sqrt[4]{x^5}$

8. ____ $\left(\sqrt[4]{x}\right)^5$ g) $\sqrt[5]{x^2}$

h) $\dfrac{1}{\left(\sqrt[5]{x}\right)^2}$

Note: Assume for all exercises that even roots are of non-negative quantities and that all denominators are nonzero.

Write an equivalent expression using radical notation and, if possible, simplify.

9. $x^{1/6}$ 10. $y^{1/5}$

11. $16^{1/2}$ 12. $8^{1/3}$

13. $32^{1/5}$ 14. $64^{1/6}$

15. $9^{1/2}$ 16. $25^{1/2}$

17. $(xyz)^{1/2}$ 18. $(ab)^{1/4}$

19. $(a^2b^2)^{1/5}$ 20. $(x^3y^3)^{1/4}$

21. $t^{2/5}$ 22. $b^{3/2}$

23. $16^{3/4}$ 24. $4^{7/2}$

25. $27^{4/3}$ 26. $9^{5/2}$

27. $(81x)^{3/4}$ 28. $(125a)^{2/3}$

29. $(25x^4)^{3/2}$ 30. $(9y^6)^{3/2}$

Write an equivalent expression using exponential notation.

31. $\sqrt[3]{20}$ 32. $\sqrt[3]{19}$

33. $\sqrt{17}$ 34. $\sqrt{6}$

35. $\sqrt{x^3}$ 36. $\sqrt{a^5}$

37. $\sqrt[5]{m^2}$ 38. $\sqrt[5]{n^4}$

39. $\sqrt[4]{cd}$ 40. $\sqrt[5]{xy}$

41. $\sqrt[5]{xy^2z}$ 42. $\sqrt[7]{x^3y^2z^2}$

43. $\left(\sqrt{3mn}\right)^3$ 44. $\left(\sqrt[3]{7xy}\right)^4$

45. $\left(\sqrt[7]{8x^2y}\right)^5$ 46. $\left(\sqrt[6]{2a^5b}\right)^7$

47. $\dfrac{2x}{\sqrt[3]{z^2}}$ 48. $\dfrac{3a}{\sqrt[5]{c^2}}$

Write an equivalent expression with positive exponents and, if possible, simplify.

49. $8^{-1/3}$ 50. $10{,}000^{-1/4}$

51. $(2rs)^{-3/4}$ 52. $(5xy)^{-5/6}$

53. $\left(\dfrac{1}{16}\right)^{-3/4}$ 54. $\left(\dfrac{1}{8}\right)^{-2/3}$

55. $\dfrac{2c}{a^{-3/5}}$ 56. $\dfrac{3b}{a^{-5/7}}$

57. $5x^{-2/3}y^{4/5}z$ 58. $2ab^{-1/2}c^{2/3}$

59. $3^{-5/2}a^3b^{-7/3}$ 60. $2^{-1/3}x^4y^{-2/7}$

61. $\left(\dfrac{2ab}{3c}\right)^{-5/6}$

62. $\left(\dfrac{7x}{8yz}\right)^{-3/5}$

63. $\dfrac{6a}{\sqrt[4]{b}}$

64. $\dfrac{7x}{\sqrt[3]{z}}$

Graph using a graphing calculator.

65. $f(x) = \sqrt[4]{x+7}$

66. $g(x) = \sqrt[5]{4-x}$

67. $r(x) = \sqrt[7]{3x-2}$

68. $q(x) = \sqrt[6]{2x+3}$

69. $f(x) = \sqrt[6]{x^3}$

70. $g(x) = \sqrt[8]{x^2}$

Approximate. Round to the nearest thousandth.

71. $\sqrt[5]{9}$

72. $\sqrt[6]{13}$

73. $\sqrt[4]{10}$

74. $\sqrt[7]{-127}$

75. $\sqrt[3]{(-3)^5}$

76. $\sqrt[10]{(1.5)^6}$

Use the laws of exponents to simplify. Do not use negative exponents in any answers.

77. $7^{3/4} \cdot 7^{1/8}$

78. $11^{2/3} \cdot 11^{1/2}$

79. $\dfrac{3^{5/8}}{3^{-1/8}}$

80. $\dfrac{8^{7/11}}{8^{-2/11}}$

81. $\dfrac{5.2^{-1/6}}{5.2^{-2/3}}$

82. $\dfrac{2.3^{-3/10}}{2.3^{-1/5}}$

83. $(10^{3/5})^{2/5}$

84. $(5^{5/4})^{3/7}$

85. $a^{2/3} \cdot a^{5/4}$

86. $x^{3/4} \cdot x^{1/3}$

Aha! **87.** $(64^{3/4})^{4/3}$

88. $(27^{-2/3})^{3/2}$

89. $(m^{2/3}n^{-1/4})^{1/2}$

90. $(x^{-1/3}y^{2/5})^{1/4}$

Use rational exponents to simplify. Do not use fraction exponents in the final answer.

91. $\sqrt[8]{x^4}$

92. $\sqrt[6]{a^2}$

93. $\sqrt[4]{a^{12}}$

94. $\sqrt[3]{x^{15}}$

95. $\sqrt[12]{y^8}$

96. $\sqrt[10]{t^6}$

97. $\left(\sqrt[7]{xy}\right)^{14}$

98. $\left(\sqrt[3]{ab}\right)^{15}$

99. $\sqrt[4]{(7a)^2}$

100. $\sqrt[8]{(3x)^2}$

101. $\left(\sqrt[8]{2x}\right)^6$

102. $\left(\sqrt[10]{3a}\right)^5$

103. $\sqrt{\sqrt[5]{m}}$

104. $\sqrt[4]{\sqrt{x}}$

105. $\sqrt[4]{(xy)^{12}}$

106. $\sqrt{(ab)^6}$

107. $\left(\sqrt[5]{a^2b^4}\right)^{15}$

108. $\left(\sqrt[3]{x^2y^5}\right)^{12}$

109. $\sqrt[3]{\sqrt[4]{xy}}$

110. $\sqrt[5]{\sqrt{2a}}$

TW **111.** If $f(x) = (x+5)^{1/2}(x+7)^{-1/2}$, find the domain of f. Explain how you found your answer.

TW **112.** Let $f(x) = 5x^{-1/3}$. Under what condition will we have $f(x) > 0$? Why?

SKILL REVIEW

SKILL REVIEW

To prepare for Section 12.3, review multiplying and factoring polynomials.

Multiply.

113. $(x+5)(x-5)$

114. $(x-2)(x^2+2x+4)$

Factor.

115. $4x^2 + 20x + 25$

116. $9a^2 - 24a + 16$

117. $5t^2 - 10t + 5$

118. $3n^2 + 12n + 12$

SYNTHESIS

TW **119.** Explain why $\sqrt[3]{x^6} = x^2$ for any value of x, whereas $\sqrt[2]{x^6} = x^3$ only when $x \geq 0$.

TW **120.** If $g(x) = x^{3/n}$, in what way does the domain of g depend on whether n is odd or even?

Use rational exponents to simplify.

121. $\sqrt{x\sqrt[3]{x^2}}$

122. $\sqrt[4]{\sqrt[3]{8x^3y^6}}$

123. $\sqrt[12]{p^2 + 2pq + q^2}$

124. *Herpetology.* The daily number of calories c needed by a reptile of weight w pounds can be approximated by $c = 10w^{3/4}$. Find the daily calorie requirement of a green iguana weighing 16 lb.
Source: www.anapsid.org

Music. *The function given by* $f(x) = k2^{x/12}$ *can be used to determine the frequency, in cycles per second, of a musical note that is x half-steps above a note with frequency k.* * Use this information for Exercises 125–127.

125. The frequency of concert A for a trumpet is 440 cycles per second. Find the frequency of the A that is two octaves (24 half-steps) above concert A. (Few trumpeters can reach this note!)

*This application was inspired by information provided by Dr. Homer B. Tilton of Pima Community College East.

126. Show that the G that is 7 half-steps (a "perfect fifth") above middle C (262 cycles per second) has a frequency that is about 1.5 times that of middle C.

127. Show that the C sharp that is 4 half-steps (a "major third") above concert A (see Exercise 125) has a frequency that is about 25% greater than that of concert A.

128. *Baseball.* The statistician Bill James has found that a baseball team's winning percentage P can be approximated by

$$P = \frac{r^{1.83}}{r^{1.83} + \sigma^{1.83}},$$

where r is the total number of runs scored by that team and σ is the total number of runs scored by their opponents. During a recent season, the San Francisco Giants scored 799 runs and their opponents scored 749 runs. Use James's formula to predict the Giants' winning percentage. (The team actually won 55.6% of their games.)
Source: M. Bittinger, *One Man's Journey Through Mathematics.* Boston: Addison-Wesley, 2004

129. *Road Pavement Messages.* In a psychological study, it was determined that the proper length L of the letters of a word printed on pavement is given by

$$L = \frac{0.000169d^{2.27}}{h},$$

where d is the distance of a car from the lettering and h is the height of the eye above the surface of the road. All units are in meters. This formula says that if a person is h meters above the surface of the road and is to be able to recognize a message d meters away, that message will be the most recognizable if the length of the letters is L. Find L to the nearest tenth of a meter, given d and h.

a) $h = 1$ m, $d = 60$ m
b) $h = 0.9906$ m, $d = 75$ m
c) $h = 2.4$ m, $d = 80$ m
d) $h = 1.1$ m, $d = 100$ m

130. *Physics.* The equation

$$m = m_0(1 - v^2c^{-2})^{-1/2},$$

developed by Albert Einstein, is used to determine the mass m of an object that is moving v meters per second and has mass m_0 before the motion begins. The constant c is the speed of light, approximately 3×10^8 m/sec. Suppose that a particle with mass 8 mg is accelerated to a speed of $\frac{9}{5} \times 10^8$ m/sec. Without using a calculator, find the new mass of the particle.

131. *Forestry.* The total wood volume T, in cubic feet, in a California black oak can be estimated using the formula

$$T = 0.936d^{1.97}h^{0.85},$$

where d is the diameter of the tree at breast height and h is the total height of the tree. How much wood is in a California black oak that is 3 ft in diameter at breast height and 80 ft high?
Source: Norman H. Pillsbury and Michael L. Kirkley, 1984. Equations for total, wood, and saw-log volume for thirteen California hardwoods, USDA Forest Service PNW Research Note No. 414: 52 p.

132. A person's body surface area (BSA) can be approximated by the DuBois formula

$$\text{BSA} = 0.007184w^{0.425}h^{0.725},$$

where w is mass, in kilograms, h is height, in centimeters, and BSA is in square meters. What is the BSA of a child who is 122 cm tall and has a mass of 29.5 kg?
Source: www.halls.md

133. Using a graphing calculator and a $[-10, 10, -1, 8]$ window, select the **MODE** SIMUL and the **FORMAT** EXPROFF. Then graph

$$y_1 = x^{1/2}, \qquad y_2 = 3x^{2/5},$$
$$y_3 = x^{4/7}, \quad \text{and} \quad y_4 = \tfrac{1}{5}x^{3/4}.$$

Looking only at coordinates, match each graph with its equation.

Are Equivalent Fractions Equivalent Exponents?

Focus: Functions and rational exponents
Time: 10–20 minutes
Group Size: 3
Materials: Graph paper

In arithmetic, we have seen that $\frac{1}{3}, \frac{1}{6} \cdot 2$, and $2 \cdot \frac{1}{6}$ all represent the same number. Interestingly,

$$f(x) = x^{1/3},$$
$$g(x) = (x^{1/6})^2, \quad \text{and}$$
$$h(x) = (x^2)^{1/6}$$

represent three *different* functions.

ACTIVITY

1. Selecting a variety of values for x and using the definition of positive rational exponents, one group member should graph f, a second group member should graph g, and a third group member should graph h. Be sure to check whether negative x-values are in the domain of the function.

2. Compare the three graphs and check each other's work. How and why do the graphs differ?

3. Decide as a group which graph, if any, would best represent the graph of $k(x) = x^{2/6}$. Then be prepared to explain your reasoning to the entire class. (*Hint*: Study the definition of $a^{m/n}$ on p. 734 carefully.)

12.3 Multiplying Radical Expressions

- Multiplying Radical Expressions
- Simplifying by Factoring
- Multiplying and Simplifying

MULTIPLYING RADICAL EXPRESSIONS

Note that $\sqrt{4}\,\sqrt{25} = 2 \cdot 5 = 10$. Also $\sqrt{4 \cdot 25} = \sqrt{100} = 10$. Likewise,

$$\sqrt[3]{27}\,\sqrt[3]{8} = 3 \cdot 2 = 6 \quad \text{and} \quad \sqrt[3]{27 \cdot 8} = \sqrt[3]{216} = 6.$$

These examples suggest the following.

> **The Product Rule for Radicals**   For any real numbers $\sqrt[n]{a}$ and $\sqrt[n]{b}$,
> $$\sqrt[n]{a} \cdot \sqrt[n]{b} = \sqrt[n]{a \cdot b}.$$

(The product of two nth roots is the nth root of the product of the two radicands.)

Rational exponents can be used to derive this rule:

$$\sqrt[n]{a} \cdot \sqrt[n]{b} = a^{1/n} \cdot b^{1/n} = (a \cdot b)^{1/n} = \sqrt[n]{a \cdot b}.$$

EXAMPLE 1   Multiply.

a) $\sqrt{3} \cdot \sqrt{5}$

b) $\sqrt{x+3}\,\sqrt{x-3}$

c) $\sqrt[3]{4} \cdot \sqrt[3]{5}$

d) $\sqrt[4]{\dfrac{y}{5}} \cdot \sqrt[4]{\dfrac{7}{x}}$

SOLUTION

a) When no index is written, roots are understood to be square roots with an unwritten index of two. We apply the product rule:

$$\sqrt{3} \cdot \sqrt{5} = \sqrt{3 \cdot 5} = \sqrt{15}.$$

b) $\sqrt{x + 3}\ \sqrt{x - 3} = \sqrt{(x + 3)(x - 3)}$ The product of two square roots is the square root of the product.

$$= \sqrt{x^2 - 9}$$

c) Both $\sqrt[3]{4}$ and $\sqrt[3]{5}$ have indices of three, so to multiply we can use the product rule:

$$\sqrt[3]{4} \cdot \sqrt[3]{5} = \sqrt[3]{4 \cdot 5} = \sqrt[3]{20}.$$

d) $\sqrt[4]{\dfrac{y}{5}} \cdot \sqrt[4]{\dfrac{7}{x}} = \sqrt[4]{\dfrac{y}{5} \cdot \dfrac{7}{x}} = \sqrt[4]{\dfrac{7y}{5x}}$ In Section 12.4, we discuss other ways to write answers like this.

Try Exercise 7.

⟨↔⟩ Connecting the Concepts

We saw in Example 1(b) that

$$\sqrt{x + 3}\ \sqrt{x - 3} = \sqrt{x^2 - 9}.$$

Is it then true that

$$f(x) = \sqrt{x + 3}\ \sqrt{x - 3} \quad \text{and} \quad g(x) = \sqrt{x^2 - 9}$$

represent the same function? To answer this, let's examine the domains of f and g.
For $f(x) = \sqrt{x + 3}\ \sqrt{x - 3}$, we must have

$$x + 3 \geq 0 \quad \text{and} \quad x - 3 \geq 0$$
$$x \geq -3 \quad \text{and} \quad x \geq 3.$$

The domain of f is thus $\{x \mid x \geq -3 \ and \ x \geq 3\}$, or $[3, \infty)$.
For $g(x) = \sqrt{x^2 - 9}$, we must have

$$x^2 - 9 \geq 0$$
$$x^2 \geq 9.$$

This is true for $x \geq 3$ or for $x \leq -3$. Thus the domain of g is $\{x \mid x \leq -3 \ or \ x \geq 3\}$, or $(-\infty, -3] \cup [3, \infty)$.
The domains are not the same, as confirmed by the following graphs. Note that the graphs do coincide where the domains coincide. We say that the expressions are equivalent because they represent the same number for all possible replacements for *both* expressions.

$y = \sqrt{x + 3}\ \sqrt{x - 3}$

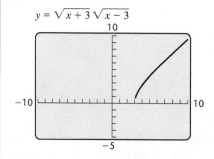

$y = \sqrt{x^2 - 9}$

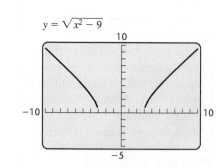

SIMPLIFYING BY FACTORING

The number p is a *perfect square* if there exists a rational number q for which $q^2 = p$. We say that p is a *perfect cube* if $q^3 = p$ for some rational number q. In general, p is a *perfect nth power* if $q^n = p$ for some rational number q. The product rule allows us to simplify $\sqrt[n]{ab}$ when a or b is a perfect nth power.

Using the Product Rule to Simplify

$\sqrt[n]{ab} = \sqrt[n]{a} \cdot \sqrt[n]{b}$.

$\left(\sqrt[n]{a} \text{ and } \sqrt[n]{b} \text{ must both be real numbers.}\right)$

To illustrate, suppose we wish to simplify $\sqrt{20}$. Since this is a *square* root, we check to see if there is a factor of 20 that is a perfect square. There is one, 4, so we express 20 as $4 \cdot 5$ and use the product rule.

$$\sqrt{20} = \sqrt{4 \cdot 5} \qquad \text{Factoring the radicand (4 is a perfect square)}$$
$$= \sqrt{4} \cdot \sqrt{5} \qquad \text{Factoring into two radicals}$$
$$= 2\sqrt{5} \qquad \text{Taking the square root of 4}$$

To Simplify a Radical Expression with Index n by Factoring

1. Express the radicand as a product in which one factor is the largest perfect nth power possible.
2. Rewrite the expression as the nth root of each factor.
3. Simplify the expression containing the perfect nth power.
4. Simplification is complete when no radicand has a factor that is a perfect nth power.

It is often safe to assume that a radicand does not represent a negative number raised to an even power. We will henceforth make this assumption—unless functions are involved—and discontinue use of absolute-value notation when taking even roots.

EXAMPLE 2 Simplify by factoring: **(a)** $\sqrt{200}$; **(b)** $\sqrt{18x^2y}$; **(c)** $\sqrt[3]{-72}$; **(d)** $\sqrt[4]{162x^6}$.

SOLUTION

a) $\sqrt{200} = \sqrt{100 \cdot 2} \qquad$ 100 is the largest perfect-square factor of 200.

$\qquad = \sqrt{100} \cdot \sqrt{2} = 10\sqrt{2}$

Express the radicand as a product.

b) $\sqrt{18x^2y} = \sqrt{9 \cdot 2 \cdot x^2 \cdot y} \qquad$ $9x^2$ is the largest perfect-square factor of $18x^2y$.

Rewrite as the nth root of each factor.

$\qquad = \sqrt{9x^2} \cdot \sqrt{2y} \qquad$ Factoring into two radicals

Simplify.

$\qquad = 3x\sqrt{2y} \qquad$ Taking the square root of $9x^2$

c) $\sqrt[3]{-72} = \sqrt[3]{-8 \cdot 9} \qquad$ -8 is a perfect-cube (third-power) factor of -72.

$\qquad = \sqrt[3]{-8} \cdot \sqrt[3]{9} = -2\sqrt[3]{9}$

d) $\sqrt[4]{162x^6} = \sqrt[4]{81 \cdot 2 \cdot x^4 \cdot x^2} \qquad$ $81 \cdot x^4$ is the largest perfect fourth-power factor of $162x^6$.

$\qquad = \sqrt[4]{81x^4} \cdot \sqrt[4]{2x^2} \qquad$ Factoring into two radicals

$\qquad = 3x\sqrt[4]{2x^2} \qquad$ Taking fourth roots

Let's look at this example another way. We write a complete factorization and look for quadruples of factors. Each quadruple makes a perfect fourth power:

$$\sqrt[4]{162x^6} = \sqrt[4]{\underline{3 \cdot 3 \cdot 3 \cdot 3} \cdot 2 \cdot \underline{x \cdot x \cdot x \cdot x} \cdot x \cdot x} \qquad \begin{array}{l} 3 \cdot 3 \cdot 3 \cdot 3 = 3^4 \text{ and} \\ x \cdot x \cdot x \cdot x = x^4 \end{array}$$

$$= 3 \cdot x \cdot \sqrt[4]{2 \cdot x \cdot x} = 3x\sqrt[4]{2x^2}.$$

Try Exercise 31.

EXAMPLE 3   If $f(x) = \sqrt{3x^2 - 6x + 3}$, find a simplified form for $f(x)$. Because we are working with a function, assume that x can be any real number.

SOLUTION

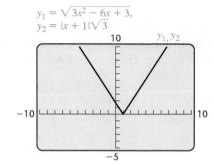

$$y_1 = \sqrt{3x^2 - 6x + 3},$$
$$y_2 = |x + 1|\sqrt{3}$$

$$\begin{aligned} f(x) &= \sqrt{3x^2 - 6x + 3} \\ &= \left.\begin{aligned} \sqrt{3(x^2 - 2x + 1)} \\ = \sqrt{(x-1)^2 \cdot 3} \end{aligned}\right\} && \text{Factoring the radicand; } x^2 - 2x + 1 \\ && \text{is a perfect square.} \\ &= \sqrt{(x-1)^2} \cdot \sqrt{3} && \text{Factoring into two radicals} \\ &= |x - 1|\sqrt{3} && \text{Taking the square root of } (x-1)^2 \end{aligned}$$

We can check by graphing $y_1 = \sqrt{3x^2 - 6x + 3}$ and $y_2 = |x - 1|\sqrt{3}$, as shown in the graph at left. It appears that the graphs coincide, and scrolling through a table of values would show us that this is indeed the case.

Try Exercise 45.

EXAMPLE 4   Simplify: **(a)** $\sqrt{x^7y^{11}z^9}$; **(b)** $\sqrt[3]{16a^7b^{14}}$.

SOLUTION

a) There are many ways to factor $x^7y^{11}z^9$. Because of the square root (index of 2), we identify the largest exponents that are multiples of 2:

$$\begin{aligned} \sqrt{x^7y^{11}z^9} &= \sqrt{x^6 \cdot x \cdot y^{10} \cdot y \cdot z^8 \cdot z} && \text{The largest perfect-square} \\ && \text{factor is } x^6y^{10}z^8. \\ &= \sqrt{x^6}\,\sqrt{y^{10}}\,\sqrt{z^8}\,\sqrt{xyz} && \text{Factoring into several radicals} \\ &= x^{6/2}\,y^{10/2}\,z^{8/2}\sqrt{xyz} && \text{Converting to rational exponents} \\ &= x^3y^5z^4\,\sqrt{xyz}. \end{aligned}$$

Check: $\left(x^3y^5z^4\sqrt{xyz}\right)^2 = (x^3)^2(y^5)^2(z^4)^2\left(\sqrt{xyz}\right)^2$
$$= x^6 \cdot y^{10} \cdot z^8 \cdot xyz = x^7y^{11}z^9$$

Our check shows that $x^3y^5z^4\sqrt{xyz}$ is the square root of $x^7y^{11}z^9$.

b) There are many ways to factor $16a^7b^{14}$. Because of the cube root (index of 3), we identify factors with the largest exponents that are multiples of 3:

$$\begin{aligned} \sqrt[3]{16a^7b^{14}} &= \sqrt[3]{8 \cdot 2 \cdot a^6 \cdot a \cdot b^{12} \cdot b^2} && \text{The largest perfect-cube} \\ && \text{factor is } 8a^6b^{12}. \\ &= \sqrt[3]{8a^6b^{12}}\,\sqrt[3]{2ab^2} && \text{Rewriting as a product} \\ && \text{of cube roots} \\ &= 2a^2b^4\sqrt[3]{2ab^2}. && \text{Simplifying the expression} \\ && \text{containing the perfect cube} \end{aligned}$$

As a check, let's redo the problem using a complete factorization of the radicand:

$$\sqrt[3]{16a^7b^{14}} = \sqrt[3]{\underline{2 \cdot 2 \cdot 2} \cdot 2 \cdot \underline{a \cdot a \cdot a} \cdot a \cdot a \cdot a \cdot a \cdot \underline{b \cdot b \cdot b} \cdot \underline{b \cdot b \cdot b} \cdot \underline{b \cdot b \cdot b} \cdot \underline{b \cdot b \cdot b} \cdot b \cdot b}$$

Each triple of factors makes a cube.

$$= 2 \cdot a \cdot a \cdot b \cdot b \cdot b \cdot b \cdot \sqrt[3]{2 \cdot a \cdot b \cdot b}$$
$$= 2a^2b^4\sqrt[3]{2ab^2}. \qquad \text{Our answer checks.}$$

Try Exercise 51.

> To simplify an *n*th root, identify factors in the radicand with exponents that are multiples of *n*.

MULTIPLYING AND SIMPLIFYING

We have used the product rule for radicals to find products and also to simplify radical expressions. For some radical expressions, it is possible to do both: First find a product and then simplify.

EXAMPLE 5 Multiply and simplify.

a) $\sqrt{15}\,\sqrt{6}$ b) $3\sqrt[3]{25} \cdot 2\sqrt[3]{5}$ c) $\sqrt[4]{8x^3y^5}\,\sqrt[4]{4x^2y^3}$

SOLUTION

a) $\sqrt{15}\sqrt{6} = \sqrt{15 \cdot 6}$ Multiplying radicands

$\qquad\qquad = \sqrt{90} = \sqrt{9 \cdot 10}$ 9 is a perfect square.

$\qquad\qquad = 3\sqrt{10}$

b) $3\sqrt[3]{25} \cdot 2\sqrt[3]{5} = 3 \cdot 2 \cdot \sqrt[3]{25 \cdot 5}$ Using a commutative law; multiplying radicands

$\qquad\qquad\qquad = 6 \cdot \sqrt[3]{125}$ 125 is a perfect cube.

$\qquad\qquad\qquad = 6 \cdot 5, \text{ or } 30$

Student Notes

To multiply $\sqrt{x} \cdot \sqrt{x}$, remember what $\sqrt{x}$ represents and go directly to the product, x. For $x \geq 0$,

$$\sqrt{x} \cdot \sqrt{x} = x,$$
$$(\sqrt{x})^2 = x, \quad \text{and}$$
$$\sqrt{x^2} = x.$$

c) $\sqrt[4]{8x^3y^5}\,\sqrt[4]{4x^2y^3} = \sqrt[4]{32x^5y^8}$ Multiplying radicands

$\qquad\qquad\qquad = \sqrt[4]{16x^4y^8 \cdot 2x}$ Identifying the largest perfect fourth-power factor

$\qquad\qquad\qquad = \sqrt[4]{16x^4y^8}\,\sqrt[4]{2x}$ Factoring into radicals

$\qquad\qquad\qquad = 2xy^2\sqrt[4]{2x}$ Finding the fourth roots; assume $x \geq 0$.

The checks are left to the student.

Try Exercise 65.

Exercise Set

↪ *Concept Reinforcement Classify each of the following statements as either true or false.*

1. For any real numbers $\sqrt[n]{a}$ and $\sqrt[n]{b}$, $\sqrt[n]{a} \cdot \sqrt[n]{b} = \sqrt[n]{ab}$.

2. For any real numbers $\sqrt[n]{a}$ and $\sqrt[n]{b}$, $\sqrt[n]{a} + \sqrt[n]{b} = \sqrt[n]{a + b}$.

3. For any real numbers $\sqrt[n]{a}$ and $\sqrt[m]{b}$, $\sqrt[n]{a} \cdot \sqrt[m]{b} = \sqrt[nm]{ab}$.

4. For $x > 0$, $\sqrt{x^2 - 9} = x - 3$.

5. The expression $\sqrt[3]{X}$ is not simplified if X contains a factor that is a perfect cube.

6. It is often possible to simplify $\sqrt{A \cdot B}$ even though $\sqrt{A}$ and $\sqrt{B}$ cannot be simplified.

Multiply.

7. $\sqrt{5}\,\sqrt{7}$

8. $\sqrt{10}\,\sqrt{3}$

9. $\sqrt[3]{3}\,\sqrt[3]{2}$

10. $\sqrt[3]{2}\,\sqrt[3]{5}$

11. $\sqrt[6]{6}\,\sqrt[4]{3}$

12. $\sqrt[4]{8}\,\sqrt[4]{9}$

13. $\sqrt{2x}\,\sqrt{13y}$

14. $\sqrt{5a}\,\sqrt{6b}$

15. $\sqrt[5]{8y^3}\,\sqrt[5]{10y}$

16. $\sqrt[5]{9t^2}\,\sqrt[5]{2t}$

17. $\sqrt{y-b}\,\sqrt{y+b}$

18. $\sqrt{x-a}\,\sqrt{x+a}$

19. $\sqrt[3]{0.7y}\,\sqrt[3]{0.3y}$

20. $\sqrt[3]{0.5x}\,\sqrt[3]{0.2x}$

21. $\sqrt[5]{x-2}\,\sqrt[5]{(x-2)^2}$

22. $\sqrt[4]{x-1}\,\sqrt[4]{x^2+x+1}$

23. $\sqrt{\dfrac{3}{t}}\,\sqrt{\dfrac{7s}{11}}$

24. $\sqrt{\dfrac{5x}{6}}\,\sqrt{\dfrac{11}{y}}$

25. $\sqrt[7]{\dfrac{x-3}{4}}\,\sqrt[7]{\dfrac{5}{x+2}}$

26. $\sqrt[6]{\dfrac{a}{b-2}}\,\sqrt[6]{\dfrac{3}{b+2}}$

Simplify by factoring.

27. $\sqrt{18}$

28. $\sqrt{50}$

29. $\sqrt{27}$

30. $\sqrt{45}$

31. $\sqrt{8x^9}$

32. $\sqrt{75y^5}$

33. $\sqrt{120}$

34. $\sqrt{350}$

35. $\sqrt{36a^4b}$

36. $\sqrt{175y^8}$

37. $\sqrt[3]{8x^3y^2}$

38. $\sqrt[3]{27ab^6}$

39. $\sqrt[3]{-16x^6}$

40. $\sqrt[3]{-32a^6}$

Find a simplified form of $f(x)$. Assume that x can be any real number.

41. $f(x)=\sqrt[3]{125x^5}$

42. $f(x)=\sqrt[3]{16x^6}$

43. $f(x)=\sqrt{49(x-3)^2}$

44. $f(x)=\sqrt{81(x-1)^2}$

45. $f(x)=\sqrt{5x^2-10x+5}$

46. $f(x)=\sqrt{2x^2+8x+8}$

Simplify. Assume that no radicands were formed by raising negative numbers to even powers.

47. $\sqrt{a^6b^7}$

48. $\sqrt{x^6y^9}$

49. $\sqrt[3]{x^5y^6z^{10}}$

50. $\sqrt[3]{a^6b^7c^{13}}$

51. $\sqrt[4]{16x^5y^{11}}$

52. $\sqrt[5]{-32a^7b^{11}}$

53. $\sqrt[5]{x^{13}y^8z^{17}}$

54. $\sqrt[5]{a^6b^8c^9}$

55. $\sqrt[3]{-80a^{14}}$

56. $\sqrt[4]{810x^9}$

Multiply and simplify. Assume that no radicands were formed by raising negative numbers to even powers.

57. $\sqrt{6}\,\sqrt{3}$

58. $\sqrt{15}\,\sqrt{5}$

59. $\sqrt{10}\,\sqrt{14}$

60. $\sqrt{6}\,\sqrt{33}$

61. $\sqrt[3]{9}\,\sqrt[3]{3}$

62. $\sqrt[3]{2}\,\sqrt[3]{4}$

Aha! **63.** $\sqrt{18a^3}\,\sqrt{18a^3}$

64. $\sqrt{75x^7}\,\sqrt{75x^7}$

65. $\sqrt[3]{5a^2}\,\sqrt[3]{2a}$

66. $\sqrt[3]{7x}\,\sqrt[3]{3x^2}$

67. $3\sqrt{2x^5}\cdot4\sqrt{10x^2}$

68. $3\sqrt{5a^7}\,2\sqrt{15a^3}$

69. $\sqrt[3]{s^2t^4}\,\sqrt[3]{s^4t^6}$

70. $\sqrt[3]{x^2y^4}\,\sqrt[3]{x^2y^6}$

71. $\sqrt[3]{(x+5)^2}\,\sqrt[3]{(x+5)^4}$

72. $\sqrt[3]{(a-b)^5}\,\sqrt[3]{(a-b)^7}$

73. $\sqrt[4]{20a^3b^7}\,\sqrt[4]{4a^2b^5}$

74. $\sqrt[4]{9x^7y^2}\,\sqrt[4]{9x^2y^9}$

75. $\sqrt[5]{x^3(y+z)^6}\,\sqrt[5]{x^3(y+z)^4}$

76. $\sqrt[5]{a^3(b-c)^4}\,\sqrt[5]{a^7(b-c)^4}$

TW **77.** Explain how you could convince a friend that
$$\sqrt{x^2-16}\neq\sqrt{x^2}-\sqrt{16}.$$

TW **78.** Why is it incorrect to say that, in general, $\sqrt{x^2}=x$?

SKILL REVIEW

Review simplifying rational expressions.

Perform the indicated operation and, if possible, simplify.

79. $\dfrac{15a^2x}{8b}\cdot\dfrac{24b^2x}{5a}$

80. $\dfrac{x^2-1}{x^2-4}\div\dfrac{x^2-x-2}{x^2+x-2}$

81. $\dfrac{x-3}{2x-10}-\dfrac{3x-5}{x^2-25}$

82. $\dfrac{6x}{25y^2}+\dfrac{3y}{10x}$

83. $\dfrac{a^{-1}+b^{-1}}{ab}$

84. $\dfrac{\dfrac{1}{x+1}-\dfrac{2}{x}}{\dfrac{3}{x}+\dfrac{1}{x+1}}$

SYNTHESIS

TW **85.** Abdul is puzzled. When he uses a graphing calculator to graph $y=\sqrt{x}\cdot\sqrt{x}$, he gets the following screen. Explain why Abdul did not get the complete line $y=x$.

TW **86.** Is the equation $\sqrt{(2x + 3)^8} = (2x + 3)^4$ always, sometimes, or never true? Why?

87. *Radar Range.* The function given by

$$R(x) = \frac{1}{2}\sqrt[4]{\frac{x \cdot 3.0 \times 10^6}{\pi^2}}$$

can be used to determine the maximum range $R(x)$, in miles, of an ARSR-3 surveillance radar with a peak power of x watts. Determine the maximum radar range when the peak power is 5×10^4 watts.
Source: Introduction to RADAR Techniques, Federal Aviation Administration, 1988

88. *Speed of a Skidding Car.* Under certain conditions, police can estimate the speed at which a car was traveling by measuring its skid marks. The function given by

$$r(L) = 2\sqrt{5L}$$

can be used, where L is the length of a skid mark, in feet, and $r(L)$ is the speed, in miles per hour. Find the exact speed and an estimate (to the nearest tenth mile per hour) for the speed of a car that left skid marks **(a)** 20 ft long; **(b)** 70 ft long; **(c)** 90 ft long. See also Exercise 101.

89. *Wind Chill Temperature.* When the temperature is T degrees Celsius and the wind speed is v meters per second, the *wind chill temperature*, T_w, is the temperature (with no wind) that it feels like. Here is a formula for finding wind chill temperature:

$$T_w = 33 - \frac{\left(10.45 + 10\sqrt{v} - v\right)(33 - T)}{22}.$$

Estimate the wind chill temperature (to the nearest tenth of a degree) for the given actual temperatures and wind speeds.

a) $T = 7°C$, $v = 8$ m/sec
b) $T = 0°C$, $v = 12$ m/sec
c) $T = -5°C$, $v = 14$ m/sec
d) $T = -23°C$, $v = 15$ m/sec

Simplify. Assume that all variables are nonnegative.

90. $\left(\sqrt{r^3 t}\right)^7$

91. $\left(\sqrt[3]{25x^4}\right)^4$

92. $\left(\sqrt[3]{a^2 b^4}\right)^5$

93. $\left(\sqrt{a^3 b^5}\right)^7$

Draw and compare the graphs of each group of functions.

94. $f(x) = \sqrt{x^2 + 2x + 1}$,
$g(x) = x + 1$,
$h(x) = |x + 1|$

95. $f(x) = \sqrt{x^2 - 2x + 1}$,
$g(x) = x - 1$,
$h(x) = |x - 1|$

96. If $f(t) = \sqrt{t^2 - 3t - 4}$, what is the domain of f?

97. What is the domain of g, if $g(x) = \sqrt{x^2 - 6x + 8}$?

Solve.

98. $\sqrt[3]{5x^{k+1}} \sqrt[3]{25x^k} = 5x^7$, for k

99. $\sqrt[5]{4a^{3k+2}} \sqrt[5]{8a^{6-k}} = 2a^4$, for k

100. Use a graphing calculator to check your answers to Exercises 21 and 41.

TW **101.** Does a car traveling twice as fast as another car leave a skid mark that is twice as long? (See Exercise 88.) Why or why not?

12.4 Dividing Radical Expressions

- Dividing and Simplifying

- Rationalizing Denominators or Numerators with One Term

DIVIDING AND SIMPLIFYING

Just as the root of a product can be expressed as the product of two roots, the root of a quotient can be expressed as the quotient of two roots. For example,

$$\sqrt[3]{\frac{27}{8}} = \frac{3}{2} \quad \text{and} \quad \frac{\sqrt[3]{27}}{\sqrt[3]{8}} = \frac{3}{2}.$$

This example suggests the following.

The Quotient Rule for Radicals For any real numbers $\sqrt[n]{a}$ and $\sqrt[n]{b}, b \neq 0$,

$$\sqrt[n]{\frac{a}{b}} = \frac{\sqrt[n]{a}}{\sqrt[n]{b}}.$$

Remember that an nth root is simplified when its radicand has no factors that are perfect nth powers. Recall too that we assume that no radicands represent negative quantities raised to an even power.

EXAMPLE 1   Simplify by taking the roots of the numerator and the denominator.

a) $\sqrt[3]{\frac{27}{125}}$ **b)** $\sqrt{\frac{25}{y^2}}$

SOLUTION

a) $\sqrt[3]{\frac{27}{125}} = \frac{\sqrt[3]{27}}{\sqrt[3]{125}} = \frac{3}{5}$ Taking the cube roots of the numerator and the denominator

b) $\sqrt{\frac{25}{y^2}} = \frac{\sqrt{25}}{\sqrt{y^2}} = \frac{5}{y}$ Taking the square roots of the numerator and the denominator. Assume $y > 0$.

Try Exercise 9.

Any radical expressions appearing in the answers should be simplified as much as possible.

EXAMPLE 2   Simplify: **(a)** $\sqrt{\frac{16x^3}{y^8}}$; **(b)** $\sqrt[3]{\frac{27y^{14}}{8x^3}}$.

SOLUTION

a) $\sqrt{\dfrac{16x^3}{y^8}} = \dfrac{\sqrt{16x^3}}{\sqrt{y^8}}$

$= \dfrac{\sqrt{16x^2 \cdot x}}{\sqrt{y^8}} = \dfrac{4x\sqrt{x}}{y^4}$ Simplifying the numerator and the denominator

b) $\sqrt[3]{\dfrac{27y^{14}}{8x^3}} = \dfrac{\sqrt[3]{27^{14}}}{\sqrt[3]{8x^3}}$

$= \dfrac{\sqrt[3]{27y^{12}y^2}}{\sqrt[3]{8x^3}} = \dfrac{\sqrt[3]{27y^{12}}\,\sqrt[3]{y^2}}{\sqrt[3]{8x^3}} = \dfrac{3y^4\sqrt[3]{y^2}}{2x}$ Simplifying the numerator and the denominator

Try Exercise 15.

If we read from right to left, the quotient rule tells us that to divide two radical expressions that have the same index, we can divide the radicands.

EXAMPLE 3   Divide and, if possible, simplify.

a) $\dfrac{\sqrt{80}}{\sqrt{5}}$ **b)** $\dfrac{5\sqrt[3]{32}}{\sqrt[3]{2}}$ **c)** $\dfrac{\sqrt{72xy}}{2\sqrt{2}}$ **d)** $\dfrac{\sqrt[4]{18a^9b^5}}{\sqrt[4]{3b}}$

Student Notes

When writing radical signs, pay careful attention to what is included as the radicand. Each of the following represents a *different* number:

$$\sqrt{\dfrac{5 \cdot 2}{3}}, \quad \dfrac{\sqrt{5 \cdot 2}}{3}, \quad \dfrac{\sqrt{5} \cdot 2}{3}.$$

SOLUTION

a) $\dfrac{\sqrt{80}}{\sqrt{5}} = \sqrt{\dfrac{80}{5}} = \sqrt{16} = 4$ **Because the indices match, we can divide the radicands.**

b) $\dfrac{5\sqrt[3]{32}}{\sqrt[3]{2}} = 5\sqrt[3]{\dfrac{32}{2}} = 5\sqrt[3]{16}$

$= 5\sqrt[3]{8 \cdot 2}$ 8 is the largest perfect-cube factor of 16.

$= 5\sqrt[3]{8}\,\sqrt[3]{2} = 5 \cdot 2\sqrt[3]{2}$

$= 10\sqrt[3]{2}$

c) $\dfrac{\sqrt{72xy}}{2\sqrt{2}} = \dfrac{1}{2}\sqrt{\dfrac{72xy}{2}}$ **Because the indices match, we can divide the radicands.**

$= \dfrac{1}{2}\sqrt{36xy} = \dfrac{1}{2} \cdot 6\sqrt{xy} = 3\sqrt{xy}$

d) $\dfrac{\sqrt[4]{18a^9b^5}}{\sqrt[4]{3b}} = \sqrt[4]{\dfrac{18a^9b^5}{3b}}$

$= \sqrt[4]{6a^9b^4} = \sqrt[4]{a^8b^4}\,\sqrt[4]{6a}$ Note that 8 is the largest power less than 9 that is a multiple of the index 4.

$= a^2b\sqrt[4]{6a}$

Try Exercise 27.

RATIONALIZING DENOMINATORS OR NUMERATORS WITH ONE TERM *

The expressions

$$\frac{1}{\sqrt{2}} \quad \text{and} \quad \frac{\sqrt{2}}{2}$$

are equivalent, but the second expression does not have a radical expression in the denominator.[†] We can **rationalize the denominator** of a radical expression if we multiply by 1 in either of two ways.

One way is to multiply by 1 *under* the radical to make the denominator of the radicand a perfect power.

EXAMPLE 4   Rationalize each denominator.

a) $\sqrt{\dfrac{7}{3}}$ **b)** $\sqrt[3]{\dfrac{5}{16}}$

SOLUTION

a) We multiply by 1 under the radical, using $\frac{3}{3}$. We do this so that the denominator of the radicand will be a perfect square:

$$\sqrt{\frac{7}{3}} = \sqrt{\frac{7}{3} \cdot \frac{3}{3}} \qquad \text{Multiplying by 1 under the radical}$$

$$= \sqrt{\frac{21}{9}} \qquad \text{The denominator, 9, is now a perfect square.}$$

$$= \frac{\sqrt{21}}{\sqrt{9}} = \frac{\sqrt{21}}{3}.$$

b) Note that $16 = 4^2$. Thus, to make the denominator a perfect cube, we multiply under the radical by $\frac{4}{4}$:

$$\sqrt[3]{\frac{5}{16}} = \sqrt[3]{\frac{5}{4 \cdot 4} \cdot \frac{4}{4}} \qquad \text{Since the index is 3, we need 3 identical factors in the denominator.}$$

$$= \sqrt[3]{\frac{20}{4^3}} \qquad \text{The denominator is now a perfect cube.}$$

$$= \frac{\sqrt[3]{20}}{\sqrt[3]{4^3}} = \frac{\sqrt[3]{20}}{4}.$$

▮ Try Exercise 41.

Another way to rationalize a denominator is to multiply by 1 *outside* the radical.

EXAMPLE 5   Rationalize each denominator.

a) $\sqrt{\dfrac{4}{5b}}$ **b)** $\dfrac{\sqrt[3]{a}}{\sqrt[3]{9x}}$

---

*Denominators and numerators with two terms are rationalized in Section 12.5.
[†]See Exercise 73 on p. 753.

SOLUTION

a) We rewrite the expression as a quotient of two radicals. Then we simplify and multiply by 1:

$$\sqrt{\frac{4}{5b}} = \frac{\sqrt{4}}{\sqrt{5b}} = \frac{2}{\sqrt{5b}} \qquad \text{We assume } b > 0.$$

$$= \frac{2}{\sqrt{5b}} \cdot \frac{\sqrt{5b}}{\sqrt{5b}} \qquad \text{Multiplying by 1}$$

$$= \frac{2\sqrt{5b}}{(\sqrt{5b})^2} \qquad \text{Try to do this step mentally.}$$

$$= \frac{2\sqrt{5b}}{5b}.$$

b) To rationalize the denominator $\sqrt[3]{9x}$, note that $9x$ is $3 \cdot 3 \cdot x$. In order for this radicand to be a cube, we need another factor of 3 and two more factors of x. Thus we multiply by 1, using $\sqrt[3]{3x^2}/\sqrt[3]{3x^2}$:

$$\frac{\sqrt[3]{a}}{\sqrt[3]{9x}} = \frac{\sqrt[3]{a}}{\sqrt[3]{9x}} \cdot \frac{\sqrt[3]{3x^2}}{\sqrt[3]{3x^2}} \qquad \text{Multiplying by 1}$$

$$= \frac{\sqrt[3]{3ax^2}}{\sqrt[3]{27x^3}} \longleftarrow \text{This radicand is now a perfect cube.}$$

$$= \frac{\sqrt[3]{3ax^2}}{3x}.$$

Try Exercise 49.

Sometimes in calculus it is necessary to rationalize a numerator. To do so, we multiply by 1 to make the radicand in the *numerator* a perfect power.

EXAMPLE 6 Rationalize each numerator.

a) $\sqrt{\dfrac{7}{5}}$
b) $\dfrac{\sqrt[3]{4a^2}}{\sqrt[3]{5b}}$

SOLUTION

a) $\sqrt{\dfrac{7}{5}} = \sqrt{\dfrac{7}{5} \cdot \dfrac{7}{7}}$ 　Multiplying by 1 under the radical. We also could have multiplied by $\sqrt{7}/\sqrt{7}$ outside the radical.

$$= \sqrt{\frac{49}{35}} \qquad \text{The numerator is now a perfect square.}$$

$$= \frac{\sqrt{49}}{\sqrt{35}} = \frac{7}{\sqrt{35}}$$

b) $\dfrac{\sqrt[3]{4a^2}}{\sqrt[3]{5b}} = \dfrac{\sqrt[3]{4a^2}}{\sqrt[3]{5b}} \cdot \dfrac{\sqrt[3]{2a}}{\sqrt[3]{2a}}$ 　Multiplying by 1

$$= \frac{\sqrt[3]{8a^3}}{\sqrt[3]{10ba}} \longleftarrow \text{This radicand is now a perfect cube.}$$

$$= \frac{2a}{\sqrt[3]{10ab}}$$

Try Exercise 59.

12.4 **Exercise Set**

↪ *Concept Reinforcement* *In each of Exercises 1–8, match the expression with an equivalent expression from the column on the right. Assume a, b > 0.*

1. — $\sqrt[3]{\dfrac{a^2}{b^6}}$

  a) $\dfrac{\sqrt[5]{a^2}\,\sqrt[5]{b^2}}{\sqrt[5]{b^5}}$

2. — $\dfrac{\sqrt[3]{a^6}}{\sqrt[3]{b^9}}$

  b) $\dfrac{a^2}{b^3}$

3. — $\sqrt[5]{\dfrac{a^6}{b^4}}$

  c) $\sqrt{\dfrac{a \cdot b}{b^3 \cdot b}}$

4. — $\sqrt{\dfrac{a}{b^3}}$

  d) $\sqrt{a}$

  e) $\dfrac{\sqrt[3]{a^2}}{b^2}$

5. — $\dfrac{\sqrt[5]{a^2}}{\sqrt[5]{b^2}}$

  f) $\sqrt[5]{\dfrac{a^6 b}{b^4 \cdot b}}$

6. — $\dfrac{\sqrt{5a^4}}{\sqrt{5a^3}}$

  g) $2a$

7. — $\dfrac{\sqrt[5]{a^2}}{\sqrt[5]{b^3}}$

  h) $\dfrac{\sqrt[5]{a^2 b^3}}{\sqrt[5]{b^5}}$

8. — $\sqrt[4]{\dfrac{16a^6}{a^2}}$

Simplify by taking the roots of the numerator and the denominator. Assume that all variables represent positive numbers.

9. $\sqrt{\dfrac{36}{25}}$

10. $\sqrt{\dfrac{100}{81}}$

11. $\sqrt[3]{\dfrac{64}{27}}$

12. $\sqrt[3]{\dfrac{343}{1000}}$

13. $\sqrt{\dfrac{49}{y^2}}$

14. $\sqrt{\dfrac{121}{x^2}}$

15. $\sqrt{\dfrac{36y^3}{x^4}}$

16. $\sqrt{\dfrac{25a^5}{b^6}}$

17. $\sqrt[3]{\dfrac{27a^4}{8b^3}}$

18. $\sqrt[3]{\dfrac{64x^7}{216y^6}}$

19. $\sqrt[4]{\dfrac{32a^4}{2b^4c^8}}$

20. $\sqrt[4]{\dfrac{81x^4}{y^8z^4}}$

21. $\sqrt[4]{\dfrac{a^5b^8}{c^{10}}}$

22. $\sqrt[4]{\dfrac{x^9y^{12}}{z^6}}$

23. $\sqrt[5]{\dfrac{32x^6}{y^{11}}}$

24. $\sqrt[5]{\dfrac{243a^9}{b^{13}}}$

25. $\sqrt[6]{\dfrac{x^6y^8}{z^{15}}}$

26. $\sqrt[6]{\dfrac{a^9b^{12}}{c^{13}}}$

Divide and, if possible, simplify. Assume that all variables represent positive numbers.

27. $\dfrac{\sqrt{18y}}{\sqrt{2y}}$

28. $\dfrac{\sqrt{700x}}{\sqrt{7x}}$

29. $\dfrac{\sqrt[3]{26}}{\sqrt[3]{13}}$

30. $\dfrac{\sqrt[3]{35}}{\sqrt[3]{5}}$

31. $\dfrac{\sqrt{40xy^3}}{\sqrt{8x}}$

32. $\dfrac{\sqrt{56ab^3}}{\sqrt{7a}}$

33. $\dfrac{\sqrt[3]{96a^4b^2}}{\sqrt[3]{12a^2b}}$

34. $\dfrac{\sqrt[3]{189x^5y^7}}{\sqrt[3]{7x^2y^2}}$

35. $\dfrac{\sqrt{100ab}}{5\sqrt{2}}$

36. $\dfrac{\sqrt{75ab}}{3\sqrt{3}}$

37. $\dfrac{\sqrt[4]{48x^9y^{13}}}{\sqrt[4]{3xy^{-2}}}$

38. $\dfrac{\sqrt[5]{64a^{11}b^{28}}}{\sqrt[5]{2ab^{-2}}}$

39. $\dfrac{\sqrt[3]{x^3 - y^3}}{\sqrt[3]{x - y}}$ ←

40. → $\dfrac{\sqrt[3]{r^3 + s^3}}{\sqrt[3]{r + s}}$

Hint: Factor and then simplify.

Rationalize each denominator. Assume that all variables represent positive numbers.

41. $\sqrt{\dfrac{3}{2}}$

42. $\sqrt{\dfrac{6}{7}}$

43. $\dfrac{2\sqrt{5}}{7\sqrt{3}}$

44. $\dfrac{3\sqrt{5}}{2\sqrt{2}}$

45. $\sqrt[3]{\dfrac{5}{4}}$

46. $\sqrt[3]{\dfrac{2}{9}}$

47. $\dfrac{\sqrt[3]{3a}}{\sqrt[3]{5c}}$

48. $\dfrac{\sqrt[3]{7x}}{\sqrt[3]{3y}}$

49. $\dfrac{\sqrt[4]{5y^6}}{\sqrt[4]{9x}}$

50. $\dfrac{\sqrt[5]{3a^4}}{\sqrt[5]{2b^7}}$

51. $\sqrt[3]{\dfrac{2}{x^2y}}$

52. $\sqrt[3]{\dfrac{5}{ab^2}}$

53. $\sqrt{\dfrac{7a}{18}}$

54. $\sqrt{\dfrac{3x}{10}}$

55. $\sqrt{\dfrac{9}{20x^2y}}$

56. $\sqrt{\dfrac{7}{32a^2b}}$

Aha! **57.** $\sqrt{\dfrac{10ab^2}{72a^3b}}$

58. $\sqrt{\dfrac{21x^2y}{75xy^5}}$

Rationalize each numerator. Assume that all variables represent positive numbers.

59. $\sqrt{\dfrac{5}{11}}$

60. $\sqrt{\dfrac{2}{3}}$

61. $\dfrac{2\sqrt{6}}{5\sqrt{7}}$

62. $\dfrac{3\sqrt{10}}{2\sqrt{3}}$

63. $\dfrac{\sqrt{8}}{2\sqrt{3x}}$

64. $\dfrac{\sqrt{12}}{\sqrt{5y}}$

65. $\dfrac{\sqrt[3]{7}}{\sqrt[3]{2}}$

66. $\dfrac{\sqrt[3]{5}}{\sqrt[3]{4}}$

67. $\sqrt{\dfrac{7x}{3y}}$

68. $\sqrt{\dfrac{7a}{6b}}$

69. $\sqrt[3]{\dfrac{2a^5}{5b}}$

70. $\sqrt[3]{\dfrac{2a^4}{7b}}$

71. $\sqrt{\dfrac{x^3y}{2}}$

72. $\sqrt{\dfrac{ab^5}{3}}$

TW **73.** Explain why it is easier to approximate

$$\dfrac{\sqrt{2}}{2} \quad \text{than} \quad \dfrac{1}{\sqrt{2}}$$

if no calculator is available and we know that $\sqrt{2} \approx 1.414213562$.

TW **74.** A student *incorrectly* claims that

$$\dfrac{5 + \sqrt{2}}{\sqrt{18}} = \dfrac{5 + \sqrt{1}}{\sqrt{9}} = \dfrac{5 + 1}{3}.$$

How could you convince the student that a mistake has been made? How would you explain the correct way of rationalizing the denominator?

SKILL REVIEW

To prepare for Section 12.5, review factoring expressions and multiplying polynomials.

Factor.

75. $3x - 8xy + 2xz$

76. $4a^2c + 9ac - 3a^3c$

Multiply.

77. $(a + b)(a - b)$

78. $(a^2 - 2y)(a^2 + 2y)$

79. $(8 + 3x)(7 - 4x)$

80. $(2y - x)(3a - c)$

SYNTHESIS

TW **81.** Is the quotient of two irrational numbers always an irrational number? Why or why not?

TW **82.** Is it possible to understand how to rationalize a denominator without knowing how to multiply rational expressions? Why or why not?

83. *Pendulums.*   The *period* of a pendulum is the time it takes to complete one cycle, swinging to and fro. For a pendulum that is L centimeters long, the period T is given by the formula

$$T = 2\pi\sqrt{\dfrac{L}{980}},$$

where T is in seconds. Find, to the nearest hundredth of a second, the period of a pendulum of length **(a)** 65 cm; **(b)** 98 cm; **(c)** 120 cm. Use a calculator's $\boxed{\pi}$ key if possible.

Perform the indicated operations.

84. $\dfrac{7\sqrt{a^2b} \ \sqrt{25xy}}{5\sqrt{a^{-4}b^{-1}} \ \sqrt{49x^{-1}y^{-3}}}$

85. $\dfrac{\left(\sqrt[3]{81mn^2}\right)^2}{\left(\sqrt[3]{mn}\right)^2}$

86. $\dfrac{\sqrt{44x^2y^9z} \ \sqrt{22y^9z^6}}{\left(\sqrt{11xy^8z^2}\right)^2}$

87. $\sqrt{a^2 - 3} - \dfrac{a^2}{\sqrt{a^2 - 3}}$

88. $5\sqrt{\dfrac{x}{y}} + 4\sqrt{\dfrac{y}{x}} - \dfrac{3}{\sqrt{xy}}$

89. Provide a reason for each step in the following derivation of the quotient rule:

$$\sqrt[n]{\dfrac{a}{b}} = \left(\dfrac{a}{b}\right)^{1/n} \quad \underline{\hspace{3cm}}$$

$$= \dfrac{a^{1/n}}{b^{1/n}} \quad \underline{\hspace{3cm}}$$

$$= \dfrac{\sqrt[n]{a}}{\sqrt[n]{b}} \quad \underline{\hspace{3cm}}$$

90. Show that $\dfrac{\sqrt[n]{a}}{\sqrt[n]{b}}$ is the nth root of $\dfrac{a}{b}$ by raising it to the nth power and simplifying.

91. Let $f(x) = \sqrt{18x^3}$ and $g(x) = \sqrt{2x}$. Find $(f/g)(x)$ and specify the domain of f/g.

92. Let $f(t) = \sqrt{2t}$ and $g(t) = \sqrt{50t^3}$. Find $(f/g)(t)$ and specify the domain of f/g.

93. Let $f(x) = \sqrt{x^2 - 9}$ and $g(x) = \sqrt{x - 3}$. Find $(f/g)(x)$ and specify the domain of f/g.

Try Exercise Answers: Section 12.4

9. $\dfrac{6}{5}$ **15.** $\dfrac{6y\sqrt{y}}{x^2}$ **27.** 3 **41.** $\dfrac{\sqrt{6}}{2}$ **49.** $\dfrac{y\sqrt[4]{45x^3y^2}}{3x}$

59. $\dfrac{5}{\sqrt{55}}$

12.5 Expressions Containing Several Radical Terms

- **Adding and Subtracting Radical Expressions**

- **Products and Quotients of Two or More Radical Terms**

- **Rationalizing Denominators and Numerators with Two Terms**

- **Terms with Differing Indices**

Radical expressions like $6\sqrt{7} + 4\sqrt{7}$ or $(\sqrt{a} + \sqrt{b})(\sqrt{a} - \sqrt{b})$ contain more than one *radical term* and can sometimes be simplified.

ADDING AND SUBTRACTING RADICAL EXPRESSIONS

When two radical expressions have the same indices and radicands, they are said to be **like radicals.** Like radicals can be combined (added or subtracted) in much the same way that we combine like terms.

EXAMPLE 1 Simplify by combining like radical terms.

a) $6\sqrt{7} + 4\sqrt{7}$

b) $\sqrt[3]{2} - 7x\sqrt[3]{2} + 5\sqrt[3]{2}$

c) $6\sqrt[5]{4x} + 3\sqrt[5]{4x} - \sqrt[3]{4x}$

SOLUTION

a) $6\sqrt{7} + 4\sqrt{7} = (6 + 4)\sqrt{7}$ Using the distributive law (factoring out $\sqrt{7}$)

$= 10\sqrt{7}$ You can think: 6 square roots of 7 plus 4 square roots of 7 results in 10 square roots of 7.

b) $\sqrt[3]{2} - 7x\sqrt[3]{2} + 5\sqrt[3]{2} = (1 - 7x + 5)\sqrt[3]{2}$ Factoring out $\sqrt[3]{2}$

$= (6 - 7x)\sqrt[3]{2}$ These parentheses are important!

Student Notes

Combining like radicals is similar to combining like terms. Recall the following:

$$3x + 8x = (3 + 8)x = 11x$$

and

$$6x^2 - 7x^2 = (6 - 7)x^2 = -x^2.$$

c) $6\sqrt[5]{4x} + 3\sqrt[5]{4x} - \sqrt[3]{4x} = (6 + 3)\sqrt[5]{4x} - \sqrt[3]{4x}$ Try to do this step mentally.

$$= 9\sqrt[5]{4x} - \sqrt[3]{4x}$$ The indices are different. We cannot combine these terms.

 Try Exercise 7.

Our ability to simplify radical expressions can help us to find like radicals even when, at first, it may appear that none exists.

EXAMPLE 2   Simplify by combining like radical terms, if possible.

a) $3\sqrt{8} - 5\sqrt{2}$

b) $9\sqrt{5} - 4\sqrt{3}$

c) $\sqrt[3]{2x^6y^4} + 7\sqrt[3]{2y}$

SOLUTION

a) $3\sqrt{8} - 5\sqrt{2} = 3\sqrt{4 \cdot 2} - 5\sqrt{2}$

$\qquad\qquad\quad = 3\sqrt{4} \cdot \sqrt{2} - 5\sqrt{2}$ Simplifying $\sqrt{8}$

$\qquad\qquad\quad = 3 \cdot 2 \cdot \sqrt{2} - 5\sqrt{2}$

$\qquad\qquad\quad = 6\sqrt{2} - 5\sqrt{2}$

$\qquad\qquad\quad = \sqrt{2}$ Combining like radicals

b) $9\sqrt{5} - 4\sqrt{3}$ cannot be simplified.   The radicands are different.

c) $\sqrt[3]{2x^6y^4} + 7\sqrt[3]{2y} = \sqrt[3]{x^6y^3 \cdot 2y} + 7\sqrt[3]{2y}$

$\qquad\qquad\qquad\quad = \sqrt[3]{x^6y^3} \cdot \sqrt[3]{2y} + 7\sqrt[3]{2y}$ Simplifying $\sqrt[3]{2x^6y^4}$

$\qquad\qquad\qquad\quad = x^2y \cdot \sqrt[3]{2y} + 7\sqrt[3]{2y}$

$\qquad\qquad\qquad\quad = (x^2y + 7)\sqrt[3]{2y}$ Factoring to combine like radical terms

Try Exercise 17.

STUDY TIP

Review Material on Your Own

Never hesitate to review earlier material in which you feel a lack of confidence. For example, if you feel unsure about how to multiply with fraction notation, be sure to review that material before studying any new material that involves multiplication of fractions. Doing (and checking) some practice problems from that section is also a good way to sharpen any skills that you may not have used for a while.

PRODUCTS AND QUOTIENTS OF TWO OR MORE RADICAL TERMS

Radical expressions often contain factors that have more than one term. Multiplying such expressions is similar to finding products of polynomials. Some products will yield like radical terms, which we can now combine.

EXAMPLE 3   Multiply.

a) $\sqrt{3}(x - \sqrt{5})$

b) $\sqrt[3]{y}(\sqrt[3]{y^2} + \sqrt[3]{2})$

c) $(4 - \sqrt{7})^2$

d) $(4\sqrt{3} + \sqrt{2})(\sqrt{3} - 5\sqrt{2})$

e) $(\sqrt{a} + \sqrt{b})(\sqrt{a} - \sqrt{b})$

SOLUTION

a) $\sqrt{3}(x - \sqrt{5}) = \sqrt{3} \cdot x - \sqrt{3} \cdot \sqrt{5}$ Using the distributive law

$\qquad\qquad\quad = x\sqrt{3} - \sqrt{15}$ Multiplying radicals

b) $\sqrt[3]{y}(\sqrt[3]{y^2} + \sqrt[3]{2}) = \sqrt[3]{y} \cdot \sqrt[3]{y^2} + \sqrt[3]{y} \cdot \sqrt[3]{2}$ Using the distributive law

$\qquad\qquad\qquad\quad = \sqrt[3]{y^3} + \sqrt[3]{2y}$ Multiplying radicals

$\qquad\qquad\qquad\quad = y + \sqrt[3]{2y}$ Simplifying $\sqrt[3]{y^3}$

c) $\left(4 - \sqrt{7}\right)^2 = \left(4 - \sqrt{7}\right)\left(4 - \sqrt{7}\right)$ We could also use the pattern
$(A - B)^2 = A^2 - 2AB + B^2$.

$$\overset{F}{= 4^2} \overset{O}{- 4\sqrt{7}} \overset{I}{- 4\sqrt{7}} \overset{L}{+ \left(\sqrt{7}\right)^2}$$

$= 16 - 8\sqrt{7} + 7$ Squaring and combining like terms

$= 23 - 8\sqrt{7}$ Adding 16 and 7

d) $\left(4\sqrt{3} + \sqrt{2}\right)\left(\sqrt{3} - 5\sqrt{2}\right) = \overset{F}{4\left(\sqrt{3}\right)^2} \overset{O}{- 20\sqrt{3} \cdot \sqrt{2}} \overset{I}{+ \sqrt{2} \cdot \sqrt{3}} \overset{L}{- 5\left(\sqrt{2}\right)^2}$

$= 4 \cdot 3 - 20\sqrt{6} + \sqrt{6} - 5 \cdot 2$ Multiplying radicals

$= 12 - 20\sqrt{6} + \sqrt{6} - 10$

$= 2 - 19\sqrt{6}$ Combining like terms

e) $\left(\sqrt{a} + \sqrt{b}\right)\left(\sqrt{a} - \sqrt{b}\right) = \left(\sqrt{a}\right)^2 - \sqrt{a}\sqrt{b} + \sqrt{a}\sqrt{b} - \left(\sqrt{b}\right)^2$

Using FOIL

$= a - b$ Combining like terms

Try Exercise 33.

In Example 3(e) above, you may have noticed that since the outer and inner products in FOIL are opposites, the result, $a - b$, is not itself a radical expression. Pairs of radical expressions like $\sqrt{a} + \sqrt{b}$ and $\sqrt{a} - \sqrt{b}$ are called **conjugates.**

RATIONALIZING DENOMINATORS AND NUMERATORS WITH TWO TERMS

The use of conjugates allows us to rationalize denominators or numerators with two terms.

EXAMPLE 4   Rationalize each denominator: **(a)** $\dfrac{4}{\sqrt{3} + x}$;   **(b)** $\dfrac{4 + \sqrt{2}}{\sqrt{5} - \sqrt{2}}$.

SOLUTION

a) $\dfrac{4}{\sqrt{3} + x} = \dfrac{4}{\sqrt{3} + x} \cdot \dfrac{\sqrt{3} - x}{\sqrt{3} - x}$ Multiplying by 1, using the conjugate of $\sqrt{3} + x$, which is $\sqrt{3} - x$

$= \dfrac{4\left(\sqrt{3} - x\right)}{\left(\sqrt{3} + x\right)\left(\sqrt{3} - x\right)}$ Multiplying numerators and denominators

$= \dfrac{4\left(\sqrt{3} - x\right)}{\left(\sqrt{3}\right)^2 - x^2}$ Using FOIL in the denominator

$= \dfrac{4\sqrt{3} - 4x}{3 - x^2}$ Simplifying. No radicals remain in the denominator.

b) $\dfrac{4 + \sqrt{2}}{\sqrt{5} - \sqrt{2}} = \dfrac{4 + \sqrt{2}}{\sqrt{5} - \sqrt{2}} \cdot \dfrac{\sqrt{5} + \sqrt{2}}{\sqrt{5} + \sqrt{2}}$ Multiplying by 1, using the conjugate of $\sqrt{5} - \sqrt{2}$, which is $\sqrt{5} + \sqrt{2}$

$= \dfrac{\left(4 + \sqrt{2}\right)\left(\sqrt{5} + \sqrt{2}\right)}{\left(\sqrt{5} - \sqrt{2}\right)\left(\sqrt{5} + \sqrt{2}\right)}$ Multiplying numerators and denominators

$= \dfrac{4\sqrt{5} + 4\sqrt{2} + \sqrt{2}\sqrt{5} + \left(\sqrt{2}\right)^2}{\left(\sqrt{5}\right)^2 - \left(\sqrt{2}\right)^2}$ Using FOIL

$= \dfrac{4\sqrt{5} + 4\sqrt{2} + \sqrt{10} + 2}{5 - 2}$ Squaring in the denominator and the numerator

$= \dfrac{4\sqrt{5} + 4\sqrt{2} + \sqrt{10} + 2}{3}$ No radicals remain in the denominator.

```
(4+√ (2))/(√ (5)−√
(2))
              6.587801273
(4√ (5)+4√ (2)+√ (1
0)+2)/3
              6.587801273
```

We can check by approximating the value of the original expression and the value of the rationalized expression, as shown at left. Care must be taken to place the parentheses properly. The approximate values are the same, so we have a check.

▌ Try Exercise 61.

To rationalize a numerator with two terms, we use the conjugate of the numerator.

EXAMPLE 5   Rationalize the numerator: $\dfrac{4 + \sqrt{2}}{\sqrt{5} - \sqrt{2}}$.

SOLUTION   We have

$\dfrac{4 + \sqrt{2}}{\sqrt{5} - \sqrt{2}} = \dfrac{4 + \sqrt{2}}{\sqrt{5} - \sqrt{2}} \cdot \dfrac{4 - \sqrt{2}}{4 - \sqrt{2}}$ Multiplying by 1, using the conjugate of $4 + \sqrt{2}$, which is $4 - \sqrt{2}$

$= \dfrac{16 - \left(\sqrt{2}\right)^2}{4\sqrt{5} - \sqrt{5}\sqrt{2} - 4\sqrt{2} + \left(\sqrt{2}\right)^2}$

$= \dfrac{14}{4\sqrt{5} - \sqrt{10} - 4\sqrt{2} + 2}$.

```
(4+√ (2))/(√ (5)−√
(2))
              6.587801273
14/(4√ (5)−√ (10)−
4√ (2)+2)
              6.587801273
```

We check by comparing the values of the original expression and the expression with a rationalized numerator, as shown at left.

▌ Try Exercise 71.

TERMS WITH DIFFERING INDICES

To multiply or divide radical terms with different indices, we can often convert to exponential notation, use the rules for exponents, and then convert back to radical notation.

Student Notes

Expressions similar to the one in Example 6 are most easily simplified by rewriting the expression using exponents in place of radicals. After simplifying, remember to write your final result in radical notation. In general, if a problem is presented in one form, it is expected that the final result be presented in the same form.

EXAMPLE 6   Divide and, if possible, simplify: $\dfrac{\sqrt[4]{(x+y)^3}}{\sqrt{x+y}}$.

SOLUTION

$$\dfrac{\sqrt[4]{(x+y)^3}}{\sqrt{x+y}} = \dfrac{(x+y)^{3/4}}{(x+y)^{1/2}}$$ Converting to exponential notation

$$= (x+y)^{3/4-1/2}$$ Since the bases are identical, we can subtract exponents: $\frac{3}{4} - \frac{1}{2} = \frac{3}{4} - \frac{2}{4} = \frac{1}{4}$.

$$\left.\begin{array}{l} = (x+y)^{1/4} \\ = \sqrt[4]{x+y} \end{array}\right\}$$ Converting back to radical notation

Try Exercise 89.

To Simplify Products or Quotients with Differing Indices

1. Convert all radical expressions to exponential notation.
2. When the bases are identical, subtract exponents to divide and add exponents to multiply. This may require finding a common denominator.
3. Convert back to radical notation and, if possible, simplify.

EXAMPLE 7   Multiply and simplify: $\sqrt{x^3}\,\sqrt[3]{x}$.

SOLUTION

$$\sqrt{x^3}\,\sqrt[3]{x} = x^{3/2} \cdot x^{1/3}$$ Converting to exponential notation

$$= x^{11/6}$$ Adding exponents: $\frac{3}{2} + \frac{1}{3} = \frac{9}{6} + \frac{2}{6}$

$$= \sqrt[6]{x^{11}}$$ Converting back to radical notation

$$\left.\begin{array}{l} = \sqrt[6]{x^6}\,\sqrt[6]{x^5} \\ = x\sqrt[6]{x^5} \end{array}\right\}$$ Simplifying

Try Exercise 79.

EXAMPLE 8   If $f(x) = \sqrt[3]{x^2}$ and $g(x) = \sqrt{x} + \sqrt[4]{x}$, find $(f \cdot g)(x)$.

SOLUTION   Recall that $(f \cdot g)(x) = f(x) \cdot g(x)$ Thus,

$$(f \cdot g)(x) = \sqrt[3]{x^2}\left(\sqrt{x} + \sqrt[4]{x}\right)$$ x is assumed to be nonnegative.

$$= x^{2/3}(x^{1/2} + x^{1/4})$$ Converting to exponential notation

$$= x^{2/3} \cdot x^{1/2} + x^{2/3} \cdot x^{1/4}$$ Using the distributive law

$$= x^{2/3+1/2} + x^{2/3+1/4}$$ Adding exponents

$$= x^{7/6} + x^{11/12}$$ $\frac{2}{3} + \frac{1}{2} = \frac{4}{6} + \frac{3}{6}; \frac{2}{3} + \frac{1}{4} = \frac{8}{12} + \frac{3}{12}$

$$= \sqrt[6]{x^7} + \sqrt[12]{x^{11}}$$ Converting back to radical notation

$$\left.\begin{array}{l} = \sqrt[6]{x^6}\,\sqrt[6]{x} + \sqrt[12]{x^{11}} \\ = x\sqrt[6]{x} + \sqrt[12]{x^{11}} \end{array}\right\}$$ Simplifying

Try Exercise 103.

We can often write a result as a single radical expression by finding a common denominator in the exponents.

EXAMPLE 9   Divide and, if possible, simplify: $\dfrac{\sqrt[3]{a^2b^4}}{\sqrt{ab}}$.

SOLUTION

$$\dfrac{\sqrt[3]{a^2b^4}}{\sqrt{ab}} = \dfrac{(a^2b^4)^{1/3}}{(ab)^{1/2}} \qquad \text{Converting to exponential notation}$$

$$= \dfrac{a^{2/3}b^{4/3}}{a^{1/2}b^{1/2}} \qquad \text{Using the product and power rules}$$

$$= a^{2/3-1/2}b^{4/3-1/2} \qquad \text{Subtracting exponents}$$

$$= a^{1/6}b^{5/6}$$

$$= \sqrt[6]{a}\,\sqrt[6]{b^5} \qquad \text{Converting to radical notation}$$

$$= \sqrt[6]{ab^5} \qquad \text{Using the product rule for radicals}$$

Try Exercise 93.

12.5   Exercise Set

FOR EXTRA HELP   *MyMathLab*   Math XL PRACTICE   WATCH   DOWNLOAD   READ   REVIEW

Concept Reinforcement   *For each of Exercises 1–6, fill in the blanks by selecting from the following words (which may be used more than once):*

radicand(s), indices, conjugate(s), base(s), denominator(s), numerator(s).

1. To add radical expressions, the _____ and the _____ must be the same.

2. To multiply radical expressions, the _____ must be the same.

3. To find a product by adding exponents, the _____ must be the same.

4. To add rational expressions, the _____ must be the same.

5. To rationalize the _____ of $\dfrac{\sqrt{c}-\sqrt{a}}{5}$, we multiply by a form of 1, using the _____ of $\sqrt{c}-\sqrt{a}$, or $\sqrt{c}+\sqrt{a}$, to write 1.

6. To find a quotient by subtracting exponents, the _____ must be the same.

Add or subtract. Simplify by combining like radical terms, if possible. Assume that all variables and radicands represent positive real numbers.

7. $2\sqrt{5}+7\sqrt{5}$

8. $4\sqrt{7}+2\sqrt{7}$

9. $7\sqrt[3]{4}-5\sqrt[3]{4}$

10. $14\sqrt[5]{2}-6\sqrt[5]{2}$

11. $\sqrt[3]{y}+9\sqrt[3]{y}$

12. $9\sqrt[4]{t}-\sqrt[4]{t}$

13. $8\sqrt{2}-\sqrt{2}+5\sqrt{2}$

14. $\sqrt{6}-8\sqrt{6}+2\sqrt{6}$

15. $9\sqrt[3]{7}-\sqrt{3}+4\sqrt[3]{7}+2\sqrt{3}$

16. $5\sqrt{7}-8\sqrt[4]{11}+\sqrt{7}+9\sqrt[4]{11}$

17. $4\sqrt{27}-3\sqrt{3}$

18. $9\sqrt{50}-4\sqrt{2}$

19. $3\sqrt{45}-8\sqrt{20}$

20. $5\sqrt{12}+16\sqrt{27}$

21. $3\sqrt[3]{16} + \sqrt[3]{54}$

22. $\sqrt[3]{27} - 5\sqrt[3]{8}$

23. $\sqrt{a} + 3\sqrt{16a^3}$

24. $2\sqrt{9x^3} - \sqrt{x}$

25. $\sqrt[3]{6x^4} - \sqrt[3]{48x}$

26. $\sqrt[3]{54x} - \sqrt[3]{2x^4}$

27. $\sqrt{4a - 4} + \sqrt{a - 1}$

28. $\sqrt{9y + 27} + \sqrt{y + 3}$

29. $\sqrt{x^3 - x^2} + \sqrt{9x - 9}$

30. $\sqrt{4x - 4} - \sqrt{x^3 - x^2}$

Multiply. Assume that all variables represent nonnegative real numbers.

31. $\sqrt{3}(4 + \sqrt{3})$

32. $\sqrt{7}(3 - \sqrt{7})$

33. $3\sqrt{5}(\sqrt{5} - \sqrt{2})$

34. $4\sqrt{2}(\sqrt{3} - \sqrt{5})$

35. $\sqrt{2}(3\sqrt{10} - 2\sqrt{2})$

36. $\sqrt{3}(2\sqrt{5} - 3\sqrt{4})$

37. $\sqrt[3]{3}(\sqrt[3]{9} - 4\sqrt[3]{21})$

38. $\sqrt[3]{2}(\sqrt[3]{4} - 2\sqrt[3]{32})$

39. $\sqrt[3]{a}(\sqrt[3]{a^2} + \sqrt[3]{24a^2})$

40. $\sqrt[3]{x}(\sqrt[3]{3x^2} - \sqrt[3]{81x^2})$

41. $(2 + \sqrt{6})(5 - \sqrt{6})$

42. $(4 - \sqrt{5})(2 + \sqrt{5})$

43. $(\sqrt{2} + \sqrt{7})(\sqrt{3} - \sqrt{7})$

44. $(\sqrt{7} - \sqrt{2})(\sqrt{5} + \sqrt{2})$

45. $(3 - \sqrt{5})(3 + \sqrt{5})$

46. $(2 + \sqrt{11})(2 - \sqrt{11})$

47. $(\sqrt{6} + \sqrt{8})(\sqrt{6} - \sqrt{8})$

48. $(\sqrt{12} - \sqrt{7})(\sqrt{12} + \sqrt{7})$

49. $(3\sqrt{7} + 2\sqrt{5})(2\sqrt{7} - 4\sqrt{5})$

50. $(4\sqrt{5} - 3\sqrt{2})(2\sqrt{5} + 4\sqrt{2})$

51. $(2 + \sqrt{3})^2$

52. $(3 + \sqrt{7})^2$

53. $(\sqrt{3} - \sqrt{2})^2$

54. $(\sqrt{5} - \sqrt{3})^2$

55. $(\sqrt{2t} + \sqrt{5})^2$

56. $(\sqrt{3x} - \sqrt{2})^2$

57. $(3 - \sqrt{x + 5})^2$

58. $(4 + \sqrt{x - 3})^2$

59. $(2\sqrt[4]{7} - \sqrt[4]{6})(3\sqrt[4]{9} + 2\sqrt[4]{5})$

60. $(4\sqrt[3]{3} + \sqrt[3]{10})(2\sqrt[3]{7} + 5\sqrt[3]{6})$

Rationalize each denominator.

61. $\dfrac{6}{3 - \sqrt{2}}$

62. $\dfrac{3}{4 - \sqrt{7}}$

63. $\dfrac{2 + \sqrt{5}}{6 + \sqrt{3}}$

64. $\dfrac{1 + \sqrt{2}}{3 + \sqrt{5}}$

65. $\dfrac{\sqrt{a}}{\sqrt{a} + \sqrt{b}}$

66. $\dfrac{\sqrt{z}}{\sqrt{x} - \sqrt{z}}$

Aha! **67.** $\dfrac{\sqrt{7} - \sqrt{3}}{\sqrt{3} - \sqrt{7}}$

68. $\dfrac{\sqrt{7} + \sqrt{5}}{\sqrt{5} + \sqrt{2}}$

69. $\dfrac{3\sqrt{2} - \sqrt{7}}{4\sqrt{2} + 2\sqrt{5}}$

70. $\dfrac{5\sqrt{3} - \sqrt{11}}{2\sqrt{3} - 5\sqrt{2}}$

Rationalize each numerator. If possible, simplify your result.

71. $\dfrac{\sqrt{5} + 1}{4}$

72. $\dfrac{\sqrt{3} + 1}{4}$

73. $\dfrac{\sqrt{6} - 2}{\sqrt{3} + 7}$

74. $\dfrac{\sqrt{10} + 4}{\sqrt{2} - 3}$

75. $\dfrac{\sqrt{x} - \sqrt{y}}{\sqrt{x} + \sqrt{y}}$

76. $\dfrac{\sqrt{a} + \sqrt{b}}{\sqrt{a} - \sqrt{b}}$

77. $\dfrac{\sqrt{a + h} - \sqrt{a}}{h}$

78. $\dfrac{\sqrt{x - h} - \sqrt{x}}{h}$

Perform the indicated operation and simplify. Assume that all variables represent positive real numbers.

79. $\sqrt[3]{a}\,\sqrt[6]{a}$

80. $\sqrt[10]{a}\,\sqrt[5]{a^2}$

81. $\sqrt[5]{b^2}\,\sqrt{b^3}$

82. $\sqrt[4]{a^3}\,\sqrt[3]{a^2}$

83. $\sqrt{xy^3}\,\sqrt[3]{x^2y}$

84. $\sqrt[5]{a^3b}\,\sqrt{ab}$

85. $\sqrt[4]{9ab^3}\,\sqrt{3a^4b}$

86. $\sqrt{2x^3y^3}\,\sqrt[3]{4xy^2}$

87. $\sqrt{a^4b^3c^4}\,\sqrt[3]{ab^2c}$

88. $\sqrt[3]{xy^2z}\,\sqrt{x^3yz^2}$

89. $\dfrac{\sqrt[3]{a^2}}{\sqrt[4]{a}}$

90. $\dfrac{\sqrt[3]{x^2}}{\sqrt[5]{x}}$

91. $\dfrac{\sqrt[4]{x^2y^3}}{\sqrt[3]{xy}}$

92. $\dfrac{\sqrt[5]{a^4b}}{\sqrt[3]{ab}}$

93. $\dfrac{\sqrt{ab^3}}{\sqrt[5]{a^2b^3}}$

94. $\dfrac{\sqrt[5]{x^3y^4}}{\sqrt{xy}}$

95. $\dfrac{\sqrt{(7 - y)^3}}{\sqrt[3]{(7 - y)^2}}$

96. $\dfrac{\sqrt[5]{(y - 9)^3}}{\sqrt{y - 9}}$

97. $\dfrac{\sqrt[4]{(5+3x)^3}}{\sqrt[3]{(5+3x)^2}}$

98. $\dfrac{\sqrt[3]{(2x+1)^2}}{\sqrt[5]{(2x+1)^2}}$

99. $\sqrt[3]{x^2y}\left(\sqrt[3]{xy} - \sqrt[5]{xy^3}\right)$

100. $\sqrt[4]{a^2b}\left(\sqrt[3]{a^2b} - \sqrt[5]{a^2b^2}\right)$

101. $\left(m + \sqrt[3]{n^2}\right)\left(2m + \sqrt[4]{n}\right)$

102. $\left(r - \sqrt[4]{s^3}\right)\left(3r - \sqrt[3]{s}\right)$

In Exercises 103–106, $f(x)$ and $g(x)$ are as given. Find $(f \cdot g)(x)$. Assume that all variables represent nonnegative real numbers.

103. $f(x) = \sqrt[4]{x}$, $g(x) = 2\sqrt{x} - \sqrt[3]{x^2}$

104. $f(x) = \sqrt[5]{x} + 5\sqrt{x}$, $g(x) = \sqrt[3]{x^2}$

105. $f(x) = x + \sqrt{7}$, $g(x) = x - \sqrt{7}$

106. $f(x) = x - \sqrt{2}$, $g(x) = x + \sqrt{6}$

Let $f(x) = x^2$. Find each of the following.

107. $f\left(5 + \sqrt{2}\right)$ **108.** $f\left(7 + \sqrt{3}\right)$

109. $f\left(\sqrt{3} - \sqrt{5}\right)$ **110.** $f\left(\sqrt{6} - \sqrt{3}\right)$

ᵀᵂ **111.** In what way(s) is combining like radical terms similar to combining like terms that are monomials?

ᵀᵂ **112.** Why do we need to know how to multiply radical expressions before learning how to add them?

SKILL REVIEW

To prepare for Section 12.6, review solving equations.
Solve.

113. $3x - 1 = 125$

114. $x + 5 - 2x = 3x + 6 - x$

115. $x^2 + 2x + 1 = 22 - 2x$

116. $9x^2 - 6x + 1 = 7 + 5x - x^2$

117. $\dfrac{1}{x} + \dfrac{1}{2} = \dfrac{1}{6}$

118. $\dfrac{x}{x-4} + \dfrac{2}{x+4} = \dfrac{x-2}{x^2-16}$

SYNTHESIS

ᵀᵂ **119.** Ramon *incorrectly* writes
$$\sqrt[5]{x^2} \cdot \sqrt{x^3} = x^{2/5} \cdot x^{3/2} = \sqrt[5]{x^3}.$$
What mistake do you suspect he is making?

ᵀᵂ **120.** After examining the expression $\sqrt[4]{25xy^3}\,\sqrt{5x^4y}$, Marika (correctly) concludes that both x and y are nonnegative. Explain how she could reach this conclusion.

Find a simplified form for $f(x)$. Assume $x \geq 0$.

121. $f(x) = \sqrt{x^3 - x^2} + \sqrt{9x^3 - 9x^2} - \sqrt{4x^3 - 4x^2}$

122. $f(x) = \sqrt{20x^2 + 4x^3} - 3x\sqrt{45 + 9x} + \sqrt{5x^2 + x^3}$

123. $f(x) = \sqrt[4]{x^5 - x^4} + 3\sqrt[4]{x^9 - x^8}$

124. $f(x) = \sqrt[4]{16x^4 + 16x^5} - 2\sqrt[4]{x^8 + x^9}$

Simplify.

125. $7x\sqrt{(x+y)^3} - 5xy\sqrt{x+y} - 2y\sqrt{(x+y)^3}$

126. $\sqrt[3]{27a^5(b+1)}\,\sqrt[3]{81a(b+1)^4}$

127. $\sqrt{8x(y+z)^5}\,\sqrt[3]{4x^2(y+z)^2}$

128. $\frac{1}{2}\sqrt{36a^5bc^4} - \frac{1}{2}\sqrt[3]{64a^4bc^6} + \frac{1}{6}\sqrt{144a^3bc^6}$

129. $\dfrac{\dfrac{1}{\sqrt{w}} - \sqrt{w}}{\dfrac{\sqrt{w}+1}{\sqrt{w}}}$

130. $\dfrac{1}{4+\sqrt{3}} + \dfrac{1}{\sqrt{3}} + \dfrac{1}{\sqrt{3}-4}$

Express each of the following as the product of two radical expressions.

131. $x - 5$

132. $y - 7$

133. $x - a$

Multiply.

134. $\sqrt{9 + 3\sqrt{5}}\,\sqrt{9 - 3\sqrt{5}}$

135. $\left(\sqrt{x+2} - \sqrt{x-2}\right)^2$

Try Exercise Answers: Section 12.5

7. $9\sqrt{5}$ **17.** $9\sqrt{3}$ **33.** $15 - 3\sqrt{10}$ **61.** $\dfrac{18 + 6\sqrt{2}}{7}$

71. $\dfrac{1}{\sqrt{5}-1}$ **79.** $\sqrt{a}$ **89.** $\sqrt[12]{a^5}$ **93.** $\sqrt[10]{ab^9}$

103. $2\sqrt[4]{x^3} - \sqrt[12]{x^{11}}$

Mid-Chapter Review

Many radical expressions can be simplified. It is important to know under which conditions radical expressions can be multiplied and divided and radical terms can be combined.

Multiplication and division: The indices must be the same.

$$\frac{\sqrt{50t^5}}{\sqrt{2t^{11}}} = \sqrt{\frac{50t^5}{2t^{11}}} = \sqrt{\frac{25}{t^6}} = \frac{5}{t^3}; \qquad \sqrt[4]{8x^3} \cdot \sqrt[4]{2x} = \sqrt[4]{16x^4} = 2x$$

Combining like terms: The indices and the radicands must both be the same.

$$\sqrt{75x} + \sqrt{12x} - \sqrt{3x} = 5\sqrt{3x} + 2\sqrt{3x} - \sqrt{3x} = 6\sqrt{3x}$$

Radical expressions with differing indices can sometimes be simplified using rational exponents.

$$\sqrt[3]{x^2}\,\sqrt{x} = x^{2/3}x^{1/2} = x^{4/6}x^{3/6} = x^{7/6} = \sqrt[6]{x^7} = x\sqrt[6]{x}$$

GUIDED SOLUTIONS

1. Multiply and simplify: $\sqrt{6x^9} \cdot \sqrt{2xy}$. [12.3]

Solution

$$\sqrt{6x^9} \cdot \sqrt{2xy} = \sqrt{6x^9 \cdot \boxed{}}$$
$$= \sqrt{12x^{10}y}$$
$$= \sqrt{\boxed{} \cdot 3y}$$
$$= \sqrt{\boxed{}} \cdot \sqrt{3y}$$
$$= \boxed{}\,\sqrt{3y} \qquad \text{Taking the square root}$$

2. Combine like terms: $\sqrt{12} - 3\sqrt{75} + \sqrt{8}$. [12.5]

Solution

$$\sqrt{12} - 3\sqrt{75} + \sqrt{8}$$
$$= \boxed{} - 3 \cdot 5\sqrt{3} + \boxed{} \qquad \begin{array}{l}\text{Simplifying each}\\\text{term}\end{array}$$
$$= 2\sqrt{3} - \boxed{} + 2\sqrt{2} \qquad \text{Multiplying}$$
$$= \boxed{} + 2\sqrt{2} \qquad \begin{array}{l}\text{Combining like}\\\text{terms}\end{array}$$

MIXED REVIEW

Simplify. Assume that variables can represent any real number.

1. $\sqrt{81}$ [12.1]

2. $-\sqrt{\dfrac{9}{100}}$ [12.1]

3. $\sqrt{64t^2}$ [12.1]

4. $\sqrt[5]{x^5}$ [12.1]

5. Find $f(-5)$ if $f(x) = \sqrt[3]{12x - 4}$. [12.1]

6. Determine the domain of g if $g(x) = \sqrt[4]{10 - x}$. [12.1]

7. Write an equivalent expression using radical notation and simplify: $8^{2/3}$. [12.2]

Simplify. Assume for the remainder of the exercises that no radicands were formed by raising negative numbers to even powers.

8. $\sqrt[6]{\sqrt{a}}$ [12.2]

9. $\sqrt[3]{y^{24}}$ [12.2]

10. $\sqrt{(t + 5)^2}$ [12.1]

11. $\sqrt[3]{-27a^{12}}$ [12.1]

12. $\sqrt{6x}\,\sqrt{15x}$ [12.3]

13. $\dfrac{\sqrt{20y}}{\sqrt{45y}}$ [12.4]

14. $\sqrt{15t} + 4\sqrt{15t}$ [12.5]

15. $\sqrt[5]{a^5b^{10}c^{11}}$ [12.1]

16. $\sqrt{6}\left(\sqrt{10} - \sqrt{33}\right)$ [12.5]

17. $\dfrac{\sqrt{t}}{\sqrt[8]{t^3}}$ [12.5]

18. $\sqrt[5]{\dfrac{3a^{12}}{96a^2}}$ [12.4]

19. $2\sqrt{3} - 5\sqrt{12}$ [12.5]

20. $\left(\sqrt{5} + 3\right)\left(\sqrt{5} - 3\right)$ [12.5]

21. $\left(\sqrt{15} + \sqrt{10}\right)^2$ [12.5]

22. $\sqrt{25x - 25} - \sqrt{9x - 9}$ [12.5]

23. $\sqrt{x^3y}\,\sqrt[5]{xy^4}$ [12.5]

24. $\sqrt[3]{5000} + \sqrt[3]{625}$ [12.5]

25. $\sqrt[3]{12x^2y^5}\,\sqrt[3]{18x^7y}$ [12.3]

12.6 Solving Radical Equations

- The Principle of Powers

- Equations with Two Radical Terms

In Sections 12.1–12.5, we learned how to manipulate radical expressions as well as expressions containing rational exponents. We performed this work to find *equivalent expressions.*

Now that we know how to work with radicals and rational exponents, we can learn how to solve a new type of equation.

THE PRINCIPLE OF POWERS

A **radical equation** is an equation in which the variable appears in a radicand. Examples are

$$\sqrt[3]{2x} + 1 = 5, \qquad \sqrt{a-2} = 7, \quad \text{and} \quad 4 - \sqrt{3x+1} = \sqrt{6-x}.$$

To solve such equations, we need a new principle. Suppose $a = b$ is true. If we square both sides, we get another true equation: $a^2 = b^2$. This can be generalized.

> **The Principle of Powers** If $a = b$, then $a^n = b^n$ for any exponent n.

Note that the principle of powers is an "if–then" statement. If we interchange the two parts of the sentence, then we have the statement

"If $a^n = b^n$ for some exponent n, then $a = b$."

This statement is *not* always true. For example, "if $x = 3$, then $x^2 = 9$" is true, but the statement "if $x^2 = 9$, then $x = 3$" is *not* true when x is replaced with -3.

Interactive Discovery

Solve each pair of equations graphically, and compare the solution sets.

1. $x = 3$; $x^2 = 9$
2. $x = -2$; $x^2 = 4$
3. $\sqrt{x} = 5$; $x = 25$
4. $\sqrt{x} = -3$; $x = 9$

Every solution of $x = a$ is a solution of $x^2 = a^2$, but not every solution of $x^2 = a^2$ is necessarily a solution of $x = a$. A similar statement can be made for any even exponent n; for example, the solution sets of $x^4 = 3^4$ and $x = 3$ are not the same.

> When we raise both sides of an equation to an even exponent, it is essential that we check the answer in the *original equation.*

EXAMPLE 1 Solve: $\sqrt{x} - 3 = 4$.

ALGEBRAIC APPROACH

Before using the principle of powers, we must isolate the radical term:

$$\sqrt{x} - 3 = 4$$
$$\sqrt{x} = 7 \qquad \text{Isolating the radical by adding 3 to both sides}$$
$$\left(\sqrt{x}\right)^2 = 7^2 \qquad \text{Using the principle of powers}$$
$$x = 49.$$

Check:
$$\frac{\sqrt{x} - 3 = 4}{\sqrt{49} - 3 \quad | \quad 4}$$
$$7 - 3 \quad |$$
$$4 \overset{?}{=} 4 \quad \text{TRUE}$$

The solution is 49.

GRAPHICAL APPROACH

We let $f(x) = \sqrt{x} - 3$ and $g(x) = 4$. We use a viewing window of $[-10, 100, -5, 5]$ and find the point of intersection. (It may require some trial and error to find an appropriate viewing window.)

We have a solution of 49, which we can check by substituting into the original equation, as shown in the algebraic approach.
    The solution is 49.

Try Exercise 7.

EXAMPLE 2 Solve: $\sqrt{x} + 5 = 3$.

ALGEBRAIC APPROACH

We have

$$\sqrt{x} + 5 = 3$$
$$\sqrt{x} = -2 \qquad \text{Isolating the radical by subtracting 5 from both sides}$$

The equation $\sqrt{x} = -2$ has no solution because the principal square root of a number is never negative. We continue as in Example 1 for comparison.

$$\left(\sqrt{x}\right)^2 = (-2)^2 \qquad \text{Using the principle of powers (squaring)}$$
$$x = 4.$$

Check:
$$\frac{\sqrt{x} + 5 = 3}{\sqrt{4} + 5 \quad | \quad 3}$$
$$2 + 5 \quad |$$
$$7 \overset{?}{=} 3 \quad \text{FALSE}$$

The number 4 does not check. Thus, $\sqrt{x} + 5 = 3$ has no solution.

GRAPHICAL APPROACH

We let $f(x) = \sqrt{x} + 5$ and $g(x) = 3$ and graph.

The graphs do not intersect. There is no real-number solution.

Try Exercise 27.

> **CAUTION!**   Raising both sides of an equation to an even power may not produce an equivalent equation. In this case, a check is essential.

Note in Example 2 that $x = 4$ has solution 4 but $\sqrt{x} + 5 = 3$ has *no* solution. Thus the equations $x = 4$ and $\sqrt{x} + 5 = 3$ are *not* equivalent.

> **To Solve an Equation with a Radical Term**
> **1.** Isolate the radical term on one side of the equation.
> **2.** Use the principle of powers and solve the resulting equation.
> **3.** Check any possible solution in the original equation.

EXAMPLE 3   Solve: $x = \sqrt{x + 7} + 5$.

ALGEBRAIC APPROACH

$$x = \sqrt{x + 7} + 5$$
$$x - 5 = \sqrt{x + 7} \quad \text{Isolating the radical by subtracting 5 from both sides}$$
$$\left.\begin{array}{l}(x - 5)^2 = \left(\sqrt{x + 7}\right)^2 \\ x^2 - 10x + 25 = x + 7\end{array}\right\} \quad \text{Using the principle of powers; squaring both sides}$$
$$x^2 - 11x + 18 = 0 \quad \text{Adding } -x - 7 \text{ to both sides to write the quadratic equation in standard form}$$
$$(x - 9)(x - 2) = 0 \quad \text{Factoring}$$
$$x = 9 \quad or \quad x = 2 \quad \text{Using the principle of zero products}$$

The possible solutions are 9 and 2. Let's check.

Check: For 9:

$$\begin{array}{c|c} x = \sqrt{x + 7} + 5 \\ \hline 9 & \sqrt{9 + 7} + 5 \\ 9 \overset{?}{=} 9 \end{array} \quad \textbf{TRUE}$$

For 2:

$$\begin{array}{c|c} x = \sqrt{x + 7} + 5 \\ \hline 2 & \sqrt{2 + 7} + 5 \\ 2 \overset{?}{=} 8 \end{array} \quad \textbf{FALSE}$$

Since 9 checks but 2 does not, the solution is 9.

GRAPHICAL APPROACH

We graph $y_1 = x$ and $y_2 = \sqrt{x + 7} + 5$ and determine any points of intersection.

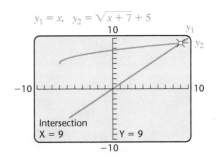

$y_1 = x, \quad y_2 = \sqrt{x + 7} + 5$

We obtain a solution of 9.

Try Exercise 39.

It is important to isolate a radical term before using the principle of powers. Suppose in Example 3 that both sides of the equation were squared *before* isolating the radical. We then would have had the expression

$$\left(\sqrt{x + 7} + 5\right)^2 \quad \text{or} \quad x + 7 + 10\sqrt{x + 7} + 25$$

in the third step of the algebraic approach, and the radical would have remained in the problem.

EXAMPLE 4 Solve: $(2x + 1)^{1/3} + 5 = 0$.

ALGEBRAIC APPROACH	GRAPHICAL APPROACH

ALGEBRAIC APPROACH

We can use exponential notation to solve:

$(2x + 1)^{1/3} + 5 = 0$

$\quad (2x + 1)^{1/3} = -5$ Subtracting 5 from both sides

$\quad [(2x + 1)^{1/3}]^3 = (-5)^3$ Cubing both sides

$\quad (2x + 1)^1 = (-5)^3$ Multiplying exponents

$\quad\quad 2x + 1 = -125$

$\quad\quad\quad\quad 2x = -126$ Subtracting 1 from both sides

$\quad\quad\quad\quad\quad x = -63.$

Because both sides were raised to an *odd* power, we need check only the accuracy of our work.

Check:

$$\begin{array}{c|c} (2x + 1)^{1/3} + 5 = 0 & \\ \hline [2(-63) + 1]^{1/3} + 5 & 0 \\ [-126 + 1]^{1/3} + 5 & \\ (-125)^{1/3} + 5 & \\ \sqrt[3]{-125} + 5 & \\ -5 + 5 & \\ 0 \overset{?}{=} 0 & \text{TRUE} \end{array}$$

GRAPHICAL APPROACH

We let $f(x) = (2x + 1)^{1/3} + 5$ and determine any values of x for which $f(x) = 0$. Using a viewing window of $[-100, 100, -10, 10]$, we find that $f(x) = 0$ when $x = -63$.

$y = (2x + 1)^{\wedge}(1/3) + 5$

Xscl = 10

Try Exercise 33.

EQUATIONS WITH TWO RADICAL TERMS

A strategy for solving equations with two or more radical terms is as follows.

> **To Solve an Equation with Two or More Radical Terms**
> 1. Isolate one of the radical terms.
> 2. Use the principle of powers.
> 3. If a radical remains, perform steps (1) and (2) again.
> 4. Solve the resulting equation.
> 5. Check possible solutions in the original equation.

EXAMPLE 5 Solve: $\sqrt{2x-5} = 1 + \sqrt{x-3}$.

ALGEBRAIC APPROACH	GRAPHICAL APPROACH

ALGEBRAIC APPROACH

We have

$$\sqrt{2x-5} = 1 + \sqrt{x-3}$$
$$\left(\sqrt{2x-5}\right)^2 = \left(1 + \sqrt{x-3}\right)^2$$

One radical is already isolated. We square both sides.

This is like squaring a binomial. We square 1, then find twice the product of 1 and $\sqrt{x-3}$, and then the square of $\sqrt{x-3}$.

$$2x - 5 = 1 + 2\sqrt{x-3} + \left(\sqrt{x-3}\right)^2$$
$$2x - 5 = 1 + 2\sqrt{x-3} + (x-3)$$
$$x - 3 = 2\sqrt{x-3}$$

Isolating the remaining radical term

$$(x-3)^2 = \left(2\sqrt{x-3}\right)^2$$

Squaring both sides

$$x^2 - 6x + 9 = 4(x-3)$$

Remember to square both the 2 and the $\sqrt{x-3}$ on the right side.

$$x^2 - 6x + 9 = 4x - 12$$
$$x^2 - 10x + 21 = 0$$
$$(x-7)(x-3) = 0$$

Factoring

$$x = 7 \quad or \quad x = 3.$$

Using the principle of zero products

The possible solutions are 7 and 3. Both 7 and 3 check in the original equation and are the solutions.

GRAPHICAL APPROACH

We let $f(x) = \sqrt{2x-5}$ and $g(x) = 1 + \sqrt{x-3}$. The domain of f is $\left[\frac{5}{2}, \infty\right)$, and the domain of g is $[3, \infty)$. Since the intersection of their domains is $[3, \infty)$, any point of intersection will occur in that interval. We choose a viewing window of $[-1, 10, -1, 5]$.

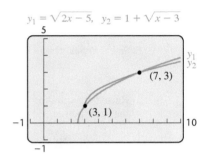

$y_1 = \sqrt{2x-5}, \quad y_2 = 1 + \sqrt{x-3}$

The graphs appear to intersect when x is approximately 3 and again when x is approximately 7. The points of intersection are $(3, 1)$ and $(7, 3)$. The solutions are 3 and 7.

Try Exercise 41.

CAUTION! A common error in solving equations like

$$\sqrt{2x-5} = 1 + \sqrt{x-3}$$

is to obtain $1 + (x-3)$ as the square of the right side. This is wrong because $(A + B)^2 \neq A^2 + B^2$. Placing parentheses around each side when squaring serves as a reminder to square the entire expression.

EXAMPLE 6   Let $f(x) = \sqrt{x + 5} - \sqrt{x - 7}$. Find all x-values for which $f(x) = 2$.

SOLUTION   We must have $f(x) = 2$, or

$$\sqrt{x + 5} - \sqrt{x - 7} = 2.\qquad \text{Substituting for } f(x)$$

To solve, we isolate one radical term and square both sides:

Isolate a radical term.	$\sqrt{x + 5} = 2 + \sqrt{x - 7}$	Adding $\sqrt{x - 7}$ to both sides. This isolates one of the radical terms.
Raise both sides to the same power.	$\left(\sqrt{x + 5}\right)^2 = \left(2 + \sqrt{x - 7}\right)^2$	Using the principle of powers (squaring both sides)
	$x + 5 = 4 + 4\sqrt{x - 7} + (x - 7)$	Using $(A + B)^2 = A^2 + 2AB + B^2$
	$5 = 4\sqrt{x - 7} - 3$	Adding $-x$ to both sides and combining like terms
Isolate a radical term.	$8 = 4\sqrt{x - 7}$	Isolating the remaining radical term
	$2 = \sqrt{x - 7}$	
Raise both sides to the same power.	$2^2 = \left(\sqrt{x - 7}\right)^2$	Squaring both sides
Solve.	$4 = x - 7$	
	$11 = x.$	

Check: $f(11) = \sqrt{11 + 5} - \sqrt{11 - 7}$

$= \sqrt{16} - \sqrt{4}$

$= 4 - 2 = 2.$

We have $f(x) = 2$ when $x = 11$.

Try Exercise 49.

12.6   Exercise Set

FOR EXTRA HELP   MyMathLab   Math XL PRACTICE   WATCH   DOWNLOAD   READ   REVIEW

↪ *Concept Reinforcement*   *Classify each of the following statements as either true or false.*

1. If $x^2 = 25$, then $x = 5$.

2. If $t = 7$, then $t^2 = 49$.

3. If $\sqrt{x} = 3$, then $\left(\sqrt{x}\right)^2 = 3^2$.

4. If $x^2 = 36$, then $x = 6$.

5. $\sqrt{x} - 8 = 7$ is equivalent to $\sqrt{x} = 15$.

6. $\sqrt{t} + 5 = 8$ is equivalent to $\sqrt{t} = 3$.

Solve.

7. $\sqrt{5x + 1} = 4$

8. $\sqrt{7x - 3} = 5$

9. $\sqrt{3x + 1} = 6$

10. $\sqrt{2x - 1} = 2$

11. $\sqrt{y + 1} - 5 = 8$

12. $\sqrt{x - 2} - 7 = -4$

13. $\sqrt{8 - x} + 7 = 10$

14. $\sqrt{y + 4} + 6 = 7$

15. $\sqrt[3]{x + 5} = 2$

16. $\sqrt[3]{x - 2} = 3$

17. $\sqrt[4]{y - 1} = 3$

18. $\sqrt[4]{x + 3} = 2$

19. $3\sqrt{x} = x$

20. $8\sqrt{y} = y$

21. $2y^{1/2} - 13 = 7$

22. $3x^{1/2} + 12 = 9$

23. $\sqrt[3]{x} = -3$

24. $\sqrt[3]{y} = -4$

25. $z^{1/4} + 8 = 10$

26. $x^{1/4} - 2 = 1$

Aha! **27.** $\sqrt{n} = -2$

28. $\sqrt{a} = -1$

29. $\sqrt[4]{3x + 1} - 4 = -1$

30. $\sqrt[4]{2x + 3} - 5 = -2$

31. $(21x + 55)^{1/3} = 10$

32. $(5y + 31)^{1/4} = 2$

33. $\sqrt[3]{3y + 6} + 7 = 8$

34. $\sqrt[3]{6x + 9} + 5 = 2$

35. $\sqrt{3t + 4} = \sqrt{4t + 3}$

36. $\sqrt{2t - 7} = \sqrt{3t - 12}$

37. $3(4 - t)^{1/4} = 6^{1/4}$

38. $2(1 - x)^{1/3} = 4^{1/3}$

39. $3 + \sqrt{5 - x} = x$

40. $x = \sqrt{x - 1} + 3$

41. $\sqrt{4x - 3} = 2 + \sqrt{2x - 5}$

42. $3 + \sqrt{z - 6} = \sqrt{z + 9}$

43. $\sqrt{20 - x} + 8 = \sqrt{9 - x} + 11$

44. $4 + \sqrt{10 - x} = 6 + \sqrt{4 - x}$

45. $\sqrt{x + 2} + \sqrt{3x + 4} = 2$

46. $\sqrt{6x + 7} - \sqrt{3x + 3} = 1$

47. If $f(x) = \sqrt{x} + \sqrt{x - 9}$, find any x for which $f(x) = 1$.

48. If $g(x) = \sqrt{x} + \sqrt{x - 5}$, find any x for which $g(x) = 5$.

49. If $f(t) = \sqrt{t - 2} - \sqrt{4t + 1}$, find any t for which $f(t) = -3$.

50. If $g(t) = \sqrt{2t + 7} - \sqrt{t + 15}$, find any t for which $g(t) = -1$.

51. If $f(x) = \sqrt{2x - 3}$ and $g(x) = \sqrt{x + 7} - 2$, find any x for which $f(x) = g(x)$.

52. If $f(x) = 2\sqrt{3x + 6}$ and $g(x) = 5 + \sqrt{4x + 9}$, find any x for which $f(x) = g(x)$.

53. If $f(t) = 4 - \sqrt{t - 3}$ and $g(t) = (t + 5)^{1/2}$, find any t for which $f(t) = g(t)$.

54. If $f(t) = 7 + \sqrt{2t - 5}$ and $g(t) = 3(t + 1)^{1/2}$, find any t for which $f(t) = g(t)$.

TW **55.** Explain in your own words why it is important to check your answers when using the principle of powers.

TW **56.** The principle of powers is an "if–then" statement that becomes false when the sentence parts are interchanged. Give an example of another such if–then statement from everyday life (answers will vary).

SKILL REVIEW

To prepare for Section 12.7, review finding dimensions of triangles and rectangles.

Solve.

57. *Sign Dimensions.* The largest sign in the United States is a rectangle with a perimeter of 430 ft. The length of the rectangle is 5 ft longer than thirteen times the width. Find the dimensions of the sign.
Source: Florida Center for Instructional Technology

58. *Sign Dimensions.* The base of a triangular sign is 4 in. longer than twice the height. The area of the sign is 255 in². Find the dimensions of the sign.

59. *Photograph Dimensions.* A rectangular family photo is 4 in. longer than it is wide. The area of the photo is 140 in². Find the dimensions of the photograph.

60. *Sidewalk Length.* The length of a rectangular lawn between classroom buildings is 2 yd less than twice the width of the lawn. A path that is 34 yd long stretches diagonally across the area. What are the dimensions of the lawn?

61. The sides of a right triangle are consecutive even integers. Find the length of each side.

62. One leg of a right triangle is 5 cm long. The hypotenuse is 1 cm longer than the other leg. Find the length of the hypotenuse.

SYNTHESIS

TW **63.** Describe a procedure that could be used to create radical equations that have no solution.

TW **64.** Is checking essential when the principle of powers is used with an odd power n? Why or why not?

65. *Firefighting.* The velocity of water flow, in feet per second, from a nozzle is given by

$$v(p) = 12.1\sqrt{p},$$

where p is the nozzle pressure, in pounds per square inch (psi). Find the nozzle pressure if the water flow is 100 feet per second.
Source: Houston Fire Department Continuing Education

66. *Firefighting.* The velocity of water flow, in feet per second, from a water tank that is h feet high is given by

$$v(h) = 8\sqrt{h}.$$

Find the height of a water tank that provides a water flow of 60 feet per second.
Source: Houston Fire Department Continuing Education

67. *Music.* The frequency of a violin string varies directly with the square root of the tension on the string. A violin string vibrates with a frequency of 260 Hz when the tension on the string is 28 N. What is the frequency when the tension is 32 N?

68. *Music.* The frequency of a violin string varies inversely with the square root of the density of the string. A nylon violin string with a density of 1200 kg/m^3 vibrates with a frequency of 250 Hz. What is the frequency of a silk violin string with a density of 1300 kg/m^3?
Source: www.speech.kth.se

Steel Manufacturing. In the production of steel and other metals, the temperature of the molten metal is so great that conventional thermometers melt. Instead, sound is transmitted across the surface of the metal to a receiver on the far side and the speed of the sound is measured. The formula

$$S(t) = 1087.7\sqrt{\frac{9t + 2617}{2457}}$$

gives the speed of sound $S(t)$, in feet per second, at a temperature of t degrees Celsius.

69. Find the temperature of a blast furnace where sound travels 1880 ft/sec.

70. Find the temperature of a blast furnace where sound travels 1502.3 ft/sec.

71. Solve the above equation for t.

Automotive Repair. For an engine with a displacement of 2.8 L, the function given by

$$d(n) = 0.75\sqrt{2.8n}$$

can be used to determine the diameter size of the carburetor's opening, in millimeters. Here n is the number of rpm's at which the engine achieves peak performance.
Source: macdizzy.com

72. If a carburetor's opening is 81 mm, for what number of rpm's will the engine produce peak power?

73. If a carburetor's opening is 84 mm, for what number of rpm's will the engine produce peak power?

Escape Velocity. A formula for the escape velocity v of a satellite is

$$v = \sqrt{2gr}\sqrt{\frac{h}{r + h}},$$

where g is the force of gravity, r is the planet or star's radius, and h is the height of the satellite above the planet or star's surface.

74. Solve for h.

75. Solve for r.

Solve.

76. $\left(\dfrac{z}{4} - 5\right)^{2/3} = \dfrac{1}{25}$

77. $\dfrac{x + \sqrt{x + 1}}{x - \sqrt{x + 1}} = \dfrac{5}{11}$

78. $\sqrt{\sqrt{y} + 49} = 7$

79. $(z^2 + 17)^{3/4} = 27$

80. $x^2 - 5x - \sqrt{x^2 - 5x - 2} = 4$
(*Hint*: Let $u = x^2 - 5x - 2$.)

81. $\sqrt{8 - b} = b\sqrt{8 - b}$

Without graphing, determine the x-intercepts of the graphs given by each of the following.

82. $f(x) = \sqrt{x - 2} - \sqrt{x + 2} + 2$

83. $g(x) = 6x^{1/2} + 6x^{-1/2} - 37$

84. $f(x) = (x^2 + 30x)^{1/2} - x - (5x)^{1/2}$

Tailgater Alert

Focus: Radical equations and problem solving
Time: 15–25 minutes
Group size: 2–3
Materials: Calculators

The faster a car is traveling, the more distance it needs to stop. Thus it is important for drivers to allow sufficient space between their vehicle and the vehicle in front of them. Police recommend that for each 10 mph of speed, a driver allow 1 car length. Thus a driver going 30 mph should have at least 3 car lengths between his or her vehicle and the one in front.

In Exercise Set 10.3, the function $r(L) = 2\sqrt{5L}$ was used to find the speed, in miles per hour, that a car was traveling when it left skid marks L feet long.

ACTIVITY

1. Each group member should estimate the length of a car in which he or she frequently travels. (Each should use a different length, if possible.)

2. Using a calculator as needed, each group member should complete the table at right. Column 1 gives a car's speed s, column 2 lists the minimum

amount of space between cars traveling s miles per hour, as recommended by police. Column 3 is the speed that a vehicle *could* travel were it forced to stop in the distance listed in column 2, using the above function.

Column 1 s (in miles per hour)	Column 2 L(s) (in feet)	Column 3 r(L) (in miles per hour)
20		
30		
40		
50		
60		
70		

3. Determine whether there are any speeds at which the "1 car length per 10 mph" guideline might not suffice. On what reasoning do you base your answer? Compare tables to determine how car length affects the results. What recommendations would your group make to a new driver?

12.7 The Distance Formula, the Midpoint Formula, and Other Applications

- Using the Pythagorean Theorem

- Two Special Triangles

- The Distance Formula and the Midpoint Formula

USING THE PYTHAGOREAN THEOREM

There are many kinds of problems that involve powers and roots. Many also involve right triangles and the Pythagorean theorem.

The Pythagorean Theorem*   In any right triangle, if a and b are the lengths of the legs and c is the length of the hypotenuse, then

$$a^2 + b^2 = c^2.$$

*The converse of the Pythagorean theorem also holds. That is, if a, b, and c are the lengths of the sides of a triangle and $a^2 + b^2 = c^2$, then the triangle is a right triangle.

In using the Pythagorean theorem, we often make use of the following principle.

The Principle of Square Roots   For any nonnegative real number n,

If $x^2 = n$, then $x = \sqrt{n}$ or $x = -\sqrt{n}$.

For most real-world applications involving length or distance, $-\sqrt{n}$ is not needed.

EXAMPLE 1   Baseball.   A baseball diamond is actually a square 90 ft on a side. Suppose a catcher fields a ball while standing on the third-base line 10 ft from home plate, as shown in the figure at left. How far is the catcher's throw to first base? Give an exact answer and an approximation to three decimal places.

SOLUTION   We make a drawing and let $d =$ the distance, in feet, to first base. Note that a right triangle is formed in which the leg from home plate to first base measures 90 ft and the leg from home plate to where the catcher fields the ball measures 10 ft.

We substitute these values into the Pythagorean theorem to find d:

$$d^2 = 90^2 + 10^2$$
$$d^2 = 8100 + 100$$
$$d^2 = 8200.$$

We now use the principle of square roots: If $d^2 = 8200$, then $d = \sqrt{8200}$ or $d = -\sqrt{8200}$. Since d represents a length, it follows that d is the positive square root of 8200:

$$d = \sqrt{8200} \text{ ft}$$ This is an exact answer.

$$d \approx 90.554 \text{ ft.}$$ Using a calculator for an approximation

 Try Exercise 19.

EXAMPLE 2   Guy Wires.   The base of a 40-ft long guy wire is located 15 ft from the telephone pole that it is anchoring. How high up the pole does the guy wire reach? Give an exact answer and an approximation to three decimal places.

SOLUTION   We make a drawing and let $h =$ the height, in feet, to which the guy wire reaches. A right triangle is formed in which one leg measures 15 ft and the hypotenuse measures 40 ft. Using the Pythagorean theorem, we have

$$h^2 + 15^2 = 40^2$$
$$h^2 + 225 = 1600$$
$$h^2 = 1375$$
$$h = \sqrt{1375}.$$ Using the positive square root

Exact answer:

$$h = \sqrt{1375} \text{ ft}$$

Approximation:

$$h \approx 37.081 \text{ ft}$$ Using a calculator

 Try Exercise 15.

TWO SPECIAL TRIANGLES

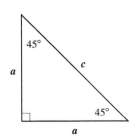

When both legs of a right triangle are the same size, as shown at left, we call the triangle an *isosceles right triangle*. If one leg of an isosceles right triangle has length a, we can find a formula for the length of the hypotenuse as follows:

$$c^2 = a^2 + b^2$$
$$c^2 = a^2 + a^2 \qquad \text{Because the triangle is isosceles, both legs are the same size: } a = b.$$
$$c^2 = 2a^2. \qquad \text{Combining like terms}$$

Next, we use the principle of square roots. Because a, b, and c are lengths, there is no need to consider negative square roots or absolute values. Thus,

$$c = \sqrt{2a^2} \qquad \text{Using the principle of square roots}$$
$$= \sqrt{a^2 \cdot 2} = a\sqrt{2}.$$

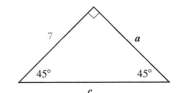

EXAMPLE 3 One leg of an isosceles right triangle measures 7 cm. Find the length of the hypotenuse. Give an exact answer and an approximation to three decimal places.

SOLUTION We substitute:

$$c = a\sqrt{2} \qquad \text{This equation is worth memorizing.}$$
$$= 7\sqrt{2}.$$

Exact answer: $c = 7\sqrt{2}$ cm

Approximation: $c \approx 9.899$ cm   Using a calculator

■ Try Exercise 29.

When the hypotenuse of an isosceles right triangle is known, the lengths of the legs can be found.

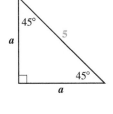

EXAMPLE 4 The hypotenuse of an isosceles right triangle is 5 ft long. Find the length of a leg. Give an exact answer and an approximation to three decimal places.

SOLUTION We replace c with 5 and solve for a:

$$5 = a\sqrt{2} \qquad \text{Substituting 5 for } c \text{ in } c = a\sqrt{2}$$
$$\frac{5}{\sqrt{2}} = a \qquad \text{Dividing both sides by } \sqrt{2}$$
$$\frac{5\sqrt{2}}{2} = a. \qquad \text{Rationalize the denominator if desired.}$$

Exact answer: $a = \dfrac{5}{\sqrt{2}}$ ft, or $\dfrac{5\sqrt{2}}{2}$ ft

Approximation: $a \approx 3.536$ ft   Using a calculator

■ Try Exercise 35.

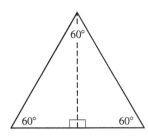

A second special triangle is known as a 30°–60°–90° right triangle, so named because of the measures of its angles. Note that in an equilateral triangle, all sides have the same length and all angles are 60°. An altitude, drawn dashed in the figure, bisects, or splits in half, one angle and one side. Two 30°–60°–90° right triangles are thus formed.

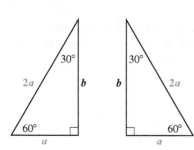

If we let a represent the length of the shorter leg in a 30°–60°–90° right triangle, then $2a$ represents the length of the hypotenuse. We have

$$a^2 + b^2 = (2a)^2 \qquad \text{Using the Pythagorean theorem}$$
$$a^2 + b^2 = 4a^2$$
$$b^2 = 3a^2 \qquad \text{Subtracting } a^2 \text{ from both sides}$$
$$b = \sqrt{3a^2} \qquad \text{Considering only the positive square root}$$
$$b = \sqrt{a^2 \cdot 3}$$
$$b = a\sqrt{3}.$$

EXAMPLE 5 The shorter leg of a 30°–60°–90° right triangle measures 8 in. Find the lengths of the other sides. Give exact answers and, where appropriate, an approximation to three decimal places.

SOLUTION The hypotenuse is twice as long as the shorter leg, so we have

$$c = 2a \qquad \text{This relationship is worth memorizing.}$$
$$= 2 \cdot 8 = 16 \text{ in.} \qquad \text{This is the length of the hypotenuse.}$$

The length of the longer leg is the length of the shorter leg times $\sqrt{3}$. This gives us

$$b = a\sqrt{3} \qquad \text{This is also worth memorizing.}$$
$$= 8\sqrt{3} \text{ in.} \qquad \text{This is the length of the longer leg.}$$

Exact answer: $c = 16$ in., $b = 8\sqrt{3}$ in.

Approximation: $b \approx 13.856$ in.

Try Exercise 37.

EXAMPLE 6 The length of the longer leg of a 30°–60°–90° right triangle is 14 cm. Find the length of the hypotenuse. Give an exact answer and an approximation to three decimal places.

SOLUTION The length of the hypotenuse is twice the length of the shorter leg. We first find a, the length of the shorter leg, by using the length of the longer leg:

$$14 = a\sqrt{3} \qquad \text{Substituting 14 for } b \text{ in } b = a\sqrt{3}$$
$$\frac{14}{\sqrt{3}} = a. \qquad \text{Dividing by } \sqrt{3}$$

Since the hypotenuse is twice as long as the shorter leg, we have

$$c = 2a$$
$$= 2 \cdot \frac{14}{\sqrt{3}} \qquad \text{Substituting}$$
$$= \frac{28}{\sqrt{3}} \text{ cm.}$$

Exact answer: $c = \dfrac{28}{\sqrt{3}}$ cm, or $\dfrac{28\sqrt{3}}{3}$ cm if the denominator is rationalized.

Approximation: $c \approx 16.166$ cm

Try Exercise 33.

Student Notes

Perhaps the easiest way to remember the important results listed in the adjacent box is to write out, on your own, the derivations shown on pp. 773 and 774.

Lengths Within Isosceles Triangles and 30°-60°-90° Right Triangles

The length of the hypotenuse in an isosceles right triangle is the length of a leg times $\sqrt{2}$.

The length of the longer leg in a 30°–60°–90° right triangle is the length of the shorter leg times $\sqrt{3}$. The hypotenuse is twice as long as the shorter leg.

THE DISTANCE FORMULA AND MIDPOINT FORMULA

We can use the Pythagorean theorem to find the distance between two points on a plane.

To find the distance between two points on the number line, we subtract. Depending on the order in which we subtract, the difference may be positive or negative. However, if we take the absolute value of the difference, we always obtain a positive value for the distance:

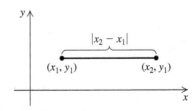

$$|4 - (-3)| = |7| = 7$$
$$|-3 - 4| = |-7| = 7$$

If two points are on a horizontal line, they have the same second coordinate. We can find the distance between them by subtracting their first coordinates and taking the absolute value of that difference.

The distance between the points (x_1, y_1) and (x_2, y_1) on a horizontal line is thus $|x_2 - x_1|$. Similarly, the distance between the points (x_2, y_1) and (x_2, y_2) on a vertical line is $|y_2 - y_1|$.

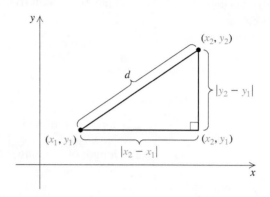

Now consider two points (x_1, y_1) and (x_2, y_2). If $x_1 \neq x_2$ and $y_1 \neq y_2$, these points, along with the point (x_2, y_1), describe a right triangle. The lengths of the legs are $|x_2 - x_1|$ and $|y_2 - y_1|$. We find d, the length of the hypotenuse, by using the Pythagorean theorem:

$$d^2 = |x_2 - x_1|^2 + |y_2 - y_1|^2.$$

Since the square of a number is the same as the square of its opposite, we can replace the absolute-value signs with parentheses:

$$d^2 = (x_2 - x_1)^2 + (y_2 - y_1)^2.$$

Taking the principal square root, we have a formula for distance.

The Distance Formula The distance d between any two points (x_1, y_1) and (x_2, y_2) is given by

$$d = \sqrt{(x_2 - x_1)^2 + (y_2 - y_1)^2}.$$

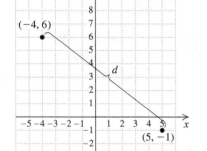

EXAMPLE 7 Find the distance between $(5, -1)$ and $(-4, 6)$. Find an exact answer and an approximation to three decimal places.

SOLUTION We substitute into the distance formula:

$$d = \sqrt{(-4 - 5)^2 + [6 - (-1)]^2}$$ Substituting. A drawing is optional.

$$= \sqrt{(-9)^2 + 7^2}$$

$$= \sqrt{130}$$ This is exact.

$$\approx 11.402.$$ Using a calculator for an approximation

Try Exercise 51.

The distance formula is needed to verify a formula for the coordinates of the *midpoint* of a segment connecting two points. We state the midpoint formula and leave its proof to the exercises.

Student Notes

To help remember the formulas correctly, note that the distance formula (a variation on the Pythagorean theorem) involves both subtraction and addition, whereas the midpoint formula does not include any subtraction.

The Midpoint Formula   If the endpoints of a segment are (x_1, y_1) and (x_2, y_2), then the coordinates of the midpoint are

$$\left(\frac{x_1 + x_2}{2}, \frac{y_1 + y_2}{2}\right).$$

(To locate the midpoint, average the x-coordinates and average the y-coordinates.)

EXAMPLE 8   Find the midpoint of the segment with endpoints $(-2, 3)$ and $(4, -6)$.

SOLUTION   Using the midpoint formula, we obtain

$$\left(\frac{-2 + 4}{2}, \frac{3 + (-6)}{2}\right), \quad \text{or} \quad \left(\frac{2}{2}, \frac{-3}{2}\right), \quad \text{or} \quad \left(1, -\frac{3}{2}\right).$$

Try Exercise 65.

12.7 Exercise Set

FOR EXTRA HELP   *MyMathLab*

Concept Reinforcement   *Complete each sentence with the best choice from the column on the right.*

1. In any ____ triangle, the square of the length of the hypotenuse is the sum of the squares of the lengths of the legs.

2. The shortest side of a right triangle is always one of the two ____.

3. The principle of ____ states that if $x^2 = n$, then $x = \sqrt{n}$ or $x = -\sqrt{n}$.

4. In a(n) ____ right triangle, both legs have the same length.

5. In a(n) ____ right triangle, the hypotenuse is twice as long as the shorter leg.

6. If both legs in a right triangle have measure a, then the ____ measures $a\sqrt{2}$.

a) Hypotenuse

b) Isosceles

c) Legs

d) Right

e) Square roots

f) $30°-60°-90°$

In a right triangle, find the length of the side not given. Give an exact answer and, where appropriate, an approximation to three decimal places.

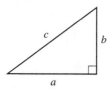

7. $a = 5, b = 3$

8. $a = 8, b = 10$

Aha! **9.** $a = 9, b = 9$

10. $a = 10, b = 10$

11. $b = 12, c = 13$

12. $a = 7, c = 25$

In Exercises 13–28, give an exact answer and, where appropriate, an approximation to three decimal places.

13. A right triangle's hypotenuse is 8 m and one leg is $4\sqrt{3}$ m. Find the length of the other leg.

14. A right triangle's hypotenuse is 6 cm and one leg is $\sqrt{5}$ cm. Find the length of the other leg.

15. The hypotenuse of a right triangle is $\sqrt{20}$ in. and one leg measures 1 in. Find the length of the other leg.

16. The hypotenuse of a right triangle is $\sqrt{15}$ ft and one leg measures 2 ft. Find the length of the other leg.

Aha! **17.** One leg of a right triangle is 1 m and the hypotenuse measures $\sqrt{2}$ m. Find the length of the other leg.

18. One leg of a right triangle is 1 yd and the hypotenuse measures 2 yd. Find the length of the other leg.

19. *Bicycling.* Amanda routinely bicycles across a rectangular parking lot on her way to class. If the lot is 200 ft long and 150 ft wide, how far does Amanda travel when she rides across the lot diagonally?

20. *Guy Wire.* How long is a guy wire if it reaches from the top of a 15-ft pole to a point on the ground 10 ft from the pole?

21. *Softball.* A slow-pitch softball diamond is actually a square 65 ft on a side. How far is it from home plate to second base?

22. *Baseball.* Suppose the catcher in Example 1 makes a throw to second base from the same location. How far is that throw?

23. *Television Sets.* What does it mean to refer to a 51-in. TV set? Such units refer to the diagonal of the screen. A 51-in. TV set has a width of 45 in. What is its height?

24. *Television Sets.* A 53-in. TV set has a screen with a height of 28 in. What is its width? (See Exercise 23.)

25. *Speaker Placement.* A stereo receiver is in a corner of a 12-ft by 14-ft room. Wire will run under a rug, diagonally, to a speaker in the far corner. If 4 ft of slack is required on each end, how long a piece of wire should be purchased?

26. *Distance over Water.* To determine the width of a pond, a surveyor locates two stakes at either end of the pond and uses instrumentation to place a third stake so that the distance across the pond is the length of a hypotenuse. If the third stake is 90 m from one stake and 70 m from the other, what is the distance across the pond?

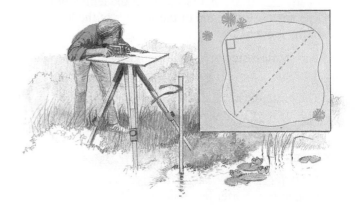

27. *Walking.* Students at Mossway Community College have worn a path that cuts diagonally across the campus "quad." If the quad is actually a rectangle that Angie measured to be 70 paces long and 40 paces wide, how many paces will Angie save by using the diagonal path?

28. *Crosswalks.* The diagonal crosswalk at the intersection of State St. and Main St. is the hypotenuse of a triangle in which the crosswalks across State St. and Main St. are the legs. If State St. is 28 ft wide and Main St. is 40 ft wide, how much shorter is the distance traveled by pedestrians using the diagonal crosswalk?

For each triangle, find the missing length(s). Give an exact answer and, where appropriate, an approximation to three decimal places.

29.

30.

31.

32.

33.

34.

35.

36.

37.

38.

39.

40.

41.

42.

43.

44.
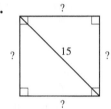

In Exercises 45–50, give an exact answer and, where appropriate, an approximation to three decimal places.

45. *Bridge Expansion.* During the summer heat, a 2-mi bridge expands 2 ft in length. If we assume that the bulge occurs straight up the middle, how high is the bulge? (The answer may surprise you. Most bridges have expansion spaces to avoid such buckling.)

46. Triangle *ABC* has sides of lengths 25 ft, 25 ft, and 30 ft. Triangle *PQR* has sides of lengths 25 ft, 25 ft, and 40 ft. Which triangle, if either, has the greater area and by how much?

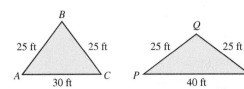

47. *Architecture.* The Rushton Triangular Lodge in Northamptonshire, England, was designed and constructed by Sir Thomas Tresham between 1593 and 1597. The building is in the shape of an equilateral triangle with walls of length 33 ft. How many square feet of land is covered by the lodge?
Source: The Internet Encyclopedia of Science

48. *Antenna Length.* As part of an emergency radio communication station, Rik sets up an "Inverted-V" antenna. He stretches a copper wire from one point on the ground to a point on a tree and then back down to the ground, forming two 30°–60°–90° triangles. If the wire is fastened to the tree 34 ft above the ground, how long is the copper wire?

49. Find all points on the *y*-axis of a Cartesian coordinate system that are 5 units from the point (3, 0).

50. Find all points on the *x*-axis of a Cartesian coordinate system that are 5 units from the point (0, 4).

Find the distance between each pair of points. Where appropriate, find an approximation to three decimal places.

51. (4, 5) and (7, 1)

52. (0, 8) and (6, 0)

53. (0, −5) and (1, −2)

54. (−1, −4) and (−3, −5)

55. (−4, 4) and (6, −6)

56. (5, 21) and (−3, 1)

Aha! **57.** (8.6, −3.4) and (−9.2, −3.4)

58. (5.9, 2) and (3.7, −7.7)

59. $\left(\frac{1}{2}, \frac{1}{3}\right)$ and $\left(\frac{5}{6}, -\frac{1}{6}\right)$

60. $\left(\frac{5}{7}, \frac{1}{14}\right)$ and $\left(\frac{1}{7}, \frac{11}{14}\right)$

61. $\left(-\sqrt{6}, \sqrt{6}\right)$ and (0, 0)

62. $\left(\sqrt{5}, -\sqrt{3}\right)$ and (0, 0)

63. (−1, −30) and (−2, −40)

64. (0.5, 100) and (1.5, −100)

Find the midpoint of each segment with the given endpoints.

65. (−2, 5) and (8, 3)

66. (1, 4) and (9, −6)

67. (2, −1) and (5, 8)

68. (−1, 2) and (1, −3)

69. (−8, −5) and (6, −1)

70. (8, −2) and (−3, 4)

71. (−3.4, 8.1) and (4.8, −8.1)

72. (4.1, 6.9) and (5.2, −8.9)

73. $\left(\frac{1}{6}, -\frac{3}{4}\right)$ and $\left(-\frac{1}{3}, \frac{5}{6}\right)$

74. $\left(-\frac{4}{5}, -\frac{2}{3}\right)$ and $\left(\frac{1}{8}, \frac{3}{4}\right)$

75. $\left(\sqrt{2}, -1\right)$ and $\left(\sqrt{3}, 4\right)$

76. $\left(9, 2\sqrt{3}\right)$ and $\left(-4, 5\sqrt{3}\right)$

TW **77.** Are there any right triangles, other than those with sides measuring 3, 4, and 5, that have consecutive numbers for the lengths of the sides? Why or why not?

TW **78.** If a 30°–60°–90° triangle and an isosceles right triangle have the same perimeter, which will have the greater area? Why?

SKILL REVIEW

Review graphing (Section 11.4).
Graph on a plane.

79. $y = 2x − 3$

80. $y < x$ [11.4]

81. $8x − 4y = 8$

82. $2y − 1 = 7$

83. $x \geq 1$

84. $x − 5 = 6 − 2y$

SYNTHESIS

TW **85.** Describe a procedure that uses the distance formula to determine whether three points, (x_1, y_1), (x_2, y_2), and (x_3, y_3), are vertices of a right triangle.

TW **86.** Outline a procedure that uses the distance formula to determine whether three points, (x_1, y_1), (x_2, y_2), and (x_3, y_3), are collinear (lie on the same line).

87. The perimeter of a regular hexagon is 72 cm. Determine the area of the shaded region shown.

88. If the perimeter of a regular hexagon is 120 ft, what is its area? (*Hint*: See Exercise 87.)

89. Each side of a regular octagon has length s. Find a formula for the distance d between the parallel sides of the octagon.

90. *Roofing.* Kit's home, which is 24 ft wide and 32 ft long, needs a new roof. By counting clapboards that are 4 in. apart, Kit determines that the peak of the roof is 6 ft higher than the sides. If one packet of shingles covers 100 ft^2, how many packets will the job require?

91. *Painting.* (Refer to Exercise 90.) A gallon of Benjamin Moore® exterior acrylic paint covers 450–500 ft^2. If Kit's house has dimensions as shown above, how many gallons of paint should be bought to paint the house? What assumption(s) is made in your answer?

92. *Contracting.* Oxford Builders has an extension cord on their generator that permits them to work, with electricity, anywhere in a circular area of 3850 ft^2. Find the dimensions of the largest square room they could work on without having to relocate the generator to reach each corner of the floor plan.

93. *Contracting.* Cleary Construction has a hose attached to their insulation blower that permits them to work, with electricity, anywhere in a circular area of 6160 ft^2. Find the dimensions of the largest square room with 12-ft ceilings in which they could reach all corners

with the hose while leaving the blower centrally located. Assume that the blower sits on the floor.

94. A cube measures 5 cm on each side. How long is the diagonal that connects two opposite corners of the cube? Give an exact answer.

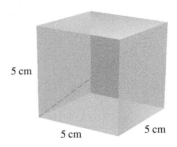

95. Prove the midpoint formula by showing that

i) the distance from (x_1, y_1) to
$$\left(\frac{x_1 + x_2}{2}, \frac{y_1 + y_2}{2} \right)$$
equals the distance from (x_2, y_2) to
$$\left(\frac{x_1 + x_2}{2}, \frac{y_1 + y_2}{2} \right);$$

and

ii) the points
$$(x_1, y_1), \left(\frac{x_1 + x_2}{2}, \frac{y_1 + y_2}{2} \right),$$
and
$$(x_2, y_2)$$
lie on the same line (see Exercise 86).

Try Exercise Answers: Section 12.7

15. $\sqrt{19}$ in.; 4.359 in.   **19.** 250 ft

29. Leg = 5; hypotenuse = $5\sqrt{2} \approx 7.071$

33. Leg = $5\sqrt{3} \approx 8.660$; hypotenuse = $10\sqrt{3} \approx 17.321$

35. Both legs = $\dfrac{13\sqrt{2}}{2} \approx 9.192$

37. Leg = $14\sqrt{3} \approx 24.249$; hypotenuse = 28

51. 5   **65.** $(3, 4)$

12.8 The Complex Numbers

IMAGINARY NUMBERS AND COMPLEX NUMBERS

Negative numbers do not have square roots in the real-number system. However, a larger number system that contains the real-number system is designed so that negative numbers *do* have square roots. That system is called the **complex-number system,** and it will allow us to solve equations like $x^2 + 1 = 0$. The complex-number system makes use of *i*, a number that is, by definition, a square root of -1.

The Number *i* *i* is the unique number for which $i = \sqrt{-1}$ and $i^2 = -1$.

We can now define the square root of a negative number as follows:

$$\sqrt{-p} = \sqrt{-1}\,\sqrt{p} = i\sqrt{p} \text{ or } \sqrt{p}i, \quad \text{for any positive number } p.$$

EXAMPLE 1 Express in terms of *i*: **(a)** $\sqrt{-7}$; **(b)** $\sqrt{-16}$; **(c)** $-\sqrt{-13}$; **(d)** $-\sqrt{-50}$.

SOLUTION

a) $\sqrt{-7} = \sqrt{-1 \cdot 7} = \sqrt{-1} \cdot \sqrt{7} = i\sqrt{7}$, or $\sqrt{7}i$ *i* is *not* under the radical.

b) $\sqrt{-16} = \sqrt{-1 \cdot 16} = \sqrt{-1} \cdot \sqrt{16} = i \cdot 4 = 4i$

c) $-\sqrt{-13} = -\sqrt{-1 \cdot 13} = -\sqrt{-1} \cdot \sqrt{13} = -i\sqrt{13}$, or $-\sqrt{13}i$

d) $-\sqrt{-50} = -\sqrt{-1} \cdot \sqrt{25} \cdot \sqrt{2} = -i \cdot 5 \cdot \sqrt{2}$
$$= -5i\sqrt{2}, \text{ or } -5\sqrt{2}i$$

■ Try Exercise 9.

Imaginary Numbers An *imaginary number* is a number that can be written in the form $a + bi$, where *a* and *b* are real numbers and $b \neq 0$.

Don't let the name "imaginary" fool you. Imaginary numbers appear in fields such as engineering and the physical sciences. The following are examples of imaginary numbers:

$5 + 4i$,   Here $a = 5, b = 4$.

$\sqrt{3} - \pi i$,   Here $a = \sqrt{3}, b = -\pi$.

$\sqrt{7}i$.   Here $a = 0, b = \sqrt{7}$.

The union of the set of all imaginary numbers and the set of all real numbers is the set of all **complex numbers.**

> Complex Numbers   A *complex number* is any number that can be written in the form $a + bi$, where a and b are real numbers. (Note that a and b both can be 0.)

The following are examples of complex numbers:

$7 + 3i$ (here $a \neq 0, b \neq 0$); $4i$ (here $a = 0, b \neq 0$);

8 (here $a \neq 0, b = 0$); 0 (here $a = 0, b = 0$).

Complex numbers like $17i$ or $4i$, in which $a = 0$ and $b \neq 0$, are called *pure imaginary numbers*. For $b = 0$, we have $a + 0i = a$, so every real number is a complex number. The relationships among various real numbers and complex numbers are shown below.

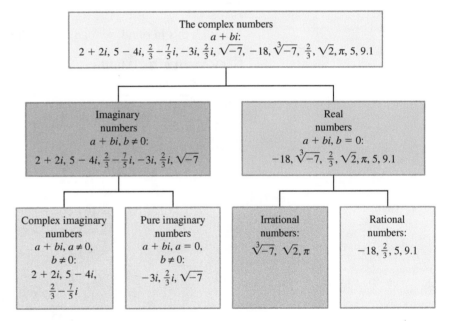

Note that although $\sqrt{-7}$ and $\sqrt[3]{-7}$ are both complex numbers, $\sqrt{-7}$ is imaginary whereas $\sqrt[3]{-7}$ is real.

ADDITION AND SUBTRACTION

The commutative, associative, and distributive laws hold for complex numbers. Thus we can add and subtract them as we do binomials.

EXAMPLE 2   Add or subtract and simplify.

a) $(8 + 6i) + (3 + 2i)$ **b)** $(4 + 5i) - (6 - 3i)$

SOLUTION

a) $(8 + 6i) + (3 + 2i) = (8 + 3) + (6i + 2i)$ Combining the real parts and the imaginary parts

$$= 11 + (6 + 2)i = 11 + 8i$$

b) $(4 + 5i) - (6 - 3i) = (4 - 6) + [5i - (-3i)]$ Note that the 6 and the $-3i$ are *both* being subtracted.

$$= -2 + 8i$$

Try Exercise 27.

Student Notes

The rule developed in Section 12.3, $\sqrt[n]{a} \cdot \sqrt[n]{b} = \sqrt[n]{a \cdot b}$, does *not* apply when *n* is 2 and either *a* or *b* is negative. Indeed this condition is stated on p. 795 when it is specified that $\sqrt[n]{a}$ and $\sqrt[n]{b}$ are both *real* numbers.

MULTIPLICATION

To multiply square roots of negative real numbers, we first express them in terms of *i*. For example,

$$\begin{aligned}
\sqrt{-2} \cdot \sqrt{-5} &= \sqrt{-1} \cdot \sqrt{2} \cdot \sqrt{-1} \cdot \sqrt{5} \\
&= i \quad \cdot \sqrt{2} \cdot \quad i \quad \cdot \sqrt{5} \\
&= i^2 \cdot \sqrt{10} \qquad \text{Since } i \text{ is a square root of } -1, i^2 = -1. \\
&= -1\sqrt{10} = -\sqrt{10} \text{ is correct!}
\end{aligned}$$

> **CAUTION!** With complex numbers, simply multiplying radicands is *incorrect* when both radicands are negative:
>
> $$\sqrt{-2} \cdot \sqrt{-5} \neq \sqrt{10}.$$

With this in mind, we can now multiply complex numbers.

EXAMPLE 3 Multiply and simplify. When possible, write answers in the form $a + bi$.

a) $\sqrt{-4} \cdot \sqrt{-25}$ **b)** $\sqrt{-5} \cdot \sqrt{-7}$ **c)** $-3i \cdot 8i$

d) $-4i(3 - 5i)$ **e)** $(1 + 2i)(4 + 3i)$

SOLUTION

a)
$$\begin{aligned}
\sqrt{-4} \cdot \sqrt{-25} &= \sqrt{-1} \cdot \sqrt{4} \cdot \sqrt{-1} \cdot \sqrt{25} \\
&= i \quad \cdot 2 \cdot \quad i \quad \cdot 5 \\
&= i^2 \cdot 10 \\
&= -1 \cdot 10 \qquad i^2 = -1 \\
&= -10
\end{aligned}$$

b)
$$\begin{aligned}
\sqrt{-5} \cdot \sqrt{-7} &= \sqrt{-1} \cdot \sqrt{5} \cdot \sqrt{-1} \cdot \sqrt{7} \qquad \text{Try to do this step mentally.} \\
&= i \quad \cdot \sqrt{5} \cdot \quad i \quad \cdot \sqrt{7} \\
&= i^2 \cdot \sqrt{35} \\
&= -1 \cdot \sqrt{35} \qquad i^2 = -1 \\
&= -\sqrt{35}
\end{aligned}$$

c)
$$\begin{aligned}
-3i \cdot 8i &= -24 \cdot i^2 \\
&= -24 \cdot (-1) \qquad i^2 = -1 \\
&= 24
\end{aligned}$$

d)
$$\begin{aligned}
-4i(3 - 5i) &= -4i \cdot 3 + (-4i)(-5i) \qquad \text{Using the distributive law} \\
&= -12i + 20i^2 \\
&= -12i - 20 \qquad i^2 = -1 \\
&= -20 - 12i \qquad \text{Writing in the form } a + bi
\end{aligned}$$

e)
$$\begin{aligned}
(1 + 2i)(4 + 3i) &= 4 + 3i + 8i + 6i^2 \qquad \text{Multiplying each term of } 4 + 3i \\
&\qquad\qquad\qquad\qquad\qquad \text{by every term of } 1 + 2i \text{ (FOIL)} \\
&= 4 + 3i + 8i - 6 \qquad i^2 = -1 \\
&= -2 + 11i \qquad \text{Combining like terms}
\end{aligned}$$

Try Exercises 39 and 45.

CONJUGATES AND DIVISION

Recall that the conjugate of $4 + \sqrt{2}$ is $4 - \sqrt{2}$.

Conjugates of complex numbers are defined in a similar manner.

> **Conjugate of a Complex Number**   The *conjugate* of a complex number $a + bi$ is $a - bi$, and the *conjugate* of $a - bi$ is $a + bi$.

EXAMPLE 4   Find the conjugate of each number.

a) $-3 - 7i$

b) $4i$

SOLUTION

a) $-3 - 7i$ The conjugate is $-3 + 7i$.

b) $4i$ The conjugate is $-4i$. Note that $4i = 0 + 4i$.

The product of a complex number and its conjugate is a real number.

EXAMPLE 5   Multiply: $(5 + 7i)(5 - 7i)$.

SOLUTION

$$\begin{aligned}(5 + 7i)(5 - 7i) &= 5^2 - (7i)^2 \quad &\text{Using } (A + B)(A - B) = A^2 - B^2\\ &= 25 - 49i^2\\ &= 25 - 49(-1) \quad &i^2 = -1\\ &= 25 + 49 = 74\end{aligned}$$

Try Exercise 55.

Conjugates are used when dividing complex numbers. The procedure is much like that used to rationalize denominators with two terms.

EXAMPLE 6   Divide and simplify to the form $a + bi$.

a) $\dfrac{-5 + 9i}{1 - 2i}$

b) $\dfrac{7 + 3i}{5i}$

SOLUTION

a) To divide and simplify $(-5 + 9i)/(1 - 2i)$, we multiply by 1, using the conjugate of the denominator to form 1:

$$\begin{aligned}\frac{-5 + 9i}{1 - 2i} &= \frac{-5 + 9i}{1 - 2i} \cdot \frac{1 + 2i}{1 + 2i} \quad &&\text{Multiplying by 1 using the conjugate of the denominator in the symbol for 1}\\ &= \frac{-5 - 10i + 9i + 18i^2}{1^2 - 4i^2} \quad &&\text{Multiplying using FOIL}\\ &= \frac{-5 - i - 18}{1 - 4(-1)} \quad &&i^2 = -1\\ &= \frac{-23 - i}{5} \quad &&\text{Writing in the form } a + bi.\\ &= -\frac{23}{5} - \frac{1}{5}i. \quad &&\text{Note that } \frac{X + Y}{Z} = \frac{X}{Z} + \frac{Y}{Z}.\end{aligned}$$

b) The conjugate of $5i$ is $-5i$, so we *could* multiply by $-5i/(-5i)$. However, when the denominator is a pure imaginary number, it is easiest if we multiply by i/i:

$$\frac{7+3i}{5i} = \frac{7+3i}{5i} \cdot \frac{i}{i} \qquad \text{Multiplying by 1 using } i/i. \text{ We can also use the conjugate of } 5i \text{ to write } -5i/(-5i).$$

$$= \frac{7i+3i^2}{5i^2} \qquad \text{Multiplying}$$

$$= \frac{7i+3(-1)}{5(-1)} \qquad i^2 = -1$$

$$= \frac{7i-3}{-5} = \frac{-3}{-5} + \frac{7}{-5}i, \text{ or } \frac{3}{5} - \frac{7}{5}i. \qquad \text{Writing in the form } a+bi$$

Try Exercise 67.

POWERS OF *i*

Answers to problems involving complex numbers are generally written in the form $a + bi$. In the following discussion, we show why there is no need to use powers of i (other than 1) when writing answers.

Recall that -1 raised to an *even* power is 1, and -1 raised to an *odd* power is -1. Simplifying powers of i can then be done by using the fact that $i^2 = -1$ and expressing the given power of i in terms of i^2. Consider the following:

$$i^2 = -1,$$
$$i^3 = i^2 \cdot i = (-1)i = -i,$$
$$i^4 = (i^2)^2 = (-1)^2 = 1,$$
$$i^5 = i^4 \cdot i = (i^2)^2 \cdot i = (-1)^2 \cdot i = i,$$
$$i^6 = (i^2)^3 = (-1)^3 = -1. \quad \longleftarrow \text{The pattern is now repeating.}$$

The powers of i cycle themselves through the values $i, -1, -i,$ and 1. Even powers of i are -1 or 1 whereas odd powers of i are i or $-i$.

EXAMPLE 7 Simplify: **(a)** i^{18}; **(b)** i^{24}.

SOLUTION

a) $i^{18} = (i^2)^9$ Using the power rule

       $= (-1)^9 = -1$ Raising -1 to a power

b) $i^{24} = (i^2)^{12} = (-1)^{12} = 1$

Try Exercise 85.

To simplify i^n when n is odd, we rewrite i^n as $i^{n-1} \cdot i$.

EXAMPLE 8 Simplify: **(a)** i^{29}; **(b)** i^{75}.

SOLUTION

a) $i^{29} = i^{28}i^1$ Using the product rule. This is a key step when i is raised to an odd power.

       $= (i^2)^{14}i$ Using the power rule

       $= (-1)^{14}i = 1 \cdot i = i$

b) $i^{75} = i^{74}i^1$ Using the product rule

       $= (i^2)^{37}i$ Using the power rule

       $= (-1)^{37}i = -1 \cdot i = -i$

Try Exercise 83.

── Complex Numbers

To perform operations with complex numbers using a calculator, you may need to first choose the a + bi setting in the MODE screen.

Press ⓘ for the complex number *i*. (ⓘ is often the 2nd option associated with the ⦁ key.) For example, to calculate $(-1 + i)(2 - i)$, press ((-) ① + ⓘ) (② - ⓘ) **ENTER**. As seen in the screen on the right above, the result is $-1 + 3i$. To calculate $\dfrac{2 - i}{3 + i}$ and write the result using fraction notation, press (② - ⓘ) ÷ (③ + ⓘ) **MATH** ① **ENTER**. Note the need for parentheses around the numerator and the denominator of the expression. The result appears in the form $a + bi$; *i* is not in the denominator of the fraction. The result is $\frac{1}{2} - \frac{1}{2}i$.

Your Turn

1. Set your calculator to complex mode.

2. Calculate $(1 - i)(3 + i)$ and $\dfrac{3 - 2i}{4 + i}$. $4 - 2i; \dfrac{10}{17} - \dfrac{11}{17}i$

3. Return your calculator to REAL mode.

12.8 Exercise Set

Concept Reinforcement   *Classify each of the following statements as either true or false.*

1. Imaginary numbers are so named because they have no real-world applications.

2. Every real number is imaginary, but not every imaginary number is real.

3. Every imaginary number is a complex number, but not every complex number is imaginary.

4. Every real number is a complex number, but not every complex number is real.

5. We multiply complex numbers by multiplying real parts and multiplying imaginary parts.

6. The product of a complex number and its conjugate is always a real number.

7. The square of a complex number is always a real number.

8. The quotient of two complex numbers is always a complex number.

Express in terms of i.

9. $\sqrt{-100}$

10. $\sqrt{-25}$

11. $\sqrt{-13}$

12. $\sqrt{-19}$

13. $\sqrt{-8}$

14. $\sqrt{-12}$

15. $-\sqrt{-3}$

16. $-\sqrt{-17}$

17. $-\sqrt{-81}$

18. $-\sqrt{-49}$

19. $-\sqrt{-300}$

20. $-\sqrt{-75}$

21. $6 - \sqrt{-84}$

22. $4 - \sqrt{-60}$

23. $-\sqrt{-76} + \sqrt{-125}$

24. $\sqrt{-4} + \sqrt{-12}$

25. $\sqrt{-18} - \sqrt{-100}$

26. $\sqrt{-72} - \sqrt{-25}$

Perform the indicated operation and simplify. Write each answer in the form a + bi.

27. $(6 + 7i) + (5 + 3i)$

28. $(4 - 5i) + (3 + 9i)$

29. $(9 + 8i) - (5 + 3i)$

30. $(9 + 7i) - (2 + 4i)$

31. $(7 - 4i) - (5 - 3i)$

32. $(5 - 3i) - (9 + 2i)$

33. $(-5 - i) - (7 + 4i)$

34. $(-2 + 6i) - (-7 + i)$

35. $7i \cdot 6i$

36. $6i \cdot 9i$

37. $(-4i)(-6i)$

38. $7i \cdot (-8i)$

39. $\sqrt{-36}\,\sqrt{-9}$

40. $\sqrt{-49}\,\sqrt{-25}$

41. $\sqrt{-5}\,\sqrt{-2}$

42. $\sqrt{-6}\,\sqrt{-7}$

43. $\sqrt{-6}\,\sqrt{-21}$

44. $\sqrt{-15}\,\sqrt{-10}$

45. $5i(2 + 6i)$

46. $2i(7 + 3i)$

47. $-7i(3 - 4i)$

48. $-4i(6 - 5i)$

49. $(1 + i)(3 + 2i)$

50. $(4 + i)(2 + 3i)$

51. $(6 - 5i)(3 + 4i)$

52. $(5 - 6i)(2 + 5i)$

53. $(7 - 2i)(2 - 6i)$

54. $(-4 + 5i)(3 - 4i)$

55. $(3 + 8i)(3 - 8i)$

56. $(1 + 2i)(1 - 2i)$

57. $(-7 + i)(-7 - i)$

58. $(-4 + 5i)(-4 - 5i)$

59. $(4 - 2i)^2$

60. $(1 - 2i)^2$

61. $(2 + 3i)^2$

62. $(3 + 2i)^2$

63. $(-2 + 3i)^2$

64. $(-5 - 2i)^2$

65. $\dfrac{10}{3 + i}$

66. $\dfrac{26}{5 + i}$

67. $\dfrac{2}{3 - 2i}$

68. $\dfrac{4}{2 - 3i}$

69. $\dfrac{2i}{5 + 3i}$

70. $\dfrac{3i}{4 + 2i}$

71. $\dfrac{5}{6i}$

72. $\dfrac{4}{7i}$

73. $\dfrac{5 - 3i}{4i}$

74. $\dfrac{2 + 7i}{5i}$

Aha! **75.** $\dfrac{7i + 14}{7i}$

76. $\dfrac{6i + 3}{3i}$

77. $\dfrac{4 + 5i}{3 - 7i}$

78. $\dfrac{5 + 3i}{7 - 4i}$

79. $\dfrac{2 + 3i}{2 + 5i}$

80. $\dfrac{3 + 2i}{4 + 3i}$

81. $\dfrac{3 - 2i}{4 + 3i}$

82. $\dfrac{5 - 2i}{3 + 6i}$

Simplify.

83. i^7

84. i^{11}

85. i^{32}

86. i^{38}

87. i^{42}

88. i^{64}

89. i^9

90. $(-i)^{71}$

91. $(-i)^6$

92. $(-i)^4$

93. $(5i)^3$

94. $(-3i)^5$

95. $i^2 + i^4$

96. $5i^5 + 4i^3$

TW **97.** Is the product of two imaginary numbers always an imaginary number? Why or why not?

TW **98.** In what way(s) are conjugates of complex numbers similar to the conjugates used in Section 12.5?

SKILL REVIEW

To prepare for Section 13.1, review solving quadratic equations.

Solve.

99. $x^2 - x - 6 = 0$

100. $(x - 5)^2 = 0$

101. $t^2 = 100$

102. $2t^2 - 50 = 0$

103. $15x^2 = 14x + 8$

104. $6x^2 = 5x + 6$

SYNTHESIS

тw **105.** Is the set of real numbers a subset of the set of complex numbers? Why or why not?

тw **106.** Is the union of the set of imaginary numbers and the set of real numbers the set of complex numbers? Why or why not?

Complex numbers are often graphed on a plane. The horizontal axis is the real axis and the vertical axis is the imaginary axis. A complex number such as $5 - 2i$ then corresponds to 5 on the real axis and -2 on the imaginary axis.

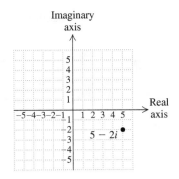

107. Graph each of the following.

   a) $3 + 2i$ **b)** $-1 + 4i$
   c) $3 - i$ **d)** $-5i$

108. Graph each of the following.

   a) $1 - 4i$ **b)** $-2 - 3i$
   c) i **d)** 4

The absolute value of a complex number $a + bi$ is its distance from the origin. Using the distance formula, we have $|a + bi| = \sqrt{a^2 + b^2}$. Find the absolute value of each complex number.

109. $|3 + 4i|$ **110.** $|8 - 6i|$

111. $|-1 + i|$ **112.** $|-3 - i|$

A function g is given by

$$g(z) = \frac{z^4 - z^2}{z - 1}.$$

113. Find $g(3i)$.

114. Find $g(1 + i)$.

115. Find $g(5i - 1)$.

116. Find $g(2 - 3i)$.

117. Evaluate

$$\frac{1}{w - w^2} \quad \text{for} \quad w = \frac{1 - i}{10}.$$

Simplify.

118. $\dfrac{i^5 + i^6 + i^7 + i^8}{(1 - i)^4}$

119. $(1 - i)^3(1 + i)^3$

120. $\dfrac{5 - \sqrt{5}i}{\sqrt{5}i}$

121. $\dfrac{6}{1 + \dfrac{3}{i}}$

122. $\left(\dfrac{1}{2} - \dfrac{1}{3}i\right)^2 - \left(\dfrac{1}{2} + \dfrac{1}{3}i\right)^2$

123. $\dfrac{i - i^{38}}{1 + i}$

Study Summary

KEY TERMS AND CONCEPTS	EXAMPLES	PRACTICE EXERCISES

SECTION 12.1: RADICAL EXPRESSIONS, FUNCTIONS, AND MODELS

KEY TERMS AND CONCEPTS	EXAMPLES	PRACTICE EXERCISES
c is a **square root** of a if $c^2 = a$. c is a **cube root** of a if $c^3 = a$. $\sqrt{a}$ indicates the **principal** square root of a. $\sqrt[n]{a}$ indicates the ***n*th root** of a. **index** $\sqrt[n]{a}$ — **radicand** **radical symbol**	The square roots of 25 are -5 and 5. The cube root of -8 is -2. $\sqrt{25} = 5$ $\sqrt[3]{-8} = -2$	*Simplify.* **1.** $-\sqrt{81}$ **2.** $\sqrt[3]{-1}$
For all a, $\sqrt[n]{a^n} = |a|$ when n is even; $\sqrt[n]{a^n} = a$ when n is odd. If a represents a nonnegative number, $\sqrt[n]{a^n} = a$.	Assume that x can represent any real number. $\sqrt{(3 + x)^2} = |3 + x|$ Assume that x represents a nonnegative number. $\sqrt{(7x)^2} = 7x$	**3.** Simplify. Assume that x can represent any real number. $\sqrt{36x^2}$ **4.** Simplify. Assume that x represents a nonnegative number. $\sqrt[4]{x^4}$

SECTION 12.2: RATIONAL NUMBERS AS EXPONENTS

KEY TERMS AND CONCEPTS	EXAMPLES	PRACTICE EXERCISES
$a^{1/n}$ means $\sqrt[n]{a}$. $a^{m/n}$ means $\left(\sqrt[n]{a}\right)^m$ or $\sqrt[n]{a^m}$. $a^{-m/n}$ means $\dfrac{1}{a^{m/n}}$.	$64^{1/2} = \sqrt{64} = 8$ $125^{2/3} = \left(\sqrt[3]{125}\right)^2 = 5^2 = 25$ $8^{-1/3} = \dfrac{1}{8^{1/3}} = \dfrac{1}{2}$	**5.** Simplify: $100^{-1/2}$.

SECTION 12.3: MULTIPLYING RADICAL EXPRESSIONS

KEY TERMS AND CONCEPTS	EXAMPLES	PRACTICE EXERCISES
The Product Rule for Radicals For any real numbers $\sqrt[n]{a}$ and $\sqrt[n]{b}$, $\sqrt[n]{a} \cdot \sqrt[n]{b} = \sqrt[n]{a \cdot b}$.	$\sqrt[3]{4x} \cdot \sqrt[3]{5y} = \sqrt[3]{20xy}$	**6.** Multiply: $\sqrt{7x} \cdot \sqrt{3y}$.
Using the Product Rule to Simplify For any real numbers $\sqrt[n]{a}$ and $\sqrt[n]{b}$, $\sqrt[n]{a \cdot b} = \sqrt[n]{a} \cdot \sqrt[n]{b}$.	$\sqrt{75x^8y^{11}} = \sqrt{25 \cdot x^8 \cdot y^{10} \cdot 3 \cdot y}$ $\phantom{\sqrt{75x^8y^{11}}} = \sqrt{25} \cdot \sqrt{x^8} \cdot \sqrt{y^{10}} \cdot \sqrt{3y}$ $\phantom{\sqrt{75x^8y^{11}}} = 5x^4y^5\sqrt{3y}$ Assuming y is nonnegative	**7.** Simplify: $\sqrt{200x^5y^{18}}$.

SECTION 12.4: DIVIDING RADICAL EXPRESSIONS

The Quotient Rule for Radicals	$\sqrt[3]{\dfrac{8y^4}{125}} = \dfrac{\sqrt[3]{8y^4}}{\sqrt[3]{125}} = \dfrac{2y\sqrt[3]{y}}{5}$	**8.** Simplify: $\sqrt{\dfrac{12x^3}{25}}$.
For any real numbers $\sqrt[n]{a}$ and $\sqrt[n]{b}, b \neq 0$, $\sqrt[n]{\dfrac{a}{b}} = \dfrac{\sqrt[n]{a}}{\sqrt[n]{b}}$.	$\dfrac{\sqrt{18a^9}}{\sqrt{2a^3}} = \sqrt{\dfrac{18a^9}{2a^3}} = \sqrt{9a^6} = 3a^3$ Assuming a is positive	
We can **rationalize a denominator** by multiplying by 1.	$\dfrac{1}{\sqrt{2}} = \dfrac{1}{\sqrt{2}} \cdot \dfrac{\sqrt{2}}{\sqrt{2}} = \dfrac{\sqrt{2}}{2}$	**9.** Rationalize the denominator: $\sqrt{\dfrac{2x}{3y^2}}$.

SECTION 12.5: EXPRESSIONS CONTAINING SEVERAL RADICAL TERMS

Like radicals have the same indices and radicands.	$\sqrt{12} + 5\sqrt{3} = \sqrt{4 \cdot 3} + 5\sqrt{3} = 2\sqrt{3} + 5\sqrt{3} = 7\sqrt{3}$	**10.** Simplify: $5\sqrt{8} - 3\sqrt{50}$.
Radical expressions are multiplied in much the same way that polynomials are multiplied.	$\begin{aligned} &(1 + 5\sqrt{6})(4 - \sqrt{6}) \\ &= 1 \cdot 4 - 1\sqrt{6} + 4 \cdot 5\sqrt{6} - 5\sqrt{6} \cdot \sqrt{6} \\ &= 4 - \sqrt{6} + 20\sqrt{6} - 5 \cdot 6 \\ &= -26 + 19\sqrt{6} \end{aligned}$	**11.** Simplify: $(2 - \sqrt{3})(5 - 7\sqrt{3})$.
To rationalize a denominator containing two terms, we use the **conjugate** of the denominator to write a form of 1.	$\dfrac{2}{1 - \sqrt{3}} = \dfrac{2}{1 - \sqrt{3}} \cdot \dfrac{1 + \sqrt{3}}{1 + \sqrt{3}}$ $1 + \sqrt{3}$ is the conjugate of $1 - \sqrt{3}$. $= \dfrac{2(1 + \sqrt{3})}{-2} = -1 - \sqrt{3}$	**12.** Rationalize the denominator: $\dfrac{\sqrt{15}}{3 + \sqrt{5}}$.
When terms have different indices, we can often use rational exponents to simplify.	$\begin{aligned} \sqrt[3]{p} \cdot \sqrt[4]{q^3} &= p^{1/3} \cdot q^{3/4} \\ &= p^{4/12} \cdot q^{9/12} \quad \text{Finding a common denominator} \\ &= \sqrt[12]{p^4 q^9} \end{aligned}$	**13.** Simplify: $\dfrac{\sqrt{x^5}}{\sqrt[3]{x}}$.

SECTION 12.6: SOLVING RADICAL EQUATIONS

The Principle of Powers	$\begin{aligned} x - 7 &= \sqrt{x - 5} \\ (x - 7)^2 &= (\sqrt{x - 5})^2 \\ x^2 - 14x + 49 &= x - 5 \\ x^2 - 15x + 54 &= 0 \\ (x - 6)(x - 9) &= 0 \\ x = 6 \quad &or \quad x = 9 \end{aligned}$ Only 9 checks and is the solution.	**14.** Solve: $\sqrt{2x + 3} = x$.
If $a = b$, then $a^n = b^n$. To solve a radical equation, use the principle of powers and the steps on pp. 765 and 766. Solutions found using the principle of powers must be checked in the original equation.	$\begin{aligned} 2 + \sqrt{t} &= \sqrt{t + 8} \\ (2 + \sqrt{t})^2 &= (\sqrt{t + 8})^2 \\ 4 + 4\sqrt{t} + t &= t + 8 \\ 4\sqrt{t} &= 4 \\ \sqrt{t} &= 1 \\ (\sqrt{t})^2 &= (1)^2 \\ t &= 1 \end{aligned}$ 1 checks and is the solution.	

SECTION 12.7: THE DISTANCE FORMULA, THE MIDPOINT FORMULA, AND OTHER APPLICATIONS

The Pythagorean Theorem

In any right triangle, if a and b are the lengths of the legs and c is the length of the hypotenuse, then

$$a^2 + b^2 = c^2.$$

Find the length of the hypotenuse of a right triangle with legs of lengths 4 and 7. Give an exact answer in radical notation, as well as a decimal approximation to three decimal places.

$$a^2 + b^2 = c^2$$
$$4^2 + 7^2 = c^2 \quad \text{Substituting}$$
$$16 + 49 = c^2$$
$$65 = c^2$$
$$\sqrt{65} = c \quad \text{This is exact.}$$
$$8.062 \approx c \quad \text{This is approximate.}$$

15. The hypotenuse of a right triangle is 10 m long, and one leg is 7 m long. Find the length of the other leg. Give an exact answer in radical notation, as well as a decimal approximation to three decimal places.

Special Triangles

The length of the hypotenuse in an isosceles right triangle is the length of a leg times $\sqrt{2}$.

The length of the longer leg in a 30°–60°–90° triangle is the length of the shorter leg times $\sqrt{3}$. The hypotenuse is twice as long as the shorter leg.

Find the missing lengths. Give an exact answer and, where appropriate, an approximation to three decimal places.

$$a = 10; \quad c = a\sqrt{2}$$
$$c = 10\sqrt{2}$$
$$c \approx 14.142$$

$$18 = a\sqrt{3} \qquad c = 2a$$
$$\frac{18}{\sqrt{3}} = a \qquad c = 2\left(\frac{18}{\sqrt{3}}\right)$$
$$10.392 \approx a; \qquad c = \frac{36}{\sqrt{3}}$$
$$c \approx 20.785$$

Find the missing lengths. Give an exact answer and, where appropriate, an approximation to three decimal places.

16.

17.

The Distance Formula

The distance d between any two points (x_1, y_1) and (x_2, y_2) is given by $d = \sqrt{(x_2 - x_1)^2 + (y_2 - y_1)^2}$.

Find the distance between $(3, -5)$ and $(-1, -2)$.

$$d = \sqrt{(-1 - 3)^2 + (-2 - (-5))^2}$$
$$= \sqrt{(-4)^2 + (3)^2}$$
$$= \sqrt{16 + 9} = \sqrt{25} = 5$$

18. Find the distance between $(-2, 1)$ and $(6, -10)$. Give an exact answer and an approximation to three decimal places.

The Midpoint Formula

If the endpoints of a segment are (x_1, y_1) and (x_2, y_2), then the coordinates of the midpoint are

$$\left(\frac{x_1 + x_2}{2}, \frac{y_1 + y_2}{2}\right).$$

Find the midpoint of the segment with endpoints $(3, -5)$ and $(-1, -2)$.

$$\left(\frac{3 + (-1)}{2}, \frac{-5 + (-2)}{2}\right), \quad \text{or} \quad \left(1, -\frac{7}{2}\right)$$

19. Find the midpoint of the segment with endpoints $(-2, 1)$ and $(6, -10)$.

SECTION 12.8: THE COMPLEX NUMBERS

A **complex number** is any number that can be written in the form $a + bi$, where a and b are real numbers,

$i = \sqrt{-1}$, and $i^2 = -1$.

$(3 + 2i) + (4 - 7i) = 7 - 5i$;

$(8 + 6i) - (5 + 2i) = 3 + 4i$;

$(2 + 3i)(4 - i) = 8 - 2i + 12i - 3i^2$

$\qquad = 8 + 10i - 3(-1) = 11 + 10i$;

$\dfrac{1 - 4i}{3 - 2i} = \dfrac{1 - 4i}{3 - 2i} \cdot \dfrac{3 + 2i}{3 + 2i}$

$\qquad = \dfrac{3 + 2i - 12i - 8i^2}{9 + 6i - 6i - 4i^2}$

$\qquad = \dfrac{3 - 10i - 8(-1)}{9 - 4(-1)} = \dfrac{11 - 10i}{13} = \dfrac{11}{13} - \dfrac{10}{13}i$

20. Add:

$\quad (5 - 3i) + (-8 - 9i)$.

21. Subtract:

$\quad (2 - i) - (-1 + i)$.

22. Multiply:

$\quad (1 - 7i)(3 - 5i)$.

23. Divide: $\dfrac{1 + i}{1 - i}$.

Review Exercises

 Concept Reinforcement   Classify each of the following statements as either true or false.

1. $\sqrt{ab} = \sqrt{a} \cdot \sqrt{b}$ for any real numbers $\sqrt{a}$ and $\sqrt{b}$. [12.3]

2. $\sqrt{a + b} = \sqrt{a} + \sqrt{b}$ for any real numbers $\sqrt{a}$ and $\sqrt{b}$. [12.5]

3. $\sqrt{a^2} = a$, for any real number a. [12.1]

4. $\sqrt[3]{a^3} = a$, for any real number a. [12.1]

5. $x^{2/5}$ means $\sqrt[5]{x^2}$ and $\left(\sqrt[5]{x}\right)^2$. [12.2]

6. The hypotenuse of a right triangle is never shorter than either leg. [12.7]

7. Some radical equations have no solution. [12.6]

8. If $f(x) = \sqrt{x - 5}$, then the domain of f is the set of all nonnegative real numbers. [12.1]

Simplify. [12.1]

9. $\sqrt{\dfrac{49}{9}}$

10. $-\sqrt{0.25}$

Let $f(x) = \sqrt{2x - 7}$. Find the following. [12.1]

11. $f(16)$

12. The domain of f

13. *Dairy Farming.*   As a calf grows, it needs more milk for nourishment. The number of pounds of milk, M, required by a calf weighing x pounds can be estimated using the formula

$$M = -5 + \sqrt{6.7x - 444}.$$

Estimate the number of pounds of milk required by a calf of the given weight: **(a)** 300 lb; **(b)** 100 lb; **(c)** 200 lb; **(d)** 400 lb. [12.1]

Source: www.ext.vt.edu

Simplify. Assume that each variable can represent any real number.

14. $\sqrt{25t^2}$ [12.1]

15. $\sqrt{(c + 8)^2}$ [12.1]

16. $\sqrt{4x^2 + 4x + 1}$ [12.1]

17. $\sqrt[5]{-32}$ [12.1]

18. Write an equivalent expression using exponential notation: $\left(\sqrt[3]{5ab}\right)^4$. [12.2]

19. Write an equivalent expression using radical notation: $(16a^6)^{3/4}$. [12.2]

Use rational exponents to simplify. Assume $x, y \ge 0$. [12.2]

20. $\sqrt[6]{x^6 y^{10}}$

21. $\left(\sqrt[6]{x^2 y}\right)^2$

Simplify. Do not use negative exponents in the answers. [12.2]

22. $(x^{-2/3})^{3/5}$

23. $\dfrac{7^{-1/3}}{7^{-1/2}}$

24. If $f(x) = \sqrt{25(x - 6)^2}$, find a simplified form for $f(x)$. [12.3]

Simplify. Write all answers using radical notation. Assume that all variables represent nonnegative numbers.

25. $\sqrt[4]{16x^{20}y^8}$ [12.3]

26. $\sqrt{250x^3y^2}$ [12.3]

27. $\sqrt{2x}\ \sqrt{3y}$ [12.3]

28. $\sqrt[3]{3x^4b}\ \sqrt[3]{9xb^2}$ [12.3]

29. $\sqrt[3]{-24x^{10}y^8}\ \sqrt[3]{18x^7y^4}$ [12.3]

30. $\dfrac{\sqrt[3]{60xy^3}}{\sqrt[3]{10x}}$ [12.4]

31. $\dfrac{\sqrt{75x}}{2\sqrt{3}}$ [12.4]

32. $\sqrt[4]{\dfrac{48a^{11}}{c^8}}$ [12.4]

33. $5\sqrt[3]{x} + 2\sqrt[3]{x}$ [12.5]

34. $2\sqrt{75} - 9\sqrt{3}$ [12.5]

35. $\sqrt[3]{8x^4} + \sqrt[3]{xy^6}$ [12.5]

36. $\sqrt{50} + 2\sqrt{18} + \sqrt{32}$ [12.5]

37. $\left(3 + \sqrt{10}\right)\left(3 - \sqrt{10}\right)$ [12.5]

38. $\left(\sqrt{3} - 3\sqrt{8}\right)\left(\sqrt{5} + 2\sqrt{8}\right)$ [12.5]

39. $\sqrt[4]{x}\ \sqrt{x}$ [12.5]

40. $\dfrac{\sqrt[3]{x^2}}{\sqrt[4]{x}}$ [12.5]

41. If $f(x) = x^2$, find $f\left(a - \sqrt{2}\right)$. [12.5]

42. Rationalize the denominator:

$$\sqrt{\dfrac{x}{8y}}.\ \text{[12.4]}$$

43. Rationalize the denominator:

$$\dfrac{4\sqrt{5}}{\sqrt{2} + \sqrt{3}}.\ \text{[12.5]}$$

44. Rationalize the numerator of the expression in Exercise 43. [12.5]

Solve. [12.6]

45. $\sqrt{y + 6} - 2 = 3$

46. $\sqrt{x} = x - 6$

47. $(x + 1)^{1/3} = -5$

48. $1 + \sqrt{x} = \sqrt{3x - 3}$

49. If $f(x) = \sqrt[4]{x + 2}$, find a such that $f(a) = 2$. [12.6]

Solve. Give an exact answer and, where appropriate, an approximation to three decimal places. [12.7]

50. The diagonal of a square has length 10 cm. Find the length of a side of the square.

51. A skate-park jump has a ramp that is 6 ft long and is 2 ft high. How long is its base?

52. Find the missing lengths. Give exact answers and, where appropriate, an approximation to three decimal places.

53. Find the distance between $(-6, 4)$ and $(-1, 5)$. Give an exact answer and an approximation to three decimal places. [12.7]

54. Find the midpoint of the segment with endpoints $(-7, -2)$ and $(3, -1)$. [12.7]

55. Express in terms of i and simplify: $\sqrt{-45}$. [12.8]

56. Add: $(-4 + 3i) + (2 - 12i)$. [12.8]

57. Subtract: $(9 - 7i) - (3 - 8i)$. [12.8]

Simplify. [12.8]

58. $(2 + 5i)(2 - 5i)$

59. i^{18}

60. $(6 - 3i)(2 - i)$

61. Divide and simplify to the form $a + bi$:

$$\dfrac{7 - 2i}{3 + 4i}.\ \text{[12.8]}$$

SYNTHESIS

TW **62.** What makes some complex numbers real and others imaginary? [12.8]

TW **63.** Explain why $\sqrt[n]{x^n} = |x|$ when n is even, but $\sqrt[n]{x^n} = x$ when n is odd. [12.1]

64. Solve:

$$\sqrt{11x + \sqrt{6 + x}} = 6.\ \text{[12.6]}$$

65. Simplify:

$$\dfrac{2}{1 - 3i} - \dfrac{3}{4 + 2i}.\ \text{[12.8]}$$

66. Write a quotient of two imaginary numbers that is a real number. (Answers may vary.) [12.8]

67. Don's Discount Shoes has two locations. The sign at the original location is shaped like an isosceles right triangle. The sign at the newer location is shaped like a 30°–60°–90° triangle. The hypotenuse of each sign measures 6 ft. Which sign has the greater area and by how much? (Round to three decimal places.) [12.7]

Chapter Test 12

Simplify. Assume that variables can represent any real number.

1. $\sqrt{50}$

2. $\sqrt[3]{-\dfrac{8}{x^6}}$

3. $\sqrt{81a^2}$

4. $\sqrt{x^2 - 8x + 16}$

5. Write an equivalent expression using exponential notation: $\sqrt{7xy}$.

6. Write an equivalent expression using radical notation: $(4a^3b)^{5/6}$.

7. If $f(x) = \sqrt{2x - 10}$, determine the domain of f.

8. If $f(x) = x^2$, find $f\left(5 + \sqrt{2}\right)$.

Simplify. Write all answers using radical notation. Assume that all variables represent positive numbers.

9. $\sqrt[5]{32x^{16}y^{10}}$

10. $\sqrt[3]{4w}\ \sqrt[3]{4v^2}$

11. $\sqrt{\dfrac{100a^4}{9b^6}}$

12. $\dfrac{\sqrt[5]{48x^6y^{10}}}{\sqrt[5]{16x^2y^9}}$

13. $\sqrt[4]{x^3}\ \sqrt{x}$

14. $\dfrac{\sqrt{y}}{\sqrt[10]{y}}$

15. $8\sqrt{2} - 2\sqrt{2}$

16. $\sqrt{x^4y} + \sqrt{9y^3}$

17. $\left(7 + \sqrt{x}\right)\left(2 - 3\sqrt{x}\right)$

18. Rationalize the denominator:

$$\dfrac{\sqrt[3]{x}}{\sqrt[3]{4y}}.$$

Solve.

19. $6 = \sqrt{x - 3} + 5$

20. $x = \sqrt{3x + 3} - 1$

21. $\sqrt{2x} = \sqrt{x + 1} + 1$

Solve. For Exercises 22–24, give exact answers and approximations to three decimal places.

22. A referee jogs diagonally from one corner of a 50-ft by 90-ft basketball court to the far corner. How far does she jog?

23. The hypotenuse of a 30°–60°–90° triangle is 10 cm long. Find the lengths of the legs.

24. Find the distance between the points $(3, 7)$ and $(-1, 8)$.

25. Find the midpoint of the segment with endpoints $(2, -5)$ and $(1, -7)$.

26. Express in terms of i and simplify: $\sqrt{-50}$.

27. Subtract: $(9 + 8i) - (-3 + 6i)$.

28. Multiply: $\sqrt{-16}\ \sqrt{-36}$.

29. Multiply. Write the answer in the form $a + bi$.
$$(4 - i)^2$$

30. Divide and simplify to the form $a + bi$:
$$\dfrac{-2 + i}{3 - 5i}.$$

31. Simplify: i^{37}.

SYNTHESIS

32. Solve:
$$\sqrt{2x - 2} + \sqrt{7x + 4} = \sqrt{13x + 10}.$$

33. Simplify:
$$\dfrac{1 - 4i}{4i(1 + 4i)^{-1}}.$$

34. The function $D(h) = 1.2\sqrt{h}$ can be used to approximate the distance D, in miles, that a person can see to the horizon from a height h, in feet. How far above sea level must a pilot fly in order to see a horizon that is 180 mi away?

13

Quadratic Functions and Equations

How Great Is America's "Sweet Tooth"?

As the graph indicates, Americans ate more candy in 2006 than in 2004, but less in 2008 than in 2006. In Example 4 of Section 13.8, we estimate how much candy Americans will have consumed in 2009 if the trend continues.

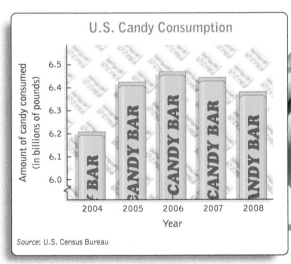

U.S. Candy Consumption

Amount of candy consumed (in billions of pounds)

6.5
6.4
6.3
6.2
6.1
6.0

2004 2005 2006 2007 2008
Year

Source: U.S. Census Bureau

The mathematical translation of a problem is often a function or an equation containing a second-degree polynomial in one variable. Such functions or equations are said to be *quadratic*. In this chapter, we examine a variety of ways to solve quadratic equations and look at graphs and applications of quadratic functions.

13.1 Quadratic Equations

- The Principle of Square Roots
- Completing the Square
- Problem Solving

The general form of a quadratic function is

$$f(x) = ax^2 + bx + c, \quad \text{with } a \neq 0.$$

The graph of a quadratic function is a *parabola*. Such graphs open up or down and can have 0, 1, or 2 x-intercepts. We learn to graph quadratic functions later in this chapter.

The graph of the quadratic function

$$f(x) = x^2 + 6x + 8$$

is shown at right. Note that $(-4, 0)$ and $(-2, 0)$ are the x-intercepts of the graph of $f(x) = x^2 + 6x + 8$.

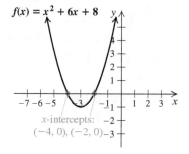

We solved equations like $x^2 + 6x + 8 = 0$ by factoring:

$$x^2 + 6x + 8 = 0$$
$$(x + 4)(x + 2) = 0 \qquad \text{Factoring}$$
$$x + 4 = 0 \quad \text{or} \quad x + 2 = 0 \qquad \text{Using the principle of zero products}$$
$$x = -4 \quad \text{or} \qquad x = -2.$$

Note that -4 and -2 are the first coordinates of the x-intercepts of the graph of $f(x)$ above.

Interactive Discovery

Graph each function and determine the number of x-intercepts.

1. $f(x) = x^2$
2. $g(x) = -x^2$
3. $h(x) = (x - 2)^2$
4. $p(x) = 2x^2 + 1$
5. $f(x) = -1.5x^2 + x - 3$
6. $g(x) = 4x^2 - 2x - 7$
7. Describe the shape of the graph of a quadratic function.

The graph of a quadratic function can have no, one, or two x-intercepts, as illustrated below. Thus a quadratic equation can have no, one, or two real-number roots. Quadratic equations can have nonreal-number roots. These must be found using algebraic methods.

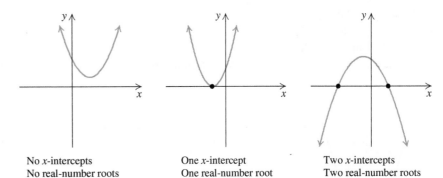

No x-intercepts   One x-intercept   Two x-intercepts
No real-number roots   One real-number root   Two real-number roots

To solve a quadratic equation by factoring, we write the equation in the *standard form $ax^2 + bx + c = 0$*, factor, and use the principle of zero products.

EXAMPLE 1   Solve: $x^2 = 25$.

SOLUTION   We have

$$x^2 = 25$$
$$x^2 - 25 = 0 \qquad \text{Writing in standard form}$$
$$(x - 5)(x + 5) = 0 \qquad \text{Factoring}$$
$$x - 5 = 0 \quad or \quad x + 5 = 0 \qquad \text{Using the principle of zero products}$$
$$x = 5 \quad or \qquad x = -5.$$

The solutions are 5 and -5. The graph at left confirms the solutions.

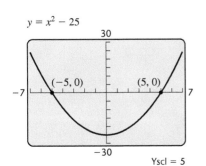

$y = x^2 - 25$

(−5, 0)   (5, 0)

Yscl = 5

Try Exercise 13.

In this section and the next, we develop algebraic methods for solving any quadratic equation, whether it is factorable or not.

THE PRINCIPLE OF SQUARE ROOTS

Consider the equation $x^2 = 25$ again. We know from Chapter 12 that the number 25 has two real-number square roots, 5 and -5, the solutions of the equation in Example 1. Thus we see that square roots provide quick solutions for equations of the type $x^2 = k$.

> **The Principle of Square Roots**   For any real number k, if $x^2 = k$, then
>
> $$x = \sqrt{k} \quad or \quad x = -\sqrt{k}.$$

CAUTION! The symbol $\pm\sqrt{2}$ represents *two* solutions: $\sqrt{2}$ and $-\sqrt{2}$.

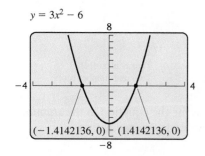

$y = 3x^2 - 6$

$(-1.4142136, 0)$ $(1.4142136, 0)$

$\left(-\dfrac{\sqrt{10}}{5}, 0\right)$ $\left(\dfrac{\sqrt{10}}{5}, 0\right)$

$g(x) = 0$ $f(x) = -5x^2 + 2$

A visualization of Example 3

EXAMPLE 2   Solve: $3x^2 = 6$. Give exact solutions and approximations to three decimal places.

SOLUTION   We have

$$3x^2 = 6$$
$$x^2 = 2 \qquad \text{Isolating } x^2$$
$$x = \sqrt{2} \quad or \quad x = -\sqrt{2}. \qquad \text{Using the principle of square roots}$$

We often use the symbol $\pm\sqrt{2}$ to represent the two numbers $\sqrt{2}$ and $-\sqrt{2}$.

Check: For $\sqrt{2}$:   For $-\sqrt{2}$:

$$\begin{array}{c|c} 3x^2 = 6 & \\ \hline 3\left(\sqrt{2}\right)^2 & 6 \\ 3\cdot 2 & \\ & 6 \overset{?}{=} 6 \quad \text{TRUE} \end{array} \qquad \begin{array}{c|c} 3x^2 = 6 & \\ \hline 3\left(-\sqrt{2}\right)^2 & 6 \\ 3\cdot 2 & \\ & 6 \overset{?}{=} 6 \quad \text{TRUE} \end{array}$$

The solutions are $\sqrt{2}$ and $-\sqrt{2}$, or $\pm\sqrt{2}$, which round to 1.414 and -1.414. A graphical solution, shown at left, yields approximate solutions, since $\sqrt{2}$ is irrational. The solutions found graphically correspond to those found algebraically.

Try Exercise 17.

EXAMPLE 3   Solve: $-5x^2 + 2 = 0$.

SOLUTION   We have

$$-5x^2 + 2 = 0$$
$$x^2 = \frac{2}{5} \qquad \text{Isolating } x^2$$
$$x = \sqrt{\frac{2}{5}} \quad or \quad x = -\sqrt{\frac{2}{5}}. \qquad \text{Using the principle of square roots}$$

The solutions are $\sqrt{\dfrac{2}{5}}$ and $-\sqrt{\dfrac{2}{5}}$. This can also be written as $\pm\sqrt{\dfrac{2}{5}}$. If we rationalize the denominator, the solutions are written $\pm\dfrac{\sqrt{10}}{5}$. The checks are left to the student.

Try Exercise 23.

Sometimes we get solutions that are imaginary numbers.

EXAMPLE 4   Solve: $4x^2 + 9 = 0$.

SOLUTION   We have

$$4x^2 + 9 = 0$$
$$x^2 = -\frac{9}{4} \qquad \text{Isolating } x^2$$
$$x = \sqrt{-\frac{9}{4}} \quad or \quad x = -\sqrt{-\frac{9}{4}} \qquad \text{Using the principle of square roots}$$
$$x = \sqrt{\frac{9}{4}}\sqrt{-1} \quad or \quad x = -\sqrt{\frac{9}{4}}\sqrt{-1}$$
$$x = \frac{3}{2}i \quad or \quad x = -\frac{3}{2}i. \qquad \text{Recall that } \sqrt{-1} = i.$$

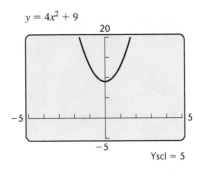

$y = 4x^2 + 9$

$Y_{scl} = 5$

Check:

For $\frac{3}{2}i$:

$$4x^2 + 9 = 0$$

$$\begin{array}{c|c} 4\left(\frac{3}{2}i\right)^2 + 9 & 0 \\ 4 \cdot \frac{9}{4} \cdot i^2 + 9 & \\ 9(-1) + 9 & \\ \hline 0 \stackrel{?}{=} 0 & \text{TRUE} \end{array}$$

For $-\frac{3}{2}i$:

$$4x^2 + 9 = 0$$

$$\begin{array}{c|c} 4\left(-\frac{3}{2}i\right)^2 + 9 & 0 \\ 4 \cdot \frac{9}{4} \cdot i^2 + 9 & \\ 9(-1) + 9 & \\ \hline 0 \stackrel{?}{=} 0 & \text{TRUE} \end{array}$$

The solutions are $\frac{3}{2}i$ and $-\frac{3}{2}i$, or $\pm\frac{3}{2}i$. The graph at left confirms that there are no real-number solutions, because there are no x-intercepts.

Try Exercise 25.

The principle of square roots can be restated in a more general form.

The Principle of Square Roots (Generalized Form)

For any real number k and any algebraic expression X,

$$\text{If } X^2 = k, \text{ then } X = \sqrt{k} \text{ or } X = -\sqrt{k}.$$

EXAMPLE 5   Let $f(x) = (x - 2)^2$. Find all x-values for which $f(x) = 7$.

SOLUTION   We are asked to find all x-values for which

$$f(x) = 7,$$

or

$$(x - 2)^2 = 7. \qquad \text{Substituting } (x-2)^2 \text{ for } f(x)$$

We solve both algebraically and graphically.

ALGEBRAIC APPROACH

The generalized principle of square roots gives us

$$x - 2 = \sqrt{7} \qquad or \qquad x - 2 = -\sqrt{7}$$
$$x = 2 + \sqrt{7} \qquad or \qquad x = 2 - \sqrt{7}.$$

Check: $f\left(2 + \sqrt{7}\right) = \left(2 + \sqrt{7} - 2\right)^2$
$$= \left(\sqrt{7}\right)^2 = 7.$$

Similarly,

$$f\left(2 - \sqrt{7}\right) = \left(2 - \sqrt{7} - 2\right)^2$$
$$= \left(-\sqrt{7}\right)^2 = 7.$$

Rounded to the nearest thousandth,

$$2 + \sqrt{7} \approx 4.646 \quad \text{and} \quad 2 - \sqrt{7} \approx -0.646,$$

so the graphical solutions match the algebraic solutions.
   The solutions are $2 + \sqrt{7}$ and $2 - \sqrt{7}$, or simply $2 \pm \sqrt{7}$.

GRAPHICAL APPROACH

We graph the equations $y_1 = (x - 2)^2$ and $y_2 = 7$. If there are any real-number x-values for which $f(x) = 7$, they will be the x-coordinates of the points of intersection of the graphs.

$y_1 = (x - 2)^2, \quad y_2 = 7$

(4.6457513, 7)

(−0.6457513, 7)

   Rounded to the nearest thousandth, the solutions are approximately -0.646 and 4.646.
   We can check the algebraic solutions using the VALUE option of the CALC menu. If we enter $2 + \sqrt{7}$ or $2 - \sqrt{7}$ for x, the corresponding value of y_1 will be 7, so the solutions check.

Try Exercise 41.

Example 5 is of the form $(x - a)^2 = c$, where a and c are constants. Sometimes we must factor to obtain this form.

EXAMPLE 6 Solve: $x^2 + 6x + 9 = 2$.

SOLUTION We have

$$x^2 + 6x + 9 = 2 \qquad \text{The left side is the square of a binomial.}$$
$$(x + 3)^2 = 2 \qquad \text{Factoring}$$
$$x + 3 = \sqrt{2} \qquad or \quad x + 3 = -\sqrt{2} \qquad \text{Using the principle of square roots}$$
$$x = -3 + \sqrt{2} \quad or \qquad x = -3 - \sqrt{2}. \qquad \text{Adding } -3 \text{ to both sides}$$

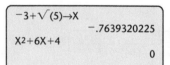

One way to check the solutions on a graphing calculator is to enter $y_1 = x^2 + 6x + 9$ and then evaluate $y_1(-3 + \sqrt{2})$ and $y_1(-3 - \sqrt{2})$, as shown at left. The second calculation can be entered quickly by copying the first entry and editing it.

The solutions are $-3 + \sqrt{2}$ and $-3 - \sqrt{2}$, or $-3 \pm \sqrt{2}$.

Try Exercise 35.

COMPLETING THE SQUARE

By using a method called *completing the square*, we can use the principle of square roots to solve *any* quadratic equation.

EXAMPLE 7 Solve: $x^2 + 6x + 4 = 0$.

SOLUTION We have

$$x^2 + 6x + 4 = 0$$
$$x^2 + 6x \qquad = -4 \qquad \text{Subtracting 4 from both sides}$$
$$x^2 + 6x + 9 = -4 + 9 \qquad \text{Adding 9 to both sides. We explain this shortly.}$$
$$(x + 3)^2 = 5 \qquad \text{Factoring the perfect-square trinomial}$$
$$x + 3 = \pm\sqrt{5} \qquad \text{Using the principle of square roots. Remember that } \pm\sqrt{5} \text{ represents two numbers.}$$
$$x = -3 \pm \sqrt{5}. \qquad \text{Adding } -3 \text{ to both sides}$$

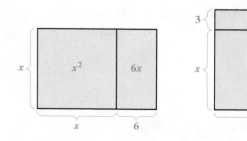

We check by storing $-3 + \sqrt{5}$ as x and evaluating $x^2 + 6x + 4$, as shown at left. We can repeat the process for $-3 - \sqrt{5}$ to check the second solution. The solutions are $-3 + \sqrt{5}$ and $-3 - \sqrt{5}$.

In Example 7, we chose to add 9 to both sides because it creates a perfect-square trinomial on the left side. The 9 was determined by taking half of the coefficient of x and squaring it.

To understand why this procedure works, examine the following drawings.

Note that the shaded areas in both figures represent the same area, $x^2 + 6x$. However, only the figure on the right, in which the $6x$ is halved, can be converted into a square with the addition of a constant term. The constant 9 is the "missing" piece that *completes* the square.

To complete the square for $x^2 + bx$, we add $\left(\dfrac{b}{2}\right)^2$.

Example 8, which follows, provides practice in finding numbers that complete the square. We will then use this skill to solve equations.

EXAMPLE 8 Replace the blanks in each equation with constants to form a true equation.

a) $x^2 + 14x + \underline{\quad} = (x + \underline{\quad})^2$

b) $x^2 - 5x + \underline{\quad} = (x - \underline{\quad})^2$

c) $x^2 + \frac{3}{4}x + \underline{\quad} = (x + \underline{\quad})^2$

SOLUTION

a) Take half of the coefficient of x: Half of 14 is 7.

Square this number: $7^2 = 49.$

Add 49 to complete the square: $x^2 + 14x + 49 = (x + 7)^2.$

b) Take half of the coefficient of x: Half of -5 is $-\dfrac{5}{2}$.

Square this number: $\left(-\dfrac{5}{2}\right)^2 = \dfrac{25}{4}.$

Add $\dfrac{25}{4}$ to complete the square: $x^2 - 5x + \dfrac{25}{4} = \left(x - \dfrac{5}{2}\right)^2.$

c) Take half of the coefficient of x: Half of $\dfrac{3}{4}$ is $\dfrac{3}{8}$.

Square this number: $\left(\dfrac{3}{8}\right)^2 = \dfrac{9}{64}.$

Add $\dfrac{9}{64}$ to complete the square: $x^2 + \dfrac{3}{4}x + \dfrac{9}{64} = \left(x + \dfrac{3}{8}\right)^2.$

Student Notes

In problems like Examples 8(b) and (c), it is best to avoid decimal notation. Most students have an easier time recognizing $\frac{9}{64}$ as $\left(\frac{3}{8}\right)^2$ than seeing 0.140625 as 0.375^2.

Try Exercise 45.

We can now use the method of completing the square to solve equations.

EXAMPLE 9 Solve: $x^2 - 8x - 7 = 0.$

SOLUTION   We begin by adding 7 to both sides:

$$x^2 - 8x - 7 = 0$$
$$x^2 - 8x \quad\ = 7 \qquad \text{Adding 7 to both sides. We can now complete the square on the left side.}$$
$$x^2 - 8x + 16 = 7 + 16 \qquad \text{Adding 16 to both sides to complete the square: } \tfrac{1}{2}(-8) = -4, \text{ and } (-4)^2 = 16$$
$$(x - 4)^2 = 23 \qquad \text{Factoring and simplifying}$$
$$x - 4 = \pm\sqrt{23} \qquad \text{Using the principle of square roots}$$
$$x = 4 \pm \sqrt{23}. \qquad \text{Adding 4 to both sides}$$

Check: For $4 + \sqrt{23}$:

$$x^2 - 8x - 7 = 0$$

$$
\begin{array}{l|l}
\left(4 + \sqrt{23}\right)^2 - 8\left(4 + \sqrt{23}\right) - 7 & 0 \\
16 + 8\sqrt{23} + 23 - 32 - 8\sqrt{23} - 7 & \\
16 + 23 - 32 - 7 + 8\sqrt{23} - 8\sqrt{23} & \\
\end{array}
$$

$$0 \overset{?}{=} 0 \quad \text{TRUE}$$

For $4 - \sqrt{23}$:

$$x^2 - 8x - 7 = 0$$

$$
\begin{array}{l|l}
\left(4 - \sqrt{23}\right)^2 - 8\left(4 - \sqrt{23}\right) - 7 & 0 \\
16 - 8\sqrt{23} + 23 - 32 + 8\sqrt{23} - 7 & \\
16 + 23 - 32 - 7 - 8\sqrt{23} + 8\sqrt{23} & \\
\end{array}
$$

$$0 \overset{?}{=} 0 \quad \text{TRUE}$$

The solutions are $4 + \sqrt{23}$ and $4 - \sqrt{23}$, or $4 \pm \sqrt{23}$.

▌ Try Exercise 57.

Recall that the value of $f(x)$ must be 0 at any x-intercept of the graph of f. If $f(a) = 0$, then $(a, 0)$ is an x-intercept of the graph.

EXAMPLE 10   Find the x-intercepts of the graph of $f(x) = x^2 + 5x - 3$.

SOLUTION   We set $f(x)$ equal to 0 and solve:

$$f(x) = 0$$

$$x^2 + 5x - 3 = 0 \qquad \text{Substituting}$$

$$x^2 + 5x = 3 \qquad \text{Adding 3 to both sides}$$

$$x^2 + 5x + \frac{25}{4} = 3 + \frac{25}{4} \qquad \begin{array}{l}\text{Completing the square:}\\ \frac{1}{2}\cdot 5 = \frac{5}{2}, \text{and } \left(\frac{5}{2}\right)^2 = \frac{25}{4}\end{array}$$

$$\left(x + \frac{5}{2}\right)^2 = \frac{37}{4} \qquad \text{Factoring and simplifying}$$

$$x + \frac{5}{2} = \pm \frac{\sqrt{37}}{2} \qquad \begin{array}{l}\text{Using the principle of square roots}\\ \text{and the quotient rule for radicals}\end{array}$$

$$x = -\frac{5}{2} \pm \frac{\sqrt{37}}{2}, \quad \text{or} \quad \frac{-5 \pm \sqrt{37}}{2}. \qquad \text{Adding } -\frac{5}{2} \text{ to both sides}$$

The x-intercepts are

$$\left(-\frac{5}{2} - \frac{\sqrt{37}}{2}, 0\right) \quad \text{and} \quad \left(-\frac{5}{2} + \frac{\sqrt{37}}{2}, 0\right), \quad \text{or}$$

$$\left(\frac{-5 - \sqrt{37}}{2}, 0\right) \quad \text{and} \quad \left(\frac{-5 + \sqrt{37}}{2}, 0\right).$$

The checks are left to the student.

▌ Try Exercise 65.

Before we complete the square in a quadratic equation, the leading coefficient must be 1. When it is not 1, we divide both sides of the equation by whatever that coefficient may be.

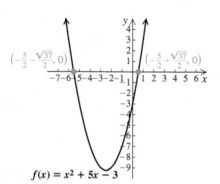

$\left(-\frac{5}{2} - \frac{\sqrt{37}}{2}, 0\right)$ $\left(-\frac{5}{2} + \frac{\sqrt{37}}{2}, 0\right)$

$f(x) = x^2 + 5x - 3$

A visualization of Example 10

> **To Solve a Quadratic Equation in x by Completing the Square**
> 1. Isolate the terms with variables on one side of the equation, and arrange them in descending order.
> 2. Divide both sides by the coefficient of x^2 if that coefficient is not 1.
> 3. Complete the square by taking half of the coefficient of x and adding its square to both sides.
> 4. Express the trinomial as the square of a binomial (factor the trinomial) and simplify the other side of the equation.
> 5. Use the principle of square roots (find the square roots of both sides).
> 6. Solve for x by adding or subtracting on both sides.

EXAMPLE 11   Solve: $3x^2 + 7x - 2 = 0$.

SOLUTION   We follow the steps listed above:

Isolate the variable terms.

Divide both sides by the x^2-coefficient.

Complete the square.

Factor the trinomial.

Use the principle of square roots.

Solve for x.

$$3x^2 + 7x - 2 = 0$$

$$3x^2 + 7x = 2 \qquad \text{Adding 2 to both sides}$$

$$x^2 + \frac{7}{3}x = \frac{2}{3} \qquad \text{Dividing both sides by 3}$$

$$x^2 + \frac{7}{3}x + \frac{49}{36} = \frac{2}{3} + \frac{49}{36} \qquad \begin{array}{l}\text{Completing the square:}\\ \left(\frac{1}{2}\cdot\frac{7}{3}\right)^2 = \frac{49}{36}\end{array}$$

$$\left(x + \frac{7}{6}\right)^2 = \frac{73}{36} \qquad \text{Factoring and simplifying}$$

$$x + \frac{7}{6} = \pm\frac{\sqrt{73}}{6} \qquad \begin{array}{l}\text{Using the principle of square roots}\\ \text{and the quotient rule for radicals}\end{array}$$

$$x = -\frac{7}{6} \pm \frac{\sqrt{73}}{6}, \quad \text{or} \quad \frac{-7 \pm \sqrt{73}}{6}. \qquad \text{Adding } -\tfrac{7}{6} \text{ to both sides}$$

The checks are left to the student. The solutions are $-\dfrac{7}{6} \pm \dfrac{\sqrt{73}}{6}$, or $\dfrac{-7 \pm \sqrt{73}}{6}$.

This can be written as

$$-\frac{7}{6} + \frac{\sqrt{73}}{6} \quad \text{and} \quad -\frac{7}{6} - \frac{\sqrt{73}}{6}, \quad \text{or} \quad \frac{-7 + \sqrt{73}}{6} \quad \text{and} \quad \frac{-7 - \sqrt{73}}{6}.$$

Try Exercise 71.

Any quadratic equation can be solved by completing the square. The procedure is also useful when graphing quadratic equations and will be used in the next section to develop a formula for solving quadratic equations.

PROBLEM SOLVING

After one year, an amount of money P, invested at 4% per year, is worth 104% of P, or $P(1.04)$. If that amount continues to earn 4% interest per year, after the second year the investment will be worth 104% of $P(1.04)$, or $P(1.04)^2$. This is called **compounding interest** since after the first time period, interest is earned on both the initial investment *and* the interest from the first time period. Continuing the above pattern, we see that after the third year, the investment will be worth 104% of $P(1.04)^2$. Generalizing, we have the following.

STUDY TIP

Choosing Tunes

Some students prefer working while listening to music. Whether listening for pleasure or to block out nearby noise, you may find that music without lyrics is most conducive to focusing your concentration on your studies. At least one study has shown that classical background music can improve one's ability to concentrate.

The Compound-Interest Formula If an amount of money P is invested at interest rate r, compounded annually, then in t years, it will grow to the amount A given by

$$A = P(1 + r)^t. \qquad (r \text{ is written in decimal notation.})$$

We can use quadratic equations to solve certain interest problems.

EXAMPLE 12 Investment Growth. Clare invested $4000 at interest rate r, compounded annually. In 2 years, it had grown to $4410. What was the interest rate?

SOLUTION

1. **Familiarize.** We are already familiar with the compound-interest formula. If we were not, we would need to consult an outside source.

2. **Translate.** The translation consists of substituting into the formula:

$$A = P(1 + r)^t$$
$$4410 = 4000(1 + r)^2. \qquad \text{Substituting}$$

3. **Carry out.** We solve for r both algebraically and graphically.

ALGEBRAIC APPROACH

We have

$$4410 = 4000(1 + r)^2$$

$\frac{4410}{4000} = (1 + r)^2$ Dividing both sides by 4000

$\frac{441}{400} = (1 + r)^2$ Simplifying

$\pm\sqrt{\frac{441}{400}} = 1 + r$ Using the principle of square roots

$\pm\frac{21}{20} = 1 + r$ Simplifying

$-\frac{20}{20} \pm \frac{21}{20} = r$ Adding -1, or $-\frac{20}{20}$, to both sides

$\frac{1}{20} = r$ or $-\frac{41}{20} = r$.

Since r represents an interest rate, we convert to decimal notation. We now have

$$r = 0.05 \quad or \quad r = -2.05.$$

GRAPHICAL APPROACH

We let $y_1 = 4410$ and $y_2 = 4000(1 + x)^2$. Using the window $[-3, 1, 0, 5000]$, we see that the graphs intersect at two points. The first coordinates of the points of intersection are -2.05 and 0.05.

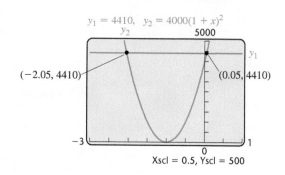

4. **Check.** Since the interest rate cannot be negative, we need only check 0.05, or 5%. If $4000 were invested at 5% interest, compounded annually, then in 2 years it would have grown to $4000(1.05)^2$, or $4410. The rate 5% checks.

5. **State.** The interest rate was 5%.

Try Exercise 81.

EXAMPLE 13 Free-Falling Objects. The formula $s = 16t^2$ is used to approximate the distance s, in feet, that an object falls freely from rest in t seconds. The highest point of the Mike O'Callaghan–Pat Tillman Memorial Bridge is 890 ft above the Colorado River. How long will it take a stone to fall from the bridge to the river? Round to the nearest tenth of a second.
Source: www.desertusa.com

SOLUTION

1. **Familiarize.** We agree to disregard air resistance and use the given formula.

2. **Translate.** We substitute into the formula:

$$s = 16t^2$$
$$890 = 16t^2.$$

3. **Carry out.** We solve for t:

$$890 = 16t^2$$
$$55.625 = t^2$$
$$\sqrt{55.625} = t \qquad \text{Using the principle of square roots;}$$

rejecting the negative square root since t cannot be negative in this problem

$$7.5 \approx t. \qquad \text{Using a calculator and rounding to the nearest tenth}$$

4. **Check.** Since $16(7.5)^2 = 900 \approx 890$, our answer checks.

5. **State.** It takes about 7.5 sec for a stone to fall freely from the bridge to the river.

Try Exercise 85.

13.1 Exercise Set

FOR EXTRA HELP   MyMathLab   Math XL PRACTICE   WATCH   DOWNLOAD   READ   REVIEW

Concept Reinforcement *Complete each of the following to form a true statement.*

1. The principle of square roots states that if $x^2 = k$, then $x =$ ____ or $x =$ ____.

2. If $(x + 5)^2 = 49$, then $x + 5 =$ ____ or $x + 5 =$ ____.

3. If $t^2 + 6t + 9 = 17$, then $($____$)^2 = 17$ and ____ $= \pm\sqrt{17}$.

4. The equations $x^2 + 8x +$ ____ $= 23$ and $x^2 + 8x = 7$ are equivalent.

5. The expressions $t^2 + 10t +$ ____ and $(t +$ ____$)^2$ are equivalent.

6. The expressions $x^2 - 6x +$ ____ and $(x -$ ____$)^2$ are equivalent.

Determine the number of real-number solutions of each equation from the given graph.

7. $x^2 + x - 12 = 0$

$y = x^2 + x - 12$

8. $-3x^2 - x - 7 = 0$

$y = -3x^2 - x - 7$

9. $4x^2 + 9 = 12x$

$y = 12x - 4x^2 - 9$

10. $2x^2 + 3 = 6x$

$y = 2x^2 + 3 - 6x$

11. $f(x) = 0$

$y = f(x)$

Yscl = 5

12. $f(x) = 0$

$y = f(x)$

51. $x^2 + 3x + \underline{\quad} = (x + \underline{\quad})^2$

52. $t^2 - 9t + \underline{\quad} = (t - \underline{\quad})^2$

53. $x^2 + \frac{2}{5}x + \underline{\quad} = (x + \underline{\quad})^2$

54. $x^2 + \frac{2}{3}x + \underline{\quad} = (x + \underline{\quad})^2$

55. $t^2 - \frac{5}{6}t + \underline{\quad} = (t - \underline{\quad})^2$

56. $t^2 - \frac{5}{3}t + \underline{\quad} = (t - \underline{\quad})^2$

Solve.

13. $x^2 = 100$

14. $t^2 = 144$

15. $p^2 - 50 = 0$

16. $c^2 - 8 = 0$

17. $4x^2 = 20$

18. $7x^2 = 21$

19. $x^2 = -4$

20. $x^2 = -9$

21. $9x^2 - 16 = 0$

22. $25x^2 - 4 = 0$

23. $5t^2 - 3 = 4$

24. $3t^2 - 1 = 6$

25. $4d^2 + 81 = 0$

26. $25y^2 + 16 = 0$

27. $(x - 1)^2 = 49$

28. $(x + 2)^2 = 25$

29. $(a - 13)^2 = 18$

30. $(a + 5)^2 = 8$

31. $(x + 1)^2 = -9$

32. $(x - 1)^2 = -49$

33. $\left(y + \frac{3}{4}\right)^2 = \frac{17}{16}$

34. $\left(t + \frac{3}{2}\right)^2 = \frac{7}{2}$

35. $x^2 - 10x + 25 = 64$

36. $x^2 - 6x + 9 = 100$

37. Let $f(x) = x^2$. Find x such that $f(x) = 19$.

38. Let $f(x) = x^2$. Find x such that $f(x) = 11$.

39. Let $f(x) = (x - 5)^2$. Find x such that $f(x) = 16$.

40. Let $g(x) = (x - 2)^2$. Find x such that $g(x) = 25$.

41. Let $F(t) = (t + 4)^2$. Find t such that $F(t) = 13$.

42. Let $f(t) = (t + 6)^2$. Find t such that $f(t) = 15$.

Aha! **43.** Let $g(x) = x^2 + 14x + 49$. Find x such that $g(x) = 49$.

44. Let $F(x) = x^2 + 8x + 16$. Find x such that $F(x) = 9$.

Replace the blanks in each equation with constants to complete the square and form a true equation.

45. $x^2 + 16x + \underline{\quad} = (x + \underline{\quad})^2$

46. $x^2 + 8x + \underline{\quad} = (x + \underline{\quad})^2$

47. $t^2 - 10t + \underline{\quad} = (t - \underline{\quad})^2$

48. $t^2 - 6t + \underline{\quad} = (t - \underline{\quad})^2$

49. $t^2 - 2t + \underline{\quad} = (t - \underline{\quad})^2$

50. $x^2 + 2x + \underline{\quad} = (x + \underline{\quad})^2$

Solve by completing the square. Show your work.

57. $x^2 + 6x = 7$

58. $x^2 + 8x = 9$

59. $t^2 - 10t = -23$

60. $t^2 - 4t = -1$

61. $x^2 + 12x + 32 = 0$

62. $x^2 + 16x + 15 = 0$

63. $t^2 + 8t - 3 = 0$

64. $t^2 + 6t - 5 = 0$

Complete the square to find the x-intercepts of each function given by the equation listed.

65. $f(x) = x^2 + 6x + 7$

66. $f(x) = x^2 + 10x - 2$

67. $g(x) = x^2 + 9x - 25$

68. $g(x) = x^2 + 5x + 2$

69. $f(x) = x^2 - 10x - 22$

70. $f(x) = x^2 - 8x - 10$

Solve by completing the square. Remember to first divide, as in Example 11, to make sure that the coefficient of x^2 is 1.

71. $9x^2 + 18x = -8$

72. $4x^2 + 8x = -3$

73. $3x^2 - 5x - 2 = 0$

74. $2x^2 - 5x - 3 = 0$

75. $5x^2 + 4x - 3 = 0$

76. $4x^2 + 3x - 5 = 0$

77. Find the x-intercepts of the function given by $f(x) = 4x^2 + 2x - 3$.

78. Find the x-intercepts of the function given by $f(x) = 3x^2 + x - 5$.

79. Find the x-intercepts of the function given by $g(x) = 2x^2 - 3x - 1$.

80. Find the x-intercepts of the function given by $g(x) = 3x^2 - 5x - 1$.

Interest. Use $A = P(1 + r)^t$ to find the interest rate in Exercises 81–84. Refer to Example 12.

81. $2000 grows to $2420 in 2 years

82. $1000 grows to $1440 in 2 years

83. $6250 grows to $6760 in 2 years

84. $6250 grows to $7290 in 2 years

Free-Falling Objects. *Use* $s = 16t^2$ *for Exercises 85–88. Refer to Example 13 and neglect air resistance.*

85. The Grand Canyon skywalk is 4000 ft above the Colorado River. How long will it take a stone to fall from the skywalk to the river?
Source: www.grandcanyonskywalk.com

86. The Sears Tower in Chicago is 1454 ft tall. How long would it take an object to fall freely from the top?

87. At 2063 ft, the KVLY-TV tower in North Dakota is the tallest supported tower in the United States. How long would it take an object to fall freely from the top?
Source: North Dakota Tourism Division

88. El Capitan in Yosemite National Park is 3593 ft high. How long would it take a carabiner to fall freely from the top?
Source: *Guinness World Records* 2008

ᴛᵂ **89.** Explain in your own words a sequence of steps that can be used to solve any quadratic equation in the quickest way.

ᴛᵂ **90.** Describe how to write a quadratic equation that can be solved algebraically but not graphically.

SKILL REVIEW

To prepare for Section 13.2, review evaluating expressions and simplifying radical expressions (Section 12.3 and 12.8)

Evaluate.

91. $b^2 - 4ac$, for $a = 3$, $b = 2$, and $c = -5$

92. $b^2 - 4ac$, for $a = 1$, $b = -1$, and $c = 4$

Simplify. [12.3], [12.8]

93. $\sqrt{200}$ **94.** $\sqrt{96}$

95. $\sqrt{-4}$ **96.** $\sqrt{-25}$

97. $\sqrt{-8}$ **98.** $\sqrt{-24}$

SYNTHESIS

ᴛᵂ **99.** What would be better: to receive 3% interest every 6 months or to receive 6% interest every 12 months? Why?

ᴛᵂ **100.** Example 12 was solved with a graphing calculator by graphing each side of
$$4410 = 4000(1 + r)^2.$$
How could you determine, from a reading of the problem, a suitable viewing window?

Find b such that each trinomial is a square.

101. $x^2 + bx + 81$ **102.** $x^2 + bx + 49$

103. If $f(x) = 2x^5 - 9x^4 - 66x^3 + 45x^2 + 280x$ and $x^2 - 5$ is a factor of $f(x)$, find all a for which $f(a) = 0$.

104. If $f(x) = \left(x - \frac{1}{3}\right)(x^2 + 6)$ and $g(x) = \left(x - \frac{1}{3}\right)\left(x^2 - \frac{2}{3}\right)$, find all a for which $(f + g)(a) = 0$.

105. *Boating.* A barge and a fishing boat leave a dock at the same time, traveling at a right angle to each other. The barge travels 7 km/h slower than the fishing boat. After 4 hr, the boats are 68 km apart. Find the speed of each boat.

106. Find three consecutive integers such that the square of the first plus the product of the other two is 67.

🟦 Try Exercise Answers: Section 13.1

13. ± 10 **17.** $\pm \sqrt{5}$ **23.** $\pm \sqrt{\frac{7}{5}}$, or $\pm \frac{\sqrt{35}}{5}$ **25.** $\pm \frac{9}{2}i$
35. $-3, 13$ **41.** $-4 \pm \sqrt{13}$ **45.** $x^2 + 16x + 64 = (x + 8)^2$
57. $-7, 1$ **65.** $\left(-3 - \sqrt{2}, 0\right), \left(-3 + \sqrt{2}, 0\right)$ **71.** $-\frac{4}{3}, -\frac{2}{3}$
81. 10%   **85.** About 15.8 sec

13.2 The Quadratic Formula

- Solving Using the Quadratic Formula

- Approximating Solutions

We can use the process of completing the square to develop a general formula for solving quadratic equations.

SOLVING USING THE QUADRATIC FORMULA

Each time we solve by completing the square, the procedure is the same. When a procedure is repeated many times, we can often develop a formula to speed up our work.

We begin with a quadratic equation in standard form,

$$ax^2 + bx + c = 0,$$

with $a > 0$. For $a < 0$, a slightly different derivation is needed (see Exercise 60), but the result is the same. Let's solve by completing the square. As the steps are performed, compare them with Example 11 on p. 805.

$$ax^2 + bx = -c \qquad \text{Adding } -c \text{ to both sides}$$

$$x^2 + \frac{b}{a}x = -\frac{c}{a} \qquad \text{Dividing both sides by } a$$

Half of $\frac{b}{a}$ is $\frac{b}{2a}$ and $\left(\frac{b}{2a}\right)^2$ is $\frac{b^2}{4a^2}$. We add $\frac{b^2}{4a^2}$ to both sides:

$$x^2 + \frac{b}{a}x + \frac{b^2}{4a^2} = -\frac{c}{a} + \frac{b^2}{4a^2} \qquad \text{Adding } \frac{b^2}{4a^2} \text{ to complete the square}$$

$$\left(x + \frac{b}{2a}\right)^2 = -\frac{4ac}{4a^2} + \frac{b^2}{4a^2} \qquad \begin{array}{l}\text{Factoring on the left side;}\\ \text{finding a common denominator}\\ \text{on the right side}\end{array}$$

$$\left(x + \frac{b}{2a}\right)^2 = \frac{b^2 - 4ac}{4a^2}$$

$$x + \frac{b}{2a} = \pm\frac{\sqrt{b^2 - 4ac}}{2a} \qquad \begin{array}{l}\text{Using the principle of square}\\ \text{roots and the quotient rule for}\\ \text{radicals; since } a > 0, \sqrt{4a^2} = 2a\end{array}$$

$$x = \frac{-b \pm \sqrt{b^2 - 4ac}}{2a}. \qquad \text{Adding } -\frac{b}{2a} \text{ to both sides}$$

It is important to remember the quadratic formula and know how to use it.

Student Notes

To avoid common errors when using the quadratic formula, use the following suggestions.

- Read "$-b$" as "the opposite of b." If b is negative, $-b$ will be positive.

- Write the fraction bar under the entire expression $-b \pm \sqrt{b^2 - 4ac}$.

- If a, b, or c is negative, use parentheses when substituting in the formula.

The Quadratic Formula The solutions of $ax^2 + bx + c = 0$, $a \neq 0$, are given by

$$x = \frac{-b \pm \sqrt{b^2 - 4ac}}{2a}.$$

EXAMPLE 1 Solve $5x^2 + 8x = -3$ using the quadratic formula.

SOLUTION We first find standard form and determine a, b, and c:

$$5x^2 + 8x + 3 = 0; \qquad \text{Adding 3 to both sides to get 0 on one side}$$

$$a = 5, \quad b = 8, \quad c = 3.$$

Next, we use the quadratic formula:

$$x = \frac{-b \pm \sqrt{b^2 - 4ac}}{2a}$$

$$x = \frac{-8 \pm \sqrt{8^2 - 4 \cdot 5 \cdot 3}}{2 \cdot 5}$$ Substituting

$$x = \frac{-8 \pm \sqrt{64 - 60}}{10}$$ **Be sure to write the fraction bar all the way across.**

$$x = \frac{-8 \pm \sqrt{4}}{10} = \frac{-8 \pm 2}{10}$$

$$x = \frac{-8 + 2}{10} \quad or \quad x = \frac{-8 - 2}{10}$$ The symbol $\pm$ indicates that there are two solutions.

$$x = \frac{-6}{10} \quad or \quad x = \frac{-10}{10}$$

$$x = -\frac{3}{5} \quad or \quad x = -1.$$

The solutions are $-\frac{3}{5}$ and -1. The checks are left to the student.

■ Try Exercise 7.

Because $5x^2 + 8x + 3$ can be factored as $(5x + 3)(x + 1)$, the quadratic formula may not have been the fastest way to solve Example 1. However, because the quadratic formula works for *any* quadratic equation, we need not spend too much time struggling to solve a quadratic equation by factoring.

To Solve a Quadratic Equation

1. If the equation can be easily written in the form $ax^2 = p$ or $(x + k)^2 = d$, use the principle of square roots as in Section 13.1.
2. If step (1) does not apply, write the equation in the form $ax^2 + bx + c = 0$.
3. Try factoring and using the principle of zero products.
4. If factoring seems difficult or impossible, use the quadratic formula. Completing the square can also be used.

The solutions of a quadratic equation can always be found using the quadratic formula. They cannot always be found by factoring.

Recall that a second-degree polynomial in one variable is said to be quadratic. Similarly, a second-degree polynomial function in one variable is said to be a **quadratic function.**

EXAMPLE 2 For the quadratic function given by $f(x) = 3x^2 - 6x - 4$, find all x for which $f(x) = 0$.

SOLUTION We substitute and solve for x:

$$f(x) = 0$$

$$3x^2 - 6x - 4 = 0$$ Substituting. We cannot factor $3x^2 - 6x - 4$.

$$a = 3, \quad b = -6, \quad c = -4.$$

We then substitute into the quadratic formula:

$$x = \frac{-(-6) \pm \sqrt{(-6)^2 - 4 \cdot 3 \cdot (-4)}}{2 \cdot 3}$$

Use parentheses when substituting negative numbers.

$$= \frac{6 \pm \sqrt{36 + 48}}{6}$$

$(-6)^2 - 4 \cdot 3 \cdot (-4) = 36 - (-48) = 36 + 48$

$$= \frac{6 \pm \sqrt{84}}{6}$$

$$= \frac{6}{6} \pm \frac{\sqrt{84}}{6}$$

Note that 4 is a perfect-square factor of 84.

$$= 1 \pm \frac{\sqrt{4}\,\sqrt{21}}{6}$$

$84 = 4 \cdot 21$

$$\left.\begin{array}{l} = 1 \pm \dfrac{2\sqrt{21}}{6} \\[2mm] = 1 \pm \dfrac{\sqrt{21}}{3}. \end{array}\right\}$$

Simplifying

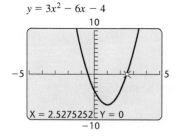

$y = 3x^2 - 6x - 4$

X = 2.5275252 Y = 0

To check, we graph $y_1 = 3x^2 - 6x - 4$, and press ⬭TRACE⬭. When we enter $1 + \sqrt{\ }(21)/3$, a rational approximation and the y-value 0 appear, as shown in the graph at left. The number $1 - \sqrt{21}/3$ also checks.

The solutions are $1 - \dfrac{\sqrt{21}}{3}$ and $1 + \dfrac{\sqrt{21}}{3}$.

Try Exercise 39.

Some quadratic equations have solutions that are imaginary numbers.

EXAMPLE 3 Solve: $x(x + 5) = 2(2x - 1)$.

SOLUTION We first find standard form:

$$x^2 + 5x = 4x - 2 \qquad \text{Multiplying}$$
$$x^2 + x + 2 = 0. \qquad \text{Subtracting } 4x \text{ and adding 2 to both sides}$$

Since we cannot factor $x^2 + x + 2$, we use the quadratic formula with $a = 1$, $b = 1$, and $c = 2$:

$$x = \frac{-1 \pm \sqrt{1^2 - 4 \cdot 1 \cdot 2}}{2 \cdot 1} \qquad \text{Substituting}$$

$$= \frac{-1 \pm \sqrt{1 - 8}}{2}$$

$$= \frac{-1 \pm \sqrt{-7}}{2}$$

$$= \frac{-1 \pm i\sqrt{7}}{2}, \text{ or } -\frac{1}{2} \pm \frac{\sqrt{7}}{2}i.$$

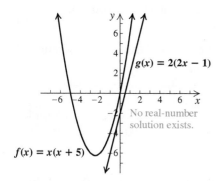

$g(x) = 2(2x - 1)$

No real-number solution exists.

$f(x) = x(x + 5)$

A visualization of Example 3

The solutions are $-\dfrac{1}{2} - \dfrac{\sqrt{7}}{2}i$ and $-\dfrac{1}{2} + \dfrac{\sqrt{7}}{2}i$. The checks are left to the student.

Try Exercise 35.

The quadratic formula can be used to solve certain rational equations.

EXAMPLE 4   If

$$f(x) = 2 + \frac{7}{x} \quad \text{and} \quad g(x) = \frac{4}{x^2},$$

find all x for which $f(x) = g(x)$.

SOLUTION   We set $f(x)$ equal to $g(x)$ and solve:

$$f(x) = g(x)$$
$$2 + \frac{7}{x} = \frac{4}{x^2}. \qquad \text{Substituting. Note that } x \neq 0.$$

This is a rational equation. To solve, we multiply both sides by the LCD, x^2 :

$$x^2\left(2 + \frac{7}{x}\right) = x^2 \cdot \frac{4}{x^2}$$
$$2x^2 + 7x = 4 \qquad \text{Simplifying}$$
$$2x^2 + 7x - 4 = 0. \qquad \text{Subtracting 4 from both sides}$$

We have

$$a = 2, \quad b = 7, \quad \text{and} \quad c = -4.$$

Substituting then gives us

$$x = \frac{-7 \pm \sqrt{7^2 - 4 \cdot 2 \cdot (-4)}}{2 \cdot 2}$$
$$= \frac{-7 \pm \sqrt{49 + 32}}{4} = \frac{-7 \pm \sqrt{81}}{4} = \frac{-7 \pm 9}{4}$$

$$x = \frac{-7 + 9}{4} = \frac{1}{2} \quad \text{or} \quad x = \frac{-7 - 9}{4} = -4. \qquad \begin{array}{l}\text{Both answers should}\\ \text{check since } x \neq 0.\end{array}$$

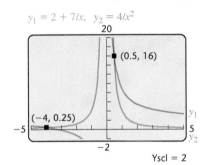

$y_1 = 2 + 7/x, \quad y_2 = 4/x^2$

(0.5, 16)

(−4, 0.25)

Yscl = 2

You can confirm that $f\left(\frac{1}{2}\right) = g\left(\frac{1}{2}\right)$ and $f(-4) = g(-4)$. The graph at left also serves as a check. The solutions are $\frac{1}{2}$ and -4.

Try Exercise 43.

APPROXIMATING SOLUTIONS

When the solution of an equation is irrational, a rational-number approximation is often useful. This is often the case in real-world applications similar to those found in Section 13.4.

EXAMPLE 5   Use a calculator to approximate, to three decimal places, the solutions of Example 2.

SOLUTION   On many graphing calculators, the following sequence of key-strokes can be used to approximate $1 + \sqrt{21}/3$:

(1) (+) (√) (2) (1) ( )) (÷) (3) **ENTER** .

Similar keystrokes can be used to approximate $1 - \sqrt{21}/3$.

The solutions are approximately 2.527525232 and -0.5275252317. Rounded to three decimal places, the solutions are approximately 2.528 and -0.528.

Try Exercise 45.

Student Notes

It is important that you understand both the rules for order of operations *and* the manner in which your calcula-tor applies those rules.

Connecting the Concepts

We have studied four different ways of solving quadratic equations. Each method has advantages and disadvantages, as outlined below. Note that although the quadratic formula can be used to solve *any* quadratic equation, the other methods are sometimes faster and easier to use.

Method	Advantages	Disadvantages	Example
Factoring	Can be very fast.	Can be used only on certain equations. Many equations are difficult or impossible to solve by factoring.	$x^2 - x - 6 = 0$ $(x - 3)(x + 2) = 0$ $x = 3 \quad or \quad x = -2$
The principle of square roots	Fastest way to solve equations of the form $X^2 = k$. Can be used to solve *any* quadratic equation.	Can be slow when original equation is not written in the form $X^2 = k$.	$(x - 5)^2 = 2$ $x - 5 = \pm\sqrt{2}$ $x = 5 \pm \sqrt{2}$
Completing the square	Works well on equations of the form $x^2 + bx = -c$, when b is even. Can be used to solve *any* quadratic equation.	Can be complicated when $a \neq 1$ or when b is not even in $x^2 + bx = -c$.	$x^2 + 14x = -2$ $x^2 + 14x + 49 = -2 + 49$ $(x + 7)^2 = 47$ $x + 7 = \pm\sqrt{47}$ $x = -7 \pm \sqrt{47}$
The quadratic formula	Can be used to solve *any* quadratic equation.	Can be slower than factoring or the principle of square roots for certain equations.	$x^2 - 2x - 5 = 0$ $x = \dfrac{-(-2) \pm \sqrt{(-2)^2 - 4(1)(-5)}}{2 \cdot 1}$ $= \dfrac{2 \pm \sqrt{24}}{2}$ $= \dfrac{2}{2} \pm \dfrac{2\sqrt{6}}{2} = 1 \pm \sqrt{6}$

13.2 Exercise Set

🔖 *Concept Reinforcement*   *Classify each of the following statements as either true or false.*

1. The quadratic formula can be used to solve *any* quadratic equation.

2. The steps used to derive the quadratic formula are the same as those used when solving by completing the square.

3. The quadratic formula does not work if solutions are imaginary numbers.

4. Solving by factoring is always slower than using the quadratic formula.

5. A quadratic equation can have as many as four solutions.

6. It is possible for a quadratic equation to have no real-number solutions.

Solve.

7. $2x^2 + 3x - 5 = 0$

8. $3x^2 - 7x + 2 = 0$

9. $u^2 + 2u - 4 = 0$

10. $u^2 - 2u - 2 = 0$

11. $3p^2 = 18p - 6$

12. $3u^2 = 8u - 5$

13. $h^2 + 4 = 6h$

14. $t^2 + 4t = 1$

15. $x^2 = 3x + 5$

16. $x^2 + 5x = -3$

17. $3t(t + 2) = 1$

18. $2t(t + 2) = 1$

19. $\dfrac{1}{x^2} - 3 = \dfrac{8}{x}$

20. $\dfrac{9}{x} - 2 = \dfrac{5}{x^2}$

21. $t^2 + 10 = 6t$

22. $t^2 + 10t + 26 = 0$

23. $x^2 + 4x + 6 = 0$

24. $x^2 + 11 = 6x$

25. $12t^2 + 17t = 40$

26. $15t^2 + 7t = 2$

27. $25x^2 - 20x + 4 = 0$

28. $36x^2 + 84x + 49 = 0$

29. $7x(x + 2) + 5 = 3x(x + 1)$

30. $5x(x - 1) - 7 = 4x(x - 2)$

31. $14(x - 4) - (x + 2) = (x + 2)(x - 4)$

32. $11(x - 2) + (x - 5) = (x + 2)(x - 6)$

33. $5x^2 = 13x + 17$

34. $25x = 3x^2 + 28$

35. $x(x - 3) = x - 9$

36. $x(x - 1) = 2x - 7$

37. $x^3 - 8 = 0$ (*Hint:* Factor the difference of cubes. Then use the quadratic formula.)

38. $x^3 + 1 = 0$

39. Let $g(x) = 4x^2 - 2x - 3$. Find x such that $g(x) = 0$.

40. Let $f(x) = 6x^2 - 7x - 20$. Find x such that $f(x) = 0$.

41. Let

$$g(x) = \frac{2}{x} + \frac{2}{x + 3}.$$

Find all x for which $g(x) = 1$.

42. Let

$$f(x) = \frac{7}{x} + \frac{7}{x + 4}.$$

Find all x for which $f(x) = 1$.

43. Let

$$F(x) = \frac{x + 3}{x} \quad \text{and} \quad G(x) = \frac{x - 4}{3}.$$

Find all x for which $F(x) = G(x)$.

44. Let

$$f(x) = \frac{3 - x}{4} \quad \text{and} \quad g(x) = \frac{1}{4x}.$$

Find all x for which $f(x) = g(x)$.

Solve. Use a calculator to approximate, to three decimal places, the solutions as rational numbers.

45. $x^2 + 4x - 7 = 0$

46. $x^2 + 6x + 4 = 0$

47. $x^2 - 6x + 4 = 0$

48. $x^2 - 4x + 1 = 0$

49. $2x^2 - 3x - 7 = 0$

50. $3x^2 - 3x - 2 = 0$

ᵀ̶ᵂ 51. Are there any equations that can be solved by the quadratic formula but not by completing the square? Why or why not?

TW **52.** Suppose you are solving a quadratic equation with no constant term $(c = 0)$. Would you use factoring or the quadratic formula to solve? Why?

SKILL REVIEW

To prepare for Section 13.3, review multiplying and simplifying radical expressions and complex-number expressions (Sections 12.3, 12.5, and 12.8).

Multiply and simplify.

53. $(x - 2i)(x + 2i)$ [12.8]

54. $\left(x - 6\sqrt{5}\right)\left(x + 6\sqrt{5}\right)$ [12.5]

55. $\left(x - \left(2 - \sqrt{7}\right)\right)\left(x - \left(2 + \sqrt{7}\right)\right)$ [12.5]

56. $(x - (-3 + 5i))(x - (-3 - 5i))$ [12.8]

Simplify.

57. $\dfrac{-6 \pm \sqrt{(-4)^2 - 4(2)(2)}}{2(2)}$ [12.3]

58. $\dfrac{-(-1) \pm \sqrt{(6)^2 - 4(3)(5)}}{2(3)}$ [12.8]

SYNTHESIS

TW **59.** Explain how you could use the quadratic formula to help factor a quadratic polynomial.

TW **60.** If $a < 0$ and $ax^2 + bx + c = 0$, then $-a$ is positive and the equivalent equation, $-ax^2 - bx - c = 0$, can be solved using the quadratic formula.

a) Find this solution, replacing a, b, and c in the formula with $-a$, $-b$, and $-c$ from the equation.

b) How does the result of part (a) indicate that the quadratic formula "works" regardless of the sign of a?

For Exercises 61–63, let
$$f(x) = \frac{x^2}{x - 2} + 1 \quad and \quad g(x) = \frac{4x - 2}{x - 2} + \frac{x + 4}{2}.$$

61. Find the x-intercepts of the graph of f.

62. Find the x-intercepts of the graph of g.

63. Find all x for which $f(x) = g(x)$.

Solve. Approximate the solutions to three decimal places.

64. $x^2 - 0.75x - 0.5 = 0$

65. $z^2 + 0.84z - 0.4 = 0$

Solve.

66. $\left(1 + \sqrt{3}\right)x^2 - \left(3 + 2\sqrt{3}\right)x + 3 = 0$

67. $\sqrt{2}x^2 + 5x + \sqrt{2} = 0$

68. $ix^2 - 2x + 1 = 0$

69. One solution of $kx^2 + 3x - k = 0$ is -2. Find the other.

TW **70.** Can a graph be used to solve *any* quadratic equation? Why or why not?

TW **71.** Solve Example 2 graphically and compare with the algebraic solution. Which method is faster? Which method is more precise?

TW **72.** Solve Example 4 graphically and compare with the algebraic solution. Which method is faster? Which method is more precise?

> Try Exercise Answers: Section 13.1
> **7.** $-\dfrac{5}{2}, 1$ **35.** $2 \pm \sqrt{5}i$ **39.** $\dfrac{1}{4} \pm \dfrac{\sqrt{13}}{4}$ **43.** $\dfrac{7}{2} \pm \dfrac{\sqrt{85}}{2}$
> **45.** $-5.317, 1.317$

13.3 Studying Solutions of Quadratic Equations

- The Discriminant

- Writing Equations from Solutions

THE DISCRIMINANT

It is sometimes enough to know what *type* of number a solution will be, without actually solving the equation. Suppose we want to know if $4x^2 + 7x - 15 = 0$ has rational solutions (and thus can be solved by factoring). Using the quadratic formula, we would have

$$x = \frac{-b \pm \sqrt{b^2 - 4ac}}{2a}$$

$$= \frac{-7 \pm \sqrt{7^2 - 4 \cdot 4 \cdot (-15)}}{2 \cdot 4}.$$

Since $7^2 - 4 \cdot 4 \cdot (-15) = 49 - 16(-15) = 289$, and since 289 is a perfect square $\left(\sqrt{289} = 17\right)$, the solutions of the equation will be two rational numbers. This means that $4x^2 + 7x - 15 = 0$ *can* be solved by factoring. Note that the radicand, 289, determines what type of number the solutions will be.

The radicand $b^2 - 4ac$ is known as the **discriminant.** If a, b, and c are rational, then we can make the following observations on the basis of the value of the discriminant.

Discriminant	Observation	Example
$b^2 - 4ac = 0$	We get the same solution twice. There is one *repeated* solution and it is rational.	$9x^2 + 6x + 1 = 0$ $b^2 - 4ac = 6^2 - 4 \cdot 9 \cdot 1 = 0$ Solving, we have $x = \dfrac{-6 \pm \sqrt{0}}{2 \cdot 9}$. The (repeated) solution is $-\frac{1}{3}$.
$b^2 - 4ac$ is positive. 1. $b^2 - 4ac$ is a perfect square. 2. $b^2 - 4ac$ is *not* a perfect square.	There are two different real-number solutions. 1. The solutions are rational numbers. 2. The solutions are irrational conjugates.	1. $6x^2 + 5x + 1 = 0$ $b^2 - 4ac = 5^2 - 4 \cdot 6 \cdot 1 = 1$ Solving, we have $x = \dfrac{-5 \pm \sqrt{1}}{2 \cdot 6}$. The solutions are $-\frac{1}{3}$ and $-\frac{1}{2}$. 2. $x^2 + 4x + 2 = 0$ $b^2 - 4ac = 4^2 - 4 \cdot 1 \cdot 2 = 8$ Solving, we have $x = \dfrac{-4 \pm \sqrt{8}}{2 \cdot 1}$. The solutions are $-2 + \sqrt{2}$ and $-2 - \sqrt{2}$.
$b^2 - 4ac$ is negative.	There are two different imaginary-number solutions. They are complex conjugates.	$x^2 + 4x + 5 = 0$ $b^2 - 4ac = 4^2 - 4 \cdot 1 \cdot 5 = -4$ Solving, we have $x = \dfrac{-4 \pm \sqrt{-4}}{2 \cdot 1}$. The solutions are $-2 + i$ and $-2 - i$.

Note that all quadratic equations have one or two solutions. They can always be found algebraically; only real-number solutions can be found graphically.

EXAMPLE 1 For each equation, determine what type of number the solutions are and how many solutions exist.

a) $9x^2 - 12x + 4 = 0$ **b)** $x^2 + 5x + 8 = 0$

c) $2x^2 + 7x - 3 = 0$

SOLUTION

a) For $9x^2 - 12x + 4 = 0$, we have

$$a = 9, \quad b = -12, \quad c = 4.$$

We substitute and compute the discriminant:

$$b^2 - 4ac = (-12)^2 - 4 \cdot 9 \cdot 4$$
$$= 144 - 144 = 0.$$

There is exactly one solution, and it is rational. This indicates that the equation $9x^2 - 12x + 4 = 0$ can be solved by factoring. The graph at left confirms that $9x^2 - 12x + 4 = 0$ has just one solution.

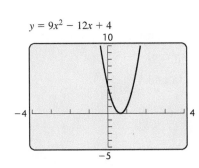

$y = 9x^2 - 12x + 4$

$y = x^2 + 5x + 8$

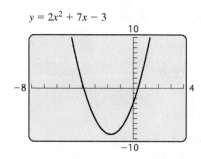

$y = 2x^2 + 7x - 3$

b) For $x^2 + 5x + 8 = 0$, we have

$$a = 1, \quad b = 5, \quad c = 8.$$

We substitute and compute the discriminant:

$$b^2 - 4ac = 5^2 - 4 \cdot 1 \cdot 8$$
$$= 25 - 32 = -7.$$

Since the discriminant is negative, there are two different imaginary-number solutions that are complex conjugates of each other. As the graph at left shows, there are no x-intercepts of the graph of $y = x^2 + 5x + 8$, and thus no real solutions of the equation $x^2 + 5x + 8 = 0$.

c) For $2x^2 + 7x - 3 = 0$, we have

$$a = 2, \quad b = 7, \quad c = -3;$$
$$b^2 - 4ac = 7^2 - 4 \cdot 2(-3)$$
$$= 49 - (-24) = 73.$$

The discriminant is a positive number that is not a perfect square. Thus there are two different irrational solutions that are conjugates of each other. From the graph at left, we see that there are two solutions of the equation. We cannot tell from simply observing the graph whether the solutions are rational or irrational.

⬛ Try Exercise 7.

Since the discriminant tells us the nature of the solutions of a quadratic equation, it also tells us the number of x-intercepts of the graph of a quadratic equation.

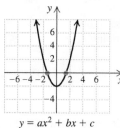

$y = ax^2 + bx + c$
$b^2 - 4ac > 0$
Two real solutions
of $ax^2 + bx + c = 0$
Two x-intercepts

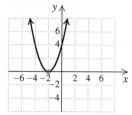

$y = ax^2 + bx + c$
$b^2 - 4ac = 0$
One real solution
of $ax^2 + bx + c = 0$
One x-intercept

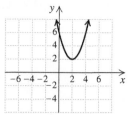

$y = ax^2 + bx + c$
$b^2 - 4ac < 0$
No real solutions
of $ax^2 + bx + c = 0$
No x-intercept

WRITING EQUATIONS FROM SOLUTIONS

We know by the principle of zero products that $(x - 2)(x + 3) = 0$ has solutions 2 and -3. If we know the solutions of an equation, we can write an equation, using the principle in reverse.

EXAMPLE 2   Find an equation for which the given numbers are solutions.

a) 3 and $-\frac{2}{5}$

b) $2i$ and $-2i$

c) $5\sqrt{7}$ and $-5\sqrt{7}$

d) $-4, 0,$ and 1

SOLUTION

a)
$$x = 3 \quad or \quad x = -\tfrac{2}{5}$$
$$x - 3 = 0 \quad or \quad x + \tfrac{2}{5} = 0 \qquad \text{Getting 0's on one side}$$
$$(x - 3)\left(x + \tfrac{2}{5}\right) = 0 \qquad \text{Using the principle of zero products (multiplying)}$$
$$x^2 + \tfrac{2}{5}x - 3x - 3 \cdot \tfrac{2}{5} = 0 \qquad \text{Multiplying}$$
$$x^2 - \tfrac{13}{5}x - \tfrac{6}{5} = 0 \qquad \text{Combining like terms}$$
$$5x^2 - 13x - 6 = 0 \qquad \text{Multiplying both sides by 5 to clear fractions}$$

Note that multiplying both sides by the LCD, 5, clears the equations of fractions. Had we preferred, we could have multiplied $x + \tfrac{2}{5} = 0$ by 5, thus clearing fractions *before* using the principle of zero products.

b)
$$x = 2i \quad or \quad x = -2i$$
$$x - 2i = 0 \quad or \quad x + 2i = 0 \qquad \text{Getting 0's on one side}$$
$$(x - 2i)(x + 2i) = 0 \qquad \text{Using the principle of zero products (multiplying)}$$
$$x^2 - (2i)^2 = 0 \qquad \text{Finding the product of a sum and a difference}$$
$$x^2 - 4i^2 = 0$$
$$x^2 + 4 = 0 \qquad i^2 = -1$$

c)
$$x = 5\sqrt{7} \quad or \quad x = -5\sqrt{7}$$
$$x - 5\sqrt{7} = 0 \quad or \quad x + 5\sqrt{7} = 0 \qquad \text{Getting 0's on one side}$$
$$\left(x - 5\sqrt{7}\right)\left(x + 5\sqrt{7}\right) = 0 \qquad \text{Using the principle of zero products}$$
$$x^2 - \left(5\sqrt{7}\right)^2 = 0 \qquad \text{Finding the product of a sum and a difference}$$
$$x^2 - 25 \cdot 7 = 0$$
$$x^2 - 175 = 0$$

d)
$$x = -4 \quad or \quad x = 0 \quad or \quad x = 1$$
$$x + 4 = 0 \quad or \quad x = 0 \quad or \quad x - 1 = 0 \qquad \text{Getting 0's on one side}$$
$$(x + 4)x(x - 1) = 0 \qquad \text{Using the principle of zero products}$$
$$x(x^2 + 3x - 4) = 0 \qquad \text{Multiplying}$$
$$x^3 + 3x^2 - 4x = 0$$

Try Exercise 29.

13.3 Exercise Set

FOR EXTRA HELP **MyMathLab**

↪ *Concept Reinforcement* *Complete each of the following statements.*

1. In the quadratic formula, the expression $b^2 - 4ac$ is called the _____.

2. When $b^2 - 4ac$ is 0, there is/are _____ solution(s).

3. When $b^2 - 4ac$ is positive, there is/are _____ solution(s).

4. When $b^2 - 4ac$ is negative, there is/are _____ solution(s).

5. When $b^2 - 4ac$ is a perfect square, the solutions are _____ numbers.

6. When $b^2 - 4ac$ is negative, the solutions are _____ numbers.

For each equation, determine what type of number the solutions are and how many solutions exist.

7. $x^2 - 7x + 5 = 0$ **8.** $x^2 - 5x + 3 = 0$

9. $x^2 + 3 = 0$ **10.** $x^2 + 5 = 0$

11. $x^2 - 5 = 0$ **12.** $x^2 - 3 = 0$

13. $4x^2 + 8x - 5 = 0$ **14.** $4x^2 - 12x + 9 = 0$

15. $x^2 + 4x + 6 = 0$ **16.** $x^2 - 2x + 4 = 0$

17. $9t^2 - 48t + 64 = 0$ **18.** $6t^2 - 19t - 20 = 0$

Aha! **19.** $9t^2 - 3t = 0$ **20.** $4m^2 + 7m = 0$

21. $x^2 + 4x = 8$ **22.** $x^2 + 5x = 9$

23. $2a^2 - 3a = -5$ **24.** $3a^2 + 5 = 7a$

25. $7x^2 = 19x$ **26.** $5x^2 = 48x$

27. $y^2 + \frac{9}{4} = 4y$ **28.** $x^2 = \frac{1}{2}x - \frac{3}{5}$

Write a quadratic equation having the given numbers as solutions.

29. $-7, 3$ **30.** $-6, 4$

31. 3, only solution (*Hint*: It must be a repeated solution.)   **32.** -5, only solution

33. $-1, -3$ **34.** $-2, -5$

35. $5, \frac{3}{4}$ **36.** $4, \frac{2}{3}$

37. $-\frac{1}{4}, -\frac{1}{2}$ **38.** $\frac{1}{2}, \frac{1}{3}$

39. $2.4, -0.4$ **40.** $-0.6, 1.4$

41. $-\sqrt{3}, \sqrt{3}$ **42.** $-\sqrt{7}, \sqrt{7}$

43. $2\sqrt{5}, -2\sqrt{5}$ **44.** $3\sqrt{2}, -3\sqrt{2}$

45. $4i, -4i$ **46.** $3i, -3i$

47. $2 - 7i, 2 + 7i$ **48.** $5 - 2i, 5 + 2i$

49. $3 - \sqrt{14}, 3 + \sqrt{14}$

50. $2 - \sqrt{10}, 2 + \sqrt{10}$

51. $1 - \dfrac{\sqrt{21}}{3}, 1 + \dfrac{\sqrt{21}}{3}$

52. $\dfrac{5}{4} - \dfrac{\sqrt{33}}{4}, \dfrac{5}{4} + \dfrac{\sqrt{33}}{4}$

Write a third-degree equation having the given numbers as solutions.

53. $-2, 1, 5$ **54.** $-5, 0, 2$

55. $-1, 0, 3$ **56.** $-2, 2, 3$

TW **57.** Explain why there are not two different solutions when the discriminant is 0.

TW **58.** While solving a quadratic equation of the form $ax^2 + bx + c = 0$ with a graphing calculator, Amberley gets the following screen. How could the sign of the discriminant help her check the graph?

SKILL REVIEW

To prepare for Section 13.4, review solving formulas and solving motion problems (Section 4.4).

Solve each formula for the specified variable.

59. $\dfrac{c}{d} = c + d$, for c

60. $\dfrac{p}{q} = \dfrac{a + b}{b}$, for b

61. $x = \dfrac{3}{1 - y}$, for y

Solve.

62. *Boating.* Kiara's motorboat took 4 hr to make a trip downstream with a 2-mph current. The return trip against the same current took 6 hr. Find the speed of the boat in still water. [4.4]

63. *Walking.* Jamal walks 1.5 mph faster than Kade. In the time it takes Jamal to walk 7 mi, Kade walks 4 mi. Find the speed of each person.

64. *Aviation.* Taryn's Cessna travels 120 mph in still air. She flies 140 mi into the wind and 140 mi with the wind in a total of 2.4 hr. Find the wind speed.

SYNTHESIS

TW **65.** If we assume that a quadratic equation has integers for coefficients, will the product of the solutions always be a real number? Why or why not?

TW **66.** Can a fourth-degree equation have exactly three irrational solutions? Why or why not?

67. The graph of an equation of the form

$$y = ax^2 + bx + c$$

is a curve similar to the one shown below. Determine a, b, and c from the information given.

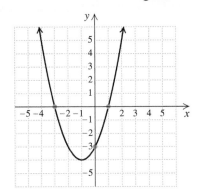

68. Show that the product of the solutions of $ax^2 + bx + c = 0$ is c/a.

For each equation under the given condition, (a) find k and (b) find the other solution.

69. $kx^2 - 2x + k = 0$; one solution is -3

70. $x^2 - kx + 2 = 0$; one solution is $1 + i$

71. $x^2 - (6 + 3i)x + k = 0$; one solution is 3

72. Show that the sum of the solutions of $ax^2 + bx + c = 0$ is $-b/a$.

73. Show that whenever there is just one solution of $ax^2 + bx + c = 0$, that solution is of the form $-b/(2a)$.

74. Find h and k, where $3x^2 - hx + 4k = 0$, the sum of the solutions is -12, and the product of the solutions is 20. (*Hint*: See Exercises 68 and 72.)

75. Suppose that $f(x) = ax^2 + bx + c$, with $f(-3) = 0, f\left(\frac{1}{2}\right) = 0$, and $f(0) = -12$. Find a, b, and c.

76. Find an equation for which $2 - \sqrt{3}, 2 + \sqrt{3}$, $5 - 2i$, and $5 + 2i$ are solutions.

Aha! **77.** Write a quadratic equation with integer coefficients for which $-\sqrt{2}$ is one solution.

78. Write a quadratic equation with integer coefficients for which $10i$ is one solution.

79. Find an equation with integer coefficients for which $1 - \sqrt{5}$ and $3 + 2i$ are two of the solutions.

TW **80.** A discriminant that is a perfect square indicates that factoring can be used to solve the quadratic equation. Why?

■ Try Exercise Answers: Section 13.3
7. Two irrational   **29.** $x^2 + 4x - 21 = 0$

13.4 Applications Involving Quadratic Equations

■ Solving Problems

■ Solving Formulas

SOLVING PROBLEMS

Some problems translate to rational equations. The solution of such rational equations can involve quadratic equations.

EXAMPLE 1 Motorcycle Travel.   Keisha rode her motorcycle 300 mi at a certain average speed. Had she averaged 10 mph more, the trip would have taken 1 hr less. Find Keisha's average speed.

SOLUTION

1. **Familiarize.** We make a drawing, labeling it with the information provided. We can create a table. We let r = the rate, in miles per hour, and t the time, in hours, for Keisha's trip.

	300 miles	
Time t		Speed r
	300 miles	
Time $t - 1$		Speed $r + 10$

Distance	Speed	Time	
300	r	t	$\longrightarrow r = \dfrac{300}{t}$
300	$r + 10$	$t - 1$	$\longrightarrow r + 10 = \dfrac{300}{t - 1}$

Recall that the definition of speed, $r = d/t$, relates the three quantities.

2. **Translate.** From the first two lines of the table, we obtain

$$r = \frac{300}{t} \quad \text{and} \quad r + 10 = \frac{300}{t - 1}.$$

3. **Carry out.** A system of equations has been formed. We substitute for r from the first equation into the second and solve the resulting equation:

$$\frac{300}{t} + 10 = \frac{300}{t - 1} \qquad \text{Substituting } 300/t \text{ for } r$$

$$t(t - 1) \cdot \left[\frac{300}{t} + 10 \right] = t(t - 1) \cdot \frac{300}{t - 1} \qquad \text{Multiplying by the LCD}$$

$$t(t - 1) \cdot \frac{300}{t} + t(t - 1) \cdot 10 = t(t - 1) \cdot \frac{300}{t - 1} \qquad \begin{array}{l} \text{Using the distributive} \\ \text{law and removing} \\ \text{factors that equal 1:} \\ \frac{t}{t} = 1; \frac{t - 1}{t - 1} = 1 \end{array}$$

$$300(t - 1) + 10(t^2 - t) = 300t$$
$$300t - 300 + 10t^2 - 10t = 300t$$
$$10t^2 - 10t - 300 = 0 \qquad \begin{array}{l} \text{Rewriting in standard} \\ \text{form} \end{array}$$
$$t^2 - t - 30 = 0 \qquad \begin{array}{l} \text{Multiplying by } \frac{1}{10} \text{ or} \\ \text{dividing by 10} \end{array}$$
$$(t - 6)(t + 5) = 0 \qquad \text{Factoring}$$
$$t = 6 \quad or \quad t = -5. \qquad \begin{array}{l} \text{Principle of zero} \\ \text{products} \end{array}$$

STUDY TIP

Keep Your Book Handy

You can supplement your regular studying by using smaller blocks of time for reviewing material. By keeping your text and notebook nearby (in your car or bag), you can review course material in a doctor's waiting room, while sitting through a child's soccer practice, while riding a bus, or whenever you find yourself with some free time.

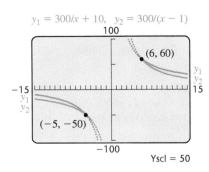

$y_1 = 300/x + 10$, $y_2 = 300/(x - 1)$

Yscl = 50

4. Check. As a partial check, we graph the equations $y_1 = 300/x + 10$ and $y_2 = 300/(x - 1)$. The graph at left shows that the solutions are -5 and 6.

Note that we have solved for t, not r as required. Since negative time has no meaning here, we disregard the -5 and use 6 hr to find r:

$$r = \frac{300 \text{ mi}}{6 \text{ hr}} = 50 \text{ mph}.$$

> **CAUTION!**   Always make sure that you find the quantity asked for in the problem.

To see if 50 mph checks, we increase the speed 10 mph to 60 mph and see how long the trip would have taken at that speed:

$$t = \frac{d}{r} = \frac{300 \text{ mi}}{60 \text{ mph}} = 5 \text{ hr.} \qquad \text{Note that mi/mph} = \text{mi} \div \frac{\text{mi}}{\text{hr}} = \text{mi} \cdot \frac{\text{hr}}{\text{mi}} = \text{hr.}$$

This is 1 hr less than the trip actually took, so the answer checks.

5. State. Keisha traveled at an average speed of 50 mph.

Try Exercise 1.

SOLVING FORMULAS

Recall that to solve a formula for a certain letter, we use the principles for solving equations to get that letter alone on one side.

EXAMPLE 2   Period of a Pendulum.   The time T required for a pendulum of length l to swing back and forth (complete one period) is given by the formula $T = 2\pi \sqrt{l/g}$, where g is the earth's gravitational constant. Solve for l.

SOLUTION   We have

$$T = 2\pi\sqrt{\frac{l}{g}} \qquad \text{This is a radical equation (see Section 12.6).}$$

$$T^2 = \left(2\pi\sqrt{\frac{l}{g}}\right)^2 \qquad \text{Principle of powers (squaring both sides)}$$

$$T^2 = 2^2\pi^2\frac{l}{g}$$

$$gT^2 = 4\pi^2 l \qquad \text{Multiplying both sides by } g \text{ to clear fractions}$$

$$\frac{gT^2}{4\pi^2} = l. \qquad \text{Dividing both sides by } 4\pi^2$$

We now have l alone on one side and l does not appear on the other side, so the formula is solved for l.

Try Exercise 21.

In formulas for which variables represent nonnegative numbers, there is no need for absolute-value signs when taking square roots.

EXAMPLE 3   Hang Time.*   An athlete's *hang time* is the amount of time that the athlete can remain airborne when jumping. A formula relating an athlete's vertical leap V, in inches, to hang time T, in seconds, is $V = 48T^2$. Solve for T.

---

*This formula is taken from an article by Peter Brancazio, "The Mechanics of a Slam Dunk," *Popular Mechanics*, November 1991. Courtesy of Professor Peter Brancazio, Brooklyn College.

SOLUTION We have

$$48T^2 = V$$

$$T^2 = \frac{V}{48} \qquad \text{Dividing by 48 to isolate } T^2$$

$$T = \frac{\sqrt{V}}{\sqrt{48}} \qquad \text{Using the principle of square roots and the quotient rule for radicals. We assume } V, T \geq 0.$$

$$= \frac{\sqrt{V}}{\sqrt{16}\,\sqrt{3}}$$

$$= \frac{\sqrt{V}}{4\sqrt{3}}$$

$$= \frac{\sqrt{V}}{4\sqrt{3}} \cdot \frac{\sqrt{3}}{\sqrt{3}} = \frac{\sqrt{3V}}{12}. \qquad \text{Rationalizing the denominator}$$

Try Exercise 15.

EXAMPLE 4 Falling Distance.   An object tossed downward with an initial speed (velocity) of v_0 will travel a distance of s meters, where $s = 4.9t^2 + v_0t$ and t is measured in seconds. Solve for t.

SOLUTION   Since t is squared in one term and raised to the first power in the other term, the equation is quadratic in t.

$$4.9t^2 + v_0t = s$$

$$4.9t^2 + v_0t - s = 0 \qquad \text{Writing standard form}$$

$$a = 4.9, \quad b = v_0, \quad c = -s$$

$$t = \frac{-v_0 \pm \sqrt{(v_0)^2 - 4(4.9)(-s)}}{2(4.9)} \qquad \text{Using the quadratic formula}$$

Since the negative square root would yield a negative value for t, we use only the positive root:

$$t = \frac{-v_0 + \sqrt{(v_0)^2 + 19.6s}}{9.8}.$$

Try Exercise 17.

The following list of steps should help you when solving formulas for a given letter. Try to remember that when solving a formula, you use the same approach that you would to solve an equation.

To Solve a Formula for a Letter—Say, h

1. Clear fractions and use the principle of powers, as needed. Perform these steps until radicals containing h are gone and h is not in any denominator.
2. Combine all like terms.
3. If the only power of h is h^1, the equation can be solved. (See Example 2.)
4. If h^2 appears but h does not, solve for h^2 and use the principle of square roots to solve for h. (See Example 3.)
5. If there are terms containing both h and h^2, put the equation in standard form and use the quadratic formula. (See Example 4.)

Solve.

1. *Car Trips.*   During the first part of a trip, Jaclyn's Honda traveled 120 mi at a certain speed. Jaclyn then drove another 100 mi at a speed that was 10 mph slower. If the total time of Jaclyn's trip was 4 hr, what was her speed on each part of the trip?

2. *Canoeing.*   During the first part of a canoe trip, Terrell covered 60 km at a certain speed. He then traveled 24 km at a speed that was 4 km/h slower. If the total time for the trip was 8 hr, what was the speed on each part of the trip?

3. *Car Trips.*   Franklin's Ford travels 200 mi averaging a certain speed. If the car had gone 10 mph faster, the trip would have taken 1 hr less. Find Franklin's average speed.

4. *Car Trips.*   Mallory's Mazda travels 280 mi averaging a certain speed. If the car had gone 5 mph faster, the trip would have taken 1 hr less. Find Mallory's average speed.

5. *Air Travel.*   A Cessna flies 600 mi at a certain speed. A Beechcraft flies 1000 mi at a speed that is 50 mph faster, but takes 1 hr longer. Find the speed of each plane.

6. *Air Travel.*   A turbo-jet flies 50 mph faster than a super-prop plane. If a turbo-jet goes 2000 mi in 3 hr less time than it takes the super-prop to go 2800 mi, find the speed of each plane.

7. *Bicycling.*   Naoki bikes the 40 mi to Hillsboro averaging a certain speed. The return trip is made at a speed that is 6 mph slower. Total time for the round trip is 14 hr. Find Naoki's average speed on each part of the trip.

8. *Car Speed.*   On a sales trip, Jay drives the 600 mi to Richmond averaging a certain speed. The return trip is made at an average speed that is 10 mph slower. Total time for the round trip is 22 hr. Find Jay's average speed on each part of the trip.

9. *Navigation.*   The Hudson River flows at a rate of 3 mph. A patrol boat travels 60 mi upriver and returns in a total time of 9 hr. What is the speed of the boat in still water?

10. *Navigation.*   The current in a typical Mississippi River shipping route flows at a rate of 4 mph. In order

for a barge to travel 24 mi upriver and then return in a total of 5 hr, approximately how fast must the barge be able to travel in still water?

11. *Filling a Pool.*   A well and a spring are filling a swimming pool. Together, they can fill the pool in 4 hr. The well, working alone, can fill the pool in 6 hr less time than the spring. How long would the spring take, working alone, to fill the pool?

12. *Filling a Tank.*   Two pipes are connected to the same tank. Working together, they can fill the tank in 2 hr. The larger pipe, working alone, can fill the tank in 3 hr less time than the smaller one. How long would the smaller one take, working alone, to fill the tank?

13. *Paddleboats.*   Antonio paddles 1 mi upstream and 1 mi back in a total time of 1 hr. The speed of the river is 2 mph. Find the speed of Antonio's paddleboat in still water.

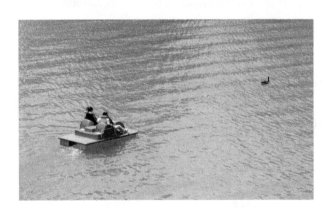

14. *Rowing.*   Sydney rows 10 km upstream and 10 km back in a total time of 3 hr. The speed of the river is 5 km/h. Find Sydney's speed in still water.

Solve each formula for the indicated letter. Assume that all variables represent nonnegative numbers.

15. $A = 4\pi r^2$, for r
(Surface area of a sphere of radius r)

16. $A = 6s^2$, for s
(Surface area of a cube with sides of length s)

17. $A = 2\pi r^2 + 2\pi rh$, for r
(Surface area of a right cylindrical solid with radius r and height h)

18. $N = \dfrac{k^2 - 3k}{2}$, for k

(Number of diagonals of a polygon with k sides)

19. $F = \dfrac{Gm_1m_2}{r^2}$, for r

(Law of gravity)

20. $N = \dfrac{kQ_1Q_2}{s^2}$, for s

(Number of phone calls between two cities)

21. $c = \sqrt{gH}$, for H

(Velocity of an ocean wave)

22. $V = 3.5\sqrt{h}$, for h

(Distance to the horizon from a height)

23. $w = \dfrac{lg^2}{800}$, for g

(An ancient fisherman's formula)

24. $V = \pi r^2 h$, for r

(Volume of a cylinder)

25. $a^2 + b^2 = c^2$, for b

(Pythagorean formula in two dimensions)

26. $a^2 + b^2 + c^2 = d^2$, for c

(Pythagorean formula in three dimensions)

27. $s = v_0 t + \dfrac{gt^2}{2}$, for t

(A motion formula)

28. $A = \pi r^2 + \pi rs$, for r

(Surface area of a cone)

29. $N = \frac{1}{2}(n^2 - n)$, for n

(Number of games if n teams play each other once)

30. $A = A_0(1 - r)^2$, for r

(A business formula)

31. $T = 2\pi\sqrt{\dfrac{l}{g}}$, for g

(A pendulum formula)

32. $W = \sqrt{\dfrac{1}{LC}}$, for L

(An electricity formula)

Aha! **33.** $at^2 + bt + c = 0$, for t

(An algebraic formula)

34. $A = P_1(1 + r)^2 + P_2(1 + r)$, for r

(Amount in an account when P_1 is invested for 2 years and P_2 for 1 year at interest rate r)

Solve.

35. *Falling Distance.*   (Use $4.9t + v_0 t = s$.)

   a) A bolt falls off an airplane at an altitude of 500 m. Approximately how long does it take the bolt to reach the ground?

   b) A ball is thrown downward at a speed of 30 m/sec from an altitude of 500 m. Approximately how long does it take the ball to reach the ground?

   c) Approximately how far will an object fall in 5 sec, when thrown downward at an initial velocity of 30 m/sec from a plane?

36. *Falling Distance.*   (Use $4.9t^2 + v_0 t = s$.)

   a) A ring is dropped from a helicopter at an altitude of 75 m. Approximately how long does it take the ring to reach the ground?

   b) A coin is tossed downward with an initial velocity of 30 m/sec from an altitude of 75 m. Approximately how long does it take the coin to reach the ground?

   c) Approximately how far will an object fall in 2 sec, if thrown downward at an initial velocity of 20 m/sec from a helicopter?

37. *Bungee Jumping.*   Jaime is tied to one end of a 40-m elasticized (bungee) cord. The other end of the cord is tied to the middle of a bridge. If Jaime jumps off the bridge, for how long will he fall before the cord begins to stretch? (Use $4.9t^2 = s$.)

40 m

38. *Bungee Jumping.*   Mariah is tied to a bungee cord (see Exercise 37) and falls for 2.5 sec before her cord begins to stretch. How long is the bungee cord?

39. *Hang Time.* The NBA's LeBron James reportedly has a vertical leap of 44 in. What is his hang time? (Use $V = 48T^2$.)
Source: www.vertcoach.com

40. *League Schedules.* In a bowling league, each team plays each of the other teams once. If a total of 66 games is played, how many teams are in the league? (See Exercise 29.)

For Exercises 41 and 42, use $4.9t^2 + v_0t = s$.

41. *Downward Speed.* An object thrown downward from a 100-m cliff travels 51.6 m in 3 sec. What was the initial velocity of the object?

42. *Downward Speed.* An object thrown downward from a 200-m cliff travels 91.2 m in 4 sec. What was the initial velocity of the object?

For Exercises 43 and 44, use
$$A = P_1(1 + r)^2 + P_2(1 + r).$$
(See Exercise 34.)

43. *Compound Interest.* A firm invests $3000 in a savings account for 2 years. At the beginning of the second year, an additional $1700 is invested. If a total of $5253.70 is in the account at the end of the second year, what is the annual interest rate?

44. *Compound Interest.* A business invests $10,000 in a savings account for 2 years. At the beginning of the second year, an additional $3500 is invested. If a total of $15,569.75 is in the account at the end of the second year, what is the annual interest rate?

45. Marti is tied to a bungee cord that is twice as long as the cord tied to Tivon. Will Marti's fall take twice as long as Tivon's before their cords begin to stretch? Why or why not? (See Exercises 37 and 38.)

46. Under what circumstances would a negative value for *t*, time, have meaning?

SKILL REVIEW

To prepare for Section 13.5, review raising a power to a power and solving rational equations and radical equations (Sections 12.2, and 10.6).

Simplify.

47. $(m^{-1})^2$

48. $(t^{1/3})^2$ [12.2]

49. $(y^{1/6})^2$ [12.2]

50. $(z^{1/4})^2$ [12.2]

Solve.

51. $t^{-1} = \dfrac{1}{2}$

52. $x^{1/4} = 3$ [12.6]

SYNTHESIS

53. Write a problem for a classmate to solve. Devise the problem so that (a) the solution is found after solving a rational equation and (b) the solution is "The express train travels 90 mph."

54. In what ways do the motion problems in this section (like Example 1) differ from the motion problems?

55. *Biochemistry.* The equation
$$A = 6.5 - \frac{20.4t}{t^2 + 36}$$
is used to calculate the acid level *A* in a person's blood *t* minutes after sugar is consumed. Solve for *t*.

56. *Special Relativity.* Einstein found that an object with initial mass m_0 and traveling velocity *v* has mass
$$m = \frac{m_0}{\sqrt{1 - \dfrac{v^2}{c^2}}},$$
where *c* is the speed of light. Solve the formula for *c*.

57. Find a number for which the reciprocal of 1 less than the number is the same as 1 more than the number.

58. *Purchasing.* A discount store bought a quantity of paperback books for $250 and sold all but 15 at a profit of $3.50 per book. With the total amount received, the manager could buy 4 more than twice as many as were bought before. Find the cost per book.

59. *Art and Aesthetics.* For over 2000 years, artists, sculptors, and architects have regarded the proportions of a "golden" rectangle as visually appealing. A rectangle of width w and length l is considered "golden" if

$$\frac{w}{l} = \frac{l}{w + l}.$$

Solve for l.

60. *Diagonal of a Cube.* Find a formula that expresses the length of the three-dimensional diagonal of a cube as a function of the cube's surface area.

61. Solve for n:

$$mn^4 - r^2pm^3 - r^2n^2 + p = 0.$$

62. *Surface Area.* Find a formula that expresses the diameter of a right cylindrical solid as a function of its surface area and its height. (See Exercise 17.)

63. A sphere is inscribed in a cube as shown in the figure below. Express the surface area of the sphere as a function of the surface area S of the cube. (See Exercise 15.)

> ■ Try Exercise Answers: Section 13.4
> **1.** First part: 60 mph; second part: 50 mph
> **15.** $r = \frac{1}{2}\sqrt{\frac{A}{\pi}}$, or $\frac{\sqrt{A\pi}}{2\pi}$ **17.** $r = \frac{-\pi h + \sqrt{\pi^2 h^2 + 2\pi A}}{2\pi}$
> **21.** $H = \frac{c^2}{g}$

13.5 Equations Reducible to Quadratic

- Recognizing Equations in Quadratic Form

- Radical Equations and Rational Equations

RECOGNIZING EQUATIONS IN QUADRATIC FORM

Certain equations that are not really quadratic can be thought of in such a way that they can be solved as quadratic. For example, because the square of x^2 is x^4, the equation $x^4 - 9x^2 + 8 = 0$ is said to be "quadratic in x^2":

$$x^4 - 9x^2 + 8 = 0$$

$$(x^2)^2 - 9(x^2) + 8 = 0 \qquad \text{Thinking of } x^4 \text{ as } (x^2)^2$$

$$u^2 - 9u + 8 = 0. \qquad \text{To make this clearer, write } u \text{ instead of } x^2.$$

The equation $u^2 - 9u + 8 = 0$ can be solved by factoring or by the quadratic formula. Then, remembering that $u = x^2$, we can solve for x. Equations that can be solved like this are *reducible to quadratic* and are said to be *in quadratic form*.

EXAMPLE 1 Solve: $x^4 - 9x^2 + 8 = 0$.

SOLUTION We solve both algebraically and graphically.

ALGEBRAIC APPROACH	GRAPHICAL APPROACH

ALGEBRAIC APPROACH

Let $u = x^2$. Then $u^2 = x^4$. We solve by substituting u for x^2 and u^2 for x^4:

$$u^2 - 9u + 8 = 0$$
$$(u - 8)(u - 1) = 0 \qquad \text{Factoring}$$
$$u - 8 = 0 \quad or \quad u - 1 = 0 \qquad \text{Principle of zero products}$$
$$u = 8 \quad or \qquad u = 1.$$

We replace u with x^2 and solve these equations:

$$x^2 = 8 \qquad or \quad x^2 = 1$$
$$x = \pm\sqrt{8} \quad or \quad x = \pm 1$$
$$x = \pm 2\sqrt{2} \quad or \quad x = \pm 1.$$

To check, note that for both $x = 2\sqrt{2}$ and $-2\sqrt{2}$, we have $x^2 = 8$ and $x^4 = 64$. Similarly, for both $x = 1$ and -1, we have $x^2 = 1$ and $x^4 = 1$. Thus instead of making four checks, we need make only two.

Check:

For $\pm 2\sqrt{2}$:

$$\begin{array}{c|c} x^4 - 9x^2 + 8 = 0 & \\ \hline \left(\pm 2\sqrt{2}\right)^4 - 9\left(\pm 2\sqrt{2}\right)^2 + 8 & 0 \\ 64 - 9 \cdot 8 + 8 & \\ & 0 \stackrel{?}{=} 0 \quad \text{TRUE} \end{array}$$

For ± 1:

$$\begin{array}{c|c} x^4 - 9x^2 + 8 = 0 & \\ \hline (\pm 1)^4 - 9(\pm 1)^2 + 8 & 0 \\ 1 - 9 + 8 & \\ & 0 \stackrel{?}{=} 0 \quad \text{TRUE} \end{array}$$

The solutions are $1, -1, 2\sqrt{2}$, and $-2\sqrt{2}$.

GRAPHICAL APPROACH

We let $f(x) = x^4 - 9x^2 + 8$ and determine the zeros of the function.

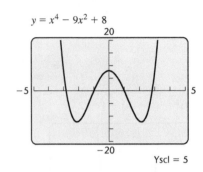

$y = x^4 - 9x^2 + 8$

Yscl = 5

It appears as though the graph has 4 x-intercepts. A fourth-degree polynomial function has at most 4 zeros, so we know that we have not missed any zeros. Using ZERO four times, we obtain the solutions -2.8284271, $-1, 1$, and 2.8284271. The solutions are ± 1 and, approximately, ± 2.8284271. Note that since $2\sqrt{2} \approx 2.8284271$, the solutions found graphically are the same as those found algebraically.

Try Exercise 15.

Equations like those in Example 1 can be solved directly by factoring:

$$x^4 - 9x^2 + 8 = 0$$
$$(x^2 - 1)(x^2 - 8) = 0$$
$$x^2 - 1 = 0 \quad or \quad x^2 - 8 = 0$$
$$x^2 = 1 \quad or \qquad x^2 = 8$$
$$x = \pm 1 \quad or \qquad x = \pm 2\sqrt{2}.$$

However, it becomes difficult to solve some equations without first making a substitution.

EXAMPLE 2 Find the x-intercepts of the graph of
$$f(x) = (x^2 - 1)^2 - (x^2 - 1) - 2.$$

SOLUTION The x-intercepts occur where $f(x) = 0$ so we must have
$$(x^2 - 1)^2 - (x^2 - 1) - 2 = 0. \qquad \text{Setting } f(x) \text{ equal to 0}$$

If we identify $x^2 - 1$ as u, then the equation can be written in quadratic form:
$$u = x^2 - 1$$
$$u^2 = (x^2 - 1)^2.$$

Substituting, we have
$$u^2 - u - 2 = 0 \qquad \text{Substituting in } (x^2 - 1)^2 - (x^2 - 1) - 2 = 0$$
$$(u - 2)(u + 1) = 0$$
$$u = 2 \quad or \quad u = -1. \qquad \text{Using the principle of zero products}$$

$y = (x^2 - 1)^2 - (x^2 - 1) - 2$

Next, we replace u with $x^2 - 1$ and solve these equations:
$$x^2 - 1 = 2 \qquad or \quad x^2 - 1 = -1$$
$$x^2 = 3 \qquad or \qquad x^2 = 0 \qquad \text{Adding 1 to both sides}$$
$$x = \pm\sqrt{3} \quad or \qquad x = 0. \qquad \text{Using the principle of square roots}$$

The x-intercepts occur at $\left(-\sqrt{3}, 0\right)$, $(0, 0)$, and $\left(\sqrt{3}, 0\right)$. These solutions are confirmed by the graph at left.

Try Exercise 49.

RADICAL EQUATIONS AND RATIONAL EQUATIONS

Sometimes rational equations, radical equations, or equations containing exponents that are fractions are reducible to quadratic. It is especially important that answers to these equations be checked in the original equation.

EXAMPLE 3 Solve: $x - 3\sqrt{x} - 4 = 0$.

SOLUTION This radical equation could be solved using the method discussed in Section 12.6. However, if we note that the square of $\sqrt{x}$ is x, we can regard the equation as "quadratic in $\sqrt{x}$."

We determine u and u^2:
$$u = \sqrt{x}$$
$$u^2 = x.$$

Substituting, we have
$$x - 3\sqrt{x} - 4 = 0$$
$$u^2 - 3u - 4 = 0 \qquad \text{Substituting}$$
$$(u - 4)(u + 1) = 0$$
$$u = 4 \quad or \quad u = -1. \qquad \text{Using the principle of zero products}$$

> **CAUTION!** A common error is to solve for u but forget to solve for x. Remember to solve for the *original* variable!

Next, we replace u with $\sqrt{x}$ and solve these equations:
$$\sqrt{x} = 4 \quad or \quad \sqrt{x} = -1.$$

Squaring gives us $x = 16$ or $x = 1$ and also makes checking essential.

Check:

For 16:
$$\begin{array}{c|c} x - 3\sqrt{x} - 4 = 0 & \\ \hline 16 - 3\sqrt{16} - 4 & 0 \\ 16 - 3 \cdot 4 - 4 & \\ & 0 \stackrel{?}{=} 0 \quad \text{TRUE} \end{array}$$

For 1:
$$\begin{array}{c|c} x - 3\sqrt{x} - 4 = 0 & \\ \hline 1 - 3\sqrt{1} - 4 & 0 \\ 1 - 3 \cdot 1 - 4 & \\ & -6 \stackrel{?}{=} 0 \quad \text{FALSE} \end{array}$$

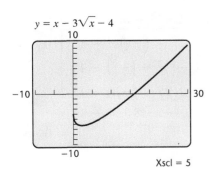

$y = x - 3\sqrt{x} - 4$

Xscl = 5

The number 16 checks, but 1 does not. Had we noticed that $\sqrt{x} = -1$ has no solution (since principal square roots are never negative), we could have solved only the equation $\sqrt{x} = 4$. The graph at left provides further evidence that although 16 is a solution, -1 is not. The solution is 16.

Try Exercise 21.

The following tips may prove useful.

To Solve an Equation That Is Reducible to Quadratic

1. The equation is quadratic in form if the variable factor in one term is the square of the variable factor in the other variable term.
2. Write down any substitutions that you are making.
3. Whenever you make a substitution, be sure to solve for the variable that is used in the original equation.
4. Check possible answers in the original equation.

EXAMPLE 4 Solve: $2m^{-2} + m^{-1} - 15 = 0$.

SOLUTION Note that the square of m^{-1} is $(m^{-1})^2$, or m^{-2}. We let $u = m^{-1}$:

Determine u and u^2.

$$u = m^{-1}$$
$$u^2 = m^{-2}.$$

Substituting, we have

Substitute.

$$2u^2 + u - 15 = 0 \qquad \text{Substituting in } 2m^{-2} + m^{-1} - 15 = 0$$

$$(2u - 5)(u + 3) = 0$$

$$2u - 5 = 0 \quad or \quad u + 3 = 0 \qquad \text{Using the principle of zero products}$$

$$2u = 5 \quad or \quad u = -3$$

Solve for u.

$$u = \frac{5}{2} \quad or \quad u = -3.$$

Now we replace u with m^{-1} and solve:

$$m^{-1} = \frac{5}{2} \quad or \quad m^{-1} = -3$$

$$\frac{1}{m} = \frac{5}{2} \quad or \quad \frac{1}{m} = -3 \qquad \text{Recall that } m^{-1} = \frac{1}{m}.$$

$$1 = \frac{5}{2}m \quad or \quad 1 = -3m \qquad \text{Multiplying both sides by } m$$

Solve for the original variable.

$$\frac{2}{5} = m \quad or \quad -\frac{1}{3} = m. \qquad \text{Solving for } m$$

Check.

Check:

For $\frac{2}{5}$:

$$\frac{2m^{-2} + m^{-1} - 15 = 0}{2\left(\frac{2}{5}\right)^{-2} + \left(\frac{2}{5}\right)^{-1} - 15 \mid 0}$$

$$2\left(\frac{5}{2}\right)^2 + \left(\frac{5}{2}\right) - 15$$

$$2\left(\frac{25}{4}\right) + \frac{5}{2} - 15$$

$$\frac{25}{2} + \frac{5}{2} - 15$$

$$\frac{30}{2} - 15$$

$$0 \overset{?}{=} 0 \quad \text{TRUE}$$

For $-\frac{1}{3}$:

$$\frac{2m^{-2} + m^{-1} - 15 = 0}{2\left(-\frac{1}{3}\right)^{-2} + \left(-\frac{1}{3}\right)^{-1} - 15 \mid 0}$$

$$2\left(-\frac{3}{1}\right)^2 + \left(-\frac{3}{1}\right) - 15$$

$$2(9) + (-3) - 15$$

$$18 - 3 - 15$$

$$0 \overset{?}{=} 0 \quad \text{TRUE}$$

We could also check the solutions using a calculator by entering $y_1 = 2x^{-2} + x^{-1} - 15$ and evaluating y_1 for both numbers, as shown on the left below.

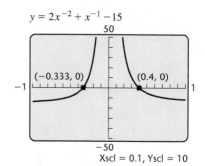

$$y = 2x^{-2} + x^{-1} - 15$$

Xscl = 0.1, Yscl = 10

As another check, we solve the equation graphically. The first coordinates of the x-intercepts of the graph on the right above give the solutions.

Both numbers check. The solutions are $-\frac{1}{3}$ and $\frac{2}{5}$, or approximately -0.333 and 0.4.

Try Exercise 31.

Note that Example 4 can also be written

$$\frac{2}{m^2} + \frac{1}{m} - 15 = 0.$$

It can then be solved by letting $u = 1/m$ and $u^2 = 1/m^2$ or by clearing fractions.

EXAMPLE 5   Solve: $t^{2/5} - t^{1/5} - 2 = 0$.

SOLUTION   Note that the square of $t^{1/5}$ is $(t^{1/5})^2$, or $t^{2/5}$. The equation is therefore quadratic in $t^{1/5}$, so we let $u = t^{1/5}$:

$$u = t^{1/5}$$
$$u^2 = t^{2/5}.$$

Substituting, we have

$$u^2 - u - 2 = 0 \qquad \text{Substituting in } t^{2/5} - t^{1/5} - 2 = 0$$
$$(u - 2)(u + 1) = 0$$
$$u = 2 \quad or \quad u = -1. \qquad \text{Using the principle of zero products}$$

Now we replace u with $t^{1/5}$ and solve:

$$t^{1/5} = 2 \quad or \quad t^{1/5} = -1$$
$$t = 32 \quad or \quad t = -1. \qquad \text{Principle of powers; raising to the 5th power}$$

Check:

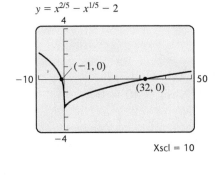

$y = x^{2/5} - x^{1/5} - 2$

(−1, 0)

−10   50

(32, 0)

−4

Xscl = 10

For 32:

$$\begin{array}{c|c} t^{2/5} - t^{1/5} - 2 = 0 & \\ \hline 32^{2/5} - 32^{1/5} - 2 & 0 \\ (32^{1/5})^2 - 32^{1/5} - 2 & \\ 2^2 - 2 - 2 & \\ & 0 \overset{?}{=} 0 \quad \text{TRUE} \end{array}$$

For −1:

$$\begin{array}{c|c} t^{2/5} - t^{1/5} - 2 = 0 & \\ \hline (-1)^{2/5} - (-1)^{1/5} - 2 & 0 \\ {[(-1)^{1/5}]}^2 - (-1)^{1/5} - 2 & \\ (-1)^2 - (-1) - 2 & \\ & 0 \overset{?}{=} 0 \quad \text{TRUE} \end{array}$$

Both numbers check and are confirmed by the graph at left. The solutions are 32 and −1.

Try Exercise 33.

EXAMPLE 6   Solve: $\left(5 + \sqrt{r}\right)^2 + 6\left(5 + \sqrt{r}\right) + 2 = 0$.

SOLUTION   We determine u and u^2:

$$u = 5 + \sqrt{r}$$
$$u^2 = \left(5 + \sqrt{r}\right)^2.$$

Substituting, we have

$$u^2 + 6u + 2 = 0$$

$$u = \frac{-6 \pm \sqrt{6^2 - 4 \cdot 1 \cdot 2}}{2 \cdot 1} \qquad \text{Using the quadratic formula}$$

$$= \frac{-6 \pm \sqrt{28}}{2}$$

$$= \frac{-6}{2} \pm \frac{2\sqrt{7}}{2} \qquad \text{Simplifying; } \sqrt{28} = \sqrt{4}\sqrt{7}$$

$$= -3 \pm \sqrt{7}.$$

Now we replace u with $5 + \sqrt{r}$ and solve for r:

$$5 + \sqrt{r} = -3 + \sqrt{7} \quad or \quad 5 + \sqrt{r} = -3 - \sqrt{7} \qquad u = -3 + \sqrt{7}$$
$$\sqrt{r} = -8 + \sqrt{7} \quad or \qquad \sqrt{r} = -8 - \sqrt{7}. \qquad or\ u = -3 - \sqrt{7}$$

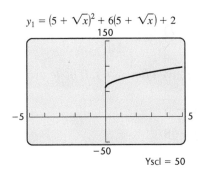

$y_1 = (5 + \sqrt{x})^2 + 6(5 + \sqrt{x}) + 2$

150

−5   5

−50

Yscl = 50

We could now solve for r and check possible solutions, but first let's examine $-8 + \sqrt{7}$ and $-8 - \sqrt{7}$. Since $\sqrt{7} \approx 2.6$, both $-8 + \sqrt{7}$ and $-8 - \sqrt{7}$ are negative. Since the principal square root of r is never negative, both values of $\sqrt{r}$ must be rejected. Note too that in the original equation, $\left(5 + \sqrt{r}\right)^2$, $6\left(5 + \sqrt{r}\right)$, and 2 are all positive. Thus it is impossible for their sum to be 0.

As another check, using the graph at left, we see that the domain of the function $f(x) = \left(5 + \sqrt{x}\right)^2 + 6\left(5 + \sqrt{x}\right) + 2$ is $(0, \infty)$, so neither value found is an allowable input. Also, there are no x-intercepts of the graph, and thus no solution of $f(x) = 0$.

The original equation has no solution.

Try Exercise 27.

13.5 Exercise Set

FOR EXTRA HELP

↪ *Concept Reinforcement* *In each of Exercises 1–8, match the equation with a substitution from the column on the right that could be used to reduce the equation to quadratic form.*

1. ___ $4x^6 - 2x^3 + 1 = 0$ a) $u = x^{-1/3}$

2. ___ $3x^4 + 4x^2 - 7 = 0$ b) $u = x^{1/3}$

3. ___ $5x^8 + 2x^4 - 3 = 0$ c) $u = x^{-2}$

4. ___ $2x^{2/3} - 5x^{1/3} + 4 = 0$ d) $u = x^2$

5. ___ $3x^{4/3} + 4x^{2/3} - 7 = 0$ e) $u = x^{-2/3}$

6. ___ $2x^{-2/3} + x^{-1/3} + 6 = 0$ f) $u = x^3$

7. ___ $4x^{-4/3} - 2x^{-2/3} + 3 = 0$ g) $u = x^{2/3}$

8. ___ $3x^{-4} + 4x^{-2} - 2 = 0$ h) $u = x^4$

Write the substitution that could be used to make each equation quadratic in u.

9. For $3p - 4\sqrt{p} + 6 = 0$, use $u =$ _____.

10. For $x^{1/2} - x^{1/4} - 2 = 0$, use $u =$ _____.

11. For $(x^2 + 3)^2 + (x^2 + 3) - 7 = 0$, use $u =$ _____.

12. For $t^{-6} + 5t^{-3} - 6 = 0$, use $u =$ _____.

13. For $(1 + t)^4 + (1 + t)^2 + 4 = 0$, use $u =$ _____.

14. For $w^{1/3} - 3w^{1/6} + 8 = 0$, use $u =$ _____.

Solve.

15. $x^4 - 5x^2 + 4 = 0$

16. $x^4 - 10x^2 + 9 = 0$

17. $x^4 - 9x^2 + 20 = 0$

18. $x^4 - 12x^2 + 27 = 0$

19. $4t^4 - 19t^2 + 12 = 0$

20. $9t^4 - 14t^2 + 5 = 0$

21. $w + 4\sqrt{w} - 12 = 0$

22. $s + 3\sqrt{s} - 40 = 0$

23. $(x^2 - 7)^2 - 3(x^2 - 7) + 2 = 0$

24. $(x^2 - 2)^2 - 12(x^2 - 2) + 20 = 0$

25. $r - 2\sqrt{r} - 6 = 0$

26. $s - 4\sqrt{s} - 1 = 0$

27. $(1 + \sqrt{x})^2 + 5(1 + \sqrt{x}) + 6 = 0$

28. $(3 + \sqrt{x})^2 + 3(3 + \sqrt{x}) - 10 = 0$

29. $x^{-2} - x^{-1} - 6 = 0$

30. $2x^{-2} - x^{-1} - 1 = 0$

31. $4y^{-2} - 3y^{-1} - 1 = 0$

32. $m^{-2} + 9m^{-1} - 10 = 0$

33. $t^{2/3} + t^{1/3} - 6 = 0$

34. $w^{2/3} - 2w^{1/3} - 8 = 0$

35. $y^{1/3} - y^{1/6} - 6 = 0$

36. $t^{1/2} + 3t^{1/4} + 2 = 0$

37. $t^{1/3} + 2t^{1/6} = 3$

38. $m^{1/2} + 6 = 5m^{1/4}$

39. $(10 - \sqrt{x})^2 - 2(10 - \sqrt{x}) - 35 = 0$

40. $(5 + \sqrt{x})^2 - 12(5 + \sqrt{x}) + 33 = 0$

41. $16\left(\dfrac{x-1}{x-8}\right)^2 + 8\left(\dfrac{x-1}{x-8}\right) + 1 = 0$

42. $9\left(\dfrac{x+2}{x+3}\right)^2 - 6\left(\dfrac{x+2}{x+3}\right) + 1 = 0$

43. $x^4 + 5x^2 - 36 = 0$

44. $x^4 + 5x^2 + 4 = 0$

45. $(n^2 + 6)^2 - 7(n^2 + 6) + 10 = 0$

46. $(m^2 + 7)^2 - 6(m^2 + 7) - 16 = 0$

Find all x-intercepts of the given function f. If none exists, state this.

47. $f(x) = 5x + 13\sqrt{x} - 6$

48. $f(x) = 3x + 10\sqrt{x} - 8$

49. $f(x) = (x^2 - 3x)^2 - 10(x^2 - 3x) + 24$

50. $f(x) = (x^2 - 6x)^2 - 2(x^2 - 6x) - 35$

51. $f(x) = x^{2/5} + x^{1/5} - 6$

52. $f(x) = x^{1/2} - x^{1/4} - 6$

Aha! **53.** $f(x) = \left(\dfrac{x^2 + 2}{x}\right)^4 + 7\left(\dfrac{x^2 + 2}{x}\right)^2 + 5$

54. $f(x) = \left(\dfrac{x^2 + 1}{x}\right)^4 + 4\left(\dfrac{x^2 + 1}{x}\right)^2 + 12$

TW **55.** To solve $25x^6 - 10x^3 + 1 = 0$, Margaret lets $u = 5x^3$ and Murray lets $u = x^3$. Can they both be correct? Why or why not?

TW **56.** While trying to solve $0.05x^4 - 0.8 = 0$ with a graphing calculator, Carmela gets the following screen. Can Carmela solve this equation with a graphing calculator? Why or why not?

$y_1 = .05x^4 - .8$

SKILL REVIEW

To prepare for Section 13.6, review graphing functions.
Graph.

57. $f(x) = x$

58. $g(x) = x + 2$

59. $h(x) = x - 2$

60. $f(x) = x^2$

61. $g(x) = x^2 + 2$

62. $h(x) = x^2 - 2$

SYNTHESIS

TW **63.** Describe a procedure that could be used to solve any equation of the form $ax^4 + bx^2 + c = 0$.

TW **64.** Describe a procedure that could be used to write an equation that is quadratic in $3x^2 - 1$. Then explain how the procedure could be adjusted to write equations that are quadratic in $3x^2 - 1$ and have no real-number solution.

Solve.

65. $5x^4 - 7x^2 + 1 = 0$

66. $3x^4 + 5x^2 - 1 = 0$

67. $(x^2 - 4x - 2)^2 - 13(x^2 - 4x - 2) + 30 = 0$

68. $(x^2 - 5x - 1)^2 - 18(x^2 - 5x - 1) + 65 = 0$

69. $\dfrac{x}{x - 1} - 6\sqrt{\dfrac{x}{x - 1}} - 40 = 0$

70. $\left(\sqrt{\dfrac{x}{x - 3}}\right)^2 - 24 = 10\sqrt{\dfrac{x}{x - 3}}$

71. $a^5(a^2 - 25) + 13a^3(25 - a^2) + 36a(a^2 - 25) = 0$

72. $a^3 - 26a^{3/2} - 27 = 0$

73. $x^6 - 28x^3 + 27 = 0$

74. $x^6 + 7x^3 - 8 = 0$

■ Try Exercise Answers: Section 13.5

15. $\pm 1, \pm 2$ **21.** 4   **27.** No solution   **31.** $-4, 1$ **33.** $-27, 8$

49. $\left(\dfrac{3}{2} + \dfrac{\sqrt{33}}{2}, 0\right), \left(\dfrac{3}{2} - \dfrac{\sqrt{33}}{2}, 0\right), (4, 0), (-1, 0)$

Mid-Chapter Review

We have discussed four methods of solving quadratic equations:

- factoring and the principle of zero products;
- the principle of square roots;
- completing the square;
- the quadratic formula.

Any of these may also be appropriate when solving an applied problem or an equation that is reducible to quadratic form.

GUIDED SOLUTIONS

1. Solve: $(x - 7)^2 = 5$.

Solution

$x - 7 = \boxed{}$ Using the principle of square roots

$x = \boxed{}$ Adding 7 to both sides

The solutions are $7 + \boxed{}$ and $7 - \boxed{}$.

2. Solve: $x^2 - 2x - 1 = 0$.

Solution

$a = \boxed{}$, $b = \boxed{}$, $c = \boxed{}$

$$x = \frac{-\left(\boxed{}\right) \pm \sqrt{\left(\boxed{}\right)^2 - 4 \cdot 1 \cdot \left(\boxed{}\right)}}{2 \cdot \boxed{}}$$

$$x = \frac{\boxed{} \pm \sqrt{\boxed{}}}{\boxed{}}$$

$$x = \frac{2}{2} \pm \frac{\boxed{}\sqrt{2}}{2}$$

The solutions are $1 + \boxed{}$ and $1 - \boxed{}$.

MIXED REVIEW

Solve. Examine each exercise carefully, and try to solve using the easiest method.

1. $x^2 - 3x - 10 = 0$ [13.1]

2. $x^2 = 121$ [13.1]

3. $x^2 + 6x = 10$ [13.1], [13.2]

4. $x^2 + x - 3 = 0$ [13.2]

5. $(x + 1)^2 = 2$ [13.1]

6. $x^2 - 10x + 25 = 0$ [13.1]

7. $4t^2 = 11$ [13.1]

8. $2t^2 + 1 = 3t$ [13.1]

9. $16c^2 = 7c$ [13.1]

10. $y^2 - 2y + 8 = 0$ [13.2]

11. $x^4 - 10x^2 + 9 = 0$ [13.5]

12. $x^4 - 8x^2 - 9 = 0$ [13.5]

13. $(t + 4)(t - 3) = 18$ [13.1]

14. $m^{-4} - 5m^{-2} + 6 = 0$ [13.5]

For each equation, determine what type of number the solutions are and how many solutions exist. [13.3]

15. $x^2 - 8x + 1 = 0$

16. $3x^2 = 4x + 7$

17. $5x^2 - x + 6 = 0$

Solve each formula for the indicated letter. Assume that all variables represent nonnegative numbers. [13.4]

18. $F = \dfrac{Av^2}{400}$, for v

(Force of wind on a sail)

19. $D^2 - 2Dd - 2hd = 0$, for D

(Dynamic load)

20. Sophie drove 225 mi south through the Smoky Mountains. It was snowing on her return trip, so her average speed on the return trip was 30 mph slower. The total driving time was 8 hr. Find Sophie's average speed on each part of the trip. [13.4]

13.6   Quadratic Functions and Their Graphs

- The Graph of $f(x) = ax^2$

- The Graph of $f(x) = a(x - h)^2$

- The Graph of $f(x) = a(x - h)^2 + k$

The graph of any *linear* function $f(x) = mx + b$ is a straight line. In this section and the next, we will see that the graph of any *quadratic* function $f(x) = ax^2 + bx + c$ is a *parabola*.

THE GRAPH OF $f(x) = ax^2$

The most basic quadratic function is $f(x) = x^2$.

EXAMPLE 1   Graph: $f(x) = x^2$.

SOLUTION   We choose some values for x and compute $f(x)$ for each. Then we plot the ordered pairs and connect them with a smooth curve.

x	$f(x) = x^2$	$(x, f(x))$
-3	9	$(-3, 9)$
-2	4	$(-2, 4)$
-1	1	$(-1, 1)$
0	0	$(0, 0)$
1	1	$(1, 1)$
2	4	$(2, 4)$
3	9	$(3, 9)$

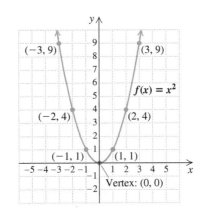

Try Exercise 15.

All quadratic functions have graphs similar to the one in Example 1. Such curves are called **parabolas.** They are U-shaped and symmetric with respect to a vertical line known as the parabola's *axis of symmetry*. For the graph of $f(x) = x^2$, the y-axis (or the line $x = 0$) is the axis of symmetry. Were the paper folded on this line, the two halves of the curve would match. The point $(0, 0)$ is known as the *vertex* of this parabola.

Since x^2 is a polynomial, we know that the domain of $f(x) = x^2$ is the set of all real numbers, or $(-\infty, \infty)$. We see from the graph and the table in Example 1 that the range of f is $\{y \mid y \geq 0\}$, or $[0, \infty)$. The function has a *minimum value* of 0. This minimum value occurs when $x = 0$.

Now let's consider a quadratic function of the form $g(x) = ax^2$. How does the constant a affect the graph of the function?

Student Notes

By paying attention to the symmetry of each parabola and the location of the vertex, you save yourself considerable work. Note too that when we are graphing ax^2, the x-values 1 unit to the right or left of the vertex are paired with the y-value a units above the vertex. Thus the graph of $y = \frac{3}{2}x^2$ includes the points $\left(-1, \frac{3}{2}\right)$ and $\left(1, \frac{3}{2}\right)$.

Interactive Discovery

Graph each of the following equations along with $y_1 = x^2$ in a $[-5, 5, -10, 10]$ window. If your calculator has a Transfrm application, run that application and graph $y_2 = Ax^2$. Then enter the values for A indicated in Exercises 1–6. For each equation, answer the following questions.

a) What is the vertex of the graph of y_2?

b) What is the axis of symmetry of the graph of y_2?

c) Does the graph of y_2 open upward or downward?

d) Is the parabola narrower or wider than the parabola given by $y_1 = x^2$?

1. $y_2 = 3x^2$ **2.** $y_2 = \frac{1}{3}x^2$ **3.** $y_2 = 0.2x^2$

4. $y_2 = -x^2$ **5.** $y_2 = -4x^2$ **6.** $y_2 = -\frac{2}{3}x^2$

7. Describe the effect of multiplying x^2 by a when $a > 1$ and when $0 < a < 1$.

8. Describe the effect of multiplying x^2 by a when $a < -1$ and when $-1 < a < 0$.

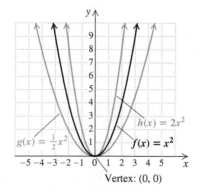

You may have noticed that for $f(x) = ax^2$, the constant a, when $|a| \neq 1$, makes the graph wider or narrower than the graph of $g(x) = x^2$. When a is negative, the graph opens downward.

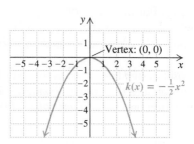

Graphing $f(x) = ax^2$

The graph of $f(x) = ax^2$ is a parabola with $x = 0$ as its axis of symmetry. Its vertex is the origin. The domain of f is $(-\infty, \infty)$.

For $a > 0$, the parabola opens upward. The range of the function is $[0, \infty)$.

For $a < 0$, the parabola opens downward. The range of the function is $(-\infty, 0]$.

If $|a|$ is greater than 1, the parabola is narrower than $y = x^2$.

If $|a|$ is between 0 and 1, the parabola is wider than $y = x^2$.

EXAMPLE 2   Graph: $g(x) = \frac{1}{2}x^2$.

SOLUTION   The function is in the form $g(x) = ax^2$, where $a = \frac{1}{2}$. The vertex is $(0, 0)$ and the axis of symmetry is $x = 0$. Since $\frac{1}{2} > 0$, the parabola opens upward. The parabola is wider than $y = x^2$ since $|\frac{1}{2}|$ is between 0 and 1.

To graph the function, we calculate and plot points. Because we know the general shape of the graph, we can sketch the graph using only a few points.

x	$g(x) = \frac{1}{2}x^2$
-3	$\frac{9}{2}$
-2	2
-1	$\frac{1}{2}$
0	0
1	$\frac{1}{2}$
2	2
3	$\frac{9}{2}$

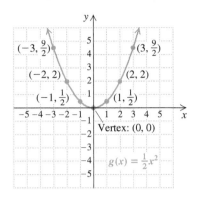

Try Exercise 19.

Note in Example 2 that since a parabola is symmetric, we can calculate function values for inputs to one side of the vertex and then plot the mirror images of those points on the other "half" of the graph.

THE GRAPH OF $f(x) = a(x - h)^2$

The width of a parabola and whether it opens upward or downward are determined by the coefficient a in $f(x) = ax^2 + bx + c$. To determine the vertex, we look first at functions of the form $f(x) = a(x - h)^2$.

Interactive Discovery

Graph each of the following pairs of equations in a $[-5, 5, -10, 10]$ window. For each pair, answer the following questions.

a) What is the vertex of the graph of y_2?

b) What is the axis of symmetry of the graph of y_2?

c) Is the graph of y_2 narrower, wider, or the same shape as the graph of y_1?

1. $y_1 = x^2$; $y_2 = (x - 3)^2$

2. $y_1 = 2x^2$; $y_2 = 2(x + 1)^2$

3. $y_1 = -\frac{1}{2}x^2$; $y_2 = -\frac{1}{2}\left(x - \frac{3}{2}\right)^2$

4. $y_1 = -3x^2$; $y_2 = -3(x + 2)^2$

5. Describe the effect of h on the graph of $g(x) = a(x - h)^2$.

The graph of $g(x) = a(x - h)^2$ looks just like the graph of $f(x) = ax^2$, except that it is moved, or *translated*, $|h|$ units horizontally.

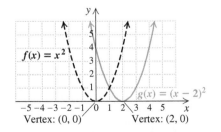

Graphing $f(x) = a(x - h)^2$

The graph of $f(x) = a(x - h)^2$ has the same shape as the graph of $y = ax^2$. The domain of f is $(-\infty, \infty)$.

If h is positive, the graph of $y = ax^2$ is shifted h units to the right.

If h is negative, the graph of $y = ax^2$ is shifted $|h|$ units to the left.

The vertex is $(h, 0)$, and the axis of symmetry is $x = h$.

EXAMPLE 3   Graph $g(x) = -2(x + 3)^2$. Label the vertex, and draw the line of symmetry.

SOLUTION   We rewrite the equation as $g(x) = -2[x - (-3)]^2$. In this case, $a = -2$ and $h = -3$, so the graph looks like that of $y = 2x^2$ translated 3 units to the left and, since $-2 < 0$, it opens downward. The vertex is $(-3, 0)$, and the axis of symmetry is $x = -3$. Plotting points as needed, we obtain the graph shown below. We say that g is a *reflection* of the graph of $f(x) = 2(x + 3)^2$ across the x-axis.

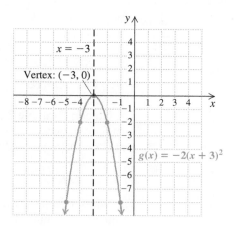

Try Exercise 25.

THE GRAPH OF $f(x) = a(x - h)^2 + k$

If we add a positive constant k to $f(x) = a(x - h)^2$, the graph of $f(x)$ is moved up. If we add a negative constant k, the graph is moved down. The axis of symmetry for the parabola remains at $x = h$, but the vertex will be at (h, k).

Because of the shape of their graphs, quadratic functions have either a *minimum* value or a *maximum* value. Many real-world applications involve finding that value. For example, a business owner is concerned with minimizing cost and maximizing profit. If a parabola opens upward ($a > 0$), the function value, or y-value, at the vertex is a least, or minimum, value. That is, it is less than the y-value at any other point on the graph. If the parabola opens downward ($a < 0$), the function value at the vertex is a greatest, or maximum, value.

Graphs of $f(x) = a(x - h)^2 + k$

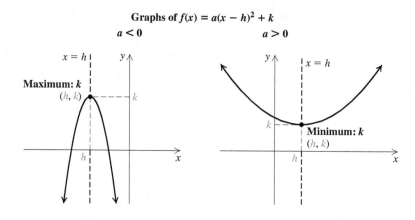

> Graphing $f(x) = a(x - h)^2 + k$
>
> The graph of $f(x) = a(x - h)^2 + k$ has the same shape as the graph of $y = a(x - h)^2$.
>
> If k is positive, the graph of $y = a(x - h)^2$ is shifted k units up.
>
> If k is negative, the graph of $y = a(x - h)^2$ is shifted $|k|$ units down.
>
> The vertex is (h, k), and the axis of symmetry is $x = h$.
>
> The domain of f is $(-\infty, \infty)$.
>
> For $a > 0$, the range of f is $[k, \infty)$. The minimum function value is k, which occurs when $x = h$.
>
> For $a < 0$, the range of f is $(-\infty, k]$. The maximum function value is k, which occurs when $x = h$.

EXAMPLE 4   Graph $g(x) = (x - 3)^2 - 5$, and find the minimum function value and the range of g.

SOLUTION   The graph will look like that of $f(x) = (x - 3)^2$ but shifted 5 units down. You can confirm this by plotting some points.

The vertex is now $(3, -5)$, and the minimum function value is -5. The range of g is $[-5, \infty)$.

x	$g(x) = (x - 3)^2 - 5$	
0	4	
1	-1	
2	-4	
3	-5	⟵ Vertex
4	-4	
5	-1	
6	4	

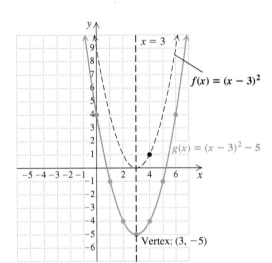

Try Exercise 45.

EXAMPLE 5 Graph $h(x) = \frac{1}{2}(x - 3)^2 + 4$, and find the minimum function value and the range of h.

SOLUTION The graph looks just like that of $f(x) = \frac{1}{2}x^2$ but moved 3 units to the right and 4 units up. The vertex is $(3, 4)$, and the axis of symmetry is $x = 3$. We draw $f(x) = \frac{1}{2}x^2$ and then shift the curve over and up.

By plotting some points, we have a check. The minimum function value is 4, and the range is $[4, \infty)$.

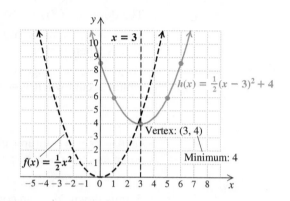

x	$h(x) = \frac{1}{2}(x - 3)^2 + 4$	
0	$8\frac{1}{2}$	
1	6	
3	4	← Vertex
5	6	
6	$8\frac{1}{2}$	

Try Exercise 49.

EXAMPLE 6 Graph $f(x) = -2(x + 3)^2 + 5$. Find the vertex, the axis of symmetry, the maximum or minimum function value, and the range of f.

SOLUTION We first express the equation in the equivalent form

$$f(x) = -2[x - (-3)]^2 + 5. \qquad \text{This is in the form } y = a(x - h)^2 + k.$$

The graph looks like that of $y = -2x^2$ translated 3 units to the left and 5 units up. The vertex is $(-3, 5)$, and the axis of symmetry is $x = -3$. Since -2 is negative, we know that 5, the second coordinate of the vertex, is the maximum function value. The range of f is $(-\infty, 5]$.

We compute a few points as needed, selecting convenient x-values on either side of the vertex. The graph is shown here.

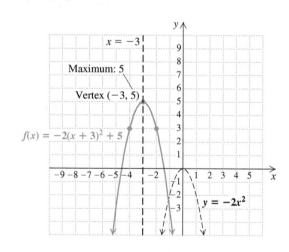

x	$f(x) = -2(x + 3)^2 + 5$	
-4	3	
-3	5	← Vertex
-2	3	

Try Exercise 59.

Connecting the Concepts

We can read information about the graph of a quadratic function directly from the constants a, h, and k in $f(x) = a(x - h)^2 + k$.

$\begin{cases} \text{Determines the width of the parabola} \\ \text{Tells whether the graph opens up or down} \\ \text{Tells whether the function has a maximum or a minimum} \end{cases}$

$$f(x) = a(x - h)^2 + k$$

Gives the axis of symmetry of the graph

Gives the maximum or minimum function value

Together, give the vertex of the graph

13.6 Exercise Set

FOR EXTRA HELP   *MyMathLab*   Math XL PRACTICE   WATCH   DOWNLOAD   READ   REVIEW

Concept Reinforcement   *In each of Exercises 1–8, match the equation with the corresponding graph from those shown.*

1. ___ $f(x) = 2(x - 1)^2 + 3$

2. ___ $f(x) = -2(x - 1)^2 + 3$

3. ___ $f(x) = 2(x + 1)^2 + 3$

4. ___ $f(x) = 2(x - 1)^2 - 3$

5. ___ $f(x) = -2(x + 1)^2 + 3$

6. ___ $f(x) = -2(x + 1)^2 - 3$

7. ___ $f(x) = 2(x + 1)^2 - 3$

8. ___ $f(x) = -2(x - 1)^2 - 3$

a)

b)

c)

d)

e)

f)

g)

h)

For each graph of a quadratic function

$$f(x) = a(x - h)^2 + k$$

in Exercises 9–14:

a) *Tell whether a is positive or negative.*
b) *Determine the vertex.*
c) *Determine the axis of symmetry.*
d) *Determine the range.*

9.

10.

11.

12.

13.

14.

Graph.

15. $f(x) = x^2$

16. $f(x) = -x^2$

17. $f(x) = -2x^2$

18. $f(x) = -3x^2$

19. $g(x) = \frac{1}{3}x^2$

20. $g(x) = \frac{1}{4}x^2$

Aha! **21.** $h(x) = -\frac{1}{3}x^2$

22. $h(x) = -\frac{1}{4}x^2$

23. $f(x) = \frac{5}{2}x^2$

24. $f(x) = \frac{3}{2}x^2$

For each of the following, graph the function, label the vertex, and draw the axis of symmetry.

25. $g(x) = (x + 1)^2$

26. $g(x) = (x + 4)^2$

27. $f(x) = (x - 2)^2$

28. $f(x) = (x - 1)^2$

29. $f(x) = -(x + 1)^2$

30. $f(x) = -(x - 1)^2$

31. $g(x) = -(x - 2)^2$

32. $g(x) = -(x + 4)^2$

33. $f(x) = 2(x + 1)^2$

34. $f(x) = 2(x + 4)^2$

35. $g(x) = 3(x - 4)^2$

36. $g(x) = 3(x - 5)^2$

37. $h(x) = -\frac{1}{2}(x - 4)^2$

38. $h(x) = -\frac{3}{2}(x - 2)^2$

39. $f(x) = \frac{1}{2}(x - 1)^2$

40. $f(x) = \frac{1}{3}(x + 2)^2$

41. $f(x) = -2(x + 5)^2$

42. $f(x) = 2(x + 7)^2$

43. $h(x) = -3\left(x - \frac{1}{2}\right)^2$

44. $h(x) = -2\left(x + \frac{1}{2}\right)^2$

For each of the following, graph the function and find the maximum value or the minimum value and the range of the function.

45. $f(x) = (x - 5)^2 + 2$

46. $f(x) = (x + 3)^2 - 2$

47. $f(x) = -(x + 2)^2 - 1$

48. $f(x) = -(x - 1)^2 + 3$

49. $g(x) = \frac{1}{2}(x + 4)^2 + 3$

50. $g(x) = 2(x - 4)^2 - 1$

51. $h(x) = -2(x - 1)^2 - 3$

52. $h(x) = -\frac{1}{2}(x + 2)^2 + 1$

For each of the following, graph the function and find the vertex, the axis of symmetry, the maximum value or the minimum value, and the range of the function.

53. $f(x) = (x + 1)^2 - 3$

54. $f(x) = (x - 1)^2 + 2$

55. $g(x) = -(x + 3)^2 + 5$

56. $g(x) = -(x - 2)^2 - 4$

57. $f(x) = \frac{1}{2}(x - 2)^2 + 1$

58. $f(x) = -\frac{1}{2}(x + 1)^2 - 1$

59. $h(x) = -2(x - 1)^2 - 3$

60. $h(x) = -2(x + 1)^2 + 4$

61. $f(x) = 2(x + 4)^2 + 1$

62. $f(x) = 2(x - 5)^2 - 3$

63. $g(x) = -\frac{3}{2}(x - 1)^2 + 4$

64. $g(x) = \frac{3}{2}(x + 2)^2 - 3$

Without graphing, find the vertex, the axis of symmetry, and the maximum value or the minimum value.

65. $f(x) = 6(x - 8)^2 + 7$

66. $f(x) = 4(x + 5)^2 - 6$

67. $h(x) = -\frac{2}{7}(x + 6)^2 + 11$

68. $h(x) = -\frac{3}{11}(x - 7)^2 - 9$

69. $f(x) = \left(x - \frac{7}{2}\right)^2 - \frac{29}{4}$

70. $f(x) = -\left(x + \frac{3}{4}\right)^2 + \frac{17}{16}$

71. $f(x) = \sqrt{2}(x + 4.58)^2 + 65\pi$

72. $f(x) = 4\pi(x - 38.2)^2 - \sqrt{34}$

TW **73.** While trying to graph $y = -\frac{1}{2}x^2 + 3x + 1$, Ibrahim gets the following screen. How can Ibrahim tell at a glance that a mistake has been made?

TW **74.** Explain, without plotting points, why the graph of $y = (x + 2)^2$ looks like the graph of $y = x^2$ translated 2 units to the left.

SKILL REVIEW

To prepare for Section 13.7, review finding intercepts and completing the square (Sections 13.1).

Find the x-intercept and the y-intercept.

75. $8x - 6y = 24$

76. $3x + 4y = 8$

Find the x-intercepts.

77. $y = x^2 + 8x + 15$

78. $y = 2x^2 - x - 3$

Replace the blanks with constants to form a true equation. [13.1]

79. $x^2 - 14x + \underline{\hspace{0.5cm}} = (x - \underline{\hspace{0.5cm}})^2$

80. $x^2 + 7x + \underline{\hspace{0.5cm}} = \left(x + \underline{\hspace{0.5cm}}\right)^2$

SYNTHESIS

TW **81.** Before graphing a quadratic function, Cassandra always plots five points. First, she calculates and plots the coordinates of the vertex. Then she plots *four* more points after calculating *two* more ordered pairs. How is this possible?

TW **82.** If the graphs of $f(x) = a_1(x - h_1)^2 + k_1$ and $g(x) = a_2(x - h_2)^2 + k_2$ have the same shape, what, if anything, can you conclude about the a's, the h's, and the k's? Why?

Write an equation for a function having a graph with the same shape as the graph of $f(x) = \frac{3}{5}x^2$, but with the given point as the vertex.

83. $(4, 1)$ **84.** $(2, 6)$ **85.** $(3, -1)$

86. $(5, -6)$ **87.** $(-2, -5)$ **88.** $(-4, -2)$

For each of the following, write the equation of the parabola that has the shape of $f(x) = 2x^2$ or $g(x) = -2x^2$ and has a maximum value or a minimum value at the specified point.

89. Minimum: $(2, 0)$

90. Minimum: $(-4, 0)$

91. Maximum: $(0, 3)$

92. Maximum: $(3, 8)$

Use the following graph of $f(x) = a(x - h)^2 + k$ for Exercises 93–96.

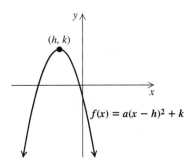

93. Describe what will happen to the graph if h is increased.

94. Describe what will happen to the graph if k is decreased.

95. Describe what will happen to the graph if a is replaced with $-a$.

96. Describe what will happen to the graph if $(x - h)$ is replaced with $(x + h)$.

Find an equation for a quadratic function F that satisfies the following conditions.

97. The graph of F is the same shape as the graph of f, where $f(x) = 3(x + 2)^2 + 7$, and $F(x)$ is a minimum at the same point that $g(x) = -2(x - 5)^2 + 1$ is a maximum.

98. The graph of F is the same shape as the graph of f, where $f(x) = -\frac{1}{3}(x - 2)^2 + 7$, and $F(x)$ is a maximum at the same point that $g(x) = 2(x + 4)^2 - 6$ is a minimum.

Functions other than parabolas can be translated. When calculating $f(x)$, if we replace x with $x - h$, where h is a constant, the graph will be moved horizontally. If we replace $f(x)$ with $f(x) + k$, the graph will be moved vertically. Use the graph below for Exercises 99–104.

Draw a graph of each of the following.

99. $y = f(x - 1)$ **100.** $y = f(x + 2)$

101. $y = f(x) + 2$ **102.** $y = f(x) - 3$

103. $y = f(x + 3) - 2$ **104.** $y = f(x - 3) + 1$

▌ Try Exercise Answers: Section 13.6

15.   **19.**

25. Vertex: $(-1, 0)$; axis of symmetry: $x = -1$

45. Minimum: 2; range: $[2, \infty)$

49. Minimum: 3; range: $[3, \infty)$

59. Vertex: $(1, -3)$; axis of symmetry: $x = 1$; maximum: -3; range: $(-\infty, -3]$

Collaborative Corner

Match the Graph

Focus: Graphing quadratic functions
Time: 15–20 minutes
Group size: 6
Materials: Index cards

ACTIVITY

1. On each of six index cards, write one of the following equations:

$$y = \tfrac{1}{2}(x - 3)^2 + 1; \qquad y = \tfrac{1}{2}(x - 1)^2 + 3;$$
$$y = \tfrac{1}{2}(x + 1)^2 - 3; \qquad y = \tfrac{1}{2}(x + 3)^2 + 1;$$
$$y = \tfrac{1}{2}(x + 3)^2 - 1; \qquad y = \tfrac{1}{2}(x + 1)^2 + 3.$$

2. Fold each index card and mix up the six cards in a hat or a bag. Then, one by one, each group member should select one of the equations. Do not let anyone see your equation.

3. Each group member should carefully graph the equation selected. Make the graph large enough so that when it is finished, it can be easily viewed by the rest of the group. Be sure to scale the axes and label the vertex, but **do not label the graph with the equation used.**

4. When all group members have drawn a graph, place the graphs in a pile. The group should then match and agree on the correct equation for each graph *with no help from the person who drew the graph.* If a mistake has been made and a graph has no match, determine what its equation *should* be.

5. Compare your group's labeled graphs with those of other groups to reach consensus within the class on the correct label for each graph.

13.7   More About Graphing Quadratic Functions

- Finding the Vertex

- Finding Intercepts

FINDING THE VERTEX

By *completing the square* (see Section 13.1), we can rewrite any polynomial $ax^2 + bx + c$ in the form $a(x - h)^2 + k$. Once that has been done, the procedures discussed in Section 13.6 will enable us to graph any quadratic function.

EXAMPLE 1   Graph: $g(x) = x^2 - 6x + 4$. Label the vertex and the axis of symmetry.

SOLUTION   We have

$$g(x) = x^2 - 6x + 4$$
$$= (x^2 - 6x) + 4.$$

To complete the square inside the parentheses, we take half of the x-coefficient, $\frac{1}{2} \cdot (-6) = -3$, and square it to get $(-3)^2 = 9$. Then we add $9 - 9$ inside the parentheses:

$$g(x) = (x^2 - 6x + 9 - 9) + 4 \qquad \text{The effect is of adding 0.}$$
$$= (x^2 - 6x + 9) + (-9 + 4) \qquad \text{Using the associative law of addition to regroup}$$
$$= (x - 3)^2 - 5. \qquad \text{Factoring and simplifying}$$

This equation appeared as Example 4 of Section 13.6. The graph is that of $f(x) = x^2$ translated 3 units to the right and 5 units down. The vertex is $(3, -5)$, and the axis of symmetry is $x = 3$.

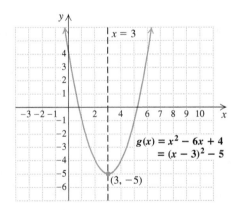

Try Exercise 19.

When the leading coefficient is not 1, we factor out that number from the first two terms. Then we complete the square and use the distributive law.

EXAMPLE 2   Graph: $f(x) = 3x^2 + 12x + 13$. Label the vertex and the axis of symmetry.

SOLUTION   Since the coefficient of x^2 is not 1, we need to factor out that number—in this case, 3—from the first two terms. Remember that we want the form $f(x) = a(x - h)^2 + k$:

$$f(x) = 3x^2 + 12x + 13 = 3(x^2 + 4x) + 13.$$

Now we complete the square as before. We take half of the x-coefficient, $\frac{1}{2} \cdot 4 = 2$, and square it: $2^2 = 4$. Then we add $4 - 4$ inside the parentheses:

$$f(x) = 3(x^2 + 4x + 4 - 4) + 13. \qquad \text{Adding } 4 - 4, \text{ or } 0, \text{ inside} \\ \text{the parentheses}$$

The distributive law allows us to separate the -4 from the perfect-square trinomial so long as it is multiplied by 3:

$$f(x) = 3(x^2 + 4x + 4) + 3(-4) + 13 \qquad \text{This leaves a perfect-} \\ \text{square trinomial inside} \\ \text{the parentheses.}$$

The -4 was added inside the parentheses. To separate it, we *must* multiply it by 3.

$$= 3(x + 2)^2 + 1. \qquad \text{Factoring and simplifying}$$

The vertex is $(-2, 1)$, and the axis of symmetry is $x = -2$. The coefficient of x^2 is 3, so the graph is narrow and opens upward. We choose a few x-values on either side of the vertex, compute y-values, and then graph the parabola.

x	$f(x) = 3(x + 2)^2 + 1$
-2	1
-3	4
-1	4

$\longleftarrow$ Vertex

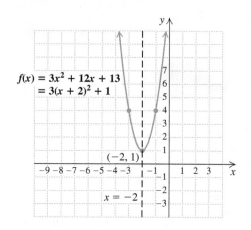

$f(x) = 3x^2 + 12x + 13$
$= 3(x + 2)^2 + 1$

$(-2, 1)$

$x = -2$

Try Exercise 23.

EXAMPLE 3 Graph $f(x) = -2x^2 + 10x - 7$, and find the maximum or minimum function value.

SOLUTION We first find the vertex by completing the square. To do so, we factor out -2 from the first two terms of the expression. This makes the coefficient of x^2 inside the parentheses 1:

Factor out a from both variable terms.

$$f(x) = -2x^2 + 10x - 7 \\ = -2(x^2 - 5x) - 7.$$

Now we complete the square as before. We take half of the x-coefficient and square it to get $\frac{25}{4}$. Then we add $\frac{25}{4} - \frac{25}{4}$ inside the parentheses:

Complete the square inside the parentheses.

$$f(x) = -2\left(x^2 - 5x + \frac{25}{4} - \frac{25}{4}\right) - 7$$

Regroup.

$$= -2\left(x^2 - 5x + \frac{25}{4}\right) + (-2)\left(-\frac{25}{4}\right) - 7 \qquad \text{Multiplying by } -2, \\ \text{using the distributive} \\ \text{law, and regrouping}$$

Factor.

$$= -2\left(x - \frac{5}{2}\right)^2 + \frac{11}{2}. \qquad \text{Factoring and} \\ \text{simplifying}$$

The vertex is $\left(\frac{5}{2}, \frac{11}{2}\right)$, and the axis of symmetry is $x = \frac{5}{2}$. The coefficient of x^2, -2, is negative, so the graph opens downward and the second coordinate of the vertex, $\frac{11}{2}$, is the maximum function value. We plot a few points on either side of the vertex, including the y-intercept, $f(0)$, and graph the parabola.

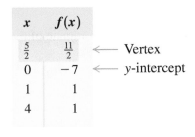

x	$f(x)$	
$\frac{5}{2}$	$\frac{11}{2}$	← Vertex
0	-7	← y-intercept
1	1	
4	1	

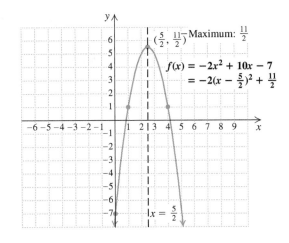

Try Exercise 39.

The method used in Examples 1–3 can be generalized to find a formula for locating the vertex. We complete the square as follows:

$$f(x) = ax^2 + bx + c$$

$$= a\left(x^2 + \frac{b}{a}x\right) + c. \qquad \text{Factoring } a \text{ out of the first two terms.}$$
Check by multiplying.

Half of the x-coefficient, $\frac{b}{a}$, is $\frac{b}{2a}$. We square it to get $\frac{b^2}{4a^2}$ and add $\frac{b^2}{4a^2} - \frac{b^2}{4a^2}$ inside the parentheses. Then we distribute the a and regroup terms:

$$f(x) = a\left(x^2 + \frac{b}{a}x + \frac{b^2}{4a^2} - \frac{b^2}{4a^2}\right) + c$$

$$= a\left(x^2 + \frac{b}{a}x + \frac{b^2}{4a^2}\right) + a\left(-\frac{b^2}{4a^2}\right) + c \qquad \text{Using the distributive law}$$

$$= a\left(x + \frac{b}{2a}\right)^2 + \frac{-b^2}{4a} + \frac{4ac}{4a} \qquad \text{Factoring and finding a common denominator}$$

$$= a\left[x - \left(-\frac{b}{2a}\right)\right]^2 + \frac{4ac - b^2}{4a}.$$

Thus we have the following.

Student Notes

It is easier to remember a formula when you understand its derivation. Check with your instructor to determine what formulas you will be expected to remember.

The Vertex of a Parabola   The vertex of the parabola given by $f(x) = ax^2 + bx + c$ is

$$\left(-\frac{b}{2a}, f\left(-\frac{b}{2a}\right)\right), \quad \text{or} \quad \left(-\frac{b}{2a}, \frac{4ac - b^2}{4a}\right).$$

- The x-coordinate of the vertex is $-b/(2a)$.
- The axis of symmetry is $x = -b/(2a)$.
- The second coordinate of the vertex is most commonly found by computing $f\left(-\frac{b}{2a}\right)$.

Let's reexamine Example 3 to see how we could have found the vertex directly. From the formula above, we see that

$$\text{the } x\text{-coordinate of the vertex is } -\frac{b}{2a} = -\frac{10}{2(-2)} = \frac{5}{2}.$$

Substituting $\frac{5}{2}$ into $f(x) = -2x^2 + 10x - 7$, we find the second coordinate of the vertex:

$$f\left(\tfrac{5}{2}\right) = -2\left(\tfrac{5}{2}\right)^2 + 10\left(\tfrac{5}{2}\right) - 7$$
$$= -2\left(\tfrac{25}{4}\right) + 25 - 7$$
$$= -\tfrac{25}{2} + 18$$
$$= -\tfrac{25}{2} + \tfrac{36}{2} = \tfrac{11}{2}.$$

The vertex is $\left(\tfrac{5}{2}, \tfrac{11}{2}\right)$. The axis of symmetry is $x = \tfrac{5}{2}$.

A quadratic function has a maximum value or a minimum value at the vertex of its graph. Thus determining the maximum value or the minimum value of the function allows us to find the vertex of the graph.

Maximums and Minimums

On most graphing calculators, a MAXIMUM or MINIMUM feature is found in the CALC menu. (CALC is the 2nd option associated with the TRACE key.)

To find a maximum or a minimum of a quadratic function, enter and graph the function, choosing a viewing window that will show the vertex. Next, press ⬚CALC⬚ and choose either the MAXIMUM or MINIMUM option in the menu. The graphing calculator will find the maximum or minimum function value over a specified interval, so the left and right endpoints, or bounds, of the interval must be entered as well as a guess near where the maximum or minimum occurs. The calculator will return the coordinates of the point for which the function value is a maximum or minimum within the interval.

Your Turn

1. Enter and graph $y_1 = x^2 - 3x - 5$, using a standard viewing window. The function is a *minimum* at the vertex.

2. Open the CALC menu and choose the minimum option.

3. The vertex occurs near $x = 1$, so enter a number less than 1 (say, 0) for the left bound.

4. Enter a number greater than 1 (say, 4) for the right bound.

5. Enter 1 as a guess. The coordinates shown are the vertex. The coordinates should be approximately $(1.5, -7.25)$.

Student Notes

It is easy to press an incorrect key when using a calculator. Always check to see if your answer is reasonable. For example, if the MINIMUM option were chosen in Example 4 instead of MAXIMUM, one endpoint of the interval would have been returned instead of the maximum. In this case, noting that the highest point on the graph is marked is a quick check that we did indeed find the maximum.

EXAMPLE 4 Use a graphing calculator to determine the vertex of the graph of the function given by $f(x) = -2x^2 + 10x - 7$.

SOLUTION The coefficient of x^2 is negative, so the parabola opens downward and the function has a maximum value. We enter and graph the function, choosing a window that will show the vertex.

We choose the MAXIMUM option from the CALC menu. For a left bound, we visually locate the vertex and either move the cursor to a point left of the vertex using the left and right arrow keys or type a value of x that is less than the x-value at the vertex. (See the graph on the left below.) After pressing (ENTER), we choose a right bound in a similar manner (as shown in the graph on the right below), and press (ENTER) again.

Finally, we enter a guess that is close to the vertex (as in the graph on the left below), and press (ENTER). The calculator indicates that the coordinates of the vertex are $(2.5, 5.5)$.

▌ Try Exercise 43.

In Example 3, we found the coordinates of the vertex of the graph of $f(x) = -2x^2 + 10x - 7$, $\left(\frac{5}{2}, \frac{11}{2}\right)$, by completing the square. On p. 850, we also found these coordinates using the formula for the vertex of a parabola. The coordinates found using a calculator in Example 4 were in decimal notation. Since $2.5000006 \approx \frac{5}{2}$, and since $5.5 = \frac{11}{2}$, the coordinates check.

We have actually developed three methods for finding the vertex. One is by completing the square, the second is by using a formula, and the third is by using a graphing calculator. You should check with your instructor about which method to use.

FINDING INTERCEPTS

All quadratic functions have a y-intercept and 0, 1, or 2 x-intercepts. For $f(x) = ax^2 + bx + c$, the y-intercept is $(0, f(0))$, or $(0, c)$. To find x-intercepts, we look for points where $y = 0$ or $f(x) = 0$. Thus, for $f(x) = ax^2 + bx + c$, the x-intercepts occur at those x-values for which $ax^2 + bx + c = 0$.

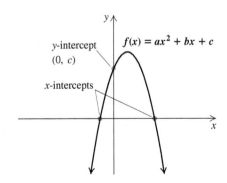

EXAMPLE 5   Find any x-intercepts and the y-intercept of the graph of $f(x) = x^2 - 2x - 2$.

SOLUTION   The y-intercept is $(0, f(0))$, or $(0, -2)$. To find the x-intercepts, we solve the equation $0 = x^2 - 2x - 2$. We are unable to factor $x^2 - 2x - 2$, so we use the quadratic formula and get $x = 1 \pm \sqrt{3}$. Thus the x-intercepts are $\left(1 - \sqrt{3}, 0\right)$ and $\left(1 + \sqrt{3}, 0\right)$.

If graphing, we would approximate, to get $(-0.7, 0)$ and $(2.7, 0)$.

Try Exercise 49.

If the solutions of $f(x) = 0$ are imaginary, the graph of f has no x-intercepts.

Connecting the Concepts

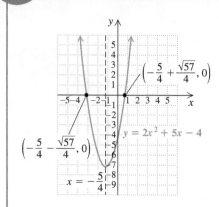

Because the graph of a quadratic equation is symmetric, the x-intercepts of the graph, if they exist, will be symmetric with respect to the axis of symmetry. This symmetry can be seen directly if the x-intercepts are found using the quadratic formula.

For example, the x-intercepts of the graph of $y = 2x^2 + 5x - 4$ are

$$\left(-\frac{5}{4} + \frac{\sqrt{57}}{4}, 0\right) \quad \text{and} \quad \left(-\frac{5}{4} - \frac{\sqrt{57}}{4}, 0\right).$$

For this equation, the axis of symmetry is $x = -\frac{5}{4}$ and the x-intercepts are $\frac{\sqrt{57}}{4}$ units to the left and right of $-\frac{5}{4}$ on the x-axis.

The Graph of a Quadratic Function Given by $f(x) = ax^2 + bx + c$ or $f(x) = a(x - h)^2 + k$

The graph is a parabola.

The vertex is (h, k) or $\left(-\dfrac{b}{2a}, f\left(-\dfrac{b}{2a}\right)\right)$.

The axis of symmetry is $x = h$.

The y-intercept of the graph is $(0, c)$.

The x-intercepts can be found by solving $ax^2 + bx + c = 0$.

   If $b^2 - 4ac > 0$, there are two x-intercepts.
   If $b^2 - 4ac = 0$, there is one x-intercept.
   If $b^2 - 4ac < 0$, there are no x-intercepts.

The domain of the function is $(-\infty, \infty)$.

If a is positive: The graph opens upward.
                   The function has a minimum value, given by k.
                      This occurs when $x = h$.
                   The range of the function is $[k, \infty)$.

If a is negative: The graph opens downward.
                   The function has a maximum value, given by k.
                      This occurs when $x = h$.
                   The range of the function is $(-\infty, k]$.

A

B

C

D

E

Visualizing for Success

Match each function with its graph.

1. $f(x) = 3x^2$

2. $f(x) = x^2 - 4$

3. $f(x) = (x - 4)^2$

4. $f(x) = x - 4$

5. $f(x) = -2x^2$

6. $f(x) = x + 3$

7. $f(x) = |x + 3|$

8. $f(x) = (x + 3)^2$

9. $f(x) = \sqrt{x + 3}$

10. $f(x) = (x + 3)^2 - 4$

Answers on page A-49

An additional, animated version of this activity appears in MyMathLab. To use MyMathLab, you need a course ID and a student access code. Contact your instructor for more information.

F

G

H

I

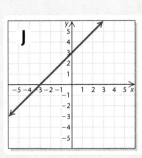

J

13.7 Exercise Set

↘ *Concept Reinforcement* *Classify each of the following statements as either true or false.*

1. The graph of $f(x) = 3x^2 - x + 6$ opens upward.

2. The function given by $g(x) = -x^2 + 3x + 1$ has a minimum value.

3. The graph of $f(x) = -2(x - 3)^2 + 7$ has its vertex at $(3, 7)$.

4. The graph of $g(x) = 4(x + 6)^2 - 2$ has its vertex at $(-6, -2)$.

5. The graph of $g(x) = \frac{1}{2}\left(x - \frac{3}{2}\right)^2 + \frac{1}{4}$ has $x = \frac{1}{4}$ as its axis of symmetry.

6. The function given by $f(x) = (x - 2)^2 - 5$ has a minimum value of -5.

7. The y-intercept of the graph of $f(x) = 2x^2 - 6x + 7$ is $(7, 0)$.

8. If the graph of a quadratic function f opens upward and has a vertex of $(1, 5)$, then the graph has no x-intercepts.

Complete the square to write each function in the form $f(x) = a(x - h)^2 + k$.

9. $f(x) = x^2 - 8x + 2$

10. $f(x) = x^2 - 6x - 1$

11. $f(x) = x^2 + 3x - 5$

12. $f(x) = x^2 + 5x + 3$

13. $f(x) = 3x^2 + 6x - 2$

14. $f(x) = 2x^2 - 20x - 3$

15. $f(x) = -x^2 - 4x - 7$

16. $f(x) = -2x^2 - 8x + 4$

17. $f(x) = 2x^2 - 5x + 10$

18. $f(x) = 3x^2 + 7x - 3$

For each quadratic function, (a) find the vertex and the axis of symmetry and (b) graph the function.

19. $f(x) = x^2 + 4x + 5$ 20. $f(x) = x^2 + 2x - 5$

21. $f(x) = x^2 + 8x + 20$

22. $f(x) = x^2 - 10x + 21$

23. $h(x) = 2x^2 - 16x + 25$

24. $h(x) = 2x^2 + 16x + 23$

25. $f(x) = -x^2 + 2x + 5$

26. $f(x) = -x^2 - 2x + 7$

27. $g(x) = x^2 + 3x - 10$

28. $g(x) = x^2 + 5x + 4$

29. $h(x) = x^2 + 7x$

30. $h(x) = x^2 - 5x$

31. $f(x) = -2x^2 - 4x - 6$

32. $f(x) = -3x^2 + 6x + 2$

For each quadratic function, (a) find the vertex, the axis of symmetry, and the maximum or minimum function value and (b) graph the function.

33. $g(x) = x^2 - 6x + 13$

34. $g(x) = x^2 - 4x + 5$

35. $g(x) = 2x^2 - 8x + 3$

36. $g(x) = 2x^2 + 5x - 1$

37. $f(x) = 3x^2 - 24x + 50$

38. $f(x) = 4x^2 + 16x + 13$

39. $f(x) = -3x^2 + 5x - 2$

40. $f(x) = -3x^2 - 7x + 2$

41. $h(x) = \frac{1}{2}x^2 + 4x + \frac{19}{3}$

42. $h(x) = \frac{1}{2}x^2 - 3x + 2$

📉 *Use a graphing calculator to find the vertex of the graph of each function.*

43. $f(x) = x^2 + x - 6$

44. $f(x) = x^2 + 2x - 5$

45. $f(x) = 5x^2 - x + 1$

46. $f(x) = -4x^2 - 3x + 7$

47. $f(x) = -0.2x^2 + 1.4x - 6.7$

48. $f(x) = 0.5x^2 + 2.4x + 3.2$

Find any x-intercepts and the y-intercept. If no x-intercepts exist, state this.

49. $f(x) = x^2 - 6x + 3$

50. $f(x) = x^2 + 5x + 2$

51. $g(x) = -x^2 + 2x + 3$

52. $g(x) = x^2 - 6x + 9$

Aha! **53.** $f(x) = x^2 - 9x$

54. $f(x) = x^2 - 7x$

55. $h(x) = -x^2 + 4x - 4$

56. $h(x) = -2x^2 - 20x - 50$

57. $g(x) = x^2 + x - 5$

58. $g(x) = 2x^2 + 3x - 1$

59. $f(x) = 2x^2 - 4x + 6$

60. $f(x) = x^2 - x + 2$

TW **61.** The graph of a quadratic function f opens downward and has no x-intercepts. In what quadrant(s) must the vertex lie? Explain your reasoning.

TW **62.** Is it possible for the graph of a quadratic function to have only one x-intercept if the vertex is off the x-axis? Why or why not?

SKILL REVIEW

To prepare for Section 13.8, review solving systems of three equations in three unknowns (Section 11.1).

Solve. [11.1]

63.
$x + y + z = 3,$
$x - y + z = 1,$
$-x - y + z = -1$

64.
$x - y + z = -6,$
$2x + y + z = 2,$
$3x + y + z = 0$

65. $z = 8,$
$x + y + z = 23,$
$2x + y - z = 17$

66. $z = -5,$
$2x - y + 3z = -27,$
$x + 2y + 7z = -26$

67. $1.5 = c,$
$52.5 = 25a + 5b + c,$
$7.5 = 4a + 2b + c$

68. $\frac{1}{2} = c,$
$5 = 9a + 6b + 2c,$
$29 = 81a + 9b + c$

SYNTHESIS

TW **69.** If the graphs of two quadratic functions have the same x-intercepts, will they also have the same vertex? Why or why not?

TW **70.** Suppose that the graph of $f(x) = ax^2 + bx + c$ has $(x_1, 0)$ and $(x_2, 0)$ as x-intercepts. Explain why the graph of $g(x) = -ax^2 - bx - c$ will also have $(x_1, 0)$ and $(x_2, 0)$ as x-intercepts.

For each quadratic function, find (a) the maximum or minimum value and (b) the x- and y-intercepts. Round to the nearest hundredth.

71. $f(x) = 2.31x^2 - 3.135x - 5.89$

72. $f(x) = -18.8x^2 + 7.92x + 6.18$

73. $g(x) = -1.25x^2 + 3.42x - 2.79$

74. $g(x) = 0.45x^2 - 1.72x + 12.92$

75. Graph the function
$$f(x) = x^2 - x - 6.$$
Then use the graph to approximate solutions to each of the following equations.

a) $x^2 - x - 6 = 2$

b) $x^2 - x - 6 = -3$

76. Graph the function
$$f(x) = \frac{x^2}{2} + x - \frac{3}{2}.$$
Then use the graph to approximate solutions to each of the following equations.

a) $\frac{x^2}{2} + x - \frac{3}{2} = 0$

b) $\frac{x^2}{2} + x - \frac{3}{2} = 1$

c) $\frac{x^2}{2} + x - \frac{3}{2} = 2$

Find an equivalent equation of the type
$$f(x) = a(x - h)^2 + k.$$

77. $f(x) = mx^2 - nx + p$

78. $f(x) = 3x^2 + mx + m^2$

79. A quadratic function has $(-1, 0)$ as one of its intercepts and $(3, -5)$ as its vertex. Find an equation for the function.

80. A quadratic function has $(4, 0)$ as one of its intercepts and $(-1, 7)$ as its vertex. Find an equation for the function.

Graph.

81. $f(x) = |x^2 - 1|$

82. $f(x) = |x^2 - 3x - 4|$

83. $f(x) = |2(x - 3)^2 - 5|$

■ Try Exercise Answers: Section 13.7

19. **(a)** Vertex: $(-2, 1)$; axis of symmetry: $x = -2$;
(b)

$f(x) = x^2 + 4x + 5$

23. **(a)** Vertex: $(4, -7)$; axis of symmetry: $x = 4$;
(b)

$h(x) = 2x^2 - 16x + 25$

39. **(a)** Vertex: $\left(\frac{5}{6}, \frac{1}{12}\right)$; axis of symmetry: $x = \frac{5}{6}$; maximum: $\frac{1}{12}$; **(b)**

$f(x) = -3x^2 + 5x - 2$

43. $(-0.5, -6.25)$ **49.** $\left(3 - \sqrt{6}, 0\right), \left(3 + \sqrt{6}, 0\right); (0, 3)$

13.8 Problem Solving and Quadratic Functions

- Maximum and Minimum Problems

- Fitting Quadratic Functions to Data

Let's look now at some of the many situations in which quadratic functions are used for problem solving.

MAXIMUM AND MINIMUM PROBLEMS

We have seen that for any quadratic function f, the value of $f(x)$ at the vertex is either a maximum or a minimum. Thus problems in which a quantity must be maximized or minimized can often be solved by finding the coordinates of a vertex, assuming the problem can be modeled with a quadratic function.

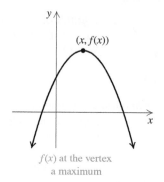

$f(x)$ at the vertex
a minimum

$f(x)$ at the vertex
a maximum

EXAMPLE 1 Sonoma Sunshine. The percent of days each month during which the sun shines in Sonoma, California, can be modeled by the quadratic function

$$s(n) = -1.625n^2 + 21.7n + 24.925,$$

where $n = 1$ represents January, $n = 2$ represents February, and so on. What month has the most sunshine, and during what percent of that month's days does the sun shine?

Source: Based on information from www.city-data.com

SOLUTION

1., 2. Familiarize and **Translate.** We are given the function that models the percent of days with sunshine in Sonoma. Since the coefficient of n^2 is negative, the quadratic function has a maximum value at the vertex of its graph.

3. Carry out. We find the vertex using the formula giving the first coordinate of the vertex:

$$n = -\frac{b}{2a} = -\frac{21.7}{2(-1.625)} = -\frac{21.7}{-3.25} \approx 6.7.$$

If we round this number, we have $n \approx 7$, which represents the month of July. The percent of days in July with sunshine would then be

$$s(7) = -1.625 \cdot 7^2 + 21.7 \cdot 7 + 24.925 = 97.2.$$

Thus the sun shines during approximately 97% of the days in July.

$y = -1.625x^2 + 21.7x + 24.925$

Yscl = 10

4. Check. Using the MAXIMUM feature of a graphing calculator, as shown at left, we find that the vertex of the graph of $s(n)$ is approximately $(6.677, 97.370)$. This is very close to our answer, allowing for rounding error.

5. State. In Sonoma, the sun shines during approximately 97% of the days in July, making July the month with the most sunshine.

Try Exercise 7.

EXAMPLE 2 Swimming Area. A lifeguard has 100 m of roped-together flotation devices with which to cordon off a rectangular swimming area at Lakeside Beach. If the shoreline forms one side of the rectangle, what dimensions will maximize the size of the area for swimming?

SOLUTION

1. **Familiarize.** We make a drawing and label it, letting $w =$ the width of the rectangle, in meters, and $l =$ the length of the rectangle, in meters.

Recall that Area $= l \cdot w$ and Perimeter $= 2w + 2l$. Since the beach forms one length of the rectangle, the flotation devices form three sides. Thus,

$$2w + l = 100.$$

To get a better feel for the problem, we can look at some possible dimensions for a rectangular area that can be enclosed with 100 m of flotation devices. All possibilities are chosen so that $2w + l = 100$.

We can make a table by hand or use a graphing calculator. To use a calculator, we let x represent the width of the swimming area. Solving $2w + l = 100$ for l, we have $l = 100 - 2w$. Thus, if $y_1 = 100 - 2x$, then the area is $y_2 = x \cdot y_1$.

$y_1 = 100 - 2x, y_2 = x \cdot y_1$

X	Y1	Y2
20	60	1200
22	56	1232
24	52	1248
26	48	1248
28	44	1232
30	40	1200
32	36	1152
X = 20		

} What choice of X will maximize Y2?

l	w	Rope Length	Area
40 m	30 m	100 m	1200 m²
30 m	35 m	100 m	1050 m²
20 m	40 m	100 m	800 m²
.	.	.	.
.	.	.	.
.	.	.	.

} What choice of l and w will maximize A?

2. **Translate.** We have two equations: One guarantees that all 100 m of flotation devices are used; the other expresses area in terms of length and width.

$$2w + l = 100,$$
$$A = l \cdot w$$

3. **Carry out.** We solve the system of equations both algebraically and graphically.

ALGEBRAIC APPROACH

We need to express A as a function of l or w but not both. To do so, we solve for l in the first equation to obtain $l = 100 - 2w$. Substituting for l in the second equation, we get a quadratic function:

$$A(w) = (100 - 2w)w \qquad \text{Substituting for } l$$
$$= 100w - 2w^2. \qquad \text{This represents a parabola opening downward, so a maximum exists.}$$

Factoring and completing the square, we get

$$A(w) = -2(w^2 - 50w + 625 - 625) \qquad \text{We could also use the vertex formula.}$$
$$= -2(w - 25)^2 + 1250. \qquad \text{This suggests a maximum of } 1250 \text{ m}^2 \text{ when } w = 25 \text{ m.}$$

There is a maximum value of 1250 when $w = 25$.

GRAPHICAL APPROACH

As in the *Familiarize* step, we let $x =$ the width. Then

$$\text{length} = y_1 = 100 - 2x, \quad \text{and}$$
$$\text{area} = y_2 = x \cdot y_1 = 100x - 2x^2.$$

We find the maximum area.

$$y = 100x - 2x^2$$

Xscl = 10, Yscl = 100

The maximum is 1250 when the width, x, is 25. If $w = 25$ m, then $l = 100 - 2 \cdot 25 = 50$ m. These dimensions give an area of 1250 m^2.

---

4. **Check.** Note that 1250 m^2 is greater than any of the values for A found in the *Familiarize* step. To be more certain, we could check values other than those used in that step. For example, if $w = 26$ m, then $l = 48$ m, and $A = 26 \cdot 48 = 1248$ m^2. Since 1250 m^2 is greater than 1248 m^2, it appears that we have a maximum.

5. **State.** The largest rectangular area for swimming that can be enclosed is 25 m by 50 m.

Try Exercise 11.

FITTING QUADRATIC FUNCTIONS TO DATA

We can now model some real-world situations using quadratic functions. As always, before attempting to fit an equation to data, we should graph the data and compare the result to the shape of the graphs of different types of functions and ask what type of function seems appropriate.

Connecting the Concepts

The general shapes of the graphs of many functions that we have studied are shown below.

Linear function:
$f(x) = mx + b$

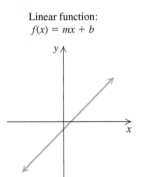

Absolute-value function:
$f(x) = |x|$

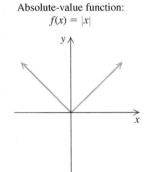

Rational function:
$f(x) = \dfrac{1}{x}$

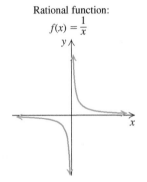

Radical function:
$f(x) = \sqrt{x}$

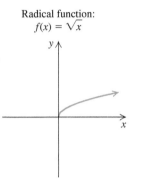

In order for a quadratic function to fit a set of data, the graph of the data must approximate the shape of a parabola. Data that resemble one half of a parabola might also be modeled using a quadratic function with a restricted domain.

Quadratic function:
$f(x) = ax^2 + bx + c, a > 0$

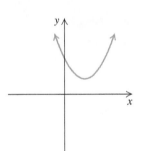

Quadratic function:
$f(x) = ax^2 + bx + c, a < 0$

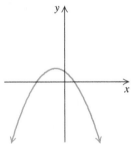

Quadratic function:
$f(x) = ax^2 + bx + c,$
$a > 0,\ x \geq 0$

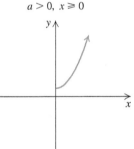

Quadratic function:
$f(x) = ax^2 + bx + c,$
$a < 0,\ x \geq 0$

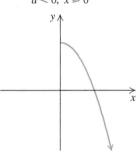

EXAMPLE 3   Determine whether a quadratic function can be used to model each of the following situations.

a) The quantity of candy consumed each year in the United States

U.S. Candy Consumption

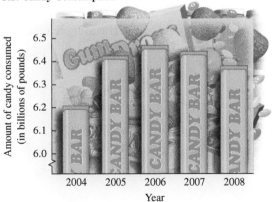

Source: U.S. Census Bureau

b) The amount of precipitation each month in Sonoma, California

Sonoma Precipitation

Source: www.city-data.com

c) The amount of precipitation each month in Atlanta, Georgia

Atlanta Precipitation

Source: www.city-data.com

d) The number of digital theater screens in the world

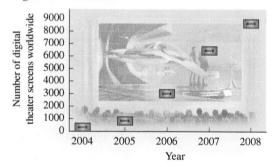

Digital Theater Screens

Source: Motion Picture Association of America, *Theatrical Market Statistics, 2008*

e) The average cinema admission price in the United States

Cinema Admission Price

Source: U.S. Bureau of Labor Statistics

SOLUTION

a) The data rise and then fall, resembling a parabola that opens downward. The situation could be modeled by a quadratic function $f(x) = ax^2 + bx + c, a < 0$.

b) The data fall and then rise, resembling a parabola that opens upward. A quadratic function $f(x) = ax^2 + bx + c, a > 0$, might be used as a model for this situation.

c) The data do not resemble a parabola. A quadratic function would not be a good model for this situation.

d) The data resemble the right half of a parabola that opens upward. We could use a quadratic function $f(x) = ax^2 + bx + c, a > 0, x \geq 0$, to model the situation.

e) The data appear nearly linear. A linear function is a better model for this situation than a quadratic function.

Try Exercise 23.

EXAMPLE 4   Candy Consumption.   The amount of candy consumed each year in the United States can be modeled by a quadratic function, as seen in Example 3(a).

Year	Years After 2004	U.S. Candy Consumption (in billions of pounds)
2004	0	6.208
2005	1	6.424
2006	2	6.468
2007	3	6.443
2008	4	6.380

a) Use the data points (0, 6.208), (2, 6.468), and (4, 6.380) to fit a quadratic function $f(x)$ to the data.

b) Use the function from part (a) to estimate the candy consumption in 2009.

c) Use the REGRESSION feature of a graphing calculator to fit a quadratic function $g(x)$ to the data.

d) Use the function from part (c) to estimate the candy consumption in 2009, and compare the estimate with the estimate from part (b).

SOLUTION

a) Only one parabola will go through any three points that are not on a straight line. We are looking for a function of the form $f(x) = ax^2 + bx + c$, where $f(x)$ is the candy consumption x years after 2004. From the given information, we can write three equations. To find a, b, and c, we will solve the system of equations.

We begin by substituting the values of x and $f(x)$ from the three data points listed:

$$6.208 = a(0)^2 + b(0) + c, \quad \text{Using the data point } (0, 6.208)$$
$$6.468 = a(2)^2 + b(2) + c, \quad \text{Using the data point } (2, 6.468)$$
$$6.380 = a(4)^2 + b(4) + c. \quad \text{Using the data point } (4, 6.380)$$

After simplifying, we have the system of three equations

$$6.208 = c,$$
$$6.468 = 4a + 2b + c,$$
$$6.380 = 16a + 4b + c.$$

From the first equation, we know that $c = 6.208$. We substitute 6.208 for c in the second and third equations, giving us a system of two equations:

$$6.468 = 4a + 2b + 6.208,$$
$$6.380 = 16a + 4b + 6.208.$$

Now we subtract 6.208 from both sides of each equation, giving us

$$0.260 = 4a + 2b,$$
$$0.172 = 16a + 4b.$$

We can solve this system using elimination.

$$\begin{array}{lll} 0.260 = 4a + 2b, & \text{Multiplying in order to} & -0.520 = -8a - 4b \\ 0.172 = 16a + 4b & \text{eliminate } b & \underline{0.172 = 16a + 4b} \\ & & -0.348 = 8a \qquad \text{Adding} \\ & & -0.0435 = a \qquad \text{Solving for } a \end{array}$$

Now that we know $a = -0.0435$, we can solve for b, using one of the equations that contain a and b:

$$0.260 = 4a + 2b$$
$$0.260 = 4(-0.0435) + 2b \qquad \text{Substituting for } a$$
$$0.260 = -0.174 + 2b$$
$$0.434 = 2b$$
$$0.217 = b. \qquad \text{Solving for } b$$

We now have values for a, b, and c, and can write the quadratic function:

$$f(x) = ax^2 + bx + c \qquad a = -0.0435, b = 0.217, c = 6.208$$
$$f(x) = -0.0435x^2 + 0.217x + 6.208.$$

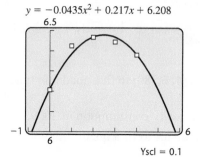

$y = -0.0435x^2 + 0.217x + 6.208$

Yscl = 0.1

As a partial check, we graph the function along with the data, as shown at left. The graph goes through the three given data points.

b) Since 2009 is 5 years after 2004, we find $f(5)$ in order to estimate the candy consumption in that year:

$$f(5) = -0.0435(5)^2 + 0.217(5) + 6.208 = 6.2055.$$

According to this model, Americans will consume 6.2055 billion pounds of candy in 2009.

c) Using regression allows us to consider all the data given in the problem, not just three points. After entering the data, we choose the QUADREG option in the

STAT CALC menu. The figure on the left below gives the coefficients of the equation. In the figure on the right, the graph of g is shown along with the data. Rounding coefficients, we obtain

$$g(x) = -0.0448x^2 + 0.2154x + 6.2224.$$

Quad Reg
$y = ax^2 + bx + c$
$a = -.0447857143$
$b = .2154428571$
$c = 6.222428571$

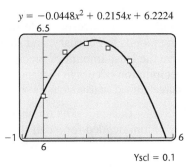

$y = -0.0448x^2 + 0.2154x + 6.2224$

6.5

−1 ⌐   ⌐ 6
  6

Yscl = 0.1

d) To estimate candy consumption in 2009, we evaluate $g(5)$ and obtain

$$g(5) = 6.1794.$$

This estimate of 6.1794 billion pounds of candy is lower than the estimate obtained in part (b). Since the second model took into consideration all the data, it is a better fit. However, without further information, it is difficult to tell which model more accurately describes the pattern of candy consumption in the United States.

Try Exercise 37.

13.8 Exercise Set

↪ *Concept Reinforcement*   *In each of Exercises 1–6, match the description with the graph that displays that characteristic.*

1. ____ A minimum value of $f(x)$ exists.

2. ____ A maximum value of $f(x)$ exists.

3. ____ No maximum or minimum value of $f(x)$ exists.

4. ____ The data points appear to suggest a linear model.

5. ____ The data points appear to suggest a quadratic model with a maximum.

6. ____ The data points appear to suggest a quadratic model with a minimum.

a)

b) $f(x)$

c) $f(x)$

d)

e) $f(x)$

f)

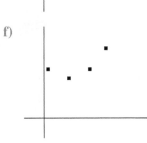

Solve.

7. *Sonoma Precipitation.* The amount of precipitation in Sonoma, California, can be approximated by

$$P(x) = 0.2x^2 - 2.8x + 9.8,$$

where $P(x)$ is in inches and x is the number of the month ($x = 1$ corresponds to January, $x = 2$ corresponds to February, and so on). In what month is there the least amount of precipitation, and how much precipitation occurs in that month?
Source: Based on data from www.city-data.com

8. *Newborn Calves.* The number of pounds of milk per day recommended for a calf that is x weeks old can be approximated by $p(x)$, where

$$p(x) = -0.2x^2 + 1.3x + 6.2.$$

When is a calf's milk consumption greatest and how much milk does it consume at that time?
Source: C. Chaloux, University of Vermont, 1998

9. *Maximizing Profit.* Recall that total profit P is the difference between total revenue R and total cost C. Given

$$R(x) = 1000x - x^2$$

and

$$C(x) = 3000 + 20x,$$

find the total profit, the maximum value of the total profit, and the value of x at which it occurs.

10. *Minimizing Cost.* Sweet Harmony Crafts has determined that when x hundred Dobros are built, the average cost per Dobro can be estimated by

$$C(x) = 0.1x^2 - 0.7x + 2.425,$$

where $C(x)$ is in hundreds of dollars. What is the minimum average cost per Dobro and how many Dobros should be built in order to achieve that minimum?

11. *Furniture Design.* A furniture builder is designing a rectangular end table with a perimeter of 128 in. What dimensions will yield the maximum area?

12. *Architecture.* An architect is designing an atrium for a hotel. The atrium is to be rectangular with a perimeter of 720 ft of brass piping. What dimensions will maximize the area of the atrium?

13. *Patio Design.* A stone mason has enough stones to enclose a rectangular patio with 60 ft of perimeter, assuming that the attached house forms one side of the rectangle. What is the maximum area that the mason can enclose? What should the dimensions of the patio be in order to yield this area?

14. *Garden Design.* Ginger is fencing in a rectangular garden, using the side of her house as one side of the rectangle. What is the maximum area that she can enclose with 40 ft of fence? What should the dimensions of the garden be in order to yield this area?

15. *Molding Plastics.* Economite Plastics plans to produce a one-compartment vertical file by bending the long side of an 8-in. by 14-in. sheet of plastic along two lines to form a U shape. How tall should the file be in order to maximize the volume that the file can hold?

16. *Composting.* A rectangular compost container is to be formed in a corner of a fenced yard, with 8 ft of chicken wire completing the other two sides of the rectangle. If the chicken wire is 3 ft high, what dimensions of the base will maximize the container's volume?

17. What is the maximum product of two numbers that add to 18? What numbers yield this product?

18. What is the maximum product of two numbers that add to 26? What numbers yield this product?

19. What is the minimum product of two numbers that differ by 8? What are the numbers?

20. What is the minimum product of two numbers that differ by 7? What are the numbers?

Aha! **21.** What is the maximum product of two numbers that add to −10? What numbers yield this product?

22. What is the maximum product of two numbers that add to −12? What numbers yield this product?

Choosing Models. **For the scatterplots and graphs in Exercises 23–32, determine which, if any, of the following functions might be used as a model for the data: Linear, with $f(x) = mx + b$; quadratic, with $f(x) = ax^2 + bx + c, a > 0$; quadratic, with $f(x) = ax^2 + bx + c, a < 0$; neither quadratic nor linear.**

23. Dorm Expense

Source: National Center for Education Statistics

24. Restaurant Industry Sales

Source: National Restaurant Association

25.

26.

27. Seniors in the Work Force

Source: U.S. Bureau of Labor Statistics

28. Doctor Visits

Sources: National Ambulatory Health Care Administration; Merritt, Hawkins & Associates; Council on Graduate Medical Education

29. **Recycling**

Source: Environmental Protection Agency

30. **Average Number of Live Births per 1000 Women**

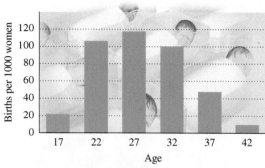

Source: U.S. Centers for Disease Control

31. **Credit Cards**

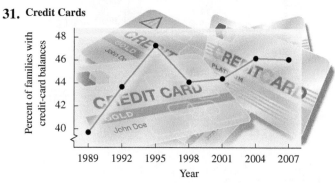

Source: http://www.federalreserve.gov/pubs/oss/oss2/2007/2007%20SCF%20Chartbook.pdf

32. **Wind Power**

Source: Energy Information Administration

Find a quadratic function that fits the set of data points.

33. $(1, 4), (-1, -2), (2, 13)$

34. $(1, 4), (-1, 6), (-2, 16)$

35. $(2, 0), (4, 3), (12, -5)$

36. $(-3, -30), (3, 0), (6, 6)$

37. a) Find a quadratic function that fits the following data.

Travel Speed (in kilometers per hour)	Number of Nighttime Accidents (for every 200 million kilometers driven)
60	400
80	250
100	250

b) Use the function to estimate the number of nighttime accidents that occur at 50 km/h.

38. a) Find a quadratic function that fits the following data.

Travel Speed (in kilometers per hour)	Number of Daytime Accidents (for every 200 million kilometers driven)
60	100
80	130
100	200

b) Use the function to estimate the number of daytime accidents that occur at 50 km/h.

39. *Archery.* The Olympic flame tower at the 1992 Summer Olympics was lit at a height of about 27 m by a flaming arrow that was launched about 63 m from the base of the tower. If the arrow landed about 63 m beyond the tower, find a quadratic function that expresses the height h of the arrow as a function of the distance d that it traveled horizontally.

40. *Pizza Prices.* Pizza Unlimited has the following prices for pizzas.

Diameter	Price
8 in.	$ 6.00
12 in.	$ 8.50
16 in.	$11.50

Is price a quadratic function of diameter? It probably should be, because the price should be proportional to the area, and the area is a quadratic function of the diameter. (The area of a circular region is given by $A = \pi r^2$ or $(\pi/4) \cdot d^2$.)

a) Express price as a quadratic function of diameter using the data points $(8, 6)$, $(12, 8.50)$, and $(16, 11.50)$.

b) Use the function to find the price of a 14-in. pizza.

41. *Hydrology.*   The drawing below shows the cross section of a river. Typically rivers are deepest in the middle, with the depth decreasing to 0 at the edges. A hydrologist measures the depths D, in feet, of a river at distances x, in feet, from one bank. The results are listed in the table below.

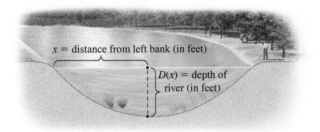

Distance x, from the Left Bank (in feet)	Depth, D, of the River (in feet)
0	0
15	10.2
25	17
50	20
90	7.2
100	0

a) Use regression to find a quadratic function that fits the data.

b) Use the function to estimate the depth of the river 70 ft from the left bank.

42. *Work Force.*   The graph in Exercise 27 indicates that the percent of the U.S. population age 65 and older that is in the work force is increasing after several decades of decrease.

a) Use regression to find a quadratic function that can be used to estimate the percent $p(x)$ of the population age 65 and older that is in the work force x years after 1957.

b) Use the function found in part (a) to predict the percent of those age 65 and older who will be in the work force in 2010.

43. *Teacher Shortages.*   The estimated shortage of math and science teachers each year is shown in the table below.

Year	Math and Science Teacher Shortage
2005	24,546
2007	25,029
2009	25,049
2011	25,781
2013	26,391
2015	27,214

Source: Based on data from National Center for Education Statistics and Council of Chief of State of School Officers

a) Use regression to find a quadratic function $t(x)$ that can be used to estimate the teacher shortage x years after 2005.

b) Use the function found in part (a) to predict the math and science teacher shortage in 2017.

44. *Restaurant Sales.*   The graph in Exercise 24 indicates that restaurant sales can be modeled as a quadratic function of the year.

a) Use regression to find a quadratic function $r(x)$ that can be used to estimate sales, in billions of dollars, x years after 1970.

b) Use the function found in part (a) to estimate restaurant sales in 2015.

TW **45.** Does every nonlinear function have a minimum value or a maximum value? Why or why not?

TW **46.** Explain how the leading coefficient of a quadratic function can be used to determine if a maximum or a minimum function value exists.

SKILL REVIEW

To prepare for Section 14.1, review function notation.

Graph each function.

47. $f(x) = x^3 - 2$

48. $g(x) = \dfrac{2}{x}$

49. If $f(x) = x + 7$, find $f\left(\dfrac{1}{a^2}\right)$.

50. If $g(x) = x^2 - 3$, find $g\left(\sqrt{a - 5}\right)$.   [12.1]

51. If $g(x) = x^2 + 2$, find $g(2a + 5)$.

52. If $f(x) = \sqrt{4x + 1}$, find $g(3a - 5)$.

SYNTHESIS

The following graphs can be used to compare the baseball statistics of pitcher Roger Clemens with the 31 other pitchers since 1968 who started at least 10 games in at least 15 seasons and pitched at least 3000 innings. Use the graphs to answer questions 53 and 54.

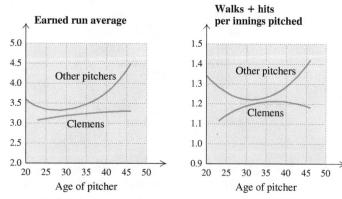

Earned run average

Other pitchers

Clemens

Age of pitcher

Walks + hits per innings pitched

Other pitchers

Clemens

Age of pitcher

Source: *The New York Times*, February 10, 2008; Eric Bradlow, Shane Jensen, Justin Wolfers and Adi Wyner

TW **53.** The earned run average describes how many runs a pitcher has allowed per game. The lower the earned run average, the better the pitcher. Compare, in terms of maximums or minimums, the earned run average of Roger Clemens with that of other pitchers. Is there any reason to suspect that the aging process was unusual for Clemens? Explain.

TW **54.** The statistic "Walks + hits per innings pitched" is related to how often a pitcher allows a batter to reach a base. The lower this statistic, the better. Compare, in terms of maximums or minimums, the "walks + hits" statistic of Roger Clemens with that of other pitchers.

55. *Bridge Design.* The cables supporting a straight-line suspension bridge are nearly parabolic in shape. Suppose that a suspension bridge is being designed with concrete supports 160 ft apart and with vertical cables 30 ft above road level at the midpoint of the bridge and 80 ft above road level at a point 50 ft from the midpoint of the bridge. How long are the longest vertical cables?

160 ft

56. *Trajectory of a Flare.* The height above the ground of a launched object is a quadratic function of the time that it is in the air. Suppose that a flare is launched from a cliff 64 ft above sea level. If 3 sec after being launched the flare is again level with the cliff, and if 2 sec after that it lands in the sea, what is the maximum height that the flare will reach?

57. *Norman Window.* A *Norman window* is a rectangle with a semicircle on top. Reid is designing a Norman window that will require 24 ft of trim. What dimensions will give the maximum area of glass?

58. *Crop Yield.* An orange grower finds that she gets an average yield of 40 bushels (bu) per tree when she plants 20 trees on an acre of ground. Each time she adds a tree to an acre, the yield per tree decreases by 1 bu, due to congestion. How many trees per acre should she plant for maximum yield?

59. *Cover Charges.* When the owner of Sweet Sounds charges a $10 cover charge, an average of 80 people will attend a show. For each 25¢ increase in admission price, the average number attending decreases by 1. What should the owner charge in order to make the most money?

60. *Minimizing Area.* A 36-in. piece of string is cut into two pieces. One piece is used to form a circle while the other is used to form a square. How should the string be cut so that the sum of the areas is a minimum?

x

36 in.

?   ?

Try Exercise Answers: Section 13.8

7. July; 0 in. **11.** 32 in. by 32 in. **23.** $f(x) = mx + b$
37. (a) $A(s) = \frac{3}{16}s^2 - \frac{135}{4}s + 1750$; (b) about 531 accidents

Study Summary

SECTION 13.1: QUADRATIC EQUATIONS

A **quadratic equation in standard form** is written $ax^2 + bx + c = 0$, with a, b, and c constant and $a \neq 0$.

Some quadratic equations can be solved by factoring.

$$x^2 - 3x - 10 = 0$$
$$(x + 2)(x - 5) = 0$$
$$x + 2 = 0 \quad \text{or} \quad x - 5 = 0$$
$$x = -2 \quad \text{or} \quad x = 5$$

1. Solve:
$$x^2 - 12x + 11 = 0.$$

The Principle of Square Roots

For any real number k, if $X^2 = k$, then $X = \sqrt{k}$ or $X = -\sqrt{k}$.

$$x^2 - 8x + 16 = 25$$
$$(x - 4)^2 = 25$$
$$x - 4 = -5 \quad \text{or} \quad x - 4 = 5$$
$$x = -1 \quad \text{or} \quad x = 9$$

2. Solve:
$$x^2 - 18x + 81 = 5.$$

Any quadratic equation can be solved by **completing the square.**

$$x^2 + 6x = 1$$
$$x^2 + 6x + \left(\tfrac{6}{2}\right)^2 = 1 + \left(\tfrac{6}{2}\right)^2$$
$$x^2 + 6x + 9 = 1 + 9$$
$$(x + 3)^2 = 10$$
$$x + 3 = \pm\sqrt{10}$$
$$x = -3 \pm \sqrt{10}$$

3. Solve by completing the square:
$$x^2 + 20x = 21.$$

SECTION 13.2: THE QUADRATIC FORMULA

The Quadratic Formula

The solutions of $ax^2 + bx + c = 0$ are given by

$$x = \frac{-b \pm \sqrt{b^2 - 4ac}}{2a}.$$

$$3x^2 - 2x - 5 = 0 \qquad a = 3, b = -2, c = -5$$
$$x = \frac{-(-2) \pm \sqrt{(-2)^2 - 4 \cdot 3(-5)}}{2 \cdot 3}$$
$$x = \frac{2 \pm \sqrt{4 + 60}}{6}$$
$$x = \frac{2 \pm \sqrt{64}}{6}$$
$$x = \frac{2 \pm 8}{6}$$
$$x = \frac{10}{6} = \frac{5}{3} \quad \text{or} \quad x = \frac{-6}{6} = -1$$

4. Solve:
$$2x^2 - 3x - 9 = 0.$$

SECTION 13.3: STUDYING SOLUTIONS OF QUADRATIC EQUATIONS

The **discriminant** of the quadratic formula is $b^2 - 4ac$.

$b^2 - 4ac = 0 \rightarrow$ One solution; a rational number

$b^2 - 4ac > 0 \rightarrow$ Two real solutions; both are rational if $b^2 - 4ac$ is a perfect square.

For $4x^2 - 12x + 9 = 0$, $b^2 - 4ac = (-12)^2 - 4(4)(9)$
$$= 144 - 144 = 0.$$

Thus, $4x^2 - 12x + 9 = 0$ has one rational solution.

For $x^2 + 6x - 2 = 0$, $b^2 - 4ac = (6)^2 - 4(1)(-2)$
$$= 36 + 8 = 44.$$

Thus, $x^2 + 6x - 2 = 0$ has two irrational real-number solutions.

5. Use the discriminant to determine the number and type of solutions of $2x^2 + 5x + 9 = 0$.

| $b^2 - 4ac < 0 \rightarrow$ Two imaginary-number solutions | For $2x^2 - 3x + 5 = 0$, $b^2 - 4ac = (-3)^2 - 4(2)(5)$ $= 9 - 40 = -31$. Thus, $2x^2 - 3x + 5 = 0$ has two imaginary-number solutions. | |

SECTION 13.4: APPLICATIONS INVOLVING QUADRATIC EQUATIONS

| To solve a formula for a letter, use the same principles used to solve equations. | Solve $y = pn^2 + dn$ for n. $$pn^2 + dn - y = 0 \qquad a = p, b = d, c = -y$$ $$n = \frac{-d \pm \sqrt{d^2 - 4p(-y)}}{2 \cdot p}$$ $$n = \frac{-d \pm \sqrt{d^2 + 4py}}{2p}$$ | **6.** Solve $a = n^2 + 1$ for n. |

SECTION 13.5: EQUATIONS REDUCIBLE TO QUADRATIC

| Equations that are **reducible to quadratic** or in **quadratic form** can be solved by making an appropriate substitution. | $$x^4 - 10x^2 + 9 = 0 \qquad \text{Let } u = x^2. \text{ Then } u^2 = x^4.$$ $$u^2 - 10u + 9 = 0 \qquad \text{Substituting}$$ $$(u - 9)(u - 1) = 0$$ $u - 9 = 0 \quad or \quad u - 1 = 0$ $u = 9 \quad or \qquad u = 1 \qquad \text{Solving for } u$ $x^2 = 9 \quad or \qquad x^2 = 1$ $x = \pm 3 \quad or \qquad x = \pm 1 \qquad \text{Solving for } x$ | **7.** Solve: $x - \sqrt{x} - 30 = 0$. |

SECTION 13.6: QUADRATIC FUNCTIONS AND THEIR GRAPHS
SECTION 13.7: MORE ABOUT GRAPHING QUADRATIC FUNCTIONS

| The graph of a quadratic function $$f(x) = ax^2 + bx + c$$ $$= a(x - h)^2 + k$$ is a **parabola.** The graph opens upward for $a > 0$ and downward for $a < 0$. The **vertex** is (h, k) and the **axis of symmetry** is $x = h$. If $a > 0$, the function has a **minimum** value of k, and if $a < 0$, the function has a **maximum** value of k. The vertex and the axis of symmetry occur at $x = -\dfrac{b}{2a}$. | | **8.** Graph $f(x) = 2x^2 - 12x + 3$. Label the vertex and the axis of symmetry, and identify the minimum or maximum function value. |

SECTION 13.8: PROBLEM SOLVING AND QUADRATIC FUNCTIONS

| Some problem situations can be **modeled** using quadratic functions. For those problems, a quantity can often be **maximized** or **minimized** by finding the coordinates of a vertex. | A lifeguard has 100 m of roped-together flotation devices with which to cordon off a rectangular swimming area at Lakeside Beach. If the shoreline forms one side of the rectangle, what dimensions will maximize the size of the area for swimming? This problem and its solution appear as Example 2 on pp. 857–858. | **9.** Loretta is putting fencing around a rectangular vegetable garden. She can afford to buy 120 ft of fencing. What dimensions should she plan for the garden in order to maximize its area? |

Review Exercises 13

🖐 *Concept Reinforcement* *Classify each of the following statements as either true or false.*

1. Every quadratic equation has two different solutions. [13.3]

2. Every quadratic equation has at least one real-number solution. [13.3]

3. If an equation cannot be solved by completing the square, it cannot be solved by the quadratic formula. [13.2]

4. A negative discriminant indicates two imaginary-number solutions of a quadratic equation. [13.3]

5. Certain radical or rational equations can be written in quadratic form. [13.5]

6. The graph of $f(x) = 2(x + 3)^2 - 4$ has its vertex at $(3, -4)$. [13.6]

7. The graph of $g(x) = 5x^2$ has $x = 0$ as its axis of symmetry. [13.6]

8. The graph of $f(x) = -2x^2 + 1$ has no minimum value. [13.6]

9. The zeros of $g(x) = x^2 - 9$ are -3 and 3. [13.6]

10. The graph of every quadratic function has at least one x-intercept. [13.7]

11. Consider the following graph of $f(x) = ax^2 + bx + c$.

    a) State the number of real-number solutions of $ax^2 + bx + c = 0$. [13.1]

    b) State whether a is positive or negative. [13.6]

    c) Determine the minimum value of f. [13.6]

$f(x) = ax^2 + bx + c$

Vertex: $(2, -3)$

Solve.

12. $9x^2 - 2 = 0$ [13.1]

13. $8x^2 + 6x = 0$ [13.1]

14. $x^2 - 12x + 36 = 9$ [13.1]

15. $x^2 - 4x + 8 = 0$ [13.2]

16. $x(3x + 4) = 4x(x - 1) + 15$ [13.2]

17. $x^2 + 9x = 1$ [13.2]

18. $x^2 - 5x - 2 = 0$. Use a calculator to approximate the solutions with rational numbers. Round to three decimal places. [13.2]

19. Let $f(x) = 4x^2 - 3x - 1$. Find x such that $f(x) = 0$. [13.2]

Replace the blanks with constants to form a true equation. [13.1]

20. $x^2 - 12x + \underline{\quad} = (x - \underline{\quad})^2$

21. $x^2 + \frac{3}{5}x + \underline{\quad} = (x + \underline{\quad})^2$

22. Solve by completing the square. Show your work.
    $$x^2 - 6x + 1 = 0 \quad [13.1]$$

23. \$2500 grows to \$2704 in 2 years. Use the formula $A = P(1 + r)^t$ to find the interest rate. [13.1]

24. The Singapore Flyer Observation Wheel is 541 ft tall. Use $s = 16t^2$ to approximate how long it would take an object to fall from the top. [13.1]

For each equation, determine whether the solutions are real or imaginary. If they are real, specify whether they are rational or irrational. [13.3]

25. $x^2 + 3x - 6 = 0$

26. $x^2 + 2x + 5 = 0$

27. Write a quadratic equation having the solutions $3i$ and $-3i$. [13.3]

28. Write a quadratic equation having -4 as its only solution. [13.3]

Solve. [13.4]

29. Horizons has a manufacturing plant located 300 mi from company headquarters. Their corporate pilot must fly from headquarters to the plant and back in 4 hr. If there is a 20-mph headwind going and a 20-mph tailwind returning, how fast must the plane be able to travel in still air?

30. Working together, Erica and Shawna can answer a day's worth of customer-service e-mails in 4 hr. Working alone, Erica takes 6 hr longer than Shawna. How long would it take Shawna to answer the e-mails alone?

31. Find all x-intercepts of the graph of
$$f(x) = x^4 - 13x^2 + 36. \text{ [13.5]}$$

Solve. [13.5]

32. $15x^{-2} - 2x^{-1} - 1 = 0$

33. $(x^2 - 4)^2 - (x^2 - 4) - 6 = 0$

34. a) Graph: $f(x) = -3(x + 2)^2 + 4$. [13.6]
 b) Label the vertex.
 c) Draw the axis of symmetry.
 d) Find the maximum or the minimum value.

35. For the function given by $f(x) = 2x^2 - 12x + 23$: [13.7]

 a) find the vertex and the axis of symmetry;
 b) graph the function.

36. Find any x-intercepts and the y-intercept of the graph of
$$f(x) = x^2 - 9x + 14. \text{ [13.7]}$$

37. Solve $N = 3\pi\sqrt{\dfrac{1}{p}}$ for p. [13.4]

38. Solve $2A + T = 3T^2$ for T. [13.4]

Determine which, if any, of the following functions might be used as a model for the data: Linear, with $f(x) = mx + b$; quadratic, with $f(x) = ax^2 + bx + c, a > 0$; quadratic, with $f(x) = ax^2 + bx + c, a < 0$; neither quadratic nor linear. [13.8]

39. Recreational Boating

40. McDonalds Restaurants

Source: McDonalds

41. Cost of Cable Television

Source: SNL Kagan

42. Eastgate Consignments wants to build a rectangular area in a corner for children to play in while their parents shop. They have 30 ft of low fencing. What is the maximum area that they can enclose? What dimensions will yield this area? [13.8]

43. *McDonalds.* The table below lists the number of McDonalds restaurants for various years (see Exercise 40). [13.8]

Year	Number of McDonalds Restaurants
1948	1
1956	14
1960	228
1968	1,000
1970	1,600
1975	3,076
1980	6,263
1984	8,300
1990	11,800
2008	32,000

a) Use the data points $(0, 1)$, $(20, 1000)$, and $(60, 32,000)$ to find a quadratic function $M(x)$ that can be used to estimate the number of McDonalds restaurants x years after 1948.

b) Use the function to estimate the number of McDonalds restaurants in 2020.

 44. a) Use the REGRESSION feature of a graphing calculator and all the data in Exercise 43 to find a quadratic

function that can be used to estimate the number $M(x)$ of McDonalds restaurants x years after 1948. [13.8]

b) Use the function to estimate the number of McDonalds restaurants in 2020. [13.8]

SYNTHESIS

TW **45.** Discuss two ways in which completing the square was used in this chapter. [13.1], [13.2], [13.7]

TW **46.** Compare the results of Exercises 43(b) and 44(b). Which model do you think gives a better prediction? [13.8]

TW **47.** What is the greatest number of solutions that an equation of the form $ax^4 + bx^2 + c = 0$ can have? Why? [13.5]

48. A quadratic function has x-intercepts at -3 and 5. If the y-intercept is at -7, find an equation for the function. [13.7]

49. Find h and k if, for $3x^2 - hx + 4k = 0$, the sum of the solutions is 20 and the product of the solutions is 80. [13.3]

50. The average of two positive integers is 171. One of the numbers is the square root of the other. Find the integers. [13.5]

Chapter Test **13**

1. Consider the following graph of $f(x) = ax^2 + bx + c$.

a) State the number of real-number solutions of $ax^2 + bx + c = 0$.

b) State whether a is positive or negative.

c) Determine the maximum function value of f.

Vertex: $(-3, -1)$

$f(x) = ax^2 + bx + c$

Solve.

2. $25x^2 - 7 = 0$

3. $4x(x - 2) - 3x(x + 1) = -18$

4. $x^2 + 2x + 3 = 0$

5. $2x + 5 = x^2$

6. $x^{-2} - x^{-1} = \frac{3}{4}$

7. $x^2 + 3x = 5$. Use a calculator to approximate the solutions with rational numbers. Round to three decimal places.

8. Let $f(x) = 12x^2 - 19x - 21$. Find x such that $f(x) = 0$.

Replace the blanks with constants to form a true equation.

9. $x^2 - 20x + \underline{\quad} = (x - \underline{\quad})^2$

10. $x^2 + \frac{2}{7}x + \underline{\quad} = \left(x + \underline{\quad}\right)^2$

11. Solve by completing the square. Show your work.
$$x^2 + 10x + 15 = 0$$

12. Determine the type of number that the solutions of $x^2 + 2x + 5 = 0$ will be.

13. Write a quadratic equation having solutions $\sqrt{11}$ and $-\sqrt{11}$.

Solve.

14. The Connecticut River flows at a rate of 4 km/h for the length of a popular scenic route. In order for a cruiser to travel 60 km upriver and then return in a total of 8 hr, how fast must the boat be able to travel in still water?

15. Dal and Kim can assemble a swing set in $1\frac{1}{2}$ hr. Working alone, it takes Kim 4 hr longer than Dal to assemble the swing set. How long would it take Dal, working alone, to assemble the swing set?

16. Find all x-intercepts of the graph of
$$f(x) = x^4 - 15x^2 - 16.$$

17. a) Graph: $f(x) = 4(x - 3)^2 + 5$.
   b) Label the vertex.
   c) Draw the axis of symmetry.
   d) Find the maximum or the minimum function value.

18. For the function $f(x) = 2x^2 + 4x - 6$:
   a) find the vertex and the axis of symmetry;
   b) graph the function.

19. Find any x-intercepts and the y-intercept of
$$f(x) = x^2 - x - 6.$$

20. Solve $V = \frac{1}{3}\pi\left(R^2 + r^2\right)$ for r. Assume that all variables are positive.

21. State whether the graph appears to represent a linear function, a quadratic function, or neither.

Chicago Air Quality

Source: The National Arbor Day Foundation

22. Jay's Metals has determined that when x hundred storage cabinets are built, the average cost per cabinet is given by
$$C(x) = 0.2x^2 - 1.3x + 3.4025,$$
where $C(x)$ is in hundreds of dollars. What is the minimum cost per cabinet and how many cabinets should be built in order to achieve that minimum?

23. Trees improve air quality in part by retaining airborne particles, called particulates, from the air. The table below shows the number of metric tons of particulates retained by trees in Chicago during the spring, summer, and autumn months. (See Exercise 21.)

Month		Amount of Particulates Retained (in metric tons)
April	(0)	35
May	(1)	235
July	(3)	325
August	(4)	310
October	(6)	200
November	(7)	35

Source: The National Arbor Day Foundation

Use the data points $(0, 35)$, $(4, 310)$, and $(6, 200)$ to find a quadratic function that can be used to estimate the number of metric tons p of particulates retained x months after April.

24. Use regression to find a quadratic function that fits all the data in Exercise 23.

SYNTHESIS

25. One solution of $kx^2 + 3x - k = 0$ is -2. Find the other solution.

26. Find a fourth-degree polynomial equation, with integer coefficients, for which $-\sqrt{3}$ and $2i$ are solutions.

27. Solve: $x^4 - 4x^2 - 1 = 0$.

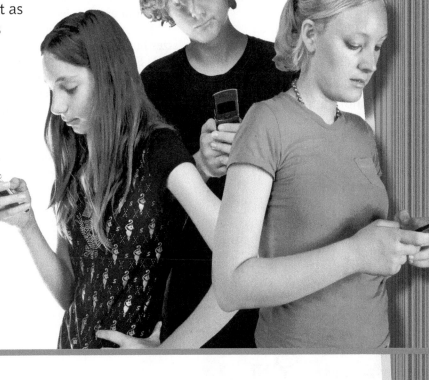

14

Exponential Functions and Logarithmic Functions

Do You Text More Than You Talk?

Beginning in 2008, Americans sent more text messages than they made phone calls. They still talk on the phone just as often, but the number of text messages has increased *exponentially*. In Example 9 of Section 14.7, we use the data in the graph shown here to estimate the number of text messages in 2011.

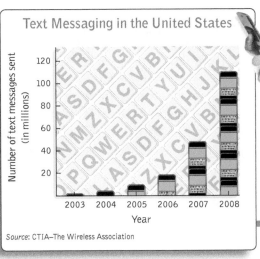

Text Messaging in the United States

Source: CTIA–The Wireless Association

14.1 Composite Functions and Inverse Functions

14.2 Exponential Functions

14.3 Logarithmic Functions

14.4 Properties of Logarithmic Functions
   MID-CHAPTER REVIEW

14.5 Natural Logarithms and Changing Bases
   VISUALIZING FOR SUCCESS

14.6 Solving Exponential and Logarithmic Equations

14.7 Applications of Exponential and Logarithmic Functions
   STUDY SUMMARY
   REVIEW EXERCISES   •   CHAPTER TEST
   CUMULATIVE REVIEW

The functions that we consider in this chapter have rich applications in many fields such as finance, epidemiology (the study of the spread of disease), and marketing. The theory centers on functions with variable exponents (*exponential functions*). We study these functions, their inverses, and their properties.

Composite Functions and Inverse Functions

- Composite Functions

- Inverses and One-to-One Functions

- Finding Formulas for Inverses

- Graphing Functions and Their Inverses

- Inverse Functions and Composition

COMPOSITE FUNCTIONS

In the real world, functions frequently occur in which some quantity depends on a variable that, in turn, depends on another variable. For instance, a firm's profits may depend on the number of items the firm produces, which may in turn depend on the number of employees hired. Such functions are called **composite functions.**

For example, the function g that gives a correspondence between women's shoe sizes in the United States and those in Britain is given by $g(x) = x - 2$, where x is the U.S. size and $g(x)$ is the British size. Thus a U.S. size 4 corresponds to a shoe size of $g(4) = 4 - 2$, or 2, in Britain.

A second function converts women's shoe sizes in Britain to those in Italy. This particular function is given by $f(x) = 2x + 28$, where x is the British size and $f(x)$ is the corresponding Italian size. Thus a British size 2 corresponds to an Italian size $f(2) = 2 \cdot 2 + 28$, or 32.

It is correct to conclude that a U.S. size 4 corresponds to an Italian size 32 and that some function h describes this correspondence.

	g			f	
	$g(x) = x - 2$			$f(x) = 2x + 28$	

U.S.	Britain	Italy
4	2	32
5	3	34
6	4	36
7	5	38

h

$$h(x) = ?$$

Size x shoes in the United States correspond to size $g(x)$ shoes in Britain, where

$$g(x) = x - 2.$$

Student Notes

Throughout this chapter, keep in mind that equations such as $g(x) = x - 2$ and $g(t) = t - 2$ describe the same function g. Both equations tell us to find a function value by subtracting 2 from the input.

Size n shoes in Britain correspond to size $f(n)$ shoes in Italy. Similarly, size $g(x)$ shoes in Britain correspond to size $f(g(x))$ shoes in Italy. Since the x in the expression $f(g(x))$ represents a U.S. shoe size, we can find the Italian shoe size that corresponds to a U.S. size x as follows:

$$f(g(x)) = f(x - 2) = 2(x - 2) + 28 \qquad \text{Using } g(x) \text{ as an input}$$
$$= 2x - 4 + 28 = 2x + 24.$$

This gives a formula for h: $h(x) = 2x + 24$. Thus U.S. size 4 corresponds to Italian size $h(4) = 2(4) + 24$, or 32. We call h the *composition* of f and g and denote it by $f \circ g$ (read "the composition of f and g," "f composed with g," or "f circle g").

> ## Composition of Functions   The *composite function $f \circ g$, the composition* of f and g, is defined as
>
> $$(f \circ g)(x) = f(g(x)).$$

We can visualize the composition of functions as follows.

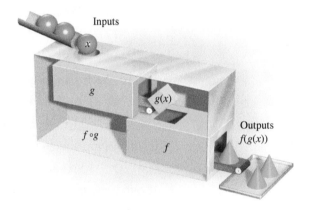

EXAMPLE 1   Given $f(x) = 3x$ and $g(x) = 1 + x^2$:

a) Find $(f \circ g)(5)$ and $(g \circ f)(5)$.

b) Find $(f \circ g)(x)$ and $(g \circ f)(x)$.

SOLUTION   Consider each function separately:

$$f(x) = 3x \qquad \text{This function multiplies each input by 3.}$$
$$\text{and} \quad g(x) = 1 + x^2. \qquad \text{This function adds 1 to the square of each input.}$$

a) To find $(f \circ g)(5)$, we first find $g(5)$ and then use that as an input for f:

$$(f \circ g)(5) = f(g(5)) = f(1 + 5^2) \qquad\qquad \text{Using } g(x) = 1 + x^2$$
$$= f(26) = 3 \cdot 26 = 78. \qquad \text{Using } f(x) = 3x$$

To find $(g \circ f)(5)$, we first find $f(5)$ and then use that as an input for g:

$$(g \circ f)(5) = g(f(5)) = g(3 \cdot 5) \qquad \text{Note that } f(5) = 3 \cdot 5 = 15.$$
$$= g(15) = 1 + 15^2 = 1 + 225 = 226.$$

b) We find $(f \circ g)(x)$ by substituting $g(x)$ for x in the equation for $f(x)$:

$$(f \circ g)(x) = f(g(x)) = f(1 + x^2) \qquad \text{Using } g(x) = 1 + x^2$$
$$= 3 \cdot (1 + x^2) = 3 + 3x^2. \qquad \text{Using } f(x) = 3x$$

To find $(g \circ f)(x)$, we substitute $f(x)$ for x in the equation for $g(x)$:

$$(g \circ f)(x) = g(f(x)) = g(3x) \qquad \text{Substituting } 3x \text{ for } f(x)$$
$$= 1 + (3x)^2 = 1 + 9x^2.$$

We can now find the function values of part (a) using the functions of part (b):

$$(f \circ g)(5) = 3 + 3(5)^2 = 3 + 3 \cdot 25 = 78;$$
$$(g \circ f)(5) = 1 + 9(5)^2 = 1 + 9 \cdot 25 = 226.$$

Try Exercise 9.

Example 1 shows that, in general, $(f \circ g)(x) \neq (g \circ f)(x)$.

EXAMPLE 2 Given $f(x) = \sqrt{x}$ and $g(x) = x - 1$, find $(f \circ g)(x)$ and $(g \circ f)(x)$.

SOLUTION We have

$$(f \circ g)(x) = f(g(x)) = f(x - 1) = \sqrt{x - 1}; \qquad \text{Using } g(x) = x - 1$$
$$(g \circ f)(x) = g(f(x)) = g(\sqrt{x}) = \sqrt{x} - 1. \qquad \text{Using } f(x) = \sqrt{x}$$

To check using a graphing calculator, let

$$y_1 = f(x) = \sqrt{x},$$
$$y_2 = g(x) = x - 1,$$
$$y_3 = \sqrt{x - 1}, \qquad \text{This is the expression we found for } (f \circ g)(x).$$
and $\quad y_4 = y_1(y_2(x)). \qquad \text{This is the notation for } f(g(x)).$

If our work is correct, y_4 will be equivalent to y_3. We form a table of values, selecting only y_3 and y_4. The table on the left below indicates that the functions are probably equivalent.

X	Y3	Y4
1	0	0
1.5	.70711	.70711
2	1	1
2.5	1.2247	1.2247
3	1.4142	1.4142
3.5	1.5811	1.5811
4	1.7321	1.7321
X = 1		

X	Y5	Y6
1	0	0
1.5	.22474	.22474
2	.41421	.41421
2.5	.58114	.58114
3	.73205	.73205
3.5	.87083	.87083
4	1	1
X = 1		

Next, we let $y_5 = \sqrt{x} - 1$ and $y_6 = y_2(y_1(x))$ and select only y_5 and y_6. The table on the right above indicates that the functions are probably equivalent. Thus we conclude that

$$(f \circ g)(x) = \sqrt{x - 1} \quad \text{and} \quad (g \circ f)(x) = \sqrt{x} - 1.$$

Try Exercise 15.

In order for us to find $f(g(a))$, the output $g(a)$ must be in the domain of f.

EXAMPLE 3 Use the following table to find each value, if possible.

a) $(y_2 \circ y_1)(3)$ **b)** $(y_1 \circ y_2)(3)$

x	y_1	y_2
0	-2	3
1	2	5
2	-1	7
3	1	9
4	0	11
5	0	13
6	-3	15

SOLUTION

a) Since $(y_2 \circ y_1)(3) = y_2(y_1(3))$, we first find $y_1(3)$. We locate 3 in the x-column and then move across to the y_1-column to find $y_1(3) = 1$.

x	y_1	y_2
0	-2	3
1	2	5 $\longleftarrow y_2(1)$
2	-1	7
3	1	9
4	0	11
5	0	13
6	-3	15

$y_1(3)$

The output 1 now becomes an input for the function y_2:

$$y_2(y_1(3)) = y_2(1).$$

To find $y_2(1)$, we locate 1 in the x-column and then move across to the y_2-column to find $y_2(1) = \mathbf{5}$. Thus, $(y_2 \circ y_1)(3) = \mathbf{5}$.

b) Since $(y_1 \circ y_2)(3) = y_1(y_2(3))$, we find $y_2(3)$ by locating 3 in the x-column and moving across to the y_2-column. We have $y_2(3) = 9$, so

$$(y_1 \circ y_2)(3) = y_1(y_2(3)) = y_1(9).$$

However, y_1 is not defined for $x = 9$, so $(y_1 \circ y_2)(3)$ is undefined.

Try Exercise 21.

In fields ranging from chemistry to geology to economics, we must recognize how a function can be regarded as the composition of two "simpler" functions. This is sometimes called *de*composition.

EXAMPLE 4   If $h(x) = (7x + 3)^2$, find f and g such that $h(x) = (f \circ g)(x)$.

SOLUTION   We can think of $h(x)$ as the result of first forming $7x + 3$ and then squaring. This suggests that $g(x) = 7x + 3$ and $f(x) = x^2$. We check by forming the composition:

$$(f \circ g)(x) = f(g(x)) = f(7x + 3) = (7x + 3)^2 = h(x), \text{ as desired.}$$

There are other less "obvious" answers. For example, if

$$f(x) = (x - 1)^2 \quad \text{and} \quad g(x) = 7x + 4,$$

then

$$(f \circ g)(x) = f(g(x)) = f(7x + 4)$$
$$= (7x + 4 - 1)^2 = (7x + 3)^2 = h(x).$$

Try Exercise 31.

INVERSES AND ONE-TO-ONE FUNCTIONS

Let's view the following two functions as relations, or correspondences.

Countries and Their Capitals

Domain (Set of Inputs)	Range (Set of Outputs)
Australia	→ Canberra
China	→ Beijing
Germany	→ Berlin
Madagascar	→ Antananaviro
Turkey	→ Ankara
United States	→ Washington, D.C.

Phone Keys

Domain (Set of Inputs)	Range (Set of Outputs)
a	
b	→ 2
c	
d	
e	→ 3
f	

Suppose we reverse the arrows. We obtain what is called the **inverse relation.** Are these inverse relations functions?

Countries and Their Capitals

Range (Set of Outputs)	Domain (Set of Inputs)
Australia ←	Canberra
China ←	Beijing
Germany ←	Berlin
Madagascar ←	Antananaviro
Turkey ←	Ankara
United States ←	Washington, D.C.

Phone Keys

Range (Set of Outputs)	Domain (Set of Inputs)
a ←	
b ←	2
c ←	
d ←	
e ←	3
f ←	

Recall that for each input, a function provides exactly one output. However, it is possible for different inputs to correspond to the same output. Only when this possibility is *excluded* will the inverse be a function. For the functions listed above, this means the inverse of the "Capitals" correspondence is a function, but the inverse of the "Phone Keys" correspondence is not.

In the Capitals function, each input has its own output, so it is a **one-to-one function.** In the Phone Keys function, a and b are both paired with 2. Thus the Phone Keys function is not a one-to-one function.

One-To-One Function A function f is *one-to-one* if different inputs have different outputs. That is, if for a and b in the domain of f with $a \neq b$, we have $f(a) \neq f(b)$, then f is one-to-one. If a function is one-to-one, then its inverse correspondence is also a function.

How can we tell graphically whether a function is one-to-one?

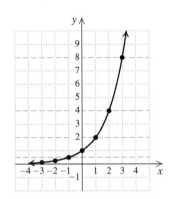

EXAMPLE 5 Shown at left is the graph of a function similar to those we will study in Section 14.2. Determine whether the function is one-to-one and thus has an inverse that is a function.

SOLUTION   A function is one-to-one if different inputs have different outputs—that is, if no two x-values have the same y-value. For this function, we cannot find two x-values that have the same y-value. Note that this means that no horizontal line can be drawn so that it crosses the graph more than once. The function is one-to-one so its inverse is a function.

Try Exercise 45.

The graph of every function must pass the vertical-line test. In order for a function to have an inverse that is a function, it must pass the *horizontal-line test* as well.

The Horizontal-Line Test If it is impossible to draw a horizontal line that intersects a function's graph more than once, then the function is one-to-one. For every one-to-one function, an inverse function exists.

EXAMPLE 6 Determine whether the function $f(x) = x^2$ is one-to-one and thus has an inverse that is a function.

SOLUTION   The graph of $f(x) = x^2$ is shown here. Many horizontal lines cross the graph more than once. For example, the line $y = 4$ crosses where the first coordinates are -2 and 2. Although these are different inputs, they have the same output. That is, $-2 \neq 2$, but $f(-2) = f(2) = 4$.

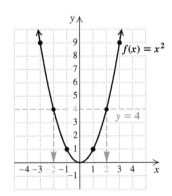

Thus the function is not one-to-one and no inverse function exists.

Try Exercise 43.

FINDING FORMULAS FOR INVERSES

When the inverse of f is also a function, it is denoted f^{-1} (read "f-inverse").

> **CAUTION!** The -1 in f^{-1} is *not* an exponent!

Suppose a function is described by a formula. If its inverse is a function, how do we find a formula for that inverse? For any equation in two variables, if we interchange the variables, we form an equation of the inverse correspondence. If it is a function, we proceed as follows to find a formula for f^{-1}.

Student Notes

Since we interchange x and y to find an equation for an inverse, the domain of the function is the range of the inverse, and the range of the function is the domain of the inverse.

> **To Find a Formula for f^{-1}**
>
> First make sure that f is one-to-one. Then:
>
> 1. Replace $f(x)$ with y.
> 2. Interchange x and y. (This gives the inverse function.)
> 3. Solve for y.
> 4. Replace y with $f^{-1}(x)$. (This is inverse function notation.)

EXAMPLE 7 Determine whether each function is one-to-one and if it is, find a formula for $f^{-1}(x)$.

a) $f(x) = x + 2$ **b)** $f(x) = 2x - 3$

SOLUTION

a) The graph of $f(x) = x + 2$ is shown at left. It passes the horizontal-line test, so it is one-to-one. Thus its inverse is a function.

1. Replace $f(x)$ with y: $y = x + 2$.
2. Interchange x and y: $x = y + 2$.   This gives the inverse function.
3. Solve for y: $x - 2 = y$.
4. Replace y with $f^{-1}(x)$: $f^{-1}(x) = x - 2$.   We also "reversed" the equation.

In this case, the function f adds 2 to all inputs. Thus, to "undo" f, the function f^{-1} must subtract 2 from its inputs.

b) The function $f(x) = 2x - 3$ is also linear. Any linear function that is not constant will pass the horizontal-line test. Thus, f is one-to-one.

1. Replace $f(x)$ with y: $y = 2x - 3$.
2. Interchange x and y: $x = 2y - 3$.
3. Solve for y: $x + 3 = 2y$
$$\frac{x + 3}{2} = y.$$

4. Replace y with $f^{-1}(x)$: $f^{-1}(x) = \dfrac{x + 3}{2}$.

In this case, the function f doubles all inputs and then subtracts 3. Thus, to "undo" f, the function f^{-1} adds 3 to each input and then divides by 2.

Try Exercise 49.

GRAPHING FUNCTIONS AND THEIR INVERSES

How do the graphs of a function and its inverse compare?

EXAMPLE 8 Graph $f(x) = 2x - 3$ and $f^{-1}(x) = (x + 3)/2$ on the same set of axes. Then compare.

SOLUTION The graph of each function follows. Note that the graph of f^{-1} can be drawn by reflecting the graph of f across the line $y = x$. That is, if we graph $f(x) = 2x - 3$ in wet ink and fold the paper along the line $y = x$, the graph of $f^{-1}(x) = (x + 3)/2$ will appear as the impression made by f.

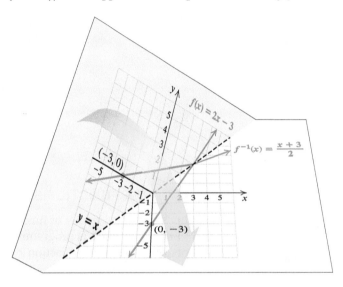

When x and y are interchanged to find a formula for the inverse, we are, in effect, reflecting or flipping the graph of $f(x) = 2x - 3$ across the line $y = x$. For example, when the coordinates of the y-intercept of the graph of f, $(0, -3)$, are reversed, we get $(-3, 0)$, the x-intercept of the graph of f^{-1}.

Try Exercise 73.

> **Visualizing Inverses** The graph of f^{-1} is a reflection of the graph of f across the line $y = x$.

EXAMPLE 9 Consider $g(x) = x^3 + 2$.

a) Determine whether the function is one-to-one.

b) If it is one-to-one, find a formula for its inverse.

c) Graph the inverse, if it exists.

SOLUTION

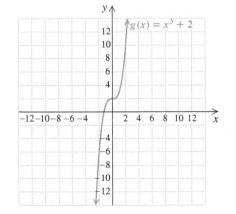

a) The graph of $g(x) = x^3 + 2$ is shown at left. It passes the horizontal-line test and thus has an inverse that is a function.

b) 1. Replace $g(x)$ with y: $y = x^3 + 2.$ Using $g(x) = x^3 + 2$

     2. Interchange x and y: $x = y^3 + 2.$

     3. Solve for y: $x - 2 = y^3$

$$\sqrt[3]{x - 2} = y.$$ Each number has only one cube root, so we can solve for y.

     4. Replace y with $g^{-1}(x)$: $g^{-1}(x) = \sqrt[3]{x - 2}.$

c) To graph g^{-1}, we can reflect the graph of $g(x) = x^3 + 2$ across the line $y = x$, as we did in Example 8. We can also graph $g^{-1}(x) = \sqrt[3]{x} - 2$ by plotting points. Note that $(2, 10)$ is on the graph of g, whereas $(10, 2)$ is on the graph of g^{-1}. The graphs of g and g^{-1} are shown together below.

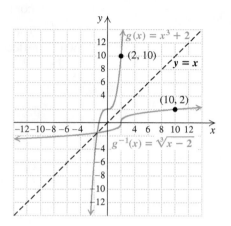

Try Exercise 75.

INVERSE FUNCTIONS AND COMPOSITION

Let's consider inverses of functions in terms of function machines. Suppose that a one-to-one function f is programmed into a machine. If the machine is run in reverse, it performs the inverse function f^{-1}. Inputs then enter at the opposite end, and the entire process is reversed.

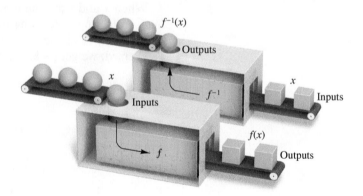

Consider $g(x) = x^3 + 2$ and $g^{-1}(x) = \sqrt[3]{x} - 2$ from Example 9. For the input 3,

$$g(3) = 3^3 + 2 = 27 + 2 = 29.$$

The output is 29. Now we use 29 for the input in the inverse:

$$g^{-1}(29) = \sqrt[3]{29 - 2} = \sqrt[3]{27} = 3.$$

The function g takes 3 to 29. The inverse function g^{-1} takes the number 29 back to 3.

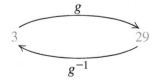

In general, if f is one-to-one, then f^{-1} takes the output $f(x)$ back to x. Similarly, f takes the output $f^{-1}(x)$ back to x.

Composition and Inverses   If a function f is one-to-one, then f^{-1} is the unique function for which

$$(f^{-1} \circ f)(x) = f^{-1}(f(x)) = x \quad \text{and} \quad (f \circ f^{-1})(x) = f(f^{-1}(x)) = x.$$

EXAMPLE 10   Let $f(x) = 2x + 1$. Show that

$$f^{-1}(x) = \frac{x-1}{2}.$$

SOLUTION   We find $(f^{-1} \circ f)(x)$ and $(f \circ f^{-1})(x)$ and check to see that each is x.

$$(f^{-1} \circ f)(x) = f^{-1}(f(x)) = f^{-1}(2x+1)$$

$$= \frac{(2x+1)-1}{2}$$

$$= \frac{2x}{2} = x \qquad \text{Thus, } (f^{-1} \circ f)(x) = x.$$

$$(f \circ f^{-1})(x) = f(f^{-1}(x)) = f\left(\frac{x-1}{2}\right)$$

$$= 2 \cdot \frac{x-1}{2} + 1$$

$$= x - 1 + 1 = x \qquad \text{Thus, } (f \circ f^{-1})(x) = x.$$

Try Exercise 83.

 —— *Inverse Functions: Graphing and Composition*

In Example 9, we found that the inverse of $y_1 = x^3 + 2$ is $y_2 = \sqrt[3]{x-2}$. There are several ways to check this result using a graphing calculator.

1. We can check visually by graphing both functions, along with the line $y = x$, on a "squared" set of axes. The graph of y_2 *appears* to be the reflection of the graph of y_1 across the line $y = x$. This is only a partial check since we are comparing graphs visually.

$y_1 = x^3 + 2, \quad y_2 = \sqrt[3]{x-2}$

(continued)

2. A second, more precise, visual check begins with graphing $y_1 = x^3 + 2$ and $y_2 = \sqrt[3]{x} - 2$ using a squared viewing window. Then press DRAW 8 VARS ▶ 1 1 ENTER to select the DrawInv option of the DRAW menu and graph the inverse. The resulting graph should coincide with the graph of y_2.

3. For a third check, note that if y_2 is the inverse of y_1, then $(y_2 \circ y_1)(x) = x$ and $(y_1 \circ y_2)(x) = x$. Enter $y_3 = y_2(y_1(x))$ and $y_4 = y_1(y_2(x))$, and form a table to compare x, y_3, and y_4. Note that for the values shown, $y_3 = y_4 = x$.

TblStart = −3, ΔTbl = 1

X	Y3	Y4
-3	-3	-3
-2	-2	-2
-1	-1	-1
0	0	0
1	1	1
2	2	2
3	3	3

X = −3

Your Turn

1. Enter $y_1 = 2x + 1$ and $y_2 = x/2 - 1$. These are *not* inverse functions, as the following three activities will demonstrate.

2. Graph y_1 and y_2 in a squared viewing window. These should not appear to be reflections across the line $y = x$.

3. From the home screen, press DRAW 8 VARS ▶ 1 1 ENTER . The graph drawn should be different from the graph of y_2.

4. Enter $y_3 = y_2(y_1(x))$ and $y_4 = y_1(y_2(x))$ and form a table. Compare x_1, y_3, and y_4. The columns should *not* be the same.

14.1 Exercise Set

FOR EXTRA HELP

↪ *Concept Reinforcement* *Classify each of the following statements as either true or false.*

1. The composition of two functions f and g is written $f \circ g$.

2. The notation $(f \circ g)(x)$ means $f(g(x))$.

3. If $f(x) = x^2$ and $g(x) = x + 3$, then $(g \circ f)(x) = (x + 3)^2$.

4. For any function h, there is only one way to decompose the function as $h = f \circ g$.

5. The function f is one-to-one if $f(1) = 1$.

6. The -1 in f^{-1} is an exponent.

7. The function f is the inverse of f^{-1}.

8. If g and h are inverses of each other, then $(g \circ h)(x) = x$.

For each pair of functions, find **(a)** $(f \circ g)(1)$; **(b)** $(g \circ f)(1)$; **(c)** $(f \circ g)(x)$; *and* **(d)** $(g \circ f)(x)$.

9. $f(x) = x^2 + 1$; $g(x) = x - 3$

10. $f(x) = x + 4$; $g(x) = x^2 - 5$

11. $f(x) = 5x + 1$; $g(x) = 2x^2 - 7$

12. $f(x) = 3x^2 + 4$; $g(x) = 4x - 1$

13. $f(x) = x + 7;$ $g(x) = 1/x^2$

14. $f(x) = 1/x^2;$ $g(x) = x + 2$

15. $f(x) = \sqrt{x};$ $g(x) = x + 3$

16. $f(x) = 10 - x;$ $g(x) = \sqrt{x}$

17. $f(x) = \sqrt{4x};$ $g(x) = 1/x$

18. $f(x) = \sqrt{x + 3};$ $g(x) = 13/x$

19. $f(x) = x^2 + 4;$ $g(x) = \sqrt{x - 1}$

20. $f(x) = x^2 + 8;$ $g(x) = \sqrt{x + 17}$

Use the following table to find each value, if possible.

X	Y₁	Y₂
-3	-4	1
-2	-1	-2
-1	2	-3
0	5	-2
1	8	1
2	11	6
3	14	11

X =

21. $(y_1 \circ y_2)(-3)$

22. $(y_2 \circ y_1)(-3)$

23. $(y_1 \circ y_2)(-1)$

24. $(y_2 \circ y_1)(-1)$

25. $(y_2 \circ y_1)(1)$

26. $(y_1 \circ y_2)(1)$

Use the table below to find each value, if possible.

x	f(x)	g(x)
1	0	1
2	3	5
3	2	8
4	6	5
5	4	1

27. $(f \circ g)(2)$

28. $(g \circ f)(4)$

29. $f(g(3))$

30. $g(f(5))$

Find $f(x)$ and $g(x)$ such that $h(x) = (f \circ g)(x)$. Answers may vary.

31. $h(x) = (3x - 5)^4$

32. $h(x) = (2x + 7)^3$

33. $h(x) = \sqrt{2x + 7}$

34. $h(x) = \sqrt[3]{4x - 5}$

35. $h(x) = \dfrac{2}{x - 3}$

36. $h(x) = \dfrac{3}{x} + 4$

37. $h(x) = \dfrac{1}{\sqrt{7x + 2}}$

38. $h(x) = \sqrt{x - 7} - 3$

39. $h(x) = \dfrac{1}{\sqrt{3x}} + \sqrt{3x}$

40. $h(x) = \dfrac{1}{\sqrt{2x}} - \sqrt{2x}$

Determine whether each function is one-to-one.

41. $f(x) = x - 5$

42. $f(x) = 5 - 2x$

43. $f(x) = x^2 + 1$

44. $f(x) = 1 - x^2$

45.

46.

47.

48.

For each function, (a) determine whether it is one-to-one and (b) if it is one-to-one, find a formula for the inverse.

49. $f(x) = x + 4$

50. $f(x) = x + 2$

51. $f(x) = 2x$

52. $f(x) = 3x$

53. $g(x) = 3x - 1$

54. $g(x) = 2x - 5$

55. $f(x) = \frac{1}{2}x + 1$

56. $f(x) = \frac{1}{3}x + 2$

57. $g(x) = x^2 + 5$

58. $g(x) = x^2 - 4$

59. $h(x) = -10 - x$

60. $h(x) = 7 - x$

Aha! **61.** $f(x) = \dfrac{1}{x}$

62. $f(x) = \dfrac{3}{x}$

63. $G(x) = 4$

64. $H(x) = 2$

65. $f(x) = \dfrac{2x + 1}{3}$

66. $f(x) = \dfrac{3x + 2}{5}$

67. $f(x) = x^3 - 5$

68. $f(x) = x^3 + 7$

69. $g(x) = (x - 2)^3$

70. $g(x) = (x + 7)^3$

71. $f(x) = \sqrt{x}$

72. $f(x) = \sqrt{x - 1}$

Graph each function and its inverse using the same set of axes.

73. $f(x) = \frac{2}{3}x + 4$

74. $g(x) = \frac{1}{4}x + 2$

75. $f(x) = x^3 + 1$

76. $f(x) = x^3 - 1$

77. $g(x) = \frac{1}{2}x^3$

78. $g(x) = \frac{1}{3}x^3$

79. $F(x) = -\sqrt{x}$

80. $f(x) = \sqrt{x}$

81. $f(x) = -x^2, x \geq 0$

82. $f(x) = x^2 - 1, x \leq 0$

83. Let $f(x) = \sqrt[3]{x - 4}$. Use composition to show that
$$f^{-1}(x) = x^3 + 4.$$

84. Let $f(x) = 3/(x + 2)$. Use composition to show that
$$f^{-1}(x) = \frac{3}{x} - 2.$$

85. Let $f(x) = (1 - x)/x$. Use composition to show that
$$f^{-1}(x) = \frac{1}{x + 1}.$$

86. Let $f(x) = x^3 - 5$. Use composition to show that
$$f^{-1}(x) = \sqrt[3]{x + 5}.$$

Use a graphing calculator to help determine whether or not the given pairs of functions are inverses of each other.

87. $f(x) = 0.75x^2 + 2;\ g(x) = \sqrt{\dfrac{4(x - 2)}{3}}$

88. $f(x) = 1.4x^3 + 3.2;\ g(x) = \sqrt[3]{\dfrac{x - 3.2}{1.4}}$

89. $f(x) = \sqrt{2.5x + 9.25};$
$g(x) = 0.4x^2 - 3.7,\ x \geq 0$

90. $f(x) = 0.8x^{1/2} + 5.23;$
$g(x) = 1.25(x^2 - 5.23),\ x \geq 0$

In Exercises 91 and 92, match the graph of each function in Column A with the graph of its inverse in Column B.

91. Column A　　　　Column B

(1) **A.**

(2) **B.**

(3) **C.**

(4) **D.**

92. Column A　　　　Column B

(1) **A.**

(2) **B.**

(3) **C.**

(4) **D.**

93. *Dress Sizes in the United States and France.*
A size-6 dress in the United States is size 38 in France. A function that converts dress sizes in the United States to those in France is
$$f(x) = x + 32.$$

a) Find the dress sizes in France that correspond to sizes 8, 10, 14, and 18 in the United States.

b) Determine whether this function has an inverse that is a function. If so, find a formula for the inverse.

c) Use the inverse function to find dress sizes in the United States that correspond to sizes 40, 42, 46, and 50 in France.

94. *Dress Sizes in the United States and Italy.* A size-6 dress in the United States is size 36 in Italy. A function that converts dress sizes in the United States to those in Italy is
$$f(x) = 2(x + 12).$$

a) Find the dress sizes in Italy that correspond to sizes 8, 10, 14, and 18 in the United States.

b) Determine whether this function has an inverse that is a function. If so, find a formula for the inverse.

c) Use the inverse function to find dress sizes in the United States that correspond to sizes 40, 44, 52, and 60 in Italy.

TW **95.** Is there a one-to-one relationship between items in a store and the price of each of those items? Why or why not?

TW **96.** Mathematicians usually try to select "logical" words when forming definitions. Does the term "one-to-one" seem logical? Why or why not?

SKILL REVIEW

To prepare for Section 14.2, review simplifying exponential expressions and graphing equations (Section 12).

Simplify.

97. 2^{-3}

98. $5^{(1-3)}$

99. $4^{5/2}$ [12.2]

100. $3^{7/10}$ [12.2]

Graph.

101. $y = x^3$

102. $x = y^3$

SYNTHESIS

TW **103.** The function $V(t) = 750(1.2)^t$ is used to predict the value, $V(t)$, of a certain rare stamp t years from 2005. Do not calculate $V^{-1}(t)$, but explain how V^{-1} could be used.

TW **104.** An organization determines that the cost per person of chartering a bus is given by the function

$$C(x) = \frac{100 + 5x}{x},$$

where x is the number of people in the group and $C(x)$ is in dollars. Determine $C^{-1}(x)$ and explain how this inverse function could be used.

For Exercises 105 and 106, graph the inverse of f.

105.

106.

107. *Dress Sizes in France and Italy.* Use the information in Exercises 93 and 94 to find a function for the French dress size that corresponds to a size x dress in Italy.

108. *Dress Sizes in Italy and France.* Use the information in Exercises 93 and 94 to find a function for the Italian dress size that corresponds to a size x dress in France.

TW **109.** What relationship exists between the answers to Exercises 107 and 108? Explain how you determined this.

110. Show that function composition is associative by showing that $((f \circ g) \circ h)(x) = (f \circ (g \circ h))(x)$.

111. Show that if $h(x) = (f \circ g)(x)$, then $h^{-1}(x) = (g^{-1} \circ f^{-1})(x)$. (*Hint*: Use Exercise 110.)

112. Match each function in Column A with its inverse from Column B.

Column A	Column B
(1) $y = 5x^3 + 10$	**A.** $y = \dfrac{\sqrt[3]{x} - 10}{5}$
(2) $y = (5x + 10)^3$	**B.** $y = \sqrt[3]{\dfrac{x}{5}} - 10$
(3) $y = 5(x + 10)^3$	**C.** $y = \sqrt[3]{\dfrac{x - 10}{5}}$
(4) $y = (5x)^3 + 10$	**D.** $y = \dfrac{\sqrt[3]{x - 10}}{5}$

TW **113.** Examine the following table. Is it possible that f and g could be inverses of each other? Why or why not?

x	$f(x)$	$g(x)$
6	6	6
7	6.5	8
8	7	10
9	7.5	12
10	8	14
11	8.5	16
12	9	18

114. Assume in Exercise 113 that f and g are both linear functions. Find equations for $f(x)$ and $g(x)$ Are f and g inverses of each other?

115. Let $c(w)$ represent the cost of mailing a package that weighs w pounds. Let $f(n)$ represent the weight, in pounds, of n copies of a certain book. Explain what $(c \circ f)(n)$ represents.

116. Let $g(a)$ represent the number of gallons of sealant needed to seal a bamboo floor with area a. Let $c(s)$ represent the cost of s gallons of sealant. Which composition makes sense: $(c \circ g)(a)$ or $(g \circ c)(s)$? What does it represent?

The following graphs show the rate of flow R, in liters per minute, of blood from the heart in a man who bicycles for 20 min, and the pressure P, in millimeters of mercury, in the artery leading to the lungs for a rate of blood flow R from the heart. (This problem was suggested by Kandace Kling, Portland Community College, Sylvania, Oregon.)

Blood Flow

Artery Pressure

117. Estimate $P(R(10))$.

118. Explain what $P(R(10))$ represents.

119. Estimate $P^{-1}(20)$.

Try Exercise Answers: Section 14.1

9. (a) $(f \circ g)(1) = 5$;
   (b) $(g \circ f)(1) = -1$;
   (c) $(f \circ g)(x) = x^2 - 6x + 10$;
   (d) $(g \circ f)(x) = x^2 - 2$
15. (a) $(f \circ g)(1) = 2$; **(b)** $(g \circ f)(1) = 4$;
   (c) $(f \circ g)(x) = \sqrt{x + 3}$; **(d)** $(g \circ f)(x) = \sqrt{x} + 3$
21. 8   **31.** $f(x) = x^4$; $g(x) = 3x - 5$
43. No   **45.** Yes
49. (a) Yes; **(b)** $f^{-1}(x) = x - 4$
73.   **75.**

83. (1) $(f^{-1} \circ f)(x) = f^{-1}(f(x))$
$$= f^{-1}\left(\sqrt[3]{x - 4}\right) = \left(\sqrt[3]{x - 4}\right)^3 + 4$$
$$= x - 4 + 4 = x;$$
   (2) $(f \circ f^{-1})(x) = f(f^{-1}(x))$
$$= f(x^3 + 4) = \sqrt[3]{x^3 + 4 - 4}$$
$$= \sqrt[3]{x^3} = x$$

14.2 Exponential Functions

- Graphing Exponential Functions

- Equations with *x* and *y* Interchanged

- Applications of Exponential Functions

In this section, we introduce a new type of function, the *exponential function*. These functions and their inverses, called *logarithmic functions*, have applications in many fields.

Consider the graph below. The rapidly rising curve approximates the graph of an *exponential function*. We now consider such functions and some of their applications.

Text Messaging in the United States

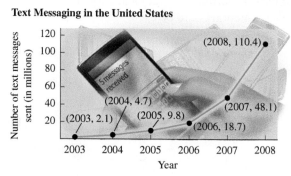

Source: U.S. Census Bureau

GRAPHING EXPONENTIAL FUNCTIONS

In Chapter 12, we studied exponential expressions with rational-number exponents, such as

$$5^{1/4}, \quad 3^{-3/4}, \quad 7^{2.34}, \quad 5^{1.73}.$$

For example, $5^{1.73}$, or $5^{173/100}$, represents the 100th root of 5 raised to the 173rd power. What about expressions with irrational exponents, such as $5^{\sqrt{3}}$ or $7^{-\pi}$? To attach meaning to $5^{\sqrt{3}}$, consider a rational approximation, r, of $\sqrt{3}$. As r gets closer to $\sqrt{3}$, the value of 5^r gets closer to some real number p.

$$\underbrace{r \text{ closes in on } \sqrt{3}.}_{}\qquad \underbrace{5^r \text{ closes in on some real number } p.}_{}$$

r closes in on $\sqrt{3}$.	5^r closes in on some real number p.
$1.7 < r < 1.8$	$15.426 \approx 5^{1.7} < p < 5^{1.8} \approx 18.119$
$1.73 < r < 1.74$	$16.189 \approx 5^{1.73} < p < 5^{1.74} \approx 16.452$
$1.732 < r < 1.733$	$16.241 \approx 5^{1.732} < p < 5^{1.733} \approx 16.267$

We define $5^{\sqrt{3}}$ to be the number p. To eight decimal places,

$$5^{\sqrt{3}} \approx 16.24245082.$$

Any positive irrational exponent can be interpreted in a similar way. Negative irrational exponents are then defined using reciprocals. Thus, so long as a is positive, a^x has meaning for *any* real number x. All of the laws of exponents still hold, but we will not prove that here. We can now define an *exponential function*.

Exponential Function   The function $f(x) = a^x$, where a is a positive constant, $a \neq 1$, and x is any real number, is called the *exponential function*, base a.

We require the base a to be positive to avoid imaginary numbers that would result from taking even roots of negative numbers. The restriction $a \neq 1$ is made to exclude the constant function $f(x) = 1^x$, or $f(x) = 1$.

The following are examples of exponential functions:

$$f(x) = 2^x, \qquad f(x) = \left(\tfrac{1}{3}\right)^x, \qquad f(x) = 5^{-3x}. \qquad \text{Note that } 5^{-3x} = (5^{-3})^x.$$

Like polynomial functions, the domain of an exponential function is the set of all real numbers. Unlike polynomial functions, exponential functions have a variable exponent. Because of this, graphs of exponential functions either rise or fall dramatically.

EXAMPLE 1   Graph the exponential function given by $y = f(x) = 2^x$.

SOLUTION   We compute some function values, thinking of y as $f(x)$, and list the results in a table. It is a good idea to start by letting $x = 0$.

$$f(0) = 2^0 = 1;$$
$$f(1) = 2^1 = 2;$$
$$f(2) = 2^2 = 4;$$
$$f(3) = 2^3 = 8;$$

$$f(-1) = 2^{-1} = \frac{1}{2^1} = \frac{1}{2};$$
$$f(-2) = 2^{-2} = \frac{1}{2^2} = \frac{1}{4};$$
$$f(-3) = 2^{-3} = \frac{1}{2^3} = \frac{1}{8}$$

x	y, or f(x)
0	1
1	2
2	4
3	8
−1	$\frac{1}{2}$
−2	$\frac{1}{4}$
−3	$\frac{1}{8}$

Next, we plot these points and connect them with a smooth curve.

The curve comes very close to the x-axis, but does not touch or cross it.

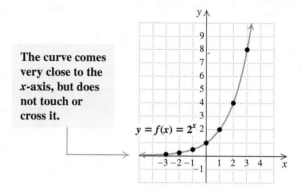

Be sure to plot enough points to determine how steeply the curve rises.

$y = f(x) = 2^x$

Note that as x increases, the function values increase without bound. As x decreases, the function values decrease, getting very close to 0. The x-axis, or the line $y = 0$, is a horizontal *asymptote*, meaning that the curve gets closer and closer to this line the further we move to the left.

Try Exercise 11.

EXAMPLE 2 Graph: $y = f(x) = \left(\frac{1}{2}\right)^x$.

SOLUTION We compute some function values, thinking of y as $f(x)$, and list the results in a table. Before we do this, note that

$$y = f(x) = \left(\tfrac{1}{2}\right)^x = (2^{-1})^x = 2^{-x}.$$

Then we have

$$f(0) = 2^{-0} = 1;$$

$$f(1) = 2^{-1} = \frac{1}{2^1} = \frac{1}{2};$$

$$f(2) = 2^{-2} = \frac{1}{2^2} = \frac{1}{4};$$

$$f(3) = 2^{-3} = \frac{1}{2^3} = \frac{1}{8};$$

$$f(-1) = 2^{-(-1)} = 2^1 = 2;$$
$$f(-2) = 2^{-(-2)} = 2^2 = 4;$$
$$f(-3) = 2^{-(-3)} = 2^3 = 8.$$

x	y, or f(x)
0	1
1	$\frac{1}{2}$
2	$\frac{1}{4}$
3	$\frac{1}{8}$
−1	2
−2	4
−3	8

Next, we plot these points and connect them with a smooth curve. This curve is a mirror image, or *reflection*, of the graph of $y = 2^x$ (see Example 1) across the y-axis. The line $y = 0$ is again the horizontal asymptote.

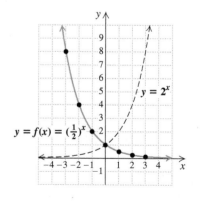

$y = f(x) = \left(\frac{1}{2}\right)^x$

$y = 2^x$

Try Exercise 23.

Interactive Discovery

If the values of $f(x)$ increase as x increases, we say that f is an *increasing function*. The function in Example 1, $f(x) = 2^x$, is increasing. If the values of $f(x)$ decrease as x increases, we say that f is a *decreasing function*. The function in Example 2, $f(x) = \left(\frac{1}{2}\right)^x$, is decreasing.

1. Graph each of the following functions, and determine whether the graph increases or decreases from left to right.

   a) $f(x) = 3^x$ **b)** $g(x) = 4^x$
   c) $h(x) = 1.5^x$ **d)** $r(x) = \left(\frac{1}{3}\right)^x$
   e) $t(x) = 0.75^x$

2. How can you tell from the number a in $f(x) = a^x$ whether the graph of f increases or decreases?

3. Compare the graphs of f, g, and h. Which curve is steepest?

4. Compare the graphs of r and t. Which curve is steeper?

We can make the following observations.

• For $a > 1$, the graph of $f(x) = a^x$ increases from left to right. The greater the value of a, the steeper the curve. (See the figure on the left below.)

 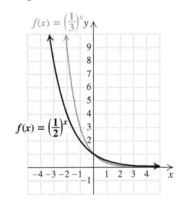

• For $0 < a < 1$, the graph of $f(x) = a^x$ decreases from left to right. For smaller values of a, the curve becomes steeper. (See the figure on the right above.)

• All graphs of $f(x) = a^x$ go through the y-intercept $(0, 1)$.

• All graphs of $f(x) = a^x$ have the x-axis as the horizontal asymptote.

• If $f(x) = a^x$, with $a > 0$, $a \neq 1$, the domain of f is all real numbers, and the range of f is all positive real numbers.

• For $a > 0$, $a \neq 1$, the function given by $f(x) = a^x$ is one-to-one. Its graph passes the horizontal-line test.

Student Notes

When using translations, make sure that you are shifting in the correct direction. When in doubt, substitute a value for x and make some calculations.

EXAMPLE 3 Graph: $y = f(x) = 2^{x-2}$.

SOLUTION We construct a table of values. Then we plot the points and connect them with a smooth curve. Here $x - 2$ is the *exponent*.

$$f(0) = 2^{0-2} = 2^{-2} = \tfrac{1}{4};$$
$$f(1) = 2^{1-2} = 2^{-1} = \tfrac{1}{2};$$
$$f(2) = 2^{2-2} = 2^{0} = 1;$$
$$f(3) = 2^{3-2} = 2^{1} = 2;$$
$$f(4) = 2^{4-2} = 2^{2} = 4;$$
$$f(-1) = 2^{-1-2} = 2^{-3} = \tfrac{1}{8};$$
$$f(-2) = 2^{-2-2} = 2^{-4} = \tfrac{1}{16}$$

x	y, or $f(x)$
0	$\frac{1}{4}$
1	$\frac{1}{2}$
2	1
3	2
4	4
-1	$\frac{1}{8}$
-2	$\frac{1}{16}$

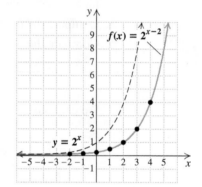

The graph looks just like the graph of $y = 2^x$, but it is translated 2 units to the right. The y-intercept of $y = 2^x$ is $(0, 1)$. The y-intercept of $y = 2^{x-2}$ is $\left(0, \tfrac{1}{4}\right)$. The line $y = 0$ is again the horizontal asymptote.

Try Exercise 19.

In general, the graph of $f(x) = 2^{x-h}$ will look like the graph of $y = 2^x$ translated right or left. Similarly, the graph of $f(x) = 2^x + k$ will look like the graph of 2^x translated up or down.

This observation is true in general.

The graph of $f(x) = a^{x-h} + k$ looks like the graph of $y = a^x$ translated $|h|$ units left or right and $|k|$ units up or down.

- If $h > 0$, $y = a^x$ is translated h units right.
- If $h < 0$, $y = a^x$ is translated $|h|$ units left.
- If $k > 0$, $y = a^x$ is translated k units up.
- If $k < 0$, $y = a^x$ is translated $|k|$ units down.

EQUATIONS WITH *x* AND *y* INTERCHANGED

It will be helpful in later work to be able to graph an equation in which the *x* and the *y* in $y = a^x$ are interchanged.

EXAMPLE 4   Graph: $x = 2^y$.

SOLUTION   Note that *x* is alone on one side of the equation. To find ordered pairs that are solutions, we choose values for *y* and then compute values for *x*:

For $y = 0$, $x = 2^0 = 1$.
For $y = 1$, $x = 2^1 = 2$.
For $y = 2$, $x = 2^2 = 4$.
For $y = 3$, $x = 2^3 = 8$.

For $y = -1$, $x = 2^{-1} = \dfrac{1}{2}$.

For $y = -2$, $x = 2^{-2} = \dfrac{1}{4}$.

For $y = -3$, $x = 2^{-3} = \dfrac{1}{8}$.

x	*y*
1	0
2	1
4	2
8	3
$\frac{1}{2}$	-1
$\frac{1}{4}$	-2
$\frac{1}{8}$	-3

(1) Choose values for *y*.
(2) Compute values for *x*.

We plot the points and connect them with a smooth curve.

The curve does not touch or cross the *y*-axis, which serves as a vertical asymptote.

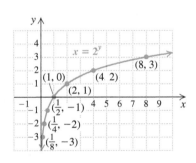

Note too that this curve looks just like the graph of $y = 2^x$, except that it is reflected across the line $y = x$, as shown here.

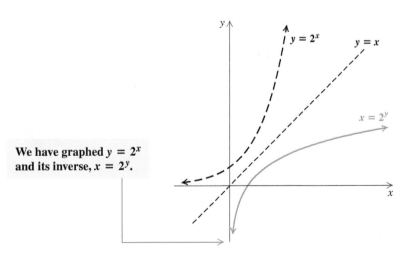

We have graphed $y = 2^x$ and its inverse, $x = 2^y$.

Try Exercise 33.

APPLICATIONS OF EXPONENTIAL FUNCTIONS

EXAMPLE 5 Interest Compounded Annually. The amount of money A that a principal P will be worth after t years at interest rate i, compounded annually, is given by the formula

$$A = P(1 + i)^t. \quad \text{You might review Example 12 in Section 13.1.}$$

Suppose that $100,000 is invested at 8% interest, compounded annually.

a) Find a function for the amount of money in the account after t years.

b) Find the amount of money in the account at $t = 0$, $t = 4$, $t = 8$, and $t = 10$.

c) Graph the function.

SOLUTION

a) If $P = \$100,000$ and $i = 8\% = 0.08$, we can substitute these values and form the following function:

$$A(t) = \$100,000(1 + 0.08)^t \quad \text{Using } A = P(1 + i)^t$$
$$= \$100,000(1.08)^t.$$

b) To find the function values, we let $y_1 = 100,000(1.08)^x$ and use the TABLE feature with Indpnt set to Ask, as shown at left. We highlight a table entry if we want to view the function value to more decimal places than is shown in the table. Large values in a table will be written in scientific notation.

Alternatively, we can use $y_1(\ )$ notation to evaluate the function for each value. Using either procedure gives us

$$A(0) = \$100,000,$$
$$A(4) \approx \$136,048.90,$$
$$A(8) \approx \$185,093.02,$$

and $A(10) \approx \$215,892.50$.

X	Y1
0	100000
4	136049
8	185093
10	215892

Y1 = 136048.896

c) We can use the function values computed in part (b), and others if we wish, to draw the graph by hand. Note that the axes will be scaled differently because of the large function values.

$A(t) = \$100,000(1.08)^t$

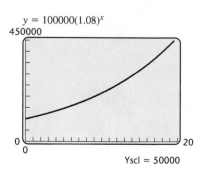

$y = 100000(1.08)^x$

450000

0

20

Yscl = 50000

Try Exercise 51.

Connecting the Concepts

Linear and Exponential Growth

Linear functions increase (or decrease) by a constant amount. The rate of change (slope) of a linear graph is constant. The rate of change of an exponential graph is not constant.

To illustrate the difference between linear growth and exponential growth, compare the salaries for two hypothetical jobs, shown in the table and the graph below. Note that the starting salaries are the same, but the salary for job A increases by a constant amount (linearly) and the salary for job B increases by a constant percent (exponentially).

Note that the salary for job A is larger for the first few years only. The rate of change of the salary for job B increases each year, since the increase is based on a larger salary each year.

	Job A	Job B
Starting salary	$50,000	$50,000
Guaranteed raise	$5000 per year	8% per year
Salary function	$f(x) = 50,000 + 5000x$	$g(x) = 50,000(1.08)^x$

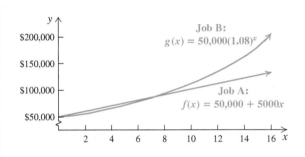

14.2   Exercise Set

FOR EXTRA HELP   *MyMathLab*   Math XL   PRACTICE   WATCH   DOWNLOAD   READ   REVIEW

↪ *Concept Reinforcement*   *Classify each of the following statements as either true or false.*

1. The graph of $f(x) = a^x$ always passes through the point $(0, 1)$.

2. The graph of $g(x) = \left(\frac{1}{2}\right)^x$ gets closer and closer to the x-axis as x gets larger and larger.

3. The graph of $f(x) = 2^{x-3}$ looks just like the graph of $y = 2^x$, but it is translated 3 units to the right.

4. The graph of $g(x) = 2^x - 3$ looks just like the graph of $y = 2^x$, but it is translated 3 units up.

5. The graph of $y = 3^x$ gets close to, but never touches, the y-axis.

6. The graph of $x = 3^y$ gets close to, but never touches, the y-axis.

Each of Exercises 7–10 shows the graph of a function $f(x) = a^x$. Determine from the graph whether $a > 1$ or $0 < a < 1$.

7.

8.

9.

10.

Graph.

11. $y = f(x) = 3^x$

12. $y = f(x) = 4^x$

13. $y = 5^x$

14. $y = 6^x$

15. $y = 2^x + 3$

16. $y = 2^x + 1$

17. $y = 3^x - 1$

18. $y = 3^x - 2$

19. $y = 2^{x-3}$

20. $y = 2^{x-1}$

21. $y = 2^{x+3}$

22. $y = 2^{x+1}$

23. $y = \left(\frac{1}{5}\right)^x$

24. $y = \left(\frac{1}{4}\right)^x$

25. $y = \left(\frac{1}{10}\right)^x$

26. $y = \left(\frac{1}{3}\right)^x$

27. $y = 2^{x-3} - 1$

28. $y = 2^{x+1} - 3$

29. $y = 1.7^x$

30. $y = 4.8^x$

31. $y = 0.15^x$

32. $y = 0.98^x$

33. $x = 3^y$

34. $x = 6^y$

35. $x = 2^{-y}$

36. $x = 3^{-y}$

37. $x = 5^y$

38. $x = 4^y$

39. $x = \left(\frac{3}{2}\right)^y$

40. $x = \left(\frac{4}{3}\right)^y$

Graph each pair of equations using the same set of axes.

41. $y = 3^x, \quad x = 3^y$

42. $y = 4^x, \quad x = 4^y$

43. $y = \left(\frac{1}{2}\right)^x, \quad x = \left(\frac{1}{2}\right)^y$

44. $y = \left(\frac{1}{4}\right)^x, \quad x = \left(\frac{1}{4}\right)^y$

Aha! *In Exercises 45–50, match each equation with one of the following graphs.*

a)

b)

c)

d)

e)

f)

45. $y = \left(\frac{5}{2}\right)^x$

46. $y = \left(\frac{2}{5}\right)^x$

47. $x = \left(\frac{5}{2}\right)^y$

48. $y = \left(\frac{2}{5}\right)^x - 3$

49. $y = \left(\frac{2}{5}\right)^{x-2}$

50. $y = \left(\frac{5}{2}\right)^x + 1$

Solve.

51. *Music Downloads.* The number $M(t)$ of single tracks downloaded, in billions, t years after 2003 can be approximated by

$$M(t) = 0.353(1.244)^t.$$

Source: Based on data from International Federation of the Phonographic Industry

a) Estimate the number of single tracks downloaded in 2006, in 2008, and in 2012.

b) Graph the function.

52. *Growth of Bacteria.* The bacteria *Escherichia coli* are commonly found in the human bladder. Suppose that 3000 of the bacteria are present at time $t = 0$. Then t minutes later, the number of bacteria present can be approximated by

$$N(t) = 3000(2)^{t/20}.$$

a) How many bacteria will be present after 10 min? 20 min? 30 min? 40 min? 60 min?

b) Graph the function.

53. *Smoking Cessation.* The percent of smokers $P(t)$ who, with telephone counseling to quit smoking, are still successful t months later can be approximated by

$$P(t) = 21.4(0.914)^t.$$

Sources: *New England Journal of Medicine*; data from California's Smokers' Hotline

a) Estimate the percent of smokers receiving telephone counseling who are successful in quitting for 1 month, 3 months, and 1 year.

b) Graph the function.

54. *Smoking Cessation.* The percent of smokers $P(t)$ who, without telephone counseling, have successfully quit smoking for t months (see Exercise 53) can be approximated by

$$P(t) = 9.02(0.93)^t.$$

Sources: *New England Journal of Medicine*; data from California's Smokers' Hotline

a) Estimate the percent of smokers not receiving telephone counseling who are successful in quitting for 1 month, 3 months, and 1 year.

b) Graph the function.

55. *Marine Biology.* Due to excessive whaling prior to the mid 1970s, the humpback whale is considered an endangered species. The worldwide population of humpbacks $P(t)$, in thousands, t years after 1900 ($t < 70$) can be approximated by

$$P(t) = 150(0.960)^t.$$

Source: Based on information from the American Cetacean Society, 2006, and the ASK Archive, 1998

a) How many humpback whales were alive in 1930? in 1960?

b) Graph the function.

56. *Salvage Value.* A laser printer is purchased for $1200. Its value each year is about 80% of the value of the preceding year. Its value, in dollars, after t years is given by the exponential function

$$V(t) = 1200(0.8)^t.$$

a) Find the value of the printer after 0 year, 1 year, 2 years, 5 years, and 10 years.

b) Graph the function.

57. *Marine Biology.* As a result of preservation efforts in most countries in which whaling was common, the humpback whale population has grown since the 1970s. The worldwide population of humpbacks $P(t)$, in thousands, t years after 1982 can be approximated by

$$P(t) = 5.5(1.08)^t.$$

Source: Based on information from the American Cetacean Society, 2006, and the ASK Archive, 1998

a) How many humpback whales were alive in 1992? in 2006?

b) Graph the function.

58. *Recycling Aluminum Cans.* About $\frac{1}{2}$ of all aluminum cans will be recycled. A beverage company distributes 250,000 cans. The number in use after t years is given by the exponential function

$$N(t) = 250{,}000\left(\tfrac{1}{2}\right)^t.$$

Source: The Aluminum Association, Inc., 2009

a) How many cans are still in use after 0 year? 1 year? 4 years? 10 years?

b) Graph the function.

59. *Invasive Species.* Ruffe is a species of freshwater fish that is considered invasive where it is not native. The function

$$R(t) = 2(1.75)^t$$

can be used to estimate the number of ruffe in a lake t years after 2 fish have been introduced to the lake.

Source: Based on information from invasivespeciesireland.com

a) How many fish will be in the lake 10 years after 2 ruffe have been introduced? after 15 years?

b) Graph the function.

60. *mp3 Players.* The number $m(t)$ of mp3 players sold per year in the United States, in millions, can be estimated by

$$m(t) = 34.3(1.25)^t,$$

where t is the number of years after 2006.

Source: Forrester Research, Inc.

a) Estimate the number of mp3 players sold in 2006, in 2010, and in 2012.

b) Graph the function.

61. Without using a calculator, explain why 2^π must be greater than 8 but less than 16.

62. Suppose that $1000 is invested for 5 years at 7% interest, compounded annually. In what year will the most interest be earned? Why?

SKILL REVIEW

Review factoring polynomials.

Factor.

63. $3x^2 - 48$

64. $x^2 - 20x + 100$

65. $6x^2 + x - 12$

66. $8x^6 - 64y^6$

67. $6y^2 + 36y - 240$

68. $5x^4 - 10x^3 - 3x^2 + 6x$

SYNTHESIS

ᵀᵂ **69.** Examine Exercise 60. Do you believe that the equation for the number of mp3 players sold in the United States will be accurate 20 years from now? Why or why not?

ᵀᵂ **70.** Why was it necessary to discuss irrational exponents before graphing exponential functions?

Determine which of the two given numbers is larger. Do not use a calculator.

71. $\pi^{1.3}$ or $\pi^{2.4}$

72. $\sqrt{8^3}$ or $8^{\sqrt{3}}$

Graph.

73. $y = 2^x + 2^{-x}$

74. $y = \left|\left(\frac{1}{2}\right)^x - 1\right|$

75. $y = |2^x - 2|$

76. $y = 2^{-(x-1)^2}$

77. $y = |2^{x^2} - 1|$

78. $y = 3^x + 3^{-x}$

Graph both equations using the same set of axes.

79. $y = 3^{-(x-1)}$, $x = 3^{-(y-1)}$

80. $y = 1^x$, $x = 1^y$

81. *Navigational Devices.* The number of GPS navigational devices in use in the United States has grown from 0.5 million in 2000 to 4 million in 2004 to 50 million in 2008. After pressing **STAT** and entering the data, use the ExpReg option in the STAT CALC menu to find an exponential function that models the number of navigational devices in use t years after 2000. Then use that function to predict the total number of devices in use in 2012.
Source: Telematics Research Group

82. *Keyboarding Speed.* Trey is studying keyboarding. After he has studied for t hours, Trey's speed, in words per minute, is given by the exponential function

$$S(t) = 200[1 - (0.99)^t].$$

Use a graph and/or table of values to predict Trey's speed after studying for 10 hr, 40 hr, and 80 hr.

ᵀᵂ **83.** The graph below shows growth in the height of ocean waves over time, assuming a steady surface wind.
Source: magicseaweed.com

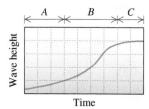

Source: magicseaweed.com

a) Consider the portions of the graph marked A, B, and C. Suppose that each portion can be labeled Exponential Growth, Linear Growth, or Saturation. How would you label each portion?

b) Small vertical movements in wind, surface roughness of water, and gravity are three forces that create waves. How might these forces be related to the shape of the wave-height graph?

ᵀᵂ **84.** Consider any exponential function of the form $f(x) = a^x$ with $a > 1$. Will it always follow that $f(3) - f(2) > f(2) - f(1)$, and, in general, $f(n + 2) - f(n + 1) > f(n + 1) - f(n)$? Why or why not? (*Hint:* Think graphically.)

85. On many graphing calculators, it is possible to enter and graph $y_1 = A\wedge(X - B) + C$ after first pressing **APPS** Transfrm. Use this application to graph $f(x) = 2.5^{x-3} + 2$, $g(x) = 2.5^{x+3} + 2$, $h(x) = 2.5^{x-3} - 2$, and $k(x) = 2.5^{x+3} - 2$.

Try Exercise Answers: Section 14.2

11.

19. $y = 2^{x-3}$

$y = f(x) = 3^x$

23. $y = \left(\frac{1}{8}\right)^x$

33. $x = 3^y$

51. **(a)** About 0.68 billion tracks; about 1.052 billion tracks; about 2.519 billion tracks;
(b)

$M(t) = 0.353(1.244)^t$

Years since 2003

The True Cost of a New Car

Focus: Car loans and exponential functions
Time: 30 minutes
Group Size: 2
Materials: Calculators with exponentiation keys

The formula

$$M = \frac{Pr}{1 - (1 + r)^{-n}}$$

is used to determine the payment size, M, when a loan of P dollars is to be repaid in n equally sized monthly payments. Here r represents the monthly interest rate. Loans repaid in this fashion are said to be *amortized* (spread out equally) over a period of n months.

ACTIVITY

1. Suppose one group member is selling the other a car for $2600, financed at 1% interest per month

for 24 months. What should be the size of each monthly payment?

2. Suppose both group members are shopping for the same model new car. Each group member visits a different dealer. One dealer offers the car for $13,000 at 10.5% interest (0.00875 monthly interest) for 60 months (no down payment). The other dealer offers the same car for $12,000, but at 12% interest (0.01 monthly interest) for 48 months (no down payment)

   a) Determine the monthly payment size for each offer. Then determine the total amount paid for the car under each offer. How much of each total is interest?

   b) Work together to find the annual interest rate for which the total cost of 60 monthly payments for the $13,000 car would equal the total cost of 48 monthly payments for the $12,000 car (as found in part (a) above).

14.3 Logarithmic Functions

- Graphs of Logarithmic Functions

- Common Logarithms

- Equivalent Equations

- Solving Certain Logarithmic Equations

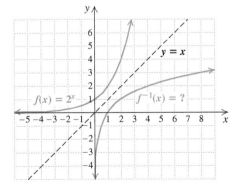

We are now ready to study inverses of exponential functions. These functions have many applications and are referred to as *logarithm*, or *logarithmic, functions*.

GRAPHS OF LOGARITHMIC FUNCTIONS

Consider the exponential function $f(x) = 2^x$. Like all exponential functions, f is one-to-one. Can a formula for f^{-1} be found? To answer this, we use the method of Section 14.1:

1. Replace $f(x)$ with y: $y = 2^x$.
2. Interchange x and y: $x = 2^y$.
3. Solve for y: y = the power to which we raise 2 to get x.
4. Replace y with $f^{-1}(x)$: $f^{-1}(x)$ = the power to which we raise 2 to get x.

We now define a new symbol to replace the words "the power to which we raise 2 to get x":

> $\log_2 x$, read "the logarithm, base 2, of x," or "log, base 2, of x," means "the exponent to which we raise 2 to get x."

Thus if $f(x) = 2^x$, then $f^{-1}(x) = \log_2 x$. Note that $f^{-1}(8) = \log_2 8 = 3$, because 3 is *the exponent to which we raise 2 to get* 8.

EXAMPLE 1 Simplify: **(a)** $\log_2 32$; **(b)** $\log_2 1$; **(c)** $\log_2 \frac{1}{8}$.

SOLUTION

a) Think of $\log_2 32$ as the exponent to which we raise 2 to get 32. That exponent is 5. Therefore, $\log_2 32 = 5$.

b) We ask ourselves: "To what exponent do we raise 2 in order to get 1?" That exponent is 0 (recall that $2^0 = 1$). Thus, $\log_2 1 = 0$.

c) To what exponent do we raise 2 in order to get $\frac{1}{8}$? Since $2^{-3} = \frac{1}{8}$, we have $\log_2 \frac{1}{8} = -3$.

Try Exercise 9.

Although numbers like $\log_2 13$ can be only approximated, we must remember that $\log_2 13$ represents *the exponent to which we raise 2 to get* 13. That is, $2^{\log_2 13} = 13$. Using an approximation, we see that $2^{3.7} \approx 13$. Therefore, $\log_2 13 \approx 3.7$.

For any exponential function $f(x) = a^x$, the inverse is called a **logarithmic function, base a.** The graph of the inverse can be drawn by reflecting the graph of $f(x) = a^x$ across the line $y = x$. It will be helpful to remember that the inverse of $f(x) = a^x$ is given by $f^{-1}(x) = \log_a x$.

The Meaning of $\log_a x$ For $x > 0$ and a a positive constant other than 1, $\log_a x$ is the exponent to which a must be raised in order to get x. Thus,

$$\log_a x = m \text{ means } a^m = x$$

or, equivalently,

$$\log_a x \text{ is that unique exponent for which } a^{\log_a x} = x.$$

Student Notes

As an aid in remembering what $\log_a x$ means, note that a is called the *base*, just as it is the base in $a^y = x$.

It is important to remember that *a logarithm is an exponent*. It might help to repeat several times: "The logarithm, base a, of a number x is the exponent to which a must be raised in order to get x."

EXAMPLE 2   Simplify: $7^{\log_7 85}$.

SOLUTION   Remember that $\log_7 85$ is the exponent to which 7 is raised to get 85. Raising 7 to that exponent, we have

$$7^{\log_7 85} = 85.$$

Try Exercise 35.

Because logarithmic functions and exponential functions are inverses of each other, the result in Example 2 should come as no surprise: If $f(x) = \log_7 x$, then

for $f(x) = \log_7 x$, we have $f^{-1}(x) = 7^x$

and $f^{-1}(f(x)) = f^{-1}(\log_7 x) = 7^{\log_7 x} = x$.

Thus, $f^{-1}(f(85)) = 7^{\log_7 85} = 85$.

The following is a comparison of exponential and logarithmic functions.

Exponential Function	Logarithmic Function
$y = a^x$	$x = a^y$
$f(x) = a^x$	$g(x) = \log_a x$
$a > 0, a \neq 1$	$a > 0, a \neq 1$
The domain is $\mathbb{R}$.	The range is $\mathbb{R}$.
The range is $(0, \infty)$.	The domain is $(0, \infty)$.
$f^{-1}(x) = \log_a x$	$g^{-1}(x) = a^x$
The graph of $f(x)$ contains the points $(0, 1)$ and $(1, a)$.	The graph of $g(x)$ contains the points $(1, 0)$ and $(a, 1)$.

Student Notes

Since $g(x) = \log_a x$ is the inverse of $f(x) = a^x$, the domain of f is the range of g, and the range of f is the domain of g.

EXAMPLE 3   Graph: $y = f(x) = \log_5 x$.

SOLUTION   If $y = \log_5 x$, then $5^y = x$. We can find ordered pairs that are solutions by choosing values for y and computing the x-values.

For $y = 0$, $x = 5^0 = 1$.
For $y = 1$, $x = 5^1 = 5$.
For $y = 2$, $x = 5^2 = 25$.
For $y = -1$, $x = 5^{-1} = \frac{1}{5}$.
For $y = -2$, $x = 5^{-2} = \frac{1}{25}$.

(1) Select y.
(2) Compute x.

This table shows the following:

$$\left. \begin{array}{l} \log_5 1 = 0; \\ \log_5 5 = 1; \\ \log_5 25 = 2; \\ \log_5 \frac{1}{5} = -1; \\ \log_5 \frac{1}{25} = -2. \end{array} \right\}$$ **These can all be checked using the equations above.**

x, or 5^y	y
1	0
5	1
25	2
$\frac{1}{5}$	-1
$\frac{1}{25}$	-2

We plot the set of ordered pairs and connect the points with a smooth curve. The graphs of $y = 5^x$ and $y = x$ are shown only for reference.

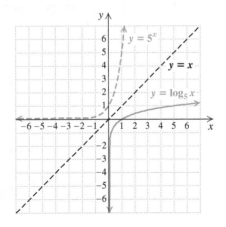

Try Exercise 37.

COMMON LOGARITHMS

Any positive number other than 1 can serve as the base of a logarithmic function. However, some logarithm bases fit into certain applications more naturally than others.

Base-10 logarithms, called **common logarithms,** are useful because they have the same base as our "commonly" used decimal system. Before calculators became so widely available, common logarithms helped with tedious calculations. In fact, that is why logarithms were developed. At first, printed tables listed common logarithms. Today we find common logarithms using calculators.

The abbreviation **log,** with no base written, is generally understood to mean logarithm base 10—that is, a common logarithm. Thus,

$$\log 17 \quad \text{means} \quad \log_{10} 17. \qquad \text{It is important to remember this abbreviation.}$$

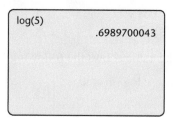

Common Logarithms

The key for common logarithms is usually marked **LOG**. Some calculators automatically supply the left parenthesis when **LOG** is pressed. You may have to supply a right parenthesis to close the expression. Even if a calculator does not require an ending parenthesis, it is a good idea to include one.

For example, if we are using a calculator that supplies the left parenthesis, log 5 can be found by pressing **LOG** **5** **)** **ENTER**. Note from the screen on the left below that log 5 ≈ 0.6990.

```
log(5)
            .6989700043
```

```
log(2/3)
               -.1760912591
log(2)/log(3)
               .6309297536
```

Parentheses must be placed carefully when evaluating expressions containing logarithms. For example, to evaluate

$$\log \frac{2}{3},$$

press **LOG** **2** **÷** **3** **)** **ENTER**. To evaluate

$$\frac{\log 2}{\log 3},$$

press **LOG** **2** **)** **÷** **LOG** **3** **)** **ENTER**. Note from the screen on the right above that $\log \dfrac{2}{3} \approx -0.1761$ and that $\dfrac{\log 2}{\log 3} \approx 0.6309$.

The inverse of $f(x) = \log_{10} x$ is $g(x) = 10^x$. Because of this, on many calculators the **LOG** key serves as the **10ˣ** key after the **2ND** key is pressed. As with logarithms, some calculators automatically supply a left parenthesis before the exponent. Using such a calculator, we find $10^{3.417}$ by pressing **10ˣ** **3** **·** **4** **1** **7** **)** **ENTER**. The result is approximately 2612.1614. If we then press **LOG** **ANS** **)** **ENTER**, the result is 3.417. This illustrates that $f(x) = \log x$ and $g(x) = 10^x$ are inverse functions.

```
10^(3.417)
                    2612.161354
log(Ans)
                          3.417
```

Your Turn

1. Find log 100.   2
2. Find $\log \frac{15}{8}$.   About 0.2730
3. Find $\dfrac{\log 15}{\log 8}$.   About 1.3023
4. Find $10^{1.2}$.   About 15.8489
5. Find log 96. Then press **10ˣ** **ANS**.   The result should be 96.

It is important to place parentheses properly when entering logarithmic expressions in a graphing calculator.

EXAMPLE 4   Graph: $f(x) = \log \dfrac{x}{5} + 1$.

SOLUTION   We enter $y = \log(x/5) + 1$. Since logarithms of negative numbers are not defined, we set the window accordingly. The graph is shown below. Note that although on the calculator the graph appears to touch the y-axis, a table of values or TRACE would show that the y-axis is indeed an asymptote.

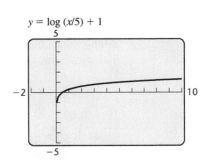

$y = \log(x/5) + 1$

Try Exercise 59.

EQUIVALENT EQUATIONS

We use the definition of logarithm to rewrite a *logarithmic equation* as an equivalent *exponential equation* or the other way around:

$$m = \log_a x \quad \text{is equivalent to} \quad a^m = x.$$

> **CAUTION!**   **Do not forget this relationship!** It is probably the most important definition in the chapter. Many times this definition will be used to justify a property we are considering.

EXAMPLE 5 Rewrite each as an equivalent exponential equation.

a) $y = \log_3 5$ **b)** $-2 = \log_a 7$

c) $a = \log_b d$

SOLUTION

a) $y = \log_3 5$ is equivalent to $3^y = 5$ The logarithm is the exponent.

                                                  The base remains the base.

b) $-2 = \log_a 7$ is equivalent to $a^{-2} = 7$

c) $a = \log_b d$ is equivalent to $b^a = d$

Try Exercise 65.

EXAMPLE 6 Rewrite each as an equivalent logarithmic equation: **(a)** $8 = 2^x$; **(b)** $y^{-1} = 4$; **(c)** $a^b = c$.

SOLUTION

a) $8 = 2^x$ is equivalent to $x = \log_2 8$ The exponent is the logarithm.

                                                  The base remains the base.

b) $y^{-1} = 4$ is equivalent to $-1 = \log_y 4$

c) $a^b = c$ is equivalent to $b = \log_a c$

Try Exercise 81.

SOLVING CERTAIN LOGARITHMIC EQUATIONS

Many logarithmic equations can be solved by rewriting them as equivalent exponential equations.

EXAMPLE 7 Solve: **(a)** $\log_2 x = -3$; **(b)** $\log_x 16 = 2$.

SOLUTION

a) $\log_2 x = -3$

      $2^{-3} = x$ Rewriting as an exponential equation

      $\frac{1}{8} = x$ Computing 2^{-3}

Check: $\log_2 \frac{1}{8}$ is the exponent to which 2 is raised to get $\frac{1}{8}$. Since that exponent is -3, we have a check. The solution is $\frac{1}{8}$.

b) $\log_x 16 = 2$

      $x^2 = 16$ Rewriting as an exponential equation

    $x = 4$ *or* $x = -4$ Principle of square roots

Check: $\log_4 16 = 2$ because $4^2 = 16$. Thus, 4 is a solution of $\log_x 16 = 2$. Because all logarithmic bases must be positive, -4 cannot be a solution. Logarithmic bases must be positive because logarithms are defined using exponential functions that require positive bases. The solution is 4.

Try Exercise 97.

One method for solving certain logarithmic equations and exponential equations relies on the following property, which results from the fact that exponential functions are one-to-one.

The Principle of Exponential Equality   For any real number b, where $b \neq -1, 0,$ or 1,

$$b^x = b^y \quad \text{is equivalent to} \quad x = y.$$

(Powers of the same base are equal if and only if the exponents are equal.)

EXAMPLE 8   Solve: **(a)** $\log_{10} 1000 = x$; **(b)** $\log_4 1 = t$.

SOLUTION

a) We rewrite $\log_{10} 1000 = x$ in exponential form and solve:

$$10^x = 1000 \qquad \text{Rewriting as an exponential equation}$$
$$10^x = 10^3 \qquad \text{Writing 1000 as a power of 10}$$
$$x = 3. \qquad \text{Equating exponents}$$

Check: This equation can also be solved directly by determining the exponent to which we raise 10 in order to get 1000. In both cases, we find that $\log_{10} 1000 = 3$, so we have a check. The solution is 3.

b) We rewrite $\log_4 1 = t$ in exponential form and solve:

$$4^t = 1 \qquad \text{Rewriting as an exponential equation}$$
$$4^t = 4^0 \qquad \text{Writing 1 as a power of 4. This can be done mentally.}$$
$$t = 0. \qquad \text{Equating exponents}$$

Check: As in part (a), this equation can be solved directly by determining the exponent to which we raise 4 in order to get 1. In both cases, we find that $\log_4 1 = 0$, so we have a check. The solution is 0.

Try Exercise 99.

Example 8 illustrates an important property of logarithms.

$\log_a 1$

The logarithm, base a, of 1 is always 0: $\log_a 1 = 0$.

This follows from the fact that $a^0 = 1$ is equivalent to the logarithmic equation $\log_a 1 = 0$. Thus, $\log_{10} 1 = 0, \log_7 1 = 0$, and so on.

Another property results from the fact that $a^1 = a$. This is equivalent to the equation $\log_a a = 1$.

$\log_a a$

The logarithm, base a, of a is always 1: $\log_a a = 1$.

Thus, $\log_{10} 10 = 1, \log_8 8 = 1$, and so on.

14.3 Exercise Set

FOR EXTRA HELP   MyMathLab   Math XL
PRACTICE   WATCH   DOWNLOAD   READ   REVIEW

Concept Reinforcement   *In each of Exercises 1–8, match the expression or equation with an equivalent expression or equation from the column on the right.*

1. _____ $\log_5 25$ a) 1

2. _____ $2^5 = x$ b) x

3. _____ $\log_5 5$ c) $x^5 = 27$

4. _____ $\log_2 1$ d) $\log_2 x = 5$

5. _____ $\log_5 5^x$ e) $\log_2 5 = x$

6. _____ $\log_x 27 = 5$ f) $\log_x 5 = -2$

7. _____ $5 = 2^x$ g) 2

8. _____ $x^{-2} = 5$ h) 0

Simplify.

9. $\log_{10} 1000$ 10. $\log_{10} 100$

11. $\log_2 16$ 12. $\log_2 8$

13. $\log_3 81$ 14. $\log_3 27$

15. $\log_4 \frac{1}{16}$ 16. $\log_4 \frac{1}{4}$

17. $\log_7 \frac{1}{7}$ 18. $\log_7 \frac{1}{49}$

19. $\log_5 625$ 20. $\log_5 125$

21. $\log_8 8$ 22. $\log_7 1$

23. $\log_8 1$ 24. $\log_8 8$

Aha! 25. $\log_9 9^5$ 26. $\log_9 9^{10}$

27. $\log_{10} 0.01$ 28. $\log_{10} 0.1$

29. $\log_9 3$ 30. $\log_{16} 4$

31. $\log_9 27$ 32. $\log_{16} 64$

33. $\log_{1000} 100$ 34. $\log_{27} 9$

35. $5^{\log_5 7}$ 36. $6^{\log_6 13}$

Graph by hand.

37. $y = \log_{10} x$ 38. $y = \log_2 x$

39. $y = \log_3 x$ 40. $y = \log_7 x$

41. $f(x) = \log_6 x$ 42. $f(x) = \log_4 x$

43. $f(x) = \log_{2.5} x$ 44. $f(x) = \log_{1/2} x$

Graph both functions using the same set of axes.

45. $f(x) = 3^x$, $f^{-1}(x) = \log_3 x$

46. $f(x) = 4^x$, $f^{-1}(x) = \log_4 x$

Use a calculator to find each of the following rounded to four decimal places.

47. $\log 4$ 48. $\log 5$

49. $\log 13{,}400$ 50. $\log 93{,}100$

51. $\log 0.527$ 52. $\log 0.493$

Use a calculator to find each of the following rounded to four decimal places.

53. $10^{2.3}$ 54. $10^{0.173}$

55. $10^{-2.9523}$ 56. $10^{4.8982}$

57. $10^{0.0012}$ 58. $10^{-3.89}$

Graph using a graphing calculator.

59. $\log (x + 2)$ 60. $\log (x - 5)$

61. $\log (2x) - 3$ 62. $\log (3x) + 2$

63. $\log (x^2)$ 64. $\log (x^2 + 1)$

Rewrite each of the following as an equivalent exponential equation. Do not solve.

65. $x = \log_{10} 8$ 66. $h = \log_7 10$

67. $\log_9 9 = 1$ 68. $\log_6 6 = 1$

69. $\log_{10} 0.1 = -1$ 70. $\log_{10} 0.01 = -2$

71. $\log_{10} 7 = 0.845$ 72. $\log_{10} 3 = 0.4771$

73. $\log_c m = 8$ 74. $\log_b n = 23$

75. $\log_t Q = r$ 76. $\log_m P = a$

77. $\log_e 0.25 = -1.3863$ 78. $\log_e 0.989 = -0.0111$

79. $\log_r T = -x$ 80. $\log_c M = -w$

Rewrite each of the following as an equivalent logarithmic equation. Do not solve.

81. $10^2 = 100$ 82. $10^4 = 10{,}000$

83. $4^{-5} = \frac{1}{1024}$ 84. $5^{-3} = \frac{1}{125}$

85. $16^{3/4} = 8$ 86. $8^{1/3} = 2$

87. $10^{0.4771} = 3$ 88. $10^{0.3010} = 2$

89. $z^m = 6$

90. $m^n = r$

91. $p^m = V$

92. $Q^t = x$

93. $e^3 = 20.0855$

94. $e^2 = 7.3891$

95. $e^{-4} = 0.0183$

96. $e^{-2} = 0.1353$

Solve.

97. $\log_3 x = 2$

98. $\log_4 x = 3$

99. $\log_5 125 = x$

100. $\log_4 64 = x$

101. $\log_x 16 = 4$

102. $\log_x 81 = 2$

103. $\log_x 7 = 1$

104. $\log_x 8 = 1$

105. $\log_x 9 = \frac{1}{2}$

106. $\log_x 11 = \frac{1}{2}$

107. $\log_3 x = -2$

108. $\log_2 x = -1$

109. $\log_{32} x = \frac{2}{5}$

110. $\log_8 x = \frac{2}{3}$

111. Explain why we say that "a logarithm is an exponent."

112. Is it easier to find x given $x = \log_9 \frac{1}{3}$ or given $9^x = \frac{1}{3}$? Explain your reasoning.

SKILL REVIEW

To prepare for Section 14.4, review rules for working with exponents.

Simplify.

113. $a^{12} \cdot a^6$

114. $x^4(x^5)$

115. $\dfrac{x^{12}}{x^4}$

116. $\dfrac{a^{15}}{a^3}$

117. $(y^3)^5$

118. $(n^{15})^2$

119. $x^2 \cdot x^3$

120. $(x^2)^3$

SYNTHESIS

121. Would a manufacturer be pleased or unhappy if sales of a product grew logarithmically? Why?

122. Explain why the number $\log_{10} 70$ must be between 1 and 2.

123. Graph both equations using the same set of axes:
$$y = \left(\tfrac{3}{2}\right)^x, \qquad y = \log_{3/2} x.$$

Graph by hand.

124. $y = \log_2 (x - 1)$

125. $y = \log_3 |x + 1|$

Solve.

126. $|\log_3 x| = 2$

127. $\log_4 (3x - 2) = 2$

128. $\log_8 (2x + 1) = -1$

129. $\log_{10} (x^2 + 21x) = 2$

Simplify.

130. $\log_{1/4} \frac{1}{64}$

131. $\log_{1/5} 25$

132. $\log_{81} 3 \cdot \log_3 81$

133. $\log_{10} (\log_4 (\log_3 81))$

134. $\log_2 (\log_2 (\log_4 256))$

135. Show that $b^x = b^y$ is *not* equivalent to $x = y$ for $b = 0$ or $b = 1$.

136. If $\log_b a = x$, does it follow that $\log_a b = 1/x$? Why or why not?

Try Exercise Answers: Section 14.3

9. 3   **35.** 7   **37.**

59. $y = \log (x + 2)$ **65.** $10^x = 8$ **81.** $2 = \log_{10} 100$ **97.** 9   **99.** 3

14.4   Properties of Logarithmic Functions

- Logarithms of Products

- Logarithms of Powers

- Logarithms of Quotients

- Using the Properties Together

Logarithmic functions are important in many applications and in more advanced mathematics. We now establish some basic properties that are useful in manipulating expressions involving logarithms.

The following Interactive Discovery explores some of these properties. In this section, we will state and prove the results you may observe. As their proofs reveal, the properties of logarithms are related to the properties of exponents.

Interactive Discovery

For each of the following, use a calculator to determine which is the equivalent logarithmic expression.

1. $\log (20 \cdot 5)$
   a) $\log (20) \cdot \log (5)$
   b) $5 \cdot \log (20)$
   c) $\log (20) + \log (5)$

2. $\log (20^5)$
   a) $\log (20) \cdot \log (5)$
   b) $5 \cdot \log (20)$
   c) $\log (20) - \log (5)$

3. $\log \left(\dfrac{20}{5} \right)$
   a) $\log (20) \cdot \log (5)$
   b) $\log (20)/\log (5)$
   c) $\log (20) - \log (5)$

4. $\log \left(\dfrac{1}{20} \right)$
   a) $-\log (20)$
   b) $\log (1)/\log (20)$
   c) $\log (1) \cdot \log (20)$

LOGARITHMS OF PRODUCTS

The first property we discuss is related to the product rule for exponents: $a^m \cdot a^n = a^{m+n}$. Its proof appears immediately after Example 2.

> **The Product Rule for Logarithms**   For any positive numbers M, N, and a ($a \neq 1$),
>
> $$\log_a (MN) = \log_a M + \log_a N.$$
>
> (The logarithm of a product is the sum of the logarithms of the factors.)

EXAMPLE 1   Express as an equivalent expression that is a sum of logarithms: $\log_2 (4 \cdot 16)$.

SOLUTION   We have

$$\log_2 (4 \cdot 16) = \log_2 4 + \log_2 16. \qquad \text{Using the product rule for logarithms}$$

As a check, note that

$$\log_2 (4 \cdot 16) = \log_2 64 = 6 \qquad 2^6 = 64$$

and that

$$\log_2 4 + \log_2 16 = 2 + 4 = 6. \qquad 2^2 = 4 \text{ and } 2^4 = 16$$

Try Exercise 7.

EXAMPLE 2   Express as an equivalent expression that is a single logarithm: $\log_b 7 + \log_b 5$.

SOLUTION   We have

$$\log_b 7 + \log_b 5 = \log_b (7 \cdot 5) \qquad \text{Using the product rule for logarithms}$$
$$= \log_b 35.$$

Try Exercise 13.

A Proof of the Product Rule.   Let $\log_a M = x$ and $\log_a N = y$. Converting to exponential equations, we have $a^x = M$ and $a^y = N$.

Now we multiply the left sides of both equations and the right sides of both equations to obtain

$$MN = a^x \cdot a^y, \quad \text{or} \quad MN = a^{x+y}.$$

Converting back to a logarithmic equation, we get

$$\log_a (MN) = x + y.$$

Recalling what x and y represent, we get

$$\log_a (MN) = \log_a M + \log_a N.$$

LOGARITHMS OF POWERS

The second basic property is related to the power rule for exponents: $(a^m)^n = a^{mn}$. Its proof follows Example 3.

> **The Power Rule for Logarithms**   For any positive numbers M and a ($a \neq 1$), and any real number p,
>
> $$\log_a M^p = p \cdot \log_a M.$$
>
> (The logarithm of a power of M is the exponent times the logarithm of M.)

To better understand the power rule, note that

$$\log_a M^3 = \log_a (M \cdot M \cdot M) = \log_a M + \log_a M + \log_a M = 3 \log_a M.$$

EXAMPLE 3   Use the power rule for logarithms to write an equivalent expression that is a product: (a) $\log_a 9^{-5}$;   (b) $\log_7 \sqrt[3]{x}$.

SOLUTION

a) $\log_a 9^{-5} = -5 \log_a 9$ Using the power rule for logarithms

b) $\log_7 \sqrt[3]{x} = \log_7 x^{1/3}$ Writing exponential notation

$\qquad\qquad = \frac{1}{3} \log_7 x$ Using the power rule for logarithms

Try Exercise 17.

Student Notes

Without understanding and *remembering* the rules of this section, it will be extremely difficult to solve the equations of Section 14.6.

A Proof of the Power Rule. Let $x = \log_a M$. The equivalent exponential equation is $a^x = M$. Raising both sides to the pth power, we get

$$(a^x)^p = M^p, \quad \text{or} \quad a^{xp} = M^p. \quad \text{Multiplying exponents}$$

Converting back to a logarithmic equation gives us

$$\log_a M^p = xp.$$

But $x = \log_a M$, so substituting, we have

$$\log_a M^p = (\log_a M)p = p \cdot \log_a M.$$

LOGARITHMS OF QUOTIENTS

The third property that we study is similar to the quotient rule for exponents: $\dfrac{a^m}{a^n} = a^{m-n}$. Its proof follows Example 5.

The Quotient Rule for Logarithms For any positive numbers M, N, and a ($a \neq 1$),

$$\log_a \frac{M}{N} = \log_a M - \log_a N.$$

(The logarithm of a quotient is the logarithm of the dividend minus the logarithm of the divisor.)

To better understand the quotient rule, note that

$$\log_2 \tfrac{8}{32} = \log_2 \tfrac{1}{4} = -2$$

and $\log_2 8 - \log_2 32 = 3 - 5 = -2.$

EXAMPLE 4 Express as an equivalent expression that is a difference of logarithms: $\log_t (6/U)$.

SOLUTION

$$\log_t \frac{6}{U} = \log_t 6 - \log_t U \quad \text{Using the quotient rule for logarithms}$$

Try Exercise 23.

EXAMPLE 5 Express as an equivalent expression that is a single logarithm: $\log_b 17 - \log_b 27$.

SOLUTION

$$\log_b 17 - \log_b 27 = \log_b \frac{17}{27} \quad \begin{array}{l}\text{Using the quotient rule for logarithms}\\ \text{"in reverse"}\end{array}$$

Try Exercise 27.

A Proof of the Quotient Rule. Our proof uses both the product rule and the power rule:

$$\log_a \frac{M}{N} = \log_a MN^{-1} \qquad \text{Rewriting } \frac{M}{N} \text{ as } MN^{-1}$$

$$= \log_a M + \log_a N^{-1} \qquad \text{Using the product rule for logarithms}$$

$$= \log_a M + (-1)\log_a N \qquad \text{Using the power rule for logarithms}$$

$$= \log_a M - \log_a N.$$

USING THE PROPERTIES TOGETHER

EXAMPLE 6 Express as an equivalent expression, using the individual logarithms of x, y, and z.

a) $\log_b \dfrac{x^3}{yz}$

b) $\log_a \sqrt[4]{\dfrac{xy}{z^3}}$

SOLUTION

a) $\log_b \dfrac{x^3}{yz} = \log_b x^3 - \log_b yz \qquad$ Using the quotient rule for logarithms

$$= 3\log_b x - \log_b yz \qquad \text{Using the power rule for logarithms}$$

$$= 3\log_b x - (\log_b y + \log_b z) \qquad \text{Using the product rule for logarithms. Because of the subtraction, parentheses are essential.}$$

$$= 3\log_b x - \log_b y - \log_b z \qquad \text{Using the distributive law}$$

b) $\log_a \sqrt[4]{\dfrac{xy}{z^3}} = \log_a \left(\dfrac{xy}{z^3}\right)^{1/4} \qquad$ Writing exponential notation

$$= \frac{1}{4} \cdot \log_a \frac{xy}{z^3} \qquad \text{Using the power rule for logarithms}$$

$$= \frac{1}{4}(\log_a xy - \log_a z^3) \qquad \text{Using the quotient rule for logarithms. Parentheses are important.}$$

$$= \frac{1}{4}(\log_a x + \log_a y - 3\log_a z) \qquad \text{Using the product rule and the power rule for logarithms}$$

> **CAUTION!** Because the product rule and the quotient rule replace one term with two, parentheses are often necessary, as in Example 6.

Try Exercise 39.

EXAMPLE 7 Express as an equivalent expression that is a single logarithm.

a) $\dfrac{1}{2}\log_a x - 7\log_a y + \log_a z$

b) $\log_a \dfrac{b}{\sqrt{x}} + \log_a \sqrt{bx}$

SOLUTION

a) $\dfrac{1}{2}\log_a x - 7\log_a y + \log_a z$

$$= \log_a x^{1/2} - \log_a y^7 + \log_a z \qquad \text{Using the power rule for logarithms}$$

$$= \left(\log_a \sqrt{x} - \log_a y^7\right) + \log_a z \qquad \text{Using parentheses to emphasize the order of operations; } x^{1/2} = \sqrt{x}$$

$$= \log_a \frac{\sqrt{x}}{y^7} + \log_a z \qquad \text{Using the quotient rule for logarithms}$$

$$= \log_a \frac{z\sqrt{x}}{y^7} \qquad \text{Using the product rule for logarithms}$$

b) $\log_a \dfrac{b}{\sqrt{x}} + \log_a \sqrt{bx} = \log_a \dfrac{b \cdot \sqrt{bx}}{\sqrt{x}}$ Using the product rule for logarithms

$$= \log_a b\sqrt{b} \qquad\qquad \text{Removing a factor equal}$$
$$\text{to } 1: \dfrac{\sqrt{x}}{\sqrt{x}} = 1$$

$$= \log_a b^{3/2}, \text{ or } \dfrac{3}{2}\log_a b \qquad \text{Since } b\sqrt{b} = b^1 \cdot b^{1/2}$$

▣ Try Exercise 51.

If we know the logarithms of two different numbers (with the same base), the properties allow us to calculate other logarithms.

EXAMPLE 8 Given $\log_a 2 = 0.431$ and $\log_a 3 = 0.683$, use the properties of logarithms to calculate a numerical value for each of the following, if possible.

a) $\log_a 6$ **b)** $\log_a \frac{2}{3}$ **c)** $\log_a 81$
d) $\log_a \frac{1}{3}$ **e)** $\log_a (2a)$ **f)** $\log_a 5$

SOLUTION

a) $\log_a 6 = \log_a (2 \cdot 3) = \log_a 2 + \log_a 3$ Using the product rule for logarithms

$$= 0.431 + 0.683 = 1.114$$

Check: $a^{1.114} = a^{0.431} \cdot a^{0.683} = 2 \cdot 3 = 6$

b) $\log_a \frac{2}{3} = \log_a 2 - \log_a 3$ Using the quotient rule for logarithms

$$= 0.431 - 0.683 = -0.252$$

c) $\log_a 81 = \log_a 3^4 = 4\log_a 3$ Using the power rule for logarithms

$$= 4(0.683) = 2.732$$

d) $\log_a \frac{1}{3} = \log_a 1 - \log_a 3$ Using the quotient rule for logarithms

$$= 0 - 0.683 = -0.683$$

e) $\log_a (2a) = \log_a 2 + \log_a a$ Using the product rule for logarithms

$$= 0.431 + 1 = 1.431$$

f) $\log_a 5$ *cannot be found using these properties.* $(\log_a 5 \neq \log_a 2 + \log_a 3)$

▣ Try Exercise 55.

A final property follows from the product rule: Since $\log_a a^k = k\log_a a$, and $\log_a a = 1$, we have $\log_a a^k = k$.

The Logarithm of the Base to an Exponent   For any base a,

$$\log_a a^k = k.$$

(The logarithm, base a, of a to an exponent is the exponent.)

This property also follows from the definition of logarithm: k is the exponent to which you raise a in order to get a^k.

EXAMPLE 9 Simplify: (a) $\log_3 3^7$; (b) $\log_{10} 10^{-5.2}$.

SOLUTION

a) $\log_3 3^7 = 7$ 7 is the exponent to which you raise 3 in order to get 3^7.

b) $\log_{10} 10^{-5.2} = -5.2$

Try Exercise 65.

We summarize the properties covered in this section as follows.

For any positive numbers M, N, and a ($a \neq 1$):

$$\log_a (MN) = \log_a M + \log_a N; \qquad \log_a M^p = p \cdot \log_a M;$$

$$\log_a \frac{M}{N} = \log_a M - \log_a N; \qquad \log_a a^k = k.$$

CAUTION! Keep in mind that, in general,

$\log_a (M + N) \neq \log_a M + \log_a N,$

$\log_a (M - N) \neq \log_a M - \log_a N,$

$\log_a (MN) \neq (\log_a M)(\log_a N),$

$\log_a \dfrac{M}{N} \neq \dfrac{\log_a M}{\log_a N}.$

14.4 Exercise Set

FOR EXTRA HELP

Concept Reinforcement *In each of Exercises 1–6, match the expression with an equivalent expression from the column on the right.*

1. _____ $\log_7 20$

2. _____ $\log_7 5^4$

3. _____ $\log_7 \frac{5}{4}$

4. _____ $\log_7 7$

5. _____ $\log_7 1$

6. _____ $\log_7 5 + \log_7 6$

a) $\log_7 5 - \log_7 4$

b) 1

c) 0

d) $\log_7 30$

e) $\log_7 5 + \log_7 4$

f) $4 \log_7 5$

Express as an equivalent expression that is a sum of logarithms.

7. $\log_3 (81 \cdot 27)$

8. $\log_2 (16 \cdot 32)$

9. $\log_4 (64 \cdot 16)$

10. $\log_5 (25 \cdot 125)$

11. $\log_c (rst)$

12. $\log_t (3ab)$

Express as an equivalent expression that is a single logarithm.

13. $\log_a 5 + \log_a 14$

14. $\log_b 65 + \log_b 2$

15. $\log_c t + \log_c y$

16. $\log_t H + \log_t M$

Express as an equivalent expression that is a product.

17. $\log_a r^8$

18. $\log_b t^5$

19. $\log_2 y^{1/3}$

20. $\log_{10} x^{1/2}$

21. $\log_b C^{-3}$

22. $\log_c M^{-5}$

Express as an equivalent expression that is a difference of two logarithms.

23. $\log_2 \frac{25}{13}$

24. $\log_3 \frac{23}{9}$

25. $\log_b \dfrac{m}{n}$

26. $\log_a \dfrac{y}{x}$

Express as an equivalent expression that is a single logarithm.

27. $\log_a 17 - \log_a 6$

28. $\log_b 32 - \log_b 7$

29. $\log_b 36 - \log_b 4$

30. $\log_a 26 - \log_a 2$

31. $\log_a x - \log_a y$

32. $\log_b c - \log_b d$

Express as an equivalent expression, using the individual logarithms of w, x, y, and z.

33. $\log_a (xyz)$

34. $\log_a (wxy)$

35. $\log_a (x^3 z^4)$

36. $\log_a (x^2 y^5)$

37. $\log_a (x^2 y^{-2} z)$

38. $\log_a (xy^2 z^{-3})$

39. $\log_a \dfrac{x^4}{y^3 z}$

40. $\log_a \dfrac{x^4}{yz^2}$

41. $\log_b \dfrac{xy^2}{wz^3}$

42. $\log_b \dfrac{w^2 x}{y^3 z}$

43. $\log_a \sqrt{\dfrac{x^7}{y^5 z^8}}$

44. $\log_c \sqrt[3]{\dfrac{x^4}{y^3 z^2}}$

45. $\log_a \sqrt[3]{\dfrac{x^6 y^3}{a^2 z^7}}$

46. $\log_a \sqrt[4]{\dfrac{x^8 y^{12}}{a^3 z^5}}$

Express as an equivalent expression that is a single logarithm and, if possible, simplify.

47. $8 \log_a x + 3 \log_a z$

48. $2 \log_b m + \frac{1}{2} \log_b n$

49. $\log_a x^2 - 2 \log_a \sqrt{x}$

50. $\log_a \dfrac{a}{\sqrt{x}} - \log_a \sqrt{ax}$

51. $\frac{1}{2} \log_a x + 5 \log_a y - 2 \log_a x$

52. $\log_a (2x) + 3(\log_a x - \log_a y)$

53. $\log_a (x^2 - 4) - \log_a (x + 2)$

54. $\log_a (2x + 10) - \log_a (x^2 - 25)$

Given $\log_b 3 = 0.792$ and $\log_b 5 = 1.161$. If possible, use the properties of logarithms to calculate numerical values for each of the following.

55. $\log_b 15$

56. $\log_b \frac{5}{3}$

57. $\log_b \frac{3}{5}$

58. $\log_b \frac{1}{3}$

59. $\log_b \frac{1}{5}$

60. $\log_b \sqrt{b}$

61. $\log_b \sqrt{b^3}$

62. $\log_b (3b)$

63. $\log_b 8$

64. $\log_b 45$

Simplify.

65. $\log_t t^7$

66. $\log_p p^4$

67. $\log_e e^m$

68. $\log_Q Q^{-2}$

Use the properties of logarithms to find each of the following.

Aha! **69.** $\log_5 (125 \cdot 625)$

70. $\log_3 (9 \cdot 81)$

71. $\log_2 16^5$

72. $\log_3 27^7$

TW **73.** Explain the difference between the phrases "the logarithm of a quotient" and "a quotient of logarithms."

TW **74.** How could you convince someone that
$$\log_a c \neq \log_c a?$$

SKILL REVIEW

To prepare for Section 14.5, review graphing functions and finding domains of functions.

Graph.

75. $f(x) = \sqrt{x} - 3$ [12.1]

76. $g(x) = \sqrt[3]{x} + 1$ [12.1]

77. $g(x) = x^3 + 2$

78. $f(x) = 1 - x^2$ [13.7]

Find the domain of each function.

79. $f(x) = \dfrac{x - 3}{x + 7}$ [11.1]

80. $f(x) = \dfrac{x}{(x - 2)(x + 3)}$ [11.1]

81. $g(x) = \sqrt{10 - x}$ [12.1]

82. $g(x) = |x^2 - 6x + 7|$

SYNTHESIS

TW **83.** A student *incorrectly* reasons that
$$\log_b \frac{1}{x} = \log_b \frac{x}{xx}$$
$$= \log_b x - \log_b x + \log_b x = \log_b x.$$
What mistake has the student made?

TW **84.** Is it true that $\log_a x + \log_b x = \log_{ab} x$? Why or why not?

Express as an equivalent expression that is a single logarithm and, if possible, simplify.

85. $\log_a (x^8 - y^8) - \log_a (x^2 + y^2)$

86. $\log_a (x + y) + \log_a (x^2 - xy + y^2)$

Express as an equivalent expression that is a sum or a difference of logarithms and, if possible, simplify.

87. $\log_a \sqrt{1 - s^2}$

88. $\log_a \dfrac{c - d}{\sqrt{c^2 - d^2}}$

89. If $\log_a x = 2$, $\log_a y = 3$, and $\log_a z = 4$, what is

$$\log_a \frac{\sqrt[3]{x^2 z}}{\sqrt[3]{y^2 z^{-2}}}?$$

90. If $\log_a x = 2$, what is $\log_a (1/x)$?

91. If $\log_a x = 2$, what is $\log_{1/a} x$?

Solve.

92. $\log_{10} 2000 - \log_{10} x = 3$

93. $\log_2 80 + \log_2 x = 5$

Classify each of the following as true or false. Assume a, x, P, and Q > 0, a ≠ 1.

94. $\log_a \left(\dfrac{P}{Q}\right)^x = x \log_a P - \log_a Q$

95. $\log_a (Q + Q^2) = \log_a Q + \log_a (Q + 1)$

96. Use graphs to show that
$$\log x^2 \neq \log x \cdot \log x.$$
(*Note*: log means $\log_{10}$.)

Try Exercise Answers: Section 14.4
7. $\log_3 81 + \log_3 27$ **13.** $\log_a (5 \cdot 14)$, or $\log_a 70$
17. $8 \log_a r$ **23.** $\log_2 25 - \log_2 13$ **27.** $\log_a \frac{17}{6}$
39. $4 \log_a x - 3 \log_a y - \log_a z$ **51.** $\log_a \dfrac{y^5}{x^{3/2}}$
55. 1.953 **65.** 7

Mid-Chapter Review

We use the following properties to simplify expressions and to rewrite equivalent logarithmic and exponential equations.

$$\log_a x = m \text{ means } x = a^m.$$
$$\log_a (MN) = \log_a M + \log_a N$$
$$\log_a \frac{M}{N} = \log_a M - \log_a N$$
$$\log_a M^p = p \cdot \log_a M$$

$$\log_a a^k = k$$
$$\log_a a = 1$$
$$\log_a 1 = 0$$
$$\log x = \log_{10} x$$

GUIDED SOLUTIONS

1. Find a formula for the inverse of $f(x) = 2x - 5$. [14.1]

Solution

$$y = 2x - 5$$

$$\boxed{} = 2\boxed{} - 5 \qquad \text{Interchanging } x \text{ and } y$$

$$\boxed{} = 2y$$

$$\frac{\boxed{}}{2} = y \qquad \text{Solving for } y$$

$$f^{-1}(x) = \boxed{}$$

2. Solve: $\log_4 x = 1$. [14.3]

Solution

$$x = \boxed{}^{\boxed{}} \qquad \text{Rewriting as an exponential equation}$$

$$x = \boxed{}$$

MIXED REVIEW

1. Find $(f \circ g)(x)$ if $f(x) = x^2 + 1$ and $g(x) = x - 5$. [14.1]

2. If $h(x) = \sqrt{5x - 3}$, find $f(x)$ and $g(x)$ such that $h(x) = (f \circ g)(x)$. Answers may vary. [14.1]

3. Find a formula for the inverse of $g(x) = 6 - x$. [14.1]

4. Graph by hand: $f(x) = 2^x + 3$. [14.2]

Simplify.

5. $\log_4 16$ [14.3]

6. $\log_5 \frac{1}{5}$ [14.3]

7. $\log_{100} 10$ [14.3]

8. $\log_b b$ [14.4]

9. $\log_8 8^{19}$ [14.4]

10. $\log_t 1$ [14.4]

Rewrite each of the following as an equivalent exponential equation.

11. $\log_x 3 = m$ [14.3]

12. $\log_2 1024 = 10$ [14.3]

Rewrite each of the following as an equivalent logarithmic equation.

13. $e^t = x$ [14.3]

14. $64^{2/3} = 16$ [14.3]

15. Express as an equivalent expression using $\log x$, $\log y$, and $\log z$:

$$\log \sqrt{\frac{x^2}{yz^3}}. \quad [14.4]$$

16. Express as an equivalent expression that is a single logarithm:

$$\log a - 2 \log b - \log c. \quad [14.4]$$

Solve. [14.3]

17. $\log_x 64 = 3$

18. $\log_3 x = -1$

19. $\log x = 5$

20. $\log_x 2 = \frac{1}{2}$

14.5   Natural Logarithms and Changing Bases

- The Base *e* and Natural Logarithms

- Changing Logarithmic Bases

- Graphs of Exponential Functions and Logarithmic Functions, Base *e*

We have already looked at base-10 logarithms, or common logarithms. Another logarithm base widely used today is an irrational number named *e*.

THE BASE *e* AND NATURAL LOGARITHMS

When interest is computed n times per year, the compound interest formula is

$$A = P\left(1 + \frac{r}{n}\right)^{nt},$$

where A is the amount that an initial investment P will be worth after t years at interest rate r. Suppose that \$1 is invested at 100% interest for 1 year (no bank would pay this). The preceding formula becomes a function A defined in terms of the number of compounding periods n:

$$A(n) = \left(1 + \frac{1}{n}\right)^n.$$

Interactive Discovery

1. What happens to the function values of $A(n) = \left(1 + \dfrac{1}{n}\right)^n$ as n gets larger?

   Use the TABLE feature with Indpnt set to Ask to fill in the table below. Round each entry to six decimal places.

n	$A(n) = \left(1 + \dfrac{1}{n}\right)^n$
1 (compounded annually)	$\left(1 + \dfrac{1}{1}\right)^1$, or \$2.00
2 (compounded semiannually)	$\left(1 + \dfrac{1}{2}\right)^2$, or \$?
3	
4 (compounded quarterly)	
12 (compounded monthly)	
52 (compounded weekly)	
365 (compounded daily)	
8760 (compounded hourly)	

2. Which of the following statements appears to be true?

   a) $A(n)$ gets very large as n gets very large.

   b) $A(n)$ gets very small as n gets very large.

   c) $A(n)$ approaches a certain number as n gets very large.

The numbers in the table approach a very important number in mathematics, called e. Because e is irrational, its decimal representation does not terminate or repeat.

The Number e $e \approx 2.7182818284\ldots$

Logarithms base e are called **natural logarithms,** or **Napierian logarithms,** in honor of John Napier (1550–1617), who first "discovered" logarithms.

The abbreviation "ln" is generally used with natural logarithms. Thus,

   ln 53   means $\log_e 53$.   Remember: $\log x$ means $\log_{10} x$, and $\ln x$ means $\log_e x$.

Natural Logarithms

On most calculators, the key for natural logarithms is marked **LN**. If we are using a calculator that supplies the left parenthesis, ln 8 can be found by pressing **LN** **8** **)** **ENTER**. Note from the screen shown below that ln 8 ≈ 2.0794.

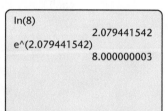

ln(8)
                    2.079441542
e^(2.079441542)
                    8.000000003

On many calculators, the **LN** key serves as the **eˣ** key after the **2ND** key is pressed. Some calculators automatically supply a left parenthesis before the exponent. If such a calculator is used,

$$e^{2.079441542}$$

is found by pressing **eˣ** **2** **.** **0** **7** **9** **4** **4** **1** **5** **4** **2** **)** **ENTER**. As shown on the screen above, $e^{2.079441542} \approx 8$, as expected, since $f(x) = e^x$ is the inverse function of $g(x) = \ln x$.

Your Turn

1. Approximate ln 5 to four decimal places.   1.6094

2. Approximate ln (5) + 1 to four decimal places. Be sure that only 5 is in parentheses.   2.6094

3. Approximate $e^{2/3}$ to four decimal places.   1.9477

4. Approximate $\dfrac{e^2}{3}$ to four decimal places. Be sure that only 2 is in parentheses.

    2.4630

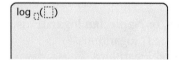
CHANGING LOGARITHMIC BASES

Most calculators can find both common logarithms and natural logarithms. To find a logarithm with some other base, a conversion formula is often needed.

The Change-of-Base Formula   For any logarithmic bases a and b, and any positive number M,

$$\log_b M = \frac{\log_a M}{\log_a b}.$$

(To find the log, base b, we typically compute $\log M / \log b$ or $\ln M / \ln b$.)

A Proof of the Change-of-Base Formula. Let $x = \log_b M$. Then,

$$b^x = M \qquad \log_b M = x \text{ is equivalent to } b^x = M.$$

$$\log_a b^x = \log_a M \qquad \text{Taking the logarithm, base } a, \text{ on both sides}$$

$$x \log_a b = \log_a M \qquad \text{Using the power rule for logarithms}$$

$$x = \frac{\log_a M}{\log_a b}. \qquad \text{Dividing both sides by } \log_a b$$

But at the outset we stated that $x = \log_b M$. Thus, by substitution, we have

$$\log_b M = \frac{\log_a M}{\log_a b}. \qquad \text{This is the change-of-base formula.}$$

EXAMPLE 1 Find $\log_5 8$ using the change-of-base formula.

SOLUTION We use the change-of-base formula with $a = 10, b = 5$, and $M = 8$:

$$\log_5 8 = \frac{\log_{10} 8}{\log_{10} 5} \qquad \text{Substituting into } \log_b M = \frac{\log_a M}{\log_a b}$$

$$\approx \frac{0.903089987}{0.6989700043} \qquad \text{Using } \boxed{\text{LOG}} \text{ twice}$$

$$\approx 1.2920. \qquad \text{When using a calculator, it is best not to round before dividing.}$$

The figure below shows the computation using a graphing calculator. To check, note that $\ln 8 / \ln 5 \approx 1.2920$. We can also use a calculator to verify that $5^{1.2920} \approx 8$.

```
log(8)/log(5)
                  1.292029674
```

Try Exercise 29.

Student Notes

The choice of the logarithm base a in the change-of-base formula should be either 10 or e so that the logarithms can be found using a calculator. Either choice will yield the same end result.

EXAMPLE 2 Find $\log_4 31$.

SOLUTION As shown in the check of Example 1, base e can also be used.

$$\log_4 31 = \frac{\log_e 31}{\log_e 4} \qquad \text{Substituting into } \log_b M = \frac{\log_a M}{\log_a b}$$

$$= \frac{\ln 31}{\ln 4} \approx \frac{3.433987204}{1.386294361} \qquad \text{Using } \boxed{\text{LN}} \text{ twice}$$

$$\approx 2.4771 \qquad \text{Check: } 4^{2.4771} \approx 31$$

```
ln(31)/ln(4)
                  2.477098155
log(31)/log(4)
                  2.477098155
4^Ans
                           31
```

The screen at left illustrates that we find the same solution using either natural logarithms or common logarithms.

Try Exercise 31.

GRAPHS OF EXPONENTIAL FUNCTIONS AND LOGARITHMIC FUNCTIONS, BASE e

EXAMPLE 3 Graph $f(x) = e^x$ and $g(x) = e^{-x}$ and state the domain and the range of f and g.

SOLUTION We use a calculator with an $\boxed{e^x}$ key to find approximate values of e^x and e^{-x}. Using these values, we can graph the functions.

x	e^x	e^{-x}
0	1	1
1	2.7	0.4
2	7.4	0.1
−1	0.4	2.7
−2	0.1	7.4

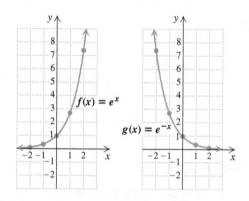

The domain of each function is $\mathbb{R}$ and the range of each function is $(0, \infty)$.

◻ Try Exercise 53.

EXAMPLE 4 Graph $f(x) = e^{-x} + 2$ and state the domain and the range of f.

SOLUTION To graph by hand, we find some solutions with a calculator, plot them, and then draw the graph. For example, $f(2) = e^{-2} + 2 \approx 2.1$. The graph is exactly like the graph of $g(x) = e^{-x}$, but is translated 2 units up.

To graph using a graphing calculator, we enter $y = e^{-x} + 2$ and choose a viewing window that shows more of the y-axis than the x-axis, since the function is exponential.

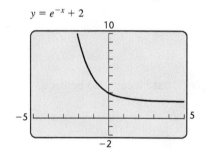

$y = e^{-x} + 2$

x	$e^{-x} + 2$
0	3
1	2.4
2	2.1
−1	4.7
−2	9.4

The domain of f is $\mathbb{R}$ and the range is $(2, \infty)$.

◻ Try Exercise 41.

EXAMPLE 5 Graph and state the domain and the range of each function.

a) $g(x) = \ln x$ **b)** $f(x) = \ln (x + 3)$

SOLUTION

a) To graph by hand, we find some solutions with a calculator and then draw the graph. As expected, the graph is a reflection across the line $y = x$ of the graph of $y = e^x$. We can also graph $y = \ln (x)$ using a graphing calculator. Since a logarithmic function is the inverse of an exponential function, we choose a viewing window that shows more of the x-axis than the y-axis.

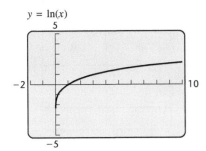

$y = \ln(x)$

x	$\ln x$
1	0
4	1.4
7	1.9
0.5	-0.7

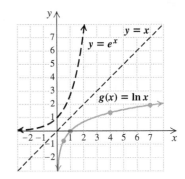

The domain of g is $(0, \infty)$ and the range is $\mathbb{R}$.

b) We find some solutions with a calculator, plot them, and draw the graph by hand. Note that the graph of $y = \ln(x + 3)$ is the graph of $y = \ln x$ translated 3 units to the left. To graph using a graphing calculator, we enter $y = \ln(x + 3)$.

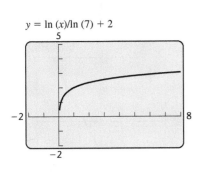

$y = \ln(x + 3)$

x	$\ln(x + 3)$
0	1.1
1	1.4
2	1.6
3	1.8
4	1.9
-1	0.7
-2	0
-2.5	-0.7

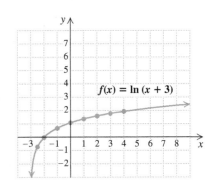

Since $x + 3$ must be positive, the domain of f is $(-3, \infty)$ and the range is $\mathbb{R}$.

Try Exercise 55.

Logarithmic functions with bases other than 10 or e can be graphed on a graphing calculator using the change-of-base formula.

EXAMPLE 6   Graph: $f(x) = \log_7 x + 2$.

SOLUTION   We use the change-of-base formula with natural logarithms. (We would get the same graph if we used common logarithms.)

$y = \ln(x)/\ln(7) + 2$

$$f(x) = \log_7 x + 2 \qquad \text{Note that this is not } \log_7(x + 2).$$

$$= \frac{\ln x}{\ln 7} + 2 \qquad \text{Using the change-of-base formula for } \log_7 x$$

We graph $y = \ln(x)/\ln(7) + 2$.

Try Exercise 67.

A

Visualizing
for Success

F

Match each function with its graph.

1. $f(x) = 2x - 3$

2. $f(x) = 2x^2 + 1$

3. $f(x) = \sqrt{x + 5}$

4. $f(x) = |4 - x|$

5. $f(x) = \ln x$

6. $f(x) = 2^{-x}$

7. $f(x) = -4$

8. $f(x) = \log x + 3$

9. $f(x) = 2^x$

10. $f(x) = 4 - x^2$

Answers on page A-55

An additional, animated version of this activity appears in MyMathLab. To use MyMathLab, you need a course ID and a student access code. Contact your instructor for more information.

B

G

C

H

D

I

E

J

14.5 Exercise Set

Concept Reinforcement   Classify each of the following statements as either true or false.

1. The expression log 23 means $\log_{10} 23$.

2. The expression ln 7 means $\log_e 7$.

3. The number e is approximately 2.7.

4. The expressions log 9 and log 18/log 2 are equivalent.

5. The expressions log 9 and log 18 − log 2 are equivalent.

6. The expressions $\log_2 9$ and ln 9/ln 2 are equivalent.

7. The expressions ln 81 and 2 ln 9 are equivalent.

8. The domain of the function given by $f(x) = \ln(x + 2)$ is $(-2, \infty)$.

9. The range of the function given by $g(x) = e^x$ is $(0, \infty)$.

10. The range of the function given by $f(x) = \ln x$ is $(-\infty, \infty)$.

Use a calculator to find each of the following to four decimal places.

11. ln 5

12. ln 2

13. ln 0.0062

14. ln 0.00073

15. $\dfrac{\ln 2300}{0.08}$

16. $\dfrac{\ln 1900}{0.07}$

17. $e^{2.71}$

18. $e^{3.06}$

19. $e^{-3.49}$

20. $e^{-2.64}$

21. log 7

22. log 2

23. $\dfrac{\log 8200}{\log 2}$

24. $\dfrac{\log 5700}{\log 5}$

25. $\log \dfrac{3}{8}$

26. $\ln \frac{2}{3}$

27. $\ln(7) + 3$

28. $\log(6) - 2$

Find each of the following logarithms using the change-of-base formula. Round answers to the nearest ten-thousandth.

29. $\log_6 92$

30. $\log_3 78$

31. $\log_2 100$

32. $\log_7 100$

33. $\log_{0.5} 5$

34. $\log_{0.1} 3$

35. $\log_2 0.2$

36. $\log_2 0.08$

37. $\log_\pi 58$

38. $\log_\pi 200$

Graph by hand or using a graphing calculator and state the domain and the range of each function.

39. $f(x) = e^x$

40. $f(x) = e^{-x}$

41. $f(x) = e^x + 3$

42. $f(x) = e^x + 2$

43. $f(x) = e^x - 2$

44. $f(x) = e^x - 3$

45. $f(x) = 0.5e^x$

46. $f(x) = 2e^x$

47. $f(x) = 0.5e^{2x}$

48. $f(x) = 2e^{-0.5x}$

49. $f(x) = e^{x-3}$

50. $f(x) = e^{x-2}$

51. $f(x) = e^{x+2}$

52. $f(x) = e^{x+3}$

53. $f(x) = -e^x$

54. $f(x) = -e^{-x}$

55. $g(x) = \ln x + 1$

56. $g(x) = \ln x + 3$

57. $g(x) = \ln x - 2$

58. $g(x) = \ln x - 1$

59. $g(x) = 2 \ln x$

60. $g(x) = 3 \ln x$

61. $g(x) = -2 \ln x$

62. $g(x) = -\ln x$

63. $g(x) = \ln(x + 2)$

64. $g(x) = \ln(x + 1)$

65. $g(x) = \ln(x - 1)$

66. $g(x) = \ln(x - 3)$

Write an equivalent expression for the function that could be graphed using a graphing calculator. Then graph the function.

67. $f(x) = \log_5 x$

68. $f(x) = \log_3 x$

69. $f(x) = \log_2(x - 5)$

70. $f(x) = \log_5(2x + 1)$

71. $f(x) = \log_3 x + x$

72. $f(x) = \log_2 x - x + 1$

TW 73. Using a calculator, Aden *incorrectly* says that log 79 is between 4 and 5. How could you convince him, without using a calculator, that he is mistaken?

TW 74. Examine Exercise 73. What mistake do you believe Aden made?

SKILL REVIEW

To prepare for Section 14.6, review solving equations.

Solve.

75. $x^2 - 3x - 28 = 0$

76. $5x^2 - 7x = 0$

77. $17x - 15 = 0$

78. $\frac{5}{3} = 2t$

79. $(x - 5) \cdot 9 = 11$ **80.** $\dfrac{x + 3}{x - 3} = 7$

81. $x^{1/2} - 6x^{1/4} + 8 = 0$ [13.5]

82. $2y - 7\sqrt{y} + 3 = 0$ [13.5]

SYNTHESIS

TW **83.** In an attempt to solve $\ln x = 1.5$, Emma gets the following graph. How can Emma tell at a glance that she has made a mistake?

TW **84.** How would you explain to a classmate why $\log_2 5 = \log 5 / \log 2$ and $\log_2 5 = \ln 5 / \ln 2$?

Knowing only that $\log 2 \approx 0.301$ *and* $\log 3 \approx 0.477$, *find each of the following.*

85. $\log_6 81$ **86.** $\log_9 16$ **87.** $\log_{12} 36$

88. Find a formula for converting common logarithms to natural logarithms.

89. Find a formula for converting natural logarithms to common logarithms.

Solve for x.

90. $\log (275x^2) = 38$

91. $\log (492x) = 5.728$

92. $\dfrac{3.01}{\ln x} = \dfrac{28}{4.31}$

93. $\log 692 + \log x = \log 3450$

⚙ *For each function given below,* **(a)** *determine the domain and the range,* **(b)** *set an appropriate window, and* **(c)** *draw the graph.*

94. $f(x) = 7.4e^x \ln x$

95. $f(x) = 3.4 \ln x - 0.25e^x$

96. $f(x) = x \ln (x - 2.1)$

97. $f(x) = 2x^3 \ln x$

▓ Try Exercise Answers: Section 14.5

29. 2.5237   **31.** 6.6439

41. Domain: $\mathbb{R}$; range: $(3, \infty)$ **53.** Domain: $\mathbb{R}$; range: $(-\infty, 0)$

55. Domain: $(0, \infty)$; range: $\mathbb{R}$ **67.** $f(x) = \log (x)/\log (5)$, or $f(x) = \ln (x)/\ln (5)$

$y = \log (x)/\log (5)$, or $y = \ln (x)/\ln (5)$

14.6   Solving Exponential and Logarithmic Equations

- Solving Exponential Equations

- Solving Logarithmic Equations

SOLVING EXPONENTIAL EQUATIONS

Equations with variables in exponents, such as $5^x = 12$ and $2^{7x} = 64$, are called **exponential equations.** In Section 14.3, we solved certain equations by using the principle of exponential equality. We restate that principle below.

> **The Principle of Exponential Equality**   For any real number b, where $b \neq -1, 0$, or 1,
>
> $$b^x = b^y \quad \text{is equivalent to} \quad x = y.$$
>
> (Powers of the same base are equal if and only if the exponents are equal.)

EXAMPLE 1   Solve: $4^{3x} = 16$.

SOLUTION   Note that $16 = 4^2$. Thus we can write each side as a power of the same base:

$$4^{3x} = 4^2 \qquad \text{Rewriting 16 as a power of 4}$$
$$3x = 2 \qquad \text{Since the base on each side is 4, the exponents are equal.}$$
$$x = \tfrac{2}{3}. \qquad \text{Solving for } x$$

Since $4^{3x} = 4^{3(2/3)} = 4^2 = 16$, the answer checks. The solution is $\tfrac{2}{3}$.

Try Exercise 9.

In Example 1, we wrote both sides of the equation as powers of 4. When it seems impossible to write both sides of an equation as powers of the same base, we use the following principle and write an equivalent logarithmic equation.

> **The Principle of Logarithmic Equality**   For any logarithmic base a, and for $x, y > 0$,
>
> $$x = y \quad \text{is equivalent to} \quad \log_a x = \log_a y.$$
>
> (Two expressions are equal if and only if the logarithms of those expressions are equal.)

Because calculators can generally find only common or natural logarithms (without resorting to the change-of-base formula), we usually take the common or natural logarithm on both sides of the equation.

The principle of logarithmic equality, used together with the power rule for logarithms, allows us to solve equations with a variable in an exponent.

EXAMPLE 2   Solve: $7^{x-2} = 60$.

SOLUTION   We have

Take the logarithm of both sides.

$$7^{x-2} = 60$$
$$\log 7^{x-2} = \log 60 \qquad \text{Using the principle of logarithmic equality to take the common logarithm on both sides. Natural logarithms also would work.}$$

Use the power rule for logarithms.

$$(x - 2)\log 7 = \log 60 \qquad \text{Using the power rule for logarithms}$$

$$x - 2 = \frac{\log 60}{\log 7} \qquad \longleftarrow \quad \boxed{\text{CAUTION!   This is } not \\ \log 60 - \log 7.}$$

$$x = \frac{\log 60}{\log 7} + 2 \qquad \text{Adding 2 to both sides}$$

Solve for x.

$$x \approx 4.1041. \qquad \text{Using a calculator and rounding to four decimal places}$$

Check.

Since $7^{4.1041-2} \approx 60.0027$, we have a check. We can also note that since $7^{4-2} = 49$, we expect a solution greater than 4. The solution is $\dfrac{\log 60}{\log 7} + 2$, or approximately 4.1041.

Try Exercise 17.

EXAMPLE 3 Solve: $e^{0.06t} = 1500$.

ALGEBRAIC APPROACH	GRAPHICAL APPROACH

ALGEBRAIC APPROACH

Since one side is a power of e, we take the *natural logarithm* on both sides:

$$\ln e^{0.06t} = \ln 1500 \qquad \text{Taking the natural logarithm on both sides}$$

$$0.06t = \ln 1500 \qquad \text{Finding the logarithm of the base to a power: } \log_a a^k = k$$

$$t = \frac{\ln 1500}{0.06} \qquad \text{Dividing both sides by 0.06}$$

$$\approx 121.887. \qquad \text{Using a calculator and rounding to three decimal places}$$

The solution is 121.887.

GRAPHICAL APPROACH

We graph $y_1 = e^{0.06x}$ and $y_2 = 1500$. Since $y_2 = 1500$, we choose a value for Ymax that is greater than 1500. It may require trial and error to choose appropriate units for the x-axis.

$y_1 = e^{0.06x}, \ y_2 = 1500$

Intersection
X = 121.88701 Y = 1500

Xscl = 50, Yscl = 500

Rounded to three decimal places, the solution is 121.887.

Try Exercise 21.

To Solve an Equation of the Form $a^t = b$ for t

1. Take the logarithm (either natural or common) of both sides.
2. Use the power rule for exponents so that the variable is no longer written as an exponent.
3. Divide both sides by the coefficient of the variable to isolate the variable.
4. If appropriate, use a calculator to find an approximate solution in decimal form.

Some equations, like the one in Example 3, are readily solved algebraically. There are other exponential equations for which we do not have the tools to solve algebraically, but we can nevertheless solve graphically.

EXAMPLE 4 Solve: $xe^{3x-1} = 5$.

SOLUTION We graph $y_1 = xe^{3x-1}$ and $y_2 = 5$ and determine the coordinates of any points of intersection.

$y_1 = xe^{3x-1}, \ y_2 = 5$

Intersection
X = .90360156   Y = 5

The x-coordinate of the point of intersection is approximately 0.90360156. Thus the solution is approximately 0.904.

Try Exercise 69.

SOLVING LOGARITHMIC EQUATIONS

Equations containing logarithmic expressions are called **logarithmic equations.** We saw in Section 14.3 that certain logarithmic equations can be solved by writing an equivalent exponential equation.

EXAMPLE 5   Solve: **(a)** $\log_4 (8x - 6) = 3$; **(b)** $\ln (5x) = 27$.

SOLUTION

a) $\log_4 (8x - 6) = 3$

$\qquad\qquad\quad 4^3 = 8x - 6$ Writing the equivalent exponential equation

$\qquad\qquad\quad 64 = 8x - 6$

$\qquad\qquad\quad 70 = 8x$ Adding 6 to both sides

$\qquad\qquad\quad x = \frac{70}{8}, \text{ or } \frac{35}{4}$

Check: $\dfrac{\log_4 (8x - 6) = 3}{\begin{array}{c|c} \log_4 \left(8 \cdot \frac{35}{4} - 6\right) & 3 \\ \log_4 (2 \cdot 35 - 6) & \\ \log_4 64 & \\ & 3 \overset{?}{=} 3 \quad \text{TRUE} \end{array}}$

The solution is $\frac{35}{4}$.

b) $\ln (5x) = 27$ Remember: $\ln (5x)$ means $\log_e (5x)$.

$\qquad e^{27} = 5x$ Writing the equivalent exponential equation

$\qquad \dfrac{e^{27}}{5} = x$ This is a very large number.

The solution is $\dfrac{e^{27}}{5}$. The check is left to the student.

Try Exercise 47.

Often the properties for logarithms are needed. The goal is to first write an equivalent equation in which the variable appears in just one logarithmic expression. We then isolate that expression and solve as in Example 5. Since logarithms of negative numbers are not defined, all possible solutions must be checked.

EXAMPLE 6   Solve: $\log x + \log (x - 3) = 1$.

SOLUTION   To increase understanding, we write in the base, 10.

$\log_{10} x + \log_{10} (x - 3) = 1$

$\qquad\quad \log_{10} [x(x - 3)] = 1$ Using the product rule for logarithms to obtain a single logarithm

$\qquad\qquad\quad x(x - 3) = 10^1$ Writing an equivalent exponential equation

$\qquad\qquad\quad x^2 - 3x = 10$

$\qquad\quad x^2 - 3x - 10 = 0$

$\qquad\quad (x + 2)(x - 5) = 0$ Factoring

$\qquad x + 2 = 0 \quad or \quad x - 5 = 0$ Using the principle of zero products

$\qquad\quad x = -2 \quad or \qquad x = 5$

Student Notes

It is essential that you remember the properties of logarithms from Section 14.4. Consider reviewing the properties before attempting to solve equations similar to those in Examples 6–8.

Find a single logarithm.

Write an equivalent exponential equation.

Solve.

Check.

$y_1 = \log(x) + \log(x - 3)$, $y_2 = 1$

Intersection
X = 5   Y = 1

Check:

For −2:

$$\frac{\log x + \log(x - 3) = 1}{\log(-2) + \log(-2 - 3) \overset{?}{=} 1} \quad \text{FALSE}$$

For 5:

$$\frac{\log x + \log(x - 3) = 1}{\log 5 + \log(5 - 3) \ \Big|\ 1}$$
$$\log 5 + \log 2$$
$$\log 10$$
$$1 \overset{?}{=} 1 \quad \text{TRUE}$$

The number −2 *does not check* because the logarithm of a negative number is undefined. Note from the graph at left that there is only one point of intersection. The solution is 5.

Try Exercise 49.

EXAMPLE 7 Solve: $\log_2(x + 7) - \log_2(x - 7) = 3$.

ALGEBRAIC APPROACH

We have

$$\log_2(x + 7) - \log_2(x - 7) = 3$$

$$\log_2 \frac{x + 7}{x - 7} = 3 \qquad \begin{array}{l}\text{Using the quotient rule}\\\text{for logarithms to obtain}\\\text{a single logarithm}\end{array}$$

$$\frac{x + 7}{x - 7} = 2^3 \qquad \begin{array}{l}\text{Writing an equivalent}\\\text{exponential equation}\end{array}$$

$$\frac{x + 7}{x - 7} = 8$$

$$x + 7 = 8(x - 7) \qquad \begin{array}{l}\text{Multiplying by the}\\\text{LCD, } x - 7\end{array}$$

$$x + 7 = 8x - 56 \qquad \begin{array}{l}\text{Using the}\\\text{distributive law}\end{array}$$

$$63 = 7x$$

$$9 = x. \qquad \text{Dividing by 7}$$

GRAPHICAL APPROACH

We first use the change-of-base formula to write the base-2 logarithms using common logarithms. Then we graph and determine the coordinates of any points of intersection.

$y_1 = \log(x + 7)/\log(2) - \log(x - 7)/\log(2)$,
$y_2 = 3$

Intersection
X = 9   Y = 3

The graphs intersect at $(9, 3)$. The solution is 9.

Check:
$$\frac{\log_2(x + 7) - \log_2(x - 7) = 3}{\log_2(9 + 7) - \log_2(9 - 7) \ \Big|\ 3}$$
$$\log_2 16 - \log_2 2$$
$$4 - 1$$
$$3 \overset{?}{=} 3 \quad \text{TRUE}$$

The solution is 9.

Try Exercise 65.

EXAMPLE 8 Solve: $\log_7 (x + 1) + \log_7 (x - 1) = \log_7 8$.

| ALGEBRAIC APPROACH | GRAPHICAL APPROACH |

ALGEBRAIC APPROACH

We have

$$\log_7 (x + 1) + \log_7 (x - 1) = \log_7 8$$
$$\log_7 [(x + 1)(x - 1)] = \log_7 8 \quad \text{Using the product rule for logarithms}$$
$$\log_7 (x^2 - 1) = \log_7 8 \quad \text{Multiplying. Note that both sides are base-7 logarithms.}$$
$$x^2 - 1 = 8 \quad \text{Using the principle of logarithmic equality. Study this step carefully.}$$
$$x^2 - 9 = 0$$
$$(x - 3)(x + 3) = 0 \quad \text{Solving the quadratic equation}$$
$$x = 3 \quad \text{or} \quad x = -3.$$

The student should confirm that 3 checks but -3 does not. The solution is 3.

GRAPHICAL APPROACH

Using the change-of-base formula, we graph

$$y_1 = \log (x + 1)/\log (7) + \log (x - 1)/\log (7)$$

and

$$y_2 = \log (8)/\log (7).$$

$y_1 = \log (x + 1)/\log (7) + \log (x - 1)/\log (7),$
$y_2 = \log (8)/\log (7)$

```
                    5
                    |
                    |
                    |            y₁
        _____|_____×_____ y₂
   -5               |          5
                    |
                    |
         Intersection
         X = 3        Y = 1.0686216
                   -5
```

The graphs intersect at $(3, 1.0686216)$. The solution is 3.

Try Exercise 57.

14.6 Exercise Set

FOR EXTRA HELP   MyMathLab
PRACTICE   WATCH   DOWNLOAD   READ   REVIEW

Concept Reinforcement *In each of Exercises 1–8, match the equation with an equivalent equation from the column on the right that could be the next step in the solution process.*

1. ___ $5^x = 3$

2. ___ $e^{5x} = 3$

3. ___ $\ln x = 3$

4. ___ $\log_x 5 = 3$

5. ___ $\log_5 x + \log_5 (x - 2) = 3$

6. ___ $\log_5 x - \log_5 (x - 2) = 3$

7. ___ $\ln x - \ln (x - 2) = 3$

8. ___ $\log x + \log (x - 2) = 3$

a) $\ln e^{5x} = \ln 3$

b) $\log_5 (x^2 - 2x) = 3$

c) $\log (x^2 - 2x) = 3$

d) $\log_5 \dfrac{x}{x - 2} = 3$

e) $\log 5^x = \log 3$

f) $e^3 = x$

g) $\ln \dfrac{x}{x - 2} = 3$

h) $x^3 = 5$

Solve. Where appropriate, include approximations to three decimal places.

9. $3^{2x} = 81$

10. $2^{3x} = 64$

11. $4^x = 32$

12. $9^x = 27$

13. $2^x = 10$

14. $2^x = 24$

15. $2^{x+5} = 16$

16. $2^{x-1} = 8$

17. $8^{x-3} = 19$

18. $5^{x+2} = 15$

19. $e^t = 50$

20. $e^t = 20$

21. $e^{-0.02t} = 8$

22. $e^{-0.01t} = 100$

23. $5 = 3^{x+1}$

24. $7 = 3^{x-1}$

25. $4.9^x - 87 = 0$

26. $7.2^x - 65 = 0$

27. $19 = 2e^{4x}$

28. $29 = 3e^{2x}$

29. $7 + 3e^{5x} = 13$

30. $4 + 5e^{4x} = 9$

Aha! **31.** $\log_3 x = 4$

32. $\log_2 x = 6$

33. $\log_2 x = -3$

34. $\log_5 x = 3$

35. $\ln x = 5$

36. $\ln x = 4$

37. $\ln (4x) = 3$

38. $\ln (3x) = 2$

39. $\log x = 2.5$

40. $\log x = 0.5$

41. $\ln (2x + 1) = 4$

42. $\ln (4x - 2) = 3$

Aha! **43.** $\ln x = 1$

44. $\log x = 1$

45. $5 \ln x = -15$

46. $3 \ln x = -3$

47. $\log_2 (8 - 6x) = 5$

48. $\log_5 (2x - 7) = 3$

49. $\log (x - 9) + \log x = 1$

50. $\log (x + 9) + \log x = 1$

51. $\log x - \log (x + 3) = 1$

52. $\log x - \log (x + 7) = -1$

Aha! **53.** $\log (2x + 1) = \log 5$

54. $\log (x + 1) - \log x = 0$

55. $\log_4 (x + 3) = 2 + \log_4 (x - 5)$

56. $\log_2 (x + 3) = 4 + \log_2 (x - 3)$

57. $\log_7 (x + 1) + \log_7 (x + 2) = \log_7 6$

58. $\log_6 (x + 3) + \log_6 (x + 2) = \log_6 20$

59. $\log_5 (x + 4) + \log_5 (x - 4) = \log_5 20$

60. $\log_4 (x + 2) + \log_4 (x - 7) = \log_4 10$

61. $\ln (x + 5) + \ln (x + 1) = \ln 12$

62. $\ln (x - 6) + \ln (x + 3) = \ln 22$

63. $\log_2 (x - 3) + \log_2 (x + 3) = 4$

64. $\log_3 (x - 4) + \log_3 (x + 4) = 2$

65. $\log_{12} (x + 5) - \log_{12} (x - 4) = \log_{12} 3$

66. $\log_6 (x + 7) - \log_6 (x - 2) = \log_6 5$

67. $\log_2 (x - 2) + \log_2 x = 3$

68. $\log_4 (x + 6) - \log_4 x = 2$

69. $e^{0.5x} - 7 = 2x + 6$

70. $e^{-x} - 3 = x^2$

71. $\ln (3x) = 3x - 8$

72. $\ln (x^2) = -x^2$

73. Find the value of x for which the natural logarithm is the same as the common logarithm.

74. Find all values of x for which the common logarithm of the square of x is the same as the square of the common logarithm of x.

TW **75.** Christina finds that the solution of $\log_3 (x + 4) = 1$ is -1, but rejects -1 as an answer because it is negative. What mistake is she making?

TW **76.** Could Example 2 have been solved by taking the natural logarithm on both sides? Why or why not?

SKILL REVIEW

To prepare for Section 14.7, review using the five-step problem-solving strategy.

Solve.

77. A rectangle is 6 ft longer than it is wide. Its perimeter is 26 ft. Find the length and the width.

78. Under one health insurance plan offered in California, the maximum co-pay for an individual is $3000 per calendar year. The co-pay for each visit to a specialist is $40, and the co-pay for a hospitalization is $1000. With hospitalizations and specialist visits, Marguerite reached the maximum co-pay in 2010. If she was hospitalized twice, how many visits to specialists did she make? [10.1]
Source: ehealthinsurance.com

79. Joanna wants to mix Golden Days bird seed containing 25% sunflower seeds with Snowy Friends bird seed containing 40% sunflower seeds. She wants 50 lb of a mixture containing 33% sunflower seeds. How much of each type should she use?

80. The outside edge of a picture frame measures 12 cm by 19 cm, and 144 cm² of picture shows. Find the width of the frame.

81. Max can key in a musical score in 2 hr. Miles takes 3 hr to key in the same score. How long would it take them, working together, to key in the score?

82. A sign is in the shape of a right triangle. The hypotenuse is 3 ft long, and the base and the height of the triangle are equal. Find the length of the base and the height. Round to the nearest tenth of a foot. [12.7]

SYNTHESIS

TW **83.** Can the principle of logarithmic equality be expanded to include all functions? That is, is the statement "$m = n$ is equivalent to $f(m) = f(n)$" true for any function f? Why or why not?

TW **84.** Explain how Exercises 39 and 40 could be solved using the graph of $f(x) = \log x$.

Solve. If no solution exists, state this.

85. $27^x = 81^{2x-3}$

86. $8^x = 16^{3x+9}$

87. $\log_x (\log_3 27) = 3$

88. $\log_6 (\log_2 x) = 0$

89. $x \log \frac{1}{8} = \log 8$

90. $\log_5 \sqrt{x^2 - 9} = 1$

91. $2^{x^2+4x} = \frac{1}{8}$

92. $\log (\log x) = 5$

93. $\log_5 |x| = 4$

94. $\log x^2 = (\log x)^2$

95. $\log \sqrt{2x} = \sqrt{\log 2x}$

96. $1000^{2x+1} = 100^{3x}$

97. $3^{x^2} \cdot 3^{4x} = \frac{1}{27}$

98. $3^{3x} \cdot 3^{x^2} = 81$

99. $\log x^{\log x} = 25$

100. $3^{2x} - 8 \cdot 3^x + 15 = 0$

101. $(81^{x-2})(27^{x+1}) = 9^{2x-3}$

102. $3^{2x} - 3^{2x-1} = 18$

103. Given that $2^y = 16^{x-3}$ and $3^{y+2} = 27^x$, find the value of $x + y$.

104. If $x = (\log_{125} 5)^{\log_5 125}$, what is the value of $\log_3 x$?

> Try Exercise Answers: Section 14.6
>
> **9.** 2   **17.** $\dfrac{\log 19}{\log 8} + 3 \approx 4.416$ **21.** $\dfrac{\ln 8}{-0.02} \approx -103.972$
> **47.** -4 **49.** 10   **57.** 1   **65.** $\frac{17}{2}$ **69.** $-6.480, 6.519$

14.7 Applications of Exponential and Logarithmic Functions

- Applications of Logarithmic Functions

- Applications of Exponential Functions

We now consider applications of exponential and logarithmic functions.

APPLICATIONS OF LOGARITHMIC FUNCTIONS

EXAMPLE 1   Sound Levels.   To measure the volume, or "loudness," of a sound, the *decibel* scale is used. The loudness L, in decibels (dB), of a sound is given by

$$L = 10 \cdot \log \frac{I}{I_0},$$

where I is the intensity of the sound, in watts per square meter (W/m²), and $I_0 = 10^{-12}$ W/m². (I_0 is approximately the intensity of the softest sound that can be heard by the human ear.)

a) The average maximum intensity of sound in a New York subway car is about 3.2×10^{-3} W/m². How loud, in decibels, is the sound level?
    Source: Columbia University Mailman School of Public Health

b) The Occupational Safety and Health Administration (OSHA) considers sustained sound levels of 90 dB and above unsafe. What is the intensity of such sounds?

SOLUTION

a) To find the loudness, in decibels, we use the above formula:

$$L = 10 \cdot \log \frac{I}{I_0}$$

$$= 10 \cdot \log \frac{3.2 \times 10^{-3}}{10^{-12}} \qquad \text{Substituting}$$

$$= 10 \cdot \log (3.2 \times 10^9) \qquad \text{Subtracting exponents}$$

$$= 10(\log 3.2 + \log 10^9) \qquad \log MN = \log M + \log N$$

$$= 10(\log 3.2 + 9) \qquad \log_{10} 10^9 = 9$$

$$\approx 10(0.5051 + 9) \qquad \text{Approximating } \log 3.2$$

$$= 10(9.5051) \qquad \text{Adding within the parentheses}$$

$$\approx 95. \qquad \text{Multiplying and rounding}$$

The volume of the sound in a subway car is about 95 decibels.

b) We substitute and solve for I:

$$L = 10 \cdot \log \frac{I}{I_0}$$

$$90 = 10 \cdot \log \frac{I}{10^{-12}} \qquad \text{Substituting}$$

$$9 = \log \frac{I}{10^{-12}} \qquad \text{Dividing both sides by 10}$$

$$9 = \log I - \log 10^{-12} \qquad \text{Using the quotient rule for logarithms}$$

$$9 = \log I - (-12) \qquad \log 10^a = a$$

$$-3 = \log I \qquad \text{Adding } -12 \text{ to both sides}$$

$$10^{-3} = I. \qquad \text{Converting to an exponential equation}$$

Sustained sounds with intensities exceeding 10^{-3} W/m^2 are considered unsafe.

 Try Exercise 15.

EXAMPLE 2 Chemistry: pH of Liquids. In chemistry, the pH of a liquid is a measure of its acidity. We calculate pH as follows:

$$\text{pH} = -\log [\text{H}^+],$$

where $[\text{H}^+]$ is the hydrogen ion concentration, in moles per liter.

a) The hydrogen ion concentration of human blood is normally about 3.98×10^{-8} moles per liter. Find the pH.
Source: www.merck.com

b) The pH of seawater is about 8.2. Find the hydrogen ion concentration.
Source: www.seafriends.org.nz

SOLUTION

a) To find the pH of blood, we use the above formula:

$$\text{pH} = -\log [\text{H}^+]$$

$$= -\log [3.98 \times 10^{-8}]$$

$$\approx -(-7.400117) \qquad \text{Using a calculator}$$

$$\approx 7.4.$$

The pH of human blood is normally about 7.4.

b) We substitute and solve for $[H^+]$:

$$8.2 = -\log[H^+] \qquad \text{Using pH} = -\log[H^+]$$
$$-8.2 = \log[H^+] \qquad \text{Dividing both sides by} -1$$
$$10^{-8.2} = [H^+] \qquad \text{Converting to an exponential equation}$$
$$6.31 \times 10^{-9} \approx [H^+]. \qquad \text{Using a calculator; writing scientific notation}$$

The hydrogen ion concentration of seawater is about 6.31×10^{-9} moles per liter.

Try Exercise 11.

APPLICATIONS OF EXPONENTIAL FUNCTIONS

EXAMPLE 3 Interest Compounded Annually. Suppose that $25,000 is invested at 4% interest, compounded annually. (See Example 5 in Section 14.2.) In t years, it will grow to the amount A given by the function

$$A(t) = 25,000(1.04)^t.$$

a) How long will it take to accumulate $80,000 in the account?

b) Find the amount of time it takes for the $25,000 to double itself.

SOLUTION

a) We set $A(t) = 80,000$ and solve for t:

$$80,000 = 25,000(1.04)^t$$
$$\frac{80,000}{25,000} = 1.04^t \qquad \text{Dividing both sides by 25,000}$$
$$3.2 = 1.04^t$$
$$\log 3.2 = \log 1.04^t \qquad \text{Taking the common logarithm on both sides}$$
$$\log 3.2 = t \log 1.04 \qquad \text{Using the power rule for logarithms}$$
$$\frac{\log 3.2}{\log 1.04} = t \qquad \text{Dividing both sides by log 1.04}$$
$$29.7 \approx t. \qquad \text{Using a calculator}$$

$y_1 = 25,000(1.04)^x, \quad y_2 = 80,000$

Intersection
X = 29.656544   Y = 80000
Xscl = 5, Yscl = 10,000

Remember that when doing a calculation like this on a calculator, it is best to wait until the end to round off. We check by solving graphically, as shown at left. At an interest rate of 4% per year, it will take about 29.7 years for $25,000 to grow to $80,000.

b) To find the *doubling time*, we replace $A(t)$ with 50,000 and solve for t:

$$50,000 = 25,000(1.04)^t$$
$$2 = (1.04)^t \qquad \text{Dividing both sides by 25,000}$$
$$\log 2 = \log (1.04)^t \qquad \text{Taking the common logarithm on both sides}$$
$$\log 2 = t \log 1.04 \qquad \text{Using the power rule for logarithms}$$
$$t = \frac{\log 2}{\log 1.04} \approx 17.7. \qquad \text{Dividing both sides by log 1.04 and using a calculator}$$

At an interest rate of 4% per year, the doubling time is about 17.7 years.

Try Exercise 5.

Student Notes

Study the different steps in the solution of Example 3(b). Note that if 50,000 and 25,000 are replaced with 8000 and 4000, the doubling time is unchanged.

Like investments, populations often grow exponentially.

Exponential Growth

An **exponential growth model** is a function of the form

$$P(t) = P_0 e^{kt}, \quad k > 0,$$

where P_0 is the population at time 0, $P(t)$ is the population at time t, and k is the **exponential growth rate** for the situation. The **doubling time** is the amount of time necessary for the population to double in size.

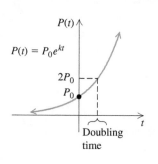

The exponential growth rate is the rate of growth of a population at any *instant* in time. Since the population is continually growing, the percent of total growth after one year will exceed the exponential growth rate.

EXAMPLE 4   Spread of a Computer Virus.   The number of computers infected by a virus t hours after it first appears usually increases exponentially. On January 12, 2009, the "Conflicker" worm had infected 2.4 million PCs. This number was increasing exponentially at a rate of 33% per day.
Source: Based on data from *PC World*

a) Find the exponential growth function that models the data.

b) Estimate the number of infected computers on January 16, 2009.

SOLUTION

a) We let $N(t)$ = the number of infected PCs, in millions. On January 12, at $t = 0$, there were 2.4 million infected PCs. Using the exponential growth function

$$N(t) = N_0 e^{kt},$$

we substitute 2.4 for N_0 and 33%, or 0.33, for k:

$$N(t) = 2.4 e^{0.33t}.$$

b) On January 16, we have $t = 4$, since 4 days have passed since January 12. We compute $N(4)$:

$$
\begin{aligned}
N(4) &= 2.4 e^{0.33(4)} \\
&= 2.4 e^{1.32} \\
&\approx 9.0. \qquad \text{Using a calculator}
\end{aligned}
$$

On January 16, 2009, the worm had infected about 9.0 million PCs.

Try Exercise 23.

EXAMPLE 5   Growth of Zebra Mussel Populations.   Zebra mussels, inadvertently imported from Europe, began fouling North American waters in 1988. These mussels are so prolific that lake and river bottoms, as well as water intake pipes, can become blanketed with them, altering an entire ecosystem. The number of zebra mussels at Prescott, Minnesota, increased exponentially from $72/\text{m}^2$ in 2005 to $574/\text{m}^2$ in 2007.
Source: *Annual Report: Quantitative Assessment of Zebra Mussels Associated with Native Mussels Beds in the Lower St. Croix River*, 2007; prepared for U.S. Army Corps of Engineers, St. Paul District St. Paul, MN, by National Park Service, St. Croix National Scenic Riverway St. Croix Falls, WI, March 2008

a) Find the exponential growth rate and the exponential growth function.

b) Assuming exponential growth, how long will it take for the density to reach 5000 mussels/m²?

SOLUTION

a) We use $P(t) = P_0 e^{kt}$, where t is the number of years since 2005. Substituting 72 for P_0 gives

$$P(t) = 72e^{kt}.$$

To find the exponential growth function, we use the fact that after 2 years, the density was 574/m²:

$$\left. \begin{array}{l} P(2) = 72e^{k \cdot 2} \\ 574 = 72e^{2k} \end{array} \right\} \qquad \text{Substituting 2 for } t \text{ and 574 for } P(2)$$

$$\frac{574}{72} = e^{2k} \qquad \text{Dividing both sides by 72}$$

$$\ln\left(\frac{574}{72}\right) = \ln e^{2k} \qquad \text{Taking the natural logarithm on both sides}$$

$$\ln\left(\frac{574}{72}\right) = 2k \qquad \ln e^a = a$$

$$\frac{\ln\left(\frac{574}{72}\right)}{2} = k \qquad \text{Dividing both sides by 2}$$

$$1.038 \approx k. \qquad \text{Using a calculator and rounding}$$

The exponential growth rate is 103.8%, and the exponential growth function is given by $P(t) = 72e^{1.038t}$.

b) To estimate how long it will take for the density to reach 5000 mussels/m², we replace $P(t)$ with 5000 and solve for t:

$$5000 = 72e^{1.038t}$$

$$\frac{5000}{72} = e^{1.038t} \qquad \text{Dividing both sides by 72}$$

$$\ln\left(\frac{5000}{72}\right) = \ln e^{1.038t} \qquad \text{Taking the natural logarithm on both sides}$$

$$\ln\left(\frac{5000}{72}\right) = 1.038t \qquad \ln e^a = a$$

$$\frac{\ln\left(\frac{5000}{72}\right)}{1.038} = t \qquad \text{Dividing both sides by 1.038}$$

$$4.1 \approx t. \qquad \text{Using a calculator}$$

It will take about 4.1 years for the density to grow to 5000 zebra mussels/m².

Try Exercise 31.

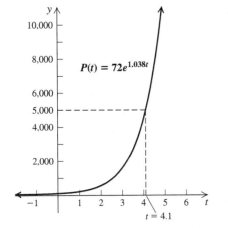

A graphical solution of Example 5

EXAMPLE 6 Interest Compounded Continuously. When an amount of money P_0 is invested at interest rate k, compounded *continuously*, interest is computed every "instant" and added to the original amount. The balance $P(t)$, after t years, is given by the exponential growth model

$$P(t) = P_0 e^{kt}.$$

a) Suppose that $30,000 is invested and grows to $44,754.75 in 5 years. Find the exponential growth function.

b) What is the doubling time?

SOLUTION

a) We have $P(0) = 30,000$. Thus the exponential growth function is

$$P(t) = 30,000 e^{kt}, \quad \text{where } k \text{ must still be determined.}$$

We substitute 5 for t and 44,754.75 for $P(5)$:

$$44,754.75 = 30,000 e^{k(5)} = 30,000 e^{5k}$$

$$\frac{44,754.75}{30,000} = e^{5k} \qquad \text{Dividing both sides by 30,000}$$

$$1.491825 = e^{5k}$$

$$\ln 1.491825 = \ln e^{5k} \qquad \text{Taking the natural logarithm on both sides}$$

$$\ln 1.491825 = 5k \qquad \ln e^a = a$$

$$\frac{\ln 1.491825}{5} = k \qquad \text{Dividing both sides by 5}$$

$$0.08 \approx k. \qquad \text{Using a calculator and rounding}$$

The interest rate is about 0.08, or 8%, compounded continuously. Because interest is being compounded continuously, the yearly interest rate is a bit more than 8%. The exponential growth function is

$$P(t) = 30,000 e^{0.08t}.$$

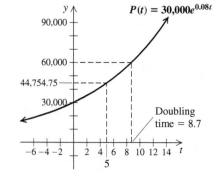

A graphical solution of Example 6

b) To find the doubling time T, we replace $P(T)$ with 60,000 and solve for T:

$$60,000 = 30,000 e^{0.08T}$$

$$2 = e^{0.08T} \qquad \text{Dividing both sides by 30,000}$$

$$\ln 2 = \ln e^{0.08T} \qquad \text{Taking the natural logarithm on both sides}$$

$$\ln 2 = 0.08T \qquad \ln e^a = a$$

$$\frac{\ln 2}{0.08} = T \qquad \text{Dividing both sides by 0.08}$$

$$8.7 \approx T. \qquad \text{Using a calculator and rounding}$$

Thus the original investment of $30,000 will double in about 8.7 years.

Try Exercise 41.

For any specified interest rate, continuous compounding gives the highest yield and the shortest doubling time.

In some real-life situations, a quantity or population is *decreasing* or *decaying* exponentially.

Exponential Decay

An **exponential decay model** is a function of the form

$$P(t) = P_0 e^{-kt}, \quad k > 0,$$

where P_0 is the quantity present at time 0, $P(t)$ is the amount present at time t, and k is the **decay rate**. The **half-life** is the amount of time necessary for half of the quantity to decay.

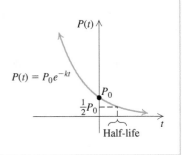

EXAMPLE 7   Carbon Dating.   The radioactive element carbon-14 has a half-life of 5750 years. The percentage of carbon-14 in the remains of organic matter can be used to determine the age of that matter. Recently, while digging near Patuxent River, Maryland, archaeologists found charcoal that had lost 8.1% of its carbon-14. The age of this charcoal indicates that this is the oldest dwelling ever discovered in Maryland. What was the age of the charcoal?

Source: Based on information from *The Baltimore Sun*, "Digging Where Indians Camped Before Columbus," by Frank D. Roylance, July 2, 2009

SOLUTION   We first find k. To do so, we use the concept of half-life. When $t = 5750$ (the half-life), $P(t)$ will be half of P_0. Then

$$0.5P_0 = P_0 e^{-k(5750)} \qquad \text{Substituting in } P(t) = P_0 e^{-kt}$$
$$0.5 = e^{-5750k} \qquad \text{Dividing both sides by } P_0$$
$$\ln 0.5 = \ln e^{-5750k} \qquad \text{Taking the natural logarithm on both sides}$$
$$\ln 0.5 = -5750k \qquad \ln e^a = a$$
$$\frac{\ln 0.5}{-5750} = k \qquad \text{Dividing}$$
$$0.00012 \approx k. \qquad \text{Using a calculator and rounding}$$

Now we have a function for the decay of carbon-14:

$$P(t) = P_0 e^{-0.00012t}. \longleftarrow \text{This completes the first part of our solution.}$$

If the charcoal has lost 8.1% of its carbon-14 from an initial amount P_0, then $100\% - 8.1\%$, or 91.9%, of P_0 is still present. To find the age t of the charcoal, we solve this equation for t:

$$0.919P_0 = P_0 e^{-0.00012t} \qquad \text{We want to find } t \text{ for which } P(t) = 0.919P_0.$$
$$0.919 = e^{-0.00012t} \qquad \text{Dividing both sides by } P_0$$
$$\ln 0.919 = \ln e^{-0.00012t} \qquad \text{Taking the natural logarithm on both sides}$$
$$\ln 0.919 = -0.00012t \qquad \ln e^a = a$$
$$\frac{\ln 0.919}{-0.00012} = t \qquad \text{Dividing}$$
$$700 \approx t. \qquad \text{Using a calculator}$$

The charcoal is about 700 years old.

 Try Exercise 35.

Student Notes

Like linear functions, two points determine an exponential function. It is important to determine whether data follow a linear model or an exponential model (if either) before fitting a function to the data.

The equation

$$P(t) = P_0 e^{-0.00012t}$$

can be used for any subsequent carbon-dating problem.

By looking at the graph of a set of data, we can tell whether a population or other quantity is growing or decaying exponentially.

EXAMPLE 8 For each of the following graphs, determine whether an exponential function might fit the data.

a) **Time to Hearing Loss**

Source: American Hearing Research Foundation

b) **Health-Care Providers and Social Workers**

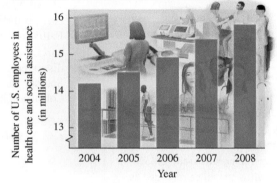

Source: U.S. Bureau of Labor Statistics

c) **Atlantic Basin Hurricanes**

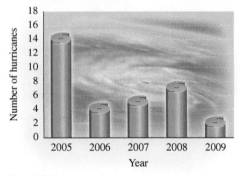

Source: NOAA

d) **Text Messaging in the United States**

Source: CTIA–The Wireless Association

SOLUTION

a) As the sound intensity increases, the safe exposure time decreases. The amount of decrease gets smaller as the intensity increases. It appears that an exponential decay function might fit the data.

Time to Hearing Loss

Source: American Hearing Research Foundation

b) The number of health-care providers and social workers increased between 2004 and 2008 at approximately the same rate each year. It does not appear that an exponential function models the data; instead, a linear function might be appropriate.

Health-Care Providers and Social Workers

Source: U.S. Bureau of Labor Statistics

c) The number of hurricanes first fell, then rose, and then fell again. This does not fit an exponential model.

d) The number of text messages increased from 2003 to 2008, and the amount of yearly growth also increased during that time. This suggests that an exponential growth function could be used to model this situation.

Text Messaging in the United States

Source: CTIA–The Wireless Association

Try Exercise 45.

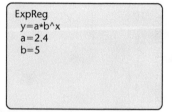

Exponential Regression

To fit an exponential function to a set of data, we use the ExpReg option in the STAT CALC menu. After entering the data, with the independent variable as L1 and the dependent variable as L2, choose the ExpReg option. For the data shown on the left below, the calculator will return a screen like that shown on the right below.

L1	L2	L3	1
1	12	------	
2	60		
3	300		
4	1500		
5	7500		
6	37500		
------	------		

L1(1)=1

```
ExpReg
  y=a*b^x
  a=2.4
  b=5
```

The exponential function found is of the form $f(x) = ab^x$.

We can use the function in this form or convert it to an exponential function of the form $f(x) = ae^{kx}$. The number a remains unchanged. To find k, we solve the equation $b^x = e^{kx}$ for k:

$$b^x = e^{kx}$$
$$b^x = (e^k)^x \qquad \text{Writing both sides as a power of } x$$
$$b = e^k \qquad \text{The bases must be equal.}$$
$$\ln b = \ln e^k \qquad \text{Taking the natural logarithm on both sides}$$
$$\ln b = k. \qquad \ln e^k = k$$

Thus to write $f(x) = 2.4(5)^x$ in the form $f(x) = ae^{kx}$, we can write

$$f(x) = 2.4e^{(\ln 5)x}, \quad \text{or} \quad f(x) = 2.4e^{1.609x}.$$

Your Turn

1. Enter the data $(0, 6), (1, 24), (2, 96), (3, 384)$.
2. Plot the points in a $[-1, 4, 0, 500]$ window, with Yscl = 50. Verify that the pattern appears to fit an exponential model.
3. Fit an exponential equation to the data. $y = 6(4)^x$
4. Write the equation in the form $y = ae^{kx}$. $a = 6, k = \ln 4; y = 6e^{1.386x}$

EXAMPLE 9 Text Messaging.   In 2003, approximately 2.1 million text messages were sent in the United States. This number increased exponentially to 110.4 million in 2008.

Year	Number of Text Messages (in billions)
2003	2.1
2004	4.7
2005	9.8
2006	18.7
2007	48.1
2008	110.4

Source: CTIA—The Wireless Association

a) Use regression to fit an exponential function to the data and graph the function.

b) Determine the exponential growth rate.

c) At this rate, how many text messages will be sent in 2011?

SOLUTION

a) We let $x =$ the number of years since 2003, and enter the data, as shown on the left below. Then we use regression to find the function. Rounding the coefficients, we have

$$f(x) = 2.0545(2.1899)^x.$$

The graph of the function, along with the data points, is shown on the right below.

$y = 2.0545 * 2.1899^x$

Yscl = 25

b) The exponential growth rate is the number k in the equation $f(x) = ae^{kx}$. To write $f(x) = 2.0545(2.1899)^x$ in the form $f(x) = ae^{kx}$, we find k:

$$k = \ln b \approx \ln 2.1899 \approx 0.7839.$$

Thus the exponential growth rate is approximately 0.784, or 78.4%. The exponential function written in the form $f(x) = ae^{kx}$ is thus

$$f(x) = 2.0545e^{0.784x}.$$ This form is equivalent to the form $f(x) = 2.0545(2.1899)^x.$

c) Since 2011 is 8 years after 2003, we find $f(8)$:

$$f(8) = 2.0545(2.1899)^8 \approx 1086.7.$$

Using the function, we estimate that there will be approximately 1.1 trillion text messages sent in the United States in 2011.

Try Exercise 47.

Connecting the Concepts

We can now add the exponential functions $f(t) = P_0 e^{kt}$ and $f(t) = P_0 e^{-kt}$, $k > 0$, and the logarithmic function $f(x) = \log_b x$, $b > 1$, to our library of functions.

Linear function:
$f(x) = mx + b$

Absolute-value function:
$f(x) = |x|$

Rational function:
$f(x) = \dfrac{1}{x}$

Radical function:
$f(x) = \sqrt{x}$

Quadratic function:
$f(x) = ax^2 + bx + c$, $a > 0$

Quadratic function:
$f(x) = ax^2 + bx + c$, $a < 0$

Exponential growth function:
$f(t) = P_0 e^{kt}$, $k > 0$

Exponential decay function:
$f(t) = P_0 e^{-kt}$, $k > 0$

Logarithmic function:
$f(x) = \log_b x$, $b > 1$

14.7 Exercise Set

FOR EXTRA HELP   MyMathLab   MathXL PRACTICE   WATCH   DOWNLOAD   READ   REVIEW

Solve.

1. *Asteroids.* The total number $A(t)$ of known asteroids t years after 1990 can be estimated by

$$A(t) = 77(1.283)^t.$$

Source: Based on data from NASA

a) Determine the year in which the number of known asteroids first reached 4000.

b) What is the doubling time for the number of known asteroids?

2. *Microfinancing.* In India, the number of micro-finance institutions, or firms offering small loans, increased rapidly from 2004 to 2009. The total amount of these loans, in millions of dollars, can be estimated by

$$m(t) = 2.05(2.2)^t,$$

where t is the number of years since 2004.

Source: Based on data from Sa-Dhan

a) In what year will the total amount of these loans reach $1 billion?

b) Find the doubling time.

3. *Health.* The rate of the number of deaths due to stroke in the United States can be estimated by

$$S(t) = 180(0.97)^t,$$

where $S(t)$ is the number of deaths per 100,000 people and t is the number of years since 1960.

Source: Based on data from Centers for Disease Control and Prevention

a) In what year was the death rate due to stroke 100 per 100,000 people?

b) In what year will the death rate due to stroke be 25 per 100,000 people?

4. *Recycling Aluminum Cans.* Approximately one-half of all aluminum cans distributed will be recycled each year. A beverage company distributes 250,000 cans. The number still in use after t years is given by the function

$$N(t) = 250{,}000\left(\tfrac{1}{2}\right)^t.$$

Source: The Aluminum Association, Inc., May 2004

a) After how many years will 60,000 cans still be in use?

b) After what amount of time will only 1000 cans still be in use?

5. *Student Loan Repayment.* A college loan of $29,000 is made at 3% interest, compounded annually. After t years, the amount due, A, is given by the function

$$A(t) = 29{,}000(1.03)^t.$$

a) After what amount of time will the amount due reach $35,000?

b) Find the doubling time.

6. *Spread of a Rumor.* The number of people who have heard a rumor increases exponentially. If all who hear a rumor repeat it to two people per day, and if 20 people start the rumor, the number N of people who have heard the rumor after t days is given by

$$N(t) = 20(3)^t.$$

a) After what amount of time will 1000 people have heard the rumor?

b) What is the doubling time for the number of people who have heard the rumor?

7. *Food Storage.* The maximum storage time, in months, for shelled corn with 13% moisture content can be estimated by

$$m(t) = 1507(0.94)^t,$$

where t is the storage temperature, in degrees Fahrenheit, $t \geq 40°$.

Source: Based on data from University of Minnesota Extension Service

a) At what temperature can corn be stored for 4 years (48 months)?

b) At what temperature can corn be stored for 15 months?

8. *Smoking.* The percentage of smokers who received telephone counseling and had successfully quit smoking for t months is given by

$$P(t) = 21.4(0.914)^t.$$

Sources: *New England Journal of Medicine*; data from California's Smoker's Hotline

a) In what month will 15% of those who quit and used telephone counseling still be smoke-free?

b) In what month will 5% of those who quit and used telephone counseling still be smoke-free?

9. *E-book Sales.* The net amount of e-book sales, in millions of dollars, can be estimated by

$$S(t) = 2.05(1.8)^t,$$

where t is the number of years since 2002.

Source: Based on data from Association of American Publishers

a) In what year will there be $1 billion in e-book net sales?

b) Find the doubling time.

10. *World Population.* The world population $P(t)$, in billions, t years after 2010 can be approximated by

$$P(t) = 6.9(1.011)^t.$$

Sources: Based on data from U.S. Census Bureau; International Data Base

a) In what year will the world population reach 10 billion?

b) Find the doubling time.

Use $\mathrm{pH} = -\log\left[\mathrm{H}^+\right]$ *for Exercises 11–14.*

11. *Chemistry.* The hydrogen ion concentration of fresh-brewed coffee is about 1.3×10^{-5} moles per liter. Find the pH.

12. *Chemistry.* The hydrogen ion concentration of milk is about 1.6×10^{-7} moles per liter. Find the pH.

13. *Medicine.* When the pH of a patient's blood drops below 7.4, a condition called *acidosis* sets in. Acidosis can be deadly when the patient's pH reaches 7.0. What would the hydrogen ion concentration of the patient's blood be at that point?

14. *Medicine.* When the pH of a patient's blood rises above 7.4, a condition called *alkalosis* sets in. Alkalosis can be deadly when the patient's pH reaches 7.8. What would the hydrogen ion concentration of the patient's blood be at that point?

Use the formula in Example 1 for Exercises 15–18.

15. *Racing.* The intensity of sound from a race car in full throttle is about 10 W/m^2. How loud in decibels is this sound level?
Source: nascar.about.com

16. *Audiology.* The intensity of sound in normal conversation is about $3.2 \times 10^{-6} \text{ W/m}^2$. How loud in decibels is this sound level?

17. *Concerts.* The crowd at a Hearsay concert at Wembley Arena in London cheered at a sound level of 128.8 dB. What is the intensity of such a sound?
Source: www.peterborough.gov.uk

18. *City Ordinances.* In Albuquerque, New Mexico, the maximum allowable sound level from a car's exhaust is 96 dB. What is the intensity of such a sound?
Source: www.cabq.gov

19. *E-mail Volume.* The SenderBase® Security Network ranks e-mail volume using a logarithmic scale. The magnitude M of a network's daily e-mail volume is given by

$$M = \log \frac{v}{1.34},$$

where v is the number of e-mail messages sent each day. How many e-mail messages are sent each day by a network that has a magnitude of 7.5?
Source: forum.spamcop.net

20. *Richter Scale.* The Richter scale, developed in 1935, has been used for years to measure earthquake magnitude. The Richter magnitude of an earthquake $m(A)$ is given by the formula

$$m(A) = \log \frac{A}{A_0},$$

where A is the maximum amplitude of the earthquake and A_0 is a constant. What is the magnitude on the Richter scale of an earthquake with an amplitude that is a million times A_0?

Use $P(t) = P_0 e^{kt}$ for Exercises 21 and 22.

21. *Interest Compounded Continuously.* Suppose that P_0 is invested in a savings account where interest is compounded continuously at 2.5% per year.
  a) Express $P(t)$ in terms of P_0 and 0.025.
  b) Suppose that $5000 is invested. What is the balance after 1 year? after 2 years?
  c) When will an investment of $5000 double itself?

22. *Interest Compounded Continuously.* Suppose that P_0 is invested in a savings account where interest is compounded continuously at 3.1% per year.
  a) Express $P(t)$ in terms of P_0 and 0.031.
  b) Suppose that $1000 is invested. What is the balance after 1 year? after 2 years?
  c) When will an investment of $1000 double itself?

23. *Population Growth.* In 2010, the population of the United States was 310 million, and the exponential growth rate was 1.0% per year.
Source: U.S. Census Bureau
  a) Find the exponential growth function.
  b) Predict the U.S. population in 2016.
  c) When will the U.S. population reach 350 million?

24. *World Population Growth.* In 2010, the world population was 6.9 billion, and the exponential growth rate was 1.1% per year.
Source: U.S. Census Bureau
  a) Find the exponential growth function.
  b) Predict the world population in 2014.
  c) When will the world population be 8.0 billion?

25. *Online College Studies.* In 2007, the number of college students studying online was 3.9 million, and the exponential growth rate was 12%. What is the doubling time for the number of online college students? 5.8 yr
Source: Based on information from "Staying the Course," Sloan Consortium, 2008

26. *Population Growth.* The exponential growth rate of the population of United Arab Emirates is 3.7% per year (one of the highest in the world). What is the doubling time? 18.7 yr
Source: Central Intelligence Agency, *The World Factbook*

27. *World Population.* The function

$$Y(x) = 87 \ln \frac{x}{6.1}$$

can be used to estimate the number of years $Y(x)$ after 2000 required for the world population to reach x billion people.
Sources: Based on data from U.S. Census Bureau; International Data Base
  a) In what year will the world population reach 10 billion?
  b) In what year will the world population reach 12 billion?
  c) Graph the function.

28. *Marine Biology.* The function

$$Y(x) = 13 \ln \frac{x}{5.5}$$

can be used to estimate the number of years $Y(x)$ after 1982 required for the world's humpback whale population to reach x thousand whales.

a) In what year will the whale population reach 40,000?

b) In what year will the whale population reach 50,000?

c) Graph the function.

29. *Forgetting.* Students in an English class took a final exam. They took equivalent forms of the exam at monthly intervals thereafter. The average score $S(t)$, in percent, after t months was found to be given by

$$S(t) = 68 - 20 \log (t + 1), \quad t \ge 0.$$

a) What was the average score when they initially took the test $(t = 0)$?

b) What was the average score after 4 months? after 24 months?

c) Graph the function.

d) After what time t was the average score 50%?

30. *Health Insurance.* The amount spent each year by the U.S. government for health insurance for children in low-income families can be estimated by

$$h(t) = 2.6 \ln t,$$

where $h(t)$ is in billions of dollars and t is the number of years after 1998.
Source: Based on data from the Congressional Budget Office

a) How much was spent on health insurance for low-income children in 2007?

b) Graph the function.

c) In what year will $7 billion be spent on health insurance for low-income children?

31. *Wind Power.* U.S. wind-power capacity has grown exponentially from about 2000 megawatts in 1990 to 35,000 megawatts in 2009.
Source: American Wind Energy Association

a) Find the exponential growth rate k, and write an equation for an exponential function that can be used to predict U.S. wind-power capacity t years after 1990.

b) Estimate the year in which wind-power capacity will reach 50,000 megawatts.

32. *Spread of a Computer Virus.* The number of computers infected by a virus t hours after it first appears usually increases exponentially. In 2004, the "MyDoom" worm spread from 100 computers to about 100,000 computers in 24 hr.
Source: Based on data from IDG News Service

a) Find the exponential growth rate k, and write an equation for an exponential function that can be used to predict the number of computers infected t hours after the virus first appeared in 100 computers.

b) Assuming exponential growth, estimate how long it took the MyDoom worm to infect 9000 computers.

33. *Cable Costs.* In 1997, the cost to construct communication cables under the ocean was approximately $8200 per gigabit per second per mile. This cost for subsea cables dropped exponentially to $500 by 2007.
Source: Based on information from TeleGeography

a) Find the exponential decay rate k, and write an equation for an exponential function that can be used to predict the cost of subsea cables t years after 1997.

b) Estimate the cost of subsea cables in 2010.

c) In what year (theoretically) will it cost only $1 per gigabit per second per mile to construct subsea cables?

34. *Decline in Farmland.* The number of acres of farmland in the United States has decreased from 945 million acres in 2000 to 920 million acres in 2008. Assume the number of acres of farmland is decreasing exponentially.
Source: *Statistical Abstract of the United States*

a) Find the value k, and write an equation for an exponential function that can predict the number of acres of U.S. farmland t years after 2000.

b) Predict the number of acres of farmland in 2015.

c) In what year (theoretically) will there be only 800 million acres of U.S. farmland remaining?

35. *Archaeology.* A date palm seedling is growing in Kibbutz Ketura, Israel, from a seed found in King Herod's palace at Masada. The seed had lost 21% of its carbon-14. How old was the seed? (See Example 7.)
Source: Based on information from www.sfgate.com

36. *Archaeology.* Soil from beneath the Kish Church in Azerbaijan was found to have lost 12% of its carbon-14. How old was the soil? (See Example 7.)
Source: Based on information from www.azer.com

37. *Chemistry.* The exponential decay rate of iodine-131 is 9.6% per day. What is its half-life?

38. *Chemistry.* The decay rate of krypton-85 is 6.3% per year. What is its half-life?

39. *Caffeine.* The half-life of caffeine in the human body for a healthy adult is approximately 5 hr.
a) What is the exponential decay rate?
b) How long will it take 95% of the caffeine consumed to leave the body?

40. *Home Construction.* The chemical urea formaldehyde was found in some insulation used in houses built during the mid to late 1960s. Unknown at the time was the fact that urea formaldehyde emitted toxic fumes as it decayed. The half-life of urea formaldehyde is 1 year.
a) What is its decay rate?
b) How long will it take 95% of the urea formaldehyde present to decay?

41. *Art Masterpieces.* As of August 2010, the highest auction price for a sculpture was $104.3 million, paid for Alberto Giacometti's bronze sculpture *Walking Man I*. The same sculpture was purchased for about $9 million in 1990.
Source: Based on information from *The New York Times*, 02/02/10

a) Find the exponential growth rate k, and determine the exponential growth function that can be used to estimate the sculpture's value $V(t)$, in millions of dollars, t years after 1990.
b) Estimate the value of the sculpture in 2020.
c) What is the doubling time for the value of the sculpture?
d) How long after 1990 will the value of the sculpture be $1 billion?

42. *Value of a Sports Card.* Legend has it that because he objected to teenagers smoking, and because his first baseball card was issued in cigarette packs, the great shortstop Honus Wagner halted production of his card before many were produced. One of these cards was purchased in 1991 by hockey great Wayne Gretzky (and a partner) for $451,000. The same card was sold in 2007 for $2.8 million. For the following questions, assume that the card's value increases exponentially, as it has for many years.

a) Find the exponential growth rate k, and determine an exponential function that can be used to estimate the dollar value, $V(t)$, of the card t years after 1991.
b) Predict the value of the card in 2012.
c) What is the doubling time for the value of the card?
d) In what year will the value of the card first exceed $4,000,000?

In Exercises 43–46, determine whether an exponential function might fit the data.

43.

Microprocessor Chip	Year Introduced	Number of Transistors
8080	1974	6,000
8086	1978	29,000
80286	1982	134,000
486 DX	1989	1,200,000
Pentium	1993	3,300,000
Pentium III	1999	9,500,000
Core2 Quad	2006	291,000,000

Sources: "Microprocessors," found on computinghistorymuseum.org; www.neoseeker.com

44. Loan Payment

45. Motor Vehicle Accidents

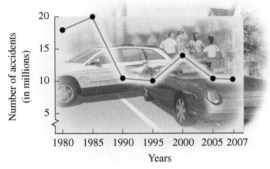

Source: National Safety Council

46. *World automobile production*

Year	Number of Automobiles Produced (in millions)
1950	11
1960	16
1970	29
1980	39
1990	49
2000	60
2008	68

Sources: American Automobile Manufacturers Association, Automotive News Data Center; R.L. Polk Marketing Systems

47. *Technology.* The number of transistors in a microchip has been increasing exponentially. The table in Exercise 43 lists the number of transistors in Intel chips introduced in various years.

a) Use regression to find an exponential function that can be used to estimate the number of transistors $n(t)$, in thousands, in a microchip t years after 1974.

b) Determine the exponential growth rate.

c) Predict the number of transistors in a microchip introduced in 2010.

48. *Stamp Collecting.* There are only two known 1¢ Z Grill stamps. The table below lists the prices paid for one of these stamps as it changed hands.

Year	Price
1975	$ 42,500
1977	90,000
1986	418,000
1998	935,000
2005	2,970,000

Source: Siegel Auctions

a) Use regression to find an exponential function that can be used to estimate the value of the stamp $v(t)$, in thousands of dollars, t years after 1975.

b) Determine the exponential growth rate.

c) Predict the value of the stamp in 2012.

49. *Hearing Loss.* Prolonged exposure to high noise levels can lead to hearing loss. The table below lists the safe exposure time, in hours, for different sound intensities.

Sound Intensity (in decibels)	Safe Exposure Time (in hours)
90	8
100	2
105	1
110	0.5
115	0.25

Source: American Hearing Research Foundation

a) Use regression to fit an exponential function of the form $f(x) = ab^x$ to the data.

b) Estimate the safe exposure time for a sound intensity of 95 dB.

50. *Loan Repayment.* The size of a monthly loan repayment decreases exponentially as the time of the loan increases. The table in Exercise 44 lists the size of monthly loan payments for a $110,000 loan at a fixed interest rate for various lengths of loans.

   a) Use regression to fit an exponential function of the form $f(x) = ab^x$ to the data.

   b) Estimate the monthly loan payment for a 15-year $110,000 loan.

TW **51.** Will the model used to predict the number of text messages in Example 9 still be realistic in 2030? Why or why not?

TW **52.** Examine the restriction on t in Exercise 29.

   a) What upper limit might be placed on t?

   b) In practice, would this upper limit ever be enforced? Why or why not?

SKILL REVIEW

To prepare for Section 15.1, review the distance and midpoint formulas, completing the square, and graphing parabolas (Sections 12.7, 13.1, and 13.7).

Find the distance between each pair of points. [12.7]

53. $(-3, 7)$ and $(-2, 6)$

54. $(1, 5)$ and $(4, 1)$

Find the coordinates of the midpoint of the segment connecting each pair of points. [12.7]

55. $(3, -8)$ and $(5, -6)$

56. $(2, -11)$ and $(-9, -8)$

Solve by completing the square. [13.1]

57. $x^2 + 8x = 1$

58. $x^2 - 10x = 15$

Graph. [13.7]

59. $y = x^2 - 5x - 6$

60. $g(x) = 2x^2 - 6x + 3$

SYNTHESIS

TW **61.** *Atmospheric Pressure.* Atmospheric pressure P at altitude a is given by
$$P(a) = P_0 e^{-0.00005a},$$
where P_0 is the pressure at sea level $\approx 14.7 \text{ lb/in}^2$ (pounds per square inch). Explain how a barometer, or some other device for measuring atmospheric pressure, can be used to find the height of a skyscraper.

TW **62.** Write a problem for a classmate to solve in which information is provided and the classmate is asked to find an exponential growth function. Make the problem as realistic as possible.

63. *Sports Salaries.* As of February 2010, Alex Rodriguez of the New York Yankees had the largest contract in sports history. As part of the 10-year $275-million deal, he will receive $20 million in 2016. How much money would need to be invested in 2008 at 4% interest, compounded continuously, in order to have $20 million for Rodriguez in 2016? (This is much like determining what $20 million in 2016 is worth in 2008 dollars.)
Source: *The San Francisco Chronicle*

64. *Supply and Demand.* The supply and demand for the sale of stereos by Sound Ideas are given by
$$S(x) = e^x \quad \text{and} \quad D(x) = 162{,}755e^{-x},$$
where $S(x)$ is the price at which the company is willing to supply x stereos and $D(x)$ is the demand price for a quantity of x stereos. Find the equilibrium point. (For reference, see Section 11.5.)

65. *Stellar Magnitude.* The apparent stellar magnitude m of a star with received intensity I is given by
$$m(I) = -(19 + 2.5 \cdot \log I),$$
where I is in watts per square meter (W/m^2). The smaller the apparent stellar magnitude, the brighter the star appears.
Source: The Columbus Optical SETI Observatory

   a) The intensity of light received from the sun is 1390 W/m^2. What is the apparent stellar magnitude of the sun?

   b) The 5-m diameter Hale telescope on Mt. Palomar can detect a star with magnitude +23. What is the received intensity of light from such a star?

66. *Growth of Bacteria.* The bacteria *Escherichia coli* (*E. coli*) are commonly found in the human bladder. Suppose that 3000 of the bacteria are present at time $t = 0$. Then t minutes later, the number of bacteria present is
$$N(t) = 3000(2)^{t/20}.$$
If 100,000,000 bacteria accumulate, a bladder infection can occur. If, at 11:00 A.M., a patient's bladder contains 25,000 *E. coli* bacteria, at what time can infection occur?

67. Show that for exponential growth at rate k, the doubling time T is given by $T = \dfrac{\ln 2}{k}$.

68. Show that for exponential decay at rate k, the half-life T is given by $T = \dfrac{\ln 2}{k}$.

Logistic Curves. *Realistically, most quantities that are growing exponentially eventually level off. The quantity may continue to increase, but at a decreasing rate. This pattern of growth can be modeled by a logistic function*

$$f(x) = \frac{c}{1 + ae^{-bx}}.$$

The general shape of this family of functions is shown by the graph below.

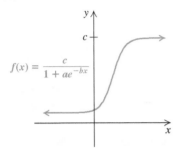

Many graphing calculators can fit a logistic function to a set of data.

69. *Internet Access.* The percent of U.S. households with Internet access for various years is listed in the table below.

Year	Percent of Households with Internet Access
1997	18.6
1998	26.2
2000	41.5
2003	54.6
2007	61.7

Source: www.ntia.doc.gov

a) Find a logistic function

$$f(x) = \frac{c}{1 + ae^{-bx}}$$

that could be used to estimate the percent of U.S. households with Internet access x years after 1997.

b) Use the function found in part (a) to predict the percent of U.S. households with Internet access in 2010.

70. *Heart Transplants.* In 1967, Dr. Christiaan Barnard of South Africa stunned the world by performing the first heart transplant. Since that time, the operation's popularity has both grown and declined, as shown in the table below.

Year	Number of Heart Transplants Worldwide
1982	189
1985	1189
1988	3157
1991	4186
1994	4402
1997	4039
2000	3246
2003	3020
2006	2200
2008	2927

Source: International Society for Heart & Lung Transplantation

a) Using 1982 as $t = 0$, graph the data.
b) Does it appear that an exponential function might have ever served as an appropriate model for these data? If so, for what years would this have been the case?
c) Considering *all* the data points on your graph, which would be the most appropriate model: a linear, quadratic, polynomial, or exponential function? Why?

Try Exercise Answers: Section 14.7
5. **(a)** 6.4 yr; **(b)** 23.4 yr **11.** 4.9 **15.** 130 dB
23. **(a)** $P(t) = 310e^{0.01t}$; **(b)** 329 million; **(c)** about 2022
31. **(a)** $k \approx 0.151$; $P(t) = 2000e^{0.151t}$; **(b)** 2011
35. About 1964 yr **41.** **(a)** $k \approx 0.123$; $V(t) = 9e^{0.123t}$;
(b) $360.4 million; **(c)** 5.6 yr; **(d)** 38.3 yr **45.** No
47. **(a)** $n(t) = 7.8(1.3725)^t$; **(b)** 31.7%;
(c) about 696,000,000 transistors

Study Summary

KEY TERMS AND CONCEPTS	EXAMPLES	PRACTICE EXERCISES

SECTION 14.1: COMPOSITE FUNCTIONS AND INVERSE FUNCTIONS

The **composition** of f and g is defined as $$(f \circ g)(x) = f(g(x)).$$	If $f(x) = \sqrt{x}$ and $g(x) = 2x - 5$, then $$(f \circ g)(x) = f(g(x)) = f(2x - 5)$$ $$= \sqrt{2x - 5}.$$	**1.** Find $(f \circ g)(x)$ if $f(x) = 1 - 6x$ and $g(x) = x^2 - 3$.
A function f is **one-to-one** if different inputs have different outputs. The graph of a one-to-one function passes the **horizontal-line test.**		**2.** Determine whether $f(x) = 5x - 7$ is one-to-one.
If f is one-to-one, it is possible to find its inverse: **1.** Replace $f(x)$ with y. **2.** Interchange x and y. **3.** Solve for y. **4.** Replace y with $f^{-1}(x)$.	If $f(x) = 2x - 3$, find $f^{-1}(x)$. **1.** $y = 2x - 3$ **2.** $x = 2y - 3$ **3.** $x + 3 = 2y$ $\dfrac{x + 3}{2} = y$ **4.** $\dfrac{x + 3}{2} = f^{-1}(x)$	**3.** If $f(x) = 5x + 1$, find $f^{-1}(x)$.

SECTION 14.2: EXPONENTIAL FUNCTIONS
SECTION 14.3: LOGARITHMIC FUNCTIONS

For an **exponential function** f: $f(x) = a^x$; $a > 0, a \neq 1$; Domain: $\mathbb{R}$; $f^{-1}(x) = \log_a x$. For a **logarithmic function** g: $g(x) = \log_a x$; $a > 0, a \neq 1$; Domain: $(0, \infty)$; $g^{-1}(x) = a^x$.		**4.** Graph by hand: $$f(x) = 2^x.$$ **5.** Graph by hand: $$f(x) = \log x.$$
$\log_a x = m$ means $a^m = x$.	Solve: $\log_8 x = 2$. $\log_8 x = 2$ $8^2 = x$ Rewriting as an exponential equation $64 = x$	**6.** Rewrite as an equivalent logarithmic equation: $$5^4 = 625.$$

SECTION 14.4: PROPERTIES OF LOGARITHMIC FUNCTIONS
SECTION 14.5: NATURAL LOGARITHMS AND CHANGING BASES

Properties of Logarithms

$$\log_a (MN) = \log_a M + \log_a N$$

$$\log_a \frac{M}{N} = \log_a M - \log_a N$$

$$\log_a M^p = p \cdot \log_a M$$

$$\log_a 1 = 0$$

$$\log_a a = 1$$

$$\log_a a^k = k$$

$$\log M = \log_{10} M$$

$$\ln M = \log_e M$$

$$\log_b M = \frac{\log_a M}{\log_a b}$$

$$\log_7 10 = \log_7 5 + \log_7 2$$

$$\log_5 \frac{14}{3} = \log_5 14 - \log_5 3$$

$$\log_8 5^{12} = 12 \log_8 5$$

$$\log_9 1 = 0$$

$$\log_4 4 = 1$$

$$\log_3 3^8 = 8$$

$$\log 43 = \log_{10} 43$$

$$\ln 37 = \log_e 37$$

$$\log_6 31 = \frac{\log 31}{\log 6} = \frac{\ln 31}{\ln 6}$$

---

7. Express as an equivalent expression that is a sum of logarithms: $\log_9 xy$.

8. Express as an equivalent expression that is a difference of logarithms: $\log_6 \frac{7}{10}$.

9. Express as an equivalent expression that is a product: $\log 7^5$.

10. Simplify: $\log_8 1$.

11. Simplify: $\log_7 7$.

12. Simplify: $\log_t t^{12}$.

13. Simplify: $\log 100$.

14. Simplify: $\ln e$.

15. Use the change-of-base formula to find $\log_2 5$.

SECTION 14.6: SOLVING EXPONENTIAL AND LOGARITHMIC EQUATIONS

The Principle of Exponential Equality

For any real number b, $b \neq -1, 0,$ or 1:

$b^x = b^y$ is equivalent to $x = y$.

Solve: $25 = 5^x$.

$$25 = 5^x$$
$$5^2 = 5^x$$
$$2 = x$$

---

16. Solve: $2^{3x} = 16$.

The Principle of Logarithmic Equality

For any logarithm base a, and for $x, y > 0$:

$x = y$ is equivalent to $\log_a x = \log_a y$.

Solve: $83 = 7^x$.

$$83 = 7^x$$
$$\log 83 = \log 7^x$$
$$\log 83 = x \log 7$$
$$\frac{\log 83}{\log 7} = x$$

---

17. Solve: $e^{0.1x} = 10$.

SECTION 14.7: APPLICATIONS OF EXPONENTIAL AND LOGARITHMIC FUNCTIONS

Exponential Growth Model

$$P(t) = P_0 e^{kt}, \quad k > 0$$

P_0 is the population at time 0.

$P(t)$ is the population at time t.

k is the **exponential growth rate**.

The **doubling time** is the amount of time necessary for the population to double in size.

If \$1000 is invested at 5%, compounded continuously, then:

- $P_0 = 1000$;
- $k = 0.05$;
- $P(t) = 1000e^{0.05t}$;
- The doubling time is 13.9 years.

---

18. The population of a town in 2010 was 15,000, and it was increasing at an exponential growth rate of 2.3% per year.

   a) Write an exponential function that describes the population $P(t)$, where t is the number of years after 2010.

   b) Find the doubling time.

Exponential Decay Model

$$P(t) = P_0 e^{-kt}, \quad k > 0$$

P_0 is the quantity present at time 0.

$P(t)$ is the amount present at time t.

k is the **exponential decay rate.**

The **half-life** is the amount of time necessary for half of the quantity to decay.

If the population of a town is 2000, and the population is decreasing exponentially at a rate of 1.5% per year, then:

- $P_0 = 2000$;
- $k = 0.015$;
- $P(t) = 2000e^{-0.015t}$;
- The half-life is 46.2 years.

19. Argon-37 has an exponential decay rate of 1.98% per day. Find the half-life.

Review Exercises 14

Concept Reinforcement Classify each of the following statements as either true or false.

1. The functions given by $f(x) = 3^x$ and $g(x) = \log_3 x$ are inverses of each other. [14.5]

2. A function's doubling time is the amount of time t for which $f(t) = 2f(0)$. [14.7]

3. A radioactive isotope's half-life is the amount of time t for which $f(t) = \frac{1}{2}f(0)$. [14.7]

4. $\ln(ab) = \ln a - \ln b$ [14.4]

5. $\log x^a = x \ln a$ [14.4]

6. $\log_a \dfrac{m}{n} = \log_a m - \log_a n$ [14.4]

7. For $f(x) = 3^x$, the domain of f is $[0, \infty)$. [14.2]

8. For $g(x) = \log_2 x$, the domain of g is $[0, \infty)$. [14.3]

9. The function F is not one-to-one if $F(-2) = F(5)$. [14.1]

10. The function g is one-to-one if it passes the vertical-line test. [14.1]

11. Find $(f \circ g)(x)$ and $(g \circ f)(x)$ if $f(x) = x^2 + 1$ and $g(x) = 2x - 3$. [14.1]

12. If $h(x) = \sqrt{3 - x}$, find $f(x)$ and $g(x)$ such that $h(x) = (f \circ g)(x)$. Answers may vary. [14.1]

13. Determine whether $f(x) = 4 - x^2$ is one-to-one. [14.1]

Find a formula for the inverse of each function. [14.1]

14. $f(x) = x - 8$

15. $g(x) = \dfrac{3x + 1}{2}$

16. $f(x) = 27x^3$

Graph by hand.

17. $f(x) = 3^x + 1$ [14.2]

18. $x = \left(\frac{1}{4}\right)^y$ [14.2]

19. $y = \log_5 x$ [14.3]

Simplify. [14.3]

20. $\log_3 9$

21. $\log_{10} \frac{1}{100}$

22. $\log_5 5^7$

23. $\log_9 3$

Rewrite as an equivalent logarithmic equation. [14.3]

24. $10^{-2} = \frac{1}{100}$

25. $25^{1/2} = 5$

Rewrite as an equivalent exponential equation. [14.3]

26. $\log_4 16 = x$

27. $\log_8 1 = 0$

Express as an equivalent expression using the individual logarithms of x, y, and z. [14.4]

28. $\log_a x^4 y^2 z^3$

29. $\log_a \dfrac{x^5}{yz^2}$

30. $\log \sqrt[4]{\dfrac{z^2}{x^3 y}}$

Express as an equivalent expression that is a single logarithm and, if possible, simplify. [14.4]

31. $\log_a 7 + \log_a 8$

32. $\log_a 72 - \log_a 12$

33. $\frac{1}{2} \log a - \log b - 2 \log c$

34. $\frac{1}{3}[\log_a x - 2 \log_a y]$

Simplify. [14.4]

35. $\log_m m$

36. $\log_m 1$

37. $\log_m m^{17}$

Given $\log_a 2 = 1.8301$ *and* $\log_a 7 = 5.0999$, *find each of the following.* [14.4]

38. $\log_a 14$

39. $\log_a \frac{2}{7}$

40. $\log_a 28$

41. $\log_a 3.5$

42. $\log_a \sqrt{7}$

43. $\log_a \frac{1}{4}$

Use a calculator to find each of the following to the nearest ten-thousandth. [14.3], [14.5]

44. $\log 75$

45. $10^{1.789}$

46. $\ln 0.05$

47. $e^{-0.98}$

Find each of the following logarithms using the change-of-base formula. Round answers to the nearest ten-thousandth. [14.5]

48. $\log_5 2$

49. $\log_{12} 70$

Graph and state the domain and the range of each function. [14.5]

50. $f(x) = e^x - 1$

51. $g(x) = 0.6 \ln x$

Solve. Where appropriate, include approximations to the nearest ten-thousandth. [14.6]

52. $2^x = 32$

53. $3^{2x} = \frac{1}{9}$

54. $\log_3 x = -4$

55. $\log_x 16 = 4$

56. $\log x = -3$

57. $3 \ln x = -6$

58. $4^{2x-5} = 19$

59. $2^x = 12$

60. $e^{-0.1t} = 0.03$

61. $2 \ln x = -6$

62. $\log(2x - 5) = 1$

63. $\log_4 x - \log_4(x - 15) = 2$

64. $\log_3(x - 4) = 3 - \log_3(x + 4)$

65. In a business class, students were tested at the end of the course with a final exam. They were then tested again 6 months later. The forgetting formula was determined to be

$$S(t) = 82 - 18 \log(t + 1),$$

where t is the time, in months, after taking the final exam. [14.7]

  a) Determine the average score when they first took the exam (when $t = 0$).

  b) What was the average score after 6 months?

  c) After what time was the average score 54?

66. A laptop computer is purchased for $1500. Its value each year is about 80% of its value in the preceding year. Its value in dollars after t years is given by the exponential function

$$V(t) = 1500(0.8)^t. \quad [14.7]$$

  a) After what amount of time will the computer's value be $900?

  b) After what amount of time will the computer's value be half the original value?

67. U.S. companies spent $1.2 billion in e-mail marketing in 2007. This amount was predicted to grow exponentially to $2.1 billion in 2012. [14.7]
Source: Jupiter Research

  a) Find the exponential growth rate k, and write a function that describes the amount $A(t)$, in billions of dollars, spent on e-mail marketing t years after 2007.

  b) Estimate the amount spent on e-mail marketing in 2015.

  c) In what year will U.S. companies spend $4 billion on e-mail marketing?

  d) Find the doubling time.

68. In 2005, consumers received, on average, 3253 spam messages. The volume of spam messages per consumer is decreasing exponentially at an exponential decay rate of 13.7% per year. [14.7]

  a) Find the exponential decay function that can be used to predict the average number of spam messages, $M(t)$, t years after 2005.

  b) Predict the number of spam messages received per consumer in 2012.

  c) In what year, theoretically, will the average consumer receive 100 spam messages?

69. *Diseases.* The number of hepatitis A cases in the United States has decreased exponentially since 1995. The number of cases for various years are listed in the table below. [14.7]

Year	Number of Hepatitis A Cases (in thousands)
1995	31.6
2000	13.4
2003	7.7
2004	5.7
2005	4.5
2006	3.6
2007	3.0

Source: U.S. Centers for Disease Control

  a) Use regression to find an exponential function of the form $f(x) = ab^x$ that can be used to estimate the number of hepatitis A cases x years after 1995.

  b) Use the function of part (a) to estimate the number of cases of hepatitis A in 2010.

  c) Find the exponential decay rate.

70. The value of Aret's stock market portfolio doubled in 6 years. What was the exponential growth rate? [14.7]

71. How long will it take $7600 to double itself if it is invested at 4.2%, compounded continuously? [14.7]

72. How old is a skull that has lost 34% of its carbon-14? (Use $P(t) = P_0 e^{-0.00012t}$.) [14.7]

73. What is the pH of coffee if its hydrogen ion concentration is 7.9×10^{-6} moles per liter? (Use pH $= -\log[H^+]$.) [14.7]

74. *Nuclear Energy.* Plutonium-239 (Pu-239) is used in nuclear energy plants. The half-life of Pu-239 is 24,360 years. How long will it take for a fuel rod of Pu-239 to lose 90% of its radioactivity? [14.7]
Source: *Microsoft Encarta 97 Encyclopedia*

75. The roar of a lion can reach a sound intensity of 2.5×10^{-1} W/m^2. How loud in decibels is this sound level? $\left(\text{Use } L = 10 \cdot \log \dfrac{I}{10^{-12} \text{ W/m}^2}. \right)$ [14.7]

Source: en.allexperts.com

SYNTHESIS

TW **76.** Explain why negative numbers do not have logarithms. [14.3]

TW **77.** Explain why taking the natural logarithm or common logarithm on each side of an equation produces an equivalent equation. [14.6]

Solve. [14.6]

78. $\ln(\ln x) = 3$ **79.** $2^{x^2 + 4x} = \frac{1}{8}$

80. Solve the system
$$5^{x+y} = 25,$$
$$2^{2x-y} = 64. \quad [14.6]$$

81. *Size of the Internet.* Chinese researchers claim that the Internet doubles in size every 5.32 years. What is the exponential growth rate?
Source: Zhang, Guo-Qing, Guo-Qiang Zhang, Qing-Feng Yang, Su-Qi Cheng, and Tao Zhou. "Evolution of the Internet and its Cores," *New Journal of Physics* **10** (2008) 123027.

Chapter Test 14

1. Find $(f \circ g)(x)$ and $(g \circ f)(x)$ if $f(x) = x + x^2$ and $g(x) = 2x + 1$.

2. If
$$h(x) = \frac{1}{2x^2 + 1},$$
find $f(x)$ and $g(x)$ such that $h(x) = (f \circ g)(x)$. Answers may vary.

3. Determine whether $f(x) = |x - 3|$ is one-to-one.

Find a formula for the inverse of each function.

4. $f(x) = 3x + 4$ **5.** $g(x) = (x + 1)^3$

Graph by hand.

6. $f(x) = 2^x - 3$ **7.** $g(x) = \log_7 x$

Simplify.

8. $\log_5 125$ **9.** $\log_{100} 10$

10. $3^{\log_3 18}$ **11.** $\log_n n$

12. $\log_c 1$ **13.** $\log_a a^{19}$

14. Rewrite as an equivalent logarithmic equation:
$$5^{-4} = \tfrac{1}{625}.$$

15. Rewrite as an equivalent exponential equation:
$$m = \log_2 \tfrac{1}{2}.$$

16. Express as an equivalent expression using the individual logarithms of a, b, and c:
$$\log \frac{a^3 b^{1/2}}{c^2}.$$

17. Express as an equivalent expression that is a single logarithm:
$$\tfrac{1}{3}\log_a x + 2\log_a z.$$

Given $\log_a 2 = 0.301$, $\log_a 6 = 0.778$, *and* $\log_a 7 = 0.845$, *find each of the following.*

18. $\log_a 14$ **19.** $\log_a 3$

20. $\log_a 16$

Use a calculator to find each of the following to the nearest ten-thousandth.

21. $\log 12.3$ **22.** $10^{-0.8}$

23. $\ln 0.4$ **24.** $e^{4.8}$

25. Find $\log_3 14$ using the change-of-base formula. Round to the nearest ten-thousandth.

Graph and state the domain and the range of each function.

26. $f(x) = e^x + 3$ **27.** $g(x) = \ln(x - 4)$

Solve. Where appropriate, include approximations to the nearest ten-thousandth.

28. $2^x = \tfrac{1}{32}$ **29.** $\log_4 x = \tfrac{1}{2}$

30. $\log x = 4$ **31.** $5^{4-3x} = 87$

32. $7^x = 1.2$ **33.** $\ln x = 3$

34. $\log(x - 3) + \log(x + 1) = \log 5$

35. The average walking speed R of people living in a city of population P is given by $R = 0.37 \ln P + 0.05$, where R is in feet per second and P is in thousands.

a) The population of Tulsa, Oklahoma, is 383,000. Find the average walking speed.

b) San Diego, California, has an average walking speed of about 3 ft/sec. Find the population.

36. The population of Austria was about 8.2 million in 2009, and the exponential growth rate was 0.052% per year.
Source: Central Intelligence Agency, *The World Factbook*

a) Write an exponential function describing the population of Austria.

b) What will the population be in 2020? in 2050?

c) When will the population be 9 million?

d) What is the doubling time?

37. The average cost of a year at a private four-year college grew exponentially from $21,855 in 2001 to $35,600 in 2010.
Source: National Center for Education Statistics

a) Find the exponential growth rate k, and write an exponential function that approximates the cost $C(t)$ of a year of college t years after 2001.

b) Predict the cost of a year of college in 2015.

c) In what year will the average cost of a year of college be $50,000?

38. *E-Book Readers.* The number of Kindle unit sales grew exponentially from 2008 to 2010, as listed in the table below.

Year	Kindle Unit Sales (in thousands)
2008	500
2009	1027
2010	3533

Source: Citi Investment Research, estimated

a) Use regression to find an exponential function of the form $f(x) = ab^x$ that can be used to estimate Kindle unit sales x years after 2008.

b) Use the function to estimate Kindle unit sales in 2012.

39. An investment with interest compounded continuously doubled itself in 15 years. What is the interest rate?

40. How old is an animal bone that has lost 43% of its carbon-14? (Use $P(t) = P_0 e^{-0.00012t}$.)

41. The sound of fireworks averages 140 dB. What is the intensity of such a sound?
$$\left(\text{Use } L = 10 \cdot \log \frac{I}{I_0}, \text{ where } I_0 = 10^{-12} \text{ W/m}^2. \right)$$

42. The hydrogen ion concentration of water is 1.0×10^{-7} moles per liter. What is the pH? (Use $\text{pH} = -\log[\text{H}^+]$.)

SYNTHESIS

43. Solve: $\log_5 |2x - 7| = 4$.

44. If $\log_a x = 2$, $\log_a y = 3$, and $\log_a z = 4$, find
$$\log_a \frac{\sqrt[3]{x^2 z}}{\sqrt[3]{y^2 z^{-1}}}.$$

Cumulative Review: Chapters 4, 9, 10–14

1. Evaluate $\dfrac{x^0 + y}{-z}$ for $x = 6$, $y = 9$, and $z = -5$.

Simplify.

2. $(-2x^2y^{-3})^{-4}$

3. $(-5x^4y^{-3}z^2)(-4x^2y^2)$

4. $\dfrac{3x^4y^6z^{-2}}{-9x^4y^2z^3}$

5. $(1.5 \times 10^{-3})(4.2 \times 10^{-12})$

6. $3^3 + 2^2 - (32 \div 4 - 16 \div 8)$

Solve.

7. $3(2x - 3) = 9 - 5(2 - x)$

8. $4x - 3y = 15,$
$\quad 3x + 5y = 4$ [4.3]

9. $\quad x + y - 3z = -1,$
$\quad 2x - y + z = 4,$
$\quad -x - y + z = 1$ [11.1]

10. $x(x - 3) = 70$

11. $\dfrac{7}{x^2 - 5x} - \dfrac{2}{x - 5} = \dfrac{4}{x}$

12. $\sqrt{4 - 5x} = 2x - 1$ [12.6]

13. $\sqrt[3]{2x} = 1$ [12.6]

14. $3x^2 + 48 = 0$ [13.1]

15. $x^4 - 13x^2 + 36 = 0$ [13.5]

16. $\log_x 81 = 2$ [14.3]

17. $3^{5x} = 7$ [14.6]

18. $\ln x - \ln (x - 8) = 1$ [14.6]

19. $x^2 + 4x > 5$ [10.4]

20. If $f(x) = x^2 + 6x$, find a such that $f(a) = 11$.
  [13.2]

21. If $f(x) = |2x - 3|$, find all x for which $f(x) \geq 7$.
  [10.2]

Solve.

22. $D = \dfrac{ab}{b + a}$, for a

23. $d = ax^2 + vx$, for x [13.4]

24. Find the domain of the function f given by

$$f(x) = \dfrac{x + 4}{3x^2 - 5x - 2}.$$

Perform the indicated operations and simplify.

25. $(5p^2q^3 + 6pq - p^2 + p) -$
$\quad (2p^2q^3 + p^2 - 5pq - 9)$

26. $(3x^2 - z^3)^2$

27. $\dfrac{1 + \dfrac{3}{x}}{x - 1 - \dfrac{12}{x}}$

28. $\dfrac{a^2 - a - 6}{a^3 - 27} \cdot \dfrac{a^2 + 3a + 9}{6}$

29. $\dfrac{3}{x + 6} - \dfrac{2}{x^2 - 36} + \dfrac{4}{x - 6}$

30. $\dfrac{\sqrt[3]{24xy^8}}{\sqrt[3]{3xy}}$ [12.4]

31. $\sqrt{x + 5} \, \sqrt[5]{x + 5}$ [12.5]

32. $\left(2 - i\sqrt{3}\right)\left(6 + i\sqrt{3}\right)$ [12.8]

33. $(x^4 - 8x^3 + 15x^2 + x - 3) \div (x - 3)$

Factor.

34. $xy + 2xz - xw$

35. $6x^2 + 8xy - 8y^2$

36. $x^4 - 4x^3 + 7x - 28$

37. $2m^2 + 12mn + 18n^2$

38. $x^4 - 16y^4$

39. Rationalize the denominator:

$$\dfrac{3 - \sqrt{y}}{2 - \sqrt{y}}. \quad [12.5]$$

40. Find the inverse of f if $f(x) = 9 - 2x$. [14.1]

41. Find a linear equation with a graph that contains the points $(0, -8)$ and $(-1, 2)$.

42. Find an equation of the line whose graph has a y-intercept of $(0, 5)$ and is perpendicular to the line given by $2x + y = 6$.

Graph by hand.

43. $5x = 15 + 3y$

44. $y = \log_3 x$ [14.3]

45. $-2x - 3y \le 12$ [10.4]

46. Graph: $f(x) = 2x^2 + 12x + 19$. [13.7]

    a) Label the vertex.
    b) Draw the axis of symmetry.
    c) Find the maximum or minimum value.

47. Graph $f(x) = 2e^x$ and determine the domain and the range. [14.5]

48. Express as a single logarithm:

$$3 \log x - \tfrac{1}{2} \log y - 2 \log z. \quad [14.4]$$

In Exercises 49–52, match each function with one of the following graphs.

a)

b)

c)

d)

49. $f(x) = -2x + 3.1$

50. $p(x) = 3x^2 + 5x - 2$ [13.6]

51. $h(x) = \dfrac{2.3}{x}$

52. $g(x) = e^{x-1}$ [14.5]

Solve.

53. *Colorado River.* The Colorado River delivers 1.5 million acre-feet of water to Mexico each year. This is only 10% of the volume of the river; the remainder is diverted at an earlier time for agricultural use. How much water is diverted each year from the Colorado River?
Source: www.sierraclub.org

54. *Desalination.* An increasing number of cities are supplying some of their fresh water through desalination, the process of removing the salt from ocean water. The worldwide desalination capacity has grown exponentially from 15 million m³ per day in 1990 to 55 million m³ per day in 2007. [14.7]
Source: Global Water Intelligence

    a) Find the exponential growth rate k, and write an equation for an exponential function that can be used to predict the worldwide desalination capacity $D(t)$, in millions of cubic meters per day, t years after 1990.
    b) Predict the worldwide desalination capacity in 2012.
    c) In what year will the worldwide desalination capacity reach 100 million m³ per day?

55. Good's Candies of Indiana makes all their chocolates by hand. It takes Abi 10 min to coat a tray of candies in chocolate. It takes Brad 12 min to coat a tray of candies. How long would it take Abi and Brad, working together, to coat the candies?

56. Joe's Thick and Tasty salad dressing gets 45% of its calories from fat. The Light and Lean dressing gets 20% of its calories from fat. How many ounces of each should be mixed in order to get 15 oz of dressing that gets 30% of its calories from fat? [4.4]

57. A fishing boat with a trolling motor can move at a speed of 5 km/h in still water. The boat travels 42 km downriver in the same time that it takes to travel 12 km upriver. What is the speed of the river?

Travel. *Prices for a massage at Passport Travel Spa in an airport waiting area are shown in the graph below. Use the graph for Exercises 58–62.*

Airport Massage

Source: Passport Travel Spa, Indianapolis International Airport

58. Determine whether the data can be modeled by a linear, quadratic, or exponential function.

59. Find the rate of change, in dollars per minute.

60. Find a linear function $f(x) = mx + b$ that fits the data, where f is the cost of the massage and x is the length, in minutes.

61. Use the function in Exercise 60 to estimate the cost of a 10-min massage.

62. For the function in Exercise 60, what do the values of m and b signify?

Life Insurance. *The monthly premium for a term life insurance policy increases as the age of the insured person increases. The graph below shows some premiums for a $250,000 policy for a male.*

Life Insurance

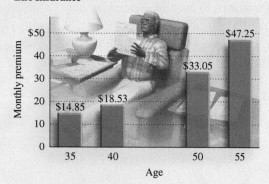

Source: Insurance company advertisement

63. Use regression to find an exponential function of the form $f(x) = ab^x$ that can be used to estimate the monthly insurance premium m for a male who is x years old. [14.7]

64. Use the function in Exercise 63 to estimate the monthly premium for a 45-year-old male. [14.7]

SYNTHESIS

Solve.

65. $\dfrac{5}{3x - 3} + \dfrac{10}{3x + 6} = \dfrac{5x}{x^2 + x - 2}$

66. $\log \sqrt{3x} = \sqrt{\log 3x}$ [14.6]

67. The Danville Express travels 280 mi at a certain speed. If the speed had been increased by 5 mph, the trip could have been made in 1 hr less time. Find the actual speed. [13.3]

Conic Sections

How Far is the Earth from the Sun?

The answer is, "It depends." The earth's orbit around the sun is not a perfect circle, but rather an ellipse with the sun at one focus. The earth is closest to the sun in January and farthest from the sun in July. In Exercise 57 of Section 15.2, we will estimate the maximum distance of the earth from the sun.

Earth's Orbit

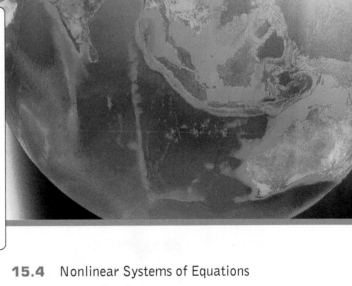

A conic section can be regarded as a cross section of a cone. This chapter presents a variety of applications and equations with graphs that are conic sections. We have already worked with two conic sections, *lines* and *parabolas*, in Chapter 13.

15.1 Conic Sections: Parabolas and Circles

- Parabolas
- Circles

This section and the next two examine curves formed by cross sections of cones. These curves are all graphs of $Ax^2 + By^2 + Cxy + Dx + Ey + F = 0$. The constants A, B, C, D, E, and F determine which of the following shapes will serve as the graph.

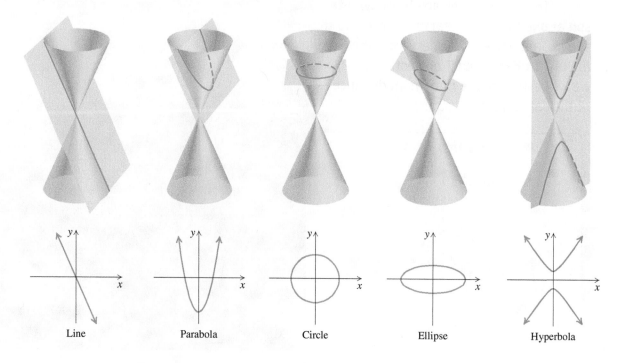

Line   Parabola   Circle   Ellipse   Hyperbola

PARABOLAS

When a cone is cut as shown in the second figure above, the conic section formed is a **parabola.** Parabolas have many applications in electricity, mechanics, and optics. A cross section of a contact lens or a satellite dish is a parabola, and arches that support certain bridges are parabolas.

Equation of a Parabola A parabola with a vertical axis of symmetry opens upward or downward and has an equation that can be written in the form

$$y = ax^2 + bx + c.$$

A parabola with a horizontal axis of symmetry opens to the right or to the left and has an equation that can be written in the form

$$x = ay^2 + by + c.$$

Parabolas with equations of the form $f(x) = ax^2 + bx + c$ were graphed in Chapter 13.

EXAMPLE 1 Graph: $y = x^2 - 4x + 9$.

SOLUTION To locate the vertex, we can use either of two approaches. One way is to complete the square:

$$y = (x^2 - 4x) + 9 \qquad \text{Note that half of } -4 \text{ is } -2, \text{ and } (-2)^2 = 4.$$
$$= (x^2 - 4x + 4 - 4) + 9 \qquad \text{Adding and subtracting 4}$$
$$= (x^2 - 4x + 4) + (-4 + 9) \qquad \text{Regrouping}$$
$$= (x - 2)^2 + 5. \qquad \text{Factoring and simplifying}$$

The vertex is $(2, 5)$.

A second way to find the vertex is to recall that the x-coordinate of the vertex of the parabola given by $y = ax^2 + bx + c$ is $-b/(2a)$:

$$x = -\frac{b}{2a} = -\frac{-4}{2(1)} = 2.$$

To find the y-coordinate of the vertex, we substitute 2 for x:

$$y = x^2 - 4x + 9 = 2^2 - 4(2) + 9 = 5.$$

Either way, the vertex is $(2, 5)$. Next, we calculate and plot some points on each side of the vertex. As expected for a positive coefficient of x^2, the graph opens upward.

x	y	
2	5	← Vertex
0	9	← y-intercept
1	6	
3	6	
4	9	

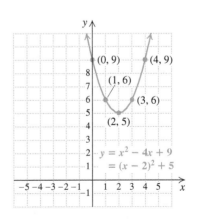

Try Exercise 11.

> ### To Graph an Equation of the Form $y = ax^2 + bx + c$
>
> **1.** Find the vertex (h, k) either by completing the square to find an equivalent equation
>
> $$y = a(x - h)^2 + k,$$
>
> or by using $-b/(2a)$ to find the x-coordinate and substituting to find the y-coordinate.
> **2.** Choose other values for x on each side of the vertex, and compute the corresponding y-values.
> **3.** The graph opens upward for $a > 0$ and downward for $a < 0$.

Any equation of the form $x = ay^2 + by + c$ represents a horizontal parabola that opens to the right for $a > 0$, opens to the left for $a < 0$, and has an axis of symmetry parallel to the x-axis.

EXAMPLE 2 Graph: $x = y^2 - 4y + 9$.

SOLUTION This equation is like that in Example 1 but with x and y interchanged. The vertex is $(5, 2)$ instead of $(2, 5)$. To find ordered pairs, we choose values for y on each side of the vertex. Then we compute values for x. Note that the x- and y-values of the table in Example 1 are now switched. You should confirm that, by completing the square, we get $x = (y - 2)^2 + 5$.

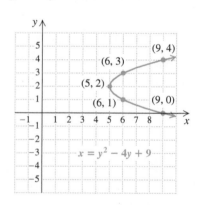

x	y	
5	2	← Vertex
9	0	← x-intercept
6	1	
6	3	
9	4	

— (1) Choose these values for y.

— (2) Compute these values for x.

Try Exercise 13.

> ### To Graph an Equation of the Form $x = ay^2 + by + c$
>
> **1.** Find the vertex (h, k) either by completing the square to find an equivalent equation
>
> $$x = a(y - k)^2 + h,$$
>
> or by using $-b/(2a)$ to find the y-coordinate and substituting to find the x-coordinate.
> **2.** Choose other values for y that are on either side of k and compute the corresponding x-values.
> **3.** The graph opens to the right if $a > 0$ and to the left if $a < 0$.

EXAMPLE 3   Graph: $x = -2y^2 + 10y - 7$.

SOLUTION   We find the vertex by completing the square:

$$x = -2y^2 + 10y - 7$$
$$= -2(y^2 - 5y \qquad) - 7$$
$$= -2\left(y^2 - 5y + \tfrac{25}{4}\right) - 7 - (-2)\tfrac{25}{4} \qquad \tfrac{1}{2}(-5) = \tfrac{-5}{2}; \left(\tfrac{-5}{2}\right)^2 = \tfrac{25}{4}; \text{ we}$$

add and subtract $(-2)\tfrac{25}{4}$.

$$= -2\left(y - \tfrac{5}{2}\right)^2 + \tfrac{11}{2}. \qquad \text{Factoring and simplifying}$$

The vertex is $\left(\tfrac{11}{2}, \tfrac{5}{2}\right)$.

For practice, we also find the vertex by first computing its y-coordinate, $-b/(2a)$, and then substituting to find the x-coordinate:

$$y = -\frac{b}{2a} = -\frac{10}{2(-2)} = \frac{5}{2}$$
$$x = -2y^2 + 10y - 7 = -2\left(\tfrac{5}{2}\right)^2 + 10\left(\tfrac{5}{2}\right) - 7$$
$$= \tfrac{11}{2}.$$

To find ordered pairs, we choose values for y on each side of the vertex and then compute values for x. A table is shown below, together with the graph. The graph opens to the left because the y^2-coefficient, -2, is negative.

x	y	
$\tfrac{11}{2}$	$\tfrac{5}{2}$	← Vertex
-7	0	← x-intercept
5	2	
5	3	
1	1	
1	4	
-7	5	

(1) Choose these values for y.
(2) Compute these values for x.

Try Exercise 27.

CIRCLES

Another conic section, the **circle,** is the set of points in a plane that are a fixed distance r, called the **radius** (plural, **radii**), from a fixed point (h, k), called the **center.** Note that the word radius can mean either any segment connecting a point on a circle to the center or the length of such a segment. Using the idea of a fixed distance r and the distance formula,

$$d = \sqrt{(x_2 - x_1)^2 + (y_2 - y_1)^2},$$

we can find the equation of a circle.

If (x, y) is on a circle of radius r, centered at (h, k), then by the definition of a circle and the distance formula, it follows that

$$r = \sqrt{(x - h)^2 + (y - k)^2}.$$

Squaring both sides gives the equation of a circle in standard form.

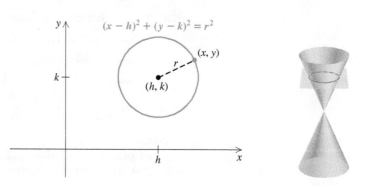

Equation of a Circle (Standard Form) The equation of a circle, centered at (h, k), with radius r, is given by

$$(x - h)^2 + (y - k)^2 = r^2.$$

Note that for $h = 0$ and $k = 0$, the circle is centered at the origin. Otherwise, the circle is translated $|h|$ units horizontally and $|k|$ units vertically.

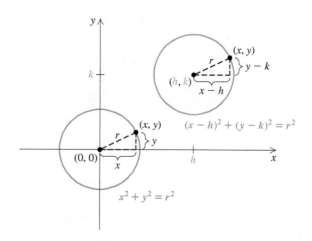

EXAMPLE 4 Find an equation of the circle having center $(4, 5)$ and radius 6.

SOLUTION Using the standard form, we obtain

$$(x - 4)^2 + (y - 5)^2 = 6^2, \qquad \text{Using } (x - h)^2 + (y - k)^2 = r^2$$

or

$$(x - 4)^2 + (y - 5)^2 = 36.$$

Try Exercise 31.

EXAMPLE 5 Find the center and the radius and then graph each circle.

a) $(x - 2)^2 + (y + 3)^2 = 4^2$
b) $x^2 + y^2 + 8x - 2y + 15 = 0$

SOLUTION

a) We write standard form:

$$(x - 2)^2 + [y - (-3)]^2 = 4^2.$$

The center is $(2, -3)$ and the radius is 4. To graph, we plot the points $(2, 1)$, $(2, -7)$, $(-2, -3)$, and $(6, -3)$, which are, respectively, 4 units above, below, left, and right of $(2, -3)$. We then either sketch a circle by hand or use a compass.

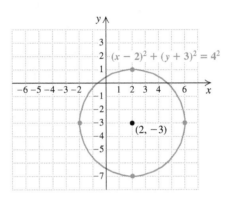

b) To write the equation $x^2 + y^2 + 8x - 2y + 15 = 0$ in standard form, we complete the square twice, once with $x^2 + 8x$ and once with $y^2 - 2y$:

$$x^2 + y^2 + 8x - 2y + 15 = 0$$

$$x^2 + 8x \qquad + y^2 - 2y \qquad = -15 \qquad \text{Grouping the } x\text{-terms and the } y\text{-terms; subtracting 15 from both sides}$$

$$x^2 + 8x + 16 + y^2 - 2y + 1 = -15 + 16 + 1 \qquad \text{Adding } \left(\tfrac{8}{2}\right)^2, \text{ or 16, and } \left(-\tfrac{2}{2}\right)^2, \text{ or 1, to both sides to get standard form}$$

$$(x + 4)^2 + (y - 1)^2 = 2 \qquad \text{Factoring}$$

$$[x - (-4)]^2 + (y - 1)^2 = \left(\sqrt{2}\right)^2. \qquad \text{Writing standard form}$$

The center is $(-4, 1)$ and the radius is $\sqrt{2}$.

Try Exercise 43.

—— *Graphing Circles*

Because most graphing calculators can graph only functions, graphing the equation of a circle usually requires two steps:

1. Solve the equation for y. The result will include a $\pm$ sign in front of a radical.

2. Graph two functions, one for the $+$ sign and the other for the $-$ sign, on the same set of axes.

For example, to graph $(x - 3)^2 + (y + 1)^2 = 16$, solve for $y + 1$ and then y:

$$(y + 1)^2 = 16 - (x - 3)^2$$
$$y + 1 = \pm\sqrt{16 - (x - 3)^2}$$
$$y = -1 \pm \sqrt{16 - (x - 3)^2}.$$

Then

$$y_1 = -1 + \sqrt{16 - (x - 3)^2}$$

and

$$y_2 = -1 - \sqrt{16 - (x - 3)^2}.$$

When both functions are graphed (in a "squared" window to eliminate distortion), the result is as follows.

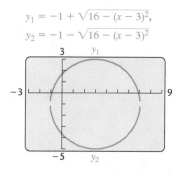

$$y_1 = -1 + \sqrt{16 - (x - 3)^2},$$
$$y_2 = -1 - \sqrt{16 - (x - 3)^2}$$

Circles can also be drawn using the CIRCLE option of the DRAW menu, but such graphs cannot be traced. Many calculators have a Conics application, accessed by pressing **APPS**. If we use this program, equations of circles in standard form can be graphed directly, and then Traced, by entering only the values of h, k, and r.

Your Turn

Graph the circle $x^2 + y^2 = 10$ using the following steps.

1. Solve $x^2 + y^2 = 10$ for y. $\qquad y = \pm\sqrt{10 - x^2}$

2. Enter $y_1 = \sqrt{10 - x^2}$ and $y_2 = -y_1$.

3. Set up a $[-6, 6, -4, 4]$ window and graph the equations.

15.1 Exercise Set

FOR EXTRA HELP   *MyMathLab*   Math XL PRACTICE   WATCH   DOWNLOAD   READ   REVIEW

Concept Reinforcement   *In each of Exercises 1–8, match the equation with the center or vertex of its graph, listed in the column on the right.*

1. ___ $(x - 2)^2 + (y + 5)^2 = 9$ a) Vertex: $(-2, 5)$

2. ___ $(x + 2)^2 + (y - 5)^2 = 9$ b) Vertex: $(5, -2)$

3. ___ $(x - 5)^2 + (y + 2)^2 = 9$ c) Vertex: $(2, -5)$

4. ___ $(x + 5)^2 + (y - 2)^2 = 9$ d) Vertex: $(-5, 2)$

5. ___ $y = (x - 2)^2 - 5$ e) Center: $(-2, 5)$

6. ___ $y = (x - 5)^2 - 2$ f) Center: $(2, -5)$

7. ___ $x = (y - 2)^2 - 5$ g) Center: $(5, -2)$

8. ___ $x = (y - 5)^2 - 2$ h) Center: $(-5, 2)$

Graph. Be sure to label each vertex.

9. $y = -x^2$ 10. $y = 2x^2$

11. $y = -x^2 + 4x - 5$ 12. $x = 4 - 3y - y^2$

13. $x = y^2 - 4y + 2$ 14. $y = x^2 + 2x + 3$

15. $x = y^2 + 3$ 16. $x = -y^2$

17. $x = 2y^2$ 18. $x = y^2 - 1$

19. $x = -y^2 - 4y$ 20. $x = y^2 + 3y$

21. $y = x^2 - 2x + 1$ 22. $y = x^2 + 2x + 1$

23. $x = -\frac{1}{2}y^2$ 24. $y = -\frac{1}{2}x^2$

25. $x = -y^2 + 2y - 1$ 26. $x = -y^2 - 2y + 3$

27. $x = -2y^2 - 4y + 1$ 28. $x = 2y^2 + 4y - 1$

Find an equation of the circle satisfying the given conditions.

29. Center $(0, 0)$, radius 6

30. Center $(0, 0)$, radius 5

31. Center $(7, 3)$, radius $\sqrt{5}$

32. Center $(5, 6)$, radius $\sqrt{2}$

33. Center $(-4, 3)$, radius $4\sqrt{3}$

34. Center $(-2, 7)$, radius $2\sqrt{5}$

35. Center $(-7, -2)$, radius $5\sqrt{2}$

36. Center $(-5, -8)$, radius $3\sqrt{2}$

Aha! 37. Center $(0, 0)$, passing through $(-3, 4)$

38. Center $(0, 0)$, passing through $(11, -10)$

39. Center $(-4, 1)$, passing through $(-2, 5)$

40. Center $(-1, -3)$, passing through $(-4, 2)$

Find the center and the radius of each circle. Then graph the circle.

41. $x^2 + y^2 = 64$ 42. $x^2 + y^2 = 36$

43. $(x + 1)^2 + (y + 3)^2 = 36$

44. $(x - 2)^2 + (y + 3)^2 = 4$

45. $(x - 4)^2 + (y + 3)^2 = 10$

46. $(x + 5)^2 + (y - 1)^2 = 15$

47. $x^2 + y^2 = 10$ 48. $x^2 + y^2 = 7$

49. $(x - 5)^2 + y^2 = \frac{1}{4}$ 50. $x^2 + (y - 1)^2 = \frac{1}{25}$

51. $x^2 + y^2 + 8x - 6y - 15 = 0$

52. $x^2 + y^2 + 6x - 4y - 15 = 0$

53. $x^2 + y^2 - 8x + 2y + 13 = 0$

54. $x^2 + y^2 + 6x + 4y + 12 = 0$

55. $x^2 + y^2 + 10y - 75 = 0$

56. $x^2 + y^2 - 8x - 84 = 0$

57. $x^2 + y^2 + 7x - 3y - 10 = 0$

58. $x^2 + y^2 - 21x - 33y + 17 = 0$

59. $36x^2 + 36y^2 = 1$

60. $4x^2 + 4y^2 = 1$

📉 *Graph using a graphing calculator.*

61. $x^2 + y^2 - 16 = 0$

62. $4x^2 + 4y^2 = 100$

63. $x^2 + y^2 + 14x - 16y + 54 = 0$

64. $x^2 + y^2 - 10x - 11 = 0$

TW **65.** Does the graph of an equation of a circle include the point that is the center? Why or why not?

TW **66.** Is a point a conic section? Why or why not?

SKILL REVIEW

To prepare for Section 15.2, review solving quadratic equations (Section 13.1).

Solve for x or for y. [13.1]

67. $\dfrac{y^2}{16} = 1$

68. $\dfrac{x^2}{a^2} = 1$

69. $\dfrac{(x - 1)^2}{25} = 1$

70. $\dfrac{(y + 5)^2}{12} = 1$

71. $\dfrac{1}{4} + \dfrac{(y + 3)^2}{36} = 1$

72. $\dfrac{1}{9} + \dfrac{(x - 2)^2}{4} = 1$

SYNTHESIS

TW **73.** On a piece of graph paper, draw a line and a point not on the line. Then plot several points that are the same distance from the point and from the line. What shape do the points appear to form? How is this set of points different from a circle?

TW **74.** If an equation has two terms with the same degree, can its graph be a parabola? Why or why not?

Find an equation of a circle satisfying the given conditions.

75. Center $(3, -5)$ and tangent to (touching at one point) the y-axis

76. Center $(-7, -4)$ and tangent to the x-axis

77. The endpoints of a diameter are $(7, 3)$ and $(-1, -3)$.

78. Center $(-3, 5)$ with a circumference of 8π units

79. Find the point on the y-axis that is equidistant from $(2, 10)$ and $(6, 2)$.

80. Find the point on the x-axis that is equidistant from $(-1, 3)$ and $(-8, -4)$.

81. *Wrestling.* The equation $x^2 + y^2 = \frac{81}{4}$, where x and y represent the number of meters from the center, can be used to draw the outer circle on a wrestling mat used in International, Olympic, and World Championship wrestling. The equation $x^2 + y^2 = 16$

can be used to draw the inner edge of the red zone. Find the area of the red zone.

Source: Based on data from the Government of Western Australia

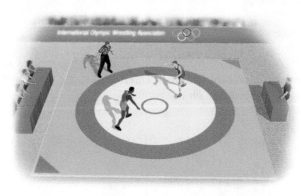

🖩 **82.** *Snowboarding.* Each side edge of the Burton X8 155 snowboard is an arc of a circle with a "running length" of 1180 mm and a "sidecut depth" of 23 mm (see the figure below).

Source: evogear.com

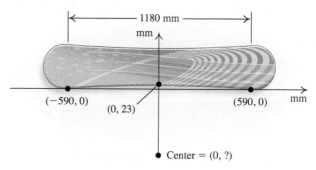

a) Using the coordinates shown, locate the center of the circle. (*Hint*: Equate distances.)

b) What radius is used for the edge of the board?

🖩 **83.** *Snowboarding.* The Never Summer Infinity 149 snowboard has a running length of 1160 mm and a sidecut depth of 23.5 mm (see Exercise 82). What radius is used for the edge of this snowboard?

Source: neversummer.com

🖩 **84.** *Skiing.* The Rossignol Blast ski, when lying flat and viewed from above, has edges that are arcs of a circle. (Actually, each edge is made of two arcs of slightly different radii. The arc for the rear half of the ski edge has a slightly larger radius.)

Source: evogear.com

a) Using the coordinates shown, locate the center of the circle. (*Hint*: Equate distances.)

b) What radius is used for the arc passing through $(0, 1.5)$ and $(72, 0)$?

85. *Doorway Construction.* Ace Carpentry needs to cut an arch for the top of an entranceway. The arch needs to be 8 ft wide and 2 ft high. To draw the arch, the carpenters will use a stretched string with chalk attached at an end as a compass.

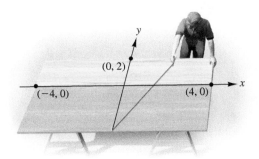

a) Using a coordinate system, locate the center of the circle.

b) What radius should the carpenters use to draw the arch?

86. *Archaeology.* During an archaeological dig, Martina finds the bowl fragment shown below. What was the original diameter of the bowl?

87. *Ferris Wheel Design.* A ferris wheel has a radius of 24.3 ft. Assuming that the center is 30.6 ft off the ground and that the origin is below the center, as in the following figure, find an equation of the circle.

88. Use a graph of the equation $x = y^2 - y - 6$ to approximate to the nearest tenth the solutions of each of the following equations.

a) $y^2 - y - 6 = 2$
(*Hint*: Graph $x = 2$ on the same set of axes as the graph of $x = y^2 - y - 6$.)

b) $y^2 - y - 6 = -3$

89. *Power of a Motor.* The horsepower of a certain kind of engine is given by the formula

$$H = \frac{D^2 N}{2.5},$$

where N is the number of cylinders and D is the diameter, in inches, of each piston. Graph this equation, assuming that $N = 6$ (a six-cylinder engine). Let D run from 2.5 to 8.

90. If the equation $x^2 + y^2 - 6x + 2y - 6 = 0$ is written as $y^2 + 2y + (x^2 - 6x - 6) = 0$, it can be regarded as quadratic in y.

a) Use the quadratic formula to solve for y.

b) Show that the graph of your answer to part (a) coincides with the graph on p. 968.

91. How could a graphing calculator best be used to help you sketch the graph of an equation of the form $x = ay^2 + by + c$?

92. Why should a graphing calculator's window be "squared" before graphing a circle?

Try Exercise Answers: Section 15.1

11. $y = -x^2 + 4x - 5$

13. $x = y^2 - 4y + 2$

27. $x = -2y^2 - 4y + 1$

31. $(x - 7)^2 + (y - 3)^2 = 5$

43. $(-1, -3); 6$

$(x + 1)^2 + (y + 3)^2 = 36$

15.2 Conic Sections: Ellipses

- Ellipses Centered at (0, 0)

- Ellipses Centered at (h, k)

When a cone is cut at an angle, as shown below, the conic section formed is an *ellipse*. To draw an ellipse, we can stick two tacks in a piece of cardboard. Then we tie a loose string to the tacks, place a pencil as shown, and draw an oval by moving the pencil while stretching the string tight.

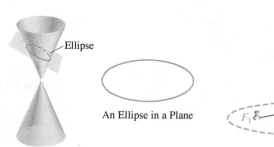

An Ellipse in a Plane

ELLIPSES CENTERED AT (0, 0)

An **ellipse** is defined as the set of all points in a plane for which the sum of the distances from two fixed points F_1 and F_2 is constant. The points F_1 and F_2 are called **foci** (pronounced (fō-sī), the plural of focus. In the figure above, the tacks are at the foci, and the length of the string is the constant sum of the distances. The midpoint of the segment F_1F_2 is the **center.** The equation of an ellipse is as follows. Its derivation is outlined in Exercise 51.

> **Equation of an Ellipse Centered at the Origin**   The equation of an ellipse centered at the origin and symmetric with respect to both axes is
>
> $$\frac{x^2}{a^2} + \frac{y^2}{b^2} = 1, \quad a, b > 0. \qquad \text{(Standard form)}$$

To graph an ellipse centered at the origin, it is helpful to first find the intercepts. If we replace x with 0, we can find the y-intercepts:

$$\frac{0^2}{a^2} + \frac{y^2}{b^2} = 1$$

$$\frac{y^2}{b^2} = 1$$

$$y^2 = b^2 \quad \text{or} \quad y = \pm b.$$

Thus the y-intercepts are $(0, b)$ and $(0, -b)$. Similarly, the x-intercepts are $(a, 0)$ and $(-a, 0)$. If $a > b$, the ellipse is said to be horizontal, and $(-a, 0)$ and $(a, 0)$ are referred to as the **vertices** (singular, **vertex**). If $b > a$, the ellipse is said to be vertical, and $(0, -b)$ and $(0, b)$ are then the vertices.

Plotting these four points and drawing an oval-shaped curve, we graph the ellipse. If a more precise graph is desired, we can plot more points.

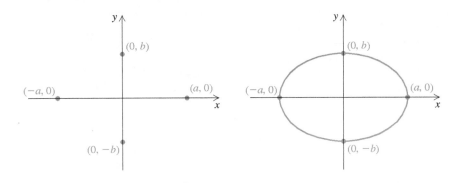

> **Using *a* and *b* to Graph an Ellipse**   For the ellipse
>
> $$\frac{x^2}{a^2} + \frac{y^2}{b^2} = 1,$$
>
> the x-intercepts are $(-a, 0)$ and $(a, 0)$. The y-intercepts are $(0, -b)$ and $(0, b)$. For $a^2 > b^2$, the ellipse is horizontal. For $b^2 > a^2$, the ellipse is vertical.

EXAMPLE 1   Graph the ellipse $\dfrac{x^2}{4} + \dfrac{y^2}{9} = 1.$

SOLUTION   Note that

$$\frac{x^2}{4} + \frac{y^2}{9} = \frac{x^2}{2^2} + \frac{y^2}{3^2}.$$ *Identifying a and b. Since $b^2 > a^2$, the ellipse is vertical.*

Since $a = 2$ and $b = 3$, the x-intercepts are $(-2, 0)$ and $(2, 0)$, and the y-intercepts are $(0, -3)$ and $(0, 3)$. We plot these points and connect them with an oval-shaped curve. To plot two other points, we let $x = 1$ and solve for y:

$$\frac{1^2}{4} + \frac{y^2}{9} = 1$$

$$36\left(\frac{1}{4} + \frac{y^2}{9}\right) = 36 \cdot 1$$

$$36 \cdot \frac{1}{4} + 36 \cdot \frac{y^2}{9} = 36$$

$$9 + 4y^2 = 36$$

$$4y^2 = 27$$

$$y^2 = \frac{27}{4}$$

$$y = \pm\sqrt{\frac{27}{4}}$$

$$y \approx \pm 2.6.$$

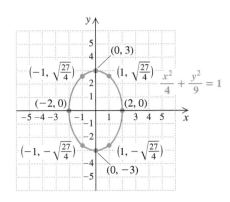

Thus, $(1, 2.6)$ and $(1, -2.6)$ can also be used to draw the graph. Similarly, the points $(-1, 2.6)$ and $(-1, -2.6)$ should appear on the graph.

Try Exercise 9.

Student Notes

Note that any equation of the form $Ax^2 + By^2 = C$ (with $A \neq B$ and $A, B > 0$) will have a graph that is an ellipse. The equation can be rewritten in standard form by dividing both sides by C.

EXAMPLE 2   Graph: $4x^2 + 25y^2 = 100$.

SOLUTION   To write the equation in standard form, we divide both sides by 100 to get 1 on the right side:

$$\frac{4x^2 + 25y^2}{100} = \frac{100}{100} \qquad \text{Dividing by 100 to get 1 on the right side}$$

$$\left.\begin{aligned} \frac{4x^2}{100} + \frac{25y^2}{100} &= 1 \\[4pt] \frac{x^2}{25} + \frac{y^2}{4} &= 1 \end{aligned}\right\} \qquad \text{Simplifying}$$

$$\frac{x^2}{5^2} + \frac{y^2}{2^2} = 1. \qquad a = 5, b = 2$$

The x-intercepts are $(-5, 0)$ and $(5, 0)$, and the y-intercepts are $(0, -2)$ and $(0, 2)$. We plot the intercepts and connect them with an oval-shaped curve. Other points can also be computed and plotted.

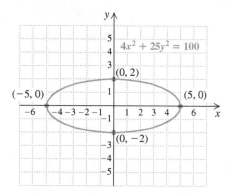

Try Exercise 13.

ELLIPSES CENTERED AT (h, k)

Horizontal and vertical translations, similar to those used in Chapter 13, can be used to graph ellipses that are not centered at the origin.

Equation of an Ellipse Centered at (h, k)   The standard form of a horizontal ellipse or a vertical ellipse centered at (h, k) is

$$\frac{(x - h)^2}{a^2} + \frac{(y - k)^2}{b^2} = 1.$$

The vertices are $(h + a, k)$ and $(h - a, k)$ if horizontal; $(h, k + b)$ and $(h, k - b)$ if vertical.

EXAMPLE 3   Graph the ellipse

$$\frac{(x - 1)^2}{4} + \frac{(y + 5)^2}{9} = 1.$$

SOLUTION   Note that

$$\frac{(x - 1)^2}{4} + \frac{(y + 5)^2}{9} = \frac{(x - 1)^2}{2^2} + \frac{(y + 5)^2}{3^2}.$$

Thus, $a = 2$ and $b = 3$. To determine the center of the ellipse, (h, k), note that

$$\frac{(x - 1)^2}{2^2} + \frac{(y + 5)^2}{3^2} = \frac{(x - 1)^2}{2^2} + \frac{(y - (-5))^2}{3^2}.$$

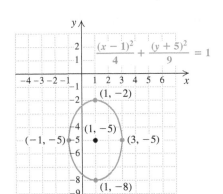

Thus the center is $(1, -5)$. We plot the points 2 units to the left and to the right of center, as well as the points 3 units above and below center. These are the points $(3, -5)$, $(-1, -5)$, $(1, -2)$, and $(1, -8)$. The graph of the ellipse is shown at left.

Note that this ellipse is the same as the ellipse in Example 1 but translated 1 unit to the right and 5 units down.

Try Exercise 27.

Ellipses have many applications. Communications satellites move in elliptical orbits with the earth as a focus while the earth itself follows an elliptical path around the sun. A medical instrument, the lithotripter, uses shock waves originating at one focus to crush a kidney stone located at the other focus.

Planetary orbit

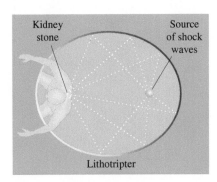

Lithotripter

In some buildings, an ellipsoidal ceiling creates a "whispering gallery" in which a person at one focus can whisper and still be heard clearly at the other focus. This happens because sound waves coming from one focus are all reflected to the other focus. Similarly, light waves bouncing off an ellipsoidal mirror are used in a dentist's or surgeon's reflector light. The light source is located at one focus while the patient's mouth or surgical field is at the other.

Graphing Ellipses

Graphing an ellipse on a graphing calculator is much like graphing a circle: We graph it in two pieces after solving for y.

To graph the ellipse given by the equation $4x^2 + 25y^2 = 100$, we first solve for y:

$$4x^2 + 25y^2 = 100$$
$$25y^2 = 100 - 4x^2$$
$$y^2 = 4 - \tfrac{4}{25}x^2$$
$$y = \pm\sqrt{4 - \tfrac{4}{25}x^2}.$$

Then, using a squared window, we graph.

$$y_1 = -\sqrt{4 - (4/25)x^2},$$
$$y_2 = \sqrt{4 - (4/25)x^2}$$

On many calculators, pressing **APPS** and selecting Conics and then Ellipse accesses a program in which equations in standard form of ellipses centered at (h, k) can be graphed directly.

Your Turn

Graph the ellipse $9x^2 + y^2 = 36$ using the following steps.

1. Solve $9x^2 + y^2 = 36$ for y. $y = \pm\sqrt{36 - 9x^2}$
2. Enter $y_1 = \sqrt{36 - 9x^2}$ and $y_2 = -y_1$.
3. Set up a $[-9, 9, -6, 6]$ window and graph both equations.

15.2 Exercise Set

FOR EXTRA HELP

Concept Reinforcement *Classify each of the following statements as either true or false.*

1. The graph of $\dfrac{x^2}{28} + \dfrac{y^2}{48} = 1$ is a vertical ellipse.

2. The graph of $\dfrac{x^2}{30} + \dfrac{y^2}{20} = 1$ is a vertical ellipse.

3. The graph of $\dfrac{x^2}{25} - \dfrac{y^2}{9} = 1$ is a horizontal ellipse.

4. The graph of $\dfrac{-x^2}{20} + \dfrac{y^2}{16} = 1$ is a horizontal ellipse.

5. The graph of $\dfrac{x^2}{9} + \dfrac{y^2}{25} = 1$ includes the points $(-3, 0)$ and $(3, 0)$.

6. The graph of $\dfrac{x^2}{36} + \dfrac{y^2}{25} = 1$ includes the points $(0, -5)$ and $(0, 5)$.

7. The graph of $\dfrac{(x + 3)^2}{25} + \dfrac{(y - 2)^2}{36} = 1$ is an ellipse centered at $(-3, 2)$.

8. The graph of $\dfrac{(x - 2)^2}{49} + \dfrac{(y + 5)^2}{9} = 1$ is an ellipse centered at $(2, -5)$.

Graph each of the following equations.

9. $\dfrac{x^2}{1} + \dfrac{y^2}{9} = 1$

10. $\dfrac{x^2}{9} + \dfrac{y^2}{1} = 1$

11. $\dfrac{x^2}{25} + \dfrac{y^2}{9} = 1$

12. $\dfrac{x^2}{16} + \dfrac{y^2}{25} = 1$

13. $4x^2 + 9y^2 = 36$

14. $9x^2 + 4y^2 = 36$

15. $16x^2 + 9y^2 = 144$

16. $9x^2 + 16y^2 = 144$

17. $2x^2 + 3y^2 = 6$

18. $5x^2 + 7y^2 = 35$

Aha! 19. $5x^2 + 5y^2 = 125$

20. $8x^2 + 5y^2 = 80$

21. $3x^2 + 7y^2 - 63 = 0$

22. $3x^2 + 8y^2 - 72 = 0$

23. $16x^2 = 16 - y^2$

24. $9y^2 = 9 - x^2$

25. $16x^2 + 25y^2 = 1$

26. $9x^2 + 4y^2 = 1$

27. $\dfrac{(x - 3)^2}{9} + \dfrac{(y - 2)^2}{25} = 1$

28. $\dfrac{(x - 2)^2}{25} + \dfrac{(y - 4)^2}{9} = 1$

29. $\dfrac{(x + 4)^2}{16} + \dfrac{(y - 3)^2}{49} = 1$

30. $\dfrac{(x + 5)^2}{4} + \dfrac{(y - 2)^2}{36} = 1$

31. $12(x - 1)^2 + 3(y + 4)^2 = 48$
    (*Hint*: Divide both sides by 48.)

32. $4(x - 6)^2 + 9(y + 2)^2 = 36$

Aha! 33. $4(x + 3)^2 + 4(y + 1)^2 - 10 = 90$

34. $9(x + 6)^2 + (y + 2)^2 - 20 = 61$

TW 35. Explain how you can tell from the equation of an ellipse whether the graph will be horizontal or vertical.

TW 36. Can an ellipse ever be the graph of a function? Why or why not?

SKILL REVIEW

Review solving equations.

Solve.

37. $x^2 - 5x + 3 = 0$ [13.2]

38. $\log_x 81 = 4$ [14.6]

39. $\dfrac{4}{x + 2} + \dfrac{3}{2x - 1} = 2$

40. $3 - \sqrt{2x - 1} = 1$ [12.6]

41. $x^2 = 11$ [13.1]

42. $x^2 + 4x = 60$

SYNTHESIS

TW 43. Explain how it is possible to recognize that the graph of $9x^2 + 18x + y^2 - 4y + 4 = 0$ is an ellipse.

TW 44. As the foci get closer to the center of an ellipse, what shape does the graph begin to resemble? Explain why this happens.

Find an equation of an ellipse that contains the following points.

45. $(-9, 0), (9, 0), (0, -11),$ and $(0, 11)$

46. $(-7, 0), (7, 0), (0, -5),$ and $(0, 5)$

47. $(-2, -1), (6, -1), (2, -4),$ and $(2, 2)$

48. $(4, 3), (-6, 3), (-1, -1)$ and $(-1, 7)$

49. *Theatrical Lighting.*   The spotlight on a violin soloist casts an ellipse of light on the floor below her that is 6 ft wide and 10 ft long. Find an equation of that ellipse if the performer is in its center, x is the distance from the performer to the side of the ellipse, and y is the distance from the performer to the top of the ellipse.

50. *Astronomy.* The maximum distance of the planet Mars from the sun is 2.48×10^8 mi. The minimum distance is 3.46×10^7 mi. The sun is at one focus of the elliptical orbit. Find the distance from the sun to the other focus.

51. Let $(-c, 0)$ and $(c, 0)$ be the foci of an ellipse. Any point $P(x, y)$ is on the ellipse if the sum of the distances from the foci to P is some constant. Use $2a$ to represent this constant.

a) Show that an equation for the ellipse is given by
$$\frac{x^2}{a^2} + \frac{y^2}{a^2 - c^2} = 1.$$

b) Substitute b^2 for $a^2 - c^2$ to get standard form.

52. *President's Office.* The Oval Office of the President of the United States is an ellipse 31 ft wide and 38 ft long. Show in a sketch precisely where the President and an adviser could sit to best hear each other using the room's acoustics. (*Hint*: See Exercise 51(b) and the discussion following Example 3.)

53. *Dentistry.* The light source in a dental lamp shines against a reflector that is shaped like a portion of an ellipse in which the light source is one focus of the ellipse. Reflected light enters a patient's mouth at the other focus of the ellipse. If the ellipse from which the reflector was formed is 2 ft wide and 6 ft long, how far should the patient's mouth be from the light source? (*Hint*: See Exercise 51(b).)

Lamp

F_2 F_1

54. *Firefighting.* The size and shape of certain forest fires can be approximated as the union of two "half-ellipses." For the blaze modeled below, the equation of the smaller ellipse—the part of the fire moving *into* the wind—is
$$\frac{x^2}{40,000} + \frac{y^2}{10,000} = 1$$

The equation of the other ellipse—the part moving *with* the wind—is
$$\frac{x^2}{250,000} + \frac{y^2}{10,000} = 1.$$

Determine the width and the length of the fire.
Source for figure: "Predicting Wind-Driven Wild Land Fire Size and Shape," Hal E. Anderson, Research Paper INT-305, U.S. Department of Agriculture, Forest Service, February 1983

For each of the following equations, complete the square as needed and find an equivalent equation in standard form. Then graph the ellipse.

55. $x^2 - 4x + 4y^2 + 8y - 8 = 0$

56. $4x^2 + 24x + y^2 - 2y - 63 = 0$

Astronomy. *The earth's orbit around the sun is an ellipse with a ≈ 149.7 million km. The sun, located at one focus of the ellipse, is approximately 2.4 million km from the center of the ellipse.*
Source: Based on information from Physical Geography.net

57. What is the maximum distance of the earth from the sun?

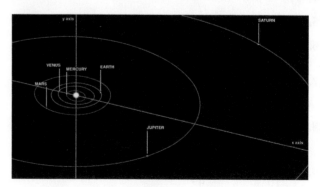

58. An *astronomical unit*, which has been defined using the mean distance of the earth from the sun, is about 149.6 million km. What is the maximum distance of the earth from the sun in astronomical units?

Collaborative Corner

A Cosmic Path

Focus: Ellipses
Time: 20–30 minutes
Group Size: 2
Materials: Scientific calculators

On May 4, 2007, Comet 17P/Holmes was at the point closest to the sun in its orbit. Comet 17P is traveling in an elliptical orbit with the sun as one focus, and one orbit takes about 6.88 years. One astronomical unit (AU) is 93,000,000 mi. One group member should do the following calculations in AU and the other in millions of miles.

Source: Harvard-Smithsonian Center for Astrophysics

ACTIVITY

1. At its *perihelion*, a comet with an elliptical orbit is at the point in its orbit closest to the sun. At its *aphelion*, the comet is at the point farthest from the sun. The perihelion distance for Comet 17P is 2.053218 AU, and the aphelion distance is 5.183610 AU. Use these distances to find *a*. (See the following diagram.)

2. Using the figure above, express b^2 as a function of *a*. Then find *b* using the value found for *a* in part (1).

3. One formula for approximating the perimeter of an ellipse is

$$P = \pi\left(3a + 3b - \sqrt{(3a + b)(a + 3b)}\right),$$

developed by the Indian mathematician S. Ramanujan in 1914. How far does Comet 17P travel in one orbit?

4. What is the speed of the comet? Find the answer in AU per year and in miles per hour.

15.3 Conic Sections: Hyperbolas

- Hyperbolas

- Hyperbolas (Nonstandard Form)

- Classifying Graphs of Equations

HYPERBOLAS

A **hyperbola** looks like a pair of parabolas, but the shapes are not quite parabolic. A hyperbola has two **vertices** and the line through the vertices is known as the **axis.** The point halfway between the vertices is called the **center.** The two curves that comprise a hyperbola are called **branches.**

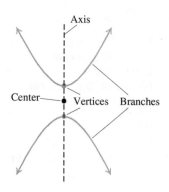

Parabola

Hyperbola in three dimensions

Hyperbola in a plane

Equation of a Hyperbola Centered at the Origin

A hyperbola with its center at the origin* has its equation as follows:

$$\frac{x^2}{a^2} - \frac{y^2}{b^2} = 1 \qquad \text{(Horizontal axis)};$$

$$\frac{y^2}{b^2} - \frac{x^2}{a^2} = 1 \qquad \text{(Vertical axis)}.$$

Note that both equations have a 1 on the right-hand side and a subtraction symbol between the terms. For the discussion that follows, we assume $a, b > 0$.

To graph a hyperbola, it helps to begin by graphing two lines called **asymptotes.** Although the asymptotes themselves are not part of the graph, they serve as guidelines for an accurate sketch.

As a hyperbola gets farther away from the origin, it gets closer and closer to its asymptotes. The asymptotes act to "constrain" the graph of a hyperbola. Parabolas are *not* constrained by any asymptotes.

---

*Hyperbolas with horizontal or vertical axes and centers *not* at the origin are discussed in Exercises 59–64.

Asymptotes of a Hyperbola   For hyperbolas with equations as shown below, the asymptotes are the lines

$$y = \frac{b}{a}x \quad \text{and} \quad y = -\frac{b}{a}x.$$

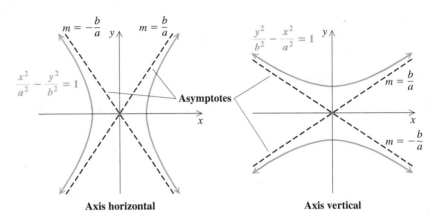

Axis horizontal   **Axis vertical**

In Section 15.2, we used a and b to determine the width and the length of an ellipse. For hyperbolas, a and b are used to determine the base and the height of a rectangle that can be used as an aid in sketching asymptotes and locating vertices.

EXAMPLE 1   Graph: $\dfrac{x^2}{4} - \dfrac{y^2}{9} = 1$.

SOLUTION   Note that

$$\frac{x^2}{4} - \frac{y^2}{9} = \frac{x^2}{2^2} - \frac{y^2}{3^2}, \qquad \text{Identifying } a \text{ and } b$$

so $a = 2$ and $b = 3$. The asymptotes are thus

$$y = \tfrac{3}{2}x \quad \text{and} \quad y = -\tfrac{3}{2}x.$$

To help us sketch asymptotes and locate vertices, we use a and b—in this case, 2 and 3—to form the pairs $(-2, 3)$, $(2, 3)$, $(2, -3)$, and $(-2, -3)$. We plot these pairs and lightly sketch a rectangle. The asymptotes pass through the corners and, since this is a horizontal hyperbola, the vertices are where the rectangle intersects the x-axis. Finally, we draw the hyperbola, as shown below.

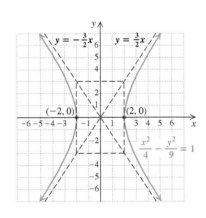

Try Exercise 11.

Student Notes

Regarding the orientation of a hyperbola, you may find it helpful to think as follows: "The axis is parallel to the x-axis if $\dfrac{x^2}{a^2}$ is the positive term.

The axis is parallel to the y-axis if $\dfrac{y^2}{b^2}$ is the positive term."

EXAMPLE 2   Graph: $\dfrac{y^2}{36} - \dfrac{x^2}{4} = 1$.

SOLUTION   Note that

$$\dfrac{y^2}{36} - \dfrac{x^2}{4} = \dfrac{y^2}{6^2} - \dfrac{x^2}{2^2} = 1.$$

> **Whether the hyperbola is horizontal or vertical is determined by which term is nonnegative. Here the y^2-term is nonnegative, so the hyperbola is vertical.**

Using ± 2 as x-coordinates and ± 6 as y-coordinates, we plot $(2, 6)$, $(2, -6)$, $(-2, 6)$, and $(-2, -6)$, and lightly sketch a rectangle through them. The asymptotes pass through the corners (see the figure on the left below). Since the hyperbola is vertical, its vertices are $(0, 6)$ and $(0, -6)$. Finally, we draw curves through the vertices toward the asymptotes, as shown below.

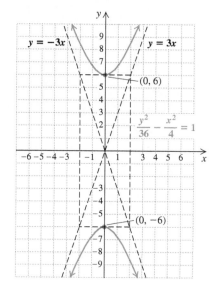

Try Exercise 9.

HYPERBOLAS (NONSTANDARD FORM)

The equations for hyperbolas just examined are the standard ones, but there are other hyperbolas. We consider some of them.

> ### Equation of a Hyperbola in Nonstandard Form   Hyperbolas
> having the x- and y-axes as asymptotes have equations as follows:
>
> $$xy = c, \quad \text{where } c \text{ is a nonzero constant.}$$

EXAMPLE 3 Graph: $xy = -8$.

SOLUTION We first solve for y:

$$y = -\frac{8}{x}.$$ Dividing both sides by x. Note that $x \neq 0$.

Next, we find some solutions and form a table. Note that x cannot be 0 and that for large values of $|x|$, the value of y will be close to 0. Thus the x- and y-axes serve as asymptotes. We plot the points and draw two curves.

x	y
2	−4
−2	4
4	−2
−4	2
1	−8
−1	8
8	−1
−8	1

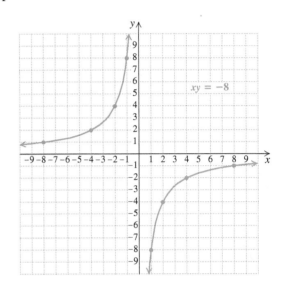

$xy = -8$

Try Exercise 19.

Hyperbolas have many applications. A jet breaking the sound barrier creates a sonic boom with a wave front the shape of a cone. The intersection of the cone with the ground is one branch of a hyperbola. Some comets travel in hyperbolic orbits, and a cross section of many lenses is hyperbolic in shape.

Graphing Hyperbolas

Graphing a hyperbola on a graphing calculator is much like graphing a circle or an ellipse.

To graph the hyperbola given by the equation

$$\frac{x^2}{25} - \frac{y^2}{49} = 1,$$

we solve for y, which gives the equations

$$y_1 = \frac{\sqrt{49x^2 - 1225}}{5} = \frac{7}{5}\sqrt{x^2 - 25}$$

and

$$y_2 = \frac{-\sqrt{49x^2 - 1225}}{5} = -\frac{7}{5}\sqrt{x^2 - 25},$$

or

$$y_2 = -y_1.$$

When the two pieces are drawn on the same squared window, the result is as shown. The gaps occur where the graph is nearly vertical.

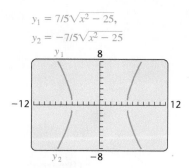

$y_1 = 7/5\sqrt{x^2 - 25},$
$y_2 = -7/5\sqrt{x^2 - 25}$

On many calculators, pressing **APPS** and selecting Conics and then Hyperbola accesses a program in which equations in standard form of hyperbolas centered at (h, k) can be graphed directly. (See Exercises 59–64.)

Your Turn

Graph the hyperbola $\dfrac{x^2}{4} - y^2 = 1$ using the following steps.

1. Solve $\dfrac{x^2}{4} - y^2 = 1$ for y. $y = \pm\sqrt{\dfrac{x^2}{4} - 1}$
2. Enter $y_1 = \sqrt{x^2/4 - 1}$ and $y_2 = -y_1$.
3. Set up a $[-6, 6, -4, 4]$ window and graph both equations.

CLASSIFYING GRAPHS OF EQUATIONS

By writing an equation of a conic section in a standard form, we can classify its graph as a parabola, a circle, an ellipse, or a hyperbola. Every conic section can also be represented by an equation of the form

$$Ax^2 + By^2 + Cxy + Dx + Ey + F = 0.$$

We can also classify graphs using values of A and B.

Graph	Standard Form		$Ax^2 + By^2 + Cxy + Dx + Ey + F = 0$
Parabola	$y = ax^2 + bx + c;$	Vertical parabola	Either $A = 0$ or $B = 0$, but not both.
	$x = ay^2 + by + c$	Horizontal parabola	
Circle	$x^2 + y^2 = r^2;$	Center at the origin	$A = B$
	$(x - h)^2 + (y - k)^2 = r^2$	Center at (h, k)	
Ellipse	$\dfrac{x^2}{a^2} + \dfrac{y^2}{b^2} = 1;$	Center at the origin	$A \neq B$, and A and B have the same sign.
	$\dfrac{(x - h)^2}{a^2} + \dfrac{(y - k)^2}{b^2} = 1$	Center at (h, k)	
Hyperbola	$\dfrac{x^2}{a^2} - \dfrac{y^2}{b^2} = 1;$	Horizontal hyperbola	A and B have opposite signs.
	$\dfrac{y^2}{b^2} - \dfrac{x^2}{a^2} = 1$	Vertical hyperbola	
	$xy = c$	Asymptotes are axes	Only C and F are nonzero.

Algebraic manipulations may be needed to express an equation in one of the preceding forms.

EXAMPLE 4   Classify the graph of each equation as a circle, an ellipse, a parabola, or a hyperbola. Refer to the above table as needed.

a) $5x^2 = 20 - 5y^2$ **b)** $x + 3 + 8y = y^2$

c) $x^2 = y^2 + 4$ **d)** $x^2 = 16 - 4y^2$

SOLUTION

a) We get the terms with variables on one side by adding $5y^2$ to both sides:

$$5x^2 + 5y^2 = 20.$$

Since *both* x and y are squared, we do not have a parabola. The fact that the squared terms are *added* tells us that we do not have a hyperbola. Do we have a circle? We factor the 5 out of both terms on the left and then divide by 5:

$$5(x^2 + y^2) = 20 \qquad \text{Factoring out 5}$$
$$x^2 + y^2 = 4 \qquad \text{Dividing both sides by 5}$$
$$x^2 + y^2 = 2^2. \qquad \text{This is an equation for a circle.}$$

We see that the graph is a circle with center at the origin and radius 2.

We can also write the equation in the form

$$5x^2 + 5y^2 - 20 = 0. \qquad A = 5, B = 5$$

Since $A = B$, the graph is a circle.

b) The equation $x + 3 + 8y = y^2$ has only one variable that is squared, so we solve for the other variable:

$$x = y^2 - 8y - 3. \qquad \text{This is an equation for a parabola.}$$

The graph is a horizontal parabola that opens to the right.

We can also write the equation in the form

$$y^2 - x - 8y - 3 = 0. \qquad A = 0, B = 1$$

Since $A = 0$ and $B \neq 0$, the graph is a parabola.

c) In $x^2 = y^2 + 4$, both variables are squared, so the graph is not a parabola. We subtract y^2 on both sides and divide by 4 to obtain

$$\frac{x^2}{2^2} - \frac{y^2}{2^2} = 1. \qquad \text{This is an equation for a hyperbola.}$$

The minus sign here indicates that the graph of this equation is a hyperbola. Because it is the x^2-term that is nonnegative, the hyperbola is horizontal.

We can also write the equation in the form

$$x^2 - y^2 - 4 = 0. \qquad A = 1, B = -1$$

Since A and B have opposite signs, the graph is a hyperbola.

d) In $x^2 = 16 - 4y^2$, both variables are squared, so the graph cannot be a parabola. We obtain the following equivalent equation:

$$x^2 + 4y^2 = 16. \qquad \text{Adding } 4y^2 \text{ to both sides}$$

If the coefficients of the terms were the same, we would have the graph of a circle, as in part (a), but they are not. Dividing both sides by 16 yields

$$\frac{x^2}{16} + \frac{y^2}{4} = 1. \qquad \text{This is an equation for an ellipse.}$$

The graph of this equation is a horizontal ellipse.

We can also write the equation in the form

$$x^2 + 4y^2 - 16 = 0. \qquad A = 1, B = 4$$

Since $A \neq B$ and both A and B are positive, the graph is an ellipse.

Try Exercises 27 and 29.

A

B

C

D

E

Visualizing for Success

Match each equation with its graph.

1. $(x - 1)^2 + (y + 3)^2 = 9$

2. $\dfrac{x^2}{9} - \dfrac{y^2}{1} = 1$

3. $y = (x - 1)^2 - 3$

4. $(x + 1)^2 + (y - 3)^2 = 9$

5. $x = (y - 1)^2 - 3$

6. $\dfrac{(x + 1)^2}{9} + \dfrac{(y - 3)^2}{1} = 1$

7. $xy = 3$

8. $y = -(x + 1)^2 + 3$

9. $\dfrac{y^2}{9} - \dfrac{x^2}{1} = 1$

10. $\dfrac{(x - 1)^2}{1} + \dfrac{(y + 3)^2}{9} = 1$

Answers on page A-62

An additional, animated version of this activity appears in MyMathLab. To use MyMathLab, you need a course ID and a student access code. Contact your instructor for more information.

F

G

H

I

J

15.3 Exercise Set

↪ *Concept Reinforcement* *In each of Exercises 1–8, match the conic section with the equation in the column on the right that represents that type of conic section.*

1. _____ A hyperbola with a horizontal axis

2. _____ A hyperbola with a vertical axis

3. _____ An ellipse with its center not at the origin

4. _____ An ellipse with its center at the origin

5. _____ A circle with its center at the origin

6. _____ A circle with its center not at the origin

7. _____ A parabola opening upward or downward

8. _____ A parabola opening to the right or to the left

a) $\dfrac{x^2}{10} + \dfrac{y^2}{12} = 1$

b) $(x + 1)^2 + (y - 3)^2 = 30$

c) $y - x^2 = 5$

d) $\dfrac{x^2}{9} - \dfrac{y^2}{10} = 1$

e) $x - 2y^2 = 3$

f) $\dfrac{y^2}{20} - \dfrac{x^2}{35} = 1$

g) $3x^2 + 3y^2 = 75$

h) $\dfrac{(x - 1)^2}{10} + \dfrac{(y - 4)^2}{8} = 1$

Graph each hyperbola. Label all vertices and sketch all asymptotes.

9. $\dfrac{y^2}{16} - \dfrac{x^2}{16} = 1$

10. $\dfrac{x^2}{9} - \dfrac{y^2}{9} = 1$

11. $\dfrac{x^2}{4} - \dfrac{y^2}{25} = 1$

12. $\dfrac{y^2}{16} - \dfrac{x^2}{9} = 1$

13. $\dfrac{y^2}{36} - \dfrac{x^2}{9} = 1$

14. $\dfrac{x^2}{25} - \dfrac{y^2}{36} = 1$

15. $y^2 - x^2 = 25$

16. $x^2 - y^2 = 4$

17. $25x^2 - 16y^2 = 400$

18. $4y^2 - 9x^2 = 36$

Graph.

19. $xy = -6$

20. $xy = 8$

21. $xy = 4$

22. $xy = -9$

23. $xy = -2$

24. $xy = -1$

25. $xy = 1$

26. $xy = 2$

Classify each of the following as the equation of a circle, an ellipse, a parabola, or a hyperbola.

27. $x^2 + y^2 - 6x + 4y - 30 = 0$

28. $y + 9 = 3x^2$

29. $9x^2 + 4y^2 - 36 = 0$

30. $x + 3y = 2y^2 - 1$

31. $4x^2 - 9y^2 - 72 = 0$

32. $y^2 + x^2 = 8$

33. $y^2 = 20 - x^2$

34. $2y + 13 + x^2 = 8x - y^2$

35. $x - 10 = y^2 - 6y$

36. $y = \dfrac{7}{x}$

37. $x - \dfrac{8}{y} = 0$

38. $9x^2 = 9 - y^2$

39. $y + 6x = x^2 + 5$

40. $x^2 = 16 + y^2$

41. $9y^2 = 36 + 4x^2$

42. $3x^2 + 5y^2 + x^2 = y^2 + 49$

43. $3x^2 + y^2 - x = 2x^2 - 9x + 10y + 40$

44. $4y^2 + 20x^2 + 1 = 8y - 5x^2$

45. $16x^2 + 5y^2 - 12x^2 + 8y^2 - 3x + 4y = 568$

46. $56x^2 - 17y^2 = 234 - 13x^2 - 38y^2$

TW 47. Explain how the equation of a hyperbola differs from the equation of an ellipse.

TW 48. Is it possible for a hyperbola to represent the graph of a function? Why or why not?

SKILL REVIEW

To prepare for Section 15.4, review solving systems of equations and solving quadratic equations (Sections 4.3 and 13.2).

Solve.

49. $5x + 2y = -3,$
$2x + 3y = 12$ [4.3]

50. $4x - 2y = 5,$
$3x + 5y = -6$ [4.3]

51. $\frac{3}{4}x^2 + x^2 = 7$ [13.2]

52. $3x^2 + 10x - 8 = 0$ [13.2]

53. $x^2 - 3x - 1 = 0$ [13.2]

54. $x^2 + \dfrac{25}{x^2} = 26$ [13.5]

SYNTHESIS

TW **55.** What is it in the equation of a hyperbola that controls how wide open the branches are? Explain your reasoning.

TW **56.** If, in

$$\frac{x^2}{a^2} - \frac{y^2}{b^2} = 1,$$

$a = b$, what are the asymptotes of the graph? Why?

Find an equation of a hyperbola satisfying the given conditions.

57. Having intercepts $(0, 6)$ and $(0, -6)$ and asymptotes $y = 3x$ and $y = -3x$

58. Having intercepts $(8, 0)$ and $(-8, 0)$ and asymptotes $y = 4x$ and $y = -4x$

The standard equations for horizontal or vertical hyperbolas centered at (h, k) are as follows:

$$\frac{(x - h)^2}{a^2} - \frac{(y - k)^2}{b^2} = 1$$

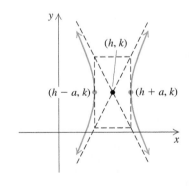

$$\frac{(y - k)^2}{b^2} - \frac{(x - h)^2}{a^2} = 1$$

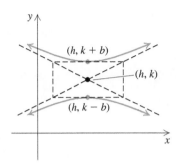

The vertices are as labeled and the asymptotes are

$$y - k = \frac{b}{a}(x - h) \quad and \quad y - k = -\frac{b}{a}(x - h).$$

For each of the following equations of hyperbolas, complete the square, if necessary, and write in standard form. Find the center, the vertices, and the asymptotes. Then graph the hyperbola.

59. $\dfrac{(x - 5)^2}{36} - \dfrac{(y - 2)^2}{25} = 1$

60. $\dfrac{(x - 2)^2}{9} - \dfrac{(y - 1)^2}{4} = 1$

61. $8(y + 3)^2 - 2(x - 4)^2 = 32$

62. $25(x - 4)^2 - 4(y + 5)^2 = 100$

63. $4x^2 - y^2 + 24x + 4y + 28 = 0$

64. $4y^2 - 25x^2 - 8y - 100x - 196 = 0$

Try Exercise Answers: Section 15.3

9.
$\frac{y^2}{16} - \frac{x^2}{16} = 1$

11.
$\frac{x^2}{4} - \frac{y^2}{25} = 1$

19.
$xy = -6$

27. Circle   **29.** Ellipse

Mid-Chapter Review

When graphing equations of conic sections, it is usually helpful to first determine what type of graph the equation represents. We then find the coordinates of key points and equations of related lines that determine the shape and the location of the graph.

Graph	Equation	Key Points	Equations of Lines
Parabola	$y = a(x - h)^2 + k$ $x = a(y - k)^2 + h$	Vertex: (h, k) Vertex: (h, k)	Axis of symmetry: $x = h$ Axis of symmetry: $y = k$
Circle	$(x - h)^2 + (y - k)^2 = r^2$	Center: (h, k)	
Ellipse	$\dfrac{x^2}{a^2} + \dfrac{y^2}{b^2} = 1$	x-intercepts: $(-a, 0), (a, 0)$; y-intercepts: $(0, -b), (0, b)$	
Hyperbola	$\dfrac{x^2}{a^2} - \dfrac{y^2}{b^2} = 1$ $\dfrac{y^2}{b^2} - \dfrac{x^2}{a^2} = 1$	Vertices: $(-a, 0), (a, 0)$ Vertices: $(0, -b), (0, b)$	Asymptotes (for both equations): $y = \dfrac{b}{a}x, y = -\dfrac{b}{a}x$
	$xy = c$		Asymptotes: $x = 0, y = 0$

GUIDED SOLUTIONS

1. Find the center and the radius of the circle
$x^2 + y^2 - 4x + 2y = 6.$ [15.1]

Solution

$$(x^2 - 4x) + (y^2 + \boxed{}) = 6$$

$$(x^2 - 4x + \boxed{}) + (y^2 + 2y + \boxed{}) =$$

$$6 + \boxed{} + \boxed{}$$

$$(x - \boxed{})^2 + (y + \boxed{})^2 = 11$$

The center of the circle is $(\boxed{}, \boxed{})$.

The radius is $\boxed{}$.

2. Classify the equation as a circle, an ellipse, a parabola, or a hyperbola:

$$x^2 - \frac{y^2}{25} = 1. \quad [15.1], [15.2], [15.3]$$

Solution

Answer each question in order to classify the equation.

1. Is there both an x^2-term and a y^2-term? $\boxed{}$

2. Do both the x^2-term and the y^2-term have the same sign? $\boxed{}$

3. The graph of the equation is a(n) $\boxed{}$.

MIXED REVIEW

1. Find the vertex and the axis of symmetry of the graph of
$y = 3(x - 4)^2 + 1.$ [15.1]

2. Find the vertex and the axis of symmetry of the graph of
$x = y^2 + 2y + 3.$ [15.1]

3. Find the center of the graph of
$(x - 3)^2 + (y - 2)^2 = 5.$ [15.1]

4. Find the center of the graph of
$x^2 + 6x + y^2 + 10y = 12.$ [15.1]

5. Find the x-intercepts and the y-intercepts of the graph of $\dfrac{x^2}{144} + \dfrac{y^2}{81} = 1$. [15.2]

6. Find the vertices of the graph of $\dfrac{x^2}{9} - \dfrac{y^2}{121} = 1$. [15.3]

7. Find the vertices of the graph of $4y^2 - x^2 = 4$. [15.3]

8. Find the asymptotes of the graph of $\dfrac{y^2}{9} - \dfrac{x^2}{4} = 1$. [15.3]

Classify each of the following as the graph of a parabola, a circle, an ellipse, or a hyperbola. Then graph.

9. $x^2 + y^2 = 36$ [15.1]

10. $y = x^2 - 5$ [15.1]

11. $\dfrac{x^2}{25} + \dfrac{y^2}{49} = 1$ [15.2]

12. $\dfrac{x^2}{25} - \dfrac{y^2}{49} = 1$ [15.3]

13. $x = (y + 3)^2 + 2$ [15.1]

14. $4x^2 + 9y^2 = 36$ [15.2]

15. $xy = -4$ [15.3]

16. $(x + 2)^2 + (y - 3)^2 = 1$ [15.1]

17. $x^2 + y^2 - 8y - 20 = 0$ [15.1]

18. $x = y^2 + 2y$ [15.1]

19. $16y^2 - x^2 = 16$ [15.3]

20. $x = \dfrac{9}{y}$ [15.3]

15.4 Nonlinear Systems of Equations

- **Systems Involving One Nonlinear Equation**
- **Systems of Two Nonlinear Equations**
- **Problem Solving**

The equations appearing in systems of two equations have thus far in our discussion always been linear. We now consider systems of two equations in which at least one equation is nonlinear.

SYSTEMS INVOLVING ONE NONLINEAR EQUATION

Suppose that a system consists of an equation of a circle and an equation of a line. In what ways can the circle and the line intersect? The figures below represent three ways in which the situation can occur. We see that such a system will have 0, 1, or 2 real solutions.

0 real solutions   1 real solution   2 real solutions

Recall that graphing, *elimination*, and *substitution* were all used to solve systems of linear equations. To solve systems in which one equation is of first degree and one is of second degree, it is preferable to use the *substitution* method.

EXAMPLE 1 Solve the system

$$x^2 + y^2 = 25, \quad (1) \quad \text{(The graph is a circle.)}$$
$$3x - 4y = 0. \quad (2) \quad \text{(The graph is a line.)}$$

SOLUTION First, we solve the linear equation, (2), for x:

$$x = \tfrac{4}{3}y. \quad (3) \qquad \text{We could have solved for } y \text{ instead.}$$

Then we substitute $\tfrac{4}{3}y$ for x in equation (1) and solve for y:

$$\left(\tfrac{4}{3}y\right)^2 + y^2 = 25$$
$$\tfrac{16}{9}y^2 + y^2 = 25$$
$$\tfrac{25}{9}y^2 = 25$$
$$y^2 = 9 \qquad \text{Multiplying both sides by } \tfrac{9}{25}$$
$$y = \pm 3. \qquad \text{Using the principle of square roots}$$

Student Notes

Be sure to list each solution of a system as an ordered pair. Remember that many of these systems will have more than one solution.

Now we substitute these numbers for y in equation (3) and solve for x:

for $y = 3$, $\quad x = \tfrac{4}{3}(3) = 4$; $\qquad$ The ordered pair is $(4, 3)$.
for $y = -3$, $\quad x = \tfrac{4}{3}(-3) = -4$. $\qquad$ The ordered pair is $(-4, -3)$.

Check: $\qquad$ For $(4, 3)$:

$$
\begin{array}{c|c}
x^2 + y^2 = 25 & 3x - 4y = 0 \\
\hline
4^2 + 3^2 \mid 25 & 3(4) - 4(3) \mid 0 \\
16 + 9 \mid & 12 - 12 \mid \\
25 \overset{?}{=} 25 \;\; \text{TRUE} & 0 \overset{?}{=} 0 \;\; \text{TRUE}
\end{array}
$$

It is left to the student to confirm that $(-4, -3)$ also checks in both equations.

The pairs $(4, 3)$ and $(-4, -3)$ check, so they are solutions. The graph at left serves as a check. Intersections occur at $(4, 3)$ and $(-4, -3)$.

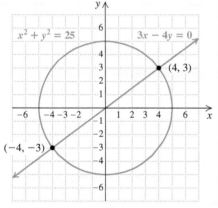

Try Exercise 7.

Even if we do not know what the graph of each equation in a system looks like, the algebraic approach of Example 1 can still be used.

EXAMPLE 2 Solve the system

$$y + 3 = 2x, \quad (1) \quad \text{(A first-degree equation)}$$
$$x^2 + 2xy = -1. \quad (2) \quad \text{(A second-degree equation)}$$

SOLUTION First, we solve the linear equation (1) for y:

$$y = 2x - 3. \quad (3)$$

Then we substitute $2x - 3$ for y in equation (2) and solve for x:

$$x^2 + 2x(2x - 3) = -1$$
$$x^2 + 4x^2 - 6x = -1$$
$$5x^2 - 6x + 1 = 0$$
$$(5x - 1)(x - 1) = 0 \qquad \text{Factoring}$$
$$5x - 1 = 0 \quad or \quad x - 1 = 0 \qquad \text{Using the principle of zero products}$$
$$x = \tfrac{1}{5} \quad or \qquad x = 1.$$

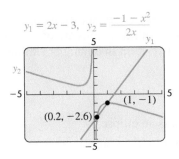

$y_1 = 2x - 3, \quad y_2 = \dfrac{-1 - x^2}{2x}$

Now we substitute these numbers for x in equation (3) and solve for y:

$$\text{for } x = \tfrac{1}{5}, \quad y = 2\left(\tfrac{1}{5}\right) - 3 = -\tfrac{13}{5};$$
$$\text{for } x = 1, \quad y = 2(1) - 3 = -1.$$

Using a graphing calculator, as shown at left, we find that the solutions are $(0.2, -2.6)$ and $(1, -1)$. You can confirm that $\left(\tfrac{1}{5}, -\tfrac{13}{5}\right)$ and $(1, -1)$ check, so they are both solutions.

Try Exercise 17.

EXAMPLE 3 Solve the system

$$x + y = 5, \qquad (1) \qquad \text{(The graph is a line.)}$$
$$y = 3 - x^2. \qquad (2) \qquad \text{(The graph is a parabola.)}$$

SOLUTION We substitute $3 - x^2$ for y in the first equation:

$$x + 3 - x^2 = 5$$
$$-x^2 + x - 2 = 0 \qquad \text{Adding } -5 \text{ to both sides and rearranging}$$
$$x^2 - x + 2 = 0. \qquad \text{Multiplying both sides by } -1$$

Since $x^2 - x + 2$ does not factor, we need the quadratic formula:

$$x = \frac{-b \pm \sqrt{b^2 - 4ac}}{2a}$$
$$= \frac{-(-1) \pm \sqrt{(-1)^2 - 4 \cdot 1 \cdot 2}}{2(1)} \qquad \text{Substituting}$$
$$= \frac{1 \pm \sqrt{1 - 8}}{2} = \frac{1 \pm \sqrt{-7}}{2} = \frac{1}{2} \pm \frac{\sqrt{7}}{2}i.$$

Solving equation (1) for y gives us $y = 5 - x$. Substituting values for x gives

$$y = 5 - \left(\frac{1}{2} + \frac{\sqrt{7}}{2}i\right) = \frac{9}{2} - \frac{\sqrt{7}}{2}i \quad \text{and}$$
$$y = 5 - \left(\frac{1}{2} - \frac{\sqrt{7}}{2}i\right) = \frac{9}{2} + \frac{\sqrt{7}}{2}i.$$

The solutions are

$$\left(\frac{1}{2} + \frac{\sqrt{7}}{2}i, \frac{9}{2} - \frac{\sqrt{7}}{2}i\right) \quad \text{and} \quad \left(\frac{1}{2} - \frac{\sqrt{7}}{2}i, \frac{9}{2} + \frac{\sqrt{7}}{2}i\right).$$

There are no real-number solutions. Note in the figure at left that the graphs do not intersect. Getting only nonreal solutions tells us that the graphs do not intersect.

Try Exercise 13.

SYSTEMS OF TWO NONLINEAR EQUATIONS

We now consider systems of two second-degree equations. Graphs of such systems can involve any two conic sections. The following figure shows some ways in which a circle and a hyperbola can intersect.

4 real solutions

3 real solutions

2 real solutions

2 real solutions

1 real solution

0 real solutions

To solve systems of two second-degree equations, we either substitute or eliminate. The elimination method is generally better when both equations are of the form $Ax^2 + By^2 = C$. Then we can eliminate an x^2- or a y^2-term in a manner similar to the procedure used in Chapter 4.

EXAMPLE 4 Solve the system

$$2x^2 + 5y^2 = 22, \quad (1) \quad \text{(The graph is an ellipse.)}$$
$$3x^2 - y^2 = -1. \quad (2) \quad \text{(The graph is a hyperbola.)}$$

SOLUTION Here we multiply equation (2) by 5 and then add:

$$
\begin{array}{ll}
2x^2 + 5y^2 = 22 & \\
\underline{15x^2 - 5y^2 = -5} & \text{Multiplying both sides of equation (2) by 5} \\
17x^2 \qquad\quad = 17 & \text{Adding} \\
\quad\ x^2 = 1 & \\
\quad\ \ x = \pm 1. &
\end{array}
$$

There is no x-term, and whether x is -1 or 1, we have $x^2 = 1$. Thus we can simultaneously substitute 1 and -1 for x in equation (2):

$$
\left.
\begin{array}{l}
3 \cdot (\pm 1)^2 - y^2 = -1 \\
3 - y^2 = -1 \\
-y^2 = -4
\end{array}
\right\}
\quad
\begin{array}{l}
\text{Since } (-1)^2 = 1^2, \text{ we can evaluate for} \\
x = -1 \text{ and } x = 1 \text{ simultaneously.}
\end{array}
$$

$$y^2 = 4 \quad \text{or} \quad y = \pm 2.$$

Thus, if $x = 1$, then $y = 2$ or $y = -2$; and if $x = -1$, then $y = 2$ or $y = -2$. The four possible solutions are $(1, 2)$, $(1, -2)$, $(-1, 2)$, and $(-1, -2)$.

Check: Since $(2)^2 = (-2)^2$ and $(1)^2 = (-1)^2$, we can check all four pairs at once.

$$
\begin{array}{c}
2x^2 + 5y^2 = 22 \\
\hline
2(\pm 1)^2 + 5(\pm 2)^2 \ \big|\ 22 \\
2 + 20 \ \big| \\
22 \overset{?}{=} 22 \quad \text{TRUE}
\end{array}
\qquad
\begin{array}{c}
3x^2 - y^2 = -1 \\
\hline
3(\pm 1)^2 - (\pm 2)^2 \ \big|\ -1 \\
3 - 4 \ \big| \\
-1 \overset{?}{=} -1 \quad \text{TRUE}
\end{array}
$$

The graph at left serves as a visual check. The solutions are $(1, 2)$, $(1, -2)$, $(-1, 2)$, and $(-1, -2)$.

$y_1 = \sqrt{(22 - 2x^2)/5}, \ y_2 = -y_1,$
$y_3 = \sqrt{3x^2 + 1}, \ y_4 = -y_3$

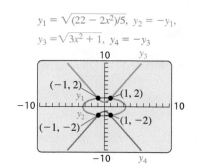

Try Exercise 33.

When a product of variables is in one equation and the other equation is of the form $Ax^2 + By^2 = C$, we often solve for a variable in the equation with the product and then use substitution.

EXAMPLE 5 Solve the system

$$x^2 + 4y^2 = 20, \quad (1) \quad \text{(The graph is an ellipse.)}$$
$$xy = 4. \quad (2) \quad \text{(The graph is a hyperbola.)}$$

SOLUTION   First, we solve equation (2) for y:

$$y = \frac{4}{x}.$$ Dividing both sides by x. Note that $x \neq 0$.

Then we substitute $4/x$ for y in equation (1) and solve for x:

$$x^2 + 4\left(\frac{4}{x}\right)^2 = 20$$

$$x^2 + \frac{64}{x^2} = 20$$

$$x^4 + 64 = 20x^2 \qquad \text{Multiplying by } x^2$$

$$x^4 - 20x^2 + 64 = 0 \qquad \begin{array}{l}\text{Obtaining standard form.}\\ \text{This equation is reducible}\\ \text{to quadratic.}\end{array}$$

$$(x^2 - 4)(x^2 - 16) = 0 \qquad \begin{array}{l}\text{Factoring. If you prefer, let}\\ u = x^2 \text{ and substitute.}\end{array}$$

$$(x - 2)(x + 2)(x - 4)(x + 4) = 0 \qquad \text{Factoring again}$$

$$x = 2 \quad or \quad x = -2 \quad or \quad x = 4 \quad or \quad x = -4. \qquad \begin{array}{l}\text{Using the principle of zero}\\ \text{products}\end{array}$$

Since $y = 4/x$, for $x = 2$, we have $y = 4/2$, or 2. Thus, $(2, 2)$ is a solution. Similarly, $(-2, -2), (4, 1)$, and $(-4, -1)$ are solutions. You can show that all four pairs check.

Try Exercise 31.

PROBLEM SOLVING

We now consider applications that can be modeled by a system of equations in which at least one equation is not linear.

EXAMPLE 6   Architecture.   For a college fitness center, an architect wants to lay out a rectangular piece of land that has a perimeter of 204 m and an area of 2565 m^2. Find the dimensions of the piece of land.

SOLUTION

1. **Familiarize.** We make a drawing and label it, letting $l =$ the length and $w =$ the width, both in meters.

2. **Translate.** We then have the following translation:

    Perimeter: $2w + 2l = 204$;

    Area: $lw = 2565.$

3. **Carry out.** We solve the system

    $$2w + 2l = 204,$$

    $$lw = 2565.$$

Solving the second equation for l gives us $l = 2565/w$. Then we substitute $2565/w$ for l in the first equation and solve for w:

$$2w + 2\left(\frac{2565}{w}\right) = 204$$

$$2w^2 + 2(2565) = 204w \qquad \text{Multiplying both sides by } w$$

$$2w^2 - 204w + 2(2565) = 0 \qquad \text{Standard form}$$

$$w^2 - 102w + 2565 = 0 \qquad \text{Multiplying by } \tfrac{1}{2}$$

> Factoring could be used instead of the quadratic formula, but the numbers are quite large.

$$w = \frac{-(-102) \pm \sqrt{(-102)^2 - 4 \cdot 1 \cdot 2565}}{2 \cdot 1}$$

$$w = \frac{102 \pm \sqrt{144}}{2} = \frac{102 \pm 12}{2}$$

$$w = 57 \quad or \quad w = 45.$$

If $w = 57$, then $l = 2565/w = 2565/57 = 45$. Similarly, if $w = 45$, then $l = 2565/w = 2565/45 = 57$. Since length is usually considered to be longer than width, we have the solution $l = 57$ and $w = 45$, or $(57, 45)$.

4. **Check.** If $l = 57$ and $w = 45$, the perimeter is $2 \cdot 57 + 2 \cdot 45$, or 204. The area is $57 \cdot 45$, or 2565. The numbers check.

5. **State.** The length is 57 m and the width is 45 m.

Try Exercise 49.

EXAMPLE 7 HDTV Dimensions. The Kaplans' new HDTV has a 40-in. diagonal screen with an area of 768 in². Find the width and the length of the screen.

SOLUTION

1. **Familiarize.** We make a drawing and label it. Note the right triangle in the figure. We let $l = $ the length and $w = $ the width, both in inches.

2. **Translate.** We translate to a system of equations:

$$l^2 + w^2 = 40^2, \qquad \text{Using the Pythagorean theorem}$$

$$lw = 768. \qquad \text{Using the formula for the area of a rectangle}$$

3. **Carry out.** We solve the system

$$\left. \begin{array}{l} l^2 + w^2 = 1600, \\ lw = 768 \end{array} \right\} \qquad \text{You should complete the solution of this system.}$$

to get $(32, 24)$, $(24, 32)$, $(-32, -24)$, and $(-24, -32)$.

4. Check. Measurements must be positive and length is usually greater than width, so we check only $(32, 24)$. In the right triangle, $32^2 + 24^2 = 1024 + 576 = 1600$, or 40^2. The area is $32 \cdot 24 = 768$, so our answer checks.

5. State. The length is 32 in. and the width is 24 in.

Try Exercise 51.

15.4 Exercise Set

FOR EXTRA HELP   MyMathLab

Concept Reinforcement   Classify each of the following statements as either true or false.

1. A system of equations that represent a line and an ellipse can have 0, 1, or 2 solutions.

2. A system of equations that represent a parabola and a circle can have up to 4 solutions.

3. A system of equations that represent a hyperbola and a circle can have no fewer than 2 solutions.

4. A system of equations that represent an ellipse and a line has either 0 or 2 solutions.

5. Systems containing one first-degree equation and one second-degree equation are most easily solved using the substitution method.

6. Systems containing two second-degree equations of the form $Ax^2 + By^2 = C$ are most easily solved using the elimination method.

Solve. Remember that graphs can be used to confirm all real solutions.

7. $x^2 + y^2 = 25$,
$y - x = 1$

8. $x^2 + y^2 = 100$,
$y - x = 2$

9. $4x^2 + 9y^2 = 36$,
$3y + 2x = 6$

10. $9x^2 + 4y^2 = 36$,
$3x + 2y = 6$

11. $y^2 = x + 3$,
$2y = x + 4$

12. $y = x^2$,
$3x = y + 2$

13. $x^2 - xy + 3y^2 = 27$,
$x - y = 2$

14. $2y^2 + xy + x^2 = 7$,
$x - 2y = 5$

15. $x^2 + 4y^2 = 25$,
$x + 2y = 7$

16. $x^2 - y^2 = 16$,
$x - 2y = 1$

17. $x^2 - xy + 3y^2 = 5$,
$x - y = 2$

18. $m^2 + 3n^2 = 10$,
$m - n = 2$

19. $3x + y = 7$,
$4x^2 + 5y = 24$

20. $2y^2 + xy = 5$,
$4y + x = 7$

21. $a + b = 6$,
$ab = 8$

22. $p + q = -6$,
$pq = -7$

23. $2a + b = 1$,
$b = 4 - a^2$

24. $4x^2 + 9y^2 = 36$,
$x + 3y = 3$

25. $a^2 + b^2 = 89$,
$a - b = 3$

26. $xy = 4$,
$x + y = 5$

Aha! **27.** $y = x^2$,
$x = y^2$

28. $x^2 + y^2 = 25$,
$y^2 = x + 5$

29. $x^2 + y^2 = 9$,
$x^2 - y^2 = 9$

30. $y^2 - 4x^2 = 25$,
$4x^2 + y^2 = 25$

31. $x^2 + y^2 = 25$,
$xy = 12$

32. $x^2 - y^2 = 16$,
$x + y^2 = 4$

33. $x^2 + y^2 = 9$,
$25x^2 + 16y^2 = 400$

34. $x^2 + y^2 = 4$,
$9x^2 + 16y^2 = 144$

35. $x^2 + y^2 = 14$,
$x^2 - y^2 = 4$

36. $x^2 + y^2 = 16$,
$y^2 - 2x^2 = 10$

37. $x^2 + y^2 = 20$,
$xy = 8$

38. $x^2 + y^2 = 5$,
$xy = 2$

39. $x^2 + 4y^2 = 20$,
$xy = 4$

40. $x^2 + y^2 = 13$,
$xy = 6$

41. $2xy + 3y^2 = 7$,
$3xy - 2y^2 = 4$

42. $3xy + x^2 = 34$,
$2xy - 3x^2 = 8$

43. $4a^2 - 25b^2 = 0$,
$2a^2 - 10b^2 = 3b + 4$

44. $xy - y^2 = 2$,
$2xy - 3y^2 = 0$

45. $ab - b^2 = -4$,
$ab - 2b^2 = -6$

46. $x^2 - y = 5$,
$x^2 + y^2 = 25$

Solve.

47. *Miniature Art.* Rachelle's miniature painting has a perimeter of 28 cm and a diagonal of length 10 cm. What are the dimensions of the painting?

48. *Tile Design.* The Old World tile company wants to make a new rectangular tile that has a perimeter of 6 in. and a diagonal of length $\sqrt{5}$ in. What should the dimensions of the tile be?

√5 in.

49. *Geometry.* A rectangle has an area of 2 yd^2 and a perimeter of 6 yd. Find its dimensions.

50. *Geometry.* A rectangle has an area of 20 in^2 and a perimeter of 18 in. Find its dimensions.

51. *Design of a Van.* The cargo area of a delivery van must be 60 ft^2, and the length of a diagonal must accommodate a 13-ft board. Find the dimensions of the cargo area.

13 ft

w   l

52. *Dimensions of a Rug.* The diagonal of a Persian rug is 25 ft. The area of the rug is 300 ft^2. Find the length and the width of the rug.

53. The product of two numbers is 90. The sum of their squares is 261. Find the numbers.

54. *Investments.* A certain amount of money saved for 1 year at a certain interest rate yielded $125 in interest. If $625 more had been invested and the rate had been 1% less, the interest would have been the same. Find the principal and the rate.

55. *Garden Design.* A garden contains two square peanut beds. Find the length of each bed if the sum of their areas is 832 ft^2 and the difference of their areas is 320 ft^2.

56. *Laptop Dimensions.* The screen on Tara's new laptop has an area of 90 in^2 and a $\sqrt{200.25}$-in. diagonal. Find the width and the length of the screen.

57. The area of a rectangle is $\sqrt{3}$ m^2, and the length of a diagonal is 2 m. Find the dimensions.

58. The area of a rectangle is $\sqrt{2}$ m^2, and the length of a diagonal is $\sqrt{3}$ m. Find the dimensions.

59. How can an understanding of conic sections be helpful when a system of nonlinear equations is being solved algebraically?

60. Suppose a system of equations is comprised of one linear equation and one nonlinear equation. Is it possible for such a system to have three solutions? Why or why not?

SKILL MAINTENANCE

To prepare for Section 16.1, review evaluating expressions. Simplify.

61. $(-1)^9(-3)^2$ **62.** $(-1)^{10}(-3)^3$

Evaluate each of the following.

63. $\dfrac{(-1)^k}{k-6}$, for $k=7$

64. $\dfrac{(-1)^k}{k-5}$, for $k=10$

65. $\dfrac{n}{2}(3+n)$, for $n=11$

66. $\dfrac{7(1-r^2)}{1-r}$, for $r=\frac{1}{2}$

SYNTHESIS

67. Write a problem that translates to a system of two equations. Design the problem so that at least one equation is nonlinear and so that no real solution exists.

68. Write a problem for a classmate to solve. Devise the problem so that a system of two nonlinear equations with exactly one real solution is solved.

69. Find the equation of a circle that passes through $(-2, 3)$ and $(-4, 1)$ and whose center is on the line $5x + 8y = -2$.

70. Find the equation of an ellipse centered at the origin that passes through the points $(2, -3)$ and $(1, \sqrt{13})$.

Solve.

71. $p^2 + q^2 = 13,$

$\dfrac{1}{pq} = -\dfrac{1}{6}$

72. $a + b = \dfrac{5}{6},$

$\dfrac{a}{b} + \dfrac{b}{a} = \dfrac{13}{6}$

73. *Fence Design.* A roll of chain-link fencing contains 100 ft of fence. The fencing is bent at a 90° angle to enclose a rectangular work area of 2475 ft², as shown. Determine the length and the width of the rectangle.

2475 ft²

74. A piece of wire 100 cm long is to be cut into two pieces and those pieces are each to be bent to make a square. The area of one square is to be 144 cm² greater than that of the other. How should the wire be cut?

75. *Box Design.* Four squares with sides 5 in. long are cut from the corners of a rectangular metal sheet that has an area of 340 in². The edges are bent up to form an open box with a volume of 350 in³. Find the dimensions of the box.

76. *Computer Screens.* The ratio of the length to the height of the screen on a computer monitor is 4 to 3. A Dell Inspiron notebook has a 15-in. diagonal screen. Find the dimensions of the screen.

15 in.

77. *HDTV Screens.* The ratio of the length to the height of an HDTV screen is 16 to 9 (see Example 7). The Sollar Lounge has an HDTV screen with a 73-in. diagonal screen. Find the dimensions of the screen.

78. *Railing Sales.* Fireside Castings finds that the total revenue R from the sale of x units of railing is given by

$$R = 100x + x^2.$$

Fireside also finds that the total cost C of producing x units of the same product is given by

$$C = 80x + 1500.$$

A break-even point is a value of x for which total revenue is the same as total cost; that is, $R = C$. How many units must be sold in order to break even?

Solve using a graphing calculator. Round all values to two decimal places.

79. $4xy - 7 = 0,$
$x - 3y - 2 = 0$

80. $x^2 + y^2 = 14,$
$16x + 7y^2 = 0$

Try Exercise Answers: Section 15.4

7. $(-4, -3), (3, 4)$

13. $\left(\dfrac{5 + \sqrt{70}}{3}, \dfrac{-1 + \sqrt{70}}{3}\right), \left(\dfrac{5 - \sqrt{70}}{3}, \dfrac{-1 - \sqrt{70}}{3}\right)$

17. $\left(\dfrac{7}{3}, \dfrac{1}{3}\right), (1, -1)$ **31.** $(-4, -3), (-3, -4), (3, 4), (4, 3)$

33. $\left(\dfrac{16}{3}, \dfrac{5\sqrt{7}}{3}i\right), \left(\dfrac{16}{3}, -\dfrac{5\sqrt{7}}{3}i\right), \left(-\dfrac{16}{3}, \dfrac{5\sqrt{7}}{3}i\right),$
$\left(-\dfrac{16}{3}, -\dfrac{5\sqrt{7}}{3}i\right)$

49. Length: 2 yd; width: 1 yd   **51.** Length: 12 ft; width: 5 ft

Study Summary

KEY TERMS AND CONCEPTS	EXAMPLES	PRACTICE EXERCISES

SECTION 15.1: CONIC SECTIONS: PARABOLAS AND CIRCLES

Parabola

$y = ax^2 + bx + c$
  $= a(x - h)^2 + k$
  Opens upward $(a > 0)$
  or downward $(a < 0)$
  Vertex: (h, k)

$x = ay^2 + by + c$
  $= a(y - k)^2 + h$
  Opens right $(a > 0)$
  or left $(a < 0)$
  Vertex: (h, k)

Parabola

$x = -y^2 + 4y - 1$
  $= -(y^2 - 4y \qquad) - 1$
  $= -(y^2 - 4y + 4) - 1 - (-1)(4)$
  $= -(y - 2)^2 + 3 \qquad a = -1;$ parabola opens left

$x = -y^2 + 4y - 1$

---

1. Graph
$$x = y^2 + 6y + 7.$$
Label the vertex.

Circle

$x^2 + y^2 = r^2$
  Radius: r
  Center: $(0, 0)$

$(x - h)^2 + (y - k)^2 = r^2$
  Radius: r
  Center: (h, k)

Circle

$$x^2 + y^2 + 2x - 6y + 6 = 0$$
$$x^2 + 2x + \qquad y^2 - 6y \qquad = -6$$
$$x^2 + 2x + 1 + y^2 - 6y + 9 = -6 + 1 + 9$$
$$(x + 1)^2 + (y - 3)^2 = 4$$
$$[x - (-1)]^2 + (y - 3)^2 = 2^2 \qquad \text{Radius: } 2$$
$$\text{Center: } (-1, 3)$$

$x^2 + y^2 + 2x - 6y + 6 = 0$

---

2. Find the center and
the radius and graph
$$x^2 + y^2 - 6x + 5 = 0.$$

1000

SECTION 15.2: CONIC SECTIONS: ELLIPSES

Ellipse

$\dfrac{x^2}{a^2} + \dfrac{y^2}{b^2} = 1$ Center: $(0, 0)$

$\dfrac{(x - h)^2}{a^2} + \dfrac{(y - k)^2}{b^2} = 1$

Center: (h, k)

Ellipse

$\dfrac{(x - 4)^2}{4} + \dfrac{(y + 1)^2}{9} = 1$

$\dfrac{(x - 4)^2}{2^2} + \dfrac{[y - (-1)]^2}{3^2} = 1$

$3 > 2$; ellipse is vertical
Center: $(4, -1)$

Vertex: $(4, 2)$
$(2, -1)$ $(6, -1)$
Vertex: $(4, -4)$

$\dfrac{(x - 4)^2}{4} + \dfrac{(y + 1)^2}{9} = 1$

3. Graph: $\dfrac{x^2}{9} + y^2 = 1$.

SECTION 15.3: CONIC SECTIONS: HYPERBOLAS

Hyperbola

$\dfrac{x^2}{a^2} - \dfrac{y^2}{b^2} = 1$

Two branches opening
right and left

$\dfrac{y^2}{b^2} - \dfrac{x^2}{a^2} = 1$

Two branches opening
upward and downward

Vertices

Hyperbola

$\dfrac{x^2}{4} - \dfrac{y^2}{1} = 1$

$\dfrac{x^2}{2^2} - \dfrac{y^2}{1^2} = 1$ Opens right and left

Asymptote: $y = \frac{1}{2}x$
Vertex: $(-2, 0)$ Vertex: $(2, 0)$
Asymptote: $y = -\frac{1}{2}x$

$\dfrac{x^2}{4} - \dfrac{y^2}{1} = 1$

4. Graph: $\dfrac{y^2}{16} - \dfrac{x^2}{4} = 1$.

SECTION 15.4: NONLINEAR SYSTEMS OF EQUATIONS

We can solve a system
containing at least one
nonlinear equation using
substitution or elimination.

Solve:

$x^2 - y = -1$,   (1)   (The graph is a parabola.)
$x + 2y = 3$.   (2)   (The graph is a line.)

$x = 3 - 2y$ Solving for x

$(3 - 2y)^2 - y = -1$ Substituting

$9 - 12y + 4y^2 - y = -1$

$4y^2 - 13y + 10 = 0$

$(4y - 5)(y - 2) = 0$

$4y - 5 = 0$ or $y - 2 = 0$

$y = \frac{5}{4}$ or $y = 2$

If $y = \frac{5}{4}$, then $x = 3 - 2\left(\frac{5}{4}\right) = \frac{1}{2}$.

If $y = 2$, then $x = 3 - 2(2) = -1$.

The solutions are $\left(\frac{1}{2}, \frac{5}{4}\right)$ and $(-1, 2)$.

5. Solve:

$x^2 + y^2 = 41$,
$y - x = 1$.

Review Exercises 15

Concept Reinforcement Classify each of the following statements as either true or false.

1. Every parabola that opens upward or downward can represent the graph of a function. [15.1]

2. The center of a circle is part of the circle itself. [15.1]

3. The foci of an ellipse are part of the ellipse itself. [15.2]

4. It is possible for a hyperbola to represent the graph of a function. [15.3]

5. If an equation of a conic section has only one term of degree 2, its graph cannot be a circle, an ellipse, or a hyperbola. [15.3]

6. Two nonlinear graphs can intersect in more than one point. [15.4]

7. Every system of nonlinear equations has at least one real solution. [15.4]

8. Both substitution and elimination can be used as methods for solving a system of nonlinear equations. [15.4]

Find the center and the radius of each circle. [15.1]

9. $(x + 3)^2 + (y - 2)^2 = 16$

10. $(x - 5)^2 + y^2 = 11$

11. $x^2 + y^2 - 6x - 2y + 1 = 0$

12. $x^2 + y^2 + 8x - 6y = 20$

13. Find an equation of the circle with center $(-4, 3)$ and radius 4. [15.1]

14. Find an equation of the circle with center $(7, -2)$ and radius $2\sqrt{5}$. [15.1]

Classify each equation as a circle, an ellipse, a parabola, or a hyperbola. Then graph. [15.1], [15.2], [15.3]

15. $5x^2 + 5y^2 = 80$

16. $9x^2 + 2y^2 = 18$

17. $y = -x^2 + 2x - 3$

18. $\dfrac{y^2}{9} - \dfrac{x^2}{4} = 1$

19. $xy = 9$

20. $x = y^2 + 2y - 2$

21. $\dfrac{(x + 1)^2}{3} + (y - 3)^2 = 1$

22. $x^2 + y^2 + 6x - 8y - 39 = 0$

Solve. [15.4]

23. $x^2 - y^2 = 21,$
    $x + y = 3$

24. $x^2 - 2x + 2y^2 = 8,$
    $2x + y = 6$

25. $x^2 - y = 5,$
    $2x - y = 5$

26. $x^2 + y^2 = 15,$
    $x^2 - y^2 = 17$

27. $x^2 - y^2 = 3,$
    $y = x^2 - 3$

28. $x^2 + y^2 = 18,$
    $2x + y = 3$

29. $x^2 + y^2 = 100,$
    $2x^2 - 3y^2 = -120$

30. $x^2 + 2y^2 = 12,$
    $xy = 4$

31. A rectangular bandstand has a perimeter of 38 m and an area of 84 m². What are the dimensions of the bandstand? [15.4]

32. One type of carton used by tableproducts.com exactly fits both a rectangular plate of area 108 in² and a candle of length 15 in., laid diagonally on top of the plate. Find the length and the width of the carton. [15.4]

15 in.

33. The perimeter of a square mirror is 12 cm more than the perimeter of another square mirror. Its area exceeds the area of the other by 39 cm². Find the perimeter of each mirror. [15.4]

34. The sum of the areas of two circles is 130π ft². The difference of the circumferences is 16π ft. Find the radius of each circle. [15.4]

SYNTHESIS

TW **35.** How does the graph of a hyperbola differ from the graph of a parabola? [15.1], [15.3]

TW **36.** Explain why function notation rarely appears in this chapter, and list the graphs discussed for which function notation could be used. [15.1], [15.2], [15.3]

37. Solve: [15.4]

$$4x^2 - x - 3y^2 = 9,$$
$$-x^2 + x + y^2 = 2.$$

38. Find the points whose distance from $(8, 0)$ and from $(-8, 0)$ is 10. [15.1]

39. Find an equation of the circle that passes through $(-2, -4)$, $(5, -5)$, and $(6, 2)$. [15.1], [15.4]

40. Find an equation of the ellipse with the following intercepts: $(-9, 0)$, $(9, 0)$, $(0, -5)$, and $(0, 5)$. [15.2]

41. Find the point on the x-axis that is equidistant from $(-3, 4)$ and $(5, 6)$. [15.1]

Chapter Test

1. Find an equation of the circle with center $(3, -4)$ and radius $2\sqrt{3}$.

Find the center and the radius of each circle.

2. $(x - 4)^2 + (y + 1)^2 = 5$

3. $x^2 + y^2 + 4x - 6y + 4 = 0$

Classify the equation as a circle, an ellipse, a parabola, or a hyperbola. Then graph.

4. $y = x^2 - 4x - 1$

5. $x^2 + y^2 + 2x + 6y + 6 = 0$

6. $\dfrac{x^2}{16} - \dfrac{y^2}{9} = 1$

7. $16x^2 + 4y^2 = 64$

8. $xy = -5$

9. $x = -y^2 + 4y$

Solve.

10. $x^2 + y^2 = 36,$
$3x + 4y = 24$

11. $x^2 - y = 3,$
$2x + y = 5$

12. $x^2 - y^2 = 3,$
$xy = 2$

13. $x^2 + y^2 = 10,$
$x^2 = y^2 + 2$

14. A rectangular bookmark with diagonal of length $5\sqrt{5}$ in. has an area of 22 in². Find the dimensions of the bookmark.

15. Two squares are such that the sum of their areas is 8 m² and the difference of their areas is 2 m². Find the length of a side of each square.

16. A rectangular dance floor has a diagonal of length 40 ft and a perimeter of 112 ft. Find the dimensions of the dance floor.

17. Brett invested a certain amount of money for 1 year and earned $72 in interest. Erin invested $240 more than Brett at an interest rate that was $\frac{5}{6}$ of the rate given to Brett, but she earned the same amount of interest. Find the principal and the interest rate for Brett's investment.

SYNTHESIS

18. Find an equation of the ellipse passing through $(6, 0)$ and $(6, 6)$ with vertices at $(1, 3)$ and $(11, 3)$.

19. Find the point on the y-axis that is equidistant from $(-3, -5)$ and $(4, -7)$.

20. The sum of two numbers is 36, and the product is 4. Find the sum of the reciprocals of the numbers.

21. *Theatrical Production.* An E.T.C. spotlight for a college's production of *Hamlet* projects an ellipse of light on a stage that is 8 ft wide and 14 ft long. Find an equation of that ellipse if an actor is in its center and x represents the number of feet, horizontally, from the actor to the edge of the ellipse and y represents the number of feet, vertically, from the actor to the edge of the ellipse.

Sequences, Series, and the Binomial Theorem

Can You Play with the Pros?

Some professional golfers can launch a golf ball flying at 180 mph. How fast must the golfer swing the golf club in order to launch the ball that fast? As the graph indicates, club speed and ball speed are not equal. In Exercise 73 of Section 16.2, we develop a formula for the general term of this *arithmetic sequence*.

Golf Ball Launch

Club speed (in miles per hour)

Ball speed (in miles per hour)

The first three sections of this chapter are devoted to sequences and series. A *sequence* is simply an ordered list. When the members of a sequence are numbers, we can discuss their sum. Such a sum is called a *series*.

Section 16.4 presents the binomial theorem, which is used to expand expressions of the form $(a + b)^n$. Such an expression is itself a series.

16.1 Sequences and Series

- Sequences

- Finding the General Term

- Sums and Series

- Sigma Notation

- Graphs of Sequences

STUDY TIP

Crunch Time for the Final

It is always best to study for a final exam over several days or more. If you have only one or two days of study time, however, begin by studying the formulas, problems, properties, and procedures in each chapter's Study Summary. Then do the exercises in the Cumulative Reviews. Make sure to attend a review session if one is offered.

SEQUENCES

Suppose that $10,000 is invested at 5%, compounded annually. The value of the account at the start of years 1, 2, 3, 4, and so on, is

$10,000, $10,500, $11,025, $11,576.25,....

We can regard this as a function that pairs 1 with $10,000, 2 with $10,500, 3 with $11,025, and so on. This is an example of a **sequence** (or **progression**). The domain of a sequence is a set of consecutive positive integers beginning with 1, and the range varies from sequence to sequence.

If we stop after a certain number of years, we obtain a **finite sequence:**

$10,000, $10,500, $11,025, $11,576.25.

If we continue listing the amounts in the account, we obtain an **infinite sequence:**

$10,000, $10,500, $11,025, $11,576.25, $12,155.06,....

The three dots at the end indicate that the sequence goes on without stopping.

Sequences An *infinite sequence* is a function having for its domain the set of natural numbers: $\{1, 2, 3, 4, 5, \ldots\}$.

A *finite sequence* is a function having for its domain a set of natural numbers: $\{1, 2, 3, 4, 5, \ldots, n\}$, for some natural number n.

As another example, consider the sequence given by

$$a(n) = 2^n, \quad \text{or} \quad a_n = 2^n.$$

The notation a_n means the same as $a(n)$ but is used more commonly with sequences. Some function values (also called *terms* of the sequence) follow:

$$a_1 = 2^1 = 2,$$
$$a_2 = 2^2 = 4,$$
$$a_3 = 2^3 = 8,$$
$$a_6 = 2^6 = 64.$$

The first term of the sequence is a_1, the fifth term is a_5, and the nth term, or **general term,** is a_n. This sequence can also be denoted in the following ways:

$$2, 4, 8, \ldots;$$

or $$2, 4, 8, \ldots, 2^n, \ldots.$$ The 2^n emphasizes that the nth term of this sequence is found by raising 2 to the nth power.

Sequences

To select the SEQUENCE mode on a graphing calculator, first press **MODE** and then move the cursor to the line that reads Func Par Pol Seq, the fourth line in the screen shown on the left below. Next, move the cursor to Seq and press **ENTER**. The functions in the equation-editor screen will be called $u(n)$ and $v(n)$ instead of y_1 and y_2, and the variable n is used instead of x; the variable is still entered using the **X,T,Θ,n** key.

Most graphing calculators will write the terms of a sequence as a list without using the SEQUENCE mode. Usually found in the LIST OPS submenu, the seq option will list a finite sequence when the general term and the beginning and ending values of n are given. The cumSum option will list the cumulative sums of the elements of a sequence.

If the seq option is used, information must be supplied in the following order:

> seq(general term, variable, value of n for the first term, value of n for the last term).

For example, to list the first 6 terms of the sequence given by

$$a_n = 2^n,$$

enter seq($2^\wedge n, n, 1, 6$). This is done by selecting seq under the LIST OPS menu, shown on the left below, and then pressing **2** **^** **X,T,Θ,n** **,** **X,T,Θ,n** **,** **1** **,** **6** **)** **ENTER**. Note that if this sequence of keystrokes is done in the FUNCTION mode, rather than the SEQUENCE mode, the variable used will be x, but the resulting sequence will be the same.

The result is shown in the screen on the right below. The first 6 terms of the sequence are 2, 4, 8, 16, 32, 64.

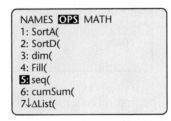

(continued)

The cumSum (cumulative sums) option can be used in connection with the seq option. Instead of listing the sequence itself, cumSum lists the first term, then the sum of the first two terms, then the sum of the first three terms, and so on. The screen on the right on the preceding page shows the cumulative sums of the sequence given by $a_n = 2^n$. The first term is 2, the sum of the first two terms is 6, the sum of the first three terms is 14, and so on. Pressing the right arrow key will show more cumulative sums of the sequence.

Your Turn

1. Put your calculator in SEQUENCE mode.
2. Press ⟨ Y= ⟩ to enter the sequence $a_n = n^2$. Define $u(n) = n^2$ by pressing ⟨ X,T,θ,n ⟩ ⟨ x^2 ⟩.
3. Press ⟨ TBLSET ⟩ and define TblStart = 1, $\triangle$Tbl = 1, and set Indpnt and Depend to Auto. Press ⟨ TABLE ⟩ to see the sequence.
4. Return your calculator to FUNCTION mode.

EXAMPLE 1 Find the first 4 terms and the 13th term of the sequence for which the general term is given by $a_n = (-1)^n n^2$.

SOLUTION We have $a_n = (-1)^n n^2$, so

$$a_1 = (-1)^1 \cdot 1^2 = -1,$$
$$a_2 = (-1)^2 \cdot 2^2 = 4,$$
$$a_3 = (-1)^3 \cdot 3^2 = -9,$$
$$a_4 = (-1)^4 \cdot 4^2 = 16,$$
$$a_{13} = (-1)^{13} \cdot 13^2 = -169.$$

n	$u(n)$
1	−1
2	4
3	−9
4	16
13	−169

$n =$

To check using a calculator in SEQUENCE mode, we define $u(n) = (-1)^\wedge n * n^2$. Then, using a table with Indpnt set to Ask, we supply 1, 2, 3, 4, and 13 as values for n. The sequence is shown in the $u(n)$ column in the figure at left.

Try Exercise 17.

Note in Example 1 that the expression $(-1)^n$ causes the signs of the terms to alternate between positive and negative, depending on whether n is even or odd.

EXAMPLE 2 Use a graphing calculator to find the first 5 terms of the sequence for which the general term is given by $a_n = n/(n + 1)^2$.

SOLUTION We use the seq feature, supplying the formula for the general term, the variable, and the values of n for the first and last terms that we wish to calculate.

seq(n/(n+1)², n,1
,5)▶Frac
{1/4 2/9 3/16 4...

Here we used ▶Frac to write each term in the sequence in fraction notation.

The first three terms are listed on the screen; the remaining can be found by pressing ⟨ ▷ ⟩. We have

$$a_1 = \tfrac{1}{4}, \qquad a_2 = \tfrac{2}{9}, \qquad a_3 = \tfrac{3}{16}, \qquad a_4 = \tfrac{4}{25}, \quad \text{and} \quad a_5 = \tfrac{5}{36}.$$

Try Exercise 29.

FINDING THE GENERAL TERM

By looking for a pattern, we can often write an expression for the general term of a sequence. When only the first few terms of a sequence are given, more than one pattern may fit.

EXAMPLE 3   For each sequence, write an expression for the general term.

a) $1, 4, 9, 16, 25, \ldots$ **b)** $2, 4, 8, \ldots$

c) $-1, 2, -4, 8, -16, \ldots$

SOLUTION

a) $1, 4, 9, 16, 25, \ldots$

These are squares of consecutive positive integers, so the general term could be n^2.

b) $2, 4, 8, \ldots$

We regard the pattern as powers of 2, in which case 16 would be the next term and 2^n the general term. The sequence could then be written with more terms as

$$2, 4, 8, 16, 32, 64, 128, \ldots.$$

c) $-1, 2, -4, 8, -16, \ldots$

These are powers of 2 with alternating signs, so the general term may be

Making sure the signs of the terms alternate

$(-1)^n [2^{n-1}].$

Raising 2 to a power that is 1 less than the term's position

To check, note that -4 is the third term, and $(-1)^3 [2^{3-1}] = -1 \cdot 2^2 = -4$.

■ Try Exercise 35.

In part (b) above, suppose that the second term is found by adding 2, the third term by adding 4, the next term by adding 6, and so on. In this case, 14 would be the next term and the sequence would be

$$2, 4, 8, 14, 22, 32, 44, 58, \ldots.$$

This illustrates that the fewer terms we are given, the greater the uncertainty about the nth term.

SUMS AND SERIES

Series   Given the infinite sequence

$$a_1, a_2, a_3, a_4, \ldots, a_n, \ldots,$$

the sum of the terms

$$a_1 + a_2 + a_3 + \cdots + a_n + \cdots$$

is called an *infinite series* and is denoted S_∞. A *partial sum* is the sum of the first n terms:

$$a_1 + a_2 + a_3 + \cdots + a_n.$$

A partial sum is also called a *finite series* and is denoted S_n.

EXAMPLE 4 For the sequence $-2,\ 4,\ -6,\ 8,\ -10,\ 12,\ -14$, find: **(a)** S_2; **(b)** S_3; **(c)** S_7.

SOLUTION

a) $S_2 = -2 + 4 = 2$ This is the sum of the first 2 terms.

b) $S_3 = -2 + 4 + (-6) = -4$ This is the sum of the first 3 terms.

c) $S_7 = -2 + 4 + (-6) + 8 + (-10) + 12 + (-14) = -8$
     This is the sum of the first 7 terms.

▌ Try Exercise 51.

We can use a graphing calculator to find partial sums of a sequence for which the general term is given by a formula.

cumSum(seq((−1)^
n/(n+1),n,1,4))▶
Frac
{−1/2 −1/6 −5/1...

EXAMPLE 5 Use a graphing calculator to find S_1, S_2, S_3, and S_4 for the sequence in which the general term is given by $a_n = (-1)^n/(n+1)$.

SOLUTION We use the cumSum and seq options in the LIST OPS menu and ▶Frac to write each sum in fraction notation. The first two sums, S_1 and S_2, are listed on the screen; S_3 and S_4 can be seen by pressing ▷. We have

$$S_1 = -\tfrac{1}{2}, \quad S_2 = -\tfrac{1}{6}, \quad S_3 = -\tfrac{5}{12}, \quad \text{and} \quad S_4 = -\tfrac{13}{60}.$$

▌ Try Exercise 55.

SIGMA NOTATION

When the general term of a sequence is known, the Greek letter Σ (capital sigma) can be used to write a series. For example, the sum of the first four terms of the sequence $3, 5, 7, 9, 11, \ldots, 2k + 1, \ldots$ can be named as follows, using *sigma notation*, or *summation notation*:

$$\sum_{k=1}^{4} (2k + 1). \qquad \begin{array}{l}\text{This represents}\\ (2\cdot 1 + 1) + (2\cdot 2 + 1) + (2\cdot 3 + 1) + (2\cdot 4 + 1).\end{array}$$

This is read "the sum as k goes from 1 to 4 of $(2k + 1)$." The letter k is called the *index of summation*. The index need not start at 1.

EXAMPLE 6 Write out and evaluate each sum.

a) $\displaystyle\sum_{k=1}^{5} k^2$ **b)** $\displaystyle\sum_{k=4}^{6} (-1)^k(2k)$ **c)** $\displaystyle\sum_{k=0}^{3} (2^k + 5)$

Student Notes

A great deal of information is condensed into sigma notation. Be careful to pay attention to what values the index of summation will take on. Evaluate the expression following sigma, the general term, for each value and then add the results.

SOLUTION

a) $\displaystyle\sum_{k=1}^{5} k^2 = 1^2 + 2^2 + 3^2 + 4^2 + 5^2 = 1 + 4 + 9 + 16 + 25 = 55$
     Evaluate k^2 for all integers from 1 through 5. Then add.

b) $\displaystyle\sum_{k=4}^{6} (-1)^k(2k) = (-1)^4(2 \cdot 4) + (-1)^5(2 \cdot 5) + (-1)^6(2 \cdot 6)$

$$= 8 - 10 + 12 = 10$$

c) $\displaystyle\sum_{k=0}^{3} (2^k + 5) = (2^0 + 5) + (2^1 + 5) + (2^2 + 5) + (2^3 + 5)$

$$= 6 + 7 + 9 + 13 = 35$$

▌ Try Exercise 59.

EXAMPLE 7 Write sigma notation for each sum.

a) $1 + 4 + 9 + 16 + 25$ **b)** $3 + 9 + 27 + 81 + \cdots$

c) $-1 + 3 - 5 + 7$

SOLUTION

a) $1 + 4 + 9 + 16 + 25$

Note that this is a sum of squares, $1^2 + 2^2 + 3^2 + 4^2 + 5^2$, so the general term is k^2. Sigma notation is

$$\sum_{k=1}^{5} k^2. \qquad \text{The sum starts with } 1^2 \text{ and ends with } 5^2.$$

Answers may vary here. For example, another—perhaps less obvious—way of writing $1 + 4 + 9 + 16 + 25$ is

$$\sum_{k=2}^{6} (k-1)^2.$$

b) $3 + 9 + 27 + 81 + \cdots$

This is a sum of powers of 3, and it is also an infinite series. We use the symbol ∞ for infinity and write the series using sigma notation:

$$\sum_{k=1}^{\infty} 3^k.$$

c) $-1 + 3 - 5 + 7$

Except for the alternating signs, this is the sum of the first four positive odd numbers. It is useful to know that $2k - 1$ is a formula for the kth positive odd number. It is also important to note that since $(-1)^k = 1$ when k is even and $(-1)^k = -1$ when k is odd, the factor $(-1)^k$ can be used to create the alternating signs. The general term is thus $(-1)^k(2k - 1)$, beginning with $k = 1$. Sigma notation is

$$\sum_{k=1}^{4} (-1)^k(2k - 1).$$

To check, we can evaluate $(-1)^k (2k - 1)$ using 1, 2, 3, and 4. Then we can write the sum of the four terms. We leave this to the student.

Try Exercise 71.

GRAPHS OF SEQUENCES

Because the domain of a sequence is a set of integers, the graph of a sequence is a set of points that are not connected. We can use the DOT mode to graph a sequence when a formula for the general term is known.

EXAMPLE 8 Graph the sequence for which the general term is given by $a_n = (-1)^n/n$.

SOLUTION We let $u(n) = (-1)^{\wedge}n/n$. In SEQUENCE mode, the default graph mode is DOT.

For the window settings, we must determine nMin and nMax, as well as Xmin, Xmax, Ymin, and Ymax. Here, nMin is the smallest value of n for which we wish to evaluate the sequence, and nMax is the largest value. We let nMin $= 1$ and nMax $= 20$, and Xmin $= 0$ and Xmax $= 20$. From the table on the left below, the terms appear to be between -1 and 1, so we let Ymin $= -1$ and Ymax $= 1$. If the graphing calculator also allows us to set PlotStart and Plot-Step, we set each of those to 1.

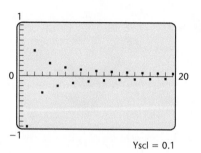

We see from the graph on the right above that the absolute value of the terms gets smaller as n gets larger. The graph also illustrates that the signs of the terms alternate.

Try Exercise 81.

16.1 Exercise Set

FOR EXTRA HELP   *MyMathLab*   Math XL   PRACTICE   WATCH   DOWNLOAD   READ   REVIEW

Concept Reinforcement In each of Exercises 1–6, match the expression with the most appropriate expression from the column on the right.

1. ____ $\sum_{k=1}^{4} k^2$

2. ____ $\sum_{k=3}^{6} (-1)^k$

3. ____ $5 + 10 + 15 + 20$

4. ____ $a_n = 5^n$

5. ____ $a_n = 3n + 2$

6. ____ $a_1 + a_2 + a_3$

a) $-1 + 1 + (-1) + 1$

b) $a_2 = 25$

c) $a_2 = 8$

d) $\sum_{k=1}^{4} 5k$

e) S_3

f) $1 + 4 + 9 + 16$

Find the indicated term of each sequence.

7. $a_n = 2n - 3$; a_8

8. $a_n = 3n + 2$; a_8

9. $a_n = (3n + 1)(2n - 5)$; a_9

10. $a_n = (3n + 2)^2$; a_6

11. $a_n = (-1)^{n-1}(3.4n - 17.3)$; a_{12}

12. $a_n = (-2)^{n-2}(45.68 - 1.2n)$; a_{23}

13. $a_n = 3n^2(9n - 100)$; a_{11}

14. $a_n = 4n^2(2n - 39)$; a_{22}

15. $a_n = \left(1 + \dfrac{1}{n}\right)^2$; a_{20}

16. $a_n = \left(1 - \dfrac{1}{n}\right)^3$; a_{15}

In each of the following, the nth term of a sequence is given. In each case, find the first 4 terms, the 10th term, a_{10}, and the 15th term, a_{15}, of the sequence.

17. $a_n = 2n + 3$

18. $a_n = 5n - 2$

19. $a_n = n^2 + 2$

20. $a_n = n^2 - 2n$

21. $a_n = \dfrac{n}{n + 1}$

22. $a_n = \dfrac{n^2 - 1}{n^2 + 1}$

23. $a_n = \left(-\dfrac{1}{2}\right)^{n-1}$

24. $a_n = (-2)^{n+1}$

25. $a_n = (-1)^n/n$

26. $a_n = (-1)^n n^2$

27. $a_n = (-1)^n(n^3 - 1)$

28. $a_n = (-1)^{n+1}(3n - 5)$

Use a graphing calculator to find the first 5 terms of each sequence.

29. $a_n = 2n - 5$

30. $a_n = 8n - 17$

31. $a_n = n^2 - 3n + 1$

32. $a_n = (n + 1)(n - 2)$

33. $a_n = \dfrac{2n}{(n + 3)^2}$

34. $a_n = \dfrac{-1}{n^2 + 1}$

Look for a pattern and then write an expression for the general term, or nth term, a_n, of each sequence. Answers may vary.

35. $2, 4, 6, 8, 10, \ldots$

36. $1, 3, 5, 7, \ldots$

37. $1, -1, 1, -1, \ldots$

38. $-1, 1, -1, 1, \ldots$

39. $-1, 2, -3, 4, \ldots$

40. $1, -2, 3, -4, \ldots$

41. $3, 5, 7, 9, \ldots$

42. $4, 6, 8, 10, \ldots$

43. $0, 3, 8, 15, 24, \ldots$

44. $2, 6, 12, 20, 30, \ldots$

45. $\frac{1}{2}, \frac{2}{3}, \frac{3}{4}, \frac{4}{5}, \frac{5}{6}, \ldots$

46. $1 \cdot 2, 2 \cdot 3, 3 \cdot 4, 4 \cdot 5, \ldots$

47. $5, 25, 125, 625, \ldots$

48. $4, 16, 64, 256, \ldots$

49. $-1, 4, -9, 16, \ldots$

50. $1, -4, 9, -16, \ldots$

Find the indicated partial sum for each sequence.

51. $1, -2, 3, -4, 5, -6, \ldots; S_7$

52. $1, -3, 5, -7, 9, -11, \ldots; S_8$

53. $2, 4, 6, 8, \ldots; S_5$

54. $1, \frac{1}{10}, \frac{1}{100}, \frac{1}{1000}, \ldots; S_6$

Use a graphing calculator to find $S_1, S_2, S_3,$ and S_4 for each of the following sequences.

55. $a_n = \dfrac{2}{n}$

56. $a_n = \dfrac{n + 1}{n}$

57. $a_n = (-1)^n(n^2)$

58. $a_n = (-1)^n(2n)$

Write out and evaluate each sum.

59. $\displaystyle\sum_{k=1}^{5} \dfrac{1}{2k}$

60. $\displaystyle\sum_{k=1}^{6} \dfrac{1}{2k - 1}$

61. $\displaystyle\sum_{k=0}^{4} 10^k$

62. $\displaystyle\sum_{k=4}^{7} \sqrt{2k + 1}$

63. $\displaystyle\sum_{k=2}^{8} \dfrac{k}{k - 1}$

64. $\displaystyle\sum_{k=2}^{5} \dfrac{k - 1}{k + 1}$

65. $\displaystyle\sum_{k=1}^{8} (-1)^{k+1} 2^k$

66. $\displaystyle\sum_{k=1}^{7} (-1)^k 4^{k+1}$

67. $\displaystyle\sum_{k=0}^{5} (k^2 - 2k + 3)$

68. $\displaystyle\sum_{k=0}^{5} (k^2 - 3k + 4)$

69. $\displaystyle\sum_{k=3}^{5} \dfrac{(-1)^k}{k(k + 1)}$

70. $\displaystyle\sum_{k=3}^{7} \dfrac{k}{2^k}$

Rewrite each sum using sigma notation. Answers may vary.

71. $\dfrac{2}{3} + \dfrac{3}{4} + \dfrac{4}{5} + \dfrac{5}{6} + \dfrac{6}{7}$

72. $\dfrac{1}{1^2} + \dfrac{1}{2^2} + \dfrac{1}{3^2} + \dfrac{1}{4^2} + \dfrac{1}{5^2}$

73. $1 + 4 + 9 + 16 + 25 + 36$

74. $1 + \sqrt{2} + \sqrt{3} + 2 + \sqrt{5} + \sqrt{6}$

75. $4 - 9 + 16 - 25 + \cdots + (-1)^n n^2$

76. $9 - 16 + 25 + \cdots + (-1)^{n+1} n^2$

77. $5 + 10 + 15 + 20 + 25 + \cdots$

78. $7 + 14 + 21 + 28 + 35 + \cdots$

79. $\dfrac{1}{1 \cdot 2} + \dfrac{1}{2 \cdot 3} + \dfrac{1}{3 \cdot 4} + \dfrac{1}{4 \cdot 5} + \cdots$

80. $\dfrac{1}{1 \cdot 2^2} + \dfrac{1}{2 \cdot 3^2} + \dfrac{1}{3 \cdot 4^2} + \dfrac{1}{4 \cdot 5^2} + \cdots$

Graph each of the following sequences.

81. $a_n = 3n + 1$

82. $a_n = 7 - 2n$

83. $a_n = (-1)^n(n^2)$

84. $a_n = (-1)^n \sqrt{n}$

85. $a_n = \dfrac{1}{n}$

86. $a_n = \dfrac{2}{n^2}$

87. $a_n = \dfrac{(-1)^n}{(n + 2)}$

88. $a_n = \dfrac{(-1)^n}{2n}$

TW **89.** The sequence $1, 4, 9, 16, \ldots$ can be written as $f(x) = x^2$ with the domain the set of all positive integers. Explain how the graph of f would compare with the graph of $y = x^2$.

TW **90.** Consider the sums

$$\sum_{k=1}^{5} 3k^2 \quad \text{and} \quad 3\sum_{k=1}^{5} k^2.$$

a) Which is easier to evaluate and why?

b) Is it true that

$$\sum_{k=1}^{n} ca_k = c\sum_{k=1}^{n} a_k?$$

Why or why not?

SKILL REVIEW

To prepare for Section 16.2, review evaluating expressions and simplifying expressions.

Evaluate.

91. $\frac{7}{2}(a_1 + a_7)$, for $a_1 = 8$ and $a_7 = 20$

92. $a_1 + (n - 1)d$, for $a_1 = 3, n = 10,$ and $d = -2$

Simplify.

93. $(a_1 + 3d) + d$

94. $(a_1 + 5d) + (a_n - 5d)$

95. $(a_1 + a_n) + (a_1 + a_n) + (a_1 + a_n)$

96. $(a_1 + 8d) - (a_1 + 7d)$

SYNTHESIS

TW **97.** Explain why the equation

$$\sum_{k=1}^{n}(a_k + b_k) = \sum_{k=1}^{n}a_k + \sum_{k=1}^{n}b_k$$

is true for any positive integer n. What laws are used to justify this result?

TW **98.** Can a finite series be formed from an infinite sequence? Can an infinite series be formed from a finite sequence? Why or why not?

Some sequences are given by a recursive *definition. The value of the first term, a_1, is given, and then we are told how to find any subsequent term from the term preceding it. Find the first six terms of each of the following recursively defined sequences.*

99. $a_1 = 1, a_{n+1} = 5a_n - 2$

100. $a_1 = 0, a_{n+1} = a_n^2 + 3$

101. *Value of a Projector.* The value of an LCD projector is $2500. Its scrap value each year is 80% of its value the year before. Write a sequence listing the scrap value of the machine at the start of each year for a 10-year period.

102. *Cell Biology.* A single cell of bacterium divides into two every 15 min. Suppose that the same rate of division is maintained for 4 hr. Give a sequence that lists the number of cells after successive 15-min periods.

103. Find S_{100} and S_{101} for the sequence in which $a_n = (-1)^n$.

Find the first five terms of each sequence. Then find S_5.

104. $a_n = \frac{1}{2^n} \log 1000^n$

105. $a_n = i^n, i = \sqrt{-1}$

106. Find all values for x that solve the following:

$$\sum_{k=1}^{x} i^k = -1.$$

107. The nth term of a sequence is given by

$$a_n = n^5 - 14n^4 + 6n^3 + 416n^2 - 655n - 1050.$$

Use a graphing calculator with a TABLE feature to determine what term in the sequence is 6144.

108. To define a sequence recursively on a graphing calculator (see Exercises 99 and 100), we use the SEQ MODE. The general term u_n or v_n can be expressed in terms of u_{n-1} or v_{n-1} by pressing (2ND) (7) or (2ND) (8). The starting values of u_n, v_n, and n are set as one of the WINDOW variables.

Use recursion to determine how many different handshakes occur when 50 people shake hands with one another. To develop the recursion formula, begin with a group of 2 and determine how many additional handshakes occur with the arrival of each new group member.

Try Exercise Answers: Section 16.1

17. $5, 7, 9, 11; 23; 33$ **29.** $-3, -1, 1, 3, 5$ **35.** $2n$

51. 4 **55.** $2, 3, \frac{11}{3}, \frac{25}{6}$ **59.** $\frac{1}{2} + \frac{1}{4} + \frac{1}{6} + \frac{1}{8} + \frac{1}{10} = \frac{137}{120}$

71. $\sum_{k=1}^{5} \frac{k+1}{k+2}$ **81.** $u = 3n + 1$

16.2 Arithmetic Sequences and Series

- Arithmetic Sequences

- Sum of the First *n* Terms of an Arithmetic Sequence

- Problem Solving

In this section, we concentrate on sequences and series that are said to be arithmetic (pronounced ar-ith-MET-ik).

ARITHMETIC SEQUENCES

In an **arithmetic sequence** (or **progression**), adding the same number to any term gives the next term in the sequence. For example, the sequence $2, 5, 8, 11, 14, 17, \ldots$ is arithmetic because adding 3 to any term produces the next term.

> **Arithmetic Sequence** A sequence is *arithmetic* if there exists a number d, called the *common difference*, such that $a_{n+1} = a_n + d$ for any integer $n \geq 1$.

EXAMPLE 1 For each arithmetic sequence, identify the first term, a_1, and the common difference, d.

a) $4, 9, 14, 19, 24, \ldots$
b) $27, 20, 13, 6, -1, -8, \ldots$

SOLUTION To find a_1, we simply use the first term listed. To find d, we choose any term beyond the first and subtract the preceding term from it.

Sequence	First Term, a_1	Common Difference, d
a) $4, 9, 14, 19, 24, \ldots$	4	$5 \longleftarrow 9 - 4 = 5$
b) $27, 20, 13, 6, -1, -8, \ldots$	27	$-7 \longleftarrow 20 - 27 = -7$

To find the common difference, we subtracted a_1 from a_2. Had we subtracted a_2 from a_3 or a_3 from a_4, we would have found the same values for d.

Check: As a check, note that when d is added to each term, the result is the next term in the sequence.

Try Exercise 9.

Student Notes

When the terms are decreasing, the common difference is negative. Try determining the sign of the common difference before calculating it.

To develop a formula for the general, *n*th, term of any arithmetic sequence, we denote the common difference by d and write out the first few terms:

$$a_1,$$
$$a_2 = a_1 + d,$$
$$a_3 = a_2 + d = (a_1 + d) + d = a_1 + 2d, \qquad \text{Substituting } a_1 + d \text{ for } a_2$$
$$a_4 = a_3 + d = (a_1 + 2d) + d = a_1 + 3d. \qquad \text{Substituting } a_1 + 2d \text{ for } a_3$$

Note that the coefficient of d in each case is 1 less than the subscript.

Generalizing, we obtain the following formula.

To Find a_n for an Arithmetic Sequence   The nth term of an arithmetic sequence with common difference d is

$$a_n = a_1 + (n - 1)d, \quad \text{for any integer } n \geq 1.$$

EXAMPLE 2   Find the 14th term of the arithmetic sequence $6, 9, 12, 15, \ldots$.

SOLUTION   First, we note that $a_1 = 6$, $d = 3$, and $n = 14$. Using the formula for the nth term of an arithmetic sequence, we have

$$a_n = a_1 + (n - 1)d$$
$$a_{14} = 6 + (14 - 1) \cdot 3 = 6 + 13 \cdot 3 = 6 + 39 = 45.$$

The 14th term is 45.

Try Exercise 17.

EXAMPLE 3   For the sequence in Example 2, which term is 300? That is, find n if $a_n = 300$.

SOLUTION   We substitute into the formula for the nth term of an arithmetic sequence and solve for n:

$$a_n = a_1 + (n - 1)d$$
$$300 = 6 + (n - 1) \cdot 3$$
$$300 = 6 + 3n - 3$$
$$297 = 3n$$
$$99 = n.$$

The term 300 is the 99th term of the sequence.

Try Exercise 23.

Given two terms and their places in an arithmetic sequence, we can construct the sequence.

EXAMPLE 4   The 3rd term of an arithmetic sequence is 14, and the 16th term is 79. Find a_1 and d and construct the sequence.

SOLUTION   We know that $a_3 = 14$ and $a_{16} = 79$. Thus we would have to add d 13 times to get from 14 to 79. That is,

$$14 + 13d = 79. \qquad a_3 \text{ and } a_{16} \text{ are 13 terms apart; } 16 - 3 = 13$$

Solving $14 + 13d = 79$, we obtain

$$13d = 65 \qquad \text{Subtracting 14 from both sides}$$
$$d = 5. \qquad \text{Dividing both sides by 13}$$

We subtract d twice from a_3 to get to a_1. Thus,

$$a_1 = 14 - 2 \cdot 5 = 4. \qquad a_1 \text{ and } a_3 \text{ are 2 terms apart; } 3 - 1 = 2$$

The sequence is $4, 9, 14, 19, \ldots$. Note that we could have subtracted d a total of 15 times from a_{16} in order to find a_1.

Try Exercise 33.

In general, d should be subtracted $(n - 1)$ times from a_n in order to find a_1. What will the graph of an arithmetic sequence look like?

Interactive Discovery

Graph each of the following arithmetic sequences. What pattern do you observe?

1. $a_n = -5 + (n - 1)3$
2. $a_n = \frac{1}{2} + (n - 1)\frac{3}{2}$
3. $a_n = 60 + (n - 1)(-5)$
4. $a_n = -1.7 + (n - 1)(-0.2)$

The pattern you may have observed above is true in general:

The graph of an arithmetic sequence is a set of points that lie on a straight line.

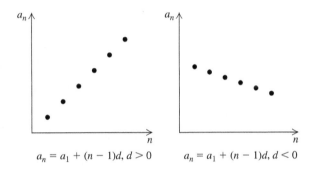

$a_n = a_1 + (n - 1)d, d > 0$ $\qquad$ $a_n = a_1 + (n - 1)d, d < 0$

SUM OF THE FIRST n TERMS OF AN ARITHMETIC SEQUENCE

When the terms of an arithmetic sequence are added, an **arithmetic series** is formed. To develop a formula for computing S_n when the series is arithmetic, we list the first n terms of the sequence as follows:

This is the next-to-last term. If we add d to this term, the result is a_n.

$$a_1, (a_1 + d), (a_1 + 2d), \ldots, (a_n - 2d), \overbrace{(a_n - d)}, a_n.$$

This term is two terms back from the end. If we add d to this term, we get the next-to-last term, $a_n - d$.

Thus, S_n is given by

$$S_n = a_1 + (a_1 + d) + (a_1 + 2d) + \cdots + (a_n - 2d) + (a_n - d) + a_n.$$

Using a commutative law, we have a second equation:

$$S_n = a_n + (a_n - d) + (a_n - 2d) + \cdots + (a_1 + 2d) + (a_1 + d) + a_1.$$

Adding corresponding terms on each side of the above equations, we get

$$2S_n = [a_1 + a_n] + [(a_1 + d) + (a_n - d)] + [(a_1 + 2d) + (a_n - 2d)]$$
$$+ \cdots + [(a_n - 2d) + (a_1 + 2d)] + [(a_n - d) + (a_1 + d)]$$
$$+ [a_n + a_1].$$

This simplifies to

$$2S_n = [a_1 + a_n] + [a_1 + a_n] + [a_1 + a_n]$$
$$+ \cdots + [a_n + a_1] + [a_n + a_1] + [a_n + a_1].$$ There are n bracketed sums.

Since $[a_1 + a_n]$ is being added n times, it follows that

$$2S_n = n[a_1 + a_n].$$

Dividing both sides by 2 leads to the following formula.

To Find S_n for an Arithmetic Sequence The sum of the first n terms of an arithmetic sequence is given by

$$S_n = \frac{n}{2}(a_1 + a_n).$$

EXAMPLE 5 Find the sum of the first 100 positive even numbers.

SOLUTION The sum is

$$2 + 4 + 6 + \cdots + 198 + 200.$$

This is the sum of the first 100 terms of the arithmetic sequence for which

$$a_1 = 2, \quad n = 100, \quad \text{and} \quad a_n = 200.$$

Substituting in the formula

$$S_n = \frac{n}{2}(a_1 + a_n),$$

we get

$$S_{100} = \frac{100}{2}(2 + 200)$$
$$= 50(202) = 10{,}100.$$

Try Exercise 39.

The formula above is useful when we know the first and last terms, a_1 and a_n. To find S_n when a_n is unknown, but a_1, n, and d are known, we can use the formula $a_n = a_1 + (n - 1)d$ to calculate a_n and then proceed as in Example 5.

EXAMPLE 6 Find the sum of the first 15 terms of the arithmetic sequence $4, 7, 10, 13, \ldots$.

SOLUTION Note that

$$a_1 = 4, \quad n = 15, \quad \text{and} \quad d = 3.$$

Before using the formula for S_n, we find a_{15}:

$$a_{15} = 4 + (15 - 1)3 \qquad \text{Substituting into the formula for } a_n$$
$$= 4 + 14 \cdot 3 = 46.$$

Thus, knowing that $a_{15} = 46$, we have

$$S_{15} = \tfrac{15}{2}(4 + 46) \qquad \text{Using the formula for } S_n$$
$$= \tfrac{15}{2}(50) = 375.$$

Try Exercise 37.

PROBLEM SOLVING

Translation of problems may involve sequences or series. There is often a variety of ways in which a problem can be solved. You should use the one that is best or easiest for you. In this chapter, however, we will try to emphasize sequences and series and their related formulas.

EXAMPLE 7 Hourly Wages. Chris accepts a job managing a music store, starting with an hourly wage of $14.60, and is promised a raise of 25¢ per hour every 2 months for 5 years. After 5 years of work, what will be Chris's hourly wage?

SOLUTION

1. **Familiarize.** It helps to write down the hourly wage for several two-month time periods.

Beginning:	14.60,
After two months:	14.85,
After four months:	15.10,

    and so on.

    What appears is a sequence of numbers: 14.60, 14.85, 15.10, ... Since the same amount is added each time, the sequence is arithmetic.

    We list what we know about arithmetic sequences. The pertinent formulas are

    $$a_n = a_1 + (n - 1)d$$

    and

    $$S_n = \frac{n}{2}(a_1 + a_n).$$

    In this case, we are not looking for a sum, so we use the first formula. We want to determine the last term in a sequence. To do so, we need to know a_1, n, and d. From our list above, we see that

    $$a_1 = 14.60 \quad \text{and} \quad d = 0.25.$$

    What is n? That is, how many terms are in the sequence? After 1 year, there will have been 6 raises, since Chris gets a raise every 2 months. There are 5 years, so the total number of raises will be $5 \cdot 6$, or 30. Altogether, there will be 31 terms: the original wage and 30 increased rates.

2. **Translate.** We want to find a_n for the arithmetic sequence in which $a_1 = 14.60$, $n = 31$, and $d = 0.25$.

3. **Carry out.** Substituting in the formula for a_n gives us

    $$a_{31} = 14.60 + (31 - 1) \cdot 0.25 = 22.10.$$

4. **Check.** We can check by redoing the calculations or we can calculate in a slightly different way for another check. For example, at the end of a year, there will be 6 raises, for a total raise of $1.50. At the end of 5 years, the total raise will be 5 × $1.50, or $7.50. If we add that to the original wage of $14.60, we obtain $22.10. The answer checks.

5. **State.** After 5 years, Chris's hourly wage will be $22.10.

Try Exercise 47.

EXAMPLE 8 Telephone Pole Storage. A stack of telephone poles has 30 poles in the bottom row. There are 29 poles in the second row, 28 in the next row, and so on. How many poles are in the stack if there are 5 poles in the top row?

SOLUTION

1. **Familiarize.** The figure below shows the ends of the poles. There are 30 poles on the bottom and one fewer in each successive row. How many rows will there be?

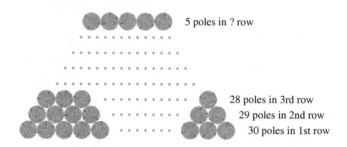

5 poles in ? row

28 poles in 3rd row
29 poles in 2nd row
30 poles in 1st row

Note that there are $30 - 1 = 29$ poles in the 2nd row, $30 - 2 = 28$ poles in the 3rd row, $30 - 3 = 27$ poles in the 4th row, and so on. The pattern leads to $30 - 25 = 5$ poles in the 26th row.

The situation is represented by the equation

$30 + 29 + 28 + \cdots + 5.$ There are 26 terms in this series.

Thus we have an arithmetic series. We recall the formula

$$S_n = \frac{n}{2}(a_1 + a_n).$$

2. **Translate.** We want to find the sum of the first 26 terms of an arithmetic sequence in which $a_1 = 30$ and $a_{26} = 5$.

3. Carry out. Substituting into the above formula gives us

$$S_{26} = \frac{26}{2}(30 + 5) = 13 \cdot 35 = 455.$$

4. Check. In this case, we can check the calculations by doing them again. A longer, harder way would be to do the entire addition:

$$30 + 29 + 28 + \cdots + 5.$$

5. State. There are 455 poles in the stack.

Try Exercise 49.

16.2 Exercise Set

FOR EXTRA HELP   *MyMathLab*

Concept Reinforcement   Classify each of the following statements as either true or false.

1. In an arithmetic sequence, the difference between any two consecutive terms is always the same.

2. In an arithmetic sequence, if $a_9 - a_8 = 4$, then $a_{13} - a_{12} = 4$ as well.

3. In an arithmetic sequence containing 17 terms, the common difference is $a_{17} - a_1$.

4. To find a_{20} in an arithmetic sequence, add the common difference to a_1 a total of 20 times.

5. The sum of the first 20 terms of an arithmetic sequence can be found by knowing just a_1 and a_{20}.

6. The sum of the first 30 terms of an arithmetic sequence can be found by knowing just a_1 and d, the common difference.

7. The notation S_5 means $a_1 + a_5$.

8. For any arithmetic sequence, $S_9 = S_8 + d$, where d is the common difference.

Find the first term and the common difference.

9. 2, 6, 10, 14, ...

10. 2.5, 3, 3.5, 4, ...

11. 7, 3, −1, −5, ...

12. −8, −5, −2, 1, ...

13. $\frac{3}{2}, \frac{9}{4}, 3, \frac{15}{4}, \ldots$

14. $\frac{3}{5}, \frac{1}{10}, -\frac{2}{5}, \ldots$

15. $5.12, $5.24, $5.36, $5.48, ...

16. $214, $211, $208, $205, ...

17. Find the 15th term of the arithmetic sequence 7, 10, 13, ...

18. Find the 17th term of the arithmetic sequence 6, 10, 14, ...

19. Find the 18th term of the arithmetic sequence 8, 2, −4, ...

20. Find the 14th term of the arithmetic sequence $3, \frac{7}{3}, \frac{5}{3}, \ldots$

21. Find the 13th term of the arithmetic sequence $1200, $964.32, $728.64, ...

22. Find the 10th term of the arithmetic sequence $2345.78, $2967.54, $3589.30, ...

23. In the sequence of Exercise 17, what term is 82?

24. In the sequence of Exercise 18, what term is 126?

25. In the sequence of Exercise 19, what term is −328?

26. In the sequence of Exercise 20, what term is −27?

27. Find a_{17} when $a_1 = 2$ and $d = 5$.

28. Find a_{20} when $a_1 = 14$ and $d = -3$.

29. Find a_1 when $d = 4$ and $a_8 = 33$.

30. Find a_1 when $d = 8$ and $a_{11} = 26$.

31. Find n when $a_1 = 5, d = -3$, and $a_n = -76$.

32. Find n when $a_1 = 25, d = -14$, and $a_n = -507$.

33. For an arithmetic sequence in which $a_{17} = -40$ and $a_{28} = -73$, find a_1 and d. Write the first five terms of the sequence.

34. In an arithmetic sequence, $a_{17} = \frac{25}{3}$ and $a_{32} = \frac{95}{6}$. Find a_1 and d. Write the first five terms of the sequence.

Aha! **35.** Find a_1 and d if $a_{13} = 13$ and $a_{54} = 54$.

36. Find a_1 and d if $a_{12} = 24$ and $a_{25} = 50$.

37. Find the sum of the first 20 terms of the arithmetic series $1 + 5 + 9 + 13 + \cdots$.

38. Find the sum of the first 14 terms of the arithmetic series $11 + 7 + 3 + \cdots$.

39. Find the sum of the first 250 natural numbers.

40. Find the sum of the first 400 natural numbers.

41. Find the sum of the even numbers from 2 to 100, inclusive.

42. Find the sum of the odd numbers from 1 to 99, inclusive.

43. Find the sum of all multiples of 6 from 6 to 102, inclusive.

44. Find the sum of all multiples of 4 that are between 15 and 521.

45. An arithmetic series has $a_1 = 4$ and $d = 5$. Find S_{20}.

46. An arithmetic series has $a_1 = 9$ and $d = -3$. Find S_{32}.

Solve.

47. *Band Formations.* The South Brighton Drum and Bugle Corps has 7 musicians in the front row, 9 in the second row, 11 in the third row, and so on, for 15 rows. How many musicians are in the last row? How many musicians are there altogether?

48. *Gardening.* A gardener is planting daffodil bulbs near an entrance to a college. She puts 50 bulbs in the front row, 46 in the second row, 42 in the third row, and so on, for 13 rows. If the pattern is consistent, how many bulbs will be in the last row? How many bulbs will there be altogether?

49. *Archaeology.* Many ancient Mayan pyramids were constructed over a span of several generations. Each layer of the pyramid has a stone perimeter, enclosing a layer of dirt or debris on which a structure once stood. One drawing of such a pyramid indicates that the perimeter of the bottom layer contains 36 stones, the next level up contains 32 stones, and so on, up to

the top row, which contains 4 stones. How many stones are in the pyramid?

50. *Telephone Pole Piles.* How many poles will be in a pile of telephone poles if there are 50 in the first layer, 49 in the second, and so on, until there are 6 in the top layer?

51. *Accumulated Savings.* If 10¢ is saved on October 1, another 20¢ on October 2, another 30¢ on October 3, and so on, how much is saved during October? (October has 31 days.)

52. *Accumulated Savings.* Renata saves money in an arithmetic sequence: $700 for the first year, another $850 the second, and so on, for 20 years. How much does she save in all (disregarding interest)?

53. *Auditorium Design.* Theaters are often built with more seats per row as the rows move toward the back. The Sanders Amphitheater has 20 seats in the first row, 22 in the second, 24 in the third, and so on, for 19 rows. How many seats are in the amphitheater?

54. *Accumulated Savings.*   Shirley sets up an investment such that it will return $5000 the first year, $6125 the second year, $7250 the third year, and so on, for 25 years. How much in all is received from the investment?

TW **55.** It is said that as a young child, the mathematician Karl F. Gauss (1777–1855) was able to compute the sum $1 + 2 + 3 + \cdots + 100$ very quickly in his head. Explain how Gauss might have done this, and present a formula for the sum of the first n natural numbers. (*Hint*: $1 + 99 = 100$.)

TW **56.** Write a problem for a classmate to solve. Devise the problem so that its solution requires computing S_{17} for an arithmetic sequence.

SKILL REVIEW

Review finding equations.

Find an equation of the line satisfying the given conditions.

57. Slope $\frac{1}{3}$, y-intercept $(0, 10)$

58. Containing the points $(2, 3)$ and $(4, -5)$

59. Containing the point $(5, 0)$ and parallel to the line given by $2x + y = 8$

60. Containing the point $(-1, -4)$ and perpendicular to the line given by $3x - 4y = 7$

Find an equation of the circle satisfying the given conditions. [15.1]

61. Center $(0, 0)$, radius 4

62. Center $(-2, 1)$, radius $2\sqrt{5}$

SYNTHESIS

TW **63.** When every term in an arithmetic sequence is an integer, S_n must also be an integer. Given that n, a_1, and a_n may each, at times, be even or odd, explain why $\frac{n}{2}(a_1 + a_n)$ is always an integer.

TW **64.** The sum of the first n terms of an arithmetic sequence is also given by

$$S_n = \frac{n}{2}[2a_1 + (n - 1)d].$$

Use the earlier formulas for a_n and S_n to explain how this equation was developed.

65. A frog is at the bottom of a 100-ft well. With each jump, the frog climbs 4 ft, but then slips back 1 ft. How many jumps does it take for the frog to reach the top of the hole?

66. Find a formula for the sum of the first n consecutive odd numbers starting with 1:

$$1 + 3 + 5 + \cdots + (2n - 1).$$

67. In an arithmetic sequence, $a_1 = \$8760$ and $d = -\$798.23$. Find the first 10 terms of the sequence.

68. Find the sum of the first 10 terms of the sequence given in Exercise 67.

69. Prove that if p, m, and q are consecutive terms in an arithmetic sequence, then

$$m = \frac{p + q}{2}.$$

70. *Straight-Line Depreciation.*   A company buys a color laser printer for $5200 on January 1 of a given year. The machine is expected to last for 8 years, at the end of which time its *trade-in*, or *salvage*, *value* will be $1100. If the company figures the decline in value to be the same each year, then the trade-in values, after t years, $0 \le t \le 8$, form an arithmetic sequence given by

$$a_t = C - t\left(\frac{C - S}{N}\right),$$

where C is the original cost of the item, N the years of expected life, and S the salvage value.

a) Find the formula for a_t for the straight-line depreciation of the printer.

b) Find the salvage value after 0 year, 1 year, 2 years, 3 years, 4 years, 7 years, and 8 years.

c) Find a formula that expresses a_t recursively.

71. Use your answer to Exercise 39 to find the sum of all integers from 501 through 750.

In Exercises 72–75, graph the data in each table, and state whether or not the graph could be the graph of an arithmetic sequence. If it can, find a formula for the general term of the sequence.

72. *Aerobic Exercise.*

Age	Target Heart Rate (in beats per minute)
20	150
40	135
60	120
80	105

73. *Golf Ball Speed.*

Ball Speed (in miles per hour)	Club Speed (in miles per hour)
100	69
110	76
120	83
130	90
140	97

74. *Video Games.*

Year	Hours Spent Playing Video Games (per person per year)
2005	78
2006	82
2007	86
2008	93
2009	96

Source: U.S. Census Bureau

75. *Internet.*

Year	Hours Spent on the Internet (per person per year)
2005	183
2006	190
2007	195
2008	200
2009	203

Source: U.S. Census Bureau

Try Exercise Answers: Section 16.2
9. $a_1 = 2, d = 4$ **17.** 49 **23.** 26th
33. $a_1 = 8; d = -3; 8, 5, 2, -1, -4$ **37.** 780 **39.** 31,375
47. 35 musicians; 315 musicians **49.** 180 stones

16.3 Geometric Sequences and Series

- Geometric Sequences

- Sum of the First *n* Terms of a Geometric Sequence

- Infinite Geometric Series

- Problem Solving

In an arithmetic sequence, a certain number is added to each term to get the next term. When each term in a sequence is *multiplied* by a certain fixed number to get the next term, the sequence is **geometric.** In this section, we examine *geometric sequences* (or *progressions*) and *geometric series*.

GEOMETRIC SEQUENCES

Consider the sequence

$$2, 6, 18, 54, 162, \ldots.$$

If we multiply each term by 3, we obtain the next term. The multiplier is called the *common ratio* because it is found by dividing any term by the preceding term.

> **Geometric Sequence**   A sequence is *geometric* if there exists a number r, called the *common ratio*, for which
>
> $$\frac{a_{n+1}}{a_n} = r, \quad \text{or} \quad a_{n+1} = a_n \cdot r, \quad \text{for any integer } n \geq 1.$$

EXAMPLE 1   For each geometric sequence, find the common ratio.

a) $4, 20, 100, 500, 2500, \ldots$

b) $3, -6, 12, -24, 48, -96, \ldots$

c) $\$5200, \$3900, \$2925, \$2193.75, \ldots$

SOLUTION

Sequence	Common Ratio	
a) $4, 20, 100, 500, 2500, \ldots$	5	$\frac{20}{4} = 5, \frac{100}{20} = 5,$ and so on
b) $3, -6, 12, -24, 48, -96, \ldots$	-2	$\frac{-6}{3} = -2, \frac{12}{-6} = -2,$ and so on
c) $\$5200, \$3900, \$2925, \$2193.75, \ldots$	0.75	$\frac{\$3900}{\$5200} = 0.75, \frac{\$2925}{\$3900} = 0.75$

Try Exercise 9.

To develop a formula for the general, or nth, term of a geometric sequence, let a_1 be the first term and let r be the common ratio. We write out the first few terms as follows:

$$a_1,$$
$$a_2 = a_1 r,$$
$$a_3 = a_2 r = (a_1 r)r = a_1 r^2, \qquad \text{Substituting } a_1 r \text{ for } a_2$$
$$a_4 = a_3 r = (a_1 r^2)r = a_1 r^3. \qquad \text{Substituting } a_1 r^2 \text{ for } a_3$$

Note that the exponent is 1 less than the subscript.

Generalizing, we obtain the following.

> **To Find a_n for a Geometric Sequence**   The nth term of a geometric sequence with common ratio r is given by
>
> $$a_n = a_1 r^{n-1}, \quad \text{for any integer } n \geq 1.$$

Student Notes

As you can observe in Example 1, when the signs of the terms alternate, the common ratio is negative. Try determining the sign of the common ratio before calculating it.

EXAMPLE 2 Find the 7th term of the geometric sequence 4, 20, 100, ...

SOLUTION First, we note that

$$a_1 = 4 \quad \text{and} \quad n = 7.$$

To find the common ratio, we can divide any term (other than the first) by the term preceding it. Since the second term is 20 and the first is 4,

$$r = \frac{20}{4}, \quad \text{or } 5.$$

The formula

$$a_n = a_1 r^{n-1}$$

gives us

$$a_7 = 4 \cdot 5^{7-1} = 4 \cdot 5^6 = 4 \cdot 15,625 = 62,500.$$

Try Exercise 19.

EXAMPLE 3 Find the 10th term of the geometric sequence

$$64, -32, 16, -8, \ldots.$$

SOLUTION First, we note that

$$a_1 = 64, \qquad n = 10, \quad \text{and} \quad r = \frac{-32}{64} = -\frac{1}{2}.$$

Then, using the formula for the nth term of a geometric sequence, we have

$$a_{10} = 64 \cdot \left(-\frac{1}{2}\right)^{10-1} = 64 \cdot \left(-\frac{1}{2}\right)^9 = 2^6 \cdot \left(-\frac{1}{2^9}\right) = -\frac{1}{2^3} = -\frac{1}{8}.$$

The 10th term is $-\frac{1}{8}$.

Try Exercise 23.

What does the graph of a geometric series look like?

Interactive Discovery

Graph each of the following geometric series. What patterns, if any, do you observe?

1. $a_n = 5 \cdot 2^{n-1}$ **2.** $a_n = \frac{1}{2} \cdot \left(\frac{5}{4}\right)^{n-1}$

3. $a_n = 2.3 \cdot (0.75)^{n-1}$ **4.** $a_n = 3\left(\frac{9}{10}\right)^{n-1}$

The pattern you may have observed is true in general for $r > 0$.

The graph of a geometric series is a set of points that lie on the graph of an exponential function.

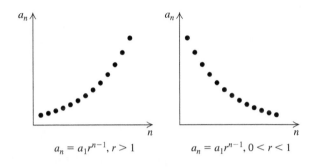

$$a_n = a_1 r^{n-1}, r > 1 \qquad\qquad a_n = a_1 r^{n-1}, 0 < r < 1$$

SUM OF THE FIRST n TERMS OF A GEOMETRIC SEQUENCE

We next develop a formula for S_n when a sequence is geometric:

$$a_1, a_1 r, a_1 r^2, a_1 r^3, \dots, a_1 r^{n-1}, \dots.$$

The **geometric series** S_n is given by

$$S_n = a_1 + a_1 r + a_1 r^2 + \cdots + a_1 r^{n-2} + a_1 r^{n-1}. \tag{1}$$

Multiplying both sides by r gives us

$$rS_n = a_1 r + a_1 r^2 + a_1 r^3 + \cdots + a_1 r^{n-1} + a_1 r^n. \tag{2}$$

When we subtract corresponding sides of equation (2) from equation (1), the color terms drop out, leaving

$$S_n - rS_n = a_1 - a_1 r^n$$
$$S_n(1 - r) = a_1(1 - r^n), \qquad \text{Factoring}$$

or

$$S_n = \frac{a_1(1 - r^n)}{1 - r}. \qquad \text{Dividing both sides by } 1 - r$$

To Find S_n for a Geometric Sequence   The sum of the first n terms of a geometric sequence with common ratio r is given by

$$S_n = \frac{a_1(1 - r^n)}{1 - r}, \quad \text{for any } r \neq 1.$$

EXAMPLE 4 Find the sum of the first 7 terms of the geometric sequence $3, 15, 75, 375, \dots$.

SOLUTION   First, we note that

$$a_1 = 3, \qquad n = 7, \quad \text{and} \quad r = \frac{15}{3} = 5.$$

Then, substituting in the formula $S_n = \dfrac{a_1(1 - r^n)}{1 - r}$, we have

$$S_7 = \frac{3(1 - 5^7)}{1 - 5} = \frac{3(1 - 78{,}125)}{-4}$$

$$= \frac{3(-78{,}124)}{-4}$$

$$= 58{,}593.$$

Try Exercise 33.

INFINITE GEOMETRIC SERIES

Suppose we consider the sum of the terms of an infinite geometric sequence, such as $2, 4, 8, 16, 32, \ldots$. We get what is called an **infinite geometric series:**

$$2 + 4 + 8 + 16 + 32 + \cdots.$$

Here, as n increases, the sum of the first n terms, S_n, increases without bound. There are also infinite series that get closer and closer to some specific number. Here is an example:

$$\frac{1}{2} + \frac{1}{4} + \frac{1}{8} + \frac{1}{16} + \cdots + \frac{1}{2^n} + \cdots.$$

Let's consider S_n for the first four values of n:

$$S_1 = \tfrac{1}{2} \qquad\qquad\qquad = \tfrac{1}{2} = 0.5,$$
$$S_2 = \tfrac{1}{2} + \tfrac{1}{4} \qquad\qquad = \tfrac{3}{4} = 0.75,$$
$$S_3 = \tfrac{1}{2} + \tfrac{1}{4} + \tfrac{1}{8} \qquad = \tfrac{7}{8} = 0.875,$$
$$S_4 = \tfrac{1}{2} + \tfrac{1}{4} + \tfrac{1}{8} + \tfrac{1}{16} = \tfrac{15}{16} = 0.9375.$$

The denominator of the sum is 2^n, where n is the subscript of S. The numerator is $2^n - 1$.

Thus, for this particular series, we have

$$S_n = \frac{2^n - 1}{2^n} = \frac{2^n}{2^n} - \frac{1}{2^n} = 1 - \frac{1}{2^n}.$$

Note that the value of S_n is less than 1 for any value of n, but as n gets larger and larger, the value of $1/2^n$ gets closer to 0 and the value of S_n gets closer to 1. We can visualize S_n by considering the area of a square with area 1. For S_1, we shade half the square. For S_2, we shade half the square plus half the remaining part, or $\tfrac{1}{4}$. For S_3, we shade the parts shaded in S_2 plus half the remaining part. Again we see that the values of S_n will continue to get close to 1 (shading the complete square).

$S_1 = \tfrac{1}{2}$

$S_2 = \tfrac{3}{4}$

$S_3 = \tfrac{7}{8}$

$S_4 = \tfrac{15}{16}$

We say that 1 is the **limit** of S_n and that 1 is the sum of this infinite geometric series. An infinite geometric series is denoted S_∞.

How can we tell if an infinite geometric series has a sum?

Interactive Discovery

For each of the following geometric sequences, **(a)** determine the common ratio, **(b)** list the first 10 partial sums, S_1 through S_{10}, and **(c)** estimate, if possible, S_∞.

1. $a_n = \left(\frac{1}{3}\right)^{n-1}$

2. $a_n = \left(-\frac{7}{2}\right)^{n-1}$

3. $a_n = 4(2)^{n-1}$

4. $a_n = 1.3(-0.4)^{n-1}$

5. What relationship do you observe between the common ratio and the existence of S_∞?

It can be shown (but we will not do so here) that the pattern you may have observed is true in general.

> **The sum of the terms of an infinite geometric sequence exists if and only if $|r| < 1$.**

To develop a formula for the sum of an infinite geometric series, we first consider the sum of the first n terms:

$$S_n = \frac{a_1(1 - r^n)}{1 - r} = \frac{a_1 - a_1 r^n}{1 - r}. \qquad \text{Using the distributive law}$$

For $|r| < 1$, it follows that the value of r^n gets closer to 0 as n gets larger. (Check this by selecting a number between -1 and 1 and finding larger and larger powers on a calculator.) As r^n gets closer to 0, so does $a_1 r^n$. Thus, S_n gets closer to $a_1/(1 - r)$.

> **The Limit of an Infinite Geometric Series**   When $|r| < 1$, the limit of an infinite geometric series is given by
>
> $$S_\infty = \frac{a_1}{1 - r}. \qquad (\text{For } |r| \geq 1, \text{ no limit exists.})$$

EXAMPLE 5   Determine whether each series has a limit. If a limit exists, find it.

a) $1 + 3 + 9 + 27 + \cdots$

b) $-2 + 1 - \frac{1}{2} + \frac{1}{4} - \frac{1}{8} + \cdots$

SOLUTION

a) Here $r = 3$, so $|r| = |3| = 3$. Since $|r| \not< 1$, the series *does not* have a limit.

b) Here $r = -\frac{1}{2}$, so $|r| = \left|-\frac{1}{2}\right| = \frac{1}{2}$. Since $|r| < 1$, the series *does* have a limit. We find the limit by substituting into the formula for S_∞:

$$S_\infty = \frac{-2}{1 - \left(-\frac{1}{2}\right)} = \frac{-2}{\frac{3}{2}} = -2 \cdot \frac{2}{3} = -\frac{4}{3}.$$

Try Exercise 41.

EXAMPLE 6 Find fraction notation for 0.63636363 . . . .

SOLUTION We can express this as

$$0.63 + 0.0063 + 0.000063 + \cdots .$$

This is an infinite geometric series, where $a_1 = 0.63$ and $r = 0.01$. Since $|r| < 1$, this series has a limit:

$$S_\infty = \frac{a_1}{1-r} = \frac{0.63}{1-0.01} = \frac{0.63}{0.99} = \frac{63}{99}.$$

Thus fraction notation for 0.63636363 . . . is $\frac{63}{99}$, or $\frac{7}{11}$.

■ Try Exercise 53.

PROBLEM SOLVING

For some problem-solving situations, the translation may involve geometric sequences or series.

EXAMPLE 7 Daily Wages. Suppose someone offered you a job for the month of September (30 days) under the following conditions. You will be paid $0.01 for the first day, $0.02 for the second, $0.04 for the third, and so on, doubling your previous day's salary each day. How much would you earn? (Would you take the job? Make a guess before reading further.)

SOLUTION

1. **Familiarize.** You earn $0.01 the first day, $0.01(2)$ the second day, $0.01(2)(2)$ the third day, and so on. Since each day's wages are a constant multiple of the previous day's wages, a geometric sequence is formed.

2. **Translate.** The amount earned is the geometric series

$$\$0.01 + \$0.01(2) + \$0.01(2^2) + \$0.01(2^3) + \cdots + \$0.01(2^{29}),$$

where

$$a_1 = \$0.01, \qquad n = 30, \quad \text{and} \quad r = 2.$$

3. **Carry out.** Using the formula

$$S_n = \frac{a_1(1-r^n)}{1-r},$$

we have

$$S_{30} = \frac{\$0.01(1-2^{30})}{1-2}$$

$$= \frac{\$0.01(-1{,}073{,}741{,}823)}{-1} \qquad \text{Using a calculator}$$

$$= \$10{,}737{,}418.23.$$

4. **Check.** The calculations can be repeated as a check.

5. **State.** The pay exceeds $10.7 million for the month. Most people would probably take the job!

■ Try Exercise 65.

EXAMPLE 8 Loan Repayment. Francine's student loan is in the amount of $6000. Interest is 9% compounded annually, and the entire amount is to be paid after 10 years. How much is to be paid back?

SOLUTION

1. **Familiarize.** Suppose we let P represent any principal amount. At the end of one year, the amount owed will be $P + 0.09P$, or $1.09P$. That amount will be the principal for the second year. The amount owed at the end of the second year will be $1.09 \times$ New principal $= 1.09(1.09P)$, or 1.09^2P. Thus the amount owed at the beginning of successive years is

$$P, \quad 1.09P, \quad 1.09^2P, \quad 1.09^3P, \quad \text{and so on.}$$

We have a geometric sequence. The amount owed at the beginning of the 11th year will be the amount owed at the end of the 10th year.

2. **Translate.** We have a geometric sequence with $a_1 = 6000, r = 1.09$, and $n = 11$. The appropriate formula is

$$a_n = a_1 r^{n-1}.$$

3. **Carry out.** We substitute and calculate:

$$a_{11} = \$6000(1.09)^{11-1} = \$6000(1.09)^{10}$$
$$\approx \$14{,}204.18. \qquad \text{Using a calculator and rounding to the nearest hundredth}$$

4. **Check.** A check, by repeating the calculations, is left to the student.

5. **State.** Francine will owe $14,204.18 at the end of 10 years.

Try Exercise 61.

EXAMPLE 9 Bungee Jumping. A bungee jumper rebounds 60% of the height jumped. Brent's bungee jump is made using a cord that stretches to 200 ft.

a) After jumping and then rebounding 9 times, how far has Brent traveled upward (the total rebound distance)?

b) Approximately how far will Brent travel upward (bounce) before coming to rest?

SOLUTION

1. **Familiarize.** Let's do some calculations and look for a pattern.

200 ft

First fall:	200 ft
First rebound:	0.6×200, or 120 ft
Second fall:	120 ft, or 0.6×200
Second rebound:	0.6×120, or $0.6(0.6 \times 200)$, which is 72 ft
Third fall:	72 ft, or $0.6(0.6 \times 200)$
Third rebound:	0.6×72, or $0.6(0.6(0.6 \times 200))$, which is 43.2 ft

The rebound distances form a geometric sequence:

$$120, \quad 0.6 \times 120, \quad 0.6^2 \times 120, \quad 0.6^3 \times 120, \dots.$$

2. Translate.

a) The total rebound distance after 9 bounces is the sum of a geometric sequence. The first term is 120 and the common ratio is 0.6. There will be 9 terms, so we can use the formula

$$S_n = \frac{a_1(1 - r^n)}{1 - r}.$$

b) Theoretically, Brent will never stop bouncing. Realistically, the bouncing will eventually stop. To approximate the actual distance, we consider an infinite number of bounces and use the formula

$$S_\infty = \frac{a_1}{1 - r}.$$ Since $r = 0.6$ and $|0.6| < 1$, we know that S_∞ exists.

3. Carry out.

a) We substitute into the formula and calculate:

$$S_9 = \frac{120\left[1 - (0.6)^9\right]}{1 - 0.6} \approx 297.$$ Using a calculator

b) We substitute and calculate:

$$S_\infty = \frac{120}{1 - 0.6} = 300.$$

4. Check. We can do the calculations again.

5. State.

a) In 9 bounces, Brent will have traveled upward a total distance of about 297 ft.

b) Brent will travel upward a total of about 300 ft before coming to rest.

Try Exercise 67.

Visualizing for Success

A

B

C

D

E

F

G

H

I

J

Match each equation with its graph.

1. $xy = 2$

2. $y = \log_2 x$

3. $y = x - 3$

4. $(x - 3)^2 + y^2 = 4$

5. $\dfrac{(x - 3)^2}{1} + \dfrac{y^2}{4} = 1$

6. $y = |x - 3|$

7. $y = (x - 3)^2$

8. $y = \dfrac{1}{x - 3}$

9. $y = 2^x$

10. $y = \sqrt{x - 3}$

Answers on page A-66

An additional, animated version of this activity appears in MyMathLab. To use MyMathLab, you need a course ID and a student access code. Contact your instructor for more information.

16.3 Exercise Set

Concept Reinforcement *Classify each of the following as an arithmetic sequence, a geometric sequence, an arithmetic series, a geometric series, or none of these.*

1. $2, 6, 18, 54, \ldots$

2. $3, 5, 7, 9, \ldots$

3. $1, 6, 11, 16, 21, \ldots$

4. $5, 15, 45, 135, 405, \ldots$

5. $4 + 20 + 100 + 500 + 2500 + 12{,}500$

6. $10 + 12 + 14 + 16 + 18 + 20$

7. $3 - \frac{3}{2} + \frac{3}{4} - \frac{3}{8} + \frac{3}{16} - \cdots$

8. $1 + \frac{1}{2} + \frac{1}{3} + \frac{1}{4} + \frac{1}{5} + \frac{1}{6} + \cdots$

Find the common ratio for each geometric sequence.

9. $10, 20, 40, 80, \ldots$

10. $5, 20, 80, 320, \ldots$

11. $6, -0.6, 0.06, -0.006, \ldots$

12. $-5, -0.5, -0.05, -0.005, \ldots$

13. $\frac{1}{2}, -\frac{1}{4}, \frac{1}{8}, -\frac{1}{16}, \ldots$

14. $\frac{2}{3}, -\frac{4}{3}, \frac{8}{3}, -\frac{16}{3}, \ldots$

15. $75, 15, 3, \frac{3}{5}, \ldots$

16. $12, -4, \frac{4}{3}, -\frac{4}{9}, \ldots$

17. $\frac{1}{m}, \frac{6}{m^2}, \frac{36}{m^3}, \frac{216}{m^4}, \ldots$

18. $4, \frac{4m}{5}, \frac{4m^2}{25}, \frac{4m^3}{125}, \ldots$

Find the indicated term for each geometric sequence.

19. $3, 6, 12, \ldots$; the 7th term

20. $2, 8, 32, \ldots$; the 9th term

21. $\sqrt{3}, 3, 3\sqrt{3}, \ldots$; the 10th term

22. $2, 2\sqrt{2}, 4, \ldots$; the 8th term

23. $-\frac{8}{243}, \frac{8}{81}, -\frac{8}{27}, \ldots$; the 14th term

24. $\frac{7}{625}, \frac{-7}{125}, \frac{7}{25}, \ldots$; the 13th term

25. $\$1000, \$1080, \$1166.40, \ldots$; the 12th term

26. $\$1000, \$1070, \$1144.90, \ldots$; the 11th term

Find the nth, or general, term for each geometric sequence.

27. $1, 5, 25, 125, \ldots$

28. $2, 4, 8, \ldots$

29. $1, -1, 1, -1, \ldots$

30. $\frac{1}{4}, \frac{1}{16}, \frac{1}{64}, \ldots$

31. $\frac{1}{x}, \frac{1}{x^2}, \frac{1}{x^3}, \ldots$

32. $5, \frac{5m}{2}, \frac{5m^2}{4}, \ldots$

For Exercises 33–40, use the formula for S_n to find the indicated sum for each geometric series.

33. S_9 for $6 + 12 + 24 + \cdots$

34. S_6 for $16 - 8 + 4 - \cdots$

35. S_7 for $\frac{1}{18} - \frac{1}{6} + \frac{1}{2} - \cdots$

Aha! 36. S_5 for $7 + 0.7 + 0.07 + \cdots$

37. S_8 for $1 + x + x^2 + x^3 + \cdots$

38. S_{10} for $1 + x^2 + x^4 + x^6 + \cdots$

39. S_{16} for $\$200 + \$200(1.06) + \$200(1.06)^2 + \cdots$

40. S_{23} for $\$1000 + \$1000(1.08) + \$1000(1.08)^2 + \cdots$

Determine whether each infinite geometric series has a limit. If a limit exists, find it.

41. $18 + 6 + 2 + \cdots$

42. $80 + 20 + 5 + \cdots$

43. $7 + 3 + \frac{9}{7} + \cdots$

44. $12 + 9 + \frac{27}{4} + \cdots$

45. $3 + 15 + 75 + \cdots$

46. $2 + 3 + \frac{9}{2} + \cdots$

47. $4 - 6 + 9 - \frac{27}{2} + \cdots$

48. $-6 + 3 - \frac{3}{2} + \frac{3}{4} - \cdots$

49. $0.43 + 0.0043 + 0.000043 + \cdots$

50. $0.37 + 0.0037 + 0.000037 + \cdots$

51. $\$500(1.02)^{-1} + \$500(1.02)^{-2} + \$500(1.02)^{-3} + \cdots$

52. $\$1000(1.08)^{-1} + \$1000(1.08)^{-2} + \$1000(1.08)^{-3} + \cdots$

Find fraction notation for each infinite sum. (Each can be regarded as an infinite geometric series.)

53. 0.7777...

54. 0.2222...

55. 8.3838...

56. 7.4747...

57. 0.15151515...

58. 0.12121212...

Solve. Use a calculator as needed for evaluating formulas.

59. *Rebound Distance.*   A ping-pong ball is dropped from a height of 20 ft and always rebounds one-fourth of the distance fallen. How high does it rebound the 6th time?

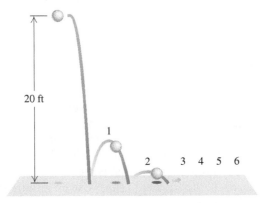

20 ft

1

2   3   4   5   6

60. *Rebound Distance.*   Approximate the total of the rebound heights of the ball in Exercise 59.

61. *Population Growth.*   Yorktown has a current population of 100,000, and the population is increasing by 3% each year. What will the population be in 15 years?

62. *Amount Owed.*   Gilberto borrows $15,000. The loan is to be repaid in 13 years at 8.5% interest, compounded annually. How much will be repaid at the end of 13 years?

63. *Shrinking Population.*   A population of 5000 fruit flies is dying off at a rate of 4% per minute. How many flies will be alive after 15 min?

64. *Shrinking Population.*   For the population of fruit flies in Exercise 63, how long will it take for only 1800 fruit flies to remain alive? (*Hint*: Use logarithms.) Round to the nearest minute.

65. *Food Service.*   Approximately 17 billion espresso-based coffees were sold in the United States in 2007. This number is expected to grow by 4% each year.

How many espresso-based coffees will be sold from 2007 through 2015?
Source: Based on data in the *Indianapolis Star*, 11/22/07

66. *Text Messaging.*   Approximately 160 billion text messages were sent worldwide in 2000. Since then, the number of text messages sent each year has grown by about 33% per year. How many text messages were sent worldwide from 2000 through 2010?
Sources: Based on data from mobilesmsmarketing.com and Global-Key Telecoms

67. *Rebound Distance.*   A superball dropped from the top of the Washington Monument (556 ft high) rebounds three-fourths of the distance fallen. How far (up and down) will the ball have traveled when it hits the ground for the 6th time?

68. *Rebound Distance.*   Approximate the total distance that the ball of Exercise 67 will have traveled when it comes to rest.

69. *Stacking Paper.*   Construction paper is about 0.02 in. thick. Beginning with just one piece, a stack is doubled again and again 10 times. Find the height of the final stack.

70. *Monthly Earnings.*   Suppose you accepted a job for the month of February (28 days) under the following conditions. You will be paid $0.01 the first day, $0.02 the second, $0.04 the third, and so on, doubling your previous day's salary each day. How much would you earn?

In Exercises 71–76, state whether the graph is that of an arithmetic sequence or a geometric sequence.

71.

72.

73.

74.

75.

76.

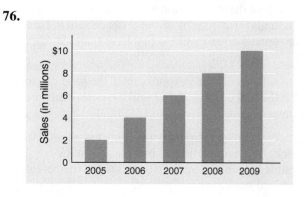

Aha!
TW **77.** Under what circumstances is it possible for the 5th term of a geometric sequence to be greater than the 4th term but less than the 7th term?

TW **78.** When r is negative, a series is said to be *alternating*. Why do you suppose this terminology is used?

SKILL REVIEW

To prepare for Section 16.4, review products of binomials.
Multiply.

79. $(x + y)^2$ **80.** $(x + y)^3$

81. $(x - y)^3$ **82.** $(x - y)^4$

83. $(2x + y)^3$ **84.** $(2x - y)^3$

SYNTHESIS

85. Using Example 5 and Exercises 41–52, explain how the graph of a geometric sequence can be used to determine whether a geometric series has a limit.

TW **86.** The infinite series

$$S_\infty = 2 + \frac{1}{2} + \frac{1}{2 \cdot 3} + \frac{1}{2 \cdot 3 \cdot 4}$$
$$+ \frac{1}{2 \cdot 3 \cdot 4 \cdot 5} + \frac{1}{2 \cdot 3 \cdot 4 \cdot 5 \cdot 6} + \cdots$$

is not geometric, but it does have a sum. Using $S_1, S_2, S_3, S_4, S_5,$ and S_6, make a conjecture about the value of S_∞ and explain your reasoning.

Calculate each of the following sums.

87. $\displaystyle\sum_{k=1}^{\infty} 6(0.9)^k$ **88.** $\displaystyle\sum_{k=1}^{\infty} 5(-0.7)^k$

89. Find the sum of the first n terms of
$$x^2 - x^3 + x^4 - x^5 + \cdots.$$

90. Find the sum of the first n terms of
$$1 + x + x^2 + x^3 + \cdots.$$

91. The sides of a square are each 16 cm long. A second square is inscribed by joining the midpoints of the sides, successively. In the second square, we repeat the process, inscribing a third square. If this process is continued indefinitely, what is the sum of all of the areas of all the squares? (*Hint*: Use an infinite geometric series.)

92. Show that $0.999 \ldots$ is 1.

Bargaining for a Used Car

Focus: Geometric series
Time: 30 minutes
Group size: 2
Materials: Graphing calculators are optional.

ACTIVITY *

1. One group member ("the seller") has a car for sale and is asking $3500. The second ("the buyer") offers $1500. The seller splits the difference ($2000 ÷ 2 = $1000) and lowers the price to $2500. The buyer then splits the difference again ($1000 ÷ 2 = $500) and counters with $2000. Continue in this manner and stop when you are able to agree on the car's selling price to the nearest penny.

2. What should the buyer's initial offer be in order to achieve a purchase price of $2000? (Check several guesses to find the appropriate initial offer.)

_____

*This activity is based on the article "Bargaining Theory, or Zeno's Used Cars," by James C. Kirby, *The College Mathematics Journal*, **27**(4), September 1996.

3. The seller's price in the bargaining above can be modeled recursively (see Exercises 99, 100, and 108 in Section 16.1) by the sequence

$$a_1 = 3500, \qquad a_n = a_{n-1} - \frac{d}{2^{2n-3}},$$

where d is the difference between the initial price and the first offer. Use this recursively defined sequence to solve parts (1) and (2) above either manually or by using the SEQ MODE and the TABLE feature of a graphing calculator.

4. The first four terms in the sequence in part (3) can be written as

$$a_1, \qquad a_1 - \frac{d}{2}, \qquad a_1 - \frac{d}{2} - \frac{d}{8},$$

$$a_1 - \frac{d}{2} - \frac{d}{8} - \frac{d}{32}.$$

Use the formula for the limit of an infinite geometric series to find a simple algebraic formula for the eventual sale price, P, when the bargaining process from above is followed. Verify the formula by using it to solve parts (1) and (2) above.

Mid-Chapter Review

A *sequence* is simply an ordered list. *Arithmetic* sequences and *geometric* sequences have formulas for general terms and for sums.

Arithmetic Sequences

$$a_n = a_1 + (n-1)d;$$

$$S_n = \frac{n}{2}(a_1 + a_n)$$

Geometric Sequences

$$a_n = a_1 r^{n-1};$$

$$S_n = \frac{a_1(1 - r^n)}{1 - r};$$

$$S_\infty = \frac{a_1}{1 - r}, |r| < 1$$

GUIDED SOLUTIONS

1. Find the 14th term of the arithmetic sequence $-6, -1, 4, 9, \ldots$.

Solution

$$a_n = a_1 + (n-1)d$$

$$n = \boxed{}, \qquad a_1 = \boxed{}, \qquad d = \boxed{}$$

$$a_{14} = \boxed{} + (\boxed{} - 1)\boxed{}$$

$$a_{14} = \boxed{}$$

2. Find the 7th term of the geometric sequence $\frac{1}{9}, -\frac{1}{3}, 1, -3, \ldots$.

Solution

$$a_n = a_1 r^{n-1}$$

$$n = \boxed{}, \qquad a_1 = \boxed{}, \qquad r = \boxed{}$$

$$a_7 = \boxed{} \cdot (\boxed{})^{\boxed{}-1}$$

$$a_7 = \boxed{}$$

MIXED REVIEW

1. Find a_{20} if $a_n = n^2 - 5n$. [16.1]

2. Write an expression for the general term a_n of the sequence $\frac{1}{2}, \frac{1}{3}, \frac{1}{4}, \frac{1}{5}, \ldots$. [16.1]

3. Find S_{12} for the sequence $1, 2, 3, 4, \ldots$. [16.1]

4. Write out and evaluate the sum

$$\sum_{k=2}^{5} k^2.$$ [16.1]

5. Rewrite using sigma notation:

$$1 - 2 + 3 - 4 + 5 - 6.$$ [16.1]

6. Find the common difference for the arithmetic sequence $115, 112, 109, 106, \ldots$. [16.2]

7. Find the 21st term of the arithmetic sequence $10, 15, 20, 25, \ldots$. [16.2]

8. Which term is 22 in the arithmetic sequence $10, 10.2, 10.4, 10.6, \ldots$? [16.2]

9. For an arithmetic sequence, find a_{25} when $a_1 = 9$ and $d = -2$. [16.2]

10. For an arithmetic sequence, find a_1 when $d = 11$ and $a_5 = 65$. [16.2]

11. For an arithmetic sequence, find n when $a_1 = 5$, $d = -\frac{1}{2}$, and $a_n = 0$. [16.2]

12. Find S_{30} for the arithmetic series $2 + 12 + 22 + 32 + \cdots$. [16.2]

13. Find the common ratio for the geometric sequence $\frac{1}{3}, -\frac{1}{6}, \frac{1}{12}, -\frac{1}{24}, \ldots$. [16.3]

14. Find the 8th term of the geometric sequence $5, 10, 20, 40, \ldots$. [16.3]

15. Find the nth, or general, term for the geometric sequence $2, -2, 2, -2, \ldots$. [16.3]

16. Find S_{10} for the geometric series $\$100 + \$100(1.03) + \$100(1.03)^2 + \cdots$. [16.3]

17. Determine whether the infinite geometric series $0.9 + 0.09 + 0.009 + \cdots$ has a limit. If a limit exists, find it. [16.3]

18. Determine whether the infinite geometric series $0.9 + 9 + 90 + \cdots$ has a limit. If a limit exists, find it. [16.3]

19. Renata earns $1 on June 1, another $2 on June 2, another $3 on June 3, another $4 on June 4, and so on. How much does she earn during the 30 days of June? [16.2]

20. Dwight earns $1 on June 1, another $2 on June 2, another $4 on June 3, another $8 on June 4, and so on. How much does he earn during the 30 days of June? [16.3]

16.4 The Binomial Theorem

- Binomial Expansion Using Pascal's Triangle

- Binomial Expansion Using Factorial Notation

The expression $(x + y)^2$ may be regarded as a series: $x^2 + 2xy + y^2$. This sum of terms is the *expansion* of $(x + y)^2$. For powers greater than 2, finding the expansion of $(x + y)^n$ can be time-consuming. In this section, we look at two methods of streamlining binomial expansion.

BINOMIAL EXPANSION USING PASCAL'S TRIANGLE

Consider the following expanded powers of $(a + b)^n$:

$$
\begin{aligned}
(a + b)^0 &= 1\\
(a + b)^1 &= a + b\\
(a + b)^2 &= a^2 + 2a^1b^1 + b^2\\
(a + b)^3 &= a^3 + 3a^2b^1 + 3a^1b^2 + b^3\\
(a + b)^4 &= a^4 + 4a^3b^1 + 6a^2b^2 + 4a^1b^3 + b^4\\
(a + b)^5 &= a^5 + 5a^4b^1 + 10a^3b^2 + 10a^2b^3 + 5a^1b^4 + b^5.
\end{aligned}
$$

Each expansion is a polynomial. There are some patterns worth noting:

1. There is one more term than the power of the binomial, n. That is, there are $n + 1$ terms in the expansion of $(a + b)^n$.

2. In each term, the sum of the exponents is the power to which the binomial is raised.

3. The exponents of a start with n, the power of the binomial, and decrease to 0. (Since $a^0 = 1$, the last term has no factor of a.) The first term has no factor of b, so powers of b start with 0 and increase to n.

4. The coefficients start at 1, increase through certain values, and then decrease through these same values back to 1.

Let's study the coefficients further. Suppose we wish to expand $(a + b)^8$. The patterns we noticed above indicate 9 terms in the expansion:

$$a^8 + c_1a^7b + c_2a^6b^2 + c_3a^5b^3 + c_4a^4b^4 + c_5a^3b^5 + c_6a^2b^6 + c_7ab^7 + b^8.$$

How can we determine the values for the c's? One simple method involves writing down the coefficients in a triangular array as follows. We form what is known as **Pascal's triangle:**

$$
\begin{array}{lccccccccccc}
(a + b)^0: & & & & & & 1 & & & & &\\
(a + b)^1: & & & & & 1 & & 1 & & & &\\
(a + b)^2: & & & & 1 & & 2 & & 1 & & &\\
(a + b)^3: & & & 1 & & 3 & & 3 & & 1 & &\\
(a + b)^4: & & 1 & & 4 & & 6 & & 4 & & 1 &\\
(a + b)^5: & 1 & & 5 & & 10 & & 10 & & 5 & & 1
\end{array}
$$

There are many patterns in the triangle. Find as many as you can.

Perhaps you discovered a way to write the next row of numbers, given the numbers in the row above it. There are always 1's on the outside. Each remaining number is the sum of the two numbers above:

We see that in the bottom (seventh) row

the 1st and last numbers are 1;

the 2nd number is $1 + 5$, or 6;

the 3rd number is $5 + 10$, or 15;

the 4th number is $10 + 10$, or 20;

the 5th number is $10 + 5$, or 15; and

the 6th number is $5 + 1$, or 6.

Thus the expansion of $(a + b)^6$ is

$$(a + b)^6 = 1a^6 + 6a^5b + 15a^4b^2 + 20a^3b^3 + 15a^2b^4 + 6ab^5 + 1b^6.$$

To expand $(a + b)^8$, we complete two more rows of Pascal's triangle:

$$
\begin{array}{ccccccccccccccccc}
 & & & & & & & & 1 & & & & & & & & \\
 & & & & & & & 1 & & 1 & & & & & & & \\
 & & & & & & 1 & & 2 & & 1 & & & & & & \\
 & & & & & 1 & & 3 & & 3 & & 1 & & & & & \\
 & & & & 1 & & 4 & & 6 & & 4 & & 1 & & & & \\
 & & & 1 & & 5 & & 10 & & 10 & & 5 & & 1 & & & \\
 & & 1 & & 6 & & 15 & & 20 & & 15 & & 6 & & 1 & & \\
 & 1 & & 7 & & 21 & & 35 & & 35 & & 21 & & 7 & & 1 & \\
1 & & 8 & & 28 & & 56 & & 70 & & 56 & & 28 & & 8 & & 1 \\
\end{array}
$$

Thus the expansion of $(a + b)^8$ has coefficients found in the 9th row above:

$$(a + b)^8 = 1a^8 + 8a^7b + 28a^6b^2 + 56a^5b^3 + 70a^4b^4 + 56a^3b^5 + 28a^2b^6 + 8ab^7 + 1b^8.$$

We can generalize our results as follows:

The Binomial Theorem (Form 1)   For any binomial $a + b$ and any natural number n,

$$(a + b)^n = c_0a^nb^0 + c_1a^{n-1}b^1 + c_2a^{n-2}b^2 + \cdots + c_{n-1}a^1b^{n-1} + c_na^0b^n,$$

where the numbers $c_0, c_1, c_2, \ldots, c_n$ are from the $(n + 1)$st row of Pascal's triangle.

EXAMPLE 1 Expand: $(u - v)^5$.

SOLUTION   Using the binomial theorem, we have $a = u, b = -v$, and $n = 5$. We use the 6th row of Pascal's triangle: 1   5   10   10   5   1. Thus,

$$(u - v)^5 = [u + (-v)]^5 \quad \text{Rewriting } u - v \text{ as a sum}$$
$$= 1(u)^5 + 5(u)^4(-v)^1 + 10(u)^3(-v)^2 + 10(u)^2(-v)^3$$
$$+ 5(u)^1(-v)^4 + 1(-v)^5$$
$$= u^5 - 5u^4v + 10u^3v^2 - 10u^2v^3 + 5uv^4 - v^5.$$

Note that the signs of the terms alternate between $+$ and $-$. When $-v$ is raised to an odd exponent, the sign is $-$; when the exponent is even, the sign is $+$.

Try Exercise 25.

EXAMPLE 2 Expand: $\left(2t + \dfrac{3}{t}\right)^6$.

SOLUTION   Note that $a = 2t, b = 3/t$, and $n = 6$. We use the 7th row of Pascal's triangle: 1   6   15   20   15   6   1. Thus,

$$\left(2t + \frac{3}{t}\right)^6 = 1(2t)^6 + 6(2t)^5\left(\frac{3}{t}\right)^1 + 15(2t)^4\left(\frac{3}{t}\right)^2 + 20(2t)^3\left(\frac{3}{t}\right)^3$$
$$+ 15(2t)^2\left(\frac{3}{t}\right)^4 + 6(2t)^1\left(\frac{3}{t}\right)^5 + 1\left(\frac{3}{t}\right)^6$$
$$= 64t^6 + 6(32t^5)\left(\frac{3}{t}\right) + 15(16t^4)\left(\frac{9}{t^2}\right) + 20(8t^3)\left(\frac{27}{t^3}\right)$$
$$+ 15(4t^2)\left(\frac{81}{t^4}\right) + 6(2t)\left(\frac{243}{t^5}\right) + \frac{729}{t^6}$$
$$= 64t^6 + 576t^4 + 2160t^2 + 4320 + 4860t^{-2} + 2916t^{-4}$$
$$+ 729t^{-6}.$$

Try Exercise 35.

BINOMIAL EXPANSION USING FACTORIAL NOTATION

The drawback to using Pascal's triangle is that we must compute all the preceding rows in the table to obtain the row we need. The following method avoids this difficulty. It will also enable us to find a specific term—say, the 8th term—without computing all the other terms in the expansion.

To develop the method, we need some new notation. Products of successive natural numbers, such as $6 \cdot 5 \cdot 4 \cdot 3 \cdot 2 \cdot 1$ and $8 \cdot 7 \cdot 6 \cdot 5 \cdot 4 \cdot 3 \cdot 2 \cdot 1$, have a special notation. For the product $6 \cdot 5 \cdot 4 \cdot 3 \cdot 2 \cdot 1$, we write 6!, read "6 factorial."

Factorial Notation   For any natural number n,
$$n! = n(n - 1)(n - 2) \cdots (3)(2)(1).$$

Here are some examples:

$$6! = 6 \cdot 5 \cdot 4 \cdot 3 \cdot 2 \cdot 1 = 720,$$
$$5! = 5 \cdot 4 \cdot 3 \cdot 2 \cdot 1 = 120,$$
$$4! = 4 \cdot 3 \cdot 2 \cdot 1 = 24,$$
$$3! = 3 \cdot 2 \cdot 1 = 6,$$
$$2! = 2 \cdot 1 = 2,$$
$$1! = 1 = 1.$$

We also define $0!$ to be 1 for reasons explained shortly.

To simplify expressions like

$$\frac{8!}{5! \, 3!},$$

note that

$$8! = 8 \cdot 7 \cdot 6 \cdot 5 \cdot 4 \cdot 3 \cdot 2 \cdot 1 = 8 \cdot 7! = 8 \cdot 7 \cdot 6! = 8 \cdot 7 \cdot 6 \cdot 5!$$

and so on.

CAUTION! $\dfrac{6!}{3!} \neq 2!$ To see this, note that

$$\frac{6!}{3!} = \frac{6 \cdot 5 \cdot 4 \cdot 3 \cdot 2 \cdot 1}{3 \cdot 2 \cdot 1} = 6 \cdot 5 \cdot 4.$$

Student Notes

It is important to recognize that factorial notation represents a product with descending factors. Thus, $7!$, $7 \cdot 6!$, and $7 \cdot 6 \cdot 5!$ all represent the same product.

EXAMPLE 3 Simplify: $\dfrac{8!}{5! \, 3!}$.

SOLUTION

$$\frac{8!}{5! \, 3!} = \frac{8 \cdot 7 \cdot 6 \cdot 5!}{5! \cdot 3 \cdot 2 \cdot 1} = 8 \cdot 7 \qquad \text{Removing a factor equal to 1:}$$
$$\frac{6 \cdot 5!}{5! \cdot 3 \cdot 2} = 1$$
$$= 56$$

Try Exercise 15.

The following notation is used in our second formulation of the binomial theorem.

$\dbinom{n}{r}$ Notation   For n, r nonnegative integers with $n \geq r$,

$$\binom{n}{r}, \quad \text{read "n choose r,"} \quad \text{means} \quad \frac{n!}{(n-r)! \, r!}.^*$$

---

*In many books and for many calculators, the notation $_nC_r$ is used instead of $\dbinom{n}{r}$.

EXAMPLE 4 Simplify: **(a)** $\begin{pmatrix} 7 \\ 2 \end{pmatrix}$; **(b)** $\begin{pmatrix} 9 \\ 6 \end{pmatrix}$; **(c)** $\begin{pmatrix} 6 \\ 6 \end{pmatrix}$.

SOLUTION

a) $\begin{pmatrix} 7 \\ 2 \end{pmatrix} = \dfrac{7!}{(7-2)!\,2!}$

$\qquad = \dfrac{7!}{5!\,2!} = \dfrac{7 \cdot 6 \cdot 5!}{5! \cdot 2 \cdot 1} = \dfrac{7 \cdot 6}{2}$ Writing 7! as $7 \cdot 6 \cdot 5!$ to help with simplification

$\qquad = 7 \cdot 3$

$\qquad = 21$

b) $\begin{pmatrix} 9 \\ 6 \end{pmatrix} = \dfrac{9!}{3!\,6!}$

$\qquad = \dfrac{9 \cdot 8 \cdot 7 \cdot 6!}{3 \cdot 2 \cdot 1 \cdot 6!} = \dfrac{9 \cdot 8 \cdot 7}{3 \cdot 2}$ Writing 9! as $9 \cdot 8 \cdot 7 \cdot 6!$

$\qquad = 3 \cdot 4 \cdot 7$

$\qquad = 84$

c) $\begin{pmatrix} 6 \\ 6 \end{pmatrix} = \dfrac{6!}{0!\,6!} = \dfrac{6!}{1 \cdot 6!}$ Since $0! = 1$

$\qquad = \dfrac{6!}{6!}$

$\qquad = 1$

Try Exercise 17.

Factorials and $\begin{pmatrix} n \\ r \end{pmatrix}$

The PRB submenu of the MATH menu provides access to both factorial calculations and $\begin{pmatrix} n \\ r \end{pmatrix}$, or $_nC_r$. In both cases, a number is entered on the home screen before the option is accessed.

To find 7!, press $\boxed{7}$, select option 4: ! from the MATH PRB menu, and press $\boxed{\text{ENTER}}$.

To find $\begin{pmatrix} 9 \\ 2 \end{pmatrix}$, press $\boxed{9}$, select option 3: nCr from the MATH PRB menu, press $\boxed{2}$, and then press $\boxed{\text{ENTER}}$.

The screen on the left below shows the options listed in the MATH PRB menu. From the screen on the right below, note that $7! = 5040$ and $\begin{pmatrix} 9 \\ 2 \end{pmatrix} = {}_9C_2 = 36$.

```
MATH NUM CPX PRB
1: rand
2: nPr
3: nCr
4: !
5: randInt(
6: randNorm(
7: randBin(
```

```
7!
                    5040
9 nCr 2
                      36
```

(continued)

Your Turn

1. Find 9! by pressing ⑨ **MATH** ⟩ ⟩ ⟩ ④ **ENTER**.   362,800

2. Find $\binom{7}{4}$ by pressing ⑦ **MATH** ⟩ ⟩ ⟩ ③ ④ **ENTER**.   35

3. The value of $n!$ increases rapidly as n increases. By trial and error, find the highest value of $n!$ that your calculator can compute.

Now we can restate the binomial theorem using our new notation.

The Binomial Theorem (Form 2)   For any binomial $a + b$ and any natural number n,

$$(a + b)^n = \binom{n}{0}a^n + \binom{n}{1}a^{n-1}b + \binom{n}{2}a^{n-2}b^2 + \cdots + \binom{n}{n}b^n.$$

EXAMPLE 5   Expand: $(3x + y)^4$.

SOLUTION   We use the binomial theorem (Form 2) with $a = 3x, b = y$, and $n = 4$:

$$(3x + y)^4 = \binom{4}{0}(3x)^4 + \binom{4}{1}(3x)^3 y + \binom{4}{2}(3x)^2 y^2 + \binom{4}{3}(3x)y^3 + \binom{4}{4}y^4$$

$$= \frac{4!}{4!\,0!}3^4 x^4 + \frac{4!}{3!\,1!}3^3 x^3 y + \frac{4!}{2!\,2!}3^2 x^2 y^2 + \frac{4!}{1!\,3!}3xy^3 + \frac{4!}{0!\,4!}y^4$$

$$= 81x^4 + 108x^3 y + 54x^2 y^2 + 12xy^3 + y^4. \qquad \text{Simplifying}$$

Try Exercise 29.

EXAMPLE 6   Expand: $(x^2 - 2y)^5$.

SOLUTION   In this case, $a = x^2, b = -2y$, and $n = 5$:

$$(x^2 - 2y)^5 = \binom{5}{0}(x^2)^5 + \binom{5}{1}(x^2)^4(-2y) + \binom{5}{2}(x^2)^3(-2y)^2$$

$$+ \binom{5}{3}(x^2)^2(-2y)^3 + \binom{5}{4}(x^2)(-2y)^4 + \binom{5}{5}(-2y)^5$$

$$= \frac{5!}{5!\,0!}x^{10} + \frac{5!}{4!\,1!}x^8(-2y) + \frac{5!}{3!\,2!}x^6(-2y)^2 + \frac{5!}{2!\,3!}x^4(-2y)^3$$

$$+ \frac{5!}{1!\,4!}x^2(-2y)^4 + \frac{5!}{0!\,5!}(-2y)^5$$

$$= x^{10} - 10x^8 y + 40x^6 y^2 - 80x^4 y^3 + 80x^2 y^4 - 32y^5.$$

Try Exercise 37.

Note that in the binomial theorem (Form 2), $\binom{n}{0}a^n b^0$ gives us the first term, $\binom{n}{1}a^{n-1}b^1$ gives us the second term, $\binom{n}{2}a^{n-2}b^2$ gives us the third term, and so on.

This can be generalized to give a method for finding a specific term without writing the entire expansion.

> **Finding a Specific Term**   When $(a + b)^n$ is expanded and written in descending powers of a, the $(r + 1)$st term is
>
> $$\binom{n}{r} a^{n-r}b^r.$$

EXAMPLE 7   Find the 5th term in the expansion of $(2x - 3y)^7$.

SOLUTION   First, we note that $5 = 4 + 1$. Thus, $r = 4, a = 2x, b = -3y$, and $n = 7$. Then the 5th term of the expansion is

$$\binom{n}{r} a^{n-r}b^r = \binom{7}{4}(2x)^{7-4}(-3y)^4, \quad \text{or} \quad \frac{7!}{3!\,4!}(2x)^3(-3y)^4, \quad \text{or} \quad 22{,}680x^3y^4.$$

■ Try Exercise 45.

It is because of the binomial theorem that $\binom{n}{r}$ is called a *binomial coefficient*.

We can now explain why 0! is defined to be 1. In the binomial expansion, $\binom{n}{0}$ must equal 1 using the definition $\binom{n}{r} = \dfrac{n!}{(n - r)!\,r!}$. Thus we must have

$$\binom{n}{0} = \frac{n!}{(n - 0)!\,0!} = \frac{n!}{n!\,0!} = 1.$$

This is satisfied only if 0! is defined to be 1.

16.4   Exercise Set

↪ *Concept Reinforcement*   *Complete each of the following statements.*

1. The last term in the expansion of $(x + 2)^5$ is
   _____ .

2. The expansion of $(x + y)^7$, when simplified, contains a total of _____ terms.

3. In the expansion of $(a + b)^9$, the exponents in each term add to _____ .

4. The expression _____ represents $4 \cdot 3 \cdot 2 \cdot 1$.

5. The expression _____ represents $\dfrac{8!}{3!\,5!}$.

6. In the expansion of $(a + b)^{10}$, the coefficient of b^{10} is _____ .

7. In the expansion of $(x + y)^9$, the coefficient of x^2y^7 is the same as the coefficient of _____ .

8. The notation $\binom{10}{4}$ is read _____ .

Simplify.

9. $4!$

10. $8!$

11. $11!$

12. $10!$

13. $\dfrac{8!}{6!}$

14. $\dfrac{7!}{4!}$

15. $\dfrac{9!}{4!\,5!}$

16. $\dfrac{10!}{6!\,4!}$

17. $\dbinom{7}{4}$

18. $\dbinom{8}{2}$

Aha! **19.** $\dbinom{9}{9}$

20. $\dbinom{7}{7}$

21. $\dbinom{30}{2}$

22. $\dbinom{51}{49}$

23. $\dbinom{40}{38}$

24. $\dbinom{35}{2}$

Expand. Use both of the methods shown in this section.

25. $(a-b)^4$

26. $(m+n)^5$

27. $(p+q)^7$

28. $(x-y)^6$

29. $(3c-d)^7$

30. $(x^2-3y)^5$

31. $(t^{-2}+2)^6$

32. $(3c-d)^6$

33. $(x-y)^5$

34. $(x-y)^3$

35. $\left(3s+\dfrac{1}{t}\right)^9$

36. $\left(x+\dfrac{2}{y}\right)^9$

37. $(x^3-2y)^5$

38. $(a^2-b^3)^5$

39. $\left(\sqrt{5}+t\right)^6$

40. $\left(\sqrt{3}-t\right)^4$

41. $\left(\dfrac{1}{\sqrt{x}}-\sqrt{x}\right)^6$

42. $(x^{-2}+x^2)^4$

Find the indicated term for each binomial expression.

43. 3rd, $(a+b)^6$

44. 6th, $(x+y)^7$

45. 12th, $(a-3)^{14}$

46. 11th, $(x-2)^{12}$

47. 5th, $\left(2x^3+\sqrt{y}\right)^8$

48. 4th, $\left(\dfrac{1}{b^2}+c\right)^7$

49. Middle, $(2u+3v^2)^{10}$

50. Middle two, $\left(\sqrt{x}+\sqrt{3}\right)^5$

Aha! **51.** 9th, $(x-y)^8$

52. 13th, $\left(a-\sqrt{b}\right)^{12}$

TW **53.** Maya claims that she can calculate mentally the first two and the last two terms of the expansion of $(a+b)^n$ for any whole number n. How do you think she does this?

TW **54.** Without performing any calculations, explain why the expansions of $(x-y)^8$ and $(y-x)^8$ must be equal.

SKILL REVIEW

Review graphing equations and inequalities.
Graph.

55. $y=x^2-5$ [13.7]

56. $y=x-5$

57. $y\ge x-5$ [11.4]

58. $y=5^x$ [14.2]

59. $f(x)=\log_5 x$ [14.3]

60. $x^2+y^2=5$ [15.1]

SYNTHESIS

TW **61.** Explain how someone can determine the x^2-term of the expansion of $\left(x-\dfrac{3}{x}\right)^{10}$ without calculating any other terms.

TW **62.** Devise two problems requiring the use of the binomial theorem. Design the problems so that one is solved more easily using Form 1 and the other is solved more easily using Form 2. Then explain what makes one form easier to use than the other in each case.

63. Show that there are exactly $\dbinom{5}{3}$ ways of choosing a subset of size 3 from $\{a,b,c,d,e\}$.

64. *Baseball.* During the 2009 season, Hanley Ramirez of the Florida Marlins had a batting average of 0.342. In that season, if someone were to randomly select 5 of his "at-bats," the probability of Ramirez getting exactly 3 hits would be the 3rd term of the binomial expansion of $(0.342+0.658)^5$. Find that term and use a calculator to estimate the probability.

65. *Widows or Divorcees.* The probability that a woman will be either widowed or divorced is 85%. If 8 women are randomly selected, the probability that exactly 5 of them will be either widowed or divorced is the 6th term of the binomial expansion of $(0.15+0.85)^8$. Use a calculator to estimate that probability.

66. *Baseball.* In reference to Exercise 64, the probability that Ramirez will get *at most* 3 hits is found by adding the last 4 terms of the binomial expansion of $(0.342+0.658)^5$. Find these terms and use a calculator to estimate the probability.

67. *Widows or Divorcees.*   In reference to Exercise 65, the probability that *at least* 6 of the women will be widowed or divorced is found by adding the last three terms of the binomial expansion of $(0.15 + 0.85)^8$. Find these terms and use a calculator to estimate the probability.

68. Find the term of

$$\left(\frac{3x^2}{2} - \frac{1}{3x}\right)^{12}$$

that does not contain x.

69. Prove that

$$\binom{n}{r} = \binom{n}{n - r}$$

for any whole numbers n and r. Assume $r \leq n$.

70. Find the middle term of $(x^2 - 6y^{3/2})^6$.

71. Find the ratio of the 4th term of

$$\left(p^2 - \frac{1}{2}p\sqrt[3]{q}\right)^5$$

to the 3rd term.

72. Find the term containing $\dfrac{1}{x^{1/6}}$ of

$$\left(\sqrt[3]{x} - \frac{1}{\sqrt{x}}\right)^7.$$

Aha! **73.** Multiply:

$$(x^2 + 2xy + y^2)(x^2 + 2xy + y^2)^2(x + y).$$

74. What is the degree of $(x^3 + 2)^4$?

Try Exercise Answers: Section 16.4

15. 126   **17.** 35   **25.** $a^4 - 4a^3b + 6a^2b^2 - 4ab^3 + b^4$
29. $2187c^7 - 5103c^6d + 5103c^5d^2 - 2835c^4d^3 + 945c^3d^4 - 189c^2d^5 + 21cd^6 - d^7$
35. $19{,}683s^9 + \dfrac{59{,}049s^8}{t} + \dfrac{78{,}732s^7}{t^2} + \dfrac{61{,}236s^6}{t^3} + \dfrac{30{,}618s^5}{t^4} + \dfrac{10{,}206s^4}{t^5} + \dfrac{2268s^3}{t^6} + \dfrac{324s^2}{t^7} + \dfrac{27s}{t^8} + \dfrac{1}{t^9}$
37. $x^{15} - 10x^{12}y + 40x^9y^2 - 80x^6y^3 + 80x^3y^4 - 32y^5$
45. $-64{,}481{,}508a^3$

Study Summary

KEY TERMS AND CONCEPTS	EXAMPLES	PRACTICE EXERCISES

SECTION 16.1: SEQUENCES AND SERIES

The **general term** of a sequence is written a_n.

The sum of the first n terms of a sequence is written S_n.

Find a_{10} if $a_n = 3n - 7$.
$$a_{10} = 3 \cdot 10 - 7 = 30 - 7 = 23$$

Find S_6 for the sequence $-1, 2, -4, 8, -16, 32, -64$.
$$S_6 = -1 + 2 + (-4) + 8 + (-16) + 32 = 21$$

1. Find a_{12} if $a_n = n^2 - 1$.

2. Find S_5 for the sequence $-9, -8, -6, -3, 1, 6, 12$.

Sigma or **Summation Notation**

k is the **index of summation**

$$\sum_{k=3}^{5} (-1)^k (k^2) = (-1)^3 (3^2) \quad \text{For } k = 3$$
$$+ (-1)^4 (4^2) \quad \text{For } k = 4$$
$$+ (-1)^5 (5^2) \quad \text{For } k = 5$$
$$= -1 \cdot 9 + 1 \cdot 16$$
$$+ (-1) \cdot 25$$
$$= -9 + 16 - 25 = -18$$

3. Write out and evaluate the sum:
$$\sum_{k=0}^{3} 5k.$$

SECTION 16.2: ARITHMETIC SEQUENCES AND SERIES

Arithmetic Sequences and Series

$a_{n+1} = a_n + d$ d is the **common difference.**

$a_n = a_1 + (n-1)d$ The nth term

$S_n = \dfrac{n}{2}(a_1 + a_n)$ The sum of the first n terms

For the arithmetic sequence $10, 7, 4, 1, \ldots$:
$$d = -3;$$
$$a_7 = 10 + (7-1)(-3) = 10 - 18 = -8;$$
$$S_7 = \frac{7}{2}(10 + (-8)) = \frac{7}{2}(2) = 7.$$

4. Find the 20th term of the arithmetic sequence
$$6, 6.5, 7, 7.5, \ldots.$$

5. Find S_{20} for the arithmetic series
$$6 + 6.5 + 7 + 7.5 + \cdots.$$

SECTION 16.3: GEOMETRIC SEQUENCES AND SERIES

Geometric Sequences and Series

$a_{n+1} = a_n \cdot r$ r is the **common ratio.**

$a_n = a_1 r^{n-1}$ The nth term

$S_n = \dfrac{a_1(1 - r^n)}{1 - r}, r \neq 1$ The sum of the first n terms

$S_\infty = \dfrac{a_1}{1 - r}, |r| < 1$ Limit of an infinite geometric series

For the geometric sequence $25, -5, 1, -\frac{1}{5}, \ldots$:
$$r = -\frac{1}{5};$$
$$a_7 = 25\left(-\frac{1}{5}\right)^{7-1} = 5^2 \cdot \frac{1}{5^6} = \frac{1}{625};$$
$$S_7 = \frac{25\left(1 - \left(-\frac{1}{5}\right)^7\right)}{1 - \left(-\frac{1}{5}\right)} = \frac{5^2\left(\frac{78,126}{5^7}\right)}{\frac{6}{5}}$$
$$= \frac{13,021}{625};$$
$$S_\infty = \frac{25}{1 - \left(-\frac{1}{5}\right)} = \frac{125}{6}.$$

6. Find the 8th term of the geometric sequence
$$-5, -10, -20, \ldots.$$

7. Find S_{12} for the geometric series
$$-5 - 10 - 20 - \cdots.$$

8. Find S_∞ for the geometric series
$$20 - 5 + \left(\frac{5}{4}\right) + \cdots.$$

SECTION 16.4: THE BINOMIAL THEOREM

Factorial Notation

$n! = n(n-1)(n-2)\cdots 3\cdot 2\cdot 1$

$7! = 7\cdot 6\cdot 5\cdot 4\cdot 3\cdot 2\cdot 1 = 5040$

9. Simplify: $11!$.

Binomial Coefficient

$\dbinom{n}{r} = {}_nC_r = \dfrac{n!}{(n-r)!\,r!}$

$\dbinom{10}{3} = {}_{10}C_3 = \dfrac{10!}{7!3!} = \dfrac{10\cdot 9\cdot 8\cdot 7!}{7!\cdot 3\cdot 2\cdot 1} = 120$

10. Simplify: $\dbinom{9}{3}$.

Binomial Theorem

$(a+b)^n = \dbinom{n}{0}a^n + \dbinom{n}{1}a^{n-1}b$

$\qquad + \cdots + \dbinom{n}{n}b^n$

$(1-2x)^3 = \dbinom{3}{0}1^3 + \dbinom{3}{1}1^2(-2x)$

$\qquad + \dbinom{3}{2}1(-2x)^2 + \dbinom{3}{3}(-2x)^3$

$\qquad = 1\cdot 1 + 3\cdot 1(-2x)$

$\qquad\quad + 3\cdot 1\cdot (4x^2) + 1\cdot (-8x^3)$

$\qquad = 1 - 6x + 12x^2 - 8x^3$

11. Expand: $(x^2-2)^5$.

$(r+1)$st term of $(a+b)^n$: $\dbinom{n}{r}a^{n-r}b^r$

3rd term of $(1-2x)^3$:

$\dbinom{3}{2}(1)^1(-2x)^2 = 12x^2 \qquad r=2$

12. Find the 4th term of $(t+3)^{10}$.

Review Exercises

> *Concept Reinforcement* *Classify each of the following statements as either true or false.*

1. The next term in the arithmetic sequence $10, 15, 20, \ldots$ is 35. [16.2]

2. The next term in the geometric sequence $2, 6, 18, 54, \ldots$ is 162. [16.3]

3. $\displaystyle\sum_{k=1}^{3} k^2$ means $1^2 + 2^2 + 3^2$. [16.1]

4. If $a_n = 3n - 1$, then $a_{17} = 19$. [16.1]

5. A geometric sequence has a common difference. [16.3]

6. The infinite geometric series $10 - 5 + \frac{5}{2} - \cdots$ has a limit. [16.3]

7. For any natural number n, $n! = n(n-1)$. [16.4]

8. When simplified, the expansion of $(x+y)^{17}$ has 19 terms. [16.4]

Find the first four terms; the 8th term, a_8; and the 12th term, a_{12}. [16.1]

9. $a_n = 4n - 3$

10. $a_n = \dfrac{n-1}{n^2+1}$

Write an expression for the general term of each sequence. Answers may vary. [16.1]

11. $-5, -10, -15, -20, \ldots$

12. $-1, 3, -5, 7, -9, \ldots$

Write out and evaluate each sum. [16.1]

13. $\displaystyle\sum_{k=1}^{5} (-2)^k$

14. $\displaystyle\sum_{k=2}^{7} (1 - 2k)$

Rewrite using sigma notation. [16.1]

15. $4 + 8 + 12 + 16 + 20$

16. $\dfrac{-1}{2} + \dfrac{1}{4} + \dfrac{-1}{8} + \dfrac{1}{16} + \dfrac{-1}{32}$

17. Find the 14th term of the arithmetic sequence $-6, 1, 8, \ldots$. [16.2]

18. An arithmetic sequence has $a_1 = 11$ and $a_{13} = 43$. Find the common difference, d. [16.2]

19. An arithmetic sequence has $a_8 = 20$ and $a_{24} = 100$. Find the first term, a_1, and the common difference, d. [16.2]

20. Find the sum of the first 17 terms of the arithmetic series $-8 + (-11) + (-14) + \cdots$. [16.2]

21. Find the sum of all the multiples of 5 from 5 to 500, inclusive. [16.2]

22. Find the 20th term of the geometric sequence $2, 2\sqrt{2}, 4, \ldots$. [16.3]

23. Find the common ratio of the geometric sequence $40, 30, \frac{45}{2}, \ldots$. [16.3]

24. Find the nth term of the geometric sequence $-2, 2, -2, \ldots$. [16.3]

25. Find the nth term of the geometric sequence $3, \frac{3}{4}x, \frac{3}{16}x^2, \ldots$. [16.3]

26. Find S_6 for the geometric series
$$3 + 12 + 48 + \cdots. \quad [16.3]$$

27. Find S_{12} for the geometric series
$$3x - 6x + 12x - \cdots. \quad [16.3]$$

Determine whether each infinite geometric series has a limit. If a limit exists, find it. [16.3]

28. $6 + 3 + 1.5 + 0.75 + \cdots$

29. $7 - 4 + \frac{16}{7} - \cdots$

30. $2 + (-2) + 2 + (-2) + \cdots$

31. $0.04 + 0.08 + 0.16 + 0.32 + \cdots$

32. $\$2000 + \$1900 + \$1805 + \$1714.75 + \cdots$

33. Find fraction notation for $0.555555\ldots$. [16.3]

34. Find fraction notation for $1.39393939\ldots$. [16.3]

35. Adam took a job working in a convenience store starting with an hourly wage of $11.50. He was promised a raise of 40¢ per hour every 3 months for 8 years. At the end of 8 years, what will be his hourly wage? [16.2]

36. A stack of poles has 42 poles in the bottom row. There are 41 poles in the second row, 40 poles in the third row, and so on, ending with 1 pole in the top row. How many poles are in the stack? [16.2]

37. Stacey's student loan is in the amount of $12,000. Interest is 4%, compounded annually, and the amount is to be paid off in 7 years. How much is to be paid back? [16.3]

38. Find the total rebound distance of a ball, given that it is dropped from a height of 12 m and each rebound is one-third of the preceding one. [16.3]

Simplify. [16.4]

39. $7!$

40. $\dbinom{8}{3}$

41. Find the 3rd term of $(a + b)^{20}$. [16.4]

42. Expand: $(x - 2y)^4$. [16.4]

SYNTHESIS

TW **43.** What happens to a_n in a geometric sequence with $|r| < 1$, as n gets larger? Why? [16.3]

TW **44.** Compare the two forms of the binomial theorem given in the text. Under what circumstances would one be more useful than the other? [16.4]

45. Find the sum of the first n terms of the geometric series $1 - x + x^2 - x^3 + \cdots$. [16.3]

46. Expand: $(x^{-3} + x^3)^5$. [16.4]

Chapter Test ⬤16

1. Find the first five terms and the 12th term of a sequence with general term $a_n = \dfrac{1}{n^2 + 1}$.

2. Write an expression for the general term of the sequence $\frac{4}{3}, \frac{4}{9}, \frac{4}{27}, \ldots$.

3. Write out and evaluate:
$$\sum_{k=2}^{5} (1 - 2^k).$$

4. Rewrite using sigma notation:
$$1 + (-8) + 27 + (-64) + 125.$$

5. Find the 13th term, a_{13}, of the arithmetic sequence $\frac{1}{2}, 1, \frac{3}{2}, 2, \ldots$.

6. Find the common difference d of an arithmetic sequence when $a_1 = 7$ and $a_7 = -11$.

7. Find a_1 and d of an arithmetic sequence when $a_5 = 16$ and $a_{10} = -4$.

8. Find the sum of all the multiples of 12 from 24 to 240, inclusive.

9. Find the 10th term of the geometric sequence $-3, 6, -12, \ldots$.

10. Find the common ratio of the geometric sequence $22\frac{1}{2}, 15, 10, \ldots$.

11. Find the nth term of the geometric sequence $3, 9, 27, \ldots$.

12. Find S_9 for the geometric series
$$11 + 22 + 44 + \cdots.$$

Determine whether each infinite geometric series has a limit. If a limit exists, find it.

13. $0.5 + 0.25 + 0.125 + \cdots$

14. $0.5 + 1 + 2 + 4 + \cdots$

15. $\$1000 + \$80 + \$6.40 + \cdots$

16. Find fraction notation for $0.85858585\ldots$.

17. An auditorium has 31 seats in the first row, 33 seats in the second row, 35 seats in the third row, and so on, for 18 rows. How many seats are in the 17th row?

18. Alyssa's uncle Ken gave her $100 for her first birthday, $200 for her second birthday, $300 for her third birthday, and so on, until her eighteenth birthday. How much did he give her in all?

19. Each week the price of a $10,000 boat will be reduced 5% of the previous week's price. If we assume that it is not sold, what will be the price after 10 weeks?

20. Find the total rebound distance of a ball that is dropped from a height of 18 m, with each rebound two-thirds of the preceding one.

21. Simplify: $\dbinom{12}{9}$.

22. Expand: $(x - 3y)^5$.

23. Find the 4th term in the expansion of $(a + x)^{12}$.

SYNTHESIS

24. Find a formula for the sum of the first n even natural numbers:
$$2 + 4 + 6 + \cdots + 2n.$$

25. Find the sum of the first n terms of
$$1 + \frac{1}{x} + \frac{1}{x^2} + \frac{1}{x^3} + \cdots.$$

Cumulative Review/Final Exam: Chapters 4, 9, 10–16

Simplify.

1. $\left| -\dfrac{2}{3} + \dfrac{1}{5} \right|$

2. $y - [3 - 4(5 - 2y) - 3y]$

3. $(10 \cdot 8 - 9 \cdot 7)^2 - 54 \div 9 - 3$

4. $(2.7 \times 10^{-24})(3.1 \times 10^9)$

5. Evaluate
$$\frac{ab - ac}{bc}$$
for $a = -2$, $b = 3$, and $c = -4$.

Perform the indicated operations to create an equivalent expression. Be sure to simplify your result if possible.

6. $(5a^2 - 3ab - 7b^2) - (2a^2 + 5ab + 8b^2)$

7. $(2a - 1)(2a + 1)$

8. $(3a^2 - 5y)^2$

9. $\dfrac{1}{x - 2} - \dfrac{4}{x^2 - 4} + \dfrac{3}{x + 2}$

10. $\dfrac{x^2 - 6x + 8}{4x + 12} \cdot \dfrac{x + 3}{x^2 - 4}$

11. $\dfrac{3x + 3y}{5x - 5y} \div \dfrac{3x^2 + 3y^2}{5x^3 - 5y^3}$

12. $\dfrac{x - \dfrac{a^2}{x}}{1 + \dfrac{a}{x}}$

13. $\sqrt{12a}\sqrt{12a^3b}$ [12.3]

14. $(-9x^2y^5)(3x^8y^{-7})$ [4.2]

15. $(125x^6y^{1/2})^{2/3}$ [12.2]

16. $\dfrac{\sqrt[3]{x^2y^5}}{\sqrt[4]{xy^2}}$ [12.5]

17. $(4 + 6i)(2 - i)$, where $i = \sqrt{-1}$ [12.8]

Factor, if possible, to form an equivalent expression.

18. $4x^2 - 12x + 9$

19. $27a^3 - 8$

20. $12s^4 - 48t^2$

21. $15y^4 + 33y^2 - 36$

22. Divide:
$$(7x^4 - 5x^3 + x^2 - 4) \div (x - 2).$$

23. For the function described by
$$f(x) = 3x^2 - 4x,$$
find $f(-2)$.

Find the domain of each function.

24. $f(x) = \sqrt{2x - 8}$ [12.1]

25. $g(x) = \dfrac{x - 4}{x^2 - 10x + 25}$ [10.1]

26. Write an equivalent expression by rationalizing the denominator:
$$\dfrac{1 - \sqrt{x}}{1 + \sqrt{x}}. \ [12.5]$$

27. Find a linear equation whose graph has a y-intercept of $(0, -8)$ and is parallel to the line whose equation is $3x - y = 6$.

28. Write a quadratic equation whose solutions are $5\sqrt{2}$ and $-5\sqrt{2}$. [13.3]

29. Find the center and the radius of the circle given by
$$x^2 + y^2 - 4x + 6y - 23 = 0. \ [15.1]$$

30. Write an equivalent expression that is a single logarithm:
$$\tfrac{2}{3}\log_a x - \tfrac{1}{2}\log_a y + 5\log_a z. \ [14.4]$$

31. Write an equivalent exponential equation:
$$\log_a c = 5. \ [14.3]$$

Use a calculator to find each of the following. Round to four decimal places. [14.5]

32. log 120

33. $\log_5 3$

34. Find the distance between the points $(-1, -5)$ and $(2, -1)$. [12.7]

35. Find the 21st term of the arithmetic sequence 19, 12, 5, ... [16.2]

36. Find the sum of the first 25 terms of the arithmetic series $-1 + 2 + 5 + \cdots$. [16.2]

37. Write an expression for the general term of the geometric sequence 16, 4, 1, ... [16.3]

38. Find the 7th term of $(a - 2b)^{10}$. [16.4]

39. Find the sum of the first nine terms of the geometric series $4 + 6 + 9 + \cdots$. [16.3]

Solve.

40. $8(x - 1) - 3(x - 2) = 1$

41. $\dfrac{6}{x} + \dfrac{6}{x + 2} = \dfrac{5}{2}$

42. $2x + 1 > 5 \ or \ x - 7 \le 3$ [10.1]

43. $5x + 6y = -2,$
$3x + 10y = 2$ [4.3]

44. $x + y - z = 0,$
$3x + y + z = 6,$
$x - y + 2z = 5$ [11.1]

45. $3\sqrt{x - 1} = 5 - x$ [12.6]

46. $x^4 - 29x^2 + 100 = 0$ [9.5]

47. $x^2 + y^2 = 8,$
$x^2 - y^2 = 2$ [15.4]

48. $4^x = 12$ [14.6]

49. $\log(x^2 - 25) - \log(x + 5) = 3$ [14.6]

50. $\log_5 x = -2$ [14.6]

51. $7^{2x+3} = 49$ [14.6]

52. $|2x - 1| \le 5$ [10.2]

53. $15x^2 + 45 = 0$ [13.1]

54. $x^2 + 4x = 3$ [13.2]

55. $y^2 + 3y > 10$ [10.4]

56. Let $f(x) = x^2 - 2x$. Find a such that $f(a) = 80$.

57. If $f(x) = \sqrt{-x+4} + 3$ and $g(x) = \sqrt{x-2} + 3$, find a such that $f(a) = g(a)$. [12.6]

58. Solve $V = P - Prt$ for r.

59. Solve $I = \dfrac{R}{R+r}$ for R.

For each of the following graphs, (a) determine whether the graph is that of a linear, a quadratic, an exponential, or a logarithmic function and (b) use the graph to find the zeros of f.

60.

[4.5]

61.

[14.3], [14.6]

62.

[13.7], [13.1]

63.

[14.2], [14.6]

Graph.

64. $3x - y = 7$

65. $x^2 + y^2 = 100$ [15.1]

66. $\dfrac{x^2}{36} - \dfrac{y^2}{9} = 1$ [15.3]

67. $y = \log_2 x$ [14.3]

68. $f(x) = 2^x - 3$ [14.2]

69. $2x - 3y < -6$ [10.3]

70. Graph: $f(x) = -2(x-3)^2 + 1$. [13.7]
   a) Label the vertex.
   b) Draw the axis of symmetry.
   c) Find the maximum or minimum value.

71. Graph $f(x) = \sqrt{4-x}$ and use the graph to estimate the domain and the range of f. [12.1]

Solve.

72. The Brighton recreation department plans to fence in a rectangular park next to a river. (Note that no fence will be needed along the river.) What is the area of the largest region that can be fenced in with 200 ft of fencing? [13.8]

73. The perimeter of a rectangular sign is 34 ft. The length of a diagonal is 13 ft. Find the dimensions of the sign. [15.4]

74. A movie club offers two types of membership. Limited members pay a fee of $40 per year and can rent movies for $2.45 each. Preferred members pay $60 per year and can rent movies for $1.65 each. For what numbers of annual movie rentals would it be less expensive to be a preferred member?

75. Cosmos Tastes mixes herbs that cost $2.68 per ounce with herbs that cost $4.60 per ounce to create a seasoning that costs $3.80 per ounce. How many ounces of each herb should be mixed together to make 24 oz of the seasoning? [4.4]

76. An airplane can fly 190 mi with the wind in the same time it takes to fly 160 mi against the wind. The speed of the wind is 30 mph. How fast can the plane fly in still air?

77. Jack can tap the sugar maple trees in Southway Farm in 21 hr. Delia can tap the trees in 14 hr. How long would it take them, working together, to tap the trees?

78. The centripetal force F of an object moving in a circle varies directly as the square of the velocity v and inversely as the radius r of the circle. If $F = 8$ when $v = 1$ and $r = 10$, what is F when $v = 2$ and $r = 16$?

79. *Credit Cards.* There were approximately 173 million credit-card holders in the United States in 2006. By 2010, 181 million Americans held credit cards.
Source: U.S. Census Bureau

a) What was the average rate of change?
b) Find a linear equation that fits the data. Let $c =$ the number of credit-card holders, in millions, and t the number of years since 2006.
c) Use the equation from part (b) to predict the number of credit-card holders in 2015.
d) Assuming the trend continues, in what year will there be 250 million Americans who have credit cards?

80. *Electronic Payments.* The amount of electronic payments made in the United States has increased exponentially from $5 billion in 1979 to $60 billion in 2006. [14.7]
Source: Based on data from Federal Reserve Board

a) Find the exponential growth rate k, and write an equation for an exponential function that can be used to predict the amount of electronic payments t years after 1979.
b) Predict the amount of electronic payments in 2012.
c) In what year will there be $200 billion in electronic payments?

81. *Retirement.* Sarita invested $2000 in a retirement account on her 22nd birthday. If the account earns 5% interest, compounded annually, how much will this investment be worth on her 62nd birthday? [14.3]

SYNTHESIS

Solve.

82. $\dfrac{9}{x} - \dfrac{9}{x + 12} = \dfrac{108}{x^2 + 12x}$

83. $\log_2 (\log_3 x) = 2$ [14.6]

84. y varies directly as the cube of x, and x is multiplied by 0.5. What is the effect on y?

85. Diaphantos, a famous mathematician, spent $\frac{1}{6}$ of his life as a child, $\frac{1}{12}$ as an adolescent, and $\frac{1}{7}$ as a bachelor. Five years after he was married, he had a son who died 4 years before his father at half his father's final age. How long did Diaphantos live? [11.2]

Answers

CHAPTER 1

Technology Connection, p. 7

1. 3438   **2.** 47,531

Translating for Success, p. 9

1. H   **2.** E   **3.** K   **4.** B   **5.** O   **6.** L   **7.** M   **8.** C
9. D   **10.** F

Exercise Set 1.1, pp. 10–12

1. Expression   **2.** Equation   **3.** Equation
4. Expression   **5.** Equation   **6.** Equation
7. Expression   **8.** Equation   **9.** Equation
10. Expression   **11.** Expression   **12.** Expression
13. 45   **15.** 8   **17.** 5   **19.** 4   **21.** 5   **23.** 3
25. $24\,\text{ft}^2$ **27.** $15\,\text{cm}^2$ **29.** 0.345   **31.** Let r represent
Ron's age; $r + 5$, or $5 + r$ **33.** $6b$, or $b \cdot 6$ **35.** $c - 9$
37. $6 + q$, or $q + 6$ **39.** Let m represent Mai's speed;
$8m$, or $m \cdot 8$ **41.** $y - x$ **43.** $x \div w$, or $\dfrac{x}{w}$ **45.** Let l
represent the length of the box and h represent the height;
$l + h$, or $h + l$ **47.** $9 \cdot 2m$, or $2m \cdot 9$ **49.** Let y
represent "some number"; $\dfrac{1}{4}y - 13$, or $\dfrac{y}{4} - 13$ **51.** Let a
and b represent the two numbers; $5(a - b)$ **53.** Let w
represent the number of women attending; 64% of w,
or $0.64w$ **55.** Yes   **57.** No   **59.** Yes   **61.** Yes
63. Let x represent the unknown number; $73 + x = 201$
65. Let x represent the unknown number; $42x = 2352$
67. Let s represent the number of unoccupied squares;
$s + 19 = 64$ **69.** Let w represent the amount of solid
waste generated, in millions of tons; 32% of $w = 79$, or
$0.32w = 79$ **71.** (f)   **73.** (d)   **75.** (g)   **77.** (e)
79. ✍   **81.** ✍   **83.** $450   **85.** 2   **87.** 6   **89.** $w + 4$
91. $l + w + l + w$, or $2l + 2w$ **93.** $t + 8$ **95.** ✍

Exercise Set 1.2, pp. 18–20

1. Commutative   **2.** Associative   **3.** Associative
4. Commutative   **5.** Distributive   **6.** Associative
7. Associative   **8.** Commutative   **9.** Commutative
10. Distributive   **11.** $t + 11$ **13.** $8x + 4$
15. $3y + 9x$ **17.** $5(1 + a)$ **19.** $x \cdot 7$ **21.** ts

23. $5 + ba$ **25.** $(a + 1)5$ **27.** $x + (8 + y)$
29. $(u + v) + 7$ **31.** $ab + (c + d)$ **33.** $8(xy)$
35. $(2a)\,b$ **37.** $(3 \cdot 2)(a + b)$
39. $(s + t) + 6; (t + 6) + s$ **41.** $17(ab); b(17a)$
43. $(1 + x) + 2 = (x + 1) + 2$ Commutative law
$\qquad\qquad\quad = x + (1 + 2)$ Associative law
$\qquad\qquad\quad = x + 3$ Simplifying
45. $(m \cdot 3)7 = m(3 \cdot 7)$ Associative law
$\qquad\qquad\ \ = m \cdot 21$ Simplifying
$\qquad\qquad\ \ = 21m$ Commutative law
47. $2x + 30$ **49.** $4 + 4a$ **51.** $24 + 8y$
53. $90x + 60$ **55.** $5r + 10 + 15t$ **57.** $2a + 2b$
59. $5x + 5y + 10$ **61.** $x, xyz, 1$ **63.** $2a, \dfrac{a}{3b}, 5b$
65. x, y **67.** $4x, 4y$ **69.** $2(a + b)$ **71.** $7(1 + y)$
73. $4(8x + 1)$ **75.** $5(x + 2 + 3y)$ **77.** $7(a + 5b)$
79. $11(4x + y + 2z)$ **81.** $5, n$ **83.** $3, (x + y)$
85. $7, a, b$ **87.** $(a - b), (x - y)$ **89.** ✍   **91.** Let k
represent Kara's salary; $\dfrac{1}{2}k$, or $\dfrac{k}{2}$ **92.** $2(m + 3)$, or
$2(3 + m)$ **93.** ✍   **95.** Yes; distributive law
97. No; for example, let $m = 1$. Then $7 \div 3 \cdot 1 = \frac{7}{3}$ and
$1 \cdot 3 \div 7 = \frac{3}{7}$.   **99.** No; for example, let $x = 1$ and
$y = 2$. Then $30 \cdot 2 + 1 \cdot 15 = 60 + 15 = 75$ and
$5[2(1 + 3 \cdot 2)] = 5[2(7)] = 5 \cdot 14 = 70$.   **101.** ✍

Exercise Set 1.3, pp. 27–29

1. (b)   **2.** (c)   **3.** (d)   **4.** (a)   **5.** Composite
7. Prime   **9.** Composite   **11.** Prime   **13.** Neither
15. $1 \cdot 50; 2 \cdot 25; 5 \cdot 10; 1, 2, 5, 10, 25, 50$
17. $1 \cdot 42; 2 \cdot 21; 3 \cdot 14; 6 \cdot 7; 1, 2, 3, 6, 7, 14, 21, 42$
19. $3 \cdot 13$ **21.** $2 \cdot 3 \cdot 5$ **23.** $3 \cdot 3 \cdot 3$ **25.** $2 \cdot 3 \cdot 5 \cdot 5$
27. $2 \cdot 2 \cdot 2 \cdot 5$ **29.** Prime   **31.** $2 \cdot 3 \cdot 5 \cdot 7$ **33.** $5 \cdot 23$
35. $\frac{3}{5}$ **37.** $\frac{2}{7}$ **39.** $\frac{1}{4}$ **41.** 4   **43.** $\frac{1}{4}$ **45.** 6
47. $\frac{21}{25}$ **49.** $\frac{60}{41}$ **51.** $\frac{15}{7}$ **53.** $\frac{3}{10}$ **55.** 6   **57.** $\frac{1}{2}$
59. $\frac{7}{6}$ **61.** $\dfrac{3b}{7a}$ **63.** $\dfrac{10}{n}$ **65.** $\frac{5}{6}$ **67.** 1   **69.** $\frac{5}{18}$
71. 0   **73.** $\frac{35}{18}$ **75.** $\frac{10}{3}$ **77.** 27   **79.** 1   **81.** $\frac{6}{35}$
83. 18   **85.** ✍   **87.** $5(3 + x)$; answers may vary
88. $7 + (b + a)$, or $(a + b) + 7$ **89.** ✍
91. Row 1: 7, 2, 36, 14, 8, 8; row 2: 9, 18, 2, 10, 12, 21
93. $\frac{2}{5}$ **95.** $\dfrac{5q}{t}$ **97.** $\frac{6}{25}$ **99.** $\dfrac{5ap}{2cm}$ **101.** $\dfrac{23r}{18t}$

103. $\frac{28}{45}$ m^2 **105.** $14\frac{2}{9}$ m   **107.** $27\frac{3}{5}$ cm

Technology Connection, p. 33

1. 2.236067977   **2.** 2.645751311   **3.** 3.605551275
4. 5.196152423   **5.** 6.164414003   **6.** 7.071067812

Exercise Set 1.4, pp. 35–37

1. Repeating   **2.** Terminating   **3.** Integer
4. Whole number   **5.** Rational number
6. Irrational number   **7.** Natural number
8. Absolute value   **9.** $-10,500, 27,482$ **11.** $136, -4$
13. $-554, 499.19$ **15.** $650, -180$ **17.** $8, -5$
19.
21.
23.   **25.** 0.875   **27.** -0.75
29. $-1.1\overline{6}$ **31.** $0.\overline{6}$ **33.** -0.5 **35.** 0.13
37.   **39.** $-\sqrt{22}$
41. $>$ **43.** $<$ **45.** $<$ **47.** $>$ **49.** $<$ **51.** $<$
53. $x < -2$ **55.** $y \geq 10$ **57.** True   **59.** False
61. True   **63.** 58   **65.** 12.2   **67.** $\sqrt{2}$ **69.** $\frac{9}{7}$ **71.** 0
73. 8   **75.** $-83, -4.7, 0, \frac{5}{9}, 2.\overline{16}, 62$ **77.** $-83, 0, 62$
79. $-83, -4.7, 0, \frac{5}{9}, 2.\overline{16}, \pi, \sqrt{17}, 62$ **81.** 🖳   **83.** 42
84. $ba + 5$, or $5 + ab$ **85.** 🖳   **87.** 🖳
89. $-23, -17, 0, 4$ **91.** $-\frac{4}{3}, \frac{4}{9}, \frac{4}{8}, \frac{4}{6}, \frac{4}{5}, \frac{4}{3}, \frac{4}{2}$ **93.** $<$ **95.** $=$
97. $-19, 19$ **99.** $-4, -3, 3, 4$ **101.** $\frac{3}{3}$ **103.** $\frac{70}{9}$
105. $x \leq 0$ **107.** $|t| \geq 20$ **109.** 🖳

Exercise Set 1.5, pp. 41–43

1. (f)   **2.** (d)   **3.** (e)   **4.** (a)   **5.** (b)   **6.** (c)
7. -3 **9.** 4   **11.** -7 **13.** -8 **15.** -35 **17.** -8
19. 0   **21.** -41 **23.** 0   **25.** 9   **27.** -2 **29.** 11
31. -43 **33.** 0   **35.** 18   **37.** -45 **39.** 0   **41.** 16
43. -0.8 **45.** -9.1 **47.** $\frac{3}{5}$ **49.** $\frac{-6}{7}$ **51.** $-\frac{1}{15}$
53. $\frac{2}{9}$ **55.** -3 **57.** 0   **59.** The price rose 29¢.
61. Her new balance was \$95.   **63.** The total gain was 20 yd.
65. The lake rose $\frac{3}{10}$ ft.   **67.** Logan owes \$85.   **69.** $17a$
71. $9x$ **73.** $25t$ **75.** $-2m$ **77.** $-10y$ **79.** $1 - 2x$
81. $12x + 17$ **83.** $7r + 8t + 16$ **85.** $18n + 16$
87. 🖳   **89.** $21z + 14y + 7$ **90.** $\frac{28}{3}$ **91.** 🖳
93. \$451.70   **95.** $-5y$ **97.** $-7m$ **99.** $-7t, -23$
101. 1 under par

Exercise Set 1.6, pp. 48–51

1. (d)   **2.** (g)   **3.** (f)   **4.** (h)   **5.** (a)   **6.** (c)
7. (b)   **8.** (e)   **9.** Six minus ten
11. Two minus negative twelve   **13.** Nine minus the
opposite of t **15.** The opposite of x minus y
17. Negative three minus the opposite of n **19.** -51
21. $\frac{11}{3}$ **23.** 3.14   **25.** 45   **27.** $\frac{14}{3}$ **29.** -0.101

31. 37   **33.** $-\frac{2}{5}$ **35.** 1   **37.** -15 **39.** -3 **41.** -6
43. -3 **45.** -7 **47.** -6 **49.** 0   **51.** -5
53. -10 **55.** -11 **57.** 0   **59.** 0   **61.** 8   **63.** -11
65. 16   **67.** -19 **69.** 1   **71.** 17   **73.** 3   **75.** -3
77. -21 **79.** 10   **81.** -8 **83.** -60 **85.** -23
87. -7.3 **89.** 1.1   **91.** -5.5 **93.** -0.928 **95.** $-\frac{7}{11}$
97. $-\frac{4}{5}$ **99.** $\frac{5}{17}$ **101.** $3.8 - (-5.2); 9$
103. $114 - (-79); 193$ **105.** -40 **107.** 43   **109.** 32
111. -62 **113.** -139 **115.** 0   **117.** $-3y, -8x$
119. $9, -5t, -3st$ **121.** $-3x$ **123.** $-5a + 4$
125. $-n - 9$ **127.** $-3x - 6$ **129.** $-8t - 7$
131. $-12x + 3y + 9$ **133.** $8x + 66$ **135.** 214°F
137. 30,347 ft   **139.** 116 m   **141.** 🖳   **143.** 432 ft^2
144. $2 \cdot 2 \cdot 2 \cdot 2 \cdot 2 \cdot 3 \cdot 3 \cdot 3$ **145.** 🖳
147. 11:00 P.M., August 14   **149.** False. For example,
let $m = -3$ and $n = -5$. Then $-3 > -5$, but
$-3 + (-5) = -8 \not> 0$.   **151.** True. For example, for
$m = 4$ and $n = -4$, $4 = -(-4)$ and $4 + (-4) = 0$; for
$m = -3$ and $n = 3$, $-3 = -3$ and $-3 + 3 = 0$.
153. (−) 9 − (−) 7 ENTER

Exercise Set 1.7, pp. 56–58

1. 1   **2.** 0   **3.** 0   **4.** 1   **5.** 0   **6.** 1   **7.** 1   **8.** 0
9. 1   **10.** 0   **11.** -40 **13.** -56 **15.** -40 **17.** 72
19. -42 **21.** 45   **23.** 190   **25.** -132 **27.** 1200
29. -126 **31.** 11.5   **33.** 0   **35.** $-\frac{2}{7}$ **37.** $\frac{1}{12}$
39. -11.13 **41.** $-\frac{5}{12}$ **43.** 252   **45.** 0   **47.** $\frac{1}{28}$
49. 150   **51.** 0   **53.** -720 **55.** $-30,240$ **57.** -9
59. -4 **61.** -7 **63.** 4   **65.** -9 **67.** 5.1   **69.** $\frac{100}{11}$
71. -8 **73.** Undefined   **75.** -4 **77.** 0   **79.** 0
81. $-\frac{8}{3}; \frac{8}{-3}$ **83.** $-\frac{29}{35}; \frac{-29}{35}$ **85.** $\frac{-7}{3}; \frac{7}{-3}$ **87.** $-\frac{x}{2}; \frac{x}{-2}$
89. $-\frac{5}{4}$ **91.** $-\frac{10}{51}$ **93.** $-\frac{1}{10}$ **95.** $\frac{1}{4.3}$, or $\frac{10}{43}$ **97.** $-\frac{4}{9}$
99. Does not exist   **101.** $\frac{21}{20}$ **103.** -1 **105.** 1
107. $\frac{3}{11}$ **109.** $-\frac{7}{4}$ **111.** 1   **113.** $\frac{1}{10}$ **115.** $-\frac{7}{6}$
117. Undefined   **119.** $-\frac{14}{15}$ **121.** 🖳   **123.** $\frac{22}{39}$
124. $12x - y - 9$ **125.** 🖳   **127.** $\dfrac{1}{a + b}$
129. $-(a + b)$ **131.** $x = -x$ **133.** For 2 and 3,
the reciprocal of the sum is $1/(2 + 3)$, or $1/5$. But
$1/5 \neq 1/2 + 1/3$.   **135.** 5°F   **137.** Positive
139. Positive   **141.** Positive   **143.** Distributive law;
law of opposites; multiplicative property of zero

Connecting the Concepts, p. 59

1. -10 **2.** 16   **3.** 4   **4.** -6 **5.** -120 **6.** -7
7. -23 **8.** -3 **9.** -1 **10.** -3 **11.** -0.8
12. -3.77 **13.** -7 **14.** -4.1 **15.** -12 **16.** $\frac{5}{3}$
17. 100   **18.** 77   **19.** 180   **20.** -52

Exercise Set 1.8, pp. 66–68

1. (a) Division; (b) subtraction; (c) addition;
(d) multiplication; (e) subtraction; (f) multiplication

2. (a) Multiplication; **(b)** subtraction; **(c)** addition; **(d)** subtraction; **(e)** division; **(f)** multiplication
3. x^6 **5.** $(-5)^3$ **7.** $(3t)^5$ **9.** $2n^4$ **11.** 16   **13.** 9
15. -9 **17.** 64   **19.** 625   **21.** 7   **23.** -32
25. $81t^4$ **27.** $-343x^3$ **29.** 26   **31.** 51   **33.** -6
35. 1   **37.** 298   **39.** 11   **41.** -36 **43.** 1291
45. 152   **47.** 36   **49.** 1   **51.** -44 **53.** 41   **55.** -10
57. -5 **59.** -19 **61.** -3 **63.** -75 **65.** 9   **67.** 30
69. 6   **71.** -17 **73.** $-9x-1$ **75.** $7n-8$
77. $-4a+3b-7c$ **79.** $-3x^2-5x+1$ **81.** $2x-7$
83. $-9x+6$ **85.** $21t-r$ **87.** $9y-25z$ **89.** x^2+6
91. $-t^3+4t$ **93.** $37a^2-23ab+35b^2$
95. $-22t^3-t^2+9t$ **97.** $2x-25$ **99.** ✍   **101.** Let n represent the number; $2n-9$ **102.** Let m and n represent the two numbers; $\frac{1}{2}(m+n)$ **103.** ✍
105. $-6r-5t+21$ **107.** $-2x-f$ **109.** ✍
111. True   **113.** False   **115.** 0   **117.** 17
119. 39,000   **121.** $44x^3$

Review Exercises: Chapter 1, pp. 73–74

1. True   **2.** True   **3.** False   **4.** True   **5.** False
6. False   **7.** True   **8.** False   **9.** False   **10.** True
11. 24   **12.** 4   **13.** -16 **14.** -15 **15.** $y-7$
16. $xz+10$, or $10+xz$ **17.** Let b represent Brandt's speed and w represent the wind speed; $15(b-w)$
18. No   **19.** Let d represent the number of digital prints, in billions, made in 2006; $14.1 = d + 3.2$ **20.** $t \cdot 3 + 5$
21. $2x+(y+z)$ **22.** $(4x)y, 4(yx),(4y)x$; answers may vary   **23.** $18x+30y$ **24.** $40x+24y+16$
25. $3(7x+5y)$ **26.** $11(2a+9b+1)$ **27.** $2\cdot2\cdot2\cdot7$
28. $\frac{5}{12}$ **29.** $\frac{9}{4}$ **30.** $\frac{19}{24}$ **31.** $\frac{3}{16}$ **32.** $\frac{3}{5}$ **33.** $\frac{27}{25}$
34. $-3600, 1350$ **35.**

$$\overset{-\frac{1}{3}}{\underset{-5\,-4\,-3\,-2\,-1\ \ 0\ \ 1\ \ 2\ \ 3\ \ 4\ \ 5}{\longleftrightarrow}}$$

36. $x>-3$ **37.** True   **38.** False   **39.** $-0.\overline{4}$ **40.** 1
41. -12 **42.** -10 **43.** $-\frac{7}{12}$ **44.** 0   **45.** -5 **46.** 8
47. $-\frac{7}{5}$ **48.** -7.9 **49.** 63   **50.** -9.18 **51.** $-\frac{2}{7}$
52. -140 **53.** -7 **54.** -3 **55.** $\frac{9}{4}$ **56.** 48
57. 168   **58.** $\frac{21}{8}$ **59.** 18   **60.** 53   **61.** $\frac{103}{17}$
62. $7a-b$ **63.** $-4x+5y$ **64.** 7   **65.** $-\frac{1}{7}$
66. $(2x)^4$ **67.** $-125x^3$ **68.** $-3a+9$ **69.** $11b-27$
70. $3x^4+10x$ **71.** $17n^2+m^2+20mn$ **72.** $5x+28$
73. ✍ The value of a constant never varies. A variable can represent a variety of numbers.   **74.** ✍ A term is one of the parts of an expression that is separated from the other parts by plus signs. A factor is part of a product.   **75.** ✍ The distributive law is used in factoring algebraic expressions, multiplying algebraic expressions, combining like terms, finding the opposite of a sum, and subtracting algebraic expressions.   **76.** ✍ A negative number raised to an even power is positive; a negative number raised to an odd power is negative.   **77.** 25,281   **78. (a)** $\frac{3}{11}$; **(b)** $\frac{10}{11}$
79. $-\frac{5}{8}$ **80.** -2.1 **81.** (i)   **82.** (j)   **83.** (a)
84. (h)   **85.** (k)   **86.** (b)   **87.** (c)   **88.** (e)
89. (d)   **90.** (f)   **91.** (g)

Test: Chapter 1, p. 75

1. [1.1] 4   **2.** [1.1] Let x and y represent the numbers; $xy-9$ **3.** [1.1] 240 ft^2 **4.** [1.2] $q+3p$
5. [1.2] $(x\cdot4)\cdot y$ **6.** [1.1] No   **7.** [1.1] Let p represent the maximum production capability; $p-4250 = 45{,}950$
8. [1.2] $35+7x$ **9.** [1.7] $-5y+10$
10. [1.2] $11(1+4x)$ **11.** [1.2] $7(x+1+7y)$
12. [1.3] $2\cdot2\cdot3\cdot5\cdot5$ **13.** [1.3] $\frac{3}{7}$ **14.** [1.4] $<$
15. [1.4] $>$ **16.** [1.4] $\frac{9}{4}$ **17.** [1.4] 3.8   **18.** [1.6] $\frac{2}{3}$
19. [1.7] $-\frac{7}{4}$ **20.** [1.6] 10   **21.** [1.4] $-5 \ge x$
22. [1.6] 7.8   **23.** [1.5] -8 **24.** [1.6] -2.5 **25.** [1.6] $-\frac{7}{8}$
26. [1.7] -48 **27.** [1.7] $\frac{2}{9}$ **28.** [1.7] -6 **29.** [1.7] $\frac{3}{4}$
30. [1.7] -9.728 **31.** [1.8] -173 **32.** [1.6] 15
33. [1.8] -64 **34.** [1.8] 448   **35.** [1.6] $21a+22y$
36. [1.8] $16x^4$ **37.** [1.8] $x+7$ **38.** [1.8] $9a-12b-7$
39. [1.8] $-y-16$ **40.** [1.1] 5
41. [1.8] $9-(3-4)+5=15$ **42.** [1.8] 15
43. [1.8] $4a$ **44.** [1.8] False

CHAPTER 2

Exercise Set 2.1, pp. 83–85

1. (c)   **2.** (b)   **3.** (f)   **4.** (a)   **5.** (d)   **6.** (e)   **7.** (d)
8. (b)   **9.** (c)   **10.** (a)   **11.** 11   **13.** -25 **15.** -31
17. 41   **19.** 19   **21.** -6 **23.** $\frac{7}{3}$ **25.** $-\frac{1}{10}$ **27.** $\frac{41}{24}$
29. $-\frac{1}{20}$ **31.** 9.1   **33.** -5 **35.** 7   **37.** 12   **39.** -38
41. 8   **43.** -7 **45.** 8   **47.** 88   **49.** 20   **51.** -54
53. $-\frac{5}{9}$ **55.** 1   **57.** $\frac{9}{2}$ **59.** -7.6 **61.** -2.5 **63.** -15
65. -5 **67.** $-\frac{7}{6}$ **69.** -128 **71.** $-\frac{1}{2}$ **73.** -15 **75.** 9
77. 310.756   **79.** ✍   **81.** -6 **82.** 2   **83.** 1
84. -16 **85.** ✍   **87.** 11.6   **89.** 2   **91.** $-23,23$
93. 9000   **95.** 250

Technology Connection, p. 88

1.   **2.**

3. 4; not reliable because, depending on the choice of ∆Tbl, it is easy to scroll past a solution without realizing it.

Exercise Set 2.2, pp. 91–92

1. (c)   **2.** (e)   **3.** (a)   **4.** (f)   **5.** (b)   **6.** (d)   **7.** 8
9. 7   **11.** 5   **13.** $\frac{10}{3}$ **15.** -7 **17.** -5 **19.** -4
21. 19   **23.** -2.8 **25.** 3   **27.** 15   **29.** -6 **31.** $-\frac{25}{2}$
33. All real numbers; identity   **35.** -3 **37.** -6 **39.** 2
41. 0   **43.** 6   **45.** No solution; contradiction   **47.** $-\frac{1}{2}$
49. 0   **51.** 10   **53.** 4   **55.** 0   **57.** No solution; contradiction   **59.** $\frac{5}{2}$ **61.** -8 **63.** $\frac{1}{6}$
65. All real numbers; identity   **67.** 2   **69.** $\frac{16}{3}$ **71.** $\frac{2}{5}$
73. 1   **75.** -4 **77.** $1.\overline{6}$ **79.** $-\frac{60}{37}$ **81.** 11   **83.** 8
85. $\frac{16}{15}$ **87.** $-\frac{1}{31}$ **89.** 2   **91.** ✍   **93.** -7 **94.** 15

95. -15 **96.** -28 **97.** ⚙   **99.** $\frac{1136}{909}$, or $1.\overline{2497}$
101. No solution; contradiction   **103.** $\frac{2}{3}$ **105.** 0
107. $\frac{52}{45}$ **109.** All real numbers; identity

Technology Connection, p. 94

1. 800

Exercise Set 2.3, pp. 97–100

1. 309.6 m   **3.** 1423 students   **5.** 8.4734   **7.** 255 mg
9. $b = \dfrac{A}{h}$ **11.** $r = \dfrac{d}{t}$ **13.** $P = \dfrac{I}{rt}$ **15.** $m = 65 - H$
17. $l = \dfrac{P - 2w}{2}$, or $l = \dfrac{P}{2} - w$ **19.** $\pi = \dfrac{A}{r^2}$
21. $h = \dfrac{2A}{b}$ **23.** $c^2 = \dfrac{E}{m}$ **25.** $d = 2Q - c$
27. $b = 3A - a - c$ **29.** $r = wf$ **31.** $C = \frac{5}{9}(F - 32)$
33. $y = 2x - 1$ **35.** $y = -\frac{2}{5}x + 2$ **37.** $y = \frac{4}{3}x - 2$
39. $y = -\frac{9}{8}x + \frac{1}{2}$ **41.** $y = \frac{3}{5}x - \frac{8}{5}$
43. $x = \dfrac{z - 13}{2} - y$, or $x = \dfrac{z - 13 - 2y}{2}$
45. $l = 4(t - 27) + w$ **47.** $t = \dfrac{A}{a + b}$ **49.** $h = \dfrac{2A}{a + b}$
51. $L = W - \dfrac{N(R - r)}{400}$, or $L = \dfrac{400W - NR + Nr}{400}$
53. ⚙   **55.** -10 **56.** -196 **57.** 0 **58.** -32
59. -13 **60.** 65 **61.** ⚙   **63.** 40 yr   **65.** 27 in³
67. $a = \dfrac{w}{c} \cdot d$ **69.** $c = \dfrac{d}{a - b}$ **71.** $a = \dfrac{c}{3 + b + d}$
73. $K = 9.632w + 19.685h - 10.54a + 102.3$

Exercise Set 2.4, pp. 104–108

1. (d)   **2.** (c)   **3.** (e)   **4.** (b)   **5.** (c)   **6.** (d)   **7.** (f)
8. (a)   **9.** (b)   **10.** (e)   **11.** 0.49   **13.** 0.01
15. 0.041   **17.** 0.2   **19.** 0.0625   **21.** 0.002   **23.** 1.75
25. 38%   **27.** 3.9%   **29.** 45%   **31.** 70%   **33.** 0.09%
35. 106%   **37.** 180%   **39.** 60%   **41.** 32%   **43.** 25%
45. 26%   **47.** $46\frac{2}{3}$, or $\frac{140}{3}$ **49.** 2.5   **51.** 10,000
53. 125%   **55.** 0.8   **57.** 50%   **59.** $33.\overline{3}\%$, or $33\frac{1}{3}\%$
61. 2.85 million Americans   **63.** 23.37 million Americans
65. 75 credits   **67.** 595 at bats   **69.** (a) 16%; (b) $29
71. $33.\overline{3}\%$, or $33\frac{1}{3}\%$; $66.\overline{6}\%$, or $66\frac{2}{3}\%$ **73.** $168
75. 285 women   **77.** $19.20 an hour   **79.** The actual
cost was 43.7% more than the estimate.   **81.** $45
83. $148.50   **85.** About 31.5 lb   **87.** About 2.45 billion
pieces of mail   **89.** About 165 calories   **91.** ⚙
93. Let l represent the length and w represent the width;
$2l + 2w$ **94.** $0.05 \cdot 180$ **95.** Let p represent the number
of points Tino scored; $p - 5$ **96.** $15 + 1.5x$ **97.** $10\left(\frac{1}{2}a\right)$
98. Let n represent the number; $3n + 10$ **99.** Let l
represent the length and w represent the width; $w = l - 2$
100. Let x represent the first number and y represent the
second number; $x = 4y$ **101.** ⚙   **103.** 18,500 people
105. About 6 ft 7 in.   **107.** About 27%   **109.** ⚙

Exercise Set 2.5, pp. 116–121

1. 11   **3.** $\frac{11}{2}$ **5.** $150   **7.** $130   **9.** About 78.4 mi
11. 160 mi   **13.** 1204 and 1205   **15.** 285 and 287
17. 32, 33, 34   **19.** Man: 103 yr; woman: 101 yr
21. Non-spam: 25 billion messages; spam: 100 billion
messages   **23.** 140 and 141   **25.** Width: 100 ft; length:
160 ft; area: 16,000 ft²   **27.** Width: 21 m; length: 25 m
29. $1\frac{3}{4}$ in. by $3\frac{1}{2}$ in.   **31.** 30°, 90°, 60°   **33.** 70°
35. Bottom: 144 ft; middle: 72 ft; top: 24 ft   **37.** 8.75 mi,
or $8\frac{3}{4}$ mi   **39.** $128\frac{1}{3}$ mi   **41.** 65°, 25°   **43.** 140°, 40°
45. Length: 27.9 cm; width: 21.6 cm   **47.** $6600
49. 830 points   **51.** $125,000   **53.** 160 chirps per
minute   **55.** ⚙   **57.** $<$ **58.** $>$ **59.** $>$ **60.** $<$
61. $-4 \le x$ **62.** $5 > x$ **63.** $y < 5$ **64.** $t \ge -10$
65. ⚙   **67.** $37   **69.** 20   **71.** Half-dollars: 5;
quarters: 10; dimes: 20; nickels: 60   **73.** $95.99
75. 5 DVDs   **77.** 6 mi   **79.** ⚙   **81.** Width: 23.31 cm;
length: 27.56 cm

Exercise Set 2.6, pp. 128–130

1. $\ge$ **2.** $\le$ **3.** $<$ **4.** $>$ **5.** Equivalent
6. Equivalent   **7.** Equivalent   **8.** Not equivalent
9. (a) Yes; (b) no; (c) no   **11.** (a) Yes; (b) no; (c) yes
13. (a) Yes; (b) yes; (c) yes   **15.** (a) No; (b) yes; (c) no
17. $y < 2$
19. $x \ge -1$
21. $0 \le t$
23. $-5 \le x < 2$
25. $-4 < x < 0$
27. $\{y \mid y < 6\}, (-\infty, 6)$
29. $\{x \mid x \ge -4\}, [-4, \infty)$
31. $\{t \mid t > -3\}, (-3, \infty)$
33. $\{x \mid x \le -7\}, (-\infty, -7]$
35. $\{x \mid x > -4\}, (-4, \infty)$ **37.** $\{x \mid x \le 2\}, (-\infty, 2]$
39. $\{x \mid x < -1\}, (-\infty, -1)$ **41.** $\{x \mid x \ge 0\}, [0, \infty)$
43. $\{y \mid y > 3\}, (3, \infty)$
45. $\{n \mid n < 17\}, (-\infty, 17)$,
47. $\{x \mid x \le -9\}, (-\infty, -9]$,
49. $\{y \mid y \le \frac{1}{2}\}, \left(-\infty, \frac{1}{2}\right]$,
51. $\{t \mid t > \frac{5}{8}\}, \left(\frac{5}{8}, \infty\right)$,
53. $\{x \mid x < 0\}, (-\infty, 0)$,
55. $\{t \mid t < 23\}, (-\infty, 23)$
57. $\{y \mid y \ge 22\}, [22, \infty)$,
59. $\{x \mid x < 7\}, (-\infty, 7)$
61. $\{t \mid t < -3\}, (-\infty, -3)$,

63. $\{n \mid n \geq -1.5\}, [-1.5, \infty)$,

65. $\{y \mid y \geq -\frac{1}{10}\}, \left[-\frac{1}{10}, \infty\right)$

67. $\{x \mid x < -\frac{4}{5}\}, \left(-\infty, -\frac{4}{5}\right)$

69. $\{x \mid x < 6\}$, or $(-\infty, 6)$ **71.** $\{t \mid t \leq 7\}$, or $(-\infty, 7]$
73. $\{x \mid x > -4\}$, or $(-4, \infty)$ **75.** $\{y \mid y < -\frac{10}{3}\}$, or
$\left(-\infty, -\frac{10}{3}\right)$ **77.** $\{x \mid x > -10\}$, or $(-10, \infty)$
79. $\{y \mid y < 0\}$, or $(-\infty, 0)$ **81.** $\{y \mid y \geq \frac{3}{2}\}$, or $\left[\frac{3}{2}, \infty\right)$
83. $\{x \mid x > -4\}$, or $(-4, \infty)$ **85.** $\{t \mid t > 1\}$, or $(1, \infty)$
87. $\{x \mid x \leq -9\}$, or $(-\infty, -9]$ **89.** $\{t \mid t < 14\}$, or
$(-\infty, 14)$ **91.** $\{y \mid y \leq -4\}$, or $(-\infty, -4]$
93. $\{t \mid t < -\frac{5}{3}\}$, or $\left(-\infty, -\frac{5}{3}\right)$ **95.** $\{r \mid r > -3\}$, or $(-3, \infty)$
97. $\{x \mid x \leq 7\}$, or $(-\infty, 7]$ **99.** $\{x \mid x > -\frac{5}{32}\}$, or $\left(-\frac{5}{32}, \infty\right)$
101. ✍   **103.** $17x - 6$ **104.** $2m - 16n$
105. $7x - 8y - 46$ **106.** $-47t + 1$
107. $35a - 20b - 17$ **108.** $-21x + 32$ **109.** ✍
111. $\{x \mid x \text{ is a real number}\}$, or $(-\infty, \infty)$
113. $\{x \mid x \leq \frac{5}{6}\}$, or $\left(-\infty, \frac{5}{6}\right]$
115. $\{x \mid x \leq -4a\}$, or $(-\infty, -4a]$
117. $\left\{x \mid x > \dfrac{y - b}{a}\right\}$, or $\left(\dfrac{y - b}{a}, \infty\right)$
119. $\{x \mid x \text{ is a real number}\}$, or $(-\infty, \infty)$

Connecting the Concepts, pp. 130–131

1. 21   **2.** $\{x \mid x \leq 21\}$, or $(-\infty, 21]$ **3.** -6
4. $\{x \mid x > -6\}$, or $(-6, \infty)$ **5.** $\{x \mid x < 6\}$, or $(-\infty, 6)$
6. 3   **7.** $-\frac{1}{3}$ **8.** $\{y \mid y < 3\}$, or $(-\infty, 3)$
9. $\{t \mid t \leq -16\}$, or $(-\infty, -16]$ **10.** $\frac{11}{2}$
11. $\{a \mid a < -1\}$, or $(-\infty, -1)$ **12.** $\{x \mid x < 10.75\}$, or
$(-\infty, 10.75)$ **13.** $\{x \mid x \geq -11\}$, or $[-11, \infty)$
14. 105   **15.** -4.24 **16.** 15   **17.** $\{y \mid y \geq 3\}$, or $[3, \infty)$
18. $\frac{14}{3}$ **19.** $\{x \mid x > \frac{22}{5}\}$, or $\left(\frac{22}{5}, \infty\right)$
20. $\{a \mid a \geq 0\}$, or $[0, \infty)$

Translating for Success, p. 134

1. F   **2.** I   **3.** C   **4.** E   **5.** D   **6.** J   **7.** O   **8.** M
9. B   **10.** L

Exercise Set 2.7, pp. 135–138

1. $b \leq a$ **2.** $b < a$ **3.** $a \leq b$ **4.** $a < b$ **5.** $b \leq a$
6. $a \leq b$ **7.** $b < a$ **8.** $a < b$ **9.** Let n represent the
number; $n < 10$ **11.** Let t represent the temperature;
$t \leq -3$ **13.** Let d represent the number of years of
driving experience; $d \geq 5$ **15.** Let a represent the age of
the altar; $a > 1200$ **17.** Let h represent Tania's hourly
wage; $12 < h < 15$ **19.** Let w represent the wind speed;
$w > 50$ **21.** Let c represent the cost of a room; $c \leq 120$
23. More than 2.375 hr   **25.** At least 2.25   **27.** Scores
greater than or equal to 97   **29.** 8 credits or more
31. At least 3 plate appearances   **33.** Lengths greater than
6 cm   **35.** Depths less than 437.5 ft   **37.** Blue-book value

is greater than or equal to $10,625   **39.** Lengths less than
55 in.   **41.** Temperatures greater than 37°C
43. No more than 3 ft tall   **45.** A serving contains at least
16 g of fat.   **47.** Dates after September 16   **49.** No more
than 134 text messages   **51.** Years after 2012
53. Mileages less than or equal to 225   **55.** ✍   **57.** -14
58. $-\frac{2}{3}$ **59.** -60 **60.** -11.1 **61.** 0   **62.** 5
63. -2 **64.** -1 **65.** ✍   **67.** Temperatures between
$-15°C$ and $-9\frac{4}{9}°C$ **69.** Lengths less than or equal to 8 cm
71. They contain at least 7.5 g of fat per serving.
73. At least $42   **75.** ✍

Review Exercises: Chapter 2, pp. 142–143

1. True   **2.** False   **3.** True   **4.** True   **5.** True
6. False   **7.** True   **8.** True   **9.** -25 **10.** 7
11. -65 **12.** 3   **13.** -20 **14.** 1.11   **15.** $\frac{1}{2}$ **16.** $-\frac{3}{2}$
17. -8 **18.** -4 **19.** $-\frac{1}{3}$ **20.** 4   **21.** No solution;
contradiction   **22.** 4   **23.** 16   **24.** 1   **25.** $-\frac{7}{5}$ **26.** 0
27. All real numbers; identity   **28.** $d = \dfrac{C}{\pi}$ **29.** $B = \dfrac{3V}{h}$
30. $y = \frac{5}{2}x - 5$ **31.** $x = \dfrac{b}{t - a}$ **32.** 0.012   **33.** 44%
34. 70%   **35.** 140   **36.** No   **37.** Yes   **38.** No
39. $5x - 6 < 2x + 3$

40. $-2 < x \leq 5$

41. $t > 0$ **42.** $\{t \mid t \geq -\frac{1}{2}\}$, or $\left[-\frac{1}{2}, \infty\right)$

43. $\{x \mid x \geq 7\}$, or $[7, \infty)$ **44.** $\{y \mid y > 3\}$, or $(3, \infty)$
45. $\{y \mid y \leq -4\}$, or $(-\infty, -4]$
46. $\{x \mid x < -11\}$, or $(-\infty, -11)$ **47.** $\{y \mid y > -7\}$, or
$(-7, \infty)$ **48.** $\{x \mid x > -6\}$, or $(-6, \infty)$
49. $\{x \mid x > -\frac{9}{11}\}$, or $\left(-\frac{9}{11}, \infty\right)$ **50.** $\{t \mid t \leq -12\}$, or
$(-\infty, -12]$ **51.** $\{x \mid x \leq -8\}$, or $(-\infty, -8]$
52. About 48%   **53.** 8 ft, 10 ft   **54.** Japanese students:
41,000; Chinese students: 62,000   **55.** 57, 59
56. Width: 11 cm; length: 17 cm   **57.** $160   **58.** About 109
million subscribers   **59.** 35°, 85°, 60°   **60.** No more than
55 g of fat   **61.** 14 or fewer copies   **62.** ✍ Multiplying
both sides of an equation by *any* nonzero number results in
an equivalent equation. When multiplying on both sides of
an inequality, the sign of the number being multiplied by
must be considered. If the number is positive, the direction
of the inequality symbol remains unchanged; if the number
is negative, the direction of the inequality symbol must be
reversed to produce an equivalent inequality.   **63.** ✍
The solutions of an equation can usually each be checked.
The solutions of an inequality are normally too numerous
to check. Checking a few numbers from the solution set
found cannot guarantee that the answer is correct, although
if any number does not check, the answer found is
incorrect.   **64.** About 1 hr 36 min   **65.** Nile: 4160 mi;
Amazon: 4225 mi   **66.** $16   **67.** $-23, 23$ **68.** $-20, 20$
69. $a = \dfrac{y - 3}{2 - b}$ **70.** $F = \dfrac{0.3(12w)}{9}$, or $F = 0.4w$

Test: Chapter 2, p. 144

1. [2.1] 9   **2.** [2.1] 15   **3.** [2.1] −3   **4.** [2.1] 49
5. [2.1] −12   **6.** [2.2] 2   **7.** [2.1] −8   **8.** [2.2] $-\frac{23}{67}$
9. [2.2] 7   **10.** [2.2] $\frac{23}{3}$ **11.** [2.2] All real numbers; identity
12. [2.6] $\{x | x > -5\}$, or $(-5, \infty)$
13. [2.6] $\{x | x > -13\}$, or $(-13, \infty)$
14. [2.6] $\{y | y \le -13\}$, or $(-\infty, -13]$
15. [2.6] $\{y | y \le -\frac{15}{2}\}$, or $(-\infty, -\frac{15}{2}]$
16. [2.6] $\{n | n < -5\}$, or $(-\infty, -5)$
17. [2.6] $\{x | x < -7\}$, or $(-\infty, -7)$
18. [2.6] $\{t | t \ge -1\}$, or $[-1, \infty)$
19. [2.6] $\{x | x \le -1\}$, or $(-\infty, -1]$

20. [2.3] $r = \dfrac{A}{2\pi h}$ **21.** [2.3] $l = 2w - P$ **22.** [2.4] 2.3

23. [2.4] 0.3%   **24.** [2.4] 14.8   **25.** [2.4] 44%
26. [2.6]

$y < 4$
<-----●-------------------->
−10 −8 −6 −4 −2 0 2 4 6 8 10

27. [2.6]

$-2 \le x \le 2$
<-----[========]----->
−5 −4 −3 −2 −1 0 1 2 3 4 5

28. [2.5] Width: 7 cm; length: 11 cm   **29.** [2.5] 525 mi
from Springer Mountain and 1575 mi from Mt. Katahdin
30. [2.5] 81 mm, 83 mm, 85 mm   **31.** [2.4] $65
32. [2.7] More than 36 one-way trips per month

33. [2.3] $d = \dfrac{a}{3}$ **34.** [1.4], [2.2] −15, 15   **35.** [2.7] Let

h = the number of hours of sun each day; $4 \le h \le 6$
36. [2.5] 60 tickets

Cumulative Review: Chapters 1–2, pp. 145–146

1. −12   **2.** $\frac{3}{4}$ **3.** −4.2   **4.** 10   **5.** 134   **6.** 149
7. $2x + 1$ **8.** $-10t + 12$ **9.** $-21n + 36$
10.

$-\frac{5}{2}$
<----●--------------------->
−5 −4 −3 −2 −1 0 1 2 3 4 5

11. 27

12. $6(2x + 3y + 5z)$ **13.** −6   **14.** 16   **15.** 9

16. $\frac{13}{18}$ **17.** 1   **18.** $-\frac{7}{2}$ **19.** $z = \dfrac{x}{4y}$ **20.** $y = \frac{4}{9}x - \frac{1}{9}$

21. $n = \dfrac{p}{a + r}$ **22.** 1.83   **23.** 37.5%
24.

$t > -\frac{5}{2}$
<----(--------------------->
$-\frac{5}{2}$
−5 −4 −3 −2 −1 0 1 2 3 4 5

25. $\{t | t \le -2\}$, or $(-\infty, -2]$

26. $\{t | t < 3\}$, or $(-\infty, 3)$ **27.** $\{x | x < 30\}$, or $(-\infty, 30)$
28. $\{n | n \ge 2\}$, or $[2, \infty)$ **29.** 48 million   **30.** 3.2 hr
31. $14\frac{1}{3}$ m   **32.** 9 ft, 15 ft   **33.** No more than $52
34. About 194%   **35.** 105°   **36.** For widths greater than
27 cm   **37.** $4t$ **38.** −5, 5   **39.** $1025

CHAPTER 3

Exercise Set 3.1, pp. 154–157

1. (a)   **2.** (c)   **3.** (b)   **4.** (d)   **5.** 2 drinks
7. The person weighs more than 140 lb.   **9.** About $5156

11. $231,856,000   **13.** About 29.2 million tons   **15.** About
3.2 million tons   **17.** About $12 billion   **19.** 2001

21.

23.

25.

27. $A(-4, 5); B(-3, -3); C(0, 4); D(3, 4); E(3, -4)$
29. $A(4, 1); B(0, -5); C(-4, 0); D(-3, -2); E(3, 0)$
31.

33.

35.

37.

39.

41. IV   **43.** III   **45.** I
47. II   **49.** I and IV
51. I and III   **53.** ✍

55. $y = \dfrac{2x}{5}$, or $y = \frac{2}{5}x$

56. $y = \dfrac{-3x}{2}$, or $y = -\frac{3}{2}x$

57. $y = x - 8$
58. $y = -\frac{2}{5}x + 2$
59. $y = -\frac{2}{3}x + \frac{5}{3}$

60. $y = \frac{5}{8}x - \frac{1}{8}$ **61.** ✍   **63.** II or IV   **65.** $(-1, -5)$

67.

Second axis / First axis

69. $\frac{65}{2}$ sq units
71. Latitude 27° North; longitude 81° West
73. 🖳

19.

$$\begin{array}{c|c} 4x - 2y = 10 \\ \hline 4 \cdot 0 - 2(-5) & 10 \\ 0 + 10 & \\ & 10 \stackrel{?}{=} 10 \quad \text{True} \end{array}$$

$$\begin{array}{c|c} 4x - 2y = 10 \\ \hline 4 \cdot 4 - 2 \cdot 3 & 10 \\ 16 - 6 & \\ & 10 \stackrel{?}{=} 10 \quad \text{True} \end{array}$$

$(2, -1)$; answers may vary

21. $y = x + 1$

23. $y = -x$

Technology Connection, p. 164

1. $y = -5x + 6.5$

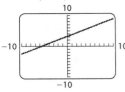

2. $y = 3x + 4.5$

3. $7y - 4x = 22$, or $y = \frac{4}{7}x + \frac{22}{7}$

4. $5y + 11x = -20$, or $y = -\frac{11}{5}x - 4$

5. $2y - x^2 = 0$, or $y = 0.5x^2$

6. $y + x^2 = 8$, or $y = -x^2 + 8$

25. $y = 2x$

27. $y = 2x + 2$

29. $y = -\frac{1}{2}x$

31. 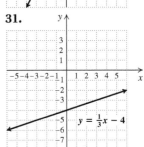 $y = \frac{1}{3}x - 4$

Exercise Set 3.2, pp. 165–167

1. False **2.** True **3.** True **4.** True **5.** True
6. False **7.** Yes **9.** No **11.** No

13.
$$\begin{array}{c|c} y = x + 3 \\ \hline 2 & -1 + 3 \\ 2 \stackrel{?}{=} 2 & \text{True} \end{array}$$

$$\begin{array}{c|c} y = x + 3 \\ \hline 7 & 4 + 3 \\ 7 \stackrel{?}{=} 7 & \text{True} \end{array}$$

$(2, 5)$; answers may vary

15.
$$\begin{array}{c|c} y = \frac{1}{2}x + 3 \\ \hline 5 & \frac{1}{2} \cdot 4 + 3 \\ & 2 + 3 \\ 5 \stackrel{?}{=} 5 & \text{True} \end{array}$$

$$\begin{array}{c|c} y = \frac{1}{2}x + 3 \\ \hline 2 & \frac{1}{2}(-2) + 3 \\ & -1 + 3 \\ 2 \stackrel{?}{=} 2 & \text{True} \end{array}$$

$(0, 3)$; answers may vary

17.
$$\begin{array}{c|c} y + 3x = 7 \\ \hline 1 + 3 \cdot 2 & 7 \\ 1 + 6 & \\ 7 \stackrel{?}{=} 7 & \text{True} \end{array}$$

$$\begin{array}{c|c} y + 3x = 7 \\ \hline -5 + 3 \cdot 4 & 7 \\ -5 + 12 & \\ 7 \stackrel{?}{=} 7 & \text{True} \end{array}$$

$(1, 4)$; answers may vary

33. $x + y = 4$

35. $x - y = -2$

37. $x + 2y = -6$

39. $y = -\frac{2}{3}x + 4$

41.
4x = 3y

43.
5x − y = 0

71.
s + n = 24
Southbound Gear
Northbound Gear

73. x + y = 5, or
y = −x + 5
75. y = x + 2

45.
6x − 3y = 9

47.
6y + 2x = 8

77.
25d + 5l = 225

Answers may vary.
1 dinner, 40 lunches;
5 dinners, 20 lunches;
8 dinners, 5 lunches

49. About $3800

51. About $49

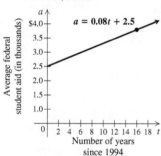
a = 0.08t + 2.5
Average federal student aid (in thousands)
Number of years since 1994

c = 3.1w + 29.07
Cost of shipping FedEx package
Weight (in pounds)

79.
y = −|x|

81.
y = x²

53. About $96

55. About 33 gal

p = 3.5n + 9
Price of assembled scrapbook
Number of pages

w = 1.6t + 16.7
Gallons of bottled water per person per year
Number of years since 2000

83.
y = −2.8x + 3.5

85.
y = 2.8x − 3.5

87.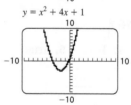
y = x² + 4x + 1

89. $56.62; 16.2 gal

57. About $1700

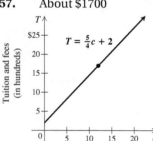
T = 5/4 c + 2
Tuition and fees (in hundreds)
Number of credits

59. 📖
61. $\frac{12}{5}$
62. $-\frac{3}{4}$
63. 3
64. $-\frac{21}{5}$
65. Q = 2A − T
66. $p = \dfrac{w}{q + 1}$
67. $y = \dfrac{C - Ax}{B}$
68. y = m(x − h) + k
69. 📖

Technology Connection, p. 171

1. y = −0.72x − 15

Xscl = 5, Yscl = 5

2. y − 2.13x = 27, or
y = 2.13x + 27

Xscl = 5, Yscl = 5

3. $5x + 6y = 84$, or
$y = -\frac{5}{6}x + 14$

Xscl = 5, Yscl = 5

4. $2x - 7y = 150$, or
$y = \frac{2}{7}x - \frac{150}{7}$

Xscl = 10, Yscl = 5

5. $19x - 17y = 200$, or
$y = \frac{19}{17}x - \frac{200}{17}$

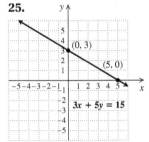

6. $6x + 5y = 159$, or
$y = -\frac{6}{5}x + \frac{159}{5}$

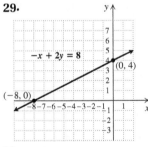

Xscl = 5, Yscl = 5

Exercise Set 3.3, pp. 173–175

1. (f)   **2.** (e)   **3.** (d)   **4.** (c)   **5.** (b)   **6.** (a)
7. (a) $(0, 5)$; **(b)** $(2, 0)$ **9. (a)** $(0, -4)$; **(b)** $(3, 0)$
11. (a) $(0, -2)$; **(b)** $(-3, 0), (3, 0)$ **13. (a)** $(0, 0)$;
(b) $(-2, 0), (0, 0), (5, 0)$ **15. (a)** $(0, 3)$; **(b)** $(5, 0)$
17. (a) $(0, -18)$; **(b)** $(4, 0)$ **19. (a)** $(0, 16)$; **(b)** $(-20, 0)$
21. (a) None; **(b)** $(12, 0)$ **23. (a)** $(0, -9)$; **(b)** none

25.

$3x + 5y = 15$

27.

$x + 2y = 4$

29.

$-x + 2y = 8$

31.

$3x + y = 9$

33.

$y = 2x - 6$

35.

$5x - 10 = 5y$

37.

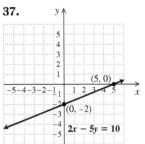

$2x - 5y = 10$

39.

$6x + 2y = 12$

41.

$4x + 3y = 16$

43.

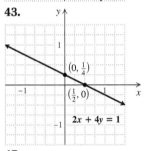

$2x + 4y = 1$

45.

$5x - 3y = 180$

47.

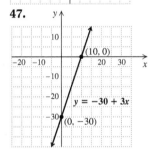

$y = -30 + 3x$

49.

$-4x = 20y + 80$

51.

$y - 3x = 0$

53.

$y = 1$

55.

$x = 3$

57.

$y = -2$

59.

$x = -1$

61.

63.

65.

67.

69.

71. $y = -1$ **73.** $x = 4$
75. $x = 0$ **77.** ✍
79. $d - 7$
80. $w + 5$, or $5 + w$
81. Let n represent the number; $7 + 4n$
82. Let n represent the number; $3n$
83. Let x and y represent the numbers; $2(x + y)$
84. Let a and b represent the numbers; $\frac{1}{2}(a + b)$
85. ✍   **87.** $y = 0$ **89.** $x = -2$ **91.** $(-3, 4)$
93. $-5x + 3y = 15$, or $y = \frac{5}{3}x + 5$ **95.** -24
97. $\left(\dfrac{C - D}{A}, 0\right)$ **99.** $\left(0, -\frac{80}{7}\right)$, or $(0, -11.\overline{428571})$; $(40, 0)$
101. $(0, -9)$; $(45, 0)$ **103.** $\left(0, \frac{1}{25}\right)$, or $(0, 0.04)$; $\left(\frac{1}{50}, 0\right)$, or $(0.02, 0)$

Exercise Set 3.4, pp. 179–184

1. Miles per hour, or $\dfrac{\text{miles}}{\text{hour}}$

2. Hours per chapter, or $\dfrac{\text{hours}}{\text{chapter}}$

3. Dollars per mile, or $\dfrac{\text{dollars}}{\text{mile}}$

4. Petunias per foot, or $\dfrac{\text{petunias}}{\text{foot}}$

5. Minutes per errand, or $\dfrac{\text{minutes}}{\text{errand}}$

6. Cups of flour per cake, or $\dfrac{\text{cups of flour}}{\text{cake}}$

7. (a) 30 mpg; (b) \$39.33/day; (c) 130 mi/day; (d) 30¢/mi
9. (a) 7 mph; (b) \$7.50/hr; (c) \$1.07/mi
11. (a) \$22/hr; (b) 20.6 pages/hr; (c) \$1.07/page
13. \$568.4 billion/yr **15.** (a) 14.5 floors/min;
(b) 4.14 sec/floor   **17.** (a) 23.42 ft/min; (b) 0.04 min/ft

19.

21.

23.

25.

27.

29. 20 calls/hr   **31.** 75 mi/hr   **33.** 12¢/min
35. -2000 people/yr   **37.** 0.02 gal/mi   **39.** (e)   **41.** (d)
43. (b)   **45.** ✍   **47.** 5   **48.** -6 **49.** -1 **50.** $-\frac{4}{3}$
51. $-\frac{4}{3}$ **52.** 1   **53.** 0   **54.** Undefined   **55.** ✍
57.
59.

61. 0.45 min/mi   **63.** About 41.6 min   **65.** 3.6 bu/hr

Exercise Set 3.5, pp. 190–196

1. Positive   **2.** Negative   **3.** Negative   **4.** Positive
5. Positive   **6.** Negative   **7.** Zero   **8.** Positive
9. Negative   **10.** Zero   **11.** \$60/blog   **13.** $-$\$6/month
15. 1 point/\$1000 income   **17.** About $-2.1°$/min   **19.** $\frac{4}{3}$
21. $\frac{3}{2}$ **23.** 2   **25.** -1 **27.** 0   **29.** $-\frac{1}{3}$

31. Undefined   **33.** $-\frac{3}{4}$ **35.** $\frac{1}{4}$ **37.** 0   **39.** $\frac{5}{4}$
41. $-\frac{4}{5}$ **43.** $\frac{2}{3}$ **45.** -1 **47.** $-\frac{1}{2}$ **49.** 0
51. 1   **53.** Undefined   **55.** 0   **57.** Undefined
59. Undefined   **61.** 0   **63.** 15%   **65.** 35%
67. $\frac{29}{98}$, or about 30%   **69.** About 5.1%; yes   **71.**
73. $y = \dfrac{c - ax}{b}$ **74.** $r = \dfrac{p + mn}{x}$ **75.** $y = \dfrac{ax - c}{b}$

76. $t = \dfrac{q - rs}{n}$

77.   **78.**

79.   **81.** 0.364, or 36.4%   **83.** $\{m \mid m \geq \frac{5}{2}\}$ **85.** $\frac{1}{2}$

Technology Connection, p. 201

1. $y_1 = -\frac{3}{4}x - 2,\ y_2 = -\frac{1}{5}x - 2,$
$y_3 = -\frac{3}{4}x - 5,\ y_4 = -\frac{1}{5}x - 5$

Exercise Set 3.6, pp. 203–205

1. (f)   **2.** (b)   **3.** (d)   **4.** (c)   **5.** (e)   **6.** (a)
7.   **9.**

11.   **13.**

15.   **17.**

19. $-\frac{2}{7}; (0, 5)$ **21.** $\frac{1}{3}; (0, 7)$ **23.** $\frac{9}{5}; (0, -4)$ **25.** $3; (0, 7)$
27. $-2; (0, 4)$ **29.** $0; (0, 3)$ **31.** $\frac{2}{5}, \left(0, \frac{8}{5}\right)$ **33.** $\frac{9}{8}; (0, 0)$
35. $y = 5x + 7$ **37.** $y = \frac{7}{8}x - 1$ **39.** $y = -\frac{5}{3}x - 8$
41. $y = \frac{1}{3}$ **43.** $y = \frac{3}{2}x + 17$, where y is the number of gallons per person and x is the number of years since 2000   **45.** $y = \frac{2}{5}x + 15$, where y is the number of jobs, in millions, and x is the number of years since 2000

47.   **49.**

51.   **53.**

55.   **57.**

59.   **61.**

63. Yes   **65.** No   **67.** Yes   **69.** Yes   **71.** No   **73.** Yes

75. $y = 5x + 11$ **77.** $y = \frac{1}{2}x$ **79.** $y = x + 3$
81. $y = x - 4$ **83.**   **85.** $y = m(x - h) + k$
86. $y = -2(x + 4) + 9$ **87.** -7 **88.** 13   **89.** -9
90. -11 **91.**   **93.** When $x = 0, y = b$, so $(0, b)$ is
on the line. When $x = 1, y = m + b$, so $(1, m + b)$ is on the
line. Then

$$\text{slope} = \frac{(m + b) - b}{1 - 0} = m.$$

95. $y = \frac{1}{3}x + 3$ **97.** $y = -\frac{5}{3}x + 3$ **99.** $y = -\frac{2}{3}x$

Connecting the Concepts, p. 206

1. (a) Yes;
(b)
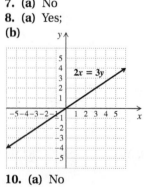

2. (a) Yes;
(b)

3. (a) Yes;
(b)

4. (a) Yes;
(b)

5. (a) Yes;
(b)

6. (a) Yes;
(b)
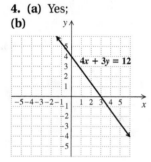

7. (a) No
8. (a) Yes;
(b)

9. (a) Yes;
(b)

10. (a) No

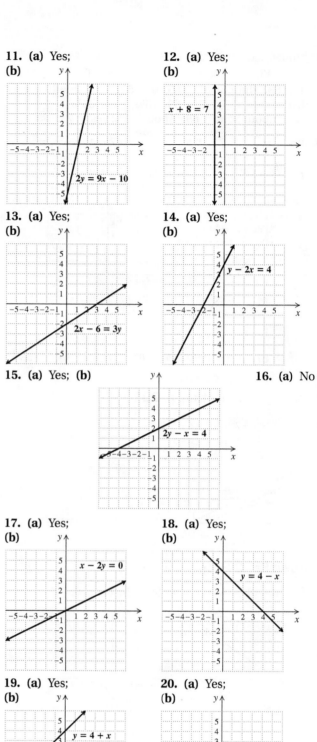

11. (a) Yes;
(b)

12. (a) Yes;
(b)

13. (a) Yes;
(b)

14. (a) Yes;
(b)

15. (a) Yes; **(b)**   **16. (a)** No

17. (a) Yes;
(b)

18. (a) Yes;
(b)

19. (a) Yes;
(b)

20. (a) Yes;
(b)

Technology Connection, p. 208

1. $y_1 = \frac{3}{4}x + 2;\ y_2 = -\frac{4}{3}x - 1$

2. $y_1 = -\frac{2}{5}x - 4;\ y_2 = \frac{5}{2}x + 3$

3. $y_1 = \frac{31}{40}x + 2;\ y_2 = -\frac{40}{30}x - 1$ No: $-\frac{40}{30} \neq -\frac{1}{\frac{31}{40}}$

Although the lines appear to be perpendicular, they are not, because the product of their slopes is not -1:
$$\frac{31}{40}\left(-\frac{40}{30}\right) = -\frac{1240}{1200} \neq -1.$$

Visualizing for Success, p. 212

1. C   **2.** G   **3.** F   **4.** B   **5.** D   **6.** A   **7.** I
8. H   **9.** J   **10.** E

Exercise Set 3.7, pp. 213-216

1. (g)   **2.** (b)   **3.** (d)   **4.** (h)   **5.** (e)   **6.** (a)
7. (f)   **8.** (c)   **9.** (c)   **10.** (b)   **11.** (d)   **12.** (a)
13. $y - 6 = 3(x - 1)$ **15.** $y - 8 = \frac{3}{5}(x - 2)$
17. $y - 1 = -4(x - 3)$ **19.** $y - (-4) = \frac{3}{2}(x - 5)$
21. $y - 6 = -\frac{5}{4}(x - (-2))$
23. $y - (-1) = -2(x - (-4))$
25. $y - 8 = 1(x - (-2))$ **27.** $y = 4x - 7$
29. $y = \frac{7}{4}x - 9$ **31.** $y = -2x + 1$ **33.** $y = -4x - 9$
35. $y = \frac{2}{3}x + \frac{8}{3}$ **37.** $y = -\frac{5}{6}x + 4$ **39.** $y = \frac{1}{2}x + 4$
41. $y = 4x - 5$ **43.** $y = -\frac{2}{3}x - \frac{13}{3}$ **45.** $x = 5$
47. $y = -\frac{3}{2}x + \frac{11}{2}$ **49.** $y = x + 6$ **51.** $y = -\frac{1}{2}x + 6$
53. $x = -3$
55.   **57.**
59.   **61.**

63.   **65.**

67.   **69.**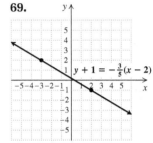

71. **(a)** 51.6 births per 1000 females; **(b)** 39.8 births per 1000 females   **73.** **(a)** About 13.1%; **(b)** 4%
75. **(a)** 16.47 million students; **(b)** 18.95 million students
77. **(a)** 33.65 million residents; **(b)** about 38.6 million residents
79. $y = -x + 5$ **81.** $y = \frac{2}{3}x + 3$ **83.** $y = \frac{2}{5}x - 2$
85. $y = 2x + 7$ **87.** ✍   **89.** -125 **90.** 64   **91.** -64
92. 8   **93.** 28   **94.** -4 **95.** ✍
97.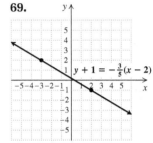
99. $y = 2x - 9$
101. $y = -\frac{4}{3}x + \frac{23}{3}$
103. $y = -4x + 7$
105. $y = \frac{10}{3}x + \frac{25}{3}$
107. $(2, 0), (0, 5)$

109. $-\frac{x}{4} + \frac{y}{3} = 1; (-4, 0), (0, 3)$ **111.** ✍

Connecting the Concepts, pp. 216-217

1. Slope–intercept form   **2.** Standard form
3. None of these   **4.** Standard form
5. Point–slope form   **6.** None of these
7. $2x - 5y = 10$ **8.** $x - y = 2$
9. $-2x + y = 7$, or $2x - y = -7$ **10.** $\frac{1}{2}x + y = 3$
11. $3x - y = -23$, or $-3x + y = 23$ **12.** $x + 0y = 18$
13. $y = \frac{2}{7}x - \frac{8}{7}$ **14.** $y = -x - 8$ **15.** $y = 8x - 3$
16. $y = -\frac{3}{5}x + 3$ **17.** $y = -\frac{8}{9}x + \frac{5}{9}$ **18.** $y = -x$
19. $y = -\frac{1}{2}$ **20.** $y = \frac{1}{2}x$

Review Exercises: Chapter 3, pp. 220-222

1. True   **2.** True   **3.** False   **4.** False   **5.** True
6. True   **7.** True   **8.** False   **9.** True   **10.** True
11. About 1.3 billion searches   **12.** About 1137 searches

13.–15.

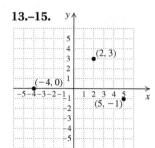

16. III **17.** IV **18.** II
19. $(-5, -1)$ **20.** $(-2, 5)$
21. $(3, 0)$

22.

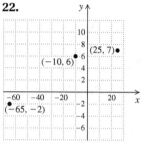

23. (a) No; **(b)** yes

24.

$$\frac{2x - y = 3}{2 \cdot 0 - (-3) \mid 3}$$
$$0 + 3 \mid$$
$$3 \overset{?}{=} 3 \quad \text{True}$$

$$\frac{2x - y = 3}{2 \cdot 2 - 1 \mid 3}$$
$$4 - 1 \mid$$
$$3 \overset{?}{=} 3 \quad \text{True}$$

$(-1, -5)$; answers may vary

25.

26.

27.

28.

29.

30.

31. About 7 million viewers

32. (a) $\frac{2}{15}$ mi/min;
(b) 7.5 min/mi
33. 12 mpg **34.** 0
35. $\frac{7}{3}$ **36.** $-\frac{3}{7}$ **37.** $-\frac{6}{5}$
38. 0 **39.** Undefined
40. 2 **41.** $8.\overline{3}\%$
42. $(16, 0), (0, -10)$
43. $-\frac{3}{5}; (0, 9)$
44. Perpendicular
45. Parallel

46. $y = \frac{3}{8}x + 7$ **47.** $y - 9 = -\frac{1}{3}(x - (-2))$
48. (a) \$1725; **(b)** \$2701 **49.** $y = 5x - 25$
50. $y = -\frac{5}{3}x - \frac{5}{3}$

51.

52.

53.

54.

55.

56. Two perpendicular lines share the same y-intercept if their point of intersection is on the y-axis.
57. The graph of a vertical line has only an x-intercept. The graph of a horizontal line has only a y-intercept. The graph of a nonvertical, non-horizontal line will have only one intercept if it passes through the origin: $(0, 0)$ is both the x-intercept and the y-intercept. **58.** -1
59. 19 **60.** Area: 45 sq units; perimeter: 28 units
61. $(0, 4), (1, 3), (-1, 3)$; answers may vary

Test: Chapter 3, pp. 222–223

1. [3.1] About 95 students **2.** [3.1] About 137 students
3. [3.1] III **4.** [3.1] II **5.** [3.1] $(3, 4)$ **6.** [3.1] $(0, -4)$
7. [3.1] $(-5, 2)$

8. [3.2]

9. [3.3]

10. [3.3]

11. [3.2]

12. [3.2]

13. [3.3]
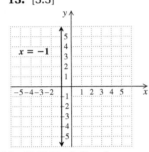

14. [3.5] 5   **15.** [3.5] $-\frac{9}{4}$ **16.** [3.5] Undefined
17. [3.4] $\frac{1}{3}$ km/min   **18.** [3.5] 31.5%
19. [3.3] $(6,0),(0,-30)$ **20.** [3.6] 8; $(0,10)$
21. [3.6] $y=-\frac{1}{3}x-11$ **22.** [3.6] Parallel
23. [3.6] Perpendicular   **24.** [3.7] $y=-\frac{5}{2}x-\frac{11}{2}$
25. [3.7] **(a)**   **(b)** 138 beats per minute

26. [3.6]

27. [3.7]

28. [3.6] $y=\frac{2}{5}x+9$ **29.** [3.1] Area: 25 sq units;
perimeter: 20 units   **30.** [3.2], [3.7] $(0,12),(-3,15),(5,7)$

Cumulative Review: Chapters 1–3, pp. 224–225

1. 7   **2.** $12a-6b+18$ **3.** $4(2x-y+1)$ **4.** $2\cdot3^3$
5. -0.15 **6.** 37   **7.** $\frac{1}{10}$ **8.** -10 **9.** 0.367   **10.** $\frac{11}{60}$
11. 2.6   **12.** 7.28   **13.** $-\frac{5}{12}$ **14.** -3 **15.** 27
16. $-2y-7$ **17.** $5x+11$ **18.** -2.6 **19.** -27
20. 16   **21.** -6 **22.** 2   **23.** $\frac{7}{9}$ **24.** -17 **25.** 2
26. $\{x|x<16\}$, or $(-\infty,16)$ **27.** $\{x|x\le-\frac{11}{8}\}$, or
$(-\infty,-\frac{11}{8}]$ **28.** $h=\dfrac{A-\pi r^2}{2\pi r}$ **29.** IV

30.

31.

32.

33.

34.

35.

36.

37.

38. $\left(\frac{21}{2},0\right),(0,-3)$
39. $\left(-\frac{5}{4},0\right),(0,5)$
40. 3; $(0,-2)$ **41.** $-\frac{1}{3}$
42. $y=\frac{2}{7}x-4$
43. $y-4=-\frac{3}{8}(x-(-6))$
44. $y=-\frac{3}{8}x+\frac{7}{4}$
45. $y=2x+1$
46. 0.5 million bicycles per year

47. (a)

$c = \frac{85}{3}r + 70$

Cycling rate
(in miles per hour)

(b) about 353 calories per hour

48. $210 billion   **49.** $54,533   **50.** 21 million Americans
51. $120   **52.** 50 m, 53 m, 40 m   **53.** 4 hr
54. $25,000   **55.** $-4, 4$ **56.** 2   **57.** -5 **58.** 3
59. No solution   **60.** $Q = \dfrac{2 - pm}{p}$
61. $y = -\frac{7}{3}x + 7; y = -\frac{7}{3}x - 7; y = \frac{7}{3}x - 7; y = \frac{7}{3}x + 7$

Chapter 4

Visualizing for Success, p. 236

1. C   **2.** H   **3.** J   **4.** G   **5.** D   **6.** I   **7.** A   **8.** F
9. E   **10.** B

Exercise Set 4.1, pp. 237–239

1. True   **2.** False   **3.** True   **4.** True   **5.** True   **6.** False
7. False   **8.** True   **9.** Yes   **11.** No   **13.** Yes   **15.** Yes
17. $(4, 1)$ **19.** $(2, -1)$ **21.** $(4, 3)$ **23.** $(-3, -2)$
25. $(-3, 2)$ **27.** $(3, -7)$ **29.** $(7, 2)$ **31.** $(4, 0)$
33. No solution   **35.** $\{(x, y) | y = 3 - x\}$ **37.** Approximately
$(1.53, 2.58)$ **39.** No solution   **41.** Approximately $(-6.37, -18.77)$
43. All except 33 and 39   **45.** 35   **47.** Full-time faculty:
$y = 9.0524x + 430.6778$; part-time faculty: $y = 14.7175x +$
185.3643; y is in thousands and x is the number of years after 1980;
in about 2023   **49.** Independent advisers: $y = 2.7x + 20.4$;
financial advisers at firms: $y = -1.5x + 61.6$; y is in thousands
and x is the number of years after 2004; in about 2014
51. TW   **53.** 15   **54.** $\frac{19}{12}$ **55.** $\frac{9}{20}$ **56.** $\frac{13}{3}$
57. $y = -\frac{3}{4}x + \frac{7}{4}$ **58.** $y = \frac{2}{5}x - \frac{9}{5}$ **59.** TW   **61.** Answers
may vary. **(a)** $x + y = 6, x - y = 4$; **(b)** $x + y = 1, 2x + 2y = 3$;
(c) $x + y = 1, 2x + 2y = 2$ **63.** $A = -\frac{17}{4}, B = -\frac{12}{5}$
65. $(0, 0), (1, 1)$ **67.** (c)   **69.** (b)   **71. (a)** $n = \frac{68}{3}t + 46$;
$n = 4t + 140$; **(b)** 2009

Exercise Set 4.2, pp. 244–246

1. False   **2.** True   **3.** True   **4.** True   **5.** $(1, 4)$ **7.** $(2, 1)$
9. $(4, 3)$ **11.** $(-20, 5)$ **13.** $(-2, 4)$ **15.** No solution
17. $(-1, -3)$ **19.** $\left(\frac{17}{3}, \frac{2}{3}\right)$ **21.** $\{(x, y) | x - 2y = 7\}$
23. $\{(x, y) | y = 2x + 5\}$ **25.** $\left(\frac{25}{8}, -\frac{11}{4}\right)$ **27.** $(6, 0)$
29. $(10, 5)$ **31.** $\{(x, y) | y = 3 - 4x\}$ **33.** $(-3, -4)$
35. No solution   **37.** 39, 44   **39.** 42, 51   **41.** 12, 28
43. $55°, 125°$ **45.** $36°, 54°$ **47.** Length: 28 in.; width: 22 in.
49. Length: 380 mi; width: 270 mi   **51.** Length: 90 yd; width: 50 yd
53. Height: 20 ft; width: 5 ft   **55.** TW   **57.** $-5x - 3y$
58. $-11x$ **59.** $-11y$ **60.** $-6y - 25$ **61.** $-11y$ **62.** $23x$
63. TW   **65.** $(7, -1)$ **67.** $(4.38, 4.33)$ **69.** 34 yr
71. $(30, 50, 100)$ **73.** TW

Exercise Set 4.3, pp. 252–253

1. False   **2.** True   **3.** True   **4.** True   **5.** $(9, 3)$ **7.** $(5, 1)$
9. $(2, 7)$ **11.** $(-1, 3)$ **13.** $\left(-1, \frac{1}{5}\right)$ **15.** $\{(a, b) | 3a - 6b = 8\}$
17. $(-3, -5)$ **19.** $(4, 5)$ **21.** $(3, 10)$ **23.** No solution
25. $\left(\frac{1}{2}, -\frac{1}{2}\right)$ **27.** $(-3, -1)$ **29.** No solution   **31.** $(50, 18)$
33. $(-2, 2)$ **35.** $(2, -1)$ **37.** $\left(\frac{231}{202}, \frac{117}{202}\right)$ **39.** 40 mi
41. $26°, 64°$ **43.** $13\frac{1}{3}$ min   **45.** $56°, 124°$ **47.** Riesling:
340 acres; Chardonnay: 480 acres   **49.** Length: 6 ft; width: 3 ft
51. TW   **53.** 0.122   **54.** 0.005   **55.** 40%   **56.** 3.06
57. Let $l =$ the number of liters; $0.12l$ **58.** Let $n =$ the number
of pounds; $0.105n$ **59.** TW   **61.** $(2, 5)$ **63.** $\left(\frac{1}{2}, -\frac{1}{2}\right)$
65. $(0, 3)$ **67.** $x = \dfrac{c - b}{a - 1}; y = \dfrac{ac - b}{a - 1}$ **69.** Rabbits: 12;
pheasants: 23   **71.** Man: 45 yr; his daughter: 10 yr

Mid-Chapter Review: Chapter 4, pp. 254–255

Guided Solutions

1. $2x - 3(x - 1) = 5$
$2x - 3x + 3 = 5$
$-x + 3 = 5$
$-x = 2$
$x = -2$

$y = x - 1$
$y = -2 - 1$
$y = -3$
The solution is $(-2, -3)$.

2. $2x - 5y = 1$
$x + 5y = 8$
$3x = 9$
$x = 3$

$x + 5y = 8$
$3 + 5y = 8$
$5y = 5$
$y = 1$
The solution is $(3, 1)$.

Mixed Review

1. $(1, 1)$ **2.** $(9, 1)$ **3.** $(4, 3)$ **4.** $(5, 7)$ **5.** $(5, 10)$
6. $\left(2, \frac{2}{5}\right)$ **7.** No solution   **8.** $\{(x, y) | x = 2 - y\}$
9. $(1, 1)$ **10.** $(0, 0)$ **11.** $(6, -1)$ **12.** No solution
13. $(3, 1)$ **14.** $\left(\frac{95}{71}, -\frac{1}{142}\right)$ **15.** $(1, 1)$ **16.** $(11, -3)$
17. $\{(x, y) | x - 2y = 5\}$ **18.** $\left(1, -\frac{1}{19}\right)$ **19.** $\left(\frac{201}{23}, -\frac{18}{23}\right)$
20. $\left(\frac{40}{9}, \frac{10}{3}\right)$

Exercise Set 4.4, pp. 265–269

1. Plant species: 601; animal species: 409   **3.** Facebook:
104 million users; MySpace: 56 million users   **5.** $119°, 61°$
7. 3-credit courses: 37; 4-credit courses: 11   **9.** 5-cent bottles or
cans: 336; 10-cent bottles or cans: 94   **11.** 2225 motorcycles
13. Nonrecycled sheets: 38; recycled sheets: 112   **15.** Gemstone
beads: 28; silver beads: 52   **17.** HP cartridges: 15; Epson cartridges: 35   **19.** Mexican: 14 lb; Peruvian: 14 lb
21. Sumac: 8 oz; thyme: 12 oz

23. 50%-acid solution: 80 mL; 80%-acid solution: 120 mL

x	y	200
50%	80%	68%
0.5x	0.8y	136

25. 50% chocolate: 7.5 lb; 10% chocolate: 12.5 lb   **27.** $7500 at 6.5%; $4500 at 7.2%   **29.** Steady State: 12.5 L; Even Flow: 7.5 L
31. 87-octane: 2.5 gal; 95-octane: 7.5 gal   **33.** Whole milk: $169\frac{3}{13}$ lb; cream: $30\frac{10}{13}$ lb   **35.** 375 km   **37.** 14 km/h
39. About 1489 mi   **41.** Foul shots: 28; two-pointers: 36
43. Landline: 85 min; wireless: 315 min   **45.** Quarters: 17; fifty-cent pieces: 13   **47.** ™

49.

50.

51.

52.

53.

54.

55. ™   **57.** $10\frac{2}{3}$ oz   **59.** 1.8 L   **61.** 12 sets   **63.** Brown: 0.8 gal; neutral: 0.2 gal   **65.** City: 261 mi; highway: 204 mi
67. Round Stic: 15 packs; Matic Grip: 9 packs

Exercise Set 4.5, pp. 276–279

1. (e)   **2.** (d)   **3.** (f)   **4.** (b)   **5.** (a)   **6.** (c)   **7.** −2
9. −4   **11.** 8   **13.** 0   **15.** 5   **17.** −2   **19.** None
21. −2, 2   **23.** 5   **25.** −20   **27.** 2.7   **29.** $-\frac{7}{3}$ **31.** 7
33. 3   **35.** 9   **37.** 1   **39.** 6   **41.** $1\frac{1}{3}$ **43.** $9500, or $4500 over $5000   **45.** 5 months   **47.** 2 hr 15 min   **49.** 250 lb
51. ™   **53.** −125   **54.** 64   **55.** −64   **56.** 8   **57.** 28
58. −4   **59.** ™   **61.** −2, 2   **63.** 1   **65.** −6, 2   **67.** −1, 2

69.

Study Summary: Chapter 4, pp. 280–282

1. $(2, -1)$ **2.** $\left(-\frac{1}{2}, \frac{1}{2}\right)$ **3.** $\left(\frac{16}{7}, -\frac{3}{7}\right)$ **4.** Roller Grip: 32 boxes; eGEL: 88 boxes   **5.** 40%-acid: 0.8 L; 15%-acid: 1.2 L   **6.** 8 mph   **7.** $\frac{1}{8}$ **8.** −1

Review Exercises: Chapter 4, pp. 282–283

1. Substitution   **2.** Elimination   **3.** Graphical   **4.** Dependent
5. Inconsistent   **6.** Contradiction   **7.** Parallel   **8.** Zero
9. Alphabetical   **10.** x-coordinate   **11.** $(4, 1)$ **12.** $(2, 1)$
13. $(-5, -13)$ **14.** No solution   **15.** $\left(-\frac{4}{5}, \frac{2}{5}\right)$ **16.** $\left(-\frac{9}{2}, -4\right)$
17. $\left(\frac{76}{17}, -\frac{2}{119}\right)$ **18.** $(-2, -3)$ **19.** $\{(x, y)|3x + 4y = 6\}$
20. Length: 265 ft; width: 165 ft   **21.** Oil: $21\frac{1}{3}$ oz; lemon juice: $10\frac{2}{3}$ oz   **22.** Private lessons: 7 students; group lessons: 5 students
23. 163°, 17°   **24.** 4 hr   **25.** 8% juice: 10 L; 15% juice: 4 L
26. 1300-word pages: 7; 1850-word pages: 5   **27.** −2   **28.** 1
29. $\frac{4}{7}$ **30.** 3   **31.** ™ A solution of a system of two equations is an ordered pair that makes both equations true. The graph of an equation represents all ordered pairs that make that equation true. So in order for an ordered pair to make *both* equations true, it must be on both graphs.   **32.** ™ Both methods involve finding the coordinates of the point of intersection of two graphs. The solution of a system of equations is the ordered pair at the point of intersection; the solution of an equation is the x-coordinate of the point of intersection.   **33.** $(0, 2), (1, 3)$ **34.** $C = 1, D = 3$ **35.** 24
36. $1800

Test: Chapter 4, p. 284

1. [4.1] $(2, 4)$ **2.** [4.1] No solution   **3.** [4.2] $\left(3, -\frac{11}{3}\right)$
4. [4.2] $\left(\frac{15}{7}, -\frac{18}{7}\right)$ **5.** [4.2] $\{(x, y)|x = 5y - 10\}$
6. [4.3] $(2, -1)$ **7.** [4.3] No solution   **8.** [4.3] $\left(-\frac{3}{2}, -\frac{3}{2}\right)$
9. [4.3] $(0, 1)$ **10.** [4.2] Length: 25 ft; width: 8 ft
11. [4.2] 38°, 52°   **12.** [4.2] Wii game machines: 3.63 million; PlayStation 3 consoles: 1.21 million   **13.** [4.4] Hardbacks: 11; paperbacks: 12   **14.** [4.4] Pepperidge Farm Goldfish: 120 g; Rold Gold Pretzels: 500 g   **15.** [4.4] 20 mph   **16.** [4.4] Nickels: 10; quarters: 3   **17.** [4.5] −2   **18.** [4.5] 10   **19.** [4.2] $(2, 0)$
20. [4.3] $(12, -6)$ **21.** [4.4] 9 people
22. [3.8], [4.3] $m = 7, b = 10$

CHAPTER 5

Exercise Set 5.1, pp. 292-293

1. (e)   **2.** (f)   **3.** (b)   **4.** (h)   **5.** (g)   **6.** (a)
7. (c)   **8.** (d)   **9.** Base: $2x$; exponent: 5

11. Base: x; exponent: 3   **13.** Base: $\dfrac{4}{y}$; exponent: 7

15. d^{13} **17.** a^7 **19.** 6^{15} **21.** $(3y)^{12}$ **23.** $(8n)^{10}$
25. $a^5 b^9$ **27.** $(x+3)^{13}$ **29.** r^{10} **31.** $m^4 n^9$ **33.** 7^3
35. t^7 **37.** $5a$ **39.** 1   **41.** $(r+s)^8$ **43.** $\frac{4}{5} d^7$
45. $4a^7 b^6$ **47.** $x^{12} y^7$ **49.** 1   **51.** 5   **53.** 2   **55.** -4
57. x^{33} **59.** 5^{32} **61.** t^{80} **63.** $100x^2$ **65.** $-8a^3$
67. $25n^{14}$ **69.** $a^{14} b^7$ **71.** $r^{17} t^{11}$ **73.** $24x^{19}$
75. $\dfrac{x^3}{125}$ **77.** $\dfrac{49}{36n^2}$ **79.** $\dfrac{a^{18}}{b^{48}}$ **81.** $\dfrac{x^8 y^4}{z^{12}}$ **83.** $\dfrac{a^{12}}{16 b^{20}}$
85. $-\dfrac{125 x^{21} y^3}{8 z^{12}}$ **87.** 1   **89.** ✍   **91.** -24 **92.** -15
93. -11 **94.** 16   **95.** -14 **96.** 4   **97.** ✍
99. ✍   **101.** Let $x = 1$; then $3x^2 = 3$, but $(3x)^2 = 9$.

103. Let $t = -1$; then $\dfrac{t^6}{t^2} = 1$, but $t^3 = -1$.   **105.** y^{6x}

107. x^t **109.** 13   **111.** <   **113.** <   **115.** >
117. 4,000,000; 4,194,304; 194,304   **119.** 2,000,000,000;
2,147,483,648; 147,483,648   **121.** 1,536,000 bytes, or
approximately 1,500,000 bytes

Technology Connection, p. 299

1. 1.71×10^{17} **2.** $5.\overline{370} \times 10^{-15}$ **3.** 3.68×10^{16}

Exercise Set 5.2, pp. 300-302

1. (c)   **2.** (d)   **3.** (a)   **4.** (b)   **5.** $\dfrac{1}{2^3} = \dfrac{1}{8}$

7. $\dfrac{1}{(-2)^6} = \dfrac{1}{64}$ **9.** $\dfrac{1}{t^9}$ **11.** $\dfrac{x}{y^2}$ **13.** $\dfrac{t}{r^5}$ **15.** a^8

17. $\dfrac{1}{7}$ **19.** $\left(\dfrac{5}{3}\right)^2 = \dfrac{25}{9}$ **21.** $\left(\dfrac{2}{x}\right)^5 = \dfrac{32}{x^5}$ **23.** $\left(\dfrac{t}{s}\right)^7 = \dfrac{t^7}{s^7}$

25. 9^{-2} **27.** y^{-3} **29.** 5^{-1} **31.** t^{-1} **33.** 2^3, or 8

35. $\dfrac{1}{x^{12}}$ **37.** $\dfrac{1}{t^2}$ **39.** $\dfrac{1}{n^{15}}$ **41.** t^{18} **43.** $\dfrac{1}{t^{12}}$

45. $\dfrac{1}{m^7 n^7}$ **47.** $\dfrac{9}{x^8}$ **49.** $\dfrac{25 t^6}{r^8}$ **51.** t^{14} **53.** $\dfrac{1}{y^4}$

55. $5y^3$ **57.** $2x^5$ **59.** $\dfrac{-3b^9}{2a^7}$ **61.** 1   **63.** $\dfrac{8y^7 z}{x^3}$

65. $3s^2 t^4 u^4$ **67.** $\dfrac{1}{x^{12} y^{15}}$ **69.** $\dfrac{m^{10} n^6}{9}$ **71.** $\dfrac{b^5 c^4}{a^8}$

73. $\dfrac{9}{a^8}$ **75.** $\dfrac{n^{12}}{m^3}$ **77.** $\dfrac{27 b^{12}}{8 a^6}$ **79.** 1   **81.** $\dfrac{2b^3}{a^4}$

83. $\dfrac{5y^4 z^{10}}{4x^{11}}$ **85.** 4920   **87.** 0.00892   **89.** 904,000,000
91. 0.000003497   **93.** 3.6×10^7 **95.** 5.83×10^{-3}
97. 7.8×10^{10} **99.** 5.27×10^{-7} **101.** 1.032×10^{-6}
103. 6×10^{13} **105.** 2.47×10^8 **107.** 3.915×10^{-16}
109. 2.5×10^{13} **111.** 5.0×10^{-6} **113.** 3×10^{-21}
115. ✍   **117.** $8x$ **118.** $-3a - 6b$ **119.** $-2x - 7$

120. $-4t - r - 5$ **121.** 1004   **122.** 9   **123.** ✍
125. 8×10^5 **127.** 2^{-12} **129.** 5   **131.** 5^6
133. $\frac{1}{3} + \frac{1}{4} = \frac{7}{12}$ **135.** 9   **137.** $6.304347826 \times 10^{25}$
139. $1.19140625 \times 10^{-15}$ **141.** 3×10^8 mi
143. $\$2.31 \times 10^8$ **145.** 2.277×10^{10} min

Connecting the Concepts, p. 303

1. x^{14} **2.** $\dfrac{1}{x^{14}}$ **3.** $\dfrac{1}{x^{14}}$ **4.** x^{14} **5.** x^{40} **6.** x^{40}

7. c^8 **8.** $\dfrac{1}{c^8}$ **9.** $16x^{12} y^4$ **10.** $\dfrac{1}{16 x^{12} y^4}$ **11.** 1

12. a^5 **13.** $\dfrac{a^{15}}{b^{20}}$ **14.** $\dfrac{b^{20}}{a^{15}}$ **15.** $\dfrac{5x^3}{2y^4}$ **16.** $\dfrac{6a^2}{7b^5}$

17. $\dfrac{7t^6}{xp^5}$ **18.** $\dfrac{16a^2}{9b^6}$ **19.** $18p^4 q^{14}$ **20.** $\dfrac{9x^3}{2y^5}$

Technology Connection, pp. 307-308

1. 9.8

Exercise Set 5.3, pp. 308-312

1. (b)   **2.** (f)   **3.** (h)   **4.** (d)   **5.** (g)   **6.** (e)
7. (a)   **8.** (c)   **9.** $8x^3, -11x^2, 6x, 1$
11. $-t^6, -3t^3, 9t, -4$ **13.** Coefficients: 8, 2; degrees: 4, 1
15. Coefficients: 9, -3, 4; degrees: 2, 1, 0
17. Coefficients: 6, 9, 1; degrees: 5, 1, 3   **19.** Coefficients:
1, -1, 4, -3; degrees: 4, 3, 1, 0   **21.** (a) 1, 3, 4; (b) $8t^4$, 8;
(c) 4   **23.** (a) 2, 0, 4; (b) $2a^4$, 2; (c) 4
25. (a) 0, 2, 1, 5; (b) $-x^5$, -1; (c) 5
27.

Term	Coefficient	Degree of the Term	Degree of the Polynomial
$8x^5$	8	5	
$-\frac{1}{2} x^4$	$-\frac{1}{2}$	4	
$-4x^3$	-4	3	5
$7x^2$	7	2	
6	6	0	

29. Trinomial   **31.** Polynomial with no special name
33. Binomial   **35.** Monomial   **37.** $11n^2 + n$ **39.** $4a^4$
41. $7x^3 + x^2 - 6x$ **43.** $11b^3 + b^2 - b$ **45.** $-x^4 - x^3$
47. $\frac{1}{15} x^4 + 10$ **49.** $-1.1a^2 + 5.3a - 7.5$ **51.** -3; 21
53. 16; 34   **55.** -38; 148   **57.** 159; 165   **59.** -39; 21
61. $\$1.93$ billion   **63.** 1112 ft   **65.** 62.8 cm
67. 153.86 m^2 **69.** About 75 donations
71. About 9 words   **73.** About 6   **75.** About 16;
about 19   **77.** ✍   **79.** $x - 3$ **80.** $-2x - 6$
81. $6a - 3$ **82.** $-t - 1$ **83.** $-t^4 + 17t$
84. $0.4a^2 - a + 11$ **85.** ✍
87. $2x^5 + 4x^4 + 6x^3 + 8$; answers may vary   **89.** $\$2510$
91. $3x^6$ **93.** 3 and 8   **95.** 85.0

97.

t	$-t^2 + 10t - 18$
3	3
4	6
5	7
6	6
7	3

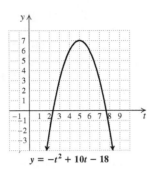

$y = -t^2 + 10t - 18$

Technology Connection, p. 316

1. In each case, let $y_1 = $ the expression before the addition or subtraction has been performed, $y_2 = $ the simplified sum or difference, and $y_3 = y_2 - y_1$; and note that the graph of y_3 coincides with the x-axis. That is, $y_3 = 0$.

Exercise Set 5.4, pp. 317–319

1. x^2 **2.** -6 **3.** $-$ **4.** $+$ **5.** $4x + 9$ **7.** $-6t + 8$
9. $-3x^2 + 6x - 2$ **11.** $9t^2 + t + 3$
13. $8m^3 - 3m - 7$ **15.** $7 + 13a - a^2 + 7a^3$
17. $2x^6 + 9x^4 + 2x^3 - 4x^2 + 5x$
19. $x^4 + \frac{1}{4}x^3 - \frac{3}{4}x^2 - \frac{5}{6}x + 3$
21. $4.2t^3 + 3.5t^2 - 6.4t - 1.8$ **23.** $-4x^3 + 4x^2 + 6x$
25. $1.3x^4 + 0.35x^3 + 9.53x^2 + 2x + 0.96$
27. $-(-3t^3 + 4t^2 - 7); 3t^3 - 4t^2 + 7$
29. $-(x^4 - 8x^3 + 6x); -x^4 + 8x^3 - 6x$
31. $-9x + 10$ **33.** $-3a^4 + 5a^2 - 1.2$
35. $4x^4 - 6x^2 - \frac{3}{4}x + 8$ **37.** $-2x - 7$
39. $-t^2 - 12t + 13$ **41.** $8a^3 + 8a^2 + a - 10$
43. $4.6x^3 + 9.2x^2 - 3.8x - 23$ **45.** 0
47. $1 + a + 12a^2 - 3a^3$ **49.** $\frac{9}{8}x^3 - \frac{1}{2}x$
51. $0.05t^3 - 0.07t^2 + 0.01t + 1$ **53.** $2x^2 + 6$
55. $-3x^4 - 8x^3 - 7x^2$ **57.** (a) $5x^2 + 4x$; (b) 145; 273
59. $16y + 26$ **61.** $(r + 11)(r + 9); 9r + 99 + 11r + r^2$
63. $(x + 3)^2; x^2 + 3x + 9 + 3x$ **65.** $m^2 - 40$
67. $\pi r^2 - 49$ **69.** $(x^2 - 12)$ ft^2 **71.** $(z^2 - 36\pi)$ ft^2
73. $\left(144 - \dfrac{d^2}{4}\pi \right)$ m^2 **75.** ✒   **77.** $2x^2 - 2x + 6$
78. $-15x^2 + 10x + 35$ **79.** x^8 **80.** y^7 **81.** $2n^3$
82. $-6n^{12}$ **83.** ✒   **85.** $9t^2 - 20t + 11$
87. $-6x + 14$ **89.** $250.591x^3 + 2.812x$ **91.** $20w + 42$
93. $2x^2 + 20x$ **95.** $8x + 24$ **97.** ✒

Technology Connection, p. 324

1. Let $y_1 = (5x^4 - 2x^2 + 3x)(x^2 + 2x)$ and
$y_2 = 5x^6 + 10x^5 - 2x^4 - x^3 + 6x^2$. With the table set in
AUTO mode, note that the values in the Y_1- and Y_2-columns
match, regardless of how far we scroll up or down.
2. Use TRACE, a table, or a boldly drawn graph to confirm
that y_3 is always 0.

Exercise Set 5.5, pp. 325–327

1. (c)   **2.** (d)   **3.** (d)   **4.** (a)   **5.** (c)   **6.** (b)
7. $21x^5$ **9.** $-x^7$ **11.** x^8 **13.** $36t^4$ **15.** $-0.12x^9$

17. $-\frac{1}{20}x^{12}$ **19.** $5n^3$ **21.** $-44x^{10}$ **23.** $72y^{10}$
25. $20x^2 + 5x$ **27.** $3a^2 - 27a$ **29.** $x^5 + x^2$
31. $-6n^3 + 24n^2 - 3n$ **33.** $-15t^3 - 30t^2$
35. $4a^9 - 8a^7 - \frac{5}{12}a^4$ **37.** $x^2 + 7x + 12$
39. $t^2 + 4t - 21$ **41.** $a^2 - 1.3a + 0.42$ **43.** $x^2 - 9$
45. $28 - 15x + 2x^2$ **47.** $t^2 + \frac{17}{6}t + 2$
49. $\frac{3}{16}a^2 + \frac{5}{4}a - 2$

51.

53.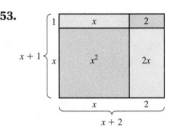

55.

57. $x^3 + 2x + 3$

59. $2a^3 - a^2 - 11a + 10$
61. $3y^6 - 21y^4 + y^3 + 2y^2 - 7y - 14$
63. $33x^2 + 25x + 2$ **65.** $x^4 + 4x^3 - 3x^2 + 16x - 3$
67. $10t^4 + 3t^3 - 20t^2 + \frac{9}{2}t - 2$
69. $x^4 + 8x^3 + 12x^2 + 9x + 4$ **71.** ✒   **73.** 0   **74.** 0
75. 8   **76.** 7   **77.** 32   **78.** 50   **79.** ✒
81. $75y^2 - 45y$ **83.** 5   **85.** $V = (4x^3 - 48x^2 + 144x)$ in^3;
$S = (-4x^2 + 144)$ in^2 **87.** $(x^3 - 5x^2 + 8x - 4)$ cm^3
89. 16 ft by 8 ft   **91.** 0   **93.** $x^3 + x^2 - 22x - 40$ **95.** 0

Visualizing for Success, p. 333

1. E, F   **2.** B, O   **3.** S, K   **4.** R, G   **5.** D, M   **6.** J, P
7. C, L   **8.** N, Q   **9.** A, H   **10.** I, T

Exercise Set 5.6, pp. 334–338

1. True   **2.** False   **3.** False   **4.** True
5. $x^3 + 3x^2 + 2x + 6$ **7.** $t^5 + 7t^4 - 2t - 14$
9. $y^2 - y - 6$ **11.** $9x^2 + 21x + 10$
13. $5x^2 + 17x - 12$ **15.** $15 - 13t + 2t^2$
17. $x^4 - 4x^2 - 21$ **19.** $p^2 - \frac{1}{16}$ **21.** $x^2 - 0.6x + 0.09$
23. $-3n^2 - 19n + 14$ **25.** $x^2 + 20x + 100$
27. $1 - 3t + 5t^2 - 15t^3$ **29.** $x^5 + 3x^3 - x^2 - 3$
31. $3x^6 - 2x^4 - 6x^2 + 4$ **33.** $4t^6 + 20t^3 + 25$
35. $8x^5 + 16x^3 + 5x^2 + 10$ **37.** $100x^4 - 9$
39. $x^2 - 64$ **41.** $4x^2 - 1$ **43.** $25m^4 - 16$
45. $81a^6 - 1$ **47.** $x^8 - 0.01$ **49.** $t^2 - \frac{9}{16}$
51. $x^2 + 6x + 9$ **53.** $49x^6 - 14x^3 + 1$
55. $a^2 - \frac{4}{5}a + \frac{4}{25}$ **57.** $t^8 + 6t^4 + 9$
59. $4 - 12x^4 + 9x^8$ **61.** $25 + 60t^2 + 36t^4$
63. $49x^2 - 4.2x + 0.09$ **65.** $14n^5 - 7n^3$
67. $a^3 - a^2 - 10a + 12$ **69.** $49 - 42x^4 + 9x^8$
71. $5x^3 + 30x^2 - 10x$ **73.** $q^{10} - 1$
75. $15t^5 - 3t^4 + 3t^3$ **77.** $36x^8 - 36x^5 + 9x^2$
79. $18a^4 + 0.8a^3 + 4.5a + 0.2$ **81.** $\frac{1}{25} - 36x^8$
83. $a^3 + 1$ **85.** $x^2 + 6x + 9$ **87.** $t^2 + 7t + 12$

89. $a^2 + 10a + 25$ **91.** $x^2 + 10x + 21$
93. $a^2 + 8a + 7$ **95.** $25t^2 + 20t + 4$
97.

99.

101.

103.

105. Washing machine: 9 kWh/mo; refrigerator: 189 kWh/mo; freezer: 99 kWh/mo   **106.** About $5.8 billion   **107.** $y = \dfrac{8}{5x}$ **108.** $a = \dfrac{c}{3b}$

109. $x = \dfrac{by + c}{a}$ **110.** $y = \dfrac{ax - c}{b}$ **111.**

113. $16x^4 - 81$ **115.** $81t^4 - 72t^2 + 16$
117. $t^{24} - 4t^{18} + 6t^{12} - 4t^6 + 1$ **119.** 396   **121.** -7
123. $17F + 7(F - 17), F^2 - (F - 17)(F - 7)$; other equivalent expressions are possible.   **125.** $(y + 1)(y - 1)$, $y(y + 1) - y - 1$; other equivalent expressions are possible.
127. $y^2 - 4y + 4$ **129.**

Connecting the Concepts, p. 337

1. Addition; $3x^2 + 3x + 3$ **2.** Subtraction; $6x + 13$
3. Multiplication; $48x^5 - 42x^3$ **4.** Multiplication; $6x^2 + x - 2$ **5.** Subtraction; $9x^3 - 5x^2 - 7x + 13$
6. Multiplication; $2x^3 + 3x^2 - 5x - 3$ **7.** Multiplication; $81x^2 - 1$ **8.** Addition; $9x^4 + 2x^3 - 5x$
9. $-6x^2 + 2x - 12$ **10.** $9x^2 + 45x + 56$
11. $40x^9 - 48x^8 + 16x^5$ **12.** $t^9 + 5t^7$
13. $4m^2 - 4m + 1$ **14.** $x^3 - 1$ **15.** $5x^3 + 3$
16. $c^2 - 9$ **17.** $16y^6 + 56y^3 + 49$
18. $3a^4 - 13a^3 - 13a^2 - 4$ **19.** $16t^4 - 25$
20. $a^8 - 5a^4 - 24$

Technology Connection, p. 341

1. 36.22   **2.** 22,312

Exercise Set 5.7, pp. 342–345

1. (a)   **2.** (b)   **3.** (b)   **4.** (a)   **5.** (c)   **6.** (c)
7. (a)   **8.** (a)   **9.** -13 **11.** -68 **13.** 3.51 L
15. 1889 calories   **17.** 73.005 in^2 **19.** 66.4 m
21. Coefficients: 3, -5, 2, -11; degrees: 3, 2, 2, 0; 3
23. Coefficients: 7, -1, 1, 9; degrees: 0, 3, 3, 3; 3
25. $2r - 6s$ **27.** $5xy^2 - 2x^2y + x + 3x^2$
29. $9u^2v - 11uv^2 + 11u^2$ **31.** $6a^2c - 7ab^2 + a^2b$
33. $11x^2 - 10xy - y^2$ **35.** $-6a^4 - 8ab + 7ab^2$
37. $-6r^2 - 5rt - t^2$ **39.** $3x^3 - x^2y + xy^2 - 3y^3$
41. $-2y^4x^3 - 3y^3x$ **43.** $-8x + 8y$
45. $12c^2 + 5cd - 2d^2$ **47.** $x^2y^2 + 4xy - 5$

49. $4a^2 - b^2$ **51.** $20r^2t^2 - 23rt + 6$
53. $m^6n^2 + 2m^3n - 48$ **55.** $30x^2 - 28xy + 6y^2$
57. $0.01 - p^2q^2$ **59.** $x^2 + 2xh + h^2$
61. $16a^2 - 40ab + 25b^2$ **63.** $a^2b^2 - c^2d^4$
65. $x^3y^2 + x^2y^3 + 2x^2y^2 + 2xy^3 + 3xy + 3y^2$
67. $a^2 + 2ab + b^2 - c^2$ **69.** $a^2 - b^2 - 2bc - c^2$
71. $x^2 + 2xy + y^2$ **73.** $\frac{1}{2}a^2b^2 - 2$
75. $a^2 + c^2 + ab + 2ac + ad + bc + bd + cd$
77. $m^2 - n^2$
79. We draw a rectangle with dimensions $r + s$ by $u + v$.   **81.**

83.   **85.** $x^2 - 8x - 4$
86. $2x^3 - x^2 - x + 4$
87. $-2x + 5$ **88.** $5x^2 + x$ **89.** $13x^2 + 1$
90. $-x - 3$ **91.**   **93.** $4xy - 4y^2$
95. $2\pi ab - \pi b^2$ **97.** $x^3 + 2y^3 + x^2y + xy^2$
99. $2x^2 - 2\pi r^2 + 4xh + 2\pi rh$ **101.**   **103.** 40
105. $P + 2Pr + Pr^2$ **107.** $15,638.03

Exercise Set 5.8, pp. 350–351

1. $8x^6 - 5x^3$ **3.** $1 - 2u + u^6$ **5.** $6t^2 - 8t + 2$
7. $7x^3 - 6x + \frac{3}{2}$ **9.** $-4t^2 - 2t + 1$ **11.** $4x - 5 + \dfrac{1}{2x}$
13. $x + 2x^3y + 3$ **15.** $-3rs - r + 2s$ **17.** $x - 6$
19. $t - 5 + \dfrac{-45}{t - 5}$ **21.** $2x - 1 + \dfrac{1}{x + 6}$
23. $t^2 - 3t + 9$ **25.** $a + 5 + \dfrac{4}{a - 5}$
27. $x - 3 - \dfrac{3}{5x - 1}$ **29.** $3a + 1 + \dfrac{3}{2a + 5}$
31. $t^2 - 3t + 1$ **33.** $x^2 + 1$ **35.** $t^2 - 1 + \dfrac{3t - 1}{t^2 + 5}$
37. $3x^2 - 3 + \dfrac{x - 1}{2x^2 + 1}$ **39.**
41.

42.

43.

44.

45. $-\frac{3}{10}$ **46.** Slope: 4; y-intercept: $\left(0, \frac{7}{2}\right)$
47. $y = -5x - 10$ **48.** $y = \frac{5}{4}x - \frac{9}{2}$ **49.** 🖘
51. $5x^{6k} - 16x^{3k} + 14$ **53.** $3t^{2h} + 2t^h - 5$
55. $a + 3 + \dfrac{5}{5a^2 - 7a - 2}$ **57.** $2x^2 + x - 3$
59. 3   **61.** -1

Review Exercises: Chapter 5, pp. 355–356

1. True   **2.** True   **3.** True   **4.** False   **5.** False
6. False   **7.** True   **8.** True   **9.** n^{12} **10.** $(7x)^{10}$
11. t^6 **12.** 4^3, or 64   **13.** 1   **14.** $-9c^4d^2$
15. $-8x^3y^6$ **16.** $18x^5$ **17.** a^7b^6 **18.** $\dfrac{4t^{10}}{9s^8}$
19. $\dfrac{1}{8^6}$ **20.** a^{-9} **21.** $\dfrac{1}{4^2}$, or $\dfrac{1}{16}$ **22.** $\dfrac{2b^9}{a^{13}}$ **23.** $\dfrac{1}{w^{15}}$
24. $\dfrac{x^6}{4y^2}$ **25.** $\dfrac{y^3}{8x^3}$ **26.** 470,000,000   **27.** 1.09×10^{-5}
28. 2.09×10^4 **29.** 5.12×10^{-5}
30. $8x^2, -x, \frac{2}{3}$ **31.** $-4y^5, 7y^2, -3y, -2$ **32.** $9, -1, 7$
33. $7, -\frac{5}{6}, -4, 10$ **34. (a)** 2, 0, 5; **(b)** $15t^5$, 15; **(c)** 5
35. (a) 5, 0, 2, 1; **(b)** $-2x^5, -2$; **(c)** 5   **36.** Trinomial
37. Polynomial with no special name   **38.** Monomial
39. $-x^2 + 7x$ **40.** $-\frac{1}{4}x^3 + 4x^2 + 7$ **41.** $t - 1$
42. $14a^5 - 2a^2 - a - \frac{2}{3}$ **43.** -24 **44.** 16
45. $x^5 + 8x^4 + 6x^3 - 2x - 9$ **46.** $6a^5 - a^3 - 12a^2$
47. $-3y^2 + 8y + 3$ **48.** $x^5 - 3x^3 - 2x^2 + 8$
49. $\frac{3}{4}x^4 + \frac{1}{4}x^3 - \frac{1}{3}x^2 - \frac{7}{4}x + \frac{3}{8}$
50. $-x^5 + x^4 - 5x^3 - 2x^2 + 2x$ **51. (a)** $4w + 6$;
(b) $w^2 + 3w$ **52.** $-30x^5$ **53.** $49x^2 + 14x + 1$
54. $a^2 - 3a - 28$ **55.** $d^2 - 64$
56. $12x^3 - 23x^2 + 13x - 2$ **57.** $x^2 - 16x + 64$
58. $15t^5 - 6t^4 + 12t^3$ **59.** $4a^2 - 81$
60. $x^2 - 1.3x + 0.4$
61. $x^7 + x^5 - 3x^4 + 3x^3 - 2x^2 + 5x - 3$
62. $16y^6 - 40y^3 + 25$ **63.** $2t^4 - 11t^2 - 21$
64. $a^2 + \frac{1}{6}a - \frac{1}{3}$ **65.** $-49 + 4n^2$ **66.** 49
67. Coefficients: 1, -7, 9, -8; degrees: 6, 2, 2, 0; 6
68. Coefficients: 1, -1, 1; degrees: 13, 22, 15; 22
69. $-4u + 4v - 7$ **70.** $6m^3 + 4m^2n - mn^2$
71. $2a^2 - 16ab$ **72.** $11x^3y^2 - 8x^2y - 6x^2 - 6x + 6$
73. $2x^2 - xy - 15y^2$ **74.** $25a^2b^2 - 10abcd^2 + c^2d^4$
75. $\frac{1}{2}x^2 - \frac{1}{2}y^2$ **76.** $y^4 - \frac{1}{3}y + 4$
77. $3x^2 - 7x + 4 + \dfrac{1}{2x + 3}$ **78.** $t^3 + 2t - 3$
79. 🖘 In the expression $5x^3$, the exponent refers only to
the x. In the expression $(5x)^3$, the entire expression $5x$ is the
base.   **80.** 🖘 It is possible to determine two possibilities
for the binomial that was squared by using the equation
$(A - B)^2 = A^2 - 2AB + B^2$ in reverse. Since, in
$x^2 - 6x + 9$, $A^2 = x^2$ and $B^2 = 9$, or 3^2, the binomial that
was squared was $A - B$, or $x - 3$. If the polynomial is
written $9 - 6x + x^2$, then $A^2 = 9$ and $B^2 = x^2$, so the
binomial that was squared was $3 - x$. We cannot determine
without further information whether the binomial squared
was $x - 3$ or $3 - x$.   **81. (a)** 9; **(b)** 28   **82.** $64x^{16}$
83. $8x^4 + 4x^3 + 5x - 2$ **84.** $-16x^6 + x^2 - 10x + 25$
85. $\frac{94}{13}$ **86.** 2.28×10^{11} platelets

Test: Chapter 5, p. 357

1. [5.1] x^{13} **2.** [5.1] 3   **3.** [5.1] 1   **4.** [5.1] t^{45}
5. [5.1] $-40x^{19}y^4$ **6.** [5.1] $\frac{6}{5}a^5b^3$ **7.** [5.2] $\dfrac{1}{y^7}$
8. [5.2] 5^{-6} **9.** [5.2] $\dfrac{1}{t^9}$ **10.** [5.2] $\dfrac{3y^5}{x^5}$ **11.** [5.2] $\dfrac{b^4}{16a^{12}}$
12. [5.2] $\dfrac{c^3}{a^3b^3}$ **13.** [5.2] 3.06×10^9 **14.** [5.2] 0.00000005
15. [5.2] 1.75×10^{17} **16.** [5.2] 1.296×10^{22}
17. [5.3] Binomial   **18.** [5.3] 3, -1, $\frac{1}{9}$ **19.** [5.3] Degrees
of terms: 3, 1, 5, 0; leading term: $7t^5$; leading coefficient: 7;
degree of polynomial: 5   **20.** [5.3] -7 **21.** [5.3] $5a^2 - 6$
22. [5.3] $\frac{7}{4}y^2 - 4y$ **23.** [5.3] $4x^3 + 4x^2 + 3$
24. [5.4] $4x^5 + x^4 + 5x^3 - 8x^2 + 2x - 7$
25. [5.4] $5x^4 + 5x^2 + x + 5$
26. [5.4] $-2a^4 + 3a^3 - a - 7$
27. [5.4] $-t^4 + 2.5t^3 - 0.6t^2 - 9$
28. [5.5] $-6x^4 + 6x^3 + 10x^2$ **29.** [5.6] $x^2 - \frac{2}{3}x + \frac{1}{9}$
30. [5.6] $25t^2 - 49$ **31.** [5.6] $6b^2 + 7b - 5$
32. [5.6] $x^{14} - 4x^8 + 4x^6 - 16$
33. [5.6] $48 + 34y - 5y^2$ **34.** [5.5] $6x^3 - 7x^2 - 11x - 3$
35. [5.6] $64a^6 + 48a^3 + 9$ **36.** [5.7] 24
37. [5.7] $-4x^3y - x^2y^2 + xy^3 - y^3 + 19$
38. [5.7] $8a^2b^2 + 6ab + 6ab^2 + ab^3 - 4b^3$
39. [5.7] $9x^{10} - y^2$ **40.** [5.8] $4x^2 + 3x - 5$
41. [5.8] $2x^2 - 4x - 2 + \dfrac{17}{3x + 2}$ **42.** [5.5], [5.6]
$V = l(l - 2)(l - 1) = l^3 - 3l^2 + 2l$ **43.** [2.2], [5.6] $\frac{100}{21}$
44. [5.2] $\frac{1}{2} - \frac{1}{4} = \frac{1}{4}$ **45.** [5.2] About 1.4×10^7 hr

Cumulative Review: Chapters 1–3, 5 pp. 358–359

1. 6   **2.** -8 **3.** $-\frac{7}{45}$ **4.** 6   **5.** $y + 10$ **6.** t^{12}
7. $-4x^5y^3$ **8.** $50a^4b^7$ **9.** $2(5a - 3b + 6)$ **10.** $\frac{11}{16}$
11. 6   **12.** $\frac{1}{4}t^3 - 5t^2 - 0.35$ **13.** II
14.

15.

16.

17.

18.

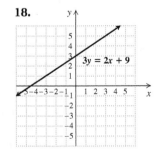

19. Slope: $\frac{1}{10}$; y-intercept: $\left(0, \frac{3}{8}\right)$ **20.** $-\frac{5}{8}$
21. $y = -\frac{2}{3}x - 10$ **22.** x-intercept: $(4, 0)$; y-intercept:
$\left(0, \frac{8}{5}\right)$ **23.** -4 **24.** $\frac{3}{5}$ **25.** $\frac{8}{3}$ **26.** 22   **27.** $\frac{5}{3}$
28. -7 **29.** $\{t \mid t \geq -8\}$, or $[-8, \infty)$ **30.** $\left\{x \mid x < \frac{1}{2}\right\}$, or
$\left(-\infty, \frac{1}{2}\right)$ **31.** $t = \dfrac{5pq}{2c}$ **32.** $7u^2v - 2uv^2 + uv + 3u^2$
33. $3x^3 - 3x^2 + 12x - 7$ **34.** $x^5 - 2x$
35. $20a - 30b + 70$ **36.** $-16x^5 - 48x^4 + 56x^3$
37. $6a^2 + 11a - 7$ **38.** $x^3 - x^2 - 7x + 10$
39. $16t^4 + 24t^2 + 9$ **40.** $\frac{1}{4}x^2 - 1$
41. $6r^4 - 5r^2s - 4s^2$ **42.** $x + \dfrac{3}{x - 1}$ **43.** $\dfrac{1}{7^{10}}$
44. $\dfrac{1}{x^7}$ **45.** $\dfrac{9}{16s^2t^{10}}$ **46.** $\dfrac{x^7y^2}{3}$ **47.** 48 thousand
megawatts   **48.** About 1298 megawatt hours
49. Washer: 20 kWh; dryer: 50 kWh
50. (a)   **(b)** 375 kWh

$w = 60n + 75$
Kilowatt hours of electricity
Number of people in household

51. No more than 6 hr   **52.** $160 billion   **53.** About 3.6
54. $\frac{12}{7}$ billion per year   **55.** 0   **56.** No solution
57. $\frac{22}{9}$ **58.** $y = \frac{1}{2}x + 4$ **59.** $\frac{1}{7} + 1 = \frac{8}{7}$ **60.** $15x^{12}$

CHAPTER 6

Technology Connection, p. 368

1. Correct   **2.** Correct   **3.** Not correct
4. Not correct   **5.** Not correct   **6.** Correct
7. Not correct   **8.** Correct

Exercise Set 6.1, pp. 368–369

1. (h)   **2.** (f)   **3.** (b)   **4.** (e)   **5.** (c)   **6.** (g)
7. (d)   **8.** (a)   **9.** Answers may vary. $(14x)(x^2)$,
$(7x^2)(2x)$, $(-2)(-7x^3)$ **11.** Answers may vary. $(-15)(a^4)$,
$(-5a)(3a^3)$, $(-3a^2)(5a^2)$ **13.** Answers may vary.
$(5t^2)(5t^3)$, $(25t)(t^4)$, $(-5t)(-5t^4)$
15. $8(x + 3)$ **17.** $6(x - 5)$ **19.** $2(x^2 + x - 4)$
21. $t(3t + 1)$ **23.** $-5y(y + 2)$ **25.** $x^2(x + 6)$
27. $8a^2(2a^2 - 3)$ **29.** $-t^2(6t^4 - 9t^2 + 4)$
31. $6x^2(x^6 + 2x^4 - 4x^2 + 5)$
33. $x^2y^2(x^3y^3 + x^2y + xy - 1)$
35. $-5a^2b^2(7ab^2 - 2b + 3a)$ **37.** $(n - 6)(n + 3)$
39. $(x + 3)(x^2 - 7)$ **41.** $(2y - 9)(y^2 + 1)$
43. $(x + 2)(x^2 + 5)$ **45.** $(a + 3)(5a^2 + 2)$
47. $(3n - 2)(3n^2 + 1)$ **49.** $(t - 5)(4t^2 + 3)$
51. $(7x + 5)(x^2 - 3)$ **53.** $(6a + 7)(a^2 + 1)$
55. $(x + 6)(2x^2 - 5)$ **57.** Not factorable by grouping
59. $(y + 8)(y^2 - 2)$ **61.** $(x - 4)(2x^2 - 9)$ **63.** 📖

65. $x^2 + 9x + 14$ **66.** $x^2 - 9x + 14$ **67.** $x^2 - 5x - 14$
68. $x^2 + 5x - 14$ **69.** $a^2 - 4a + 3$ **70.** $t^2 + 8t + 15$
71. $t^2 + 5t - 50$ **72.** $a^2 - 2a - 24$ **73.** 📖
75. $(2x^3 + 3)(2x^2 + 3)$ **77.** $2x(x + 1)(x^2 - 2)$
79. $(x - 1)(5x^4 + x^2 + 3)$ **81.** Answers may vary.
$8x^4y^3 - 24x^2y^4 + 16x^3y^4$

Exercise Set 6.2, pp. 375–376

1. Positive; positive   **2.** Negative; negative
3. Negative; positive   **4.** Positive; positive
5. Positive   **6.** Negative   **7.** $(x + 4)(x + 4)$
9. $(x + 1)(x + 10)$ **11.** $(x + 3)(x + 7)$
13. $(t - 2)(t - 7)$ **15.** $(b - 4)(b - 1)$
17. $(a - 3)(a - 4)$ **19.** $(d - 2)(d - 5)$
21. $(x - 5)(x + 3)$ **23.** $(x + 5)(x - 3)$
25. $2(x + 2)(x - 9)$ **27.** $-x(x + 2)(x - 8)$
29. $(y - 5)(y + 9)$ **31.** $(x - 6)(x + 12)$
33. $-5(b - 3)(b + 10)$ **35.** $x^3(x - 2)(x + 1)$
37. Prime   **39.** $(t + 4)(t + 8)$ **41.** $(x + 9)(x + 11)$
43. $3x(x - 25)(x + 4)$ **45.** $-2(x - 24)(x + 3)$
47. $(y - 12)(y - 8)$ **49.** $-a^4(a - 6)(a + 15)$
51. $\left(t + \frac{1}{3}\right)^2$ **53.** Prime   **55.** $(p - 5q)(p - 2q)$
57. Prime   **59.** $(s - 6t)(s + 2t)$ **61.** $6a^8(a - 2)(a + 7)$
63. 📖   **65.** $6x^2 + 17x + 12$ **66.** $6x^2 + x - 12$
67. $6x^2 - x - 12$ **68.** $6x^2 - 17x + 12$
69. $5x^2 - 36x + 7$ **70.** $3x^2 + 13x - 30$
71. 📖   **73.** $-5, 5, -23, 23, -49, 49$
75. $(y + 0.2)(y - 0.4)$ **77.** $-\frac{1}{3}a(a - 3)(a + 2)$
79. $(x^m + 4)(x^m + 7)$ **81.** $(a + 1)(x + 2)(x + 1)$
83. $(x + 3)^3$, or $(x^3 + 9x^2 + 27x + 27)$ cubic meters
85. $x^2\left(\frac{3}{4}\pi + 2\right)$, or $\frac{1}{4}x^2(3\pi + 8)$ **87.** $x^2\left(9 - \frac{1}{2}\pi\right)$
89. $(x + 4)(x + 5)$

Exercise Set 6.3, pp. 385–386

1. (c)   **2.** (a)   **3.** (d)   **4.** (b)   **5.** $(2x - 1)(x + 4)$
7. $(3x + 1)(x - 6)$ **9.** $(2t + 1)(2t + 5)$
11. $(5a - 3)(3a - 1)$ **13.** $(3x + 4)(2x + 3)$
15. $2(3x + 1)(x - 2)$ **17.** $t(7t + 1)(t + 2)$
19. $(4x - 5)(3x - 2)$ **21.** $-1(7x + 4)(5x + 2)$, or
$-(7x + 4)(5x + 2)$ **23.** Prime   **25.** $(5x + 4)^2$
27. $(20y - 1)(y + 3)$ **29.** $(7x + 5)(2x + 9)$
31. $-1(x - 3)(2x + 5)$, or $-(x - 3)(2x + 5)$
33. $-3(2x + 1)(x + 5)$ **35.** $2(a + 1)(5a - 9)$
37. $4(3x - 1)(x + 6)$ **39.** $(3x + 1)(x + 1)$
41. $(x + 3)(x - 2)$ **43.** $(4t - 3)(2t - 7)$
45. $(3x + 2)(2x + 5)$ **47.** $(y + 4)(2y - 1)$
49. $(3a - 4)(2a - 1)$ **51.** $(16t + 7)(t + 1)$
53. $-1(3x + 1)(3x + 5)$, or $-(3x + 1)(3x + 5)$
55. $10(x^2 + 3x - 7)$ **57.** $3x(3x - 1)(2x + 3)$
59. $(x + 1)(25x + 64)$ **61.** $3x(7x + 1)(8x + 1)$
63. $-t^2(2t - 3)(7t + 1)$ **65.** $2(2y + 9)(8y - 3)$
67. $(2a - b)(a - 2b)$ **69.** $2(s + t)(4s + 7t)$
71. $3(3x - 4y)^2$ **73.** $-2(3a - 2b)(4a - 3b)$
75. $x^2(2x + 3)(7x - 1)$ **77.** $a^6(3a + 4)(3a + 2)$
79. 📖   **81.** $x^2 - 4x + 4$ **82.** $x^2 + 4x + 4$
83. $x^2 - 4$ **84.** $25t^2 - 30t + 9$ **85.** $16a^2 + 8a + 1$
86. $4n^2 - 49$ **87.** $9c^2 - 60c + 100$

88. $1 - 10a + 25a^2$ **89.** $64n^2 - 9$ **90.** $81 - y^2$
91. 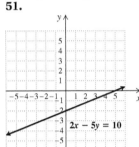 **93.** $(3xy + 2)(6xy - 5)$ **95.** Prime
97. $(4t^5 - 1)^2$ **99.** $-1(5x^m - 2)(3x^m - 4)$, or
$-(5x^m - 2)(3x^m - 4)$ **101.** $(3a^{3n} + 1)(a^{3n} - 1)$
103. $[7(t - 3)^n - 2][(t - 3)^n + 1]$

Connecting the Concepts, pp. 386–387

1. $6x^2(x^3 - 3)$ **2.** $(x + 2)(x + 8)$ **3.** $(x + 7)(2x - 1)$
4. $(x + 3)(x^2 + 2)$ **5.** $5(x - 2)(x + 10)$ **6.** Prime
7. $7y(x - 4)(x + 1)$ **8.** $3a^2(5a^2 - 9b^2 + 7b)$
9. $(b - 7)^2$ **10.** $(3x - 1)(4x + 1)$
11. $(c + 1)(c + 2)(c - 2)$ **12.** $2(x - 5)(x + 20)$
13. Prime **14.** $15(d^2 - 2d + 5)$
15. $(3p + 2q)(5p + 2q)$ **16.** $-2t(t + 2)(t + 3)$
17. $(x + 11)(x - 7)$ **18.** $10(c + 1)^2$
19. $-1(2x - 5)(x + 1)$ **20.** $2n(m - 5)(m^2 - 3)$

Exercise Set 6.4, pp. 392–393

1. Prime polynomial **2.** Difference of squares
3. Difference of squares **4.** None of these
5. Perfect-square trinomial **6.** Perfect-square trinomial
7. None of these **8.** Prime polynomial
9. Difference of squares **10.** Perfect-square trinomial
11. Yes **13.** No **15.** No **17.** Yes **19.** $(x + 8)^2$
21. $(x - 5)^2$ **23.** $5(p + 2)^2$ **25.** $(1 - t)^2$, or $(t - 1)^2$
27. $2(3x + 1)^2$ **29.** $(7 - 4y)^2$, or $(4y - 7)^2$
31. $-x^3(x - 9)^2$ **33.** $2n(n + 10)^2$ **35.** $5(2x + 5)^2$
37. $(7 - 3x)^2$, or $(3x - 7)^2$ **39.** $(4x + 3)^2$
41. $2(1 + 5x)^2$, or $2(5x + 1)^2$ **43.** $(3p + 2q)^2$
45. Prime **47.** $-1(8m + n)^2$, or $-(8m + n)^2$
49. $-2(4s - 5t)^2$ **51.** Yes **53.** No **55.** Yes
57. $(x + 5)(x - 5)$ **59.** $(p + 3)(p - 3)$
61. $(7 + t)(-7 + t)$, or $(t + 7)(t - 7)$
63. $6(a + 2)(a - 2)$ **65.** $(7x - 1)^2$
67. $2(10 + t)(10 - t)$ **69.** $-5(4a + 3)(4a - 3)$
71. $5(t + 4)(t - 4)$ **73.** $2(2x + 9)(2x - 9)$
75. $x(6 + 7x)(6 - 7x)$ **77.** Prime
79. $(t^2 + 1)(t + 1)(t - 1)$ **81.** $-3x(x - 4)^2$
83. $3t(5t + 3)(5t - 3)$ **85.** $a^6(a - 1)^2$
87. $10(a + b)(a - b)$ **89.** $(4x^2 + y^2)(2x + y)(2x - y)$
91. $2(3t + 2s)(3t - 2s)$ **93.** 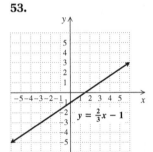 **95.** $8x^6y^{12}$
96. $-125x^6y^3$ **97.** $x^3 + 3x^2 + 3x + 1$
98. $x^3 - 3x^2 + 3x - 1$ **99.** $p^3 + 3p^2q + 3pq^2 + q^3$
100. $p^3 - 3p^2q + 3pq^2 - q^3$ **101.**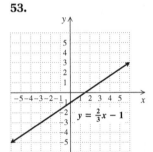
103. $(x^4 + 2^4)(x^2 + 2^2)(x + 2)(x - 2)$, or
$(x^4 + 16)(x^2 + 4)(x + 2)(x - 2)$
105. $2x(3x - \frac{2}{5})(3x + \frac{2}{5})$
107. $[(y - 5)^2 + z^4][(y - 5) + z^2][(y - 5) - z^2]$, or
$(y^2 - 10y + 25 + z^4)(y - 5 + z^2)(y - 5 - z^2)$
109. $-1(x^2 + 1)(x + 3)(x - 3)$, or $-(x^2 + 1)(x + 3)(x - 3)$
111. $(y + 4)^2$ **113.** $(3p + 5)(3p - 5)^2$
115. $(9 + b^{2k})(3 + b^k)(3 - b^k)$ **117.** $2x^3 - x^2 - 1$
119. $(y + x + 7)(y - x - 1)$ **121.** 16
123. $(x + 1)^2 - x^2 = [(x + 1) + x][(x + 1) - x] = 2x + 1 = (x + 1) + x$

Exercise Set 6.5, p. 397

1. Difference of cubes **2.** Sum of cubes **3.** Difference
of squares **4.** None of these **5.** Sum of cubes
6. Difference of cubes **7.** None of these **8.** Difference
of squares **9.** Difference of cubes **10.** None of these
11. $(x - 4)(x^2 + 4x + 16)$ **13.** $(z + 1)(z^2 - z + 1)$
15. $(t - 10)(t^2 + 10t + 100)$
17. $(3x + 1)(9x^2 - 3x + 1)$
19. $(4 - 5x)(16 + 20x + 25x^2)$
21. $(x - y)(x^2 + xy + y^2)$ **23.** $(a + \frac{1}{2})(a^2 - \frac{1}{2}a + \frac{1}{4})$
25. $8(t - 1)(t^2 + t + 1)$ **27.** $2(3x + 1)(9x^2 - 3x + 1)$
29. $rs(s + 4)(s^2 - 4s + 16)$
31. $5(x - 2z)(x^2 + 2xz + 4z^2)$
33. $(y - \frac{1}{10})(y^2 + \frac{1}{10}y + \frac{1}{100})$
35. $(x + 0.1)(x^2 - 0.1x + 0.01)$
37. $8(2x^2 - t^2)(4x^4 + 2x^2t^2 + t^4)$
39. $2y(3y - 4)(9y^2 + 12y + 16)$
41. $(z + 1)(z^2 - z + 1)(z - 1)(z^2 + z + 1)$
43. $(t^2 + 4y^2)(t^4 - 4t^2y^2 + 16y^4)$
45. $(x^4 - yz^4)(x^8 + x^4yz^4 + y^2z^8)$ **47.**
49. $-\frac{1}{5}$ **50.** $\frac{1}{4}$
51.

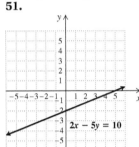

$2x - 5y = 10$

52.

$-5x = 10$

53.

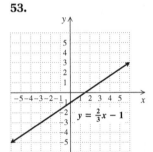

$y = \frac{2}{3}x - 1$

54.

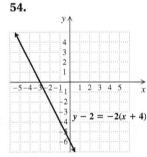

$y - 2 = -2(x + 4)$

55. **57.** $(x^{2a} - y^b)(x^{4a} + x^{2a}y^b + y^{2b})$
59. $2x(x^2 + 75)$ **61.** $5(xy^2 - \frac{1}{2})(x^2y^4 + \frac{1}{2}xy^2 + \frac{1}{4})$
63. $-(3x^{4a} + 3x^{2a} + 1)$ **65.** $(t - 8)(t - 1)(t^2 + t + 1)$

Exercise Set 6.6, pp. 401–402

1. Common factor **2.** Perfect-square trinomial
3. Grouping **4.** Multiplying **5.** $5(a + 5)(a - 5)$
7. $(y - 7)^2$ **9.** $(3t + 7)(t + 3)$ **11.** $x(x + 9)^2$
13. $(x - 5)^2(x + 5)$ **15.** $3t(3t + 1)(3t - 1)$
17. $3x(3x - 5)(x + 3)$ **19.** Prime **21.** $6(y - 5)(y + 8)$
23. $-2a^4(a - 2)^2$ **25.** $5x(x^2 + 4)(x + 2)(x - 2)$
27. $(t^2 + 3)(t^2 - 3)$ **29.** $-x^4(x^2 - 2x + 7)$
31. $(x - y)(x^2 + xy + y^2)$ **33.** $a(x^2 + y^2)$
35. $2\pi r(h + r)$ **37.** $(a + b)(5a + 3b)$
39. $(x + 1)(x + y)$ **41.** $(a - 2)(a - y)$

43. $(3x - 2y)(x + 5y)$ **45.** $8mn(m^2 - 4mn + 3)$
47. $(a - 2b)^2$ **49.** $(4x + 3y)^2$ **51.** Prime
53. $(a^2b^2 + 4)(ab + 2)(ab - 2)$ **55.** $4c(4d - c)(5d - c)$
57. $(2t + 1)(4t^2 - 2t + 1)(2t - 1)(4t^2 + 2t + 1)$
59. $-1(xy + 2)(xy + 6)$, or $-(xy + 2)(xy + 6)$
61. $5(pq + 6)(pq - 1)$
63. $2a(3a + 2b)(9a^2 - 6ab + 4b^2)$
65. $x^4(x + 2y)(x - y)$ **67.** $\left(6a - \frac{5}{4}\right)^2$ **69.** $\left(\frac{1}{9}x - \frac{4}{3}\right)^2$
71. $(1 + 4x^6y^6)(1 + 2x^3y^3)(1 - 2x^3y^3)$ **73.** $(2ab + 3)^2$
75. $z(z + 6)(z^2 - 6)$ **77.** ✍   **79.** $\frac{9}{8}$ **80.** $-\frac{5}{3}$
81. $-\frac{7}{2}$ **82.** $\frac{1}{4}$ **83.** 3   **84.** 11   **85.** -1 **86.** 3
87. ✍   **89.** $-x(x^2 + 9)(x^2 - 2)$
91. $-1(x^2 + 2)(x + 3)(x - 3)$, or
$-(x^2 + 2)(x + 3)(x - 3)$ **93.** $(y + 1)(y - 7)(y + 3)$
95. $(y + 4 + x)^2$ **97.** $(a + 3)^2(2a + b + 4)(a - b + 5)$
99. $(7x^2 + 1 + 5x^3)(7x^2 + 1 - 5x^3)$

Technology Connection, p. 409

1. $-4.65, 0.65$ **2.** $-0.37, 5.37$ **3.** $-8.98, -4.56$
4. No solution   **5.** $0, 2.76$

Exercise Set 6.7, pp. 409–411

1. (c)   **2.** (a)   **3.** (d)   **4.** (b)   **5.** $-9, -2$ **7.** $-6, \frac{3}{2}$
9. $\frac{1}{7}, \frac{3}{10}$ **11.** $0, 7$ **13.** $\frac{1}{21}, \frac{18}{11}$ **15.** $-\frac{8}{3}, 0$ **17.** $50, 70$
19. $-5, \frac{2}{3}, 1$ **21.** $1, 6$ **23.** $-7, 3$ **25.** $-9, -2$ **27.** $0, 10$
29. $-6, 0$ **31.** $-6, 6$ **33.** $-\frac{7}{2}, \frac{7}{2}$ **35.** -5 **37.** 8
39. $0, 2$ **41.** $-\frac{5}{4}, 3$ **43.** 3   **45.** $0, \frac{4}{3}$ **47.** $-\frac{7}{6}, \frac{7}{6}$
49. $-4, -\frac{2}{3}$ **51.** $-3, 1$ **53.** $-1, 0, \frac{3}{2}$ **55.** $-7, -\frac{8}{3}, \frac{5}{2}$
57. $-1, 4$ **59.** $-3, 2$ **61.** $(-2, 0), (3, 0)$ **63.** $(-4, 0)$,
$(2, 0)$ **65.** $(-3, 0), \left(\frac{3}{2}, 0\right)$ **67.** ✍   **69.** Let m and n
represent the numbers; $(m + n)^2$ **70.** Let m and n repre-
sent the numbers; $m^2 + n^2$ **71.** Let x represent the first
integer; then $x + 1$ represents the second integer; $x(x + 1)$
72. Mother's Day: $13.8 billion; Father's Day: $9 billion
73. $140°, 35°, 5°$ **74.** Length: 64 in.; width: 32 in.
75. ✍   **77.** **(a)** $x^2 - x - 20 = 0$; **(b)** $x^2 - 6x - 7 = 0$;
(c) $4x^2 - 13x + 3 = 0$; **(d)** $6x^2 - 5x + 1 = 0$;
(e) $12x^2 - 17x + 6 = 0$; **(f)** $x^3 - 4x^2 + x + 6 = 0$
79. $-5, 4$ **81.** $-\frac{3}{5}, \frac{3}{5}$ **83.** $-4, 2$
85. **(a)** $2x^2 + 20x - 4 = 0$; **(b)** $x^2 - 3x - 18 = 0$;
(c) $(x + 1)(5x - 5) = 0$; **(d)** $(2x + 8)(2x - 5) = 0$;
(e) $4x^2 + 8x + 36 = 0$; **(f)** $9x^2 - 12x + 24 = 0$
87. ✍   **89.** $2.33, 6.77$ **91.** $-9.15, -4.59$ **93.** $-3.76, 0$

Connecting the Concepts, p. 412

1. Expression   **2.** Equation   **3.** Equation
4. Expression   **5.** Expression   **6.** Equation
7. $2x^3 + x^2 - 8x$ **8.** $-2x^2 - 11$ **9.** $-10, 10$
10. $6a^2 - 19a + 10$ **11.** $(n - 1)(n - 9)$ **12.** $2, 8$
13. $-\frac{5}{2}$ **14.** $7x^3 + 2x - 7$ **15.** $(4x + 9)(4x - 9)$
16. $-3, 8$ **17.** $-4a^2 - a - 11$
18. $2x^2(9x^2 - 12x + 10)$ **19.** $-1, -\frac{2}{3}$
20. $8x^5 - 20x^4 + 12x^2$

Translating for Success, p. 419

1. O   **2.** M   **3.** K   **4.** I   **5.** G   **6.** E   **7.** C
8. A   **9.** H   **10.** B

Exercise Set 6.8, pp. 420–424

1. $-2, 3$ **3.** 6 m, 8 m, 10 m   **5.** 11, 12
7. -14 and -12; 12 and 14   **9.** Length: 30 ft; width: 6 ft
11. Length: 6 cm; width: 4 cm   **13.** Base: 12 in.; height: 9 in.
15. Foot: 7 ft; height: 12 ft   **17.** 1 min, 3 min   **19.** In 2008
21. 16 teams   **23.** 66 handshakes   **25.** 12 players
27. 9 ft   **29.** 32 ft   **31.** 300 ft by 400 ft by 500 ft
33. Dining room: 12 ft by 12 ft; kitchen: 12 ft by 10 ft
35. 20 ft   **37.** 1 sec, 2 sec   **39.** ✍   **41.** $-\frac{12}{35}$ **42.** $-\frac{21}{20}$
43. -1 **44.** $-\frac{7}{4}$ **45.** $\frac{1}{4}$ **46.** $\frac{4}{5}$ **47.** $\frac{53}{168}$ **48.** $\frac{19}{18}$
49. ✍   **51.** $180   **53.** 39 cm   **55.** 4 in., 6 in.
57. 35 ft   **59.** 2 hr, 4.2 hr   **61.** 3 hr

Review Exercises: Chapter 6, pp. 427–429

1. False   **2.** True   **3.** True   **4.** False   **5.** False
6. True   **7.** True   **8.** False   **9.** Answers may vary.
$(4x)(5x^2), (-2x^2)(-10x), (x^3)(20)$
10. Answers may vary. $(-3x^2)(6x^3), (2x^4)(-9x)$,
$(-18x)(x^4)$ **11.** $6x^3(2x - 3)$ **12.** $4a(2a - 3)$
13. $(10t + 1)(10t - 1)$ **14.** $(x + 4)(x - 3)$
15. $(x + 7)^2$ **16.** $3x(2x + 1)^2$ **17.** $(2x + 3)(3x^2 + 1)$
18. $(6a - 5)(a + 1)$ **19.** $(5t - 3)^2$
20. $2(24t^2 - 14t + 3)$ **21.** $(9a^2 + 1)(3a + 1)(3a - 1)$
22. $3x(3x - 5)(x + 3)$ **23.** $2(x - 5)(x^2 + 5x + 25)$
24. $(x + 4)(x^3 - 2)$ **25.** $(ab^2 + 8)(ab^2 - 8)$
26. $-4x^4(2x^2 - 8x + 1)$ **27.** $3(2x - 5)^2$
28. Prime   **29.** $-t(t + 6)(t - 7)$ **30.** $(2x + 5)(2x - 5)$
31. $(n + 6)(n - 10)$ **32.** $5(z^2 - 6z + 2)$
33. $(4t + 5)(t + 2)$ **34.** $(2t + 1)(t - 4)$
35. $7x(x + 1)(x + 4)$ **36.** $(2y + 3x^2)(4y^2 - 6x^2y + 9x^4)$
37. $5(2x - 1)^2$ **38.** $-6x(x + 5)(x - 5)$
39. $(5 - x)(3 - x)$ **40.** Prime   **41.** $(xy + 8)(xy - 2)$
42. $3(2a + 7b)^2$ **43.** $(m + 5)(m + t)$
44. $32(x^2 + 2y^2z^2)(x^2 - 2y^2z^2)$ **45.** $(2m + n)(3m + n)$
46. $(3r + 5s)(2r - 3s)$ **47.** $-11, 9$ **48.** $-7, 5$
49. $-\frac{3}{4}, \frac{3}{4}$ **50.** $\frac{2}{3}, 1$ **51.** $-\frac{5}{2}, 6$ **52.** $-2, 3$ **53.** $0, \frac{3}{5}$
54. 1   **55.** $-3, 4$ **56.** 10 teams   **57.** $(-1, 0), \left(\frac{5}{2}, 0\right)$
58. Height: 14 ft; base: 14 ft   **59.** 10 holes
60. ✍ Answers may vary. Because Celia did not first factor
out the largest common factor, 4, her factorization will not be
"complete" until she removes a common factor of 2 from each
binomial. The answer should be $4(x - 5)(x + 5)$. Awarding 3
to 7 points would seem reasonable.   **61.** ✍ The equations
solved in this chapter have an x^2-term (are quadratic),
whereas those solved previously have no x^2-term (are
linear). The principle of zero products is used to solve
quadratic equations and is not used to solve linear
equations.   **62.** 2.5 cm   **63.** $0, 2$ **64.** Length: 12 cm;
width: 6 cm   **65.** 100 cm^2, 225 cm^2 **66.** $-3, 2, \frac{5}{2}$
67. No real solution

Test: Chapter 6, pp. 429–430

1. [6.1] Answers may vary. $(3x^2)(4x^2)$, $(-2x)(-6x^3)$, $(12x^3)(x)$ **2.** [6.2] $(x-4)(x-9)$ **3.** [6.4] $(x-5)^2$
4. [6.1] $2y^2(2y^2-4y+3)$ **5.** [6.1] $(x+1)(x^2+2)$
6. [6.1] $t^5(t^2-3)$ **7.** [6.2] $a(a+4)(a-1)$
8. [6.3] $2(5x-6)(x+4)$ **9.** [6.4] $(2t+5)(2t-5)$
10. [6.2] $(x+2)(x-3)$ **11.** [6.3] $-3m(2m+1)(m+1)$
12. [6.5] $3(r-1)(r^2+r+1)$ **13.** [6.4] $5(3r+2)^2$
14. [6.4] $3(x^2+4)(x+2)(x-2)$ **15.** [6.4] $(7t+6)^2$
16. [6.1] $(x+2)(x^3-3)$ **17.** [6.2] Prime
18. [6.3] $(2x+3)(2x-5)$ **19.** [6.3] $3t(2t+5)(t-1)$
20. [6.3] $3(m-5n)(m+2n)$ **21.** [6.7] $1,5$
22. [6.7] $-\frac{3}{2},5$ **23.** [6.7] $0,\frac{2}{5}$ **24.** [6.7] $-\frac{1}{5},\frac{1}{5}$
25. [6.7] $-4,5$ **26.** [6.7] $(-1,0),\left(\frac{8}{3},0\right)$
27. [6.8] Length: 10 m; width: 4 m   **28.** [6.8] 10 people
29. [6.8] 5 ft   **30.** [6.8] 15 cm by 30 cm
31. [6.2] $(a-4)(a+8)$ **32.** [6.7] $-\frac{8}{3},0,\frac{2}{5}$

Cumulative Review: Chapters 1–3, 5–6 pp. 430–431

1. $\frac{1}{2}$ **2.** $\frac{9}{32}$ **3.** $\frac{9}{8}$ **4.** 29   **5.** $\frac{1}{9x^4y^6}$ **6.** t^{10}
7. $3x^4+5x^3+x-10$ **8.** $-3a^2b-ab^2+2b^3$
9. $\frac{t^8}{4s^2}$ **10.** $-\frac{8x^6y^3}{27z^{12}}$ **11.** 8   **12.** -8 **13.** $-x^4$
14. $2x^3-5x^2+\frac{1}{2}x-1$ **15.** $-4t^{11}+8t^9+20t^8$
16. $9x^2-30x+25$ **17.** $100x^{10}-y^2$
18. x^3-2x^2+1 **19.** $(c+1)(c-1)$
20. $5(x+y)(1+2x)$ **21.** $(2r-t)^2$
22. $(2x-5)(3x-2)$ **23.** $10(y^2+4)$
24. $y(x-1)(x-2)$ **25.** $(3x-2y)(4x+y)$
26. $(5a+4b)(25a^2-20ab+16b^2)$ **27.** $\frac{1}{12}$
28. 1   **29.** $-\frac{9}{4}$ **30.** $\{x|x\geq 1\}$, or $[1,\infty)$ **31.** $-3,1$
32. $-4,3$ **33.** $-2,2$ **34.** $0,4$ **35.** $c=\frac{a}{b+d}$ **36.** 0
37. $-2;(0,5)$ **38.** $y=5x-\frac{1}{3}$ **39.** $y=5x+\frac{5}{3}$

40.

41.

42.

43.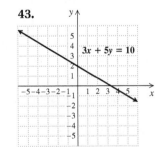

44.

45. 372 min
46. 11,616,000 subscribers per year   **47.** 60,000,000 users   **48.** 101,180 people
49. Bottom of ladder to building: 5 ft; top of ladder to ground: 12 ft
50. Length: 12 ft; width: 2 ft
51. Scores that are 9 and higher
52. (a)   **(b)** 950 mg per serving

53. $b=\frac{2}{a+1}$ **54.** $y=-8$
55. (a) $9y^2+12y+4-x^2$; **(b)** $(3y+2+x)(3y+2-x)$
56. $-1,0,\frac{1}{3}$

CHAPTER 7

Technology Connection, p. 437

1. Correct   **2.** Correct   **3.** Not correct   **4.** Not correct

Exercise Set 7.1, pp. 439–440

1. (e)   **2.** (a)   **3.** (d)   **4.** (b)   **5.** (c)   **6.** (f)
7. 0   **9.** -5 **11.** 5   **13.** $-4,7$ **15.** $-6,\frac{1}{2}$ **17.** $\frac{5a}{4b^2}$
19. $\frac{t+2}{t-3}$ **21.** $\frac{7}{8}$ **23.** $\frac{a-3}{a+1}$ **25.** $-\frac{2x^3}{3}$ **27.** $\frac{y-3}{4y}$
29. $\frac{t-4}{t-5}$ **31.** $\frac{a+4}{2(a-4)}$ **33.** $\frac{x-4}{x+4}$ **35.** $\frac{1}{n^2+2n+4}$
37. $t-1$ **39.** $\frac{y^2+4}{y+2}$ **41.** $\frac{1}{2}$ **43.** $\frac{y}{2y+1}$
45. $\frac{2x-3}{5x+2}$ **47.** -1 **49.** -7 **51.** $-\frac{1}{4}$ **53.** $-\frac{3}{2}$
55. -1 **57.** ✏️   **59.** $-\frac{4}{21}$ **60.** $-\frac{5}{3}$ **61.** $-\frac{15}{4}$
62. $-\frac{21}{16}$ **63.** $\frac{13}{63}$ **64.** $\frac{5}{48}$ **65.** ✏️   **67.** $-(2y+x)$
69. $\frac{x^3+4}{(x^3+2)(x^2+2)}$ **71.** $\frac{(t-1)(t-9)^2}{(t+1)(t^2+9)}$
73. $\frac{(x-y)^3}{(x+y)^2(x-5y)}$ **75.** ✏️

Technology Connection, pp. 443–444

1. Let $y_1=((x^2+3x+2)/(x^2+4))/(5x^2+10x)$ and $y_2=(x+1)/((x^2+4)(5x))$. With the tables set in AUTO mode, note that the values in the Y1- and Y2-columns match except for $x = -2$.   **2.** ERROR messages occur when division by 0 is attempted. Since the simplified expression has no factor of $x + 5$ or $x + 1$ in a denominator, no ERROR message occurs in Y2 for $x = -5$ or -1.

Exercise Set 7.2, pp. 444–446

1. $\dfrac{3x(x + 2)}{8(5x - 1)}$ **3.** $\dfrac{(a - 4)(a + 2)}{(a + 6)^2}$ **5.** $\dfrac{(2x + 3)(x + 1)}{4(x - 5)}$

7. $\dfrac{(n - 4)(n + 4)}{(n^2 + 4)(n^2 - 4)}$ **9.** $\dfrac{(y + 6)(y - 3)}{(1 + y)(y + 3)}$ **11.** $\dfrac{6t}{5}$

13. $\dfrac{4}{c^2 d}$ **15.** $\dfrac{(x - 5)(x + 2)}{x - 2}$ **17.** $\dfrac{(n - 5)(n - 1)(n - 6)}{(n + 6)(n^2 + 36)}$

19. $\dfrac{7(a + 3)}{a(a + 4)}$ **21.** $\dfrac{3v}{v - 2}$ **23.** $\dfrac{t - 5}{t + 5}$ **25.** $\dfrac{9(y - 5)}{10(y - 1)}$

27. 1   **29.** $\dfrac{(t - 2)(t + 5)}{(t - 5)(t - 5)}$ **31.** $(2x - 1)^2$ **33.** $c(c - 2)$

35. $\dfrac{9}{2x}$ **37.** $\dfrac{1}{a^4 + 3a}$ **39.** $\frac{20}{27}$ **41.** $\dfrac{x^2}{20}$ **43.** $\dfrac{a^3}{b^3}$

45. $\dfrac{4(t - 3)}{3(t + 1)}$ **47.** $4(y - 2)$ **49.** $-\dfrac{a}{b}$

51. $\dfrac{(n + 3)(n + 3)}{n - 2}$ **53.** $\frac{15}{16}$ **55.** $\dfrac{-x^2 - 4}{x + 2}$

57. $\dfrac{a - 5}{3(a - 1)}$ **59.** $\dfrac{(2x - 1)(2x + 1)}{x - 5}$

61. $\dfrac{(w - 7)(w - 8)}{(2w - 7)(3w + 1)}$ **63.** $\dfrac{1}{(c - 5)(5c - 3)}$

65. $\dfrac{(x - 4y)(x - y)}{(x + y)^3}$ **67.** $\dfrac{x^2 + 4x + 16}{(x + 4)^2}$ **69.** $\dfrac{(2a + b)^2}{2(a + b)}$

71. ✍   **73.** $\frac{19}{12}$ **74.** $\frac{41}{24}$ **75.** $\frac{1}{18}$ **76.** $-\frac{1}{6}$ **77.** $x^2 + 3$

78. $-2x^2 - 4x + 1$ **79.** ✍   **81.** $\dfrac{3}{7x}$ **83.** 1

85. $\dfrac{1}{(x + y)^3(3x + y)}$ **87.** $\dfrac{a^2 - 2b}{a^2 + 3b}$ **89.** $\dfrac{(z + 4)^3}{3(z - 4)^2}$

91. $\dfrac{a - 3b}{c}$ **93.** 📊

Exercise Set 7.3, pp. 453–455

1. Numerators; denominator   **2.** Term   **3.** Least common denominator; LCD   **4.** Factorizations; denominators   **5.** $\dfrac{8}{t}$ **7.** $\dfrac{3x + 5}{12}$ **9.** $\dfrac{9}{a + 3}$

11. $\dfrac{8}{4x - 7}$ **13.** $\dfrac{2y + 7}{2y}$ **15.** 6   **17.** $\dfrac{4(x - 1)}{x + 3}$

19. $a + 5$ **21.** $y - 7$ **23.** 0   **25.** $\dfrac{1}{x + 2}$ **27.** $\dfrac{t - 4}{t + 3}$

29. $\dfrac{y + 2}{y - 4}$ **31.** $-\dfrac{5}{x - 4}$, or $\dfrac{5}{4 - x}$ **33.** $-\dfrac{1}{x - 1}$, or $\dfrac{1}{1 - x}$

35. 180   **37.** 72   **39.** 60   **41.** $18t^5$ **43.** $30a^4b^8$

45. $6(y - 3)$ **47.** $(x - 5)(x + 3)(x - 3)$

49. $t(t - 4)(t + 2)^2$ **51.** $120x^2y^3z^2$

53. $(a + 1)(a - 1)^2$ **55.** $(2n - 1)(n + 1)(n + 2)$

57. $12x^3(x - 5)(x - 3)(x - 1)$

59. $2(x + 1)(x - 1)(x^2 + x + 1)$ **61.** $\dfrac{15}{18t^4}, \dfrac{st^2}{18t^4}$

63. $\dfrac{21y}{9x^4y^3}, \dfrac{4x^3}{9x^4y^3}$ **65.** $\dfrac{2x(x + 3)}{(x - 2)(x + 2)(x + 3)}$,

$\dfrac{4x(x - 2)}{(x - 2)(x + 2)(x + 3)}$ **67.** ✍   **69.** $\frac{-5}{8}, \frac{5}{-8}$

70. $\frac{-4}{11}, -\frac{4}{11}$ **71.** $-x + y$, or $y - x$ **72.** $-3 + a$, or $a - 3$

73. $-2x + 7$, or $7 - 2x$ **74.** $-a + b$, or $b - a$ **75.** ✍

77. $\dfrac{18x + 5}{x - 1}$ **79.** $\dfrac{x}{3x + 1}$ **81.** 30 strands

83. 60 strands   **85.** $(2x + 5)(2x - 5)(3x + 4)^4$

87. 30 sec   **89.** 7:55 A.M.   **91.** ✍

Exercise Set 7.4, pp. 460–462

1. LCD   **2.** Missing; denominator   **3.** Numerators; LCD

4. Simplify   **5.** $\dfrac{3 + 5x}{x^2}$ **7.** $-\dfrac{5}{24r}$ **9.** $\dfrac{3u^2 + 4v}{u^3v^2}$

11. $\dfrac{-2(xy + 9)}{3x^2y^3}$ **13.** $\dfrac{7x + 1}{24}$ **15.** $\dfrac{-x - 4}{6}$

17. $\dfrac{a^2 + 13a - 5}{15a^2}$ **19.** $\dfrac{7z - 12}{12z}$ **21.** $\dfrac{(3c - d)(c + d)}{c^2d^2}$

23. $\dfrac{4x^2 - 13xt + 9t^2}{3x^2t^2}$ **25.** $\dfrac{6x}{(x + 2)(x - 2)}$

27. $\dfrac{(t - 3)(t + 1)}{(t - 1)(t + 3)}$ **29.** $\dfrac{11x + 2}{3x(x + 1)}$ **31.** $\dfrac{-5t + 3}{2t(t - 1)}$

33. $\dfrac{a^2}{(a - 3)(a + 3)}$ **35.** $\dfrac{16}{3(z + 4)}$ **37.** $\dfrac{5q - 3}{(q - 1)^2}$

39. $\dfrac{1}{t^2 + t + 1}$ **41.** $\dfrac{9a}{4(a - 5)}$ **43.** 0

45. $\dfrac{10}{(a - 3)(a + 2)}$ **47.** $\dfrac{x - 5}{(x + 5)(x + 3)}$

49. $\dfrac{3z^2 + 19z - 20}{(z - 2)^2(z + 3)}$ **51.** $\dfrac{-7}{x^2 + 25x + 24}$ **53.** $\dfrac{3x - 1}{2}$

55. $y + 3$ **57.** 0   **59.** $\dfrac{p^2 + 7p + 1}{(p - 5)(p + 5)}$

61. $\dfrac{(x + 1)(x + 3)}{(x - 4)(x + 4)}$ **63.** $\dfrac{-a - 2}{(a + 1)(a - 1)}$, or

$\dfrac{a + 2}{(1 + a)(1 - a)}$ **65.** $\dfrac{2(5x + 3y)}{(x - y)(x + y)}$ **67.** $\dfrac{2x - 3}{2 - x}$

69. 3   **71.** 0   **73.** ✍   **75.** $-\frac{3}{22}$ **76.** $\frac{7}{9}$ **77.** $\frac{9}{10}$

78. $\frac{16}{27}$ **79.** $\frac{2}{3}$ **80.** $\dfrac{(x - 3)(x + 2)}{(x - 2)(x + 3)}$ **81.** ✍

83. Perimeter: $\dfrac{2(5x - 7)}{(x - 5)(x + 4)}$; area: $\dfrac{6}{(x - 5)(x + 4)}$

85. $\dfrac{x}{3x + 1}$ **87.** $\dfrac{x^4 + 4x^3 - 5x^2 - 126x - 441}{(x + 2)^2(x + 7)^2}$

89. $\dfrac{5(a^2 + 2ab - b^2)}{(a - b)(3a + b)(3a - b)}$ **91.** $\dfrac{a}{a - b} + \dfrac{3b}{b - a}$;

answers may vary.   **93.** ✍, 📊

Connecting the Concepts, pp. 462–463

1. Addition; $\dfrac{3x + 10}{5x^2}$ **2.** Multiplication; $\dfrac{6}{5x^3}$

3. Division; $\dfrac{3x}{10}$ **4.** Subtraction; $\dfrac{3x - 10}{5x^2}$

5. Multiplication; $\dfrac{x - 3}{15(x - 2)}$ **6.** Multiplication;

$\dfrac{6}{(x + 3)(x + 4)}$ **7.** Division; $\frac{1}{3}$ **8.** Subtraction;

$\dfrac{x^2 - 2x - 2}{(x - 1)(x + 2)}$ **9.** Addition; $\dfrac{5x + 17}{(x + 3)(x + 4)}$

10. Addition; -5 **11.** Subtraction; $\dfrac{5}{x - 4}$ **12.** Division;

$\dfrac{(2x + 3)(x + 3)}{(x + 1)^2}$ **13.** Subtraction; $\frac{1}{6}$ **14.** Multiplication;

$\dfrac{x(x + 4)}{(x - 1)^2}$ **15.** Addition; $\dfrac{x + 7}{(x - 5)(x + 1)}$ **16.** Division;

$\dfrac{9(u - 1)}{16}$ **17.** Addition; $\dfrac{7t + 8}{30}$ **18.** Multiplication;

$(t + 5)^2$ **19.** Division; $\dfrac{a - 1}{(a + 2)(a - 2)^2}$

20. Subtraction; $\dfrac{-3x^2 + 9x - 14}{2x}$

Technology Connection, p. 467

1. $(1 - 1/x)/(1 - 1/x^2)$ **2.** Parentheses are needed to group separate terms into factors. When a fraction bar is replaced with a division sign, we need parentheses to preserve the groupings that had been created by the fraction bar. This holds for denominators and numerators alike.

Exercise Set 7.5, pp. 467–469

1. (d)   **2.** (a)   **3.** (b)   **4.** (c)   **5.** $\frac{5}{11}$ **7.** 10

9. $\dfrac{5x^2}{4(x^2 + 4)}$ **11.** $\dfrac{-10t}{5t - 2}$ **13.** $\dfrac{2(2a - 5)}{a - 7}$

15. $\dfrac{x^2 - 18}{2(x + 3)}$ **17.** $-\frac{1}{5}$ **19.** $\dfrac{1 + t^2}{t(1 - t)}$ **21.** $\dfrac{x}{x - y}$

23. $\dfrac{c(4c + 7)}{3(2c^2 - 1)}$ **25.** $\dfrac{15(4 - a^3)}{14a^2(9 + 2a)}$ **27.** 1

29. $\dfrac{3a^2 + 4b^3}{b^3(5 - 3a^2)}$ **31.** $\dfrac{(t - 3)(t + 3)}{t^2 + 4}$ **33.** $\dfrac{a^2b^2}{b^2 - ab + a^2}$

35. $\dfrac{a(3ab^3 + 4)}{b^2(3 + a)}$ **37.** $\dfrac{t^2 + 5t + 3}{(t + 1)^2}$ **39.** $\dfrac{x^2 - 2x - 1}{x^2 - 5x - 4}$

41.   **43.** -4 **44.** -4 **45.** $\frac{19}{3}$ **46.** $-\frac{14}{27}$ **47.** 3, 4

48. $-15, 2$ **49.**   **51.** 6, 7, 8   **53.** $-3, -\frac{4}{5}, 3$

55. $\dfrac{A}{B} \div \dfrac{C}{D} = \dfrac{\dfrac{A}{B}}{\dfrac{C}{D}} = \dfrac{\dfrac{A}{B}}{\dfrac{C}{D}} \cdot \dfrac{BD}{BD} = \dfrac{AD}{BC} = \dfrac{A}{B} \cdot \dfrac{D}{C}$

57. $\dfrac{x^2 + 5x + 15}{-x^2 + 10}$ **59.** 0   **61.** $\dfrac{2z(5z - 2)}{(z + 2)(13z - 6)}$

63.

Exercise Set 7.6, pp. 475–476

1. False   **2.** True   **3.** True   **4.** True   **5.** $-\frac{2}{5}$ **7.** $\frac{6}{7}$

9. $\frac{24}{5}$ **11.** $-4, -1$ **13.** $-6, 6$ **15.** 12   **17.** $\frac{14}{3}$

19. -10 **21.** $-4, -3$ **23.** $\frac{23}{2}$ **25.** $\frac{5}{2}$ **27.** -1

29. No solution   **31.** -10 **33.** $-\frac{7}{3}$ **35.** $-2, \frac{7}{3}$
37. $-3, 13$ **39.** 2   **41.** -8 **43.** No solution
45. $-6, 6$ **47.**   **49.** 137, 139   **50.** 14 yd
51. Base: 9 cm; height: 12 cm   **52.** $-8, -6; 6, 8$
53. 0.06 cm per day   **54.** 0.28 in. per day   **55.**
57. -2 **59.** 3   **61.** 4   **63.** 4   **65.** -2 **67.**

Connecting the Concepts, pp. 476–477

1. Expression; $\dfrac{x - 2}{x + 1}$ **2.** Expression; $\dfrac{19n - 2}{5n(2n - 1)}$

3. Equation; 8   **4.** Expression; $\dfrac{(z + 1)^2(z - 1)}{z}$

5. Equation; $-\frac{1}{2}$ **6.** Expression; $\dfrac{8(t + 1)}{(t - 1)(2t - 1)}$

7. Expression; $\dfrac{2a}{a - 1}$ **8.** Equation; $-5, 3$

9. Expression; $\dfrac{3x}{10}$ **10.** Equation; $-10, 10$

Translating for Success, p. 487

1. K   **2.** E   **3.** C   **4.** N   **5.** D   **6.** O   **7.** F   **8.** H
9. B   **10.** A

Exercise Set 7.7, pp. 488–493

1. $\frac{1}{2}$ cake per hour   **2.** $\frac{1}{3}$ cake per hour   **3.** $\frac{5}{6}$ cake per hour
4. 1 lawn per hour   **5.** $\frac{1}{3}$ lawn per hour   **6.** $\frac{2}{3}$ lawn per hour
7. $3\frac{3}{7}$ hr   **9.** $\frac{42}{13}$ min, or $3\frac{3}{13}$ min   **11.** $19\frac{1}{11}$ min
13. H470: 135 min; K5400: $67\frac{1}{2}$ min   **15.** Austin: 15 min;
Airgle: 30 min   **17.** 300 min, or 5 hr
19.

	Distance (in km)	Speed (in km/h)	Time (in hours)
B & M	330	$r - 14$	$\dfrac{330}{r - 14}$
AMTRAK	400	r	$\dfrac{400}{r}$

AMTRAK: 80 km/h; B & M: 66 km/h
21. 7 mph   **23.** 5.2 ft/sec   **25.** 3 hr   **27.** 9 km/h
29. 2 km/h   **31.** 20 mph   **33.** 10.5   **35.** $\frac{8}{3}$ **37.** $3\frac{3}{4}$ in.
39. 20 ft   **41.** 15 ft   **43.** 12.6   **45.** 1440 messages
47. About 231,000 people   **49.** 18 gal   **51.** $26\frac{2}{3}$ cm
53. 52 bulbs   **55.** $7\frac{1}{2}$ oz   **57.** 90 whales
59. (a) 1.92 T; (b) 28.8 lb   **61.**
63.   **64.**

65.

66.

67.

68.

69. ✍   **71.** $49\frac{1}{2}$ hr   **73.** 2250 people per hour
75. $14\frac{7}{8}$ mi   **77.** About 57%   **79.** Page 278
81. $\dfrac{B}{A} = \dfrac{D}{C}; \dfrac{A}{C} = \dfrac{B}{D}; \dfrac{C}{A} = \dfrac{D}{B}$ **83.** $51\frac{3}{7}$ mph   **85.** ✍

Review Exercises: Chapter 7, pp. 497–498

1. False   **2.** True   **3.** False   **4.** True   **5.** True
6. False   **7.** False   **8.** False   **9.** 0   **10.** −5
11. −6, 6   **12.** −6, 5   **13.** −2   **14.** $\dfrac{x-3}{x+5}$ **15.** $\dfrac{7x+3}{x-3}$
16. $\dfrac{3(y-3)}{2(y+3)}$ **17.** $-5(x+2y)$ **18.** $\dfrac{a-6}{5}$
19. $\dfrac{3(y-2)^2}{4(2y-1)(y-1)}$ **20.** $-32t$ **21.** $\dfrac{2x(x-1)}{x+1}$
22. $\dfrac{(x^2+1)(2x+1)}{(x-2)(x+1)}$ **23.** $\dfrac{(t+4)^2}{t+1}$ **24.** $60a^5b^8$
25. $x^4(x-1)(x+1)$ **26.** $(y-2)(y+2)(y+1)$
27. $\dfrac{15-3x}{x+3}$ **28.** $\dfrac{4}{x-4}$ **29.** $\dfrac{x+5}{2x}$
30. $\dfrac{2a^2-21ab+15b^2}{5a^2b^2}$ **31.** $y-4$ **32.** $\dfrac{t(t-2)}{(t-1)(t+1)}$
33. $d+2$ **34.** $\dfrac{-x^2+x+26}{(x+1)(x-5)(x+5)}$ **35.** $\dfrac{2(x-2)}{x+2}$
36. $\dfrac{3(7t+2)}{4t(3t+2)}$ **37.** $\dfrac{z}{1-z}$ **38.** $\dfrac{10x}{3x^2+16}$ **39.** $c-d$
40. 4   **41.** $\frac{7}{2}$ **42.** −6, −1   **43.** $5\frac{1}{7}$ hr   **44.** Core 2
Duo: 45 sec; Core 2 Quad: 30 sec   **45.** Car: 105 km/h;
train: 90 km/h   **46.** 24 mph   **47.** 55 seals
48. 6   **49.** ✍ The LCM of denominators is used to clear
fractions when simplifying a complex rational expression
using the method of multiplying by the LCD, and when
solving rational equations.   **50.** ✍ Although multiplying
the denominators of the expressions being added results in a
common denominator, it is often not the *least* common
denominator. Using a common denominator other than the

LCD makes the expressions more complicated, requires
additional simplifying after the addition has been performed,
and leaves more room for error.   **51.** $\dfrac{5(a+3)^2}{a}$
52. $\dfrac{10a}{(a-b)(b-c)}$ **53.** 0

Test: Chapter 7, pp. 498–499

1. [7.1] 0   **2.** [7.1] −8   **3.** [7.1] −1, 1   **4.** [7.1] 1, 2
5. [7.1] $\dfrac{3x+7}{x+3}$ **6.** [7.2] $\dfrac{2t(t+3)}{3(t-1)}$
7. [7.2] $\dfrac{(5y+1)(y+1)}{3y(y+2)}$ **8.** [7.2] $\dfrac{(2a+1)(4a^2+1)}{4a^2(2a-1)}$
9. [7.2] $(x+3)(x-3)$ **10.** [7.3] $(y-3)(y+3)(y+7)$
11. [7.3] $\dfrac{-3x+9}{x^3}$ **12.** [7.3] $\dfrac{-2t+8}{t^2+1}$ **13.** [7.4] 1
14. [7.4] $\dfrac{3x-5}{x-3}$ **15.** [7.4] $\dfrac{11t-8}{t(t-2)}$
16. [7.4] $\dfrac{y^2+3}{(y-1)(y+3)^2}$ **17.** [7.4] $\dfrac{x^2+2x-7}{(x+1)(x-1)^2}$
18. [7.5] $\dfrac{3y+1}{y}$ **19.** [7.5] $x-8$ **20.** [7.6] $\frac{8}{3}$
21. [7.6] −3, 5   **22.** [7.7] 12 min   **23.** [7.7] $1\frac{1}{4}$ mi
24. [7.7] Ryan: 65 km/h; Alicia: 45 km/h   **25.** [7.7] Rema:
4 hr; Pe'rez: 10 hr   **26.** [7.5] a **27.** [7.7] −1

Cumulative Review: Chapters 1–3, 5–7, pp. 499–500

1. $a+cb$ **2.** −25   **3.** 25   **4.** $-3x+33$ **5.** 10
6. −7, 7   **7.** $-\frac{5}{3}$ **8.** $\frac{8}{5}$ **9.** 4   **10.** −10, −1   **11.** −8
12. 1, 4   **13.** $\left\{y \mid y \le -\frac{2}{3}\right\}$ **14.** −17   **15.** $-4, \frac{1}{2}$
16. $\{x \mid x > 43\}$ **17.** 5   **18.** $-\frac{7}{2}, 5$ **19.** −13
20. $b = 3a - c + 9$ **21.** $y = \dfrac{4z-3x}{6}$
22.

23.

24.

25.

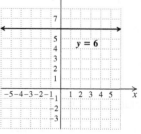

26. -2 **27.** Slope: $\frac{1}{2}$; y-intercept: $\left(0, -\frac{1}{4}\right)$

28. $y = -\frac{5}{8}x - 4$ **29.** $\frac{1}{x^2}$ **30.** y^{-7}, or $\frac{1}{y^7}$

31. $-4a^4b^{14}$ **32.** $-y^3 - 2y^2 - 2y + 7$

33. $-15a + 10b - 5c$ **34.** $2x^5 + x^3 - 6x^2 - x + 3$

35. $36x^2 - 60xy + 25y^2$ **36.** $3n^2 - 13n - 10$

37. $4x^6 - 1$ **38.** $2x(3 - x - 12x^3)$

39. $(4x + 9)(4x - 9)$ **40.** $10(t + 1)(t^2 - t + 1)$

41. $(4x + 3)(2x + 1)$ **42.** $2(3x - 2)(x - 4)$

43. $(5t + 4)^2$ **44.** $(xy - 5)(xy + 4)$

45. $(x + 2)(x^3 - 3)$ **46.** $\dfrac{4}{t + 4}$ **47.** 1

48. $\dfrac{a^2 + 7ab + b^2}{(a + b)(a - b)}$ **49.** $\dfrac{2x + 5}{4 - x}$ **50.** $\dfrac{x}{x - 2}$

51. $\dfrac{y(3y^2 + 2)}{y^3 - 3}$ **52.** $6x^2 - 5x + 2 + \dfrac{4}{x} + \dfrac{1}{x^2}$

53. $15x^3 - 57x^2 + 177x - 529 + \dfrac{1605}{x + 3}$ **54.** 15 books

55. About 340.8 billion admissions   **56.** $33{,}339{,}507$ and $33{,}339{,}508$ **57.** 12 ft   **58.** $\frac{75}{4}$ min, or $18\frac{3}{4}$ min

59. 90 antelope   **60.** 150 calories   **61.** $-144, 144$

62. $16y^6 - y^4 + 6y^2 - 9$ **63.** $-7, 4, 12$ **64.** 18

CHAPTER 8

Exercise Set 8.1, pp. 508-513

1. Correspondence   **2.** Exactly   **3.** Domain
4. Range   **5.** Horizontal   **6.** Vertical   **7.** "f of 3," "f at 3,"
or "the value of f at 3"   **8.** Vertical   **9.** Yes   **11.** Yes
13. No   **15.** Yes   **17.** Function   **19.** Function
21. (a) -1; (b) -3 **23.** (a) 3; (b) 3 **25.** (a) 3; (b) 0
27. (a) 3; (b) -3 **29.** (a) 1; (b) 3 **31.** (a) 4; (b) $-1, 3$
33. (a) 2; (b) $\{x \mid 0 < x \le 2\}$, or $(0, 2]$ **35.** Yes   **37.** Yes
39. No   **41.** (a) 5; (b) -3; (c) -9; (d) 21;
(e) $2a + 9$; (f) $2a + 7$ **43.** (a) 0; (b) 1; (c) 57;
(d) $5t^2 + 4t$; (e) $20a^2 + 8a$; (f) 48 **45.** (a) $\frac{3}{5}$; (b) $\frac{1}{3}$; (c) $\frac{4}{7}$;
(d) 0; (e) $\dfrac{x - 1}{2x - 1}$; (f) $\dfrac{a + h - 3}{2a + 2h - 5}$
47. $4\sqrt{3}$ cm$^2 \approx 6.93$ cm^2 **49.** 36π in$^2 \approx 113.10$ in^2
51. 164.98 cm   **53.** $23°$F   **55.** 75 heart attacks per $10{,}000$ men   **57.** 500 movies
59. 19 watts; 30 watts

61. 3.5 drinks; 6 drinks

63. $\$257{,}000$; $\$306{,}000$

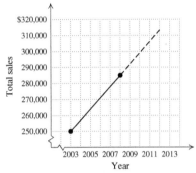

65. 〣   **67.** 6
68. $-6, 6$ **69.** $-\frac{1}{2}$
70. $-1, 1$
71. $-4, 3$ **72.** $\frac{9}{32}$
73. $\frac{1}{7}$ **74.** $-4, 8$
75. 〣   **77.** $26; 99$
79. Worm
81. About 2 min 50 sec
83. 1 every 3 min

85.

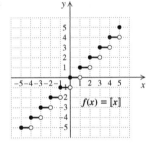

Exercise Set 8.2, pp. 519-521

1. (c)   **2.** (d)   **3.** (d)   **4.** (b)   **5.** (c)   **6.** (b)
7. Domain: $\{2, 9, -2, -4\}$; range: $\{8, 3, 10, 4\}$
9. Domain: $\{0, 4, -5, -1\}$; range: $\{0, -2\}$
11. Domain: $\{-4, -2, 0, 2, 4\}$; range: $\{-2, -1, 0, 1, 2\}$
13. Domain: $\{-5, -3, -1, 0, 2, 4\}$; range: $\{-1, 1\}$
15. Domain: $\{x \mid -4 \le x \le 3\}$, or $[-4, 3]$; range: $\{y \mid -3 \le y \le 4\}$, or $[-3, 4]$ **17.** Domain: $\{x \mid -4 \le x \le 5\}$, or $[-4, 5]$; range: $\{y \mid -2 \le y \le 4\}$, or $[-2, 4]$ **19.** Domain: $\{x \mid -4 \le x \le 4\}$, or $[-4, 4]$; range: $\{-3, -1, 1\}$ **21.** Domain: $\mathbb{R}$; range: $\mathbb{R}$
23. Domain: $\mathbb{R}$; range: $\{4\}$ **25.** Domain: $\mathbb{R}$; range: $\{y \mid y \ge 1\}$, or $[1, \infty)$ **27.** Domain: $\{x \mid x$ is a real number and $x \ne -2\}$; range: $\{y \mid y$ is a real number and $y \ne -4\}$
29. Domain: $\{x \mid x \ge 0\}$, or $[0, \infty)$; range: $\{y \mid y \ge 0\}$, or $[0, \infty)$ **31.** $\{x \mid x$ is a real number and $x \ne 3\}$
33. $\left\{x \mid x$ is a real number and $x \ne \frac{1}{2}\right\}$ **35.** $\mathbb{R}$ **37.** $\mathbb{R}$
39. $\{x \mid x$ is a real number and $x \ne 3$ and $x \ne -3\}$ **41.** $\mathbb{R}$
43. $\{x \mid x$ is a real number and $x \ne -1$ and $x \ne -7\}$
45. $\{t \mid 0 \le t < 624\}$, or $[0, 624)$

47. $\{p \mid \$0 \le p \le \$10.60\}$, or $[0, 10.60]$ **49.** $\{d \mid d \ge 0\}$, or $[0, \infty)$ **51.** $\{t \mid 0 \le t \le 5\}$, or $[0, 5]$ **53.** (a) -5; (b) 1; (c) 21 **55.** (a) 0; (b) 2; (c) 7 **57.** (a) 100; (b) 100; (c) 131 **59.**

61.   **62.**

63. Slope: $\frac{2}{3}$; y-intercept: $(0, -4)$
64. Slope: $-\frac{1}{4}$; y-intercept: $(0, 6)$

65. Slope: $\frac{4}{3}$; y-intercept: $(0, 0)$
66. Slope: -5; y-intercept: $(0, 0)$ **67.**

69.   **71.**

73. Domain: $\{x \mid x$ is a real number *and* $x \neq 0\}$; range: $\{y \mid y$ is a real number *and* $y \neq 0\}$
75. Domain: $\{x \mid x < -2$ *or* $x > 0\}$; range: $\{y \mid y < -2$ *or* $y > 3\}$ **77.** Domain: $\mathbb{R}$; range: $\{y \mid y \ge 0\}$, or $[0, \infty)$ **79.** Domain: $\{x \mid x$ is a real number *and* $x \neq 2\}$; range: $\{y \mid y$ is a real number *and* $y \neq 0\}$
81. $\{h \mid 0 \le h \le 144\}$, or $[0, 144]$
83.   **85.**

87.   **89.**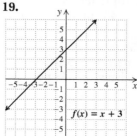

Visualizing for Success, p. 527

1. D **2.** J **3.** A **4.** E **5.** B **6.** C **7.** I **8.** F **9.** G **10.** H

Exercise Set 8.3, pp. 528–531

1. False **2.** True **3.** False **4.** True
5. True **6.** True
7.   **9.**

11.   **13.**

15.   **17.**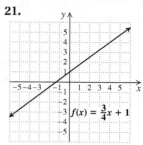

19.   **21.**

23.

25. $C(d) = 0.75d + 30$; 60 miles
27. $L(t) = \frac{1}{2}t + 5$; 20 months after the haircut
29. $A(t) = 849t + 5960$; 5 years after 2006, or 2011
31. (a) $a(t) = 0.9t + 12.7$; (b) 24.4 million cars; (c) about 2014
33. (a) $E(t) = 0.14t + 78.44$; (b) 81.52 yr

35. (a) $A(t) = 22.525t + 236.95$; (b) \$462.2 million
37. (a) $N(t) = 9.4t + 16$; (b) 110 million Americans;
(c) 2015   **39.** (a) $A(t) = \frac{41}{110}t + \frac{1615}{22}$;
(b) about 80.9 million acres   **41.** Linear function; $\mathbb{R}$
43. Quadratic function; $\mathbb{R}$ **45.** Rational function;
$\{t \mid t$ is a real number $and\ t \neq -\frac{4}{3}\}$ **47.** Polynomial function; $\mathbb{R}$
49. Rational function; $\{x \mid x$ is a real number $and\ x \neq \frac{5}{2}\}$
51. Rational function; $\{n \mid n$ is a real number $and\ n \neq -1$
$and\ n \neq -2\}$ **53.** Linear function; $\mathbb{R}$ **55.** $\{y \mid y \geq 0\}$, or
$[0, \infty)$ **57.** $\mathbb{R}$ **59.** $\{y \mid y \leq 0\}$, or $(-\infty, 0]$

61.

63.

Domain: $\mathbb{R}$; range: $\mathbb{R}$ Domain: $\mathbb{R}$; range: $\{-1\}$

65.

67.

Domain: $\mathbb{R}$;   Domain: $\mathbb{R}$;
range: $\{y \mid y \geq 1\}$, or $[1, \infty)$ range: $\{y \mid y \geq 0\}$, or $[0, \infty)$
69. ✍   **71.** $4x^2 + 2x - 1$ **72.** $2x^3 - x^2 - x + 7$
73. $2x^2 - 13x - 7$ **74.** $x^2 + x - 12$
75. $x^3 - 2x^2 - 3x + 5$ **76.** $x^3 + 2x^2 + x + 4$
77. ✍   **79.** False   **81.** False   **83.** 21.1°C   **85.** \$60
87. (a) $g(x) = x - 8$; (b) -10; (c) 83

Connecting the Concepts, p. 532

1. $\{-1, 0, 3, 4\}$ **2.** $\{-2, 0, 6, 8\}$ **3.** -2
4.
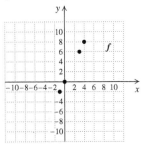
5. $\mathbb{R}$

6. $\{x \mid x$ is a real number $and\ x \neq 0\}$ **7.** $\frac{1}{5}$ **8.** 2   **9.** 3
10. $\{x \mid x$ is a real number $and\ x \neq 0\ and\ x \neq 1\}$
11. Linear function   **12.** Rational function
13. Range: $\mathbb{R}$

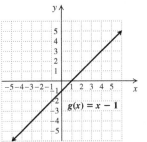

14. Yes   **15.** -4
16. $\{x \mid x \geq -3\}$, or $[-3, \infty)$
17. $\{y \mid y \geq -4\}$, or $[-4, \infty)$
18. 4   **19.** 10   **20.** 13

Exercise Set 8.4, pp. 538-541

1. Sum   **2.** Subtract   **3.** Evaluate   **4.** Domains
5. Excluding   **6.** Sum   **7.** 1   **9.** 5   **11.** -7 **13.** 1
15. -5 **17.** $x^2 - 2x - 2$ **19.** $x^2 - x + 3$ **21.** 5
23. $-a^3 + 5a^2 + 2a - 10$ **25.** $\frac{x^2 - 2}{5 - x}, x \neq 5$ **27.** $\frac{7}{2}$
29. -2 **31.** $1.2 + 2.9 = 4.1$ million   **33.** 4%
35. About 95 million; the number of tons of municipal solid
waste that was composted or recycled in 2005   **37.** About
215 million; the number of tons of municipal solid waste
in 1996   **39.** About 230 million; the number of tons of
municipal solid waste that was not composted in 2004
41. $\mathbb{R}$ **43.** $\{x \mid x$ is a real number $and\ x \neq -5\}$
45. $\{x \mid x$ is a real number $and\ x \neq 0\}$
47. $\{x \mid x$ is a real number $and\ x \neq 1\}$
49. $\{x \mid x$ is a real number $and\ x \neq -\frac{9}{2}\ and\ x \neq 1\}$
51. $\{x \mid x$ is a real number $and\ x \neq 3\}$
53. $\{x \mid x$ is a real number $and\ x \neq -4\}$
55. $\{x \mid x$ is a real number $and\ x \neq 4\ and\ x \neq 5\}$
57. $\{x \mid x$ is a real number $and\ x \neq -1\ and\ x \neq -\frac{5}{2}\}$
59. 4; 3   **61.** 5; -1 **63.** $\{x \mid 0 \leq x \leq 9\}$;
$\{x \mid 3 \leq x \leq 10\}$; $\{x \mid 3 \leq x \leq 9\}$; $\{x \mid 3 \leq x \leq 9\}$

65.

67. ✍   **69.** $c = \frac{b}{a}$
70. $w = \frac{x - y}{z}$
71. $q = \frac{st}{p - r}$
72. $b = \frac{d}{a + c}$
73. $b = \frac{cd + d}{a - 3}$
74. $d = \frac{ab - 3b}{c + 1}$

75. 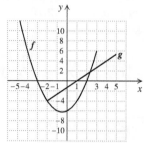 **77.** $\{x\,|\,x$ is a real number *and* $x \neq 4$ *and* $x \neq 3$ *and* $x \neq 2$ *and* $x \neq -2\}$
79. Answers may vary.

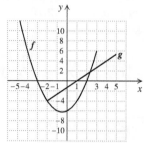

81. $\{x\,|\,x$ is a real number *and* $-1 < x < 5$ *and* $x \neq \frac{3}{2}\}$
83. Answers may vary. $f(x) = \dfrac{1}{x + 2}, g(x) = \dfrac{1}{x - 5}$

85.

Exercise Set 8.5, pp. 548–553

1. (d) **2.** (f) **3.** (e) **4.** (b) **5.** (a) **6.** (c)
7. Inverse **8.** Direct **9.** Direct **10.** Inverse
11. Inverse **12.** Direct **13.** $d = \dfrac{L}{f}$
15. $v_1 = \dfrac{2s}{t} - v_2$, or $\dfrac{2s - tv_2}{t}$ **17.** $b = \dfrac{at}{a - t}$
19. $g = \dfrac{Rs}{s - R}$ **21.** $n = \dfrac{IR}{E - Ir}$ **23.** $q = \dfrac{pf}{p - f}$
25. $t_1 = \dfrac{H}{Sm} + t_2$, or $\dfrac{H + Smt_2}{Sm}$ **27.** $r = \dfrac{Re}{E - e}$
29. $r = 1 - \dfrac{a}{S}$, or $\dfrac{S - a}{S}$ **31.** $a + b = \dfrac{f}{c^2}$
33. $r = \dfrac{A}{P} - 1$, or $\dfrac{A - P}{P}$
35. $t_1 = t_2 - \dfrac{d_2 - d_1}{v}$, or $\dfrac{vt_2 - d_2 + d_1}{v}$ **37.** $t = \dfrac{ab}{b + a}$
39. $Q = \dfrac{2Tt - 2AT}{A - q}$ **41.** $w = \dfrac{4.15c - 98.42}{p + 0.082}$
43. $k = 6; y = 6x$ **45.** $k = 1.7; y = 1.7x$
47. $k = 10; y = 10x$ **49.** $k = 100; y = \dfrac{100}{x}$
51. $k = 44; y = \dfrac{44}{x}$ **53.** $k = 9; y = \dfrac{9}{x}$ **55.** $33\frac{1}{3}$ cm
57. 3.5 hr **59.** 56 in. **61.** 32 kg **63.** 286 Hz
65. About 21 min **67.** About 110,000,000 tons
69. $y = \frac{1}{2}x^2$ **71.** $y = \dfrac{5000}{x^2}$ **73.** $y = 1.5xz$
75. $y = \dfrac{4wx^2}{z}$ **77.** 61.3 ft **79.** 308 cm³
81. About 57 mph **83.** **85.** $y = \frac{1}{6}x - \frac{1}{2}$
86. $y = \frac{3}{8}x - \frac{5}{8}$ **87.** $y = -\frac{5}{2}x - \frac{3}{2}$ **88.** $y = -\frac{1}{8}x + \frac{1}{2}$

89. Let n represent the number; $2n + 5 = 49$ **90.** Let x represent the number; $\frac{1}{2}x - 3 = 57$ **91.** Let x represent the number; $x + (x + 1) = 145$ **92.** Let n represent the number; $n - (-n) = 20$ **93.** **95.** 567 mi
97. Ratio is $\dfrac{a + 12}{a + 6}$; percent increase is $\dfrac{6}{a + 6} \cdot 100\%$, or $\dfrac{600}{a + 6}\%$ **99.** $t_1 = t_2 + \dfrac{(d_2 - d_1)(t_4 - t_3)}{a(t_4 - t_2)(t_4 - t_3) + d_3 - d_4}$
101. The intensity is halved. **103.** About 1.7 m
105. $d(s) = \dfrac{28}{s}$; 70 yd

Review Exercises: Chapter 8, pp. 556–558

1. True **2.** True **3.** False **4.** True **5.** False
6. True **7.** True **8.** True **9.** True **10.** False
11. (a) 3; (b) $\{x\,|\,-2 \le x \le 4\}$, or $[-2, 4]$; (c) -1;
(d) $\{y\,|\,1 \le y \le 5\}$, or $[1, 5]$ **12.** $\frac{3}{2}$ **13.** $4a^2 + 4a - 3$
14. 10.53 yr **15.** About \$9.30;

16. (a) Yes; (b) Domain: $\mathbb{R}$; range: $\{y\,|\,y \ge 0\}$, or $[0, \infty)$
17. (a) No **18.** (a) No **19.** (a) Yes; (b) Domain: $\mathbb{R}$; range: $\{-2\}$ **20.** $\mathbb{R}$
21. $\{x\,|\,x$ is a real number *and* $x \neq 1\}$
22. $\{t\,|\,t$ is a real number *and* $t \neq -1$ *and* $t \neq -4\}$
23. $\{t\,|\,0 \le t \le 60\}$, or $[0, 60]$ **24.** (a) 5; (b) 4;
(c) 16; (d) 35 **25.** $C(t) = 30t + 90$; 7 months
26. (a) $R(t) = -\frac{43}{2400}t + \frac{15,843}{800}$; (b) about 19.21 sec; about
19.09 sec **27.** Absolute-value function **28.** Polynomial function **29.** Quadratic function **30.** Linear function
31. Rational function

32.

Domain: $\mathbb{R}$; range: $\{3\}$

33.

Domain: $\mathbb{R}$; range: $\mathbb{R}$

34.

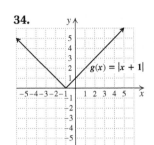

Domain: $\mathbb{R}$; range: $\{y|y \geq 0\}$,
or $[0, \infty)$

35. 102   **36.** −17
37. $-\frac{9}{2}$ **38.** $\mathbb{R}$

39. $\{x|x \text{ is a real number } and \text{ } x \neq 2\}$ **40.** $r = \dfrac{2V - IR}{2I}$,
or $\dfrac{V}{I} - \dfrac{R}{2}$ **41.** $m = \dfrac{H}{S(t_1 - t_2)}$ **42.** $c = \dfrac{b + 3a}{2}$
43. $t_1 = \dfrac{-A}{vT} + t_2$, or $\dfrac{-A + vTt_2}{vT}$ **44.** $y = \frac{15}{2}x$
45. $y = \dfrac{\frac{3}{4}}{x}$ **46.** $y = \dfrac{1}{2}\dfrac{xw^2}{z}$ **47.** 15 min
48. 22.5 lb   **49.** About 2.9 sec   **50.** ✍ Two functions
that have the same domain and range are not necessarily
identical. For example, the functions f: $\{(-2, 1), (-3, 2)\}$
and g: $\{(-2, 2), (-3, 1)\}$ have the same domain and range
but are different functions.   **51.** ✍ Jenna is not correct.
Any value of the variable that makes a denominator 0
is not in the domain; 0 itself may or may not make a
denominator 0.   **52.** $f(x) = 10.94x + 20$ **53.** Domain:
$\{x|x \geq -4 \text{ } and \text{ } x \neq 2\}$; range: $\{y|y \geq 0 \text{ } and \text{ } y \neq 3\}$

Test: Chapter 8, pp. 559–560

1. [8.1], [8.2] **(a)** 1; **(b)** $\{x|-3 \leq x \leq 4\}$, or $[-3, 4]$; **(c)** 3;
(d) $\{y|-1 \leq y \leq 2\}$, or $[-1, 2]$ **2.** [8.1] About 49 million
international visitors   **3.** **(a)** [8.1] Yes; **(b)** [8.2] domain: $\mathbb{R}$;
range: $\mathbb{R}$ **4.** **(a)** [8.1] Yes; **(b)** [8.2] domain: $\mathbb{R}$;
range: $\{y|y \geq 1\}$, or $[1, \infty)$ **5.** **(a)** [8.1] No
6. [8.2] $\{t|0 \leq t \leq 4\}$, or $[0, 4]$ **7.** [8.2] **(a)** −5; **(b)** 10
8. [8.3] $C(t) = 55t + 180$; 12 months
9. [8.3] **(a)** $C(m) = 0.3m + 25$; **(b)** $175
10. [8.3] Linear function; $\mathbb{R}$ **11.** [8.3] Rational function;
$\{x|x \text{ is a real number } and \text{ } x \neq -4 \text{ } and \text{ } x \neq 4\}$
12. [8.3] Quadratic function; $\mathbb{R}$
13. [8.3]   **14.** [8.3]

Domain: $\mathbb{R}$; range: $\mathbb{R}$

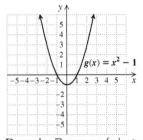

Domain: $\mathbb{R}$; range: $\{y|y \geq -1\}$,
or $[-1, \infty)$

15. [8.3]

Domain: $\mathbb{R}$; range: $\left\{-\frac{1}{2}\right\}$

16. [8.1] −1
17. [8.1] $10a + 1$
18. [8.4] $\frac{1}{x} + 2x + 1$

19. [8.1] $\{x|x \text{ is a real number } and \text{ } x \neq 0\}$
20. [8.4] $\{x|x \text{ is a real number } and \text{ } x \neq 0\}$
21. [8.4] $\left\{x|x \text{ is a real number } and \text{ } x \neq 0 \text{ } and \text{ } x \neq -\frac{1}{2}\right\}$
22. [8.5] $s = \dfrac{Rg}{g - R}$ **23.** [8.5] $y = \frac{1}{2}x$ **24.** [8.5] 30 workers
25. [8.5] 637 in^2 **26.** [8.3] **(a)** 30 mi; **(b)** 15 mph
27. [8.4] $h(x) = 7x - 2$

Cumulative Review: Chapters 1–3, 5–8, pp. 560–562

1. 10   **2.** 3.91×10^8 **3.** Slope: $\frac{7}{4}$; y-intercept: $(0, -3)$
4. $y = -2x + 5$ **5.** **(a)** 0; **(b)** $\{x|x \text{ is a real number } and$
$x \neq 5 \text{ } and \text{ } x \neq 6\}$
6.

7.

8.

9.

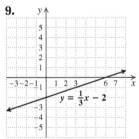

10. $-24x^4y^4$ **11.** $15x^4 - x^3 - 9x^2 + 5x - 2$
12. $9x^4 + 6x^2y + y^2$ **13.** $4x^4 - 81$
14. $-m^3n^2 - m^2n^2 - 5mn^3$ **15.** $\dfrac{y - 6}{2}$ **16.** $x - 1$
17. $\dfrac{a^2 + 7ab + b^2}{(a - b)(a + b)}$ **18.** $\dfrac{-m^2 + 5m - 6}{(m + 1)(m - 5)}$ **19.** $\dfrac{3y^2 - 2}{3y}$
20. $\dfrac{y - x}{xy(x + y)}$ **21.** $4x(x^2 + 100)$ **22.** $(x - 6)(x + 14)$
23. $(4y - 5)(4y + 5)$ **24.** $8(2x + 1)(4x^2 - 2x + 1)$
25. $(t - 8)^2$ **26.** $x^2(x - 1)(x + 1)(x^2 + 1)$
27. $\left(\frac{1}{2}b - c\right)\left(\frac{1}{4}b^2 + \frac{1}{2}bc + c^2\right)$ **28.** $(3t - 4)(t + 7)$
29. $(x^2 - y)(x^3 + y)$ **30.** $\frac{1}{4}$ **31.** $-12, 12$

32. $\{x \mid x \ge -1\}$, or $[-1, \infty)$ **33.** $\frac{3}{5}$ **34.** -1
35. No solution   **36.** $a = \dfrac{Pb}{4 - P}$ **37.** -5 **38.** 8
39. 0   **40.** $y = -x + 3$ **41.** 99   **42.** $\dfrac{x^2 - 1}{x + 5}$
43. $\{x \mid x \text{ is a real number } and\ x \neq -6\}$
44. Domain: $\{x \mid -4 \le x \le 3\}$; or $[-4, 3]$;
range: $\{y \mid -3 \le y \le 0\ or\ y = 2\}$
45. (a) $r(t) = 45.95t + 20$; **(b)** \$1076.85 million; **(c)** in
2016–2017   **46.** 34 performances per month, or 408 performances per year   **47.** 72 in.   **48.** IQAir HealthPro:
10 min; Austin Healthmate: 15 min   **49.** 12 billion hr
50. $22\frac{1}{2}$ min   **51.** \$1.09 billion
52. $x^3 - 12x^2 + 48x - 64$ **53.** $-3, 3, -5, 5$
54. All real numbers except 9 and -5 **55.** $-\frac{1}{4}, 0, \frac{1}{4}$
56. $C(x) = \begin{cases} 12, & \text{if } x \le 20, \\ 12 + 0.75(x - 20), & \text{if } x > 20 \end{cases}$

Chapter 9

Exercise Set 9.1, pp. 569–570

1. False   **3.** True   **5.** True   **7.** 4   **9.** 1.3   **11.** -25
13. $-\frac{11}{15}$ **15.** -6.5 **17.** -15 **19.** 0   **21.** $-\frac{1}{2}$ **23.** 5.8
25. -3 **27.** 39   **29.** 175   **31.** -32 **33.** 16   **35.** -6
37. 9   **39.** -3 **41.** -16 **43.** 100   **45.** 2   **47.** -23
49. 36   **51.** 10   **53.** 10   **55.** -7 **57.** 32   **59.** 28 cm^2
61. $8x + 28$ **63.** $-30 + 6x$ **65.** $8a + 12b - 6c$
67. $-6x + 3y - 3z$ **69.** $2(4x + 3y)$ **71.** $3(1 + w)$
73. $10(x + 5y + 10)$ **75.** p **77.** $-m + 22$ **79.** $3x + 7$
81. $6p - 7$ **83.** $-x + 12y$ **85.** $36a - 48b$
87. $-10x + 104y + 9$ **89.** Yes   **91.** No   **93.** Yes
95. Let n represent the number; $3n = 348$ **97.** Let c represent
the number of calories in a Taco Bell Beef Burrito; $c + 69 = 500$
99. Let l represent the amount of water used to produce 1 lb of
lettuce; $42 = 2l$

Exercise Set 9.2, pp. 578–579

1. 16   **3.** $-\frac{1}{12}$ **5.** -0.8 **7.** $-\frac{5}{3}$ **9.** 42   **11.** -5
13. 2   **15.** $\frac{25}{3}$ **17.** $-\frac{4}{9}$
19. -4 **21.** $\frac{69}{5}$
23. $\frac{9}{32}$ **25.** -2 **27.** -15 **29.** $\frac{43}{2}$ **31.** $-\frac{61}{115}$
33. $l = \dfrac{A}{w}$ **35.** $q = \dfrac{p}{30}$ **37.** $P = IV$ **39.** $p = 2q - r$
41. $\pi = \dfrac{A}{r^2 + r^2 h}$ **43. (a)** No; **(b)** yes; **(c)** no; **(d)** yes
45. $\{x \mid x \le 12\}$, or $(-\infty, 12]$
47. $\{m \mid m > 12\}$, or $(12, \infty)$
49. $\{x \mid x \ge -\frac{3}{2}\}$, or $[-\frac{3}{2}, \infty)$
51. $\{t \mid t < -3\}$, or $(-\infty, -3)$
53. $\{y \mid y > 10\}$, or $(10, \infty)$ **55.** $\{a \mid a \ge 1\}$, or $[1, \infty)$
57. $\{x \mid x \ge \frac{64}{17}\}$, or $[\frac{64}{17}, \infty)$ **59.** $\{x \mid x > \frac{39}{11}\}$, or $(\frac{39}{11}, \infty)$
61. $\{x \mid x \le -10.875\}$, or $(-\infty, -10.875]$ **63.** 7
65. 16, 18   **67.** $166\frac{2}{3}$ pages   **69.** 4.5 cm, 9.5 cm
71. 900 cubic feet   **73.** 80¢   **75.** 30 min or more
77. For $2\frac{7}{9}$ hr or less

Exercise Set 9.3, pp. 587–588

1.
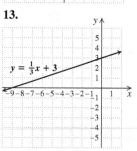

3. I   **5.** IV
7. I, IV   **9.** No
11. Yes

13.

15.

17. $y = x^2 - 7$

19. $y = |x + 3|$

21. $y = \sqrt{x^2 + 1}$
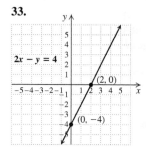

23. 1   **25.** -5 **27.** 0

29. Slope: 2; y-intercept: $(0, -5)$
31. Slope: $-\frac{2}{7}$; y-intercept: $\left(0, \frac{1}{7}\right)$

33.

35.

37.

39.

41.

43. 0

45. Undefined

47. $y = \frac{1}{3}x + 1$ **49.** $y = -x + 3$ **51.** Perpendicular
53. Neither   **55. (a)** 6; **(b)** $8\frac{1}{3}$; **(c)** $\frac{1}{3}a + 8$
57. (a) 6; **(b)** 3; **(c)** $20a^2 + 4a + 3$ **59.** No   **61.** Yes
63. $\{x \mid x$ is a real number *and* $x \neq 3\}$ **65.** $\mathbb{R}$
67. $\{x \mid x \geq -6\}$, or $[-6, \infty)$

Exercise Set 9.4, pp. 596–598

1. $(4, 3)$ **3.** $(1, 3)$ **5.** $(2, -1)$ **7.** No solution
9. $(6, -1)$ **11.** $\left\{(x, y) \mid y = \frac{1}{5}x + 4\right\}$ **13.** $(2, -3)$
15. $(-4, 3)$ **17.** $(2, -2)$ **19.** $\{(x, y) \mid 2x - 3 = y\}$
21. $\left(\frac{25}{23}, -\frac{11}{23}\right)$ **23.** No solution   **25.** $(1, 2)$ **27.** $(2, 7)$
29. $(-1, 2)$ **31.** $\left(\frac{15}{14}, \frac{4}{7}\right)$ **33.** $(6, 2)$ **35.** No solution
37. $\{(x, y) \mid -4x + 2y = 5\}$ **39.** 43, 46   **41.** 49°, 131°
43. Two-pointers: 32; three-pointers: 4
45. Private lessons: 6 students; group lessons: 8 students
47. Peanuts: 135 lb; Brazil nuts: 345 lb
49.

x	y	90
12%	30%	20%
0.12x	0.3y	0.2(90)

Streakfree: 50 oz;
Sunstream: 40 oz

51. 3 hr   **53.** Headwind: 40 mph; plane: 620 mph   **55.** 7
57. $-\frac{9}{2}$ **59.** -6 **61.** 3   **63.** 0.666667, or $\frac{2}{3}$

Exercise Set 9.5, pp. 605–606

1. 1   **3.** -3 **5.** $\frac{1}{8^2} = \frac{1}{64}$ **7.** $\frac{10}{x^5}$ **9.** $\frac{1}{(ab)^2}$
11. y^{10} **13.** y^{-4} **15.** x^{-t} **17.** x^{13} **19.** a^6 **21.** $(4x)^8$
23. 7^{40} **25.** x^8y^{12} **27.** $\frac{y^6}{64}$ **29.** $\frac{9q^8}{4p^6}$
31. $8x^3, -6x^2, x, -7$ **33.** $18, 36, -7, 3; 3, 9, 1, 0; 9$
35. $-1, 4, -2; 3, 3, 2; 3$ **37.** $8p^4; 8$ **39.** $x^4 + 3x^3$
41. $-7t^2 + 5t + 10$ **43.** 36   **45.** -14 **47.** 144 ft   **49.** 11
51. -4 **53.** $4x^3 - 3x^2 + 8x + 7$ **55.** $-y^2 + 5y - 2$
57. $-3x^2y - y^2 + 8y$ **59.** $12x^5 - 28x^3 + 28x^2$
61. $8a^2 + 2ab + 4ay + by$ **63.** $x^3 + 4x^2 - 20x + 7$

65. $x^2 - 49$ **67.** $x^2 + 2xy + y^2$ **69.** $6x^4 + 17x^2 - 14$
71. $a^2 - 6ab + 9b^2$ **73.** $42a^2 - 17ay - 15y^2$
75. $-t^4 - 3t^2 + 2t - 5$ **77.** $5x + 3$
79. $2x^2 - 3x + 3 + \dfrac{-2}{x + 1}$ **81.** $5x + 3 + \dfrac{3}{x^2 - 1}$

Exercise Set 9.6, p. 616

1. $6t^3(3t^2 - 2t + 1)$ **3.** $(y - 3)^2$ **5.** $(p + 2)(2p^3 + 1)$
7. Prime   **9.** $(2t + 3)(4t^2 - 6t + 9)$
11. $(m + 6)(m + 7)$ **13.** $(x^2 + 9)(x + 3)(x - 3)$
15. $(2x + 3)(4x + 5)$ **17.** $(x + 2)(x + 1)(x - 1)$
19. $(0.1t^2 - 0.2)(0.01t^4 + 0.02t^2 + 0.04)$
21. $\left(x^2 + \frac{1}{4}\right)\left(x + \frac{1}{2}\right)\left(x - \frac{1}{2}\right)$ **23.** $(n - 2)(m + 3)$
25. $(m + 15n)(m - 10n)$ **27.** $2y(3x + 1)(4x - 3)$
29. $(y + 11)(y - 11)$ **31.** $-7, 2$ **33.** $0, 11$ **35.** $-10, 10$
37. $-\frac{5}{2}, 7$ **39.** $0, 5$ **41.** $-2, 6$ **43.** $-11, 5$ **45.** -5
47. Base: 8 ft; height: 6 ft   **49.** 8 ft, 15 ft

Chapter 10

Interactive Discovery, p. 626

1. Domain of $f = (-\infty, 3]$; domain of $g = [-1, \infty)$
2. Domain of $f + g =$ domain of $f - g =$ domain of
$f \cdot g = [-1, 3]$ **3.** By finding the intersection of the
domains of f and g

Exercise Set 10.1, pp. 627–632

1. (h)   **2.** (j)   **3.** (f)   **4.** (a)   **5.** (e)   **6.** (d)
7. (b)   **8.** (g)   **9.** (c)   **10.** (i)
11. $\{x \mid x \geq 2\}$, or $[2, \infty)$ **13.** $\{x \mid x < 3\}$, or $(-\infty, 3)$
15. (a) $\{x \mid x \leq -2\}$, or $(-\infty, -2]$; **(b)** $\left\{x \mid x > \frac{8}{3}\right\}$, or $\left(\frac{8}{3}, \infty\right)$;
(c) $\left\{x \mid x > \frac{4}{5}\right\}$, or $\left(\frac{4}{5}, \infty\right)$ **17.** $\{x \mid x < 7\}$, or $(-\infty, 7)$
19. $\{x \mid x \geq 2\}$, or $[2, \infty)$ **21.** $\{x \mid x < 8\}$, or $(-\infty, 8)$
23. $\{x \mid x \leq 2\}$, or $(-\infty, 2]$ **25.** $\left\{x \mid x \leq -\frac{4}{9}\right\}$, or $\left(-\infty, -\frac{4}{9}\right]$
27. At least 625 people
29. $r(x) = -0.04x + 2.0233$; years after 2013
31. $n(x) = -6.4x + 56.5, t(x) = 3.7x + 12$; years after 2010
33. $f(x) = -0.0826x + 54.541$; years after 2045
35. $\{9, 11\}$ **37.** $\{0, 5, 10, 15, 20\}$ **39.** $\{b, d, f\}$
41. $\{r, s, t, u, v\}$ **43.** $\varnothing$ **45.** $\{3, 5, 7\}$
47. ⟨─┼─┼─(─┼─┼─)─┼─┼─┼⟩ (3, 7)
    0 1 2 3 4 5 6 7 8 9 10
49. ⟨─┼─[─┼─┼─┼─┼─┼─]─┼─┼⟩ [-6, 0]
    -8 -7 -6 -5 -4 -3 -2 -1 0 1 2
51. ⟨─┼─┼─┼)─┼─┼─(─┼─┼─┼⟩ $(-\infty, -1) \cup (4, \infty)$
    -3 -2 -1 0 1 2 3 4 5 6 7
53. ⟨─┼─┼─]─┼─┼─(─┼─┼─┼─┼⟩ $(-\infty, -2] \cup (1, \infty)$
    -5 -4 -3 -2 -1 0 1 2 3 4 5
55. ⟨─┼─┼─(─┼─┼─┼─)─┼─┼─┼⟩ $(-2, 4)$
    -5 -4 -3 -2 -1 0 1 2 3 4 5
57. ⟨─┼─┼─(─┼─┼─┼─]─┼─┼─┼⟩ $(-2, 4]$
    -5 -4 -3 -2 -1 0 1 2 3 4 5
59. ⟨─┼─┼─┼─┼─)─┼─(─┼─┼⟩ $(-\infty, 5) \cup (7, \infty)$
    -1 0 1 2 3 4 5 6 7 8 9
61. ⟨─]─┼─┼─┼─┼─┼─[─┼─┼⟩ $(-\infty, -4] \cup [5, \infty)$
    -5 -4 -3 -2 -1 0 1 2 3 4 5
63. ⟨─┼─[─┼─┼─┼─┼─┼─┼─)─┼⟩ $[-3, 7)$
    -3 -2 -1 0 1 2 3 4 5 6 7
65. ⟨─┼─┼─┼─┼─[─┼─┼─┼─)─⟩ $[3, 7)$
    -2 -1 0 1 2 3 4 5 6 7 8

67. $(-\infty, 5)$

69. $\{t \mid -3 < t < 7\}$, or $(-3, 7)$

71. $\{x \mid 0 < x < 4\}$, or $(0, 4)$

73. $\{a \mid a \le -2 \text{ or } a > 2\}$, or $(-\infty, -2] \cup (2, \infty)$

75. $\mathbb{R}$, or $(-\infty, \infty)$

77. $\{x \mid -3 \le x \le 2\}$, or $[-3, 2]$

79. $\{x \mid 7 < x < 23\}$, or $(7, 23)$

81. $\{x \mid -32 \le x \le 8\}$, or $[-32, 8]$

83. $\{x \mid 1 \le x \le 3\}$, or $[1, 3]$

85. $\{x \mid -\frac{7}{2} < x \le 7\}$, or $\left(-\frac{7}{2}, 7\right]$

87. $\{t \mid t < 0 \text{ or } t > 1\}$, or $(-\infty, 0) \cup (1, \infty)$

89. $\left\{a \mid a < \frac{7}{2}\right\}$, or $\left(-\infty, \frac{7}{2}\right)$

91. $\{a \mid a < -5\}$, or $(-\infty, -5)$

93. $\varnothing$ **95.** $\{t \mid t \le 6\}$, or $(-\infty, 6]$

97. $(-1, 6)$ **99.** $(-\infty, -8) \cup (-8, \infty)$

101. $(-\infty, 0) \cup (0, \infty)$ **103.** $[6, \infty)$ **105.** $\left[-\frac{7}{2}, \infty\right)$

107. $(-\infty, 4]$ **109.** $[5, \infty)$ **111.** $\left[\frac{2}{3}, 3\right]$ **113.** TW

115.

$g(x) = 2x$

116.

$f(x) = 4$

117.

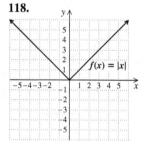

$g(x) = -3$

118.

$f(x) = |x|$

119. -1 **120.** -4 **121.** TW

123. Between 2003 and 2009   **125.** Sizes between 6 and 13

127. Densities between 1.03 kg/L and 1.04 kg/L

129. $\left\{m \mid m < \frac{6}{5}\right\}$, or $\left(-\infty, \frac{6}{5}\right)$

131. $\left\{x \mid -\frac{1}{8} < x < \frac{1}{2}\right\}$, or $\left(-\frac{1}{8}, \frac{1}{2}\right)$

133. True   **135.** False   **137.** $(-\infty, -7) \cup \left(-7, \frac{3}{4}\right]$

139.

---

1. True   **2.** False   **3.** True   **4.** True   **5.** True

6. True   **7.** False   **8.** False   **9.** (g)   **10.** (h)

11. (d)   **12.** (a)   **13.** (a)   **14.** (b)   **15.** $\{-5, 1\}$

16. $[-5, 1]$ **17.** $(-5, 1)$ **18.** $(-\infty, -5) \cup (1, \infty)$

19. $(-\infty, -5] \cup [1, \infty)$ **20.** $\varnothing$ **21.** $\{-7, 7\}$

23. $\varnothing$ **25.** $\{0\}$ **27.** $\left\{-\frac{1}{2}, \frac{7}{2}\right\}$ **29.** $\varnothing$ **31.** $\{-4, 8\}$

33. $\{2, 8\}$ **35.** $\{-5.5, 5.5\}$ **37.** $\{-8, 8\}$ **39.** $\left\{-\frac{11}{7}, \frac{11}{7}\right\}$

41. $\left\{-\frac{11}{2}, \frac{13}{2}\right\}$ **43.** $\{-2, 12\}$ **45.** $\left\{-\frac{1}{3}, 3\right\}$ **47.** $\{-7, 1\}$

49. $\{-8.7, 8.7\}$ **51.** $\left\{-\frac{8}{3}, 4\right\}$ **53.** $\{1, 11\}$ **55.** $\left\{-\frac{1}{2}\right\}$

57. $\left\{-\frac{3}{5}, 5\right\}$ **59.** $\mathbb{R}$ **61.** $\left\{\frac{1}{4}\right\}$

63. $\{a \mid -9 \le a \le 9\}$, or $[-9, 9]$

65. $\{t \mid t < 0 \text{ or } t > 0\}$, or $(-\infty, 0) \cup (0, \infty)$

67. $\{x \mid -3 < x < 5\}$, or $(-3, 5)$

69. $\{x \mid -8 \le x \le 4\}$, or $[-8, 4]$

71. $\{x \mid x < -2 \text{ or } x > 8\}$, or $(-\infty, -2) \cup (8, \infty)$

73. $\mathbb{R}$, or $(-\infty, \infty)$

75. $\left\{a \mid a \le -\frac{2}{3} \text{ or } a \ge \frac{10}{3}\right\}$, or $\left(-\infty, -\frac{2}{3}\right] \cup \left[\frac{10}{3}, \infty\right)$

77. $\{y \mid -9 < y < 15\}$, or $(-9, 15)$

79. $\{x \mid x \le -8 \text{ or } x \ge 0\}$, or $(-\infty, -8] \cup [0, \infty)$

81. $\left\{x \mid x < -\frac{1}{2} \text{ or } x > \frac{7}{2}\right\}$, or $\left(-\infty, -\frac{1}{2}\right) \cup \left(\frac{7}{2}, \infty\right)$

83. $\varnothing$ **85.** $\left\{x \mid x \le -\frac{2}{15} \text{ or } x \ge \frac{14}{15}\right\}$, or $\left(-\infty, -\frac{2}{15}\right] \cup \left[\frac{14}{15}, \infty\right)$

87. $\{m \mid -9 \le m \le 3\}$, or $[-9, 3]$

89. $\{a \mid -6 < a < 0\}$, or $(-6, 0)$

91. $\left\{x \mid -\frac{1}{2} \le x \le \frac{7}{2}\right\}$, or $\left[-\frac{1}{2}, \frac{7}{2}\right]$

93. $\left\{x \mid x \le -\frac{7}{3} \text{ or } x \ge 5\right\}$, or $\left(-\infty, -\frac{7}{3}\right] \cup [5, \infty)$

95. $\{x \mid -4 < x < 5\}$, or $(-4, 5)$

97. TW

99.

$3x - y = 6$

100.

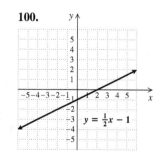

$y = \frac{1}{2}x - 1$

101.

$x = -2$

102.

$y = 4$

103. $\left(4, -\frac{4}{3}\right)$ **104.** $(5, 1)$ **105.** $\left(\frac{5}{7}, -\frac{18}{7}\right)$ **106.** $(-2, -5)$
107. TW **109.** $\left\{t \mid t \ge \frac{5}{3}\right\}$, or $\left[\frac{5}{3}, \infty\right)$ **111.** $\mathbb{R}$, or $(-\infty, \infty)$
113. $\left\{-\frac{1}{7}, \frac{7}{3}\right\}$ **115.** $|x| < 3$ **117.** $|x + 3| > 5$
119. $|x - 7| < 2$, or $|7 - x| < 2$ **121.** $|x - 3| \le 4$
123. $|x + 4| < 3$ **125.** Between 80 ft and 100 ft

Mid-Chapter Review: Chapter 10, pp. 644–645

Guided Solutions

1. $2 < x < 11$
The solution is $(2, 11)$.
2. $x - 1 < -9$ *or* $9 < x - 1$
    $x < -8$ *or* $10 < x$
The solution is $(-\infty, -8) \cup (10, \infty)$.

Mixed Review

1. $\{-15, 15\}$ **2.** $\{t \mid -10 < t < 10\}$, or $(-10, 10)$
3. $\{p \mid p < -15 \text{ or } p > 15\}$, or $(-\infty, -15) \cup (15, \infty)$
4. $\{-4, 3\}$ **5.** $\{x \mid 2 < x < 11\}$, or $(2, 11)$
6. $\{t \mid -4 < t < 4\}$, or $(-4, 4)$
7. $\{x \mid x < -6 \text{ or } x > 13\}$, or $(-\infty, -6) \cup (13, \infty)$
8. $\{x \mid -7 \le x \le 3\}$, or $[-7, 3]$ **9.** $\left\{-\frac{8}{3}, \frac{8}{3}\right\}$
10. $\{x \mid -7 \le x \le 13\}$, or $[-7, 13]$
11. $\left\{n \mid -9 < n \le \frac{8}{3}\right\}$, or $\left(-9, \frac{8}{3}\right]$ **12.** $\varnothing$
13. $\left\{x \mid x \le -\frac{17}{2} \text{ or } x \ge \frac{7}{2}\right\}$, or $\left(-\infty, -\frac{17}{2}\right] \cup \left[\frac{7}{2}, \infty\right)$
14. $\varnothing$ **15.** $\{m \mid -24 < m < 12\}$, or $(-24, 12)$
16. $\{-42, 38\}$
17. $\{t \mid t \le 4 \text{ or } t \ge 10\}$, or $(-\infty, 4] \cup [10, \infty)$
18. $\varnothing$ **19.** $\{a \mid -7 < a < -5\}$, or $(-7, -5)$
20. $\mathbb{R}$, or $(-\infty, \infty)$

Visualizing for Success, p. 655

1. B **2.** F **3.** J **4.** A **5.** E **6.** G **7.** C
8. D **9.** I **10.** H

Exercise Set 10.3, pp. 656–658

1. (e) **2.** (c) **3.** (d) **4.** (a) **5.** (b)
6. (f) **7.** Yes **9.** No

11.

$y \ge \frac{1}{2}x$

13.

$y > x - 3$

15.

$y \le x + 5$

17.

$x - y \le 4$

19.

$2x + 3y > 6$

21.

$2y - x \le 4$

23.

$2x - 2y \ge 8 + 2y$

25.

$x > -2$

27.

$y \le 6$

29.

$-2 < y < 7$

31.

$-4 \le x \le 2$

33.

$0 \le y \le 3$

35. $y > x + 3.5$

37. $8x - 2y < 11$

39.

41.

73.

75.

43.

45.

77.
$$w > 0,$$
$$h > 0,$$
$$w + h + 30 \le 62, \text{ or}$$
$$w + h \le 32,$$
$$2w + 2h + 30 \le 130, \text{ or}$$
$$w + h \le 50$$

47.

49.

79. $h \le 2w,$
$w \le 1.5h,$
$h \le 3200,$
$h \ge 0,$
$w \ge 0$

51.

53.

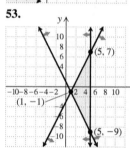

81. $q + v \le 1150,$
$q \ge 700,$
$q \le 800,$
$v \ge 400,$
$v \le 800$

55.

57.

83. $y \le x,$ **85.** $y \le x + 2,$
    $y \le 2$ $y \le -x + 4,$
                        $y \ge 0$

Exercise Set 10.4, pp. 664–666

1. True   **2.** False   **3.** True   **4.** True   **5.** False
6. True   **7.** $\left[-4, \frac{3}{2}\right]$, or $\left\{x \mid -4 \le x \le \frac{3}{2}\right\}$
9. $(-\infty, -2) \cup (0, 2) \cup (3, \infty)$, or
$\{x \mid x < -2 \text{ or } 0 < x < 2 \text{ or } x > 3\}$
11. $\left(-\infty, -\frac{7}{2}\right) \cup (-2, \infty)$, or $\left\{x \mid x < -\frac{7}{2} \text{ or } x > -2\right\}$
13. $(-4, 3)$, or $\{x \mid -4 < x < 3\}$
15. $(-\infty, -7] \cup [2, \infty)$, or $\{x \mid x \le -7 \text{ or } x \ge 2\}$
17. $(-\infty, -1) \cup (2, \infty)$, or $\{x \mid x < -1 \text{ or } x > 2\}$
19. $\varnothing$ **21.** $(-2, 6)$, or $\{x \mid -2 < x < 6\}$
23. $(-\infty, -2) \cup (0, 2)$, or $\{x \mid x < -2 \text{ or } 0 < x < 2\}$
25. $[-2, 1] \cup [4, \infty)$, or $\{x \mid -2 \le x \le 1 \text{ or } x \ge 4\}$
27. $[-0.78, 1.59]$, or $\{x \mid -0.78 \le x \le 1.59\}$
29. $(-\infty, -2) \cup (1, 3)$, or $\{x \mid x < -2 \text{ or } 1 < x < 3\}$
31. $[-2, 2]$, or $\{x \mid -2 \le x \le 2\}$
33. $(-1, 2) \cup (3, \infty)$, or $\{x \mid -1 < x < 2 \text{ or } x > 3\}$
35. $(-\infty, 0] \cup [2, 5]$, or $\{x \mid x \le 0 \text{ or } 2 \le x \le 5\}$

59.

61. ⒯ⓦ   **63.** $-1, 1$
64. $-\frac{3}{5}, 1$ **65.** $0, 1, 2$
66. $-2, 0, 3$ **67.** $-\frac{23}{4}$
68. No solution   **69.** 0
70. $-6, 9$ **71.** ⒯ⓦ

37. $(-\infty, -5)$, or $\{x \mid x < -5\}$

39. $(-\infty, -1] \cup (3, \infty)$, or $\{x \mid x \le -1 \text{ or } x > 3\}$

41. $(-\infty, -6)$, or $\{x \mid x < -6\}$

43. $(-\infty, -1] \cup [2, 5)$, or $\{x \mid x \le -1 \text{ or } 2 \le x < 5\}$

45. $(-\infty, -3) \cup [0, \infty)$, or $\{x \mid x < -3 \text{ or } x \ge 0\}$

47. $(0, \infty)$, or $\{x \mid x > 0\}$

49. $(-\infty, -4) \cup [1, 3)$, or $\{x \mid x < -4 \text{ or } 1 \le x < 3\}$

51. $\left(-\frac{3}{4}, \frac{5}{2}\right]$, or $\left\{x \mid -\frac{3}{4} < x \le \frac{5}{2}\right\}$

53. $(-\infty, 2) \cup [3, \infty)$, or $\{x \mid x < 2 \text{ or } x \ge 3\}$ **55.** TW

57. $\left(2, -\frac{1}{2}\right)$ **58.** $\left(\frac{23}{4}, -\frac{1}{4}\right)$ **59.** $(2, 1)$ **60.** $\left(\frac{3}{7}, \frac{1}{7}\right)$

61. $\left(-\frac{3}{8}, \frac{1}{8}\right)$ **62.** $(-2, -3)$ **63.** TW **65.** $\varnothing$ **67.** $\{0\}$

69. (a) $(10, 200)$, or $\{x \mid 10 < x < 200\}$;

(b) $[0, 10) \cup (200, \infty)$, or $\{x \mid 0 \le x < 10 \text{ or } x > 200\}$

71. $\{n \mid n \text{ is an integer } and\ 12 \le n \le 25\}$ **73.** $f(x)$ has no zeros; $f(x) < 0$ for $(-\infty, 0)$, or $\{x \mid x < 0\}$; $f(x) > 0$ for $(0, \infty)$, or $\{x \mid x > 0\}$ **75.** $f(x) = 0$ for $x = -1, 0$; $f(x) < 0$ for $(-\infty, -3) \cup (-1, 0)$, or $\{x \mid x < -3 \text{ or } -1 < x < 0\}$; $f(x) > 0$ for $(-3, -1) \cup (0, 2) \cup (2, \infty)$, or $\{x \mid -3 < x < -1 \text{ or } 0 < x < 2 \text{ or } x > 2\}$

77. $(-\infty, -5] \cup [9, \infty)$, or $\{x \mid x \le -5 \text{ or } x \ge 9\}$

79. $(-\infty, -8] \cup [0, \infty)$, or $\{x \mid x \le -8 \text{ or } x \ge 0\}$

Study Summary: Chapter 10, pp. 667–668

1. $\{x \mid x < 1\}$, or $(-\infty, 1)$

2. $\left\{x \mid -2 < x \le -\frac{3}{4}\right\}$, or $\left(-2, -\frac{3}{4}\right]$

3. $\{x \mid x \le 13 \text{ or } x > 22\}$, or $(-\infty, 13] \cup (22, \infty)$

4. $\left\{-1, \frac{9}{2}\right\}$ **5.** $\{x \mid 11 \le x \le 13\}$, or $[11, 13]$

6. $\{x \mid x < -5 \text{ or } x > 2\}$, or $(-\infty, -5) \cup (2, \infty)$

7.

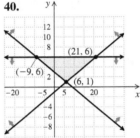

8. $\{x \mid -1 < x < 12\}$, or $(-1, 12)$

Review Exercises: Chapter 10, p. 669

1. True **2.** False **3.** True **4.** True **5.** False

6. True **7.** True **8.** False **9.** False **10.** True

11. $\{x \mid x < 1\}$, or $(-\infty, 1)$ **12.** $\{x \mid x > -4\}$, or $(-4, \infty)$

13. $\{x \mid x \ge -6\}$, or $[-6, \infty)$ **14.** $\{x \mid x \le 2\}$, or $(-\infty, 2]$

15. $\{1, 5, 9\}$ **16.** $\{1, 2, 3, 5, 6, 9\}$

17. $(-3, 2]$

18. $(-\infty, \infty)$

19. $\{x \mid -12 < x \le -3\}$, or $(-12, -3]$

20. $\left\{x \mid -\frac{5}{4} < x < \frac{5}{2}\right\}$, or $\left(-\frac{5}{4}, \frac{5}{2}\right)$

21. $\{x \mid x < -3 \text{ or } x > 1\}$, or $(-\infty, -3) \cup (1, \infty)$

22. $\{x \mid x < -11 \text{ or } x \ge -6\}$, or $(-\infty, -11) \cup [-6, \infty)$

23. $\{x \mid x \le -6 \text{ or } x \ge 8\}$, or $(-\infty, -6] \cup [8, \infty)$

24. $\left\{x \mid x < -\frac{2}{5} \text{ or } x > \frac{8}{5}\right\}$, or $\left(-\infty, -\frac{2}{5}\right) \cup \left(\frac{8}{5}, \infty\right)$

25. $(-\infty, 8) \cup (8, \infty)$ **26.** $[-5, \infty)$ **27.** $\left(-\infty, \frac{8}{3}\right]$

28. $\{-5, 5\}$ **29.** $\{t \mid t \le -21 \text{ or } t \ge 21\}$, or $(-\infty, -21] \cup [21, \infty)$ **30.** $\{-4, 10\}$

31. $\left\{a \mid -\frac{7}{2} < a < 2\right\}$, or $\left(-\frac{7}{2}, 2\right)$

32. $\left\{x \mid x \le -\frac{11}{3} \text{ or } x \ge \frac{19}{3}\right\}$, or $\left(-\infty, -\frac{11}{3}\right] \cup \left[\frac{19}{3}, \infty\right)$

33. $\left\{-14, \frac{4}{3}\right\}$ **34.** $\varnothing$

35. $\{x \mid -16 \le x \le 8\}$, or $[-16, 8]$

36. $\{x \mid x < 0 \text{ or } x > 10\}$, or $(-\infty, 0) \cup (10, \infty)$ **37.** $\varnothing$

38.

39.

40.

41. $(-1, 0) \cup (3, \infty)$, or $\{x \mid -1 < x < 0 \text{ or } x > 3\}$

42. $(-3, 5]$, or $\{x \mid -3 < x \le 5\}$

43. TW The equation $|X| = p$ has two solutions when p is positive because X can be either p or $-p$. The same equation has no solution when p is negative because no number has a negative absolute value. **44.** TW The solution set of a system of inequalities is all ordered pairs that make *all* the individual inequalities true. This consists of ordered pairs that are common to all the individual solution sets, or the intersection of the graphs.

45. $\left\{x \mid -\frac{8}{3} \le x \le -2\right\}$, or $\left[-\frac{8}{3}, -2\right]$

46. $|t - 21.5| \le 3.5$, where t is in thousandths of an inch

Test: Chapter 10, p. 670

1. [10.1] $\{x \mid x > 1\}$, or $(1, \infty)$ **2.** [10.1] $\{x \mid x \ge 4\}$, or $[4, \infty)$

3. [10.1] $\{3, 5\}$ **4.** [10.1] $\{1, 3, 5, 7, 9, 11, 13\}$

5. [10.1] $(-\infty, 2]$ **6.** [10.1] $(-\infty, 7) \cup (7, \infty)$

7. [10.1] $\{x \mid 1 < x < 8\}$, or $(1, 8)$

8. [10.1] $\left\{t \mid -\frac{2}{5} < t \le \frac{9}{5}\right\}$, or $\left(-\frac{2}{5}, \frac{9}{5}\right]$

9. $[10.1]$ $\{x \mid x < 3 \, or \, x > 6\}$, or $(-\infty, 3) \cup (6, \infty)$

10. $[10.1]$ $\{x \mid x < -4 \, or \, x > -\frac{5}{2}\}$, or $(-\infty, -4) \cup (-\frac{5}{2}, \infty)$

11. $[10.2]$ $\{-13, 13\}$

12. $[10.2]$ $\{a \mid a < -7 \, or \, a > 7\}$, or $(-\infty, -7) \cup (7, \infty)$

13. $[10.2]$ $\{x \mid -2 < x < \frac{8}{3}\}$, or $(-2, \frac{8}{3})$

14. $[10.2]$ $\{t \mid t \le -\frac{13}{5} \, or \, t \ge \frac{7}{5}\}$, or $(-\infty, -\frac{13}{5}] \cup [\frac{7}{5}, \infty)$

15. $[10.2]$ $\varnothing$

16. $[10.1]$ $\{x \mid x < \frac{1}{2} \, or \, x > \frac{7}{2}\}$, or $(-\infty, \frac{1}{2}) \cup (\frac{7}{2}, \infty)$

17. $[10.2]$ $\{1\}$

18. $[10.3]$

$y \le 2x + 1$

19. $[10.3]$

$(4, -1)$

20. $[10.3]$

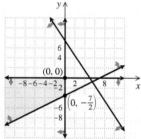

$(0, 0)$ $(0, -\frac{7}{2})$

21. $[10.4]$ $[-6, 1]$, or $\{x \mid -6 \le x \le 1\}$
22. $[10.4]$ $(-1, 0) \cup (1, \infty)$, or $\{x \mid -1 < x < 0 \, or \, x > 1\}$
23. $[10.2]$ $[-1, 0] \cup [4, 6]$ **24.** $[10.1]$ $\left(\frac{1}{5}, \frac{4}{5}\right)$
25. $[10.2]$ $|x + 3| \le 5$

Chapter 11

Exercise Set 11.1, pp. 678–680

1. True   **2.** False   **3.** False   **4.** True   **5.** True   **6.** False
7. Yes   **9.** $(3, 1, 2)$ **11.** $(1, -2, 2)$ **13.** $(2, -5, -6)$
15. No solution   **17.** $(-2, 0, 5)$ **19.** $(21, -14, -2)$
21. The equations are dependent.   **23.** $\left(3, \frac{1}{2}, -4\right)$
25. $\left(\frac{1}{2}, \frac{1}{3}, \frac{1}{6}\right)$ **27.** $\left(\frac{1}{2}, \frac{2}{3}, -\frac{5}{6}\right)$ **29.** $(15, 33, 9)$
31. $(3, 4, -1)$ **33.** $(10, 23, 50)$ **35.** No solution

37. The equations are dependent.
39. TW   **41.** Let x and y represent the numbers; $x = \frac{1}{2}y$
42. Let x and y represent the numbers; $x - y = 2x$
43. Let x represent the first number;
$x + (x + 1) + (x + 2) = 100$
44. Let x, y, and z represent the numbers; $x + y + z = 100$
45. Let x, y, and z represent the numbers; $xy = 5z$
46. Let x and y represent the numbers; $xy = 2(x + y)$
47. TW   **49.** $(1, -1, 2)$ **51.** $(-3, -1, 0, 4)$
53. $\left(-\frac{1}{2}, -1, -\frac{1}{3}\right)$ **55.** 14   **57.** $z = 8 - 2x - 4y$

Exercise Set 11.2, pp. 684–686

1. 16, 19, 22   **3.** 8, 21, -3   **5.** 32°, 96°, 52°
7. Reading: 501; mathematics: 515; writing: 493
9. Bran muffin: 1.5 g; banana: 3 g; 1 cup Wheaties: 3 g
11. Basic price: $23,800; satellite radio: $310; car cover: $230
13. 12-oz cups: 17; 16-oz cups: 25; 20-oz cups: 13
15. Bank loan: $15,000; small-business loan: $35,000;
mortgage: $70,000   **17.** Gold: $30/g; silver: $3/g;
copper: $0.02/g   **19.** Roast beef: 2 servings; baked potato:
1 serving; broccoli: 2 servings   **21.** First mezzanine: 8 tickets;
main floor: 12 tickets; second mezzanine: 20 tickets
23. Two-point field goals: 32; three-point field goals: 5; foul shots: 13
25. TW   **27.** $-4x + 6y$ **28.** $-x + 6y$ **29.** $7y$ **30.** $11a$
31. $-2a + b + 6c$ **32.** $-50a - 30b + 10c$
33. $-12x + 5y - 8z$ **34.** $23x - 13z$ **35.** TW
37. Applicant: $83; spouse: $52; first child: $19; second child: $19
39. 20 yr   **41.** 35 tickets

Exercise Set 11.3, pp. 693–694

1. Matrix   **2.** Horizontal; columns   **3.** Entry   **4.** Matrices
5. Rows   **6.** First   **7.** $(3, 4)$ **9.** $(-4, 3)$ **11.** $\left(\frac{3}{2}, \frac{5}{2}\right)$
13. $\left(2, \frac{1}{2}, -2\right)$ **15.** $(2, -2, 1)$ **17.** $\left(4, \frac{1}{2}, -\frac{1}{2}\right)$
19. $(1, -3, -2, -1)$ **21.** Dimes: 18; nickels: 24
23. Dried fruit: 9 lb; macadamia nuts: 6 lb
25. $400 at 7%; $500 at 8%; $1600 at 9%   **27.** TW
29. 13   **30.** -22   **31.** 37   **32.** 422   **33.** TW   **35.** 1324

Mid-Chapter Review: Chapter 11, pp. 694–695

Guided Solutions

1.
$$x - y + z = 4$$
$$x + y - 2z = 3$$
$$\overline{2x \qquad - z = 7}$$

$$x + y - 2z = 3$$
$$2x - y - z = 9$$
$$\overline{3x \qquad - 3z = 12}$$

$$2x - z = 7$$
$$3x - 3z = 12$$

$$x = 3, z = -1$$
$$x + y - 2z = 3$$
$$3 + y - 2(-1) = 3$$
$$y = -2$$
The solution is $(3, -2, -1)$.

2. $\begin{bmatrix} 2 & 3 & | & 6 \\ 4 & -5 & | & 1 \end{bmatrix}$

$\begin{bmatrix} 2 & 3 & | & 6 \\ 0 & -11 & | & -11 \end{bmatrix}$

$2x + 3y = 6$

$-11y = -11$

$y = 1$

$2x + 3(1) = 6$

$x = \frac{3}{2}$

The solution is $\left(\frac{3}{2}, 1\right)$.

Mixed Review

1. $(2, -1, 4)$ **2.** $(-3, 2, -2)$ **3.** $(1, 0, 5)$ **4.** $\left(\frac{23}{10}, -\frac{1}{2}, \frac{11}{10}\right)$
5. $\left(\frac{16}{7}, \frac{32}{7}, -\frac{6}{7}\right)$ **6.** No solution **7.** $\left(-\frac{11}{2}, \frac{5}{2}\right)$ **8.** $(1, -1)$
9. $\left(\frac{4}{3}, -1, \frac{5}{3}\right)$ **10.** $\left(\frac{11}{8}, 0, \frac{3}{4}\right)$ **11.** $10, -2, 7$ **12.** $28°, 56°, 96°$
13. Brownies: 45; bags of chips: 30; hot dogs: 50
14. 2%: \$2800; 1%: \$3500; 1.5%: \$4000

Exercise Set 11.4, p. 700

1. True **2.** True **3.** True **4.** False **5.** False **6.** False
7. 18 **9.** -50 **11.** 27 **13.** -5 **15.** $(-3, 2)$
17. $\left(\frac{9}{19}, \frac{51}{38}\right)$ **19.** $\left(-1, -\frac{6}{7}, \frac{11}{7}\right)$ **21.** $(2, -1, 4)$ **23.** $(1, 2, 3)$
25. ᵀᵂ **27.** 9700 **28.** $70x - 2500$ **29.** -1800
30. 4500 **31.** $\frac{250}{7}$ **32.** $\frac{250}{7}$ **33.** ᵀᵂ **35.** 12 **37.** 10

Visualizing for Success, p. 705

1. A **2.** D **3.** J **4.** H **5.** I **6.** B **7.** E
8. F **9.** C **10.** G

Exercise Set 11.5, pp. 706–708

1. (b) **2.** (a) **3.** (e) **4.** (f) **5.** (h) **6.** (c)
7. (g) **8.** (d) **9.** (a) $P(x) = 20x - 300,000$;
(b) (15,000 units, \$975,000) **11.** (a) $P(x) = 25x - 3100$;
(b) (124 units, \$4960) **13.** (a) $P(x) = 45x - 22,500$;
(b) (500 units, \$42,500) **15.** (a) $P(x) = 16x - 50,000$;
(b) (3125 units, \$125,000) **17.** (a) $P(x) = 50x - 100,000$;
(b) (2000 units, \$250,000) **19.** (\$70, 300)
21. (\$22, 474) **23.** (\$50, 6250) **25.** (\$10, 1070)
27. (a) $C(x) = 45,000 + 40x$; (b) $R(x) = 130x$;
(c) $P(x) = 90x - 45,000$; (d) \$225,000 profit, \$9000 loss
(e) (500 phones, \$65,000) **29.** (a) $C(x) = 10,000 + 30x$;
(b) $R(x) = 80x$; (c) $P(x) = 50x - 10,000$; (d) \$90,000 profit,
\$7500 loss; (e) (200 seats, \$16,000) **31.** (a) \$8.74;
(b) 24,509 units **33.** ᵀᵂ **35.** $4a - 7 + h$
36. $4a + 4h - 7$ **37.** $\left\{x \,|\, x \text{ is a real number } and \ x \neq -\frac{1}{2}\right\}$, or
$\left(-\infty, -\frac{1}{2}\right) \cup \left(-\frac{1}{2}, \infty\right)$ **38.** $\mathbb{R}$
39. $\{x \,|\, x \geq -4\}$, or $[-4, \infty)$
40. $\{x \,|\, x \text{ is a real number } and \ x \neq -1 \ and \ x \neq 1\}$, or
$(-\infty, -1) \cup (-1, 1) \cup (1, \infty)$ **41.** ᵀᵂ
43. (\$5, 300 yo-yo's) **45.** (a) $S(p) = 15.97p - 1.05$;
(b) $D(p) = -11.26p + 41.16$; (c) (\$1.55, 23.7 million jars)

Study Summary: Chapter 11, pp. 709–711

1. $\left(2, -\frac{1}{2}, -5\right)$ **2.** $(2.5, 3.5, 3)$ **3.** $(4, 1)$ **4.** 28
5. -25 **6.** $\left(\frac{11}{4}, -\frac{3}{4}\right)$ **7.** (a) $P(x) = 75x - 9000$;
(b) (120, \$10,800) **8.** (\$9, 141)

Review Exercises: Chapter 11, pp. 711–712

1. Elimination **2.** Consistent **3.** $180°$ **4.** 1
5. Square **6.** Determinant **7.** Total profit **8.** Fixed
9. Equilibrium point **10.** Zero **11.** $(4, -8, 10)$
12. The equations are dependent. **13.** $(2, 0, 4)$ **14.** No solution
15. $\left(\frac{8}{9}, -\frac{2}{3}, \frac{10}{9}\right)$ **16.** A: 90°; B: 67.5°; C: 22.5°
17. Man: 1.4; woman: 5.3; one-year-old child: 50 **18.** $\left(55, -\frac{89}{2}\right)$
19. $(-1, 1, 3)$ **20.** -5 **21.** 9 **22.** $(6, -2)$
23. $(-3, 0, 4)$ **24.** (a) $P(x) = 20x - 15,800$;
(b) (790 units, \$39,500) **25.** (\$3, 81)
26. (a) $C(x) = 4.75x + 54,000$; (b) $R(x) = 9.25x$;
(c) $P(x) = 4.5x - 54,000$; (d) \$31,500 loss; \$13,500 profit;
(e) (12,000 pints of honey, \$111,000) **27.** ᵀᵂ To solve a
problem involving four variables, go through the *Familiarize* and
Translate steps as usual. The resulting system of equations can be
solved using the elimination method just as for three variables but
likely with more steps. **28.** ᵀᵂ A system of equations can be
both dependent and inconsistent if it is equivalent to a system with
fewer equations that has no solution. An example is a system of three
equations in three unknowns in which two of the equations represent
the same plane, and the third represents a parallel plane.
29. 20,000 pints
30. $a = -\frac{2}{3}, b = -\frac{4}{3}, c = 3; f(x) = -\frac{2}{3}x^2 - \frac{4}{3}x + 3$

Test: Chapter 11, p. 713

1. [11.1] The equations are dependent. **2.** [11.1] $\left(2, -\frac{1}{2}, -1\right)$
3. [11.1] No solution **4.** [11.1] $(0, 1, 0)$ **5.** [11.3] $\left(\frac{22}{5}, -\frac{28}{5}\right)$
6. [11.3] $(3, 1, -2)$ **7.** [11.4] -14 **8.** [11.4] -59
9. [11.4] $\left(\frac{7}{13}, -\frac{17}{26}\right)$ **10.** [11.2] A: 15°; B: 40°; C: 125°
11. [11.2] Electrician: 3.5 hr; carpenter: 8 hr; plumber: 10 hr
12. [11.5] (\$3, 55) **13.** [11.5] (a) $C(x) = 25x + 44,000$;
(b) $R(x) = 80x$; (c) $P(x) = 55x - 44,000$;
(d) \$27,500 loss, \$5500 profit; (e) (880 hammocks, \$64,000)
14. [11.1] $(1, -1, 0, 2)$ **15.** [11.2] Adults' tickets: 1346; senior
citizens' tickets: 335; children's tickets: 1651

Cumulative Review: Chapters 4, 8–14, pp. 714–716

1. 22 **2.** $c - 6$ **3.** $-\frac{1}{100}$ **4.** $-\frac{6x^4}{y^3}$ **5.** $\frac{9a^6}{4b^4}$
6. $\frac{2}{x^2 + 5x + 25}$ **7.** $x^2 - 25$ **8.** $15n^2 + 11n - 14$
9. $\frac{-10}{(x + 5)(x - 5)}$ **10.** $\frac{(x - 3)^2}{x^2(2x - 3)}$ **11.** $\frac{3y^2 + 2}{3y}$
12. $2x^2(2x + 9)$ **13.** $(x - 6)(x + 14)$
14. $(4y - 9)(4y + 9)$ **15.** $8(2x + 1)(4x^2 - 2x + 1)$
16. $(t - 8)^2$ **17.** $x^2(x - 1)(x + 1)(x^2 + 1)$
18. $(0.3b - 0.2c)(0.09b^2 + 0.06bc + 0.04c^2)$

19. $(4x - 1)(5x + 3)$ **20.** 5 **21.** $\mathbb{R}$ **22.** $-2, 4$
23. $-4, 3$ **24.** No solution **25.** $(5, 1)$ **26.** $(-2, -3, 1)$
27. $\left\{-\frac{7}{2}, \frac{9}{2}\right\}$ **28.** $\left\{x \mid x < \frac{13}{2}\right\}$, or $\left(-\infty, \frac{13}{2}\right)$
29. $\{t \mid t < -3 \ or \ t > 3\}$, or $(-\infty, -3) \cup (3, \infty)$
30. $\left\{x \mid -2 \le x \le \frac{10}{3}\right\}$, or $\left[-2, \frac{10}{3}\right]$ **31.** (b) **32.** (a)
33. (d) **34.** (c)

35.

$y = \frac{2}{3}x - 4$

36.

$x = -3$

37.

$3x - y = 3$

38.

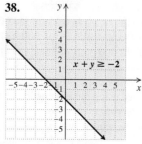

$x + y \ge -2$

39.

$f(x) = -x + 1$

40.

41. Slope: $\frac{4}{9}$; y-intercept: $(0, -2)$ **42.** $y = -7x - 25$
43. $y = \frac{2}{3}x + 4$ **44.** Domain: $\mathbb{R}$; range: $\{y \mid y \ge -2\}$, or $[-2, \infty)$ **45.** $\left\{x \mid x \text{ is a real number } and \ x \neq -\frac{5}{2}\right\}$, or $\left(-\infty, -\frac{5}{2}\right) \cup \left(-\frac{5}{2}, \infty\right)$ **46.** 22 **47.** $x^2 + 6x - 9$
48.

49. $\left\{x \mid x \text{ is a real number } and \ x \neq 0 \ and \ x \neq \frac{1}{3}\right\}$
50. $t = \dfrac{c}{a - d}$ **51.** 1 **52.** $\{x \mid x \ge 1\}$, or $[1, \infty)$
53. $(2, -3)$ **54.** 2 **55.** 1 **56.** 183 cannons
57. Beef: 9300 gal; wheat: 2300 gal
58. **(a)** More than \$40; **(b)** costs greater than \$30
59. Length: 10 cm; width: 6 cm **60.** \$640
61. **(a)** $f(t) = -\frac{5}{3}t + 19$; **(b)** 9 times per month; **(c)** 2015
62. **(a)** $c(t) = 93.5t + 672.5$; **(b)** about 1047 truckloads
63. $[-4, 0) \cup (0, \infty)$ **64.** 2^{11a-16} **65.** $-3, 3, -5, 5$
66. $\{x \mid -3 \le x \le -1 \ or \ 7 \le x \le 9\}$, or $[-3, -1] \cup [7, 9]$
67. All real numbers except 9 and -5

Chapter 12

Interactive Discovery, p. 720

1. Not an identity **2.** Not an identity **3.** Identity
4. Not an identity **5.** Identity **6.** Identity

Visualizing for Success, p. 728

1. B **2.** H **3.** C **4.** I **5.** D **6.** A **7.** F
8. J **9.** G **10.** E

Exercise Set 12.1, pp. 729–732

1. Two **2.** Negative **3.** Positive **4.** Negative **5.** Irrational
6. Real **7.** Nonnegative **8.** Negative **9.** $7, -7$
11. $12, -12$ **13.** $20, -20$ **15.** $30, -30$ **17.** 7 **19.** -4
21. $\frac{6}{7}$ **23.** $-\frac{4}{9}$ **25.** 0.2 **27.** 0.09 **29.** $p^2; 2$
31. $\dfrac{x}{y + 4}; 5$ **33.** $\sqrt{5}; 0$; does not exist; does not exist
35. -7; does not exist; -1; does not exist **37.** 1; $\sqrt{2}$; $\sqrt{101}$
39. $|8x|$, or $8|x|$ **41.** $|-4b|$, or $4|b|$ **43.** $|8 - t|$
45. $|y + 8|$ **47.** $|2x + 7|$ **49.** -4 **51.** -1 **53.** $\frac{2}{3}$
55. $|x|$ **57.** t **59.** $|6a|$, or $6|a|$ **61.** 6 **63.** $|a + b|$
65. $|a^{11}|$ **67.** Cannot be simplified **69.** $4x$ **71.** $-3t$
73. $a + 1$ **75.** $3t - 2$ **77.** $3a$ **79.** $2x$ **81.** $x - 1$
83. $5y$ **85.** t^9 **87.** $(x - 2)^4$ **89.** 2; 3; -2; -4
91. 2; does not exist; does not exist; 3
93. $\{x \mid x \ge 6\}$, or $[6, \infty)$ **95.** $\{t \mid t \ge -8\}$, or $[-8, \infty)$
97. $\{x \mid x \ge 5\}$, or $[5, \infty)$ **99.** $\mathbb{R}$
101. $\left\{z \mid z \ge -\frac{2}{5}\right\}$, or $\left[-\frac{2}{5}, \infty\right)$ **103.** $\mathbb{R}$
105. Domain: $\{x \mid x \le 5\}$, or $(-\infty, 5]$;
range: $\{y \mid y \ge 0\}$, or $[0, \infty)$
107. Domain: $\{x \mid x \ge -1\}$, or $[-1, \infty)$;
range: $\{y \mid y \le 1\}$, or $(-\infty, 1]$
109. Domain: $\mathbb{R}$; range: $\{y \mid y \ge 5\}$, or $[5, \infty)$ **111.** (c)
113. (d) **115.** Yes **117.** Yes **119.** No
121. Approximately 840 GPM; approximately 1572 GPM

123. TW **125.** $a^6 b^2$ **126.** $15x^3 y^9$ **127.** $\dfrac{125x^6}{y^9}$ **128.** $\dfrac{a^3}{8b^6 c^3}$

129. $\dfrac{x^3}{2y^6}$ **130.** $\dfrac{y^4 z^8}{16x^4}$ **131.** TW **133.** TW

135. **(a)** 13; **(b)** 15; **(c)** 18; **(d)** 20
137. $\{x \mid x \ge -5\}$, or $[-5, \infty)$ **139.** $\{x \mid x \ge 0\}$, or $[0, \infty)$

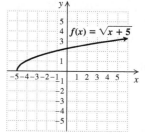

$f(x) = \sqrt{x + 5}$

$g(x) = \sqrt{x} - 2$

141. $\{x \mid -4 < x \le 5\}$, or $(-4, 5]$ **143.** Cubic

Exercise Set 12.2, pp. 738–740

1. (g) **2.** (c) **3.** (e) **4.** (h) **5.** (a) **6.** (d)
7. (b) **8.** (f) **9.** $\sqrt[6]{x}$ **11.** 4 **13.** 2 **15.** 3
17. $\sqrt{xyz}$ **19.** $\sqrt[5]{a^2b^2}$ **21.** $\sqrt[5]{t^2}$ **23.** 8 **25.** 81
27. $27\sqrt[4]{x^3}$ **29.** $125x^6$ **31.** $20^{1/3}$ **33.** $17^{1/2}$
35. $x^{3/2}$ **37.** $m^{2/5}$ **39.** $(cd)^{1/4}$ **41.** $(xy^2z)^{1/5}$

43. $(3mn)^{3/2}$ **45.** $(8x^2y)^{5/7}$ **47.** $\dfrac{2x}{z^{2/3}}$ **49.** $\frac{1}{2}$

51. $\dfrac{1}{(2rs)^{3/4}}$ **53.** 8 **55.** $2a^{3/5}c$ **57.** $\dfrac{5y^{4/5}z}{x^{2/3}}$

59. $\dfrac{a^3}{3^{5/2}b^{7/3}}$ **61.** $\left(\dfrac{3c}{2ab}\right)^{5/6}$ **63.** $\dfrac{6a}{b^{1/4}}$

65. $y = (x + 7)\wedge(1/4)$

67. $y = (3x - 2)\wedge(1/7)$

69. $y = x\wedge(3/6)$

Xscl = 5

71. 1.552 **73.** 1.778
75. -6.240 **77.** $7^{7/8}$
79. $3^{3/4}$ **81.** $5.2^{1/2}$
83. $10^{6/25}$ **85.** $a^{23/12}$

87. 64 **89.** $\dfrac{m^{1/3}}{n^{1/8}}$

91. $\sqrt{x}$ **93.** a^3

95. $\sqrt[3]{y^2}$ **97.** x^2y^2 **99.** $\sqrt{7a}$ **101.** $\sqrt[4]{8x^3}$
103. $\sqrt[10]{m}$ **105.** x^3y^3 **107.** a^6b^{12} **109.** $\sqrt[12]{xy}$
111. TW **113.** $x^2 - 25$ **114.** $x^3 - 8$ **115.** $(2x + 5)^2$
116. $(3a - 4)^2$ **117.** $5(t - 1)^2$ **118.** $3(n + 2)^2$
119. TW **121.** $\sqrt[6]{x^5}$ **123.** $\sqrt[6]{p + q}$
125. 1760 cycles per second
127. $2^{4/12} \approx 1.2599 \approx 1.25$, which is 25% greater than 1.
129. (a) 1.8 m; (b) 3.1 m; (c) 1.5 m; (d) 5.3 m
131. 338 cubic feet **133.** ▨

Exercise Set 12.3, pp. 745–747

1. True **2.** False **3.** False **4.** False **5.** True
6. True **7.** $\sqrt{35}$ **9.** $\sqrt[3]{6}$ **11.** $\sqrt[4]{18}$ **13.** $\sqrt{26xy}$
15. $\sqrt[5]{80y^4}$ **17.** $\sqrt{y^2 - b^2}$ **19.** $\sqrt[3]{0.21y^2}$
21. $\sqrt[5]{(x - 2)^3}$ **23.** $\sqrt{\dfrac{21s}{11t}}$ **25.** $\sqrt[7]{\dfrac{5x - 15}{4x + 8}}$ **27.** $3\sqrt{2}$
29. $3\sqrt{3}$ **31.** $2x^4\sqrt{2x}$ **33.** $2\sqrt{30}$ **35.** $6a^2\sqrt{b}$
37. $2x\sqrt[3]{y^2}$ **39.** $-2x^2\sqrt[3]{2}$ **41.** $f(x) = 5x\sqrt[3]{x^2}$
43. $f(x) = |7(x - 3)|$, or $7|x - 3|$ **45.** $f(x) = |x - 1|\sqrt{5}$
47. $a^3b^3\sqrt{b}$ **49.** $xy^2z^3\sqrt[3]{x^2z}$ **51.** $2xy^2\sqrt[4]{xy^3}$
53. $x^2yz^3\sqrt[5]{x^3y^3z^2}$ **55.** $-2a^4\sqrt[3]{10a^2}$ **57.** $3\sqrt{2}$
59. $2\sqrt{35}$ **61.** 3 **63.** $18a^3$ **65.** $a\sqrt[3]{10}$ **67.** $24x^3\sqrt{5x}$
69. $s^2t^3\sqrt[3]{t}$ **71.** $(x + 5)^2$ **73.** $2ab^3\sqrt[4]{5a}$

75. $x(y + z)^2\sqrt[5]{x}$ **77.** TW **79.** $9abx^2$ **80.** $\dfrac{(x - 1)^2}{(x - 2)^2}$

81. $\dfrac{x + 1}{2(x + 5)}$ **82.** $\dfrac{3(4x^2 + 5y^3)}{50xy^2}$ **83.** $\dfrac{b + a}{a^2b^2}$

84. $\dfrac{-x - 2}{4x + 3}$ **85.** TW, ▨ **87.** 175.6 mi
89. (a) $-3.3°C$; (b) $-16.6°C$; (c) $-25.5°C$; (d) $-54.0°C$
91. $25x^5\sqrt[3]{25x}$ **93.** $a^{10}b^{17}\sqrt{ab}$
95.

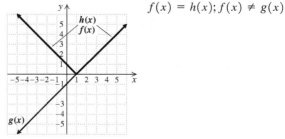

$f(x) = h(x); f(x) \neq g(x)$

97. $\{x \mid x \le 2 \ or \ x \ge 4\}$, or $(-\infty, 2] \cup [4, \infty)$ **99.** 6
101. TW

Exercise Set 12.4, pp. 752–754

1. (e) **2.** (b) **3.** (f) **4.** (c) **5.** (h) **6.** (d) **7.** (a)
8. (g) **9.** $\frac{6}{5}$ **11.** $\frac{4}{3}$ **13.** $\dfrac{7}{y}$ **15.** $\dfrac{6y\sqrt{y}}{x^2}$ **17.** $\dfrac{3a\sqrt[3]{a}}{2b}$

19. $\dfrac{2a}{bc^2}$ **21.** $\dfrac{ab^2}{c^2}\sqrt[4]{\dfrac{a}{c^2}}$ **23.** $\dfrac{2x}{y^2}\sqrt[5]{\dfrac{x}{y}}$ **25.** $\dfrac{xy}{z^2}\sqrt[6]{\dfrac{y^2}{z^3}}$

27. 3 **29.** $\sqrt[3]{2}$ **31.** $y\sqrt{5y}$ **33.** $2\sqrt[3]{a^2b}$ **35.** $\sqrt{2ab}$

37. $2x^2y^3\sqrt[4]{y^3}$ **39.** $\sqrt[3]{x^2 + xy + y^2}$ **41.** $\dfrac{\sqrt{6}}{2}$ **43.** $\dfrac{2\sqrt{15}}{21}$

45. $\dfrac{\sqrt[3]{10}}{2}$ **47.** $\dfrac{\sqrt[3]{75ac^2}}{5c}$ **49.** $\dfrac{y\sqrt[4]{45x^3y^2}}{3x}$ **51.** $\dfrac{\sqrt[3]{2xy^2}}{xy}$

53. $\dfrac{\sqrt{14a}}{6}$ **55.** $\dfrac{3\sqrt{5y}}{10xy}$ **57.** $\dfrac{\sqrt{5b}}{6a}$ **59.** $\dfrac{5}{\sqrt{55}}$ **61.** $\dfrac{12}{5\sqrt{42}}$

63. $\dfrac{2}{\sqrt{6x}}$ **65.** $\dfrac{7}{\sqrt[3]{98}}$ **67.** $\dfrac{7x}{\sqrt{21xy}}$ **69.** $\dfrac{2a^2}{\sqrt[3]{20ab}}$

71. $\dfrac{x^2y}{\sqrt{2xy}}$ **73.** TW **75.** $x(3 - 8y + 2z)$
76. $ac(4a + 9 - 3a^2)$ **77.** $a^2 - b^2$ **78.** $a^4 - 4y^2$
79. $56 - 11x - 12x^2$ **80.** $6ay - 2cy - 3ax + cx$
81. TW **83.** (a) 1.62 sec; (b) 1.99 sec; (c) 2.20 sec
85. $9\sqrt[3]{9n^2}$ **87.** $\dfrac{-3\sqrt{a^2 - 3}}{a^2 - 3}$, or $\dfrac{-3}{\sqrt{a^2 - 3}}$

89. Step 1: $\sqrt[n]{a} = a^{1/n}$, by definition; Step 2: $\left(\dfrac{a}{b}\right)^n = \dfrac{a^n}{b^n}$, raising
a quotient to a power; Step 3: $a^{1/n} = \sqrt[n]{a}$, by definition
91. $(f/g)(x) = 3x$, where x is a real number and $x > 0$
93. $(f/g)(x) = \sqrt{x + 3}$, where x is a real number and $x > 3$

Exercise Set 12.5, pp. 759–761

1. Radicands; indices **2.** Indices **3.** Bases
4. Denominators **5.** Numerator; conjugate **6.** Bases
7. $9\sqrt{5}$ **9.** $2\sqrt[3]{4}$ **11.** $10\sqrt[3]{y}$ **13.** $12\sqrt{2}$
15. $13\sqrt[3]{7} + \sqrt{3}$ **17.** $9\sqrt{3}$ **19.** $-7\sqrt{5}$ **21.** $9\sqrt[3]{2}$
23. $(1 + 12a)\sqrt{a}$ **25.** $(x - 2)\sqrt[3]{6x}$ **27.** $3\sqrt{a - 1}$
29. $(x + 3)\sqrt{x - 1}$ **31.** $4\sqrt{3} + 3$ **33.** $15 - 3\sqrt{10}$
35. $6\sqrt{5} - 4$ **37.** $3 - 4\sqrt[3]{63}$ **39.** $a + 2a\sqrt[3]{3}$
41. $4 + 3\sqrt{6}$ **43.** $\sqrt{6} - \sqrt{14} + \sqrt{21} - 7$ **45.** 4
47. -2 **49.** $2 - 8\sqrt{35}$ **51.** $7 + 4\sqrt{3}$ **53.** $5 - 2\sqrt{6}$

55. $2t + 5 + 2\sqrt{10t}$ **57.** $14 + x - 6\sqrt{x+5}$

59. $6\sqrt[4]{63} + 4\sqrt[4]{35} - 3\sqrt[4]{54} - 2\sqrt[4]{30}$ **61.** $\dfrac{18 + 6\sqrt{2}}{7}$

63. $\dfrac{12 - 2\sqrt{3} + 6\sqrt{5} - \sqrt{15}}{33}$ **65.** $\dfrac{a - \sqrt{ab}}{a - b}$

67. -1 **69.** $\dfrac{12 - 3\sqrt{10} - 2\sqrt{14} + \sqrt{35}}{6}$ **71.** $\dfrac{1}{\sqrt{5}-1}$

73. $\dfrac{2}{14 + 2\sqrt{3} + 3\sqrt{2} + 7\sqrt{6}}$ **75.** $\dfrac{x - y}{x + 2\sqrt{xy} + y}$

77. $\dfrac{1}{\sqrt{a+h} + \sqrt{a}}$ **79.** $\sqrt{a}$ **81.** $b\sqrt[10]{b^9}$

83. $xy\sqrt[6]{xy^5}$ **85.** $3a^2b\sqrt[4]{ab}$ **87.** $a^2b^2c^2\sqrt[6]{a^2bc^2}$

89. $\sqrt[12]{a^5}$ **91.** $\sqrt[12]{x^2y^5}$ **93.** $\sqrt[10]{ab^9}$ **95.** $\sqrt[6]{(7-y)^5}$

97. $\sqrt[12]{5+3x}$ **99.** $x\sqrt[6]{xy^5} - \sqrt[15]{x^{13}y^{14}}$

101. $2m^2 + m\sqrt[4]{n} + 2m\sqrt[3]{n^2} + \sqrt[12]{n^{11}}$

103. $2\sqrt[4]{x^3} - \sqrt[12]{x^{11}}$ **105.** $x^2 - 7$ **107.** $27 + 10\sqrt{2}$

109. $8 - 2\sqrt{15}$ **111.** TW **113.** 42 **114.** $-\frac{1}{3}$

115. $-7, 3$ **116.** $-\frac{2}{5}, \frac{3}{2}$ **117.** -3 **118.** $-6, 1$ **119.** TW

121. $f(x) = 2x\sqrt{x-1}$ **123.** $f(x) = (x + 3x^2)\sqrt[4]{x-1}$

125. $(7x^2 - 2y^2)\sqrt{x+y}$ **127.** $4x(y+z)^3\sqrt[6]{2x(y+z)}$

129. $1 - \sqrt{w}$ **131.** $\left(\sqrt{x} + \sqrt{5}\right)\left(\sqrt{x} - \sqrt{5}\right)$

133. $\left(\sqrt{x} + \sqrt{a}\right)\left(\sqrt{x} - \sqrt{a}\right)$ **135.** $2x - 2\sqrt{x^2 - 4}$

Mid-Chapter Review: Chapter 12, p. 762

Guided Solutions

1. $\sqrt{6x^9} \cdot \sqrt{2xy} = \sqrt{6x^9 \cdot 2xy}$
$= \sqrt{12x^{10}y}$
$= \sqrt{4x^{10} \cdot 3y}$
$= \sqrt{4x^{10}} \cdot \sqrt{3y}$
$= 2x^5\sqrt{3y}$

2. $\sqrt{12} - 3\sqrt{75} + \sqrt{8} = 2\sqrt{3} - 3 \cdot 5\sqrt{3} + 2\sqrt{2}$
$= 2\sqrt{3} - 15\sqrt{3} + 2\sqrt{2}$
$= -13\sqrt{3} + 2\sqrt{2}$

Mixed Review

1. 9 **2.** $-\frac{3}{10}$ **3.** $|8t|$, or $8|t|$ **4.** x **5.** -4
6. $\{x \mid x \leq 10\}$, or $(-\infty, 10]$ **7.** 4 **8.** $\sqrt[12]{a}$
9. y^8 **10.** $t + 5$ **11.** $-3a^4$ **12.** $3x\sqrt{10}$ **13.** $\frac{2}{3}$
14. $5\sqrt{15t}$ **15.** $ab^2c^2\sqrt[5]{c}$ **16.** $2\sqrt{15} - 3\sqrt{22}$
17. $\sqrt[8]{t}$ **18.** $\dfrac{a^2}{2}$ **19.** $-8\sqrt{3}$ **20.** -4 **21.** $25 + 10\sqrt{6}$
22. $2\sqrt{x-1}$ **23.** $xy\sqrt[10]{x^7y^3}$ **24.** $15\sqrt[3]{5}$ **25.** $6x^3y^2$

Interactive Discovery, p. 763

1. $\{3\}; \{-3, 3\}$ **2.** $\{-2\}; \{-2, 2\}$ **3.** $\{25\}; \{25\}$
4. $\varnothing; \{9\}$

Exercise Set 12.6, pp. 768–770

1. False **2.** True **3.** True **4.** False **5.** True **6.** True
7. 3 **9.** $\frac{25}{3}$ **11.** 168 **13.** -1 **15.** 3 **17.** 82 **19.** $0, 9$
21. 100 **23.** -27 **25.** 16 **27.** No solution **29.** $\frac{80}{3}$
31. 45 **33.** $-\frac{5}{3}$ **35.** 1 **37.** $\frac{106}{27}$ **39.** 4 **41.** $3, 7$

43. $\frac{80}{9}$ **45.** -1 **47.** No solution **49.** $2, 6$ **51.** 2 **53.** 4
55. TW **57.** Length: 200 ft; width: 15 ft **58.** Base: 34 in.;
height: 15 in. **59.** Length: 14 in.; width: 10 in. **60.** Length:
30 yd; width: 16 yd **61.** $6, 8, 10$ **62.** 13 cm **63.** TW
65. About 68 psi **67.** About 278 Hz **69.** $524.8°C$

71. $t = \dfrac{1}{9}\left(\dfrac{S^2 \cdot 2457}{1087.7^2} - 2617\right)$ **73.** 4480 rpm

75. $r = \dfrac{v^2h}{2gh - v^2}$ **77.** $-\frac{8}{9}$ **79.** $-8, 8$ **81.** $1, 8$
83. $\left(\frac{1}{36}, 0\right), (36, 0)$

Exercise Set 12.7, pp. 777–781

1. (d) **2.** (c) **3.** (e) **4.** (b) **5.** (f) **6.** (a)
7. $\sqrt{34}; 5.831$ **9.** $9\sqrt{2}; 12.728$ **11.** 5 **13.** 4 m
15. $\sqrt{19}$ in.; 4.359 in. **17.** 1 m **19.** 250 ft
21. $\sqrt{8450}$, or $65\sqrt{2}$ ft; 91.924 ft **23.** 24 in.
25. $\left(\sqrt{340} + 8\right)$ ft; 26.439 ft
27. $\left(110 - \sqrt{6500}\right)$ paces; 29.377 paces
29. Leg $= 5$; hypotenuse $= 5\sqrt{2} \approx 7.071$
31. Shorter leg $= 7$; longer leg $= 7\sqrt{3} \approx 12.124$
33. Leg $= 5\sqrt{3} \approx 8.660$; hypotenuse $= 10\sqrt{3} \approx 17.321$
35. Both legs $= \dfrac{13\sqrt{2}}{2} \approx 9.192$
37. Leg $= 14\sqrt{3} \approx 24.249$; hypotenuse $= 28$
39. $3\sqrt{3} \approx 5.196$ **41.** $13\sqrt{2} \approx 18.385$
43. $\dfrac{19\sqrt{2}}{2} \approx 13.435$ **45.** $\sqrt{10{,}561}$ ft ≈ 102.767 ft

47. $\dfrac{1089}{4}\sqrt{3}$ ft$^2 \approx 471.551$ ft^2 **49.** $(0, -4), (0, 4)$

51. 5 **53.** $\sqrt{10} \approx 3.162$ **55.** $\sqrt{200} \approx 14.142$ **57.** 17.8
59. $\dfrac{\sqrt{13}}{6} \approx 0.601$ **61.** $\sqrt{12} \approx 3.464$ **63.** $\sqrt{101} \approx 10.050$

65. $(3, 4)$ **67.** $\left(\frac{7}{2}, \frac{7}{2}\right)$ **69.** $(-1, -3)$ **71.** $(0.7, 0)$

73. $\left(-\frac{1}{12}, \frac{1}{24}\right)$ **75.** $\left(\dfrac{\sqrt{2} + \sqrt{3}}{2}, \dfrac{3}{2}\right)$ **77.** TW

79.

$y = 2x - 3$

80.

$y < x$

81.

$8x - 4y = 8$

82.

$2y - 1 = 7$

83.

84.

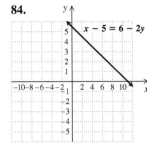

$x - 5 = 6 - 2y$

85. TW   **87.** $36\sqrt{3}$ cm²; 62.354 cm²   **89.** $d = s + s\sqrt{2}$
91. 5 gal. The total area of the doors and windows is 134 ft² or more.
93. 60.28 ft by 60.28 ft
95. Let $P_1 = (x_1, y_1), P_2 = (x_2, y_2)$, and
$$M = \left(\frac{x_1 + x_2}{2}, \frac{y_1 + y_2}{2}\right).$$
Let $d(AB)$ denote the distance from point A to point B.

(i) $d(P_1M) = \sqrt{\left(\frac{x_1 + x_2}{2} - x_1\right)^2 + \left(\frac{y_1 + y_2}{2} - y_1\right)^2}$

$= \frac{1}{2}\sqrt{(x_2 - x_1)^2 + (y_2 - y_1)^2};$

$d(P_2M) = \sqrt{\left(\frac{x_1 + x_2}{2} - x_2\right)^2 + \left(\frac{y_1 + y_2}{2} - y_2\right)^2}$

$= \frac{1}{2}\sqrt{(x_1 - x_2)^2 + (y_1 - y_2)^2}$

$= \frac{1}{2}\sqrt{(x_2 - x_1)^2 + (y_2 - y_1)^2} = d(P_1M).$

(ii) $d(P_1M) + d(P_2M) = \frac{1}{2}\sqrt{(x_2 - x_1)^2 + (y_2 - y_1)^2}$

$+ \frac{1}{2}\sqrt{(x_2 - x_1)^2 + (y_2 - y_1)^2}$

$= \sqrt{(x_2 - x_1)^2 + (y_2 - y_1)^2}$

$= d(P_1P_2).$

Exercise Set 12.8, pp. 787–789

1. False   **2.** False   **3.** True   **4.** True   **5.** False   **6.** True
7. False   **8.** True   **9.** $10i$ **11.** $i\sqrt{13}$, or $\sqrt{13}i$
13. $2i\sqrt{2}$, or $2\sqrt{2}i$ **15.** $-i\sqrt{3}$, or $-\sqrt{3}i$ **17.** $-9i$
19. $-10i\sqrt{3}$, or $-10\sqrt{3}i$ **21.** $6 - 2i\sqrt{21}$, or $6 - 2\sqrt{21}i$
23. $\left(-2\sqrt{19} + 5\sqrt{5}\right)i$ **25.** $\left(3\sqrt{2} - 10\right)i$ **27.** $11 + 10i$
29. $4 + 5i$ **31.** $2 - i$ **33.** $-12 - 5i$ **35.** -42
37. -24 **39.** -18 **41.** $-\sqrt{10}$ **43.** $-3\sqrt{14}$
45. $-30 + 10i$ **47.** $-28 - 21i$ **49.** $1 + 5i$ **51.** $38 + 9i$
53. $2 - 46i$ **55.** 73 **57.** 50 **59.** $12 - 16i$
61. $-5 + 12i$ **63.** $-5 - 12i$ **65.** $3 - i$ **67.** $\frac{6}{13} + \frac{4}{13}i$
69. $\frac{3}{17} + \frac{5}{17}i$ **71.** $-\frac{5}{6}i$ **73.** $-\frac{3}{4} - \frac{5}{4}i$ **75.** $1 - 2i$
77. $-\frac{23}{58} + \frac{43}{58}i$ **79.** $\frac{19}{29} - \frac{4}{29}i$ **81.** $\frac{6}{25} - \frac{17}{25}i$ **83.** $-i$
85. 1 **87.** -1 **89.** i **91.** -1 **93.** $-125i$ **95.** 0
97. TW   **99.** $-2, 3$ **100.** 5 **101.** $-10, 10$ **102.** $-5, 5$
103. $-\frac{2}{5}, \frac{4}{3}$ **104.** $-\frac{3}{3}, \frac{3}{2}$ **105.** TW

107.

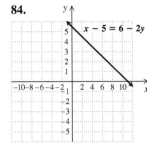

109. 5
111. $\sqrt{2}$
113. $-9 - 27i$
115. $50 - 120i$
117. $\frac{250}{41} + \frac{200}{41}i$
119. 8
121. $\frac{3}{5} + \frac{9}{5}i$
123. 1

Study Summary: Chapter 12, pp. 790–793

1. -9 **2.** -1 **3.** $|6x|$, or $6|x|$ **4.** x **5.** $\frac{1}{10}$
6. $\sqrt{21xy}$ **7.** $10x^2y^9\sqrt{2x}$ **8.** $\frac{2x\sqrt{3x}}{5}$ **9.** $\frac{\sqrt{6x}}{3y}$
10. $-5\sqrt{2}$ **11.** $31 - 19\sqrt{3}$ **12.** $\frac{3\sqrt{15} - 5\sqrt{3}}{4}$
13. $\sqrt[6]{x^{13}}$ **14.** 3 **15.** $\sqrt{51}$ m ≈ 7.141 m   **16.** $a = 6$
17. $b = 5\sqrt{3} \approx 8.660; c = 10$ **18.** $\sqrt{185} \approx 13.601$
19. $\left(2, -\frac{9}{2}\right)$ **20.** $-3 - 12i$ **21.** $3 - 2i$
22. $-32 - 26i$ **23.** i

Review Exercises: Chapter 12, pp. 793–794

1. True   **2.** False   **3.** False   **4.** True   **5.** True   **6.** True
7. True   **8.** False   **9.** $\frac{7}{3}$ **10.** -0.5 **11.** 5
12. $\left\{x | x \geq \frac{7}{2}\right\}$, or $\left[\frac{7}{2}, \infty\right)$ **13.** **(a)** 34.6 lb; **(b)** 10.0 lb;
(c) 24.9 lb; **(d)** 42.3 lb   **14.** $|5t|$, or $5|t|$ **15.** $|c + 8|$
16. $|2x + 1|$ **17.** -2 **18.** $(5ab)^{4/3}$ **19.** $8a^4\sqrt{a}$
20. x^3y^5 **21.** $\sqrt[3]{x^2y}$ **22.** $\frac{1}{x^{2/5}}$ **23.** $7^{1/6}$
24. $f(x) = 5|x - 6|$ **25.** $2x^5y^2$ **26.** $5xy\sqrt{10x}$
27. $\sqrt{6xy}$ **28.** $3xb\sqrt[3]{x^2}$ **29.** $-6x^5y^4\sqrt[3]{2x^2}$ **30.** $y\sqrt[3]{6}$
31. $\frac{5\sqrt{x}}{2}$ **32.** $\frac{2a^2\sqrt[4]{3a^3}}{c^2}$ **33.** $7\sqrt[3]{x}$ **34.** $\sqrt{3}$
35. $(2x + y^2)\sqrt[3]{x}$ **36.** $15\sqrt{2}$ **37.** -1
38. $\sqrt{15} + 4\sqrt{6} - 6\sqrt{10} - 48$ **39.** $\sqrt[4]{x^3}$ **40.** $\sqrt[12]{x^5}$
41. $a^2 - 2a\sqrt{2} + 2$ **42.** $\frac{\sqrt{2xy}}{4y}$ **43.** $-4\sqrt{10} + 4\sqrt{15}$
44. $\frac{20}{\sqrt{10} + \sqrt{15}}$ **45.** 19 **46.** 9 **47.** -126 **48.** 4
49. 14 **50.** $5\sqrt{2}$ cm; 7.071 cm   **51.** $\sqrt{32}$ ft; 5.657 ft
52. Short leg = 10; long leg = $10\sqrt{3} \approx 17.321$
53. $\sqrt{26} \approx 5.099$ **54.** $\left(-2, -\frac{3}{2}\right)$ **55.** $3i\sqrt{5}$, or $3\sqrt{5}i$
56. $-2 - 9i$ **57.** $6 + i$ **58.** 29 **59.** -1 **60.** $9 - 12i$
61. $\frac{13}{25} - \frac{34}{25}i$ **62.** TW   A complex number $a + bi$ is real when
$b = 0$. It is imaginary when $b \neq 0$.   **63.** TW   An absolute-value
sign must be used to simplify $\sqrt[n]{x^n}$ when n is even, since x may be
negative. If x is negative while n is even, the radical expression
cannot be simplified to x, since $\sqrt[n]{x^n}$ represents the principal, or
positive, root. When n is odd, there is only one root, and it will be
positive or negative depending on the sign of x. Thus there is no
absolute-value sign when n is odd.   **64.** 3 **65.** $-\frac{2}{5} + \frac{9}{10}i$
66. $\frac{2i}{3i}$; answers may vary   **67.** The isosceles triangle is larger
by about 1.206 ft².

Test: Chapter 12, p. 795

1. [12.3] $5\sqrt{2}$ **2.** [12.4] $-\dfrac{2}{x^2}$ **3.** [12.1] $|9a|$, or $9|a|$

4. [12.1] $|x - 4|$ **5.** [12.2] $(7xy)^{1/2}$ **6.** [12.2] $\sqrt[6]{(4a^3b)^5}$

7. [12.1] $\{x | x \geq 5\}$, or $[5, \infty)$ **8.** [12.5] $27 + 10\sqrt{2}$

9. [12.3] $2x^3y^2\sqrt[5]{x}$ **10.** [12.3] $2\sqrt[3]{2wv^2}$

11. [12.4] $\dfrac{10a^2}{3b^3}$ **12.** [12.4] $\sqrt[5]{3x^4y}$ **13.** [12.5] $x\sqrt[4]{x}$

14. [12.5] $\sqrt[5]{y^2}$ **15.** [12.5] $6\sqrt{2}$ **16.** [12.5] $(x^2 + 3y)\sqrt{y}$

17. [12.5] $14 - 19\sqrt{x} - 3x$ **18.** [12.4] $\dfrac{\sqrt[3]{2xy^2}}{2y}$

19. [12.6] 4 **20.** [12.6] $-1, 2$ **21.** [12.6] 8

22. [12.7] $\sqrt{10{,}600}$ ft ≈ 102.956 ft

23. [12.7] 5 cm; $5\sqrt{3}$ cm ≈ 8.660 cm

24. [12.7] $\sqrt{17} \approx 4.123$ **25.** [12.7] $\left(\frac{3}{2}, -6\right)$

26. [12.8] $5i\sqrt{2}$, or $5\sqrt{2}i$ **27.** [12.8] $12 + 2i$

28. [12.8] -24 **29.** [12.8] $15 - 8i$ **30.** [12.8] $-\frac{11}{34} - \frac{7}{34}i$

31. [12.8] i **32.** [12.6] 3 **33.** [12.8] $-\frac{17}{4}i$

34. [12.6] 22,500 ft

Chapter 13

Interactive Discovery, p. 798

1. 1 **2.** 1 **3.** 1 **4.** 0 **5.** 0 **6.** 2

7. A cup-shaped curve opening up or down

Exercise Set 13.1, pp. 807–809

1. $\sqrt{k}; -\sqrt{k}$ **2.** $7; -7$ **3.** $t + 3; t + 3$ **4.** 16

5. $25; 5$ **6.** $9; 3$ **7.** 2 **8.** 0 **9.** 1 **10.** 2 **11.** 0

12. 1 **13.** ± 10 **15.** $\pm 5\sqrt{2}$ **17.** $\pm\sqrt{5}$ **19.** $\pm 2i$

21. $\pm\frac{4}{3}$ **23.** $\pm\sqrt{\dfrac{7}{5}}$, or $\pm\dfrac{\sqrt{35}}{5}$ **25.** $\pm\frac{9}{2}i$ **27.** $-6, 8$

29. $13 \pm 3\sqrt{2}$ **31.** $-1 \pm 3i$ **33.** $-\dfrac{3}{4} \pm \dfrac{\sqrt{17}}{4}$, or $\dfrac{-3 \pm \sqrt{17}}{4}$

35. $-3, 13$ **37.** $\pm\sqrt{19}$ **39.** $1, 9$ **41.** $-4 \pm \sqrt{13}$

43. $-14, 0$ **45.** $x^2 + 16x + 64 = (x + 8)^2$

47. $t^2 - 10t + 25 = (t - 5)^2$ **49.** $t^2 - 2t + 1 = (t - 1)^2$

51. $x^2 + 3x + \frac{9}{4} = \left(x + \frac{3}{2}\right)^2$ **53.** $x^2 + \frac{2}{5}x + \frac{1}{25} = \left(x + \frac{1}{5}\right)^2$

55. $t^2 - \frac{5}{6}t + \frac{25}{144} = \left(t - \frac{5}{12}\right)^2$ **57.** $-7, 1$ **59.** $5 \pm \sqrt{2}$

61. $-8, -4$ **63.** $-4 \pm \sqrt{19}$

65. $\left(-3 - \sqrt{2}, 0\right), \left(-3 + \sqrt{2}, 0\right)$

67. $\left(-\dfrac{9}{2} - \dfrac{\sqrt{181}}{2}, 0\right), \left(-\dfrac{9}{2} + \dfrac{\sqrt{181}}{2}, 0\right)$, or

$\left(\dfrac{-9 - \sqrt{181}}{2}, 0\right), \left(\dfrac{-9 + \sqrt{181}}{2}, 0\right)$

69. $\left(5 - \sqrt{47}, 0\right), \left(5 + \sqrt{47}, 0\right)$ **71.** $-\frac{4}{3}, -\frac{2}{3}$ **73.** $-\frac{1}{3}, 2$

75. $-\dfrac{2}{5} \pm \dfrac{\sqrt{19}}{5}$, or $\dfrac{-2 \pm \sqrt{19}}{5}$

77. $\left(-\dfrac{1}{4} - \dfrac{\sqrt{13}}{4}, 0\right), \left(-\dfrac{1}{4} + \dfrac{\sqrt{13}}{4}, 0\right)$, or

$\left(\dfrac{-1 - \sqrt{13}}{4}, 0\right), \left(\dfrac{-1 + \sqrt{13}}{4}, 0\right)$

79. $\left(\dfrac{3}{4} - \dfrac{\sqrt{17}}{4}, 0\right), \left(\dfrac{3}{4} + \dfrac{\sqrt{17}}{4}, 0\right)$, or

$\left(\dfrac{3 - \sqrt{17}}{4}, 0\right), \left(\dfrac{3 + \sqrt{17}}{4}, 0\right)$ **81.** 10% **83.** 4%

85. About 15.8 sec **87.** About 11.4 sec **89.** TW **91.** 64

92. -15 **93.** $10\sqrt{2}$ **94.** $4\sqrt{6}$ **95.** $2i$ **96.** $5i$

97. $2i\sqrt{2}$, or $2\sqrt{2}i$ **98.** $2i\sqrt{6}$, or $2\sqrt{6}i$ **99.** TW

101. ± 18 **103.** $-\frac{7}{2}, -\sqrt{5}, 0, \sqrt{5}, 8$

105. Barge: 8 km/h; fishing boat: 15 km/h

Exercise Set 13.2, pp. 815–816

1. True **2.** True **3.** False **4.** False **5.** False **6.** True

7. $-\frac{5}{2}, 1$ **9.** $-1 \pm \sqrt{5}$ **11.** $3 \pm \sqrt{7}$ **13.** $3 \pm \sqrt{5}$

15. $\dfrac{3}{2} \pm \dfrac{\sqrt{29}}{2}$ **17.** $-1 \pm \dfrac{2\sqrt{3}}{3}$ **19.** $-\dfrac{4}{3} \pm \dfrac{\sqrt{19}}{3}$

21. $3 \pm i$ **23.** $-2 \pm \sqrt{2}i$ **25.** $-\frac{8}{3}, \frac{5}{4}$ **27.** $\frac{2}{5}$

29. $-\dfrac{11}{8} \pm \dfrac{\sqrt{41}}{8}$ **31.** $5, 10$ **33.** $\dfrac{13}{10} \pm \dfrac{\sqrt{509}}{10}$

35. $2 \pm \sqrt{5}i$ **37.** $2, -1 \pm \sqrt{3}i$ **39.** $\dfrac{1}{4} \pm \dfrac{\sqrt{13}}{4}$ **41.** $-2, 3$

43. $\dfrac{7}{2} \pm \dfrac{\sqrt{85}}{2}$ **45.** $-5.317, 1.317$ **47.** $0.764, 5.236$

49. $-1.266, 2.766$ **51.** TW **53.** $x^2 + 4$ **54.** $x^2 - 180$

55. $x^2 - 4x - 3$ **56.** $x^2 + 6x + 34$ **57.** $-\frac{3}{2}$

58. $\dfrac{1}{6} \pm \dfrac{\sqrt{6}}{3}i$ **59.** TW **61.** $(-2, 0), (1, 0)$

63. $4 - 2\sqrt{2}, 4 + 2\sqrt{2}$ **65.** $-1.179, 0.339$

67. $\dfrac{-5\sqrt{2}}{4} \pm \dfrac{\sqrt{34}}{4}$ **69.** $\frac{1}{2}$ **71.** TW

Exercise Set 13.3, pp. 819–821

1. Discriminant **2.** One **3.** Two **4.** Two **5.** Rational

6. Imaginary **7.** Two irrational **9.** Two imaginary

11. Two irrational **13.** Two rational **15.** Two imaginary

17. One rational **19.** Two rational **21.** Two irrational

23. Two imaginary **25.** Two rational **27.** Two irrational

29. $x^2 + 4x - 21 = 0$ **31.** $x^2 - 6x + 9 = 0$

33. $x^2 + 4x + 3 = 0$ **35.** $4x^2 - 23x + 15 = 0$

37. $8x^2 + 6x + 1 = 0$ **39.** $x^2 - 2x - 0.96 = 0$

41. $x^2 - 3 = 0$ **43.** $x^2 - 20 = 0$ **45.** $x^2 + 16 = 0$

47. $x^2 - 4x + 53 = 0$ **49.** $x^2 - 6x - 5 = 0$

51. $3x^2 - 6x - 4 = 0$ **53.** $x^3 - 4x^2 - 7x + 10 = 0$

55. $x^3 - 2x^2 - 3x = 0$ **57.** TW **59.** $c = \dfrac{d^2}{1 - d}$

60. $b = \dfrac{aq}{p - q}$ **61.** $y = \dfrac{x - 3}{x}$, or $1 - \dfrac{3}{x}$ **62.** 10 mph

63. Jamal: 3.5 mph; Kade: 2 mph **64.** 20 mph **65.** TW

67. $a = 1, b = 2, c = -3$ **69.** (a) $-\frac{3}{5}$; (b) $-\frac{1}{3}$

71. (a) $9 + 9i$; (b) $3 + 3i$

73. The solutions of $ax^2 + bx + c = 0$ are

$x = \dfrac{-b \pm \sqrt{b^2 - 4ac}}{2a}$. When there is just one solution,

$b^2 - 4ac$ must be 0, so $x = \dfrac{-b \pm 0}{2a} = \dfrac{-b}{2a}$.

75. $a = 8, b = 20, c = -12$ **77.** $x^2 - 2 = 0$
79. $x^4 - 8x^3 + 21x^2 - 2x - 52 = 0$

Exercise Set 13.4, pp. 825–828

1. First part: 60 mph; second part: 50 mph   **3.** 40 mph
5. Cessna: 150 mph, Beechcraft: 200 mph; or Cessna: 200 mph,
Beechcraft: 250 mph   **7.** To Hillsboro: 10 mph; return trip: 4 mph
9. About 14 mph   **11.** 12 hr   **13.** About 3.24 mph
15. $r = \dfrac{1}{2}\sqrt{\dfrac{A}{\pi}}$, or $\dfrac{\sqrt{A\pi}}{2\pi}$ **17.** $r = \dfrac{-\pi h + \sqrt{\pi^2 h^2 + 2\pi A}}{2\pi}$
19. $r = \sqrt{\dfrac{Gm_1 m_2}{F}}$, or $\dfrac{\sqrt{FGm_1 m_2}}{F}$ **21.** $H = \dfrac{c^2}{g}$
23. $g = \sqrt{\dfrac{800w}{l}}$, or $\dfrac{20\sqrt{2lw}}{l}$ **25.** $b = \sqrt{c^2 - a^2}$
27. $t = \dfrac{-v_0 + \sqrt{(v_0)^2 + 2gs}}{g}$ **29.** $n = \dfrac{1 + \sqrt{1 + 8N}}{2}$
31. $g = \dfrac{4\pi^2 l}{T^2}$ **33.** $t = \dfrac{-b \pm \sqrt{b^2 - 4ac}}{2a}$
35. (a) 10.1 sec; (b) 7.49 sec; (c) 272.5 m   **37.** 2.9 sec
39. 0.957 sec   **41.** 2.5 m/sec   **43.** 7%   **45.** TW
47. m^{-2}, or $\dfrac{1}{m^2}$ **48.** $t^{2/3}$ **49.** $y^{1/3}$ **50.** $z^{1/2}$ **51.** 2
52. 81   **53.** TW   **55.** $t = \dfrac{-10.2 + 6\sqrt{-A^2 + 13A - 39.36}}{A - 6.5}$
57. $\pm\sqrt{2}$ **59.** $l = \dfrac{w + w\sqrt{5}}{2}$
61. $n = \pm\sqrt{\dfrac{r^2 \pm \sqrt{r^4 + 4m^4 r^2 p - 4mp}}{2m}}$ **63.** $A(S) = \dfrac{\pi S}{6}$

Exercise Set 13.5, pp. 834–835

1. (f)   **2.** (d)   **3.** (h)   **4.** (b)   **5.** (g)   **6.** (a)   **7.** (e)
8. (c)   **9.** $\sqrt{p}$ **10.** $x^{1/4}$ **11.** $x^2 + 3$ **12.** t^{-3}
13. $(1 + t)^2$ **14.** $w^{1/6}$ **15.** $\pm 1, \pm 2$ **17.** $\pm\sqrt{5}, \pm 2$
19. $\pm\dfrac{\sqrt{3}}{2}, \pm 2$ **21.** 4   **23.** $\pm 2\sqrt{2}, \pm 3$ **25.** $8 + 2\sqrt{7}$
27. No solution   **29.** $-\frac{1}{2}, \frac{1}{3}$ **31.** $-4, 1$ **33.** $-27, 8$
35. 729   **37.** 1   **39.** 9, 225   **41.** $\frac{12}{5}$ **43.** $\pm 2, \pm 3i$
45. $\pm i, \pm 2i$ **47.** $\left(\frac{4}{25}, 0\right)$
49. $\left(\dfrac{3}{2} + \dfrac{\sqrt{33}}{2}, 0\right), \left(\dfrac{3}{2} - \dfrac{\sqrt{33}}{2}, 0\right), (4, 0), (-1, 0)$
51. $(-243, 0), (32, 0)$ **53.** No x-intercepts   **55.** TW
57.

58.

59.

60.

61.

62.

63. TW   **65.** $\pm\sqrt{\dfrac{7 \pm \sqrt{29}}{10}}$ **67.** $-2, -1, 5, 6$
69. $\frac{100}{99}$ **71.** $-5, -3, -2, 0, 2, 3, 5$
73. $1, 3, -\dfrac{1}{2} + \dfrac{\sqrt{3}}{2}i, -\dfrac{1}{2} - \dfrac{\sqrt{3}}{2}i, -\dfrac{3}{2} + \dfrac{3\sqrt{3}}{2}i, -\dfrac{3}{2} - \dfrac{3\sqrt{3}}{2}i$

Mid-Chapter Review: Chapter 13, pp. 835–836

Guided Solutions

1. $x - 7 = \pm\sqrt{5}$
  $x = 7 \pm \sqrt{5}$
  The solutions are $7 + \sqrt{5}$ and $7 - \sqrt{5}$.
2. $a = 1, b = -2, c = -1$
  $x = \dfrac{-(-2) \pm \sqrt{(-2)^2 - 4 \cdot 1 \cdot (-1)}}{2 \cdot 1}$
  $x = \dfrac{2 \pm \sqrt{8}}{2}$
  $x = \dfrac{2}{2} \pm \dfrac{2\sqrt{2}}{2}$
  The solutions are $1 + \sqrt{2}$ and $1 - \sqrt{2}$.

Mixed Review

1. $-2, 5$ **2.** ± 11 **3.** $-3 \pm \sqrt{19}$ **4.** $-\dfrac{1}{2} \pm \dfrac{\sqrt{13}}{2}$
5. $-1 \pm \sqrt{2}$ **6.** 5   **7.** $\pm\dfrac{\sqrt{11}}{2}$ **8.** $\frac{1}{2}, 1$ **9.** $0, \frac{7}{16}$
10. $1 \pm \sqrt{7}i$ **11.** $\pm 1, \pm 3$ **12.** $\pm 3, \pm i$ **13.** $-6, 5$
14. $\pm\dfrac{\sqrt{3}}{3}, \pm\dfrac{\sqrt{2}}{2}$ **15.** Two irrational
16. Two rational   **17.** Two imaginary   **18.** $v = 20\sqrt{\dfrac{F}{A}}$, or
$\dfrac{20\sqrt{FA}}{A}$ **19.** $D = d + \sqrt{d^2 + 2hd}$
20. South: 75 mph; north: 45 mph

Interactive Discovery, p. 838

1. (a) $(0, 0)$; **(b)** $x = 0$; **(c)** upward; **(d)** narrower
2. (a) $(0, 0)$; **(b)** $x = 0$; **(c)** upward; **(d)** wider
3. (a) $(0, 0)$; **(b)** $x = 0$; **(c)** upward; **(d)** wider
4. (a) $(0, 0)$; **(b)** $x = 0$; **(c)** downward; **(d)** neither narrower
nor wider **5. (a)** $(0, 0)$; **(b)** $x = 0$; **(c)** downward;
(d) narrower **6. (a)** $(0, 0)$; **(b)** $x = 0$; **(c)** downward;
(d) wider **7.** When $a > 1$, the graph of $y = ax^2$ is narrower
than the graph of $y = x^2$. When $0 < a < 1$, the graph of $y = ax^2$
is wider than the graph of $y = x^2$. **8.** When $a < -1$, the graph
of $y = ax^2$ is narrower than the graph of $y = x^2$ and the graph
opens downward. When $-1 < a < 0$, the graph of $y = ax^2$ is
wider than the graph of $y = x^2$ and the graph opens downward.

Interactive Discovery, p. 839

1. (a) $(3, 0)$; **(b)** $x = 3$; **(c)** same shape **2. (a)** $(-1, 0)$;
(b) $x = -1$; **(c)** same shape **3. (a)** $\left(\frac{3}{2}, 0\right)$; **(b)** $x = \frac{3}{2}$;
(c) same shape **4. (a)** $(-2, 0)$; **(b)** $x = -2$;
(c) same shape **5.** The graph of $g(x) = a(x - h)^2$ looks like
the graph of $f(x) = ax^2$, except that it is moved left or right.

Exercise Set 13.6, pp. 843–846

1. (h) **2.** (g) **3.** (f) **4.** (d) **5.** (b) **6.** (c)
7. (e) **8.** (a) **9. (a)** Positive; **(b)** $(3, 1)$; **(c)** $x = 3$;
(d) $[1, \infty)$ **10. (a)** Negative; **(b)** $(-1, 2)$; **(c)** $x = -1$;
(d) $(-\infty, 2]$ **11. (a)** Negative; **(b)** $(-2, -3)$;
(c) $x = -2$; **(d)** $(-\infty, -3]$ **12. (a)** Positive; **(b)** $(2, 0)$;
(c) $x = 2$; **(d)** $[0, \infty)$ **13. (a)** Positive; **(b)** $(-3, 0)$;
(c) $x = -3$; **(d)** $[0, \infty)$ **14. (a)** Negative; **(b)** $(1, -2)$;
(c) $x = 1$; **(d)** $(-\infty, -2]$

15.

17.

19.

21.

23.

25. Vertex: $(-1, 0)$;
axis of symmetry: $x = -1$

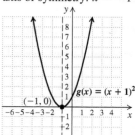

27. Vertex: $(2, 0)$;
axis of symmetry: $x = 2$

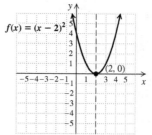

29. Vertex: $(-1, 0)$;
axis of symmetry: $x = -1$

31. Vertex: $(2, 0)$;
axis of symmetry: $x = 2$

33. Vertex: $(-1, 0)$;
axis of symmetry: $x = -1$

35. Vertex: $(4, 0)$;
axis of symmetry: $x = 4$

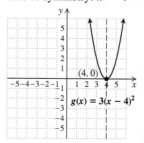

37. Vertex: $(4, 0)$;
axis of symmetry: $x = 4$

39. Vertex: $(1, 0)$;
axis of symmetry: $x = 1$

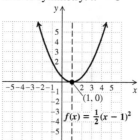

41. Vertex: $(-5, 0)$;
axis of symmetry: $x = -5$

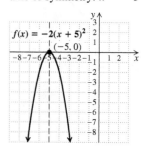

43. Vertex: $\left(\frac{1}{2}, 0\right)$; axis of symmetry: $x = \frac{1}{2}$

45. Minimum: 2; range: $[2, \infty)$

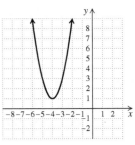

$f(x) = 2(x + 4)^2 + 1$

63. Vertex: axis of symmetry: maximum: 4; range:

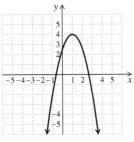

$g(x) = -\frac{3}{2}(x - 1)^2 + 4$

47. Maximum: -1; range: $(-\infty, -1]$

49. Minimum: 3; range: $[3, \infty)$

65. Vertex: $(8, 7)$; axis of symmetry: $x = 8$; minimum: 7

67. Vertex: $(-6, 11)$; axis of symmetry: $x = -6$; maximum: 11

69. Vertex: $\left(\frac{7}{2}, -\frac{29}{4}\right)$; axis of symmetry: $x = \frac{7}{2}$; minimum: $-\frac{29}{4}$

71. Vertex: $(-4.58, 65\pi)$; axis of symmetry: $x = -4.58$; minimum: 65π **73.** TW **75.** x-intercept: $(3, 0)$; y-intercept: $(0, -4)$ **76.** x-intercept: $\left(\frac{8}{3}, 0\right)$; y-intercept: $(0, 2)$

77. $(-5, 0), (-3, 0)$ **78.** $(-1, 0), \left(\frac{3}{2}, 0\right)$

79. $x^2 - 14x + 49 = (x - 7)^2$

80. $x^2 + 7x + \frac{49}{4} = \left(x + \frac{7}{2}\right)^2$ **81.** TW

83. $f(x) = \frac{3}{5}(x - 4)^2 + 1$ **85.** $f(x) = \frac{3}{5}(x - 3)^2 - 1$

87. $f(x) = \frac{3}{5}(x + 2)^2 - 5$ **89.** $f(x) = 2(x - 2)^2$

91. $g(x) = -2x^2 + 3$ **93.** The graph will move to the right.

95. The graph will be reflected across the x-axis.

97. $F(x) = 3(x - 5)^2 + 1$

51. Maximum: -3; range: $(-\infty, -3]$

53. Vertex: $(-1, -3)$; axis of symmetry: $x = -1$; minimum: -3; range: $[-3, \infty)$

$f(x) = (x + 1)^2 - 3$

99.

$y = f(x - 1)$

101.

$y = f(x) + 2$

103.

$y = f(x + 3) - 2$

55. Vertex: $(-3, 5)$; axis of symmetry: $x = -3$; maximum: 5; range: $(-\infty, 5]$

57. Vertex: $(2, 1)$; axis of symmetry: $x = 2$; minimum: 1; range: $[1, \infty)$

$f(x) = \frac{1}{2}(x - 2)^2 + 1$

59. Vertex: $(1, -3)$; axis of symmetry: $x = 1$; maximum: -3; range: $(-\infty, -3]$

61. Vertex: $(-4, 1)$; axis of symmetry: $x = -4$; minimum: 1; range: $[1, \infty)$

Visualizing for Success, p. 853

1. B   **2.** E   **3.** A   **4.** H   **5.** C   **6.** J   **7.** F
8. G   **9.** I   **10.** D

Exercise Set 13.7, pp. 854–855

1. True   **2.** False   **3.** True   **4.** True   **5.** False
6. True   **7.** False   **8.** True
9. $f(x) = (x - 4)^2 + (-14)$
11. $f(x) = \left(x - \left(-\frac{3}{2}\right)\right)^2 + \left(-\frac{29}{4}\right)$
13. $f(x) = 3(x - (-1))^2 + (-5)$
15. $f(x) = -(x - (-2))^2 + (-3)$
17. $f(x) = 2\left(x - \frac{5}{4}\right)^2 + \frac{55}{8}$
19. (a) Vertex: $(-2, 1)$;
axis of symmetry: $x = -2$;
(b)

21. (a) Vertex: $(-4, 4)$;
axis of symmetry: $x = -4$;
(b)

$f(x) = x^2 + 8x + 20$

23. (a) Vertex: $(4, -7)$;
axis of symmetry: $x = 4$;
(b)

$h(x) = 2x^2 - 16x + 25$

25. (a) Vertex: $(1, 6)$;
axis of symmetry: $x = 1$;
(b)

$f(x) = -x^2 + 2x + 5$

27. (a) Vertex: $\left(-\frac{3}{2}, -\frac{49}{4}\right)$;
axis of symmetry: $x = -\frac{3}{2}$;
(b)

$g(x) = x^2 + 3x - 10$

29. (a) Vertex: $\left(-\frac{7}{2}, -\frac{49}{4}\right)$;
axis of symmetry: $x = -\frac{7}{2}$;
(b)

$h(x) = x^2 + 7x$

31. (a) Vertex: $(-1, -4)$;
axis of symmetry: $x = -1$;
(b)

$f(x) = -2x^2 - 4x - 6$

33. (a) Vertex: $(3, 4)$; axis of
symmetry: $x = 3$; minimum: 4;
(b)

$g(x) = x^2 - 6x + 13$

35. (a) Vertex: $(2, -5)$;
axis of symmetry: $x = 2$;
minimum: -5;
(b)

$g(x) = 2x^2 - 8x + 3$

37. (a) Vertex: $(4, 2)$; axis of
symmetry: $x = 4$; minimum: 2;
(b)

$f(x) = 3x^2 - 24x + 50$

39. (a) Vertex: $\left(\frac{5}{6}, \frac{1}{12}\right)$;
axis of symmetry: $x = \frac{5}{6}$;
maximum: $\frac{1}{12}$;
(b)

$f(x) = -3x^2 + 5x - 2$

41. (a) Vertex: $\left(-4, -\frac{5}{3}\right)$;
axis of symmetry: $x = -4$;
minimum: $-\frac{5}{3}$;
(b)

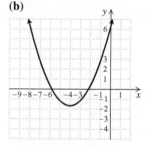

$h(x) = \frac{1}{2}x^2 + 4x + \frac{19}{3}$

43. $(-0.5, -6.25)$ **45.** $(0.1, 0.95)$ **47.** $(3.5, -4.25)$
49. $(3 - \sqrt{6}, 0)$, $(3 + \sqrt{6}, 0)$; $(0, 3)$
51. $(-1, 0)$, $(3, 0)$; $(0, 3)$ **53.** $(0, 0)$, $(9, 0)$; $(0, 0)$
55. $(2, 0)$; $(0, -4)$
57. $\left(-\frac{1}{2} - \frac{\sqrt{21}}{2}, 0\right)$, $\left(-\frac{1}{2} + \frac{\sqrt{21}}{2}, 0\right)$; $(0, -5)$
59. No x-intercept; $(0, 6)$ **61.** TW   **63.** $(1, 1, 1)$
64. $(-2, 5, 1)$ **65.** $(10, 5, 8)$ **66.** $(-3, 6, -5)$
67. $(2.4, -1.8, 1.5)$ **68.** $\left(\frac{1}{3}, \frac{1}{6}, \frac{1}{2}\right)$ **69.** TW
71. (a) Minimum: -6.95; (b) $(-1.06, 0)$, $(2.41, 0)$; $(0, -5.89)$

73. (a) Maximum: -0.45; (b) no x-intercept; $(0, -2.79)$
75. (a) $-2.4, 3.4$; (b) $-1.3, 2.3$
77. $f(x) = m\left(x - \dfrac{n}{2m}\right)^2 + \dfrac{4mp - n^2}{4m}$
79. $f(x) = \frac{5}{16}x^2 - \frac{15}{8}x - \frac{35}{16}$, or $f(x) = \frac{5}{16}(x - 3)^2 - 5$
81.

$f(x) = |x^2 - 1|$

83.

$f(x) = |2(x - 3)^2 - 5|$

Exercise Set 13.8, pp. 863–868

1. (e) **2.** (b) **3.** (c) **4.** (a) **5.** (d) **6.** (f)
7. July; 0 in.
9. $P(x) = -x^2 + 980x - 3000$; $237,100 at $x = 490$
11. 32 in. by 32 in. **13.** 450 ft^2; 15 ft by 30 ft (The house serves as a 30-ft side.) **15.** 3.5 in. **17.** 81; 9 and 9
19. -16; 4 and -4 **21.** 25; -5 and -5
23. $f(x) = mx + b$ **25.** $f(x) = ax^2 + bx + c, a < 0$
27. $f(x) = ax^2 + bx + c, a > 0$
29. $f(x) = ax^2 + bx + c, a > 0$
31. Neither quadratic nor linear **33.** $f(x) = 2x^2 + 3x - 1$
35. $f(x) = -\frac{1}{4}x^2 + 3x - 5$
37. (a) $A(s) = \frac{3}{16}s^2 - \frac{135}{4}s + 1750$; (b) about 531 accidents
39. $h(d) = -0.0068d^2 + 0.8571d$
41. (a) $D(x) = -0.0083x^2 + 0.8243x + 0.2122$; (b) 17.325 ft
43. (a) $t(x) = 18.125x^2 + 78.15x + 24,613$; 28,161 teachers
45. TW
47.

$f(x) = x^3 - 2$

48.

$g(x) = \dfrac{2}{x}$

49. $\dfrac{1}{a^2} + 7$ **50.** $a - 8$ **51.** $4a^2 + 20a + 27$
52. $\sqrt{12a - 19}$ **53.** TW **55.** 158 ft **57.** The radius of the circular portion of the window and the height of the rectangular portion should each be $\dfrac{24}{\pi + 4}$ ft. **59.** $15

Study Summary: Chapter 13, pp. 869–870

1. 1, 11 **2.** $9 \pm \sqrt{5}$ **3.** $-21, 1$ **4.** $-\frac{3}{2}, 3$ **5.** Two imaginary-number solutions **6.** $n = \pm\sqrt{a - 1}$ **7.** 36

8.

Axis of symmetry: $x = 3$

$f(x) = 2x^2 - 12x + 3$

Vertex: $(3, -15)$
Minimum: -15

9. 30 ft by 30 ft

Review Exercises: Chapter 13, pp. 871–873

1. False **2.** True **3.** True **4.** True **5.** True
6. False **7.** True **8.** True **9.** True **10.** False
11. (a) 2; (b) positive; (c) -3 **12.** $\pm\dfrac{\sqrt{2}}{3}$ **13.** $0, -\frac{3}{4}$
14. 3, 9 **15.** $2 \pm 2i$ **16.** 3, 5 **17.** $-\dfrac{9}{2} \pm \dfrac{\sqrt{85}}{2}$
18. $-0.372, 5.372$ **19.** $-\frac{1}{4}, 1$
20. $x^2 - 12x + 36 = (x - 6)^2$
21. $x^2 + \frac{3}{5}x + \frac{9}{100} = \left(x + \frac{3}{10}\right)^2$ **22.** $3 \pm 2\sqrt{2}$ **23.** 4%
24. 5.8 sec **25.** Two irrational real numbers
26. Two imaginary numbers **27.** $x^2 + 9 = 0$
28. $x^2 + 8x + 16 = 0$ **29.** About 153 mph **30.** 6 hr
31. $(-3, 0), (-2, 0), (2, 0), (3, 0)$ **32.** $-5, 3$
33. $\pm\sqrt{2}, \pm\sqrt{7}$
34.

$x = -2$
$(-2, 4)$
$f(x) = -3(x + 2)^2 + 4$
Maximum: 4

35. (a) Vertex: $(3, 5)$; axis of symmetry: $x = 3$;
(b)

$f(x) = 2x^2 - 12x + 23$

36. $(2, 0), (7, 0)$; $(0, 14)$ **37.** $p = \dfrac{9\pi^2}{N^2}$
38. $T = \dfrac{1 \pm \sqrt{1 + 24A}}{6}$ **39.** Neither quadratic nor linear
40. $f(x) = ax^2 + bx + c, a > 0$ **41.** $f(x) = mx + b$
42. 225 ft^2; 15 ft by 15 ft
43. (a) $M(x) = \dfrac{14,501}{1200}x^2 - \dfrac{2876}{15}x + 1$; (b) 48,841 restaurants
44. (a) $M(x) = 12.6207x^2 - 242.2557x + 706.6461$;
(b) 48,690 restaurants **45.** TW Completing the square was used to solve quadratic equations and to graph quadratic functions by rewriting the function in the form $f(x) = a(x - h)^2 + k$.
46. TW The model found in Exercise 44 predicts 151 fewer restaurants in 2020 than the model from Exercise 43. Since the

function in Exercise 44 considers all the data, we would expect it to be a better model.   **47.** TW The equation can have at most four solutions. If we substitute u for x^2, we see that $au^2 + bu + c = 0$ can have at most two solutions. Suppose $u = m$ or $u = n$. Then $x^2 = m$ or $x^2 = n$, and $x = \pm\sqrt{m}$ or $x = \pm\sqrt{n}$. When $m \neq n$, this gives four solutions, the maximum number possible.
48. $f(x) = \frac{7}{15}x^2 - \frac{14}{15}x - 7$ **49.** $h = 60, k = 60$
50. 18, 324

Test: Chapter 13, pp. 873–874

1. (a) [13.1] 0; (b) [11.6] negative; (c) [13.6] -1

2. [13.1] $\pm\dfrac{\sqrt{7}}{5}$ **3.** [13.2] 2, 9   **4.** [13.2] $-1 \pm \sqrt{2}i$

5. [13.2] $1 \pm \sqrt{6}$ **6.** [13.5] $-2, \frac{2}{3}$ **7.** [13.2] $-4.193, 1.193$
8. [13.2] $-\frac{3}{4}, \frac{7}{3}$ **9.** [13.1] $x^2 - 20x + 100 = (x - 10)^2$
10. [13.1] $x^2 + \frac{2}{7}x + \frac{1}{49} = \left(x + \frac{1}{7}\right)^2$ **11.** [13.1] $-5 \pm \sqrt{10}$
12. [13.3] Two imaginary numbers   **13.** [13.3] $x^2 - 11 = 0$
14. [13.4] 16 km/h   **15.** [13.4] 2 hr   **16.** [13.5] $(-4, 0), (4, 0)$
17. [13.6]

$f(x) = 4(x - 3)^2 + 5$
Minimum: 5

18. [13.7]
(a) $(-1, -8), x = -1$;
(b)

$f(x) = 2x^2 + 4x - 6$

19. [13.7] $(-2, 0), (3, 0); (0, -6)$

20. [13.4] $r = \sqrt{\dfrac{3V}{\pi} - R^2}$ **21.** [11.8] Quadratic; the data

approximate a parabola opening downward.
22. [13.8] Minimum \$129 per cabinet when 325 cabinets are built
23. [13.8] $p(x) = -\frac{165}{8}x^2 + \frac{605}{4}x + 35$
24. [13.8] $p(x) = -23.5417x^2 + 162.2583x + 57.6167$
25. [13.3] $\frac{1}{2}$ **26.** [13.3] $x^4 + x^2 - 12 = 0$; answers may vary
27. [13.5] $\pm\sqrt{\sqrt{5} + 2}, \pm\sqrt{\sqrt{5} - 2}i$

Chapter 14

Exercise Set 14.1, pp. 886–890

1. True   **2.** True   **3.** False   **4.** False   **5.** False
6. False   **7.** True   **8.** True
9. (a) $(f \circ g)(1) = 5$; (b) $(g \circ f)(1) = -1$;
(c) $(f \circ g)(x) = x^2 - 6x + 10$; (d) $(g \circ f)(x) = x^2 - 2$
11. (a) $(f \circ g)(1) = -24$; (b) $(g \circ f)(1) = 65$;
(c) $(f \circ g)(x) = 10x^2 - 34$; (d) $(g \circ f)(x) = 50x^2 + 20x - 5$
13. (a) $(f \circ g)(1) = 8$; (b) $(g \circ f)(1) = \frac{1}{64}$;
(c) $(f \circ g)(x) = \dfrac{1}{x^2} + 7$; (d) $(g \circ f)(x) = \dfrac{1}{(x + 7)^2}$

15. (a) $(f \circ g)(1) = 2$; (b) $(g \circ f)(1) = 4$;
(c) $(f \circ g)(x) = \sqrt{x + 3}$; (d) $(g \circ f)(x) = \sqrt{x} + 3$
17. (a) $(f \circ g)(1) = 2$; (b) $(g \circ f)(1) = \frac{1}{2}$;
(c) $(f \circ g)(x) = \sqrt{\dfrac{4}{x}}$; (d) $(g \circ f)(x) = \dfrac{1}{\sqrt{4x}}$
19. (a) $(f \circ g)(1) = 4$; (b) $(g \circ f)(1) = 2$;
(c) $(f \circ g)(x) = x + 3$; (d) $(g \circ f)(x) = \sqrt{x^2 + 3}$ **21.** 8
23. -4 **25.** Not defined   **27.** 4   **29.** Not defined
31. $f(x) = x^4; g(x) = 3x - 5$ **33.** $f(x) = \sqrt{x}$;
$g(x) = 2x + 7$ **35.** $f(x) = \dfrac{2}{x}; g(x) = x - 3$

37. $f(x) = \dfrac{1}{\sqrt{x}}; g(x) = 7x + 2$ **39.** $f(x) = \dfrac{1}{x} + x$;
$g(x) = \sqrt{3x}$ **41.** Yes   **43.** No   **45.** Yes   **47.** No
49. (a) Yes; (b) $f^{-1}(x) = x - 4$ **51.** (a) Yes;
(b) $f^{-1}(x) = \dfrac{x}{2}$ **53.** (a) Yes; (b) $g^{-1}(x) = \dfrac{x + 1}{3}$
55. (a) Yes; (b) $f^{-1}(x) = 2x - 2$ **57.** (a) No   **59.** (a) Yes;
(b) $h^{-1}(x) = -10 - x$ **61.** (a) Yes; (b) $f^{-1}(x) = \dfrac{1}{x}$

63. (a) No   **65.** (a) Yes; (b) $f^{-1}(x) = \dfrac{3x - 1}{2}$
67. (a) Yes; (b) $f^{-1}(x) = \sqrt[3]{x + 5}$ **69.** (a) Yes;
(b) $g^{-1}(x) = \sqrt[3]{x} + 2$ **71.** (a) Yes; (b) $f^{-1}(x) = x^2, x \geq 0$
73.

$f(x) = \frac{2}{3}x + 4$
$f^{-1}(x) = \frac{3}{2}x - 6$

75.

$f(x) = x^3 + 1$
$f^{-1}(x) = \sqrt[3]{x} - 1$

77.

$g(x) = \frac{1}{2}x^3$
$g^{-1}(x) = \sqrt[3]{2x}$

79.

$F^{-1}(x) = x^2,$
$x \leq 0$
$F(x) = -\sqrt{x}$

81.

$f^{-1}(x) = \sqrt{-x},$
$x \leq 0$
$f(x) = -x^2,$
$x \geq 0$

83. (1) $(f^{-1} \circ f)(x) = f^{-1}(f(x))$
$$= f^{-1}\left(\sqrt[3]{x-4}\right) = \left(\sqrt[3]{x-4}\right)^3 + 4$$
$$= x - 4 + 4 = x;$$
(2) $(f \circ f^{-1})(x) = f(f^{-1}(x))$
$$= f(x^3 + 4) = \sqrt[3]{x^3 + 4 - 4}$$
$$= \sqrt[3]{x^3} = x$$

85. (1) $(f^1 \circ f)(x) = f^{-1}(f(x)) = f^{-1}\left(\dfrac{1-x}{x}\right)$
$$= \dfrac{1}{\left(\dfrac{1-x}{x}\right) + 1}$$
$$= \dfrac{1}{\dfrac{1-x+x}{x}}$$
$$= x;$$
(2) $(f \circ f^{-1})(x) = f(f^{-1}(x)) = f\left(\dfrac{1}{x+1}\right)$
$$= \dfrac{1 - \left(\dfrac{1}{x+1}\right)}{\left(\dfrac{1}{x+1}\right)}$$
$$= \dfrac{\dfrac{x+1-1}{x+1}}{\dfrac{1}{x+1}} = x$$

87. No   **89.** Yes   **91.** (1) C; (2) D; (3) B; (4) A
93. (a) 40, 42, 46, 50; (b) yes; $f^{-1}(x) = x - 32$;
(c) 8, 10, 14, 18   **95.** ᵀᵂ   **97.** $\frac{1}{8}$ **98.** $\frac{1}{25}$
99. 32   **100.** Approximately 2.1577

101.

102.

103. ᵀᵂ   **105.**

107. $g(x) = \dfrac{x}{2} + 20$ **109.** ᵀᵂ

111. Suppose that $h(x) = (f \circ g)(x)$. First, note that for
$I(x) = x, (f \circ I)(x) = f(I(x)) = f(x)$ for any function f.
(**i**) $((g^{-1} \circ f^{-1}) \circ h)(x) = ((g^{-1} \circ f^{-1}) \circ (f \circ g))(x)$
$$= ((g^{-1} \circ (f^{-1} \circ f)) \circ g)(x)$$
$$= ((g^{-1} \circ I) \circ g)(x)$$
$$= (g^{-1} \circ g)(x) = x$$
(**ii**) $(h \circ (g^{-1} \circ f^{-1}))(x) = ((f \circ g) \circ (g^{-1} \circ f^{-1}))(x)$
$$= ((f \circ (g \circ g^{-1})) \circ f^{-1})(x)$$
$$= ((f \circ I) \circ f^{-1})(x)$$
$$= (f \circ f^{-1})(x) = x.$$
Therefore, $(g^{-1} \circ f^{-1})(x) = h^{-1}(x)$.
113. ᵀᵂ   **115.** The cost of mailing n copies of the book
117. 22 mm   **119.** 15 L/min

Interactive Discovery, p. 893

1. (a) Increases; (b) increases; (c) increases; (d) decreases;
(e) decreases   **2.** If $a > 1$, the graph increases; if $0 < a < 1$,
the graph decreases.   **3.** g   **4.** r

Exercise Set 14.2, pp. 897–900

1. True   **2.** True   **3.** True   **4.** False   **5.** False
6. True   **7.** $a > 1$ **9.** $0 < a < 1$
11.

13.

15.

17.

19.

21.

23.

$y = \left(\frac{1}{5}\right)^x$

25.

$y = \left(\frac{1}{10}\right)^x$

27.

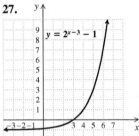

$y = 2^{x-3} - 1$

29.

$y = 1.7^x$

Yscl = 10

31.

$y = 0.15^x$

Yscl = 10

33.

$x = 3^y$

35.

$x = 2^{-y}$

37.

$x = 5^y$

39.

$x = \left(\frac{3}{2}\right)^y$

41.

$y = 3^x$

$x = 3^y$

43.

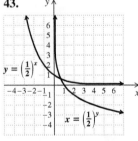

$y = \left(\frac{1}{2}\right)^x$

$x = \left(\frac{1}{2}\right)^y$

45. (d)

47. (f)

49. (c)

51. (a) About 0.68 billion tracks; about 1.052 billion tracks; about 2.519 billion tracks;

(b)

$M(t) = 0.353(1.244)^t$

Years since 2003

53. (a) 19.6%; 16.3%; 7.3%;

(b)

$P(t) = 21.4(0.914)^t$

Months after counseling

55. (a) About 44,079 whales; about 12,953 whales;

(b)

$P(t) = 150(0.960)^t$

Years since 1900

57. (a) About 11,874 whales; about 34,876 whales;

(b)

$P(t) = 5.5(1.08)^t$

Years since 1982

59. (a) About 539 fish; about 8843 fish;

(b)

$R(t) = 2(1.75)^t$

Years after introduction

61. TW   **63.** $3(x+4)(x-4)$ **64.** $(x-10)^2$
65. $(2x+3)(3x-4)$
66. $8(x^2-2y^2)(x^4+2x^2y^2+4y^4)$ **67.** $6(y-4)(y+10)$
68. $x(x-2)(5x^2-3)$ **69.** TW   **71.** $\pi^{2.4}$

73.

$y = 2^x + 2^{-x}$

75.

$y = |2^x - 2|$

77.

$y = |2^{x^2} - 1|$

79.

$y = 3^{-(x-1)}$
$x = 3^{-(y-1)}$

81. $N(t) = 0.464(1.778)^t$; about 464 million devices
83. TW   **85.**

Exercise Set 14.3, pp. 908–909

1. (g)   **2.** (d)   **3.** (a)   **4.** (h)   **5.** (b)   **6.** (c)
7. (e)   **8.** (f)   **9.** 3   **11.** 4   **13.** 4   **15.** -2
17. -1 **19.** 4   **21.** 1   **23.** 0   **25.** 5   **27.** -2
29. $\frac{1}{2}$ **31.** $\frac{3}{2}$ **33.** $\frac{2}{3}$ **35.** 7

37.

$y = \log_{10} x$

39.

$y = \log_3 x$

41.

$f(x) = \log_6 x$

43.

$f(x) = \log_{2.5} x$

45.

$f(x) = 3^x$
$f^{-1}(x) = \log_3 x$

47. 0.6021   **49.** 4.1271

51. -0.2782 **53.** 199.5262   **55.** 0.0011   **57.** 1.0028

59.

$y = \log(x+2)$

61.

$y = \log(2x) - 3$

63.

$y = \log(x^2)$

65. $10^x = 8$ **67.** $9^1 = 9$

69. $10^{-1} = 0.1$ **71.** $10^{0.845} = 7$ **73.** $c^8 = m$
75. $t^r = Q$ **77.** $e^{-1.3863} = 0.25$ **79.** $r^{-x} = T$
81. $2 = \log_{10} 100$ **83.** $-5 = \log_4 \frac{1}{1024}$ **85.** $\frac{3}{4} = \log_{16} 8$
87. $0.4771 = \log_{10} 3$ **89.** $m = \log_z 6$ **91.** $m = \log_p V$
93. $3 = \log_e 20.0855$ **95.** $-4 = \log_e 0.0183$ **97.** 9
99. 3   **101.** 2   **103.** 7   **105.** 81   **107.** $\frac{1}{9}$ **109.** 4
111. TW   **113.** a^{18} **114.** x^9 **115.** x^8 **116.** a^{12}
117. y^{15} **118.** n^{30} **119.** x^5 **120.** x^6 **121.** TW

123.

$y = \left(\frac{3}{2}\right)^x$
$y = \log_{3/2} x$

125.

$y = \log_3 |x+1|$

127. 6   **129.** $-25, 4$ **131.** -2 **133.** 0
135. Let $b = 0$, and suppose that $x = 1$ and $y = 2$. Then $0^1 = 0^2$, but $1 \neq 2$. Then let $b = 1$, and suppose that $x = 1$ and $y = 2$. Then $1^1 = 1^2$, but $1 \neq 2$.

Interactive Discovery, p. 910

1. (c)   **2.** (b)   **3.** (c)   **4.** (a)

Exercise Set 14.4, pp. 915–917

1. (e)   **2.** (f)   **3.** (a)   **4.** (b)   **5.** (c)   **6.** (d)
7. $\log_3 81 + \log_3 27$ **9.** $\log_4 64 + \log_4 16$
11. $\log_c r + \log_c s + \log_c t$ **13.** $\log_a (5 \cdot 14)$, or $\log_a 70$

15. $\log_c (t \cdot y)$ **17.** $8 \log_a r$ **19.** $\frac{1}{3} \log_2 y$
21. $-3 \log_b C$ **23.** $\log_2 25 - \log_2 13$
25. $\log_b m - \log_b n$ **27.** $\log_a \frac{17}{6}$ **29.** $\log_b \frac{36}{4}$, or $\log_b 9$

31. $\log_a \dfrac{x}{y}$ **33.** $\log_a x + \log_a y + \log_a z$

35. $3 \log_a x + 4 \log_a z$ **37.** $2 \log_a x - 2 \log_a y + \log_a z$
39. $4 \log_a x - 3 \log_a y - \log_a z$
41. $\log_b x + 2 \log_b y - \log_b w - 3 \log_b z$
43. $\frac{1}{2} (7 \log_a x - 5 \log_a y - 8 \log_a z)$
45. $\frac{1}{3} (6 \log_a x + 3 \log_a y - 2 - 7 \log_a z)$ **47.** $\log_a (x^8 z^3)$

49. $\log_a x$ **51.** $\log_a \dfrac{y^5}{x^{3/2}}$ **53.** $\log_a (x - 2)$ **55.** 1.953

57. -0.369 **59.** -1.161 **61.** $\frac{3}{2}$ **63.** Cannot be found
65. 7 **67.** m **69.** $\log_5 125 + \log_5 625 = 7$
71. $5 \cdot \log_2 16 = 20$ **73.** TW

75.

76.

77.

78.

79. $(-\infty, -7) \cup (-7, \infty)$, or
$\{x \mid x \text{ is a real number } and\ x \ne -7\}$
80. $(-\infty, -3) \cup (-3, 2) \cup (2, \infty)$, or
$\{x \mid x \text{ is a real number } and\ x \ne -3\ and\ x \ne 2\}$
81. $(-\infty, 10]$, or $\{x \mid x \le 10\}$ **82.** $(-\infty, \infty)$, or $\mathbb{R}$
83. TW **85.** $\log_a (x^6 - x^4 y^2 + x^2 y^4 - y^6)$
87. $\frac{1}{2} \log_a (1 - s) + \frac{1}{2} \log_a (1 + s)$ **89.** $\frac{10}{3}$ **91.** -2
93. $\frac{2}{5}$ **95.** True

Mid-Chapter Review: Chapter 14, pp. 917–918

Guided Solutions

1.
$$y = 2x - 5$$
$$x = 2y - 5$$
$$x + 5 = 2y$$
$$\dfrac{x + 5}{2} = y$$
$$f^{-1}(x) = \dfrac{x + 5}{2}$$

2. $x = 4^1$
$x = 4$

Mixed Review

1. $x^2 - 10x + 26$ **2.** $f(x) = \sqrt{x}; g(x) = 5x - 3$
3. $g^{-1}(x) = 6 - x$ **4.**

5. 2 **6.** -1 **7.** $\frac{1}{2}$ **8.** 1 **9.** 19 **10.** 0 **11.** $x^m = 3$
12. $2^{10} = 1024$ **13.** $t = \log_e x$ **14.** $\frac{2}{3} = \log_{64} 16$
15. $\log x - \frac{1}{2} \log y - \frac{3}{2} \log z$ **16.** $\log \dfrac{a}{b^2 c}$ **17.** 4
18. $\frac{1}{3}$ **19.** 100,000 **20.** 4

Interactive Discovery, p. 919

1. $2.25; \$2.370370; \$2.441406; \$2.613035; \$2.692597;$
$\$2.714567; \$2.718127$ **2.** (c)

Visualizing for Success, p. 924

1. J **2.** D **3.** B **4.** G **5.** H **6.** C **7.** F
8. I **9.** E **10.** A

Exercise Set 14.5, pp. 925–926

1. True **2.** True **3.** True **4.** False **5.** True
6. True **7.** True **8.** True **9.** True **10.** True
11. 1.6094 **13.** -5.0832 **15.** 96.7583 **17.** 15.0293
19. 0.0305 **21.** 0.8451 **23.** 13.0014 **25.** -0.4260
27. 4.9459 **29.** 2.5237 **31.** 6.6439 **33.** -2.3219
35. -2.3219 **37.** 3.5471
39. Domain: $\mathbb{R}$; range: $(0, \infty)$ **43.** Domain: $\mathbb{R}$; range:
41. Domain: $\mathbb{R}$; range: $(3, \infty)$ $(-2, \infty)$

45. Domain: $\mathbb{R}$; range: $(0, \infty)$ **47.** Domain: $\mathbb{R}$; range:

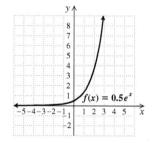

49. Domain: $\mathbb{R}$; range: $(0, \infty)$

51. Domain: $\mathbb{R}$; range: $(0, \infty)$

53. Domain: $\mathbb{R}$; range: $(-\infty, 0)$

55. Domain: $(0, \infty)$; range: $\mathbb{R}$

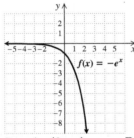

57. Domain: $(0, \infty)$; range: $\mathbb{R}$

59. Domain: $(0, \infty)$; range: $\mathbb{R}$

61. Domain: $(0, \infty)$; range: $\mathbb{R}$

63. Domain: $(-2, \infty)$; range: $\mathbb{R}$

65. Domain: $(1, \infty)$; range: $\mathbb{R}$

$f(x) = \log(x)/\log(5)$, or

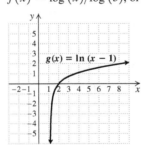

67.
$f(x) = \ln(x)/\ln(5)$

$y = \log(x)/\log(5)$, or
$y = \ln(x)/\ln(5)$

69. $f(x) = \log(x-5)/\log(2)$, or
$f(x) = \ln(x-5)/\ln(2)$

$y = \log(x-5)/\log(2)$, or
$y = \ln(x-5)/\ln(2)$

71. $f(x) = \log(x)/\log(3) + x$, or
$f(x) = \ln(x)/\ln(3) + x$

$y = \log(x)/\log(3) + x$, or
$y = \ln(x)/\ln(3) + x$

73. TW   **75.** $-4, 7$ **76.** $0, \frac{7}{5}$ **77.** $\frac{15}{17}$ **78.** $\frac{5}{6}$

79. $\frac{56}{9}$ **80.** 4   **81.** 16, 256   **82.** $\frac{1}{4}, 9$ **83.** TW

85. 2.452   **87.** 1.442   **89.** $\log M = \dfrac{\ln M}{\ln 10}$

91. 1086.5129   **93.** 4.9855

95. **(a)** Domain: $\{x \mid x > 0\}$, or $(0, \infty)$; range: $\{y \mid y < 0.5135\}$, or $(-\infty, 0.5135)$; **(b)** $[-1, 5, -10, 5]$; **(c)**

$y = 3.4 \ln x - 0.25e^x$

97. **(a)** Domain: $\{x \mid x > 0\}$, or $(0, \infty)$; range: $\{y \mid y > -0.2453\}$, or $(-0.2453, \infty)$; **(b)** $[-1, 5, -1, 10]$; **(c)**

$y = 2x^3 \ln x$

Exercise Set 14.6, pp. 931–933

1. (e)   **2.** (a)   **3.** (f)   **4.** (h)   **5.** (b)   **6.** (d)

7. (g)   **8.** (c)   **9.** 2   **11.** $\frac{5}{2}$ **13.** $\dfrac{\log 10}{\log 2} \approx 3.322$

15. -1 **17.** $\dfrac{\log 19}{\log 8} + 3 \approx 4.416$ **19.** $\ln 50 \approx 3.912$

21. $\dfrac{\ln 8}{-0.02} \approx -103.972$ **23.** $\dfrac{\log 5}{\log 3} - 1 \approx 0.465$

25. $\dfrac{\log 87}{\log 4.9} \approx 2.810$ **27.** $\dfrac{\ln\left(\frac{19}{2}\right)}{4} \approx 0.563$ **29.** $\dfrac{\ln 2}{5} \approx 0.139$

31. 81 **33.** $\frac{1}{8}$ **35.** $e^5 \approx 148.413$ **37.** $\dfrac{e^3}{4} \approx 5.021$

39. $10^{2.5} \approx 316.228$ **41.** $\dfrac{e^4 - 1}{2} \approx 26.799$ **43.** $e \approx 2.718$

45. $e^{-3} \approx 0.050$ **47.** -4 **49.** 10 **51.** No solution
53. 2 **55.** $\frac{83}{15}$ **57.** 1 **59.** 6 **61.** 1 **63.** 5
65. $\frac{17}{2}$ **67.** 4 **69.** $-6.480, 6.519$ **71.** $0.000112, 3.445$
73. 1 **75.** TW **77.** Length: 9.5 ft; width: 3.5 ft
78. 25 visits or more **79.** Golden Days; $23\frac{1}{3}$ lb; Snowy Friends:
$26\frac{2}{3}$ lb **80.** 1.5 cm **81.** $1\frac{1}{5}$ hr **82.** Approximately 2.1 ft
83. TW **85.** $\frac{12}{5}$ **87.** $\sqrt[3]{3}$ **89.** -1 **91.** $-3, -1$
93. $-625, 625$ **95.** $\frac{1}{2}, 5000$ **97.** $-3, -1$
99. $\frac{1}{100,000}, 100,000$ **101.** $-\frac{1}{3}$ **103.** 38

Exercise Set 14.7, pp. 944–951

1. (a) About 2006; (b) 2.8 yr **3.** (a) About 1979; (b) about
2025 **5.** (a) 6.4 yr; (b) 23.4 yr **7.** (a) About 56°F;
(b) about 75°F **9.** (a) About 2013; (b) 1.2 yr **11.** 4.9
13. 10^{-7} moles per liter **15.** 130 dB **17.** 7.6 W/m^2
19. Approximately 42.4 million messages per day
21. (a) $P(t) = P_0 e^{0.025t}$; (b) \$5126.58; \$5256.36; (c) 27.7 yr
23. (a) $P(t) = 310 e^{0.01t}$; (b) 329 million; (c) about 2022
25. 5.8 yr **27.** (a) About 2043; (b) about 2059;
(c)

$f(x) = 87 \ln \dfrac{x}{6.1}$

Years since 2000 (vertical axis); World population (in billions) (horizontal axis)

29. (a) 68%; (b) 54%; 40%
(c) **(d)** 6.9 months

$S(t) = 68 - 20 \log(t + 1), t \geq 0$

Score (in percents) (vertical axis); Months (horizontal axis)

31. (a) $k \approx 0.151$; $P(t) = 2000 e^{0.151t}$; (b) 2011
33. (a) $k \approx 0.280$; $P(t) = 8200 e^{-0.280t}$;

(b) \$215 per gigabit per second per mile; (c) 2029
35. About 1964 yr **37.** About 7.2 days **39.** (a) 13.9% per hour;
(b) 21.6 hr **41.** (a) $k \approx 0.123$; $V(t) = 9 e^{0.123t}$;
(b) \$360.4 million; (c) 5.6 yr; (d) 38.3 yr **43.** Yes **45.** No
47. (a) $n(t) = 7.8(1.3725)^t$; (b) 31.7%; (c) about 696,000,000
transistors **49.** (a) $f(x) = 2,097,152(0.8706)^x$; (b) 4 hr
51. TW **53.** $\sqrt{2}$ **54.** 5 **55.** $(4, -7)$
56. $\left(-\frac{7}{2}, -\frac{19}{2}\right)$ **57.** $-4 \pm \sqrt{17}$ **58.** $5 \pm 2\sqrt{10}$
59. **60.**

$y = x^2 - 5x - 6$ $g(x) = 2x^2 - 6x + 3$

61. TW **63.** \$14.5 million
65. (a) -26.9; (b) 1.58×10^{-17} W/m^2
67. Consider an exponential growth function $P(t) = P_0 e^{kt}$. At
time T, $P(T) = 2P_0$.
Solve for T:
$$2P_0 = P_0 e^{kT}$$
$$2 = e^{kT}$$
$$\ln 2 = kT$$
$$\frac{\ln 2}{k} = T.$$

69. (a) $f(x) = \dfrac{62.2245}{1 + 2.2661 e^{-0.4893x}}$; (b) 62.0%

Study Summary: Chapter 14, pp. 952–954

1. $(f \circ g)(x) = 19 - 6x^2$ **2.** Yes **3.** $f^{-1}(x) = \dfrac{x - 1}{5}$
4. **5.**

$f(x) = 2^x$ $f(x) = \log x$

6. $\log_5 625 = 4$ **7.** $\log_9 x + \log_9 y$ **8.** $\log_6 7 - \log_6 10$
9. $5 \log 7$ **10.** 0 **11.** 1 **12.** 12 **13.** 2 **14.** 1

15. 2.3219 **16.** $\frac{4}{3}$ **17.** $\dfrac{\ln 10}{0.1} \approx 23.0259$

18. (a) $P(t) = 15,000 e^{0.023t}$; (b) 30.1 yr **19.** 35 days

Review Exercises: Chapter 14, pp. 954–956

1. True **2.** True **3.** True **4.** False **5.** False
6. True **7.** False **8.** False **9.** True **10.** False
11. $(f \circ g)(x) = 4x^2 - 12x + 10$; $(g \circ f)(x) = 2x^2 - 1$

12. $f(x) = \sqrt{x}$; $g(x) = 3 - x$ **13.** No

14. $f^{-1}(x) = x + 8$ **15.** $g^{-1}(x) = \dfrac{2x - 1}{3}$

16. $f^{-1}(x) = \dfrac{\sqrt[3]{x}}{3}$

17.

18.

19.
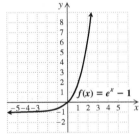

20. 2
21. -2
22. 7
23. $\frac{1}{2}$
24. $\log_{10} \frac{1}{100} = -2$
25. $\log_{25} 5 = \frac{1}{2}$
26. $16 = 4^x$
27. $1 = 8^0$

28. $4 \log_a x + 2 \log_a y + 3 \log_a z$
29. $5 \log_a x - (\log_a y + 2 \log_a z)$, or $5 \log_a x - \log_a y - 2 \log_a z$
30. $\frac{1}{4}(2 \log z - 3 \log x - \log y)$ **31.** $\log_a (7 \cdot 8)$, or $\log_a 56$
32. $\log_a \frac{72}{12}$, or $\log_a 6$ **33.** $\log \dfrac{a^{1/2}}{bc^2}$ **34.** $\log_a \sqrt[3]{\dfrac{x}{y^2}}$
35. 1   **36.** 0   **37.** 17   **38.** 6.93   **39.** -3.2698
40. 8.7601   **41.** 3.2698   **42.** 2.54995   **43.** -3.6602
44. 1.8751   **45.** 61.5177   **46.** -2.9957 **47.** 0.3753
48. 0.4307   **49.** 1.7097
50. Domain: $\mathbb{R}$; range: $(-1, \infty)$ **51.** Domain: $(0, \infty)$; range: $\mathbb{R}$

52. 5   **53.** -1 **54.** $\frac{1}{81}$ **55.** 2   **56.** $\frac{1}{1000}$
57. $e^{-2} \approx 0.1353$ **58.** $\frac{1}{2}\left(\dfrac{\log 19}{\log 4} + 5\right) \approx 3.5620$
59. $\dfrac{\log 12}{\log 2} \approx 3.5850$ **60.** $\dfrac{\ln 0.03}{-0.1} \approx 35.0656$
61. $e^{-3} \approx 0.0498$ **62.** $\frac{15}{2}$ **63.** 16   **64.** $\sqrt{43}$
65. (a) 82; (b) 66.8; (c) 35 months   **66.** (a) 2.3 yr; (b) 3.1 yr
67. (a) $k \approx 0.112$; $A(t) = 1.2e^{0.112t}$; (b) \$2.9 billion; (c) 2018; (d) 6.2 yr   **68.** (a) $M(t) = 3253e^{-0.137t}$; (b) 1247 spam messages per consumer; (c) 2030
69. (a) $f(x) = 33.8684(0.8196)^x$; (b) about 1700 cases; (c) 19.9%   **70.** 11.553% per year   **71.** 16.5 yr

72. 3463 yr   **73.** 5.1   **74.** About 80,922 yr, or with rounding of k, about 80,792 yr   **75.** About 114 dB
76. ᵀᵂ Negative numbers do not have logarithms because logarithm bases are positive, and there is no exponent to which a positive number can be raised to yield a negative number.
77. ᵀᵂ Taking the logarithm on each side of an equation produces an equivalent equation because the logarithm function is one-to-one. If two quantities are equal, their logarithms must be equal, and if the logarithms of two quantities are equal, the quantities must be the same.
78. e^{e^3} **79.** $-3, -1$ **80.** $\left(\frac{8}{3}, -\frac{2}{3}\right)$ **81.** 13.03%

Test: Chapter 14, pp. 956–957

1. [14.1] $(f \circ g)(x) = 2 + 6x + 4x^2$; $(g \circ f)(x) = 2x^2 + 2x + 1$
2. [14.1] $f(x) = \dfrac{1}{x}$; $g(x) = 2x^2 + 1$ **3.** [14.1] No
4. [14.1] $f^{-1}(x) = \dfrac{x - 4}{3}$ **5.** [14.1] $g^{-1}(x) = \sqrt[3]{x} - 1$

6. [14.2]

7. [14.3]

8. [14.3] 3   **9.** [14.3] $\frac{1}{2}$ **10.** [14.3] 18   **11.** [14.4] 1
12. [14.4] 0   **13.** [14.4] 19   **14.** [14.3] $\log_5 \frac{1}{625} = -4$
15. [14.3] $2^m = \frac{1}{2}$ **16.** [14.4] $3 \log a + \frac{1}{2} \log b - 2 \log c$
17. [14.4] $\log_a \left(z^2 \sqrt[3]{x}\right)$ **18.** [14.4] 1.146   **19.** [14.4] 0.477
20. [14.4] 1.204   **21.** [14.3] 1.0899   **22.** [14.3] 0.1585
23. [14.5] -0.9163 **24.** [14.5] 121.5104   **25.** [14.5] 2.4022
26. [14.5] Domain: $\mathbb{R}$; range: $(3, \infty)$
27. [14.5] Domain: $(4, \infty)$; range: $\mathbb{R}$

28. [14.6] -5 **29.** [14.6] 2   **30.** [14.6] 10,000
31. [14.6] $-\frac{1}{3}\left(\dfrac{\log 87}{\log 5} - 4\right) \approx 0.4084$
32. [14.6] $\dfrac{\log 1.2}{\log 7} \approx 0.0937$ **33.** [14.6] $e^3 \approx 20.0855$
34. [14.6] 4   **35.** [14.7] (a) 2.25 ft/sec; (b) 2,901,000
36. [14.7] (a) $P(t) = 8.2e^{0.00052t}$, where t is the number of years after 2009 and $P(t)$ is in millions; (b) 8.25 million; 8.38 million; (c) 2188; (d) 1333 yr   **37.** [14.7] (a) $k \approx 0.054$; $C(t) = 21,855e^{0.054t}$; (b) \$46,545; (c) 2016   **38.** [14.7] (a) $f(x) = 458.8188(2.6582)^x$, where $f(x)$ is in thousands; (b) about 22,908,000 units

39. [14.7] 4.6%   **40.** [14.7] About 4684 yr   **41.** [14.7] 10^2 W/m^2
42. [14.7] 7.0   **43.** [14.6] $-309, 316$ **44.** [14.4] 2

Cumulative Review: Chapters 4, 8–14, pp. 958–960

1. 2   **2.** $\dfrac{y^{12}}{16x^8}$ **3.** $\dfrac{20x^6z^2}{y}$ **4.** $-\dfrac{y^4}{3z^5}$ **5.** 6.3×10^{-15}

6. 25   **7.** 8   **8.** $(3, -1)$ **9.** $(1, -2, 0)$ **10.** $-7, 10$

11. $\dfrac{9}{2}$ **12.** $\dfrac{3}{4}$ **13.** $\dfrac{1}{2}$ **14.** $\pm 4i$ **15.** $\pm 2, \pm 3$ **16.** 9

17. $\dfrac{\log 7}{5 \log 3} \approx 0.3542$ **18.** $\dfrac{8e}{e-1} \approx 12.6558$

19. $(-\infty, -5) \cup (1, \infty)$, or $\{x | x < -5 \text{ or } x > 1\}$
20. $-3 \pm 2\sqrt{5}$ **21.** $\{x | x \le -2 \text{ or } x \ge 5\}$, or

$(-\infty, -2] \cup [5, \infty)$ **22.** $a = \dfrac{Db}{b-D}$

23. $x = \dfrac{-v \pm \sqrt{v^2 + 4ad}}{2a}$

24. $\{x | x \text{ is a real number } and \ x \ne -\frac{1}{3} \text{ and } x \ne 2\}$, or
$\left(-\infty, -\frac{1}{3}\right) \cup \left(-\frac{1}{3}, 2\right) \cup (2, \infty)$

25. $3p^2q^3 + 11pq - 2p^2 + p + 9$ **26.** $9x^4 - 6x^2z^3 + z^6$

27. $\dfrac{1}{x-4}$ **28.** $\dfrac{a+2}{6}$ **29.** $\dfrac{7x+4}{(x+6)(x-6)}$ **30.** $2y^2 \sqrt[3]{y}$

31. $\sqrt[10]{(x+5)^7}$ **32.** $15 - 4\sqrt{3}i$ **33.** $x^3 - 5x^2 + 1$
34. $x(y + 2z - w)$ **35.** $2(3x - 2y)(x + 2y)$
36. $(x - 4)(x^3 + 7)$ **37.** $2(m + 3n)^2$

38. $(x - 2y)(x + 2y)(x^2 + 4y^2)$ **39.** $\dfrac{6 + \sqrt{y} - y}{4 - y}$

40. $f^{-1}(x) = \dfrac{x-9}{-2}$, or $f^{-1}(x) = \dfrac{9-x}{2}$
41. $f(x) = -10x - 8$ **42.** $y = \frac{1}{2}x + 5$
43.

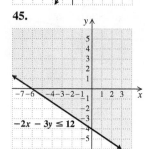

44.

$y = \log_3 x$

45.

$-2x - 3y \le 12$

46.

$x = -3$

$(-3, 1)$

$f(x) = 2x^2 + 12x + 19$
Minimum: 1

47. Domain: $\mathbb{R}$; range: $(0, \infty)$

$f(x) = 2e^x$

48. $\log\left(\dfrac{x^3}{y^{1/2}z^2}\right)$

49. (c)
50. (b)
51. (a)
52. (d)
53. 13.5 million acre-feet

54. (a) $k \approx 0.076$; $D(t) = 15e^{0.076t}$; (b) 79.8 million cubic meters
per day; (c) 2015   **55.** $5\frac{5}{11}$ min   **56.** Thick and Tasty: 6 oz;
Light and Lean: 9 oz   **57.** $2\frac{7}{9}$ km/h   **58.** Linear
59. $1/min   **60.** $f(x) = x + 3$ **61.** $13
62. $m = 1$ signifies the cost per minute; $b = 3$ signifies the startup
cost of each massage   **63.** $m(x) = 1.8937(1.0596)^x$
64. $25.63   **65.** All real numbers except 1 and -2
66. $\frac{1}{3}, \frac{10,000}{3}$ **67.** 35 mph

Chapter 15

Exercise Set 15.1, pp. 969–971

1. (f)   **2.** (e)   **3.** (g)   **4.** (h)   **5.** (c)
6. (b)   **7.** (d)   **8.** (a)
9.

$(0, 0)$

$y = -x^2$

11.

$y = -x^2 + 4x - 5$

$(2, -1)$

13.

$(-2, 2)$

$x = y^2 - 4y + 2$

15.

$(3, 0)$

$x = y^2 + 3$

17.

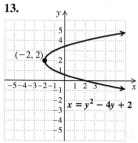

$x = 2y^2$

$(0, 0)$

19.

$x = -y^2 - 4y$

$(4, -2)$

21.
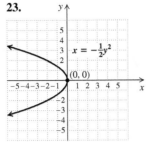
$y = x^2 - 2x + 1$

23.
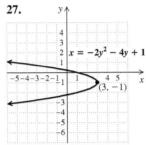
$x = -\frac{1}{2}y^2$

53. $(4, -1); 2$

$x^2 + y^2 - 8x + 2y + 13 = 0$

55. $(0, -5); 10$

$x^2 + y^2 + 10y - 75 = 0$

25.
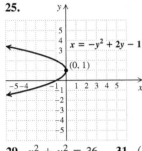
$x = -y^2 + 2y - 1$

27.

$x = -2y^2 - 4y + 1$

57. $\left(-\frac{7}{2}, \frac{3}{2}\right); \sqrt{\frac{98}{4}}, \text{ or } \frac{7\sqrt{2}}{2}$

$x^2 + y^2 + 7x - 3y - 10 = 0$

59. $(0, 0); \frac{1}{6}$
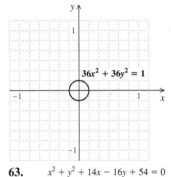
$36x^2 + 36y^2 = 1$

29. $x^2 + y^2 = 36$ **31.** $(x - 7)^2 + (y - 3)^2 = 5$
33. $(x + 4)^2 + (y - 3)^2 = 48$
35. $(x + 7)^2 + (y + 2)^2 = 50$
37. $x^2 + y^2 = 25$ **39.** $(x + 4)^2 + (y - 1)^2 = 20$
41. $(0, 0); 8$

43. $(-1, -3); 6$

$x^2 + y^2 = 64$

$(x + 1)^2 + (y + 3)^2 = 36$

61. $x^2 + y^2 - 16 = 0$

63. $x^2 + y^2 + 14x - 16y + 54 = 0$
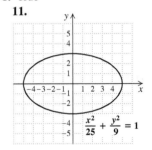

65. TW   **67.** ± 4 **68.** $\pm a$ **69.** $-4, 6$ **70.** $-5 \pm 2\sqrt{3}$
71. $-3 \pm 3\sqrt{3}$ **72.** $2 \pm \frac{4\sqrt{2}}{3}$ **73.** TW

45. $(4, -3); \sqrt{10}$

47. $(0, 0); \sqrt{10}$

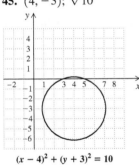
$(x - 4)^2 + (y + 3)^2 = 10$

$x^2 + y^2 = 10$

75. $(x - 3)^2 + (y + 5)^2 = 9$ **77.** $(x - 3)^2 + y^2 = 25$
79. $(0, 4)$ **81.** $\frac{17}{4}\pi$ m², or approximately 13.4 m²
83. 7169 mm   **85. (a)** $(0, -3)$; **(b)** 5 ft
87. $x^2 + (y - 30.6)^2 = 590.49$

49. $(5, 0); \frac{1}{2}$

51. $(-4, 3); \sqrt{40}, \text{ or } 2\sqrt{10}$

$(x - 5)^2 + y^2 = \frac{1}{4}$

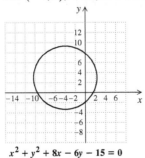
$x^2 + y^2 + 8x - 6y - 15 = 0$

Exercise Set 15.2, pp. 976–979

1. True   **2.** False   **3.** False   **4.** False
5. True   **6.** True   **7.** True   **8.** True
9.

$\frac{x^2}{1} + \frac{y^2}{9} = 1$

11.

$\frac{x^2}{25} + \frac{y^2}{9} = 1$

13.

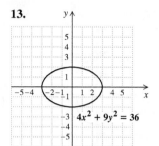

$4x^2 + 9y^2 = 36$

15.

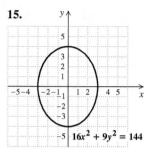

$16x^2 + 9y^2 = 144$

17.

$2x^2 + 3y^2 = 6$

19.

$5x^2 + 5y^2 = 125$

21.

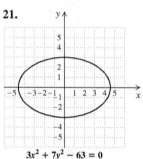

$3x^2 + 7y^2 - 63 = 0$

23.

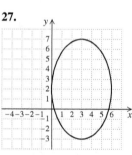

$16x^2 = 16 - y^2$

$\dfrac{(x-3)^2}{9} + \dfrac{(y-2)^2}{25} = 1$

25.

$16x^2 + 25y^2 = 1$

27.

29.

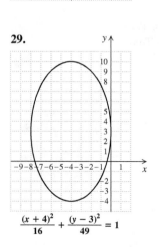

$\dfrac{(x+4)^2}{16} + \dfrac{(y-3)^2}{49} = 1$

31.

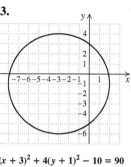

$12(x-1)^2 + 3(y+4)^2 = 48$

33.

$4(x+3)^2 + 4(y+1)^2 - 10 = 90$

47. $\dfrac{(x-2)^2}{16} + \dfrac{(y+1)^2}{9} = 1$

51. (a) Let $F_1 = (-c, 0)$ and $F_2 = (c, 0)$. Then the sum of the distances from the foci to P is $2a$. By the distance formula,
$$\sqrt{(x+c)^2 + y^2} + \sqrt{(x-c)^2 + y^2} = 2a, \text{ or}$$
$$\sqrt{(x+c)^2 + y^2} = 2a - \sqrt{(x-c)^2 + y^2}.$$
Squaring, we get
$$(x+c)^2 + y^2 = 4a^2 - 4a\sqrt{(x-c)^2 + y^2} + (x-c)^2 + y^2,$$
or
$$x^2 + 2cx + c^2 + y^2 = 4a^2 - 4a\sqrt{(x-c)^2 + y^2}$$
$$+ x^2 - 2cx + c^2 + y^2.$$
Thus
$$-4a^2 + 4cx = -4a\sqrt{(x-c)^2 + y^2}$$
$$a^2 - cx = a\sqrt{(x-c)^2 + y^2}.$$
Squaring again, we get
$$a^4 - 2a^2cx + c^2x^2 = a^2(x^2 - 2cx + c^2 + y^2)$$
$$a^4 - 2a^2cx + c^2x^2 = a^2x^2 - 2a^2cx + a^2c^2 + a^2y^2,$$
or
$$x^2(a^2 - c^2) + a^2y^2 = a^2(a^2 - c^2)$$
$$\frac{x^2}{a^2} + \frac{y^2}{a^2 - c^2} = 1.$$

(b) When P is at $(0, b)$, it follows that $b^2 = a^2 - c^2$. Substituting, we have
$$\frac{x^2}{a^2} + \frac{y^2}{b^2} = 1.$$

53. 5.66 ft

55.

$\dfrac{(x-2)^2}{16} + \dfrac{(y+1)^2}{4} = 1$

35. TW

37. $\dfrac{5}{2} \pm \dfrac{\sqrt{13}}{2}$

38. 3

39. $-\dfrac{3}{4}, 2$

40. $\dfrac{5}{2}$

41. $-\sqrt{11}, \sqrt{11}$

42. $-10, 6$

43. TW

45. $\dfrac{x^2}{81} + \dfrac{y^2}{121} = 1$

49. $\dfrac{x^2}{9} + \dfrac{y^2}{25} = 1$

57. 152.1 million km

Visualizing for Success, p. 987

1. C **2.** A **3.** F **4.** B **5.** J **6.** D **7.** H
8. I **9.** G **10.** E

Exercise Set 15.3, pp. 988–989

1. (d) **2.** (f) **3.** (h) **4.** (a) **5.** (g) **6.** (b)
7. (c) **8.** (e)

9.

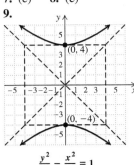

$$\frac{y^2}{16} - \frac{x^2}{16} = 1$$

11.

$$\frac{x^2}{4} - \frac{y^2}{25} = 1$$

13.

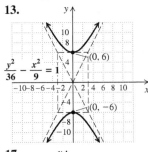

$$\frac{y^2}{36} - \frac{x^2}{9} = 1$$

15.

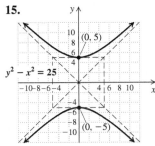

$$y^2 - x^2 = 25$$

17.

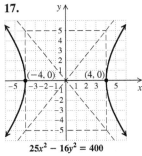

$$25x^2 - 16y^2 = 400$$

19.

$$xy = -6$$

21.

$$xy = 4$$

23.

$$xy = -2$$

25.

$$xy = 1$$

27. Circle
29. Ellipse
31. Hyperbola
33. Circle
35. Parabola
37. Hyperbola
39. Parabola
41. Hyperbola
43. Circle
45. Ellipse

47. TW   **49.** $(-3, 6)$ **50.** $\left(\frac{1}{2}, -\frac{3}{2}\right)$ **51.** $-2, 2$

52. $-4, \frac{2}{3}$ **53.** $\frac{3}{2} \pm \frac{\sqrt{13}}{2}$ **54.** $\pm 1, \pm 5$ **55.** TW

57. $\frac{y^2}{36} - \frac{x^2}{4} = 1$ **59.** C: $(5, 2)$; V: $(-1, 2)$, $(11, 2)$;
asymptotes: $y - 2 = \frac{5}{6}(x - 5)$, $y - 2 = -\frac{5}{6}(x - 5)$

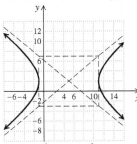

$$\frac{(x - 5)^2}{36} - \frac{(y - 2)^2}{25} = 1$$

61. $\frac{(y + 3)^2}{4} - \frac{(x - 4)^2}{16} = 1$; C: $(4, -3)$; V: $(4, -5)$, $(4, -1)$;
asymptotes: $y + 3 = \frac{1}{2}(x - 4)$, $y + 3 = -\frac{1}{2}(x - 4)$

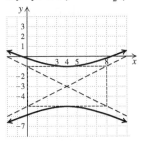

$$8(y + 3)^2 - 2(x - 4)^2 = 32$$

63. $\frac{(x + 3)^2}{1} - \frac{(y - 2)^2}{4} = 1$; C: $(-3, 2)$; V: $(-4, 2)$, $(-2, 2)$;
asymptotes: $y - 2 = 2(x + 3)$, $y - 2 = -2(x + 3)$

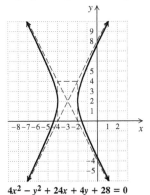

$$4x^2 - y^2 + 24x + 4y + 28 = 0$$

Mid-Chapter Review: Chapter 15, pp. 990–991

Guided Solutions

1.
$$(x^2 - 4x) + (y^2 + 2y) = 6$$
$$(x^2 - 4x + 4) + (y^2 + 2y + 1) = 6 + 4 + 1$$
$$(x - 2)^2 + (y + 1)^2 = 11$$
The center of the circle is $(2, -1)$. The radius is $\sqrt{11}$.

2. 1. Is there both an x^2-term and a y^2-term? Yes
   2. Do both the x^2-term and the y^2-term have the same sign? No
   3. The graph of the equation is a hyperbola.

Mixed Review

1. $(4, 1)$; $x = 4$ **2.** $(2, -1)$; $y = -1$ **3.** $(3, 2)$
4. $(-3, -5)$ **5.** $(-12, 0), (12, 0), (0, -9), (0, 9)$
6. $(-3, 0), (3, 0)$ **7.** $(0, -1), (0, 1)$ **8.** $y = \frac{3}{2}x, y = -\frac{3}{2}x$
9. Circle

$x^2 + y^2 = 36$

10. Parabola

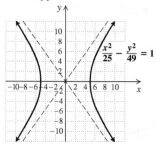
$y = x^2 - 5$

11. Ellipse

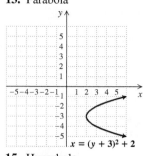
$\frac{x^2}{25} + \frac{y^2}{49} = 1$

12. Hyperbola

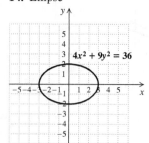
$\frac{x^2}{25} - \frac{y^2}{49} = 1$

13. Parabola

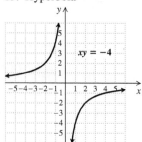
$x = (y + 3)^2 + 2$

14. Ellipse

$4x^2 + 9y^2 = 36$

15. Hyperbola

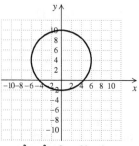
$xy = -4$

16. Circle

$(x + 2)^2 + (y - 3)^2 = 1$

17. Circle

$x^2 + y^2 - 8y - 20 = 0$

18. Parabola

$x = y^2 + 2y$

19. Hyperbola

$16y^2 - x^2 = 16$

20. Hyperbola

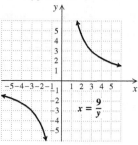
$x = \dfrac{9}{y}$

Exercise Set 15.4, pp. 997–999

1. True   **2.** True   **3.** False   **4.** False   **5.** True
6. True   **7.** $(-4, -3), (3, 4)$ **9.** $(0, 2), (3, 0)$ **11.** $(-2, 1)$
13. $\left(\dfrac{5 + \sqrt{70}}{3}, \dfrac{-1 + \sqrt{70}}{3} \right), \left(\dfrac{5 - \sqrt{70}}{3}, \dfrac{-1 - \sqrt{70}}{3} \right)$
15. $\left(4, \frac{3}{2}\right), (3, 2)$ **17.** $\left(\frac{7}{3}, \frac{1}{3}\right), (1, -1)$ **19.** $\left(\frac{11}{4}, -\frac{5}{4}\right), (1, 4)$
21. $(2, 4), (4, 2)$ **23.** $(3, -5), (-1, 3)$ **25.** $(-5, -8), (8, 5)$
27. $(0, 0), (1, 1), \left(-\dfrac{1}{2} + \dfrac{\sqrt{3}}{2}i, -\dfrac{1}{2} - \dfrac{\sqrt{3}}{2}i \right),$
$\left(-\dfrac{1}{2} - \dfrac{\sqrt{3}}{2}i, -\dfrac{1}{2} + \dfrac{\sqrt{3}}{2}i \right)$ **29.** $(-3, 0), (3, 0)$
31. $(-4, -3), (-3, -4), (3, 4), (4, 3)$
33. $\left(\dfrac{16}{3}, \dfrac{5\sqrt{7}}{3}i \right), \left(\dfrac{16}{3}, -\dfrac{5\sqrt{7}}{3}i \right), \left(-\dfrac{16}{3}, \dfrac{5\sqrt{7}}{3}i \right),$
$\left(-\dfrac{16}{3}, -\dfrac{5\sqrt{7}}{3}i \right)$ **35.** $(-3, -\sqrt{5}), (-3, \sqrt{5}), (3, -\sqrt{5}),$
$(3, \sqrt{5})$ **37.** $(4, 2), (-4, -2), (2, 4), (-2, -4)$
39. $(4, 1), (-4, -1), (2, 2), (-2, -2)$ **41.** $(2, 1), (-2, -1)$
43. $\left(2, -\frac{4}{5}\right), \left(-2, -\frac{4}{5}\right), (5, 2), (-5, 2)$
45. $\left(-\sqrt{2}, \sqrt{2}\right), \left(\sqrt{2}, -\sqrt{2}\right)$ **47.** Length: 8 cm; width: 6 cm
49. Length: 2 yd; width: 1 yd   **51.** Length: 12 ft; width: 5 ft
53. 6 and 15; -6 and -15 **55.** 24 ft, 16 ft
57. Length: $\sqrt{3}$ m; width: 1 m   **59.** TW   **61.** -9 **62.** -27
63. -1 **64.** $\frac{1}{5}$ **65.** 77   **66.** $\frac{21}{2}$ **67.** TW
69. $(x + 2)^2 + (y - 1)^2 = 4$
71. $(-2, 3), (2, -3), (-3, 2), (3, -2)$ **73.** Length: 55 ft;
width: 45 ft   **75.** 10 in. by 7 in. by 5 in.   **77.** Length: 63.6 in.;
height: 35.8 in.   **79.** $(-1.50, -1.17); (3.50, 0.50)$

Study Summary: Chapter 15, pp. 1000–1001

1.

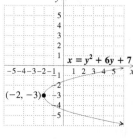
$x = y^2 + 6y + 7$
$(-2, -3)$

2. Center: $(3, 0)$; radius 2

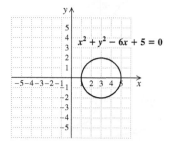
$x^2 + y^2 - 6x + 5 = 0$

3.

$$\frac{x^2}{9} + y^2 = 1$$

4.

$$\frac{y^2}{16} - \frac{x^2}{4} = 1$$

5. $(-5, -4), (4, 5)$

Review Exercises: Chapter 15, pp. 1002–1003

1. True **2.** False **3.** False **4.** True **5.** True
6. True **7.** False **8.** True **9.** $(-3, 2), 4$
10. $(5, 0), \sqrt{11}$ **11.** $(3, 1), 3$ **12.** $(-4, 3), 3\sqrt{5}$
13. $(x + 4)^2 + (y - 3)^2 = 16$ **14.** $(x - 7)^2 + (y + 2)^2 = 20$
15. Circle **16.** Ellipse

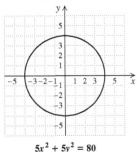

$$5x^2 + 5y^2 = 80$$

17. Parabola

18. Hyperbola

19. Hyperbola

$xy = 9$

20. Parabola

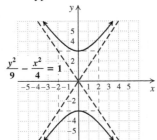

$x = y^2 + 2y - 2$

21. Ellipse

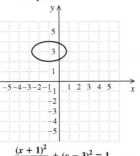

$$\frac{(x + 1)^2}{3} + (y - 3)^2 = 1$$

22. Circle

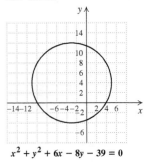

$$x^2 + y^2 + 6x - 8y - 39 = 0$$

23. $(5, -2)$ **24.** $(2, 2), \left(\frac{32}{9}, -\frac{10}{9}\right)$ **25.** $(0, -5), (2, -1)$
26. $(4, i), (4, -i), (-4, i), (-4, -i)$
27. $(2, 1), \left(\sqrt{3}, 0\right), (-2, 1), \left(-\sqrt{3}, 0\right)$
28. $(3, -3), \left(-\frac{3}{5}, \frac{21}{5}\right)$ **29.** $(6, 8), (6, -8), (-6, 8), (-6, -8)$
30. $(2, 2), (-2, -2), \left(2\sqrt{2}, \sqrt{2}\right), \left(-2\sqrt{2}, -\sqrt{2}\right)$
31. Length: 12 m; width: 7 m **32.** Length: 12 in.; width: 9 in.
33. 32 cm, 20 cm **34.** 3 ft, 11 ft **35.** ᵀᵂ The graph of a
parabola has one branch whereas the graph of a hyperbola has two
branches. A hyperbola has asymptotes, but a parabola does not.
36. ᵀᵂ Function notation rarely appears in this chapter
because many of the relations are not functions. Function
notation could be used for vertical parabolas and for
hyperbolas that have the axes as asymptotes.
37. $\left(-5, -4\sqrt{2}\right), \left(-5, 4\sqrt{2}\right), \left(3, -2\sqrt{2}\right), \left(3, 2\sqrt{2}\right)$
38. $(0, 6), (0, -6)$ **39.** $(x - 2)^2 + (y + 1)^2 = 25$
40. $\frac{x^2}{81} + \frac{y^2}{25} = 1$ **41.** $\left(\frac{9}{4}, 0\right)$

Test: Chapter 15, p. 1003

1. [15.1] $(x - 3)^2 + (y + 4)^2 = 12$
2. [15.1] $(4, -1), \sqrt{5}$ **3.** [15.1] $(-2, 3), 3$
4. [15.1], [15.3] Parabola **5.** [15.1], [15.3] Circle

$y = x^2 - 4x - 1$

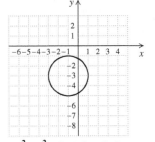

$$x^2 + y^2 + 2x + 6y + 6 = 0$$

6. [15.3] Hyperbola **7.** [15.2], [15.3] Ellipse

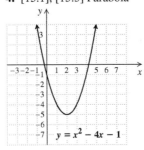

$$\frac{x^2}{16} - \frac{y^2}{9} = 1$$

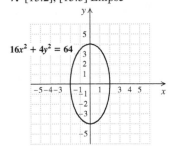

$16x^2 + 4y^2 = 64$

8. [15.3] Hyperbola

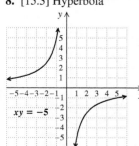

$xy = -5$

9. [15.1], [15.3] Parabola

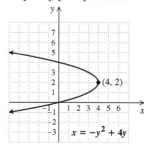

(4, 2)

$x = -y^2 + 4y$

10. [15.4] $(0, 6), \left(\frac{144}{25}, \frac{42}{25}\right)$ **11.** [15.4] $(-4, 13), (2, 1)$

12. [15.4] $(2, 1), (-2, -1), (i, -2i), (-i, 2i)$

13. [15.4] $\left(\sqrt{6}, 2\right), \left(\sqrt{6}, -2\right), \left(-\sqrt{6}, 2\right), \left(-\sqrt{6}, -2\right)$

14. [15.4] 2 in. by 11 in.   **15.** [15.4] $\sqrt{5}$ m, $\sqrt{3}$ m

16. [15.4] Length: 32 ft; width: 24 ft   **17.** [15.4] $1200, 6%

18. [15.2] $\dfrac{(x-6)^2}{25} + \dfrac{(y-3)^2}{9} = 1$ **19.** [15.1] $\left(0, -\frac{31}{4}\right)$

20. [15.4] 9   **21.** [15.2] $\dfrac{x^2}{16} + \dfrac{y^2}{49} = 1$

Chapter 16

Exercise Set 16.1, pp. 1012–1014

1. (f)   **2.** (a)   **3.** (d)   **4.** (b)   **5.** (c)   **6.** (e)

7. 13   **9.** 364   **11.** -23.5 **13.** -363 **15.** $\dfrac{441}{400}$

17. $5, 7, 9, 11; 23; 33$ **19.** $3, 6, 11, 18; 102; 227$

21. $\frac{1}{2}, \frac{2}{3}, \frac{3}{4}, \frac{4}{5}, \frac{10}{11}, \frac{15}{16}$ **23.** $1, -\frac{1}{2}, \frac{1}{4}, -\frac{1}{8}, -\frac{1}{512}, \frac{1}{16,384}$

25. $-1, \frac{1}{2}, -\frac{1}{3}, \frac{1}{4}, \frac{1}{10}, -\frac{1}{15}$ **27.** $0, 7, -26, 63; 999; -3374$

29. $-3, -1, 1, 3, 5$ **31.** $-1, -1, 1, 5, 11$ **33.** $\frac{1}{8}, \frac{4}{25}, \frac{1}{6}, \frac{8}{49}, \frac{5}{32}$

35. $2n$ **37.** $(-1)^{n+1}$ **39.** $(-1)^n \cdot n$ **41.** $2n + 1$

43. $n^2 - 1$, or $(n+1)(n-1)$ **45.** $\dfrac{n}{n+1}$ **47.** 5^n

49. $(-1)^n \cdot n^2$ **51.** 4   **53.** 30   **55.** $2, 3, \frac{11}{3}, \frac{25}{6}$

57. $-1, 3, -6, 10$ **59.** $\frac{1}{2} + \frac{1}{4} + \frac{1}{6} + \frac{1}{8} + \frac{1}{10} = \frac{137}{120}$

61. $10^0 + 10^1 + 10^2 + 10^3 + 10^4 = 11,111$

63. $2 + \frac{3}{2} + \frac{4}{3} + \frac{5}{4} + \frac{6}{5} + \frac{7}{6} + \frac{8}{7} = \frac{1343}{140}$

65. $(-1)^2 2^1 + (-1)^3 2^2 + (-1)^4 2^3 + (-1)^5 2^4 + (-1)^6 2^5 + (-1)^7 2^6 + (-1)^8 2^7 + (-1)^9 2^8 = -170$

67. $(0^2 - 2 \cdot 0 + 3) + (1^2 - 2 \cdot 1 + 3) + (2^2 - 2 \cdot 2 + 3) + (3^2 - 2 \cdot 3 + 3) + (4^2 - 2 \cdot 4 + 3) + (5^2 - 2 \cdot 5 + 3) = 43$

69. $\dfrac{(-1)^3}{3 \cdot 4} + \dfrac{(-1)^4}{4 \cdot 5} + \dfrac{(-1)^5}{5 \cdot 6} = -\dfrac{1}{15}$

71. $\displaystyle\sum_{k=1}^{5} \dfrac{k+1}{k+2}$ **73.** $\displaystyle\sum_{k=1}^{6} k^2$ **75.** $\displaystyle\sum_{k=2}^{n} (-1)^k k^2$

77. $\displaystyle\sum_{k=1}^{\infty} 5k$ **79.** $\displaystyle\sum_{k=1}^{\infty} \dfrac{1}{k(k+1)}$

81. $u = 3n + 1$

Yscl = 5

83. $u = (-1)^n(n^2)$

Yscl = 10

85. $u = 1/n$

Yscl = 0.1

87. $u = (-1)^n/(n+2)$

Yscl = 0.5

89. TW   **91.** 98   **92.** -15 **93.** $a_1 + 4d$ **94.** $a_1 + a_n$

95. $3(a_1 + a_n)$, or $3a_1 + 3a_n$ **96.** d **97.** TW

99. $1, 3, 13, 63, 313, 1563$ **101.** $2500, $2000, $1600, $1280, $1024, $819.20, $655.36, $524.29, $419.43, $335.54

103. $S_{100} = 0; S_{101} = -1$ **105.** $i, -1, -i, 1, i; i$

107. 11th term

Interactive Discovery, p. 1017

1. The points lie on a straight line with positive slope.
2. The points lie on a straight line with positive slope.
3. The points lie on a straight line with negative slope.
4. The points lie on a straight line with negative slope.

Exercise Set 16.2, pp. 1021–1024

1. True   **2.** True   **3.** False   **4.** False   **5.** True

6. True   **7.** False   **8.** False   **9.** $a_1 = 2, d = 4$

11. $a_1 = 7, d = -4$ **13.** $a_1 = \frac{3}{2}, d = \frac{3}{4}$

15. $a_1 = $5.12, d = 0.12 **17.** 49   **19.** -94

21. $-$1628.16$ **23.** 26th   **25.** 57th   **27.** 82   **29.** 5

31. 28   **33.** $a_1 = 8; d = -3; 8, 5, 2, -1, -4$

35. $a_1 = 1; d = 1$ **37.** 780   **39.** 31,375   **41.** 2550

43. 918   **45.** 1030   **47.** 35 musicians; 315 musicians

49. 180 stones   **51.** $49.60   **53.** 722 seats   **55.** TW

57. $y = \frac{1}{3}x + 10$ **58.** $y = -4x + 11$ **59.** $y = -2x + 10$

60. $y = -\frac{4}{3}x - \frac{16}{3}$ **61.** $x^2 + y^2 = 16$

62. $(x+2)^2 + (y-1)^2 = 20$ **63.** TW   **65.** 33 jumps

67. $8760, $7961.77, $7163.54, $6365.31, $5567.08; $4768.85, $3970.62, $3172.39, $2374.16, $1575.93   **69.** Let $d =$ the common difference. Since $p, m,$ and q form an arithmetic sequence, $m = p + d$ and $q = p + 2d$. Then
$$\dfrac{p+q}{2} = \dfrac{p + (p + 2d)}{2} = p + d = m.$$

71. 156,375   **73.** Arithmetic; $a_n = 0.7n + 68.3$, where $n = 1$ corresponds to a ball speed of 100 mph, $n = 2$ corresponds to a ball speed of 101 mph, and so on   **75.** Not arithmetic

Interactive Discovery, p. 1026

1. The points lie on an exponential curve with $a > 1$.
2. The points lie on an exponential curve with $a > 1$.
3. The points lie on an exponential curve with $0 < a < 1$.
4. The points lie on an exponential curve with $0 < a < 1$.

Interactive Discovery, p. 1029

1. (a) $\frac{1}{3}$; **(b)** 1, 1.33333, 1.44444, 1.48148, 1.49383, 1.49794, 1.49931, 1.49977, 1.49992, 1.49997 (sums are rounded to 5 decimal places); **(c)** 1.5   **2. (a)** $-\frac{7}{2}$; **(b)** 1, -2.5, 9.75, -33.125, 116.9375, -408.28125, 1429.984375, -5003.945313, 17514.80859, -61300.83008; **(c)** does not exist   **3. (a)** 2; **(b)** 4, 12, 28, 60, 124, 252, 508, 1020, 2044, 4092; **(c)** does not exist   **4. (a)** -0.4; **(b)** 1.3, 0.78, 0.988, 0.9048, 0.93808, 0.92477, 0.93009, 0.92796, 0.92881, 0.92847 (sums are rounded to 5 decimal places); **(c)** 0.928   **5.** S_∞ does not exist if $|r| > 1$.

Visualizing for Success, p. 1033

1. J   **2.** G   **3.** A   **4.** H   **5.** I   **6.** B   **7.** E
8. D   **9.** F   **10.** C

Exercise Set 16.3, pp. 1034–1036

1. Geometric sequence   **2.** Arithmetic sequence
3. Arithmetic sequence   **4.** Geometric sequence
5. Geometric series   **6.** Arithmetic series
7. Geometric series   **8.** None of these   **9.** 2

11. -0.1 **13.** $-\frac{1}{2}$ **15.** $\frac{1}{5}$ **17.** $\frac{6}{m}$ **19.** 192

21. 243   **23.** 52,488   **25.** $2331.64   **27.** $a_n = 5^{n-1}$
29. $a_n = (-1)^{n-1}$, or $a_n = (-1)^{n+1}$

31. $a_n = \dfrac{1}{x^n}$, or $a_n = x^{-n}$ **33.** 3066   **35.** $\frac{547}{18}$

37. $\dfrac{1 - x^8}{1 - x}$, or $(1 + x)(1 + x^2)(1 + x^4)$ **39.** $5134.51

41. 27   **43.** $\frac{49}{4}$ **45.** No   **47.** No   **49.** $\frac{43}{99}$ **51.** $25,000

53. $\frac{7}{9}$ **55.** $\frac{830}{99}$ **57.** $\frac{5}{33}$ **59.** $\frac{5}{1024}$ ft   **61.** 155,797
63. 2710 flies   **65.** Approximately 179.9 billion coffees
67. 3100.35 ft   **69.** 20.48 in.   **71.** Arithmetic
73. Geometric   **75.** Geometric   **77.** TW
79. $x^2 + 2xy + y^2$ **80.** $x^3 + 3x^2y + 3xy^2 + y^3$
81. $x^3 - 3x^2y + 3xy^2 - y^3$
82. $x^4 - 4x^3y + 6x^2y^2 - 4xy^3 + y^4$
83. $8x^3 + 12x^2y + 6xy^2 + y^3$
84. $8x^3 - 12x^2y + 6xy^2 - y^3$ **85.** TW   **87.** 54

89. $\dfrac{x^2[1 - (-x)^n]}{1 + x}$ **91.** 512 cm²

Mid-Chapter Review: Chapter 16, pp. 1037–1038

Guided Solutions

1. $a_n = a_1 + (n - 1)d$
$n = 14, a_1 = -6, d = 5$
$a_{14} = -6 + (14 - 1)5$
$a_{14} = 59$

2. $a_n = a_1 r^{n-1}$
$n = 7, a_1 = \frac{1}{9}, r = -3$
$a_7 = \frac{1}{9} \cdot (-3)^{7-1}$
$a_7 = 81$

Mixed Review

1. 300   **2.** $\dfrac{1}{n + 1}$ **3.** 78   **4.** $2^2 + 3^2 + 4^2 + 5^2 = 54$

5. $\displaystyle\sum_{k=1}^{6} (-1)^{k+1} \cdot k$ **6.** -3 **7.** 110   **8.** 61st   **9.** -39
10. 21   **11.** 11   **12.** 4410   **13.** $-\frac{1}{2}$ **14.** 640

15. $2(-1)^{n+1}$ **16.** $1146.39   **17.** 1   **18.** No
19. $465   **20.** $1,073,741,823

Exercise Set 16.4, pp. 1045–1047

1. 2^5, or 32   **2.** 8   **3.** 9   **4.** 4!   **5.** $\dbinom{8}{5}$, or $\dbinom{8}{3}$

6. 1   **7.** x^7y^2 **8.** 10 choose 4   **9.** 24   **11.** 39,916,800
13. 56   **15.** 126   **17.** 35   **19.** 1   **21.** 435   **23.** 780
25. $a^4 - 4a^3b + 6a^2b^2 - 4ab^3 + b^4$
27. $p^7 + 7p^6q + 21p^5q^2 + 35p^4q^3 + 35p^3q^4 + 21p^2q^5 + 7pq^6 + q^7$ **29.** $2187c^7 - 5103c^6d + 5103c^5d^2 - 2835c^4d^3 + 945c^3d^4 - 189c^2d^5 + 21cd^6 - d^7$
31. $t^{-12} + 12t^{-10} + 60t^{-8} + 160t^{-6} + 240t^{-4} + 192t^{-2} + 64$
33. $x^5 - 5x^4y + 10x^3y^2 - 10x^2y^3 + 5xy^4 - y^5$

35. $19,683s^9 + \dfrac{59,049s^8}{t} + \dfrac{78,732s^7}{t^2} + \dfrac{61,236s^6}{t^3} + \dfrac{30,618s^5}{t^4} + \dfrac{10,206s^4}{t^5} + \dfrac{2268s^3}{t^6} + \dfrac{324s^2}{t^7} + \dfrac{27s}{t^8} + \dfrac{1}{t^9}$
37. $x^{15} - 10x^{12}y + 40x^9y^2 - 80x^6y^3 + 80x^3y^4 - 32y^5$
39. $125 + 150\sqrt{5}t + 375t^2 + 100\sqrt{5}t^3 + 75t^4 + 6\sqrt{5}t^5 + t^6$
41. $x^{-3} - 6x^{-2} + 15x^{-1} - 20 + 15x - 6x^2 + x^3$
43. $15a^4b^2$ **45.** $-64,481,508a^3$ **47.** $1120x^{12}y^2$
49. $1,959,552u^5v^{10}$ **51.** y^8 **53.** TW

55.
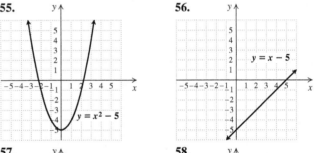

56.
$y = x - 5$

57.

$y \geq x - 5$

58.

$y = 5^x$

59.
$f(x) = \log_5 x$

60.

$x^2 + y^2 = 5$

61. TW   **63.** List all the subsets of size 3: $\{a, b, c\}$, $\{a, b, d\}$, $\{a, b, e\}$, $\{a, c, d\}$, $\{a, c, e\}$, $\{a, d, e\}$, $\{b, c, d\}$, $\{b, c, e\}$, $\{b, d, e\}$, $\{c, d, e\}$. There are exactly 10 subsets of size 3 and $\dbinom{5}{3} = 10$, so there are exactly $\dbinom{5}{3}$ ways of forming a subset of size 3 from $\{a, b, c, d, e\}$.

65. $\binom{8}{5}(0.15)^3(0.85)^5 \approx 0.084$

67. $\binom{8}{6}(0.15)^2(0.85)^6 + \binom{8}{7}(0.15)(0.85)^7 +$
$\binom{8}{8}(0.85)^8 \approx 0.89$

69. $\binom{n}{n-r} = \dfrac{n!}{[n-(n-r)]!\,(n-r)!}$
$= \dfrac{n!}{r!\,(n-r)!} = \binom{n}{r}$

71. $\dfrac{-\sqrt[3]{q}}{2p}$ **73.** $x^7 + 7x^6y + 21x^5y^2 + 35x^4y^3 +$
$35x^3y^4 + 21x^2y^5 + 7xy^6 + y^7$

Study Summary: Chapter 16, pp. 1048–1049

1. 143   **2.** -25 **3.** $5\cdot 0 + 5\cdot 1 + 5\cdot 2 + 5\cdot 3 = 30$
4. 15.5   **5.** 215   **6.** -640 **7.** $-20{,}475$
8. 16   **9.** 39,916,800   **10.** 84
11. $x^{10} - 10x^8 + 40x^6 - 80x^4 + 80x^2 - 32$ **12.** $3240t^7$

Review Exercises: Chapter 16, pp. 1049–1050

1. False   **2.** True   **3.** True   **4.** False   **5.** False
6. True   **7.** False   **8.** False   **9.** 1, 5, 9, 13; 29; 45
10. $0, \frac{1}{5}, \frac{1}{5}, \frac{3}{17}, \frac{7}{65}, \frac{11}{145}$ **11.** $a_n = -5n$
12. $a_n = (-1)^n(2n-1)$
13. $-2 + 4 + (-8) + 16 + (-32) = -22$
14. $-3 + (-5) + (-7) + (-9) + (-11) + (-13) = -48$
15. $\sum\limits_{k=1}^{5} 4k$ **16.** $\sum\limits_{k=1}^{5} \dfrac{1}{(-2)^k}$ **17.** 85   **18.** $\frac{8}{3}$
19. $a_1 = -15, d = 5$ **20.** -544 **21.** 25,250
22. $1024\sqrt{2}$ **23.** $\frac{3}{4}$ **24.** $a_n = 2(-1)^n$
25. $a_n = 3\left(\dfrac{x}{4}\right)^{n-1}$ **26.** 4095   **27.** $-4095x$ **28.** 12
29. $\frac{49}{11}$ **30.** No   **31.** No   **32.** \$40,000   **33.** $\frac{5}{9}$ **34.** $\frac{46}{33}$
35. \$24.30   **36.** 903 poles   **37.** \$15,791.18   **38.** 6 m
39. 5040   **40.** 56   **41.** $190a^{18}b^2$
42. $x^4 - 8x^3y + 24x^2y^2 - 32xy^3 + 16y^4$
43. TW For a geometric sequence with $|r| < 1$, as n gets larger, the absolute value of the terms gets smaller, since $|r^n|$ gets smaller.
44. TW The first form of the binomial theorem draws the coefficients from Pascal's triangle; the second form uses factorial notation. The second form avoids the need to compute all preceding rows of Pascal's triangle, and is generally easier to use when only one term of an expansion is needed. When several terms of an expansion are needed and n is not large (say, $n \leq 8$), it is often easier to use Pascal's triangle.
45. $\dfrac{1 - (-x)^n}{x + 1}$
46. $x^{-15} + 5x^{-9} + 10x^{-3} + 10x^3 + 5x^9 + x^{15}$

Test: Chapter 16, pp. 1050–1051

1. [16.1] $\frac{1}{2}, \frac{1}{5}, \frac{1}{10}, \frac{1}{17}, \frac{1}{26}; \frac{1}{145}$ **2.** [16.1] $a_n = 4\left(\frac{1}{3}\right)^n$
3. [16.1] $-3 + (-7) + (-15) + (-31) = -56$
4. [16.1] $\sum\limits_{k=1}^{5} (-1)^{k+1}k^3$ **5.** [16.2] $\frac{13}{2}$ **6.** [16.2] -3
7. [16.2] $a_1 = 32; d = -4$ **8.** [16.2] 2508

9. [16.3] 1536   **10.** [16.3] $\frac{2}{3}$ **11.** [16.3] 3^n
12. [16.3] 5621   **13.** [16.3] 1   **14.** [16.3] No
15. [16.3] $\frac{\$25{,}000}{23} \approx \$1086.96$ **16.** [16.3] $\frac{85}{99}$
17. [16.2] 63 seats   **18.** [16.2] \$17,100
19. [16.3] \$5987.37   **20.** [16.3] 36 m   **21.** [16.4] 220
22. [16.4] $x^5 - 15x^4y + 90x^3y^2 - 270x^2y^3 +$
$405xy^4 - 243y^5$ **23.** [16.4] $220a^9x^3$ **24.** [16.2] $n(n+1)$
25. [16.3] $\dfrac{1 - \left(\frac{1}{x}\right)^n}{1 - \frac{1}{x}}$, or $\dfrac{x^n - 1}{x^{n-1}(x-1)}$

Cumulative Review/Final Exam: Chapters 4, 10–16, pp. 1051–1054

1. $\frac{7}{15}$ **2.** $-4y + 17$ **3.** 280   **4.** 8.4×10^{-15}
5. $\frac{7}{6}$ **6.** $3a^2 - 8ab - 15b^2$ **7.** $4a^2 - 1$
8. $9a^4 - 30a^2y + 25y^2$ **9.** $\dfrac{4}{x+2}$ **10.** $\dfrac{x-4}{4(x+2)}$
11. $\dfrac{(x+y)(x^2 + xy + y^2)}{x^2 + y^2}$ **12.** $x - a$ **13.** $12a^2\sqrt{b}$
14. $-27x^{10}y^{-2}$, or $-\dfrac{27x^{10}}{y^2}$ **15.** $25x^4y^{1/3}$
16. $y\sqrt[12]{x^5y^2}, y \geq 0$ **17.** $14 + 8i$ **18.** $(2x - 3)^2$
19. $(3a - 2)(9a^2 + 6a + 4)$ **20.** $12(s^2 + 2t)(s^2 - 2t)$
21. $3(y^2 + 3)(5y^2 - 4)$
22. $7x^3 + 9x^2 + 19x + 38 + \dfrac{72}{x-2}$ **23.** 20   **24.** $[4, \infty)$, or
$\{x | x \geq 4\}$ **25.** $(-\infty, 5) \cup (5, \infty)$, or $\{x | x \neq 5\}$
26. $\dfrac{1 - 2\sqrt{x} + x}{1 - x}$ **27.** $y = 3x - 8$ **28.** $x^2 - 50 = 0$
29. $(2, -3); 6$ **30.** $\log_a \dfrac{\sqrt[3]{x^2} \cdot z^5}{\sqrt{y}}$ **31.** $a^5 = c$ **32.** 2.0792
33. 0.6826   **34.** 5   **35.** -121 **36.** 875   **37.** $16\left(\frac{1}{4}\right)^{n-1}$
38. $13{,}440a^4b^6$ **39.** $\frac{19{,}171}{64}$, or 299.546875   **40.** $\frac{3}{5}$ **41.** $-\frac{6}{5}, 4$
42. $\mathbb{R}$, or $(-\infty, \infty)$ **43.** $\left(-1, \frac{1}{2}\right)$ **44.** $(2, -1, 1)$
45. 2   **46.** $\pm 2, \pm 5$ **47.** $\left(\sqrt{5}, \sqrt{3}\right), \left(\sqrt{5}, -\sqrt{3}\right),$
$\left(-\sqrt{5}, \sqrt{3}\right), \left(-\sqrt{5}, -\sqrt{3}\right)$ **48.** 1.7925   **49.** 1005   **50.** $\frac{1}{25}$
51. $-\frac{1}{2}$ **52.** $\{x | -2 \leq x \leq 3\}$, or $[-2, 3]$ **53.** $\pm i\sqrt{3}$
54. $-2 \pm \sqrt{7}$ **55.** $\{y | y < -5 \text{ or } y > 2\}$, or
$(-\infty, -5) \cup (2, \infty)$ **56.** $-8, 10$ **57.** 3
58. $r = \dfrac{V - P}{-Pt}$, or $\dfrac{P - V}{Pt}$ **59.** $R = \dfrac{Ir}{1 - I}$
60. (a) Linear; (b) 2   **61.** (a) Logarithmic; (b) -1
62. (a) Quadratic; (b) $-1, 4$ **63.** (a) Exponential; (b) no real zeros

64.

65.

66.

$$\frac{x^2}{36} - \frac{y^2}{9} = 1$$

67.

$y = \log_2 x$

68.

$f(x) = 2^x - 3$

69.

$2x - 3y < -6$

70.

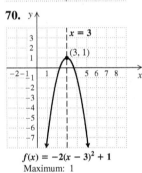

$x = 3$

$(3, 1)$

$f(x) = -2(x - 3)^2 + 1$
Maximum: 1

71. $y = \sqrt{(4 - x)}$

Domain: $(-\infty, 4]$;
range: $[0, \infty)$

72. 5000 ft^2 **73.** 5 ft by 12 ft   **74.** More than 25 rentals
75. \$2.68 herb: 10 oz; \$4.60 herb: 14 oz   **76.** 350 mph
77. $8\frac{2}{5}$ hr, or 8 hr 24 min   **78.** 20   **79. (a)** 2 million card
holders/year; **(b)** $c = 2t + 173$; **(c)** 191 million card holders;
(d) 2044   **80. (a)** $k \approx 0.092$; $P(t) = 5e^{0.092t}$, where $P(t)$ is in
billions of dollars; **(b)** \$104 billion; **(c)** 2019   **81.** \$14,079.98
82. All real numbers except 0 and -12 **83.** 81
84. y gets divided by 8   **85.** 84 yr

Glossary

Arithmetic sequence (or **progression**) [16.2]   A sequence in which adding the same number to any term gives the next term in the sequence

Arithmetic series [16.2]   A series for which the associated sequence is arithmetic

Axis of symmetry [13.6]   A line that can be drawn through a graph such that the part of the graph on one side of the line is an exact reflection of the part on the opposite side

Branches [15.3]   The two or more curves that comprise the graph of some relations

Break-even point [11.5]   In business, the point of intersection of the revenue function and the cost function

Circle [15.1]   A set of points in a plane that are a fixed distance r, called the radius, from a fixed point (h, k), called the center

Columns of a matrix [11.3]   The vertical elements of a matrix

Common logarithm [14.3]   A logarithm with base 10

Completing the square [13.1]   A method of adding a particular constant to an expression so that the resulting sum is a perfect square

Complex number [12.8]   Any number that can be written in the form $a + bi$, where a and b are real numbers and $i = \sqrt{-1}$

Complex-number system [12.8]   A number system that contains the real-number system and is designed so that negative numbers have defined square roots

Composite function [14.1]   A function in which a quantity depends on a variable that, in turn, depends on another variable

Compound inequality [10.1]   A statement in which two or more inequalities are joined by the word "and" or the word "or"

Compound interest [13.1]   Interest computed on the sum of an original principal and the interest previously accrued by that principal

Conic section [15.1]   A curve formed by the intersection of a plane and a cone

Conjugates [12.5]   Pairs of radical expressions, like $\sqrt{a} + \sqrt{b}$ and $\sqrt{a} - \sqrt{b}$, for which the product does not have a radical term

Conjugate of a complex number [12.8]   The *conjugate* of a complex number $a + bi$ is $a - bi$, and the *conjugate* of $a - bi$ is $a + bi$.

Conjunction [10.1]   A sentence in which two or more sentences are joined by the word "and"

Consistent system of equations [4.1]   A system of equations that has at least one solution

Cube root [12.1]   The number c is the *cube root* of a if $c^3 = a$.

Demand function [11.5]   A function modeling the relationship between the price of a good and the quantity of that good demanded

Dependent equations [4.1], [11.1]   Equations in a system are dependent if one equation can be removed without changing the solution set.

Determinant [11.4]   A descriptor of a square matrix. The determinant of a two-by-two matrix $\begin{bmatrix} a & c \\ b & d \end{bmatrix}$ is denoted by $\begin{vmatrix} a & c \\ b & d \end{vmatrix}$ and is defined as $ad - bc$.

Discriminant [13.3]   The radicand $b^2 - 4ac$ from the quadratic formula

Disjunction [10.1]   A sentence in which two or more sentences are joined by the word "or"

Doubling time [14.7]   The amount of time necessary for a population to double in size

Elements of a matrix [11.3]   The individual numbers in a matrix; also called *entries*

Elimination method [4.3]   An algebraic method that uses the addition principle to solve a system of equations

Ellipse [15.2]   The set of all points in a plane for which the sum of the distances from two fixed points F_1 and F_2 is constant

Equilibrium point [11.5]   The point of intersection between the demand function and the supply function

Equivalent systems of equations [11.3]   Systems of equations with the same solutions

Exponential decay [14.7]   A decrease in quantity over time that can be modeled by an exponential function of the form $P(t) = P_0 e^{-kt}$, $k > 0$, where P_0 is the quantity present at time 0, $P(t)$ is the amount present at time t, and k is the decay rate

Exponential equation [14.6]   An equation in which a variable appears as an exponent

Exponential function [14.2]   A function that can be described by an exponential equation

Exponential growth [14.7]   An increase in quantity over time that can be modeled by an exponential function of the form $P(t) = P_0 e^{kt}$, $k > 0$, where P_0 is the population at time 0, $P(t)$ is the population at time t, and k is the exponential growth rate

Finite sequence [16.1]   A function having for its domain a set of natural numbers: $\{1, 2, 3, 4, 5, \ldots, n\}$, for some natural number n

Finite series [16.1]   The sum of the first n terms of a sequence: $a_1 + a_2 + a_3 + \cdots + a_n$; also called *partial sum*

Fixed costs [11.5]   In business, costs that are incurred whether or not a product is produced

Foci (plural of focus) [15.2]   Two fixed points that determine the points of an ellipse

General term of a sequence [16.1]   The nth term, denoted a_n

Geometric sequence [16.3]   A sequence in which multiplying a certain fixed number by any term gives the next term in the sequence

Geometric series [16.3]   A series for which the associated sequence is geometric

Half-life [14.7]   The amount of time necessary for half of a quantity to decay

Half-plane [10.3]   A region of a plane consisting of all points on one side of a straight line

Horizontal-line test [14.1]   If it is impossible to draw a horizontal line that intersects a function's graph more than once, then the function is one-to-one.

Hyperbola [11.3]   The set of all points P in a plane such that the difference of the distance from P to two fixed points is constant

i [12.8]   The square root of -1; $i = \sqrt{-1}$ and $i^2 = -1$

Imaginary number [12.8]   A number that can be written in the form $a + bi$, where a and b are real numbers and $b \neq 0$

Inconsistent system of equations [4.1]   A system of equations for which there is no solution

Independent equations [4.1]   Equations that are not dependent

Index [12.1]   In the radical $\sqrt[n]{a}$, the number n is called the index.

Infinite geometric series [16.3]   The sum of the terms of an infinite geometric sequence

Infinite sequence [16.1]   A function having for its domain the set of natural numbers: $\{1, 2, 3, 4, 5, \ldots\}$

Infinite series [16.1]   Given the infinite sequence $a_1, a_2, a_3, a_4, \ldots a_n, \ldots$, the sum of the terms $a_1 + a_2 + a_3 + a_4 + \cdots + a_n + \cdots$ is called an infinite series.

Intersection of A and B [10.1]   The set of all elements that are common to *both* A and B; denoted $A \cap B$

Inverse relation [14.1]   The relation formed by interchanging the members of the domain and the range of a relation

Isosceles right triangle [12.7]   A right triangle in which both legs have the same length

Like radicals [12.5]   Radical expressions that have the same indices and radicands

Linear equation in three variables [11.1]   An equation equivalent to one in the form $Ax + By + Cz = D$, where x, y, and z are variables

Linear inequality [10.3]   An inequality whose related equation is a linear equation

Logarithmic equation [14.6]   An equation containing a logarithmic expression

Logarithmic function, base a [14.3]   The inverse of an exponential function $f(x) = a^x$

Matrix [11.3]   A rectangular array of numbers

Maximum value [13.6]   The greatest function value (output) achieved by a function

Minimum value [13.6]   The least function value (output) achieved by a function

Motion problem [4.4]   A problem that deals with distance, speed (rate), and time

Natural logarithm [14.5]   A logarithm with base e; also called *Napierian logarithm*

nth root [12.1]   A number c is called the nth root of a if $c^n = a$.

Odd root [12.1]   A root with an odd index

One-to-one function [14.1]   A function for which different inputs have different outputs

Parabola [13.6]   A graph of a second-degree polynomial in one variable

Partial sum [16.1]   The sum of the first n terms of a sequence: $a_1 + a_2 + a_3 + \cdots + a_n$; also called *finite series*

Pascal's triangle [16.4]   A triangular array of coefficients of the expansion $(a + b)^n$ for $n = 0, 1, 2, \ldots$

Polynomial inequality [10.4]   An inequality that is equivalent to an inequality with a polynomial as one side and 0 as the other

Principal square root [12.1]   The nonnegative square root of a number

Pure imaginary number [12.8]   A complex number of the form $a + bi$, in which $a = 0$ and $b \neq 0$

Quadratic equation [13.1]   An equation equivalent to one of the form $ax^2 + bx + c = 0$, where $a \neq 0$

Quadratic formula [13.2]   The solutions of $ax^2 + bx + c = 0, a \neq 0$, are given by the equation $x = \left(-b \pm \sqrt{b^2 - 4ac}\right)/(2a)$

Quadratic function [13.2]   A second-degree polynomial function in one variable

Quadratic inequality [10.4]   A second-degree polynomial inequality in one variable

Radical equation [12.6]   An equation in which a variable appears in a radicand

Radical expression [12.1]   An algebraic expression in which a radical sign appears

Radical function [12.1]   A function that can be described by a radical equation

Radical sign [12.1]   The symbol $\sqrt{}$

Radical term [12.5]   A term in which a radical sign appears

Radicand [12.1]   The expression under the radical sign

Radius [15.1]   The distance from the center of a circle to a point on the circle; a segment connecting a point on the circle to the center of the circle

Rational inequality [10.4]   An inequality involving rational expressions

Rationalizing the denominator [12.4]   A procedure for finding an equivalent expression without a radical in the denominator

Rationalizing the numerator [12.4]   A procedure for finding an equivalent expression without a radical in the numerator

Reflection [13.6]   The mirror image of a graph

Row-equivalent operations [11.3]   Operations used to produce equivalent systems of equations

Rows of a matrix [11.3]   The horizontal elements of a matrix

Sequence [16.1]   A function for which the domain is a set of consecutive positive integers beginning with 1

Series [16.1]   The sum of specified terms in a sequence

Sigma notation [16.1]   The naming of a sum using the Greek letter Σ (sigma) as part of an abbreviated form; also called *summation notation*

Square matrix [11.4]   A matrix with the same number of rows and columns

Square root [12.1]   The number c is a *square root* of a if $c^2 = a$.

Supply function [11.5]   A function modeling the relationship between the price of a good and the quantity of that good supplied

System of equations [4.1]   A set of two or more equations, in two or more variables, for which we seek a common solution

Total cost [11.5]   The money spent to produce a product

Total profit [11.5]   The money taken in less the money spent, or total revenue minus total cost

Total revenue [11.5]   The amount taken in from the sale of a product

Union of A and B [10.1]   The collection of elements belonging to A and/or B; denoted $A \cup B$

Variable costs [11.5]   In business, costs that vary according to the amount being produced

Vertex [13.7], [15.1], [15.2], [15.3]   The point at which a parabola, an ellipse, or a hyperbola crosses its axis of symmetry

Zero of a function [4.5]   An input whose corresponding output is 0; if a is a zero of the function f, then $f(a) = 0$.

Photo Credits

Index

---

*Page numbers followed by an asterisk pertain to Chapters 15 and 16.

Index of Applications

*Page numbers followed by an asterisk pertain to Chapters 15 and 16.

Frequently Used Symbols and Formulas

A Key to the Icons Appearing in the Exercise Sets

↪   Concept reinforcement exercises, indicated by purple exercise numbers, provide basic practice with the new concepts and vocabulary.

1   Following most examples, students are directed to Try Exercise. These selected exercises are identified with a color block around the exercise numbers.

Aha!   Exercises labeled Aha! can often be solved quickly with the proper insight.

▦   Calculator exercises are designed to be worked using a scientific calculator or a graphing calculator.

〰   Graphing calculator exercises are designed to be worked using a graphing calculator.

TW   Writing exercises are designed to be answered using one or more complete sentences.

Symbols

$=$	Is equal to
$\approx$	Is approximately equal to
$>$	Is greater than
$<$	Is less than
$\geq$	Is greater than or equal to
$\leq$	Is less than or equal to
$\in$	Is an element of
$\subseteq$	Is a subset of
$\lvert x \rvert$	The absolute value of x
$\{x \mid x \dots\}$	The set of all x such that $x \dots$
$-x$	The opposite of x
$\sqrt{x}$	The square root of x
$\sqrt[n]{x}$	The nth root of x
LCM	Least Common Multiple
LCD	Least Common Denominator
π	Pi
i	$\sqrt{-1}$
$f(x)$	f of x, or f at x
$f^{-1}(x)$	f inverse of x
$(f \circ g)(x)$	$f(g(x))$
e	Approximately 2.7
Σ	Summation
$n!$	Factorial notation

Formulas

$m = \dfrac{y_2 - y_1}{x_2 - x_1}$	Slope of a line
$y = mx + b$	Slope–intercept form of a linear equation
$y - y_1 = m(x - x_1)$	Point–slope form of a linear equation
$(A + B)(A - B) = A^2 - B^2$	Product of the sum and the difference of the same two terms
$\left.\begin{array}{l}(A + B)^2 = A^2 + 2AB + B^2, \\ (A - B)^2 = A^2 - 2AB + B^2\end{array}\right\}$	Square of a binomial
$d = rt$	Formula for distance traveled
$\dfrac{1}{a} \cdot t + \dfrac{1}{b} \cdot t = 1$	Work principle
$s = 16t^2$	Free-fall distance
$y = kx$	Direct variation
$y = \dfrac{k}{x}$	Inverse variation
$x = \dfrac{-b \pm \sqrt{b^2 - 4ac}}{2a}$	Quadratic formula
$P(t) = P_0 e^{kt}, k > 0$	Exponential growth
$P(t) = P_0 e^{-kt}, k > 0$	Exponential decay
$d = \sqrt{(x_2 - x_1)^2 + (y_2 - y_1)^2}$	Distance formula
$\dbinom{n}{r} = \dfrac{n!}{(n - r)!\, r!}$	$\dbinom{n}{r}$ notation

A Library of Functions

Constant Function
$y = b$

Linear Function
$y = mx + b$

Squaring Function
$y = x^2$

Quadratic Function
$y = ax^2 + bx + c, a > 0$

Quadratic Function
$y = ax^2 + bx + c, a < 0$

Square Root Function
$y = \sqrt{x}$

Cubing Function
$y = x^3$

Cube Root Function
$y = \sqrt[3]{x}$

Reciprocal Function
$y = \dfrac{1}{x}$

Absolute Value Function
$y = |x|$

Exponential Function
$y = ab^x$, or ae^{kx}
$a, b > 0, k > 0$

Exponential Function
$y = ab^{-x}$, or ae^{-kx}
$a, b > 0, k > 0$

Logarithmic Function
$y = a + b \ln x$